BirdLife Conse

MW01089724

ENDEMIC BIRD AREAS OF THE WORLD
Priorities for Biodiversity Conservation

Alison J. Stattersfield, Michael J. Crosby,
Adrian J. Long and David C. Wege

Maps by Andrew P. Rayner

BirdLife
INTERNATIONAL

Dedication   *Endemic Bird Areas of the World: Priorities for Biodiversity Conservation* is dedicated to Robert B. Wallace – in recognition of his vision of, commitment to and support for BirdLife International's Biodiversity Programme.

© 1998 BirdLife International
Wellbrook Court, Girton Road, Cambridge CB3 0NA, UK
tel. +44-(0)1223-277318   fax +44-(0)1223-277200   email birdlife@birdlife.org.uk

BirdLife International is a UK registered charity

ISBN 0 946888 33 7

A catalogue record for this book is available from the British Library

Series editor   Duncan Brooks
Design   Duncan Brooks and CBA (Cambridge)
Layout, text preparation and graphics   Duncan Brooks, Regina Pfaff, Michelle Berry
Cover (*design and graphics*)   Andrew Rayner

Text set in Times (9/11 pt) and Optima

Printed on 90 gsm Sequel Satin, made from sustainable forest by a totally chlorine-free process

Imageset, printed and bound in Great Britain by The Burlington Press (Cambridge) Ltd.

The publication of this book has been generously supported by

the Government of the Netherlands
Ministry of Foreign Affairs,
Directoraat Generaal Internationale Samenwerking (DGIS)

and by the following members of BirdLife International's

Rare Bird Club

Mario Albek	André C. A. van Gils	HRH Prince Bernhard of
Mrs Hortense Anda-Bührle	Tom Gullick	the Netherlands
André Baar	Dr Cynthia O. Harris	HRH Princess Juliana of
Barlow Rand Limited	Juan de Herrera, Marqués de	the Netherlands
Jacques Bemberg	Viesca de la Sierra	Gerard J. M. Nieuwe Weme
Mrs James Bond	Mr & Mrs André Hoffmann	Jacques Ormond
Henk Brusse	Luc Hoffmann	Jaime Ortiz-Patiño
Club 300	M. F. Keeley	Drs G. G. W. M. Peters
Henry Coebergh	A. P. Leventis	Mrs J. M. Relly
Bruce Coleman	Mr & Mrs H. K. Leventis	The Dr Mortimer and
W. Baron van Dedem	HRH the Grand Duke of	Theresa Sackler
Stephen D. Eccles	Luxembourg	Foundation
Edinburgh Trust	Will Marx	HSH Prince Sadruddin
Mr & Mrs John Flemer	Mrs Vera Michalski-	Aga Khan
J. E. Francis	Hoffmann	Dr Peter Wallenberg
Fritz Gerber	Christopher B. Mitchell	Alan N. Weeden
		R. E. van Zuylen

Specially bound copies of *Endemic Bird Areas of the World* have been presented to
His Royal Highness Prince Bernhard of the Netherlands, Honorary President of
the Rare Bird Club, and to Her Majesty Queen Noor of Jordan, Honorary President of
BirdLife International

This book is an output from the BirdLife International Biodiversity Programme,
which has been generously supported by

Conservation, Food and Health Foundation
The Education Foundation of America
The IBM Corporation
The John D. and Catherine T. MacArthur Foundation
The Pew Charitable Trust
Wallace Genetic Foundation, Inc.
The World Bank

BirdLife International is grateful to the following individuals
who also supported this programme

Mr and Mrs Howard P. Brokaw, James Cadbury, Mrs Jean W. Douglas, Wallace C. Dayton,
John Hunting, Mrs Bremner H. Jackson, Stephen C. Rockefeller,
Mr and Mrs Roger Sant, Robert B. Wallace, Thomas J. Watson, Jr.

CONTENTS

ENDEMIC BIRD AREAS

FOREWORD

by

Her Majesty Queen Noor of Jordan
Honorary President of BirdLife International

PLANNING for the wise use of natural resources is an investment with perpetual rewards. To do this, we need to know how biodiversity is distributed and what the priorities are for its conservation. Our knowledge of birds and the popular enthusiasm for their survival is a most powerful combination. In a previous publication, the award-winning *Putting biodiversity on the map*, BirdLife mapped concentrations of birds with small ranges—many of them threatened with extinction. This new book follows this approach through with an abundance of supporting detail and demonstrates clearly the value of birds as indicators of places which are important for biodiversity conservation overall.

The publication of this up-to-date material, and the advocacy programme which will deliver its message to decision-makers around the world, is funded by an innovative collaboration between the Dutch Government (Directoraat-Generaal voor Internationale Samenwerking) and members of BirdLife International's Rare Bird Club. It shows what can be achieved when the commitment of a government and the enthusiasm of individuals are combined with the common goal of focusing world attention on some of the most threatened birds and the fragile habitats on which they depend. The result is a unique, effective and valuable contribution to biodiversity conservation.

I hope and believe that this book will unite grass-roots support and environmental decision-makers and so help meet one of the greatest challenges facing mankind: the conservation and sustainable development of our biological natural resources.

ACKNOWLEDGEMENTS

THIS BOOK is the culmination of 10 years of work at BirdLife International's Secretariat, but has only been possible through the guidance and support of BirdLife's Partner organizations and worldwide network of contacts. We have relied on the firsthand experience of hundreds of ornithologists and conservationists who during the evolution of the project have, in many cases, been asked for information and clarification several times. We very warmly and gratefully thank these people who have freely given us the benefits of their knowledge and of their time (see list of names, below). We simply would not have been able to complete the task without their contributions.

In addition, we have drawn on data from several other BirdLife research projects, and contributors to these may not be personally acknowledged here. We therefore also extend thanks to the many people who provided information to these, notably to *Putting biodiversity on the map: priority areas for global conservation* (ICBP 1992)—the first publication of the results of this project—but also to *Threatened birds of Africa and related islands* (Collar and Stuart 1985), *Threatened birds of the Americas* (Collar *et al.* 1992), *Birds to watch 2: the world list of threatened birds* (Collar *et al.* 1994) and *Key areas for threatened birds in the Neotropics* (Wege and Long 1995), publications which have all contributed significantly to our understanding of Endemic Bird Areas and their birds.

We acknowledge our many colleagues whom we feel privileged to have worked with. We are honoured to be the authors of this book for we are very aware that in truth its publication represents a mighty team effort by all the staff. In particular we thank Nigel Collar (Research Fellow, BirdLife) who was the main instigator of this project and who is, for all of us, both a mentor and friend. His own work has laid the foundations and standards for most of BirdLife's research, and he has read all the Endemic Bird Area accounts and the introductory sections, and commented extensively. We also thank Colin Bibby (Director of Science and Policy, BirdLife) for generally overseeing our work and for providing us with scientific guidance, and our other directors, Lindsay Derry, Christoph Imboden and Mike Rands who worked hard against the odds to keep us to schedule.

We are especially appreciative of Andrew Rayner (our Geographic Information System expert) whose maps are such a key element of this book and whose general computer wizardry has been invaluable over the last three years. We also remember Mike Adams, who was our original GIS expert and who helped us to establish our mapping and database protocols at a time when the software was decidedly unfriendly. Other key players include Martin Jenkins (World Conservation Monitoring Centre, UK) who took the lead in writing three of the introductory chapters and whose insight into overall biodiversity conservation has helped us to broaden our bird perspective, and Andrew Balmford (University of Sheffield, UK), Tom Brooks (University of Tennessee, USA) and Tony Payne (Research Assistant, BirdLife) who helped to guide us through the pitfalls of numerical evaluation.

We draw special attention to our co-authors of *Putting biodiversity on the map*—Colin Bibby, Nigel Collar, Melanie Heath, Christoph Imboden, Tim Johnson and Simon Thirgood. They helped to lay the foundations for this book and we have made extensive use of their ideas and information in our introductory chapters. We especially thank Melanie Heath who, along with the four of us, was one of the main data-gatherers and who prepared some of the early drafts of the EBA accounts. We also acknowledge the other people who helped us to gather the bird distribution data on which the analyses are based including Paul Andrew, Mike Barker, Leticia Brandão, George Green, Frank Lambert, Craig Robson and Tony Stones, and many of the people listed below and members of the BirdLife staff. We have been helped along the way by a stream of willing volunteers including Tim Allwood, David Butler, Francis Brearley, Jonathan Ekstrom (who organised the picture research) and Tony Payne, and we thank them all for their enthusiastic commitment.

We thank all the staff in BirdLife's regional teams and offices for their input and support, in particular Gary Allport, Bas van Balen, Yusup Cahyadin, Nonie Coulthard, Nguyen Cu, Guy Duke, Jonathan Eames, Mike Evans, John Fanshawe, Lincoln Fishpool, Richard Grimmett, Paul Jepson, Martin Kelsey, James Lowen, Jane Lyons, Richard Porter, Michael Poulsen, Peter Robertson, Rudyanto and Sujatnika.

We applaud Duncan Brooks (Scientific Editor, BirdLife) who guided us through a lengthy and complicated publication process. His attention to detail and logical approach has greatly improved the quality of the text and we thank him, in particular, for remaining calm throughout despite so many requests for changes. We also thank Regina Pfaff and Michelle Berry who were responsible for much of the layout and graphical presentation in the book, and who have done such an excellent job in dealing with our messy manuscripts.

We acknowledge John Fanshawe, Jane Fenton and Judi James who successfully sought funding for the project and turned publication and advocacy into reality. We also thank Peter Herkenrath (Biodiversity Officer, BirdLife) for help with the policy aspects of the introductory chapters, and wish him success in using the information which we have compiled to good conservation effect through its application to the Biodiversity Convention. We also thank our library staff, Sue Squire and Christine Alder, who kept us fuelled with new information right up to going to press. We thank the staff at the many other libraries which we used, including the Edward Grey Institute (and especially Linda Birch), the Natural History Museum at Tring and the Map Room in the University Library, Cambridge.

Finally we thank our partners, John Croxall, Linping Crosby, Melanie Heath and Nicky Wege for giving us home support throughout this lengthy project, especially at times when we didn't believe that we would ever finish this book.

Contributors to the project The names and organizations listed below (and the countries of residence) give some indication of the amount and breadth of help that we have received. However, it has been difficult to maintain accurate records during the course of this long project, and we sincerely apologise if we have inadvertently missed any of our supporters from this list. (Organizations and countries relate to time of correspondence and may not be current. The list does not include contributors mentioned in the main text above.)

W. J. Adsett, Panama Audubon Society

P. D. Alexander-Marrack, Netherlands

D. G. Allan, Avian Demography Unit, South Africa

D. Allen, Japan

O. Al-Saghier, BirdLife Yemen

P. Alström, Sweden

M. A. de Andrade, Intituto Estadual de Florestas, Brazil

P. Andrew, Australia

G. Angehr, Smithsonian Tropical Research Institute, Panama

N. Arlott, UK

J. S. Ash, UK

The late D. Aspinwall, Zambia

A. Aspiroz, GUPECA, Uruguay

J. Atkins, UK

P. W. Atkinson, UK

C. Attié, CBC-CNRS, Réunion

N. E. Baker, Tanzania

D. J. Baker-Gabb, Royal Australasian Ornithologists' Union

C. Balchin, UK

E. Bani, Environment Unit, Vanuatu

M. A. Barker, UK

K. Barnes, Avian Demography Unit, South Africa

N. Barré, EMVT-CIRAD, France

J. Barrio, Peru

M. Beaman, UK

B. M. Beehler, Office of Ecology and Terrestrial Conservation, USA

A. J. Begazo, Peru

B. D. Bell, Wildlife Management International Ltd., New Zealand

L. A. Bennun, Kenya

A. Berruti, Durban National Science Museum, South Africa

B. J. Best, UK

R. Beyers, Belgium

P. C. Bhattacharjee, Gauhati University, India

B. Bhushan, Smithsonian Institution, USA

M. Biscoito, Museu Municipal do Funchal, Madeira

K. D. Bishop, Australia

P. Bison, Ornithological Society of the Middle East, UK

W. V. Bleisch, New York Zoological Society, USA

P. Boesman, Venezuela

N. Bostock, UK

M. Boulet, Service de l'Environnement et de la Gestion des Parcs et Réserves, New Caledonia

C. G. R. and L. Bowden, Mount Kupe Forest Project, Cameroon

J. Bowen, UK

J. Bowler, UK

R. C. Brace, University of Nottingham, UK

H. Bregulla, Germany

V. Bretagnolle, CNRS, France

N. Brickle, UK

M. de L. Brooke, University of Cambridge, UK

P. J. Bubb, Pronatura, Mexico

A. Burbidge, Royal Australasian Ornithologists' Union

N. D. Burgess, Zoological Museum, Copenhagen, Denmark

H. Burn, UK

I. Burrows, University of Papua New Guinea

R. Burrows, UK

S. M. H. Butchart, UK

D. J. Butler, Department of Lands and Environment, Western Samoa

P. J. Butler, RARE Center for Tropical Conservation, USA

C. Byres, UK

P. Canevari, Red Hemisférica de Reservas de Aves, Argentina

M. Carswell, UK

A. Challenger, Mexico

J. C. Chebez, Delegación Técnica Regional NEA, Argentina

P. Clarke, Frontier Tanzania, UK

R. P. Clay, UK

B. J. Coates, Australia

J. Collie, Division of the Environment, Seychelles

J. A. Colon, USA

J. Cooper, Percy FitzPatrick Institute, South Africa

P. Coopmans, Belgium

H. Corrigan, Department of Forests, Vanuatu

B. Cox, Ecuador

C. Cox, Forest and Lands Department, St Lucia

N. Cricks, Island Resources Foundation, Antigua and Barbuda

Nguyen Cu, IBER, Vietnam

D. Cunningham, Department of Conservation, New Zealand

E. Curio, Ruhr-Universität Bochum, Germany

R. L. Curry, Villanova University, USA

R. Daniels, Ornithological Society of India

P. Davidson, UK

M. Davies, Royal Society for the Protection of Birds, UK

S. Davis, Bolivia

W. R. J. Dean, Tierberg Karoo Research Centre, South Africa

R. W. R. J. Dekker, Natuurhistorisch Museum, Leiden, Netherlands

R. Demey, Belgium

J. M. Diamond, University of California, USA

E. Dickinson, UK

Ding Chang-qing, Chinese Academy of Sciences

R. Donaghey, Australia

R. J. Douthwaite, UK

S. D. Dowell, Partridge Quail and Francolin Specialist Group, UK

A. C. Downer, Jamaica

R. J. Dowsett, *Tauraco*, Belgium

F. Dowsett-Lemaire, *Tauraco*, Belgium

C. Dranzoa, Uganda

J. W. Duckworth, UK

D. J. Du Puy, Royal Botanic Gardens, UK

A. Duncan, Ligue pour la Protection des Oiseaux, France

G. C. L. Dutson, UK

P. Dutton, Oceanographic Research Institute

M. F. Ebreo, Philippines

U. Ekanayake, Sri Lanka

G. Ekstrom, Sweden

C. Elphick, UK

J. Engbring, Fish and Wildlife Service, USA

E. C. Enkerlin, Mexico

P. Evans, University of Oxford, UK

T. D. Evans, UK

E. Faull, UK

P. Feldmann, CIRAD-CA, Guadeloupe

B. W. Finch, Kenya

A. and J. Fitter, UK

C. Fitzgibbon, Kenya

K. Fitzherbert, Royal Australasian Ornithologists' Union

J. Fjeldså, Zoologisk Museum, Copenhagen, Denmark

A. Flamenco, CIES, Mexico

B. Fletcher, UK

J. Flynn, UK

P. S. M. Fonseca, Brazil

I. S. Francis, Royal Society for the Protection of Birds, UK

M. W. Fraser, South Africa

S. Garnett, Queensland Department of Environment and Heritage, Australia

M. C. Garnett, UK

K. L. Garrett, Natural History Museum of Los Angeles County, USA

O. Garrido, Museo National de Historia Natural, Cuba

P. J. Garson, Pheasant Specialist Group, UK

A. J. Gaston, National Wildlife Research Centre, Canada

R. Gerlach, Nature Protection Trust of Seychelles

D. Gibbs, UK

P. Glass, Fish and Wildlife Service, USA

L. P. Gonzaga, Ararajuba, Brazil

C. Gonzalez, Universidad de la Laguna, Canary Islands

S. M. Goodman, Field Museum of Natural History, USA

M. L. Goodwin, Sociedad Conservationista Audubon de Venezuela

M. E. J. Gore, Government House, Cayman Islands

P. D. Goriup, The Nature Conservation Bureau Ltd., UK

A. Grajal, NYZS, The Wildlife Conservation Society, USA

P. Gregory, Papua New Guinea Bird Society

A. Gretton, UK

P. Hall, UK

F. Hannecart, Service de l'Environnement et de la Gestion des Parcs et Réserves, New Caledonia

L. A. Hansen, Denmark

C. Harcourt, UK

S. Harrap, UK

G. N. Harrington, Royal Australasian Ornithologists' Union

J. Harrison, Avian Demography Unit, South Africa

J. Harrison, World Conservation Monitoring Centre, UK

A. F. A. Hawkins, WWF Madagascar

P. V. Hayman, UK

C. J. Hazevoet, Universiteit van Amsterdam, Netherlands

He Fen-qi, Chinese Academy of Sciences

C. J. Heij, Natuur Museum Rotterdam, Netherlands

S. Henson, UK

R. Hill, Royal Australasian Ornithologists' Union

J. C. Hillman, Ethiopian Wildlife Conservation

R. K. Hills, Vanuatu Protected Areas Initiative, UK

S. L. Hilty, USA

T. Hjarsen, University of Copenhagen, Denmark

P. A. R. Hockey, Percy FitzPatrick Institute, South Africa

T. W. Hoffman, Ceylon Bird Club, Sri Lanka

D. A. Holmes, Indonesian Ornithological Society (Kukila)

D. T. Holyoak, UK

J. Hornbuckle, UK

J. Hornskov, Denmark

S. N. G. Howell, Point Reyes Bird Observatory, USA

T. R. Howell, USA

G. R. Hunt, Massey University, New Zealand

S. A. Hussain, BirdLife Asia Council, India

M. A. Hutt, Barbados, West Indies

N. Ichida, Wild Bird Society of Japan

C. Inskipp, UK

T. P. Inskipp, World Conservation Monitoring Centre, UK

M. P. S. Irwin, Zimbabwe

I. Isherwood, UK

M. Isler, USA

L. Jammes, Fundación Armonía, Bolivia

S. Javed, Aligarh Muslim University, India

J. J. Jeffrey, USA

M. C. Jennings, UK

A. Jensen, Dansk Ornitologisk Forening

B. Jiménez Ruiz, Asociación Nacional para la Conservación de la Naturaleza, Panama

N. Jivan Shah, ENVIRO, Seychelles

L. John, Forest and Lands Department, St Lucia

M. A. Johnston, University of the West of England, UK

C. G. Jones, Mauritius

M. J. Jones, Manchester Metropolitan University, UK

P. J. Jones, University of Edinburgh, UK

S. Kanyamibwa, World Conservation Monitoring Centre, UK

M. Katti, University of California San Diego, USA

R. Kaul, India

K. Kazmierczak, UK

A. Keith, USA

C. Kennedy, UK

L. F. Kiff, Peregrine Fund, USA

B. King, KingBird Tours Inc., USA

J. Komdeur, National Environment Research Institute, Denmark

E. Kosaka, Fish and Wildlife Service, USA

S. W. Kotagama, Field Ornithology Group, University of Sri Lanka

N. Krabbe, Ecuador

U. Lachungpa, Wildlife Department, Government of Sikkim, India

F. R. Lambert, IUCN, Thailand

M. Lammertink, Netherlands

T. Leary, Nature Conservancy, Solomon Islands

A. Lees, Maruia Society, New Zealand

M. Lentino, Colección Ornitológica Phelps, Venezuela

Y. Létocart, Service de l'Environnement et de la Gestion des Parcs et Réserves, New Caledonia

C. Levy, Gosse Bird Club, Jamaica

A. D. Lewis, UK

A. Lieberman, Peregrine Fund, USA

M. Linsley, UK

J. A. Lorenzo, Universidad de la Laguna, Canary Islands

M. Louette, Koninklijk Museum voor Midden-Afrika, Belgium

J. Lovett, Botanical Museum, Denmark

A. Luy, Sociedad Conservacionista Audubon de Venezuela

G. Mackey, UK

J. MacKinnon, Asian Bureau for Conservation, UK

G. Maclean, University of Natal, South Africa

G. Magnin, DHKD (Society for the Protection of Nature), Turkey

N. A. D. Mallari, Haribon Foundation, Philippines

A. Marogh, Gosse Bird Club, Jamaica

C. Martin, WWF, Switzerland

R. P. Martins, UK

G. McCormack, Cook Islands Natural Heritage Project

N. McCulloch, Royal Society for the Protection of Birds, UK

K. McDermond, Fish and Wildlife Service, USA

P. McGowan, Partridge Quail and Francolin Specialist Group, UK

D. McNiven, Royal Society for the Protection of Birds, UK

D. V. Merton, Department of Conservation, New Zealand

J. Meza, Chile

B. and C. Miller, Wildlife Conservation Society, Belize

J. Minton, Wild Bird Society of Japan

A. Mitchell, UK

R. Mittermeier, Conservation International, USA

C. W. Moeliker, Natuur Museum Rotterdam, Netherlands

T. V. Mora, Departamento de Vida Silvestre, Dominican Republic

S. Mori, New York Botanical Garden, USA

P. Morris, Birdquest, UK

D. C. Moyer, Louisiana State University, USA

J. T. Moyer, Mijake-jima Nature Center, Japan

A. G. Navarro, Museo de Zoologa, Mexico

A. J. Negret, Museo de Historia Natural, Universidad del Cauca, Colombia

M. Nogales, Universidad de La Laguna, Canary Islands

M. Nores, Universidad Nacional de Cordoba, Argentina

R. Noske, Northern Territory University, Australia

C. M. C. Nozawa, Haribon Foundation, Philippines

Y. Ntiamoa-Baidu, Ghana Wildlife Society, Ghana

D. A. S. Nuñez, Departamento de Vida Silvestre, Dominican Republic

J. Oglethorpe, KIRCP, Kenya

L. G. Olarte, Colombia

W. L. R. Oliver, Flora and Fauna International, UK

U. Olsson, Sweden

J. A. Ottenwalder, Florida State Museum, USA

R. Paalan, Silliman University, Philippines

The late T. A. Parker, Louisiana State University, USA

J. and H. Parrot, UK

M. Pearman, UK

N. B. Peet, University of East Anglia, UK

C. Perennun, Wetlands International, Netherlands

J. Pérez del Val, Spain

P. K. D. Perng, Taiwan Endemic Species Research Institute

A. H. Perry, TREX, USA

A. T. Peterson, University of Kansas, USA

S. L. Pimm, University of Tennessee, USA

M. A. Plenge, Peru

D. E. Pomeroy, Makarere University, Uganda

R. Pople, UK

R. Potapov, Zoological Institute, Russia

G. V. N. Powell, RARE Centre for Tropical Conservation, Costa Rica

S. N. Prasad, SACON, India

H. D. Pratt, Louisana State University, USA

T. Pratt, USA
R. P. Prys-Jones, Natural History Museum, UK
R. Pyle, Bishop Museum, USA
A. Rahmani, Bombay Natural History Society, India
M. Rank, UK
B. Raynor, Nature Conservancy, Micronesia
N. J. Redman, UK
B. Reed, UK
H. Rienhard, Bruce Coleman Ltd., UK
J. van Remsen Jr., Louisiana State University, USA
L. M. Renjifo, University of Missouri–St Louis, USA
R. S. Ridgely, Philadelphia Academy of Natural Sciences, USA
D. Rinke, Brehm-Fonds Sudsee Expedition, Germany
D. Riven, Environment Planning Group, Barbados
M. R. Robbins, Museum of Natural History, University of Kansas, USA
T. J. Roberts, UK
A. Robertson, UK
H. Robertson, Department of Conservation, New Zealand
S. A. Robertson, Kenya
C. R. Robson, UK
G. Rocamora, Division of the Environment, Seychelles
P. Rodewald, University of Arkansas, USA
C. Rose, UK
L. A. Ruedas, Cincinati Museum of Natural History, USA
P. Ryan, Percy FitzPatrick Institute, South Africa
R. J. Safford, Royal Holloway Institute for Environmental Research, UK
P. Salaman, Edward Grey Institute, UK
T. Salathé, Tour du Valat, France

R. S. Sankaran, SACON, India
D. E. Sargeant, Netherlands
A. Schubert, Departamento de Vida Silvestre, Dominican Republic
T. S. Schulenberg, Field Museum of Natural History, USA
P. Scofield, Royal Australasian Ornithologists' Union
J. M. Scott, Idaho Cooperative Fish and Wildlife Research Unit, USA
N. Seddon, UK
R. Seitre, France
L. L. Severinghaus, Chinese Wild Bird Federation, Taiwan
V. Sharma, State College, India
C. J. Sharpe, Venezuela
T. W. Sherry, Cooperación Técnica, Honduras
C. G. Sibley, USA
B. Simpson, UK
P. Singh, Wildlife Institute of India
S. Sirgouant, Service de l'Environnemnent et de la Gestion des Parcs et Réserves, New Caledonia
A. Skerrett, Seychelles
E. Smith, UK
N. G. Smith, Smithsonian Tropical Research Institute, Panama
T. Smith, San Francisco State University, USA
D. W. Snow, Natural History Museum, UK
G. J. Speight, UK
C. Spottiswoode, South Africa
D. W. Steadman, New York State Museum, USA
J. Stevenson, Royal Society for the Protection of Birds, UK

T. Stevenson, Kenya
F. G. Stiles, Instituto de Ciencias Naturales, Colombia
D. W. Stinson, Department of Natural Resources, Northern Mariana Islands
T. Stokes, Great Barrier Reef Marine Park Authority, Australia
F. C. Straube, Museu de Historia Natural 'Capão de Inbúia', Brazil
N. Stronach, Ireland
S. N. Stuart, IUCN Species Survival Commission, Switzerland
S. Subramanya, University of Agricultural Sciences, Bangalore, India
M. and S. Sulley, UK
A. and R. Sutton, Jamaica
J. O. Svendsen, Denmark
P. Sweet, American Museum of Natural History, USA
P. O. Syversten, University of Oslo, Norway
B. Tabaranza, Haribon Foundation, Philippines
L. Tacconi, University of New South Wales, Australia
B. Taylor, University of Natal, South Africa
R. Taylor, Natal Parks Board, South Africa
J.-C. Thibault, France
J.-M. Thiollay, École Normale Supérieure, Paris, France
G. and V. Thompson, Windrush, UK
R. Thorpe, New Zealand
R. J. Timmins, UK
B. Torres, Brazil
P. W. Trail, Department of Marine and Wildlife Resources, American Samoa
D. A. Turner, Kenya
J.-P. Vande weghe, Uganda
J. P. Vannini, Guatemala

P. Verbelen, Belgium
C. J. Vernon, East London Museum, South Africa
L. Vijayan, SACON, India
F. J. Vilella, US Fish and Wildlife Service, Puerto Rico
P. Villard, CIRAD-CA, Guadeloupe
J. Vincent, South Africa
Wang Sung, Chinese Academy of Sciences
Wang Xian-pu, China Plant Specialist Group
D. Watling, Fiji
J. Watson, Nature Conservancy Council, UK
H. P. Webb, USA
S. Webb, USA
D. R. Wells, UK
D. Weyer, Belize
B. M. Whitney, Field Guides Inc., USA
A. J. Whitten, World Bank, Washington, USA
G. J. Wiles, Department of Agriculture, Guam
J. W. Wiley, USA
J. C. Z. Woinarsksi, Conservation Commission, Australia
P. Wood, Royal Society for the Protection of Birds, UK
The late Wu Zhi-kang, Guizhou Institute of Biology, China
J. M. Wunderle, Institute of Tropical Forestry, Puerto Rico
Xu Wei-shu, China Ornithological Society
V. J. Zacharias, Project Tiger, India
Zhang Zheng-wang, Beijing Normal University, China
Zheng Guang-mei, China Ornithological Society
Zhou Fang, Guangxi, China
F. Zino, Madeira

Photographs We thank the following people for sending us, or allowing us to use, their photographs or copies of their paintings free of charge. These have helped to bring the text alive by showing readers the amazing range of habitats and birds (and other wildlife) which occur in Endemic Bird Areas, and also some of the threats which face some of these places.

P. Alström, J. K. Archer, J. S. Ash, C. Balchin, B. Beehler, A. J. Begazo, B. D. Bell, K. D. Bishop, P. Bison, P. Boesman, R. Brace, M. de L. Brooke, D. J. Brooks, T. Brooks, S. Butchart, A. Challenger, N. J. Collar, B. Cox, J. Croxall, M. Davies, R. J. Douthwaite, G. Duke, G. C. L. Dutson, M. Edwards, G. Ekstrom, J. M. M. Ekstrom, P. G. H. Evans, J. H. Fanshawe, E. Faull, A. and J. Fitter, C. Fitzgibbon, J. Fjeldså, J. Flynn, B. Forester, P. D. Goriup, R. F. A. Grimmett, C. T. Hanashiro, C. Harcourt, S. Harrap, F. Hawkins, M. F. Heath, R. Hill, T. Hjarsen, S. N. G. Howell, I. Isherwood, L. Jammes, J. J. Jeffrey, P. Jepson, P. J. Jones, C. Kennedy, M. Lammertink, C. Levy, J. Lowen, G. Mackey, G. Magnin, A. Marogh, R. P. Martins, S. Miller, R. Mittermeier, P. Morris, J. Moyer, C. Mullen, R. Noske, U. Olsson, J. P. O'Neill, R. Pople, R. F. Porter, M. K. Poulsen, H. D. Pratt, T. Pratt, T. Pridham, H. B. Rajao, H. Reinhard, C. Robson, G. Rocamora, R. J. Safford, P. G. W. Salaman, T. Salathé, N. Seddon, R. Seitre, C. Sharpe, B. Simpson, C. Spottiswoode, K. Takehara, H. Taylor, J. Tobias, J. Watson, S. Webb.

We are especially grateful to Norman Arlott, Hilary Burn, Peter Hayman, Chris Rose and Clive Byers for allowing us to reproduce their paintings which were specially commissioned for members of the Rare Bird Club, many of whom have sponsored this book (see p. 3).

SUMMARY

The problem

Biodiversity—the total variety of life on earth—is being lost at an increasing pace. Despite growing popular support to stem this loss, conservation is hindered because financial resources are limited and the knowledge of the distribution of most organisms is poor.

Towards a solution

BirdLife International's *Biodiversity Project* makes a unique contribution to the identification of priorities for biodiversity conservation by using *birds*—one of the best-known groups of animals—as *indicators of areas of high endemism*. Limited conservation resources can most effectively be directed at these places.

The Biodiversity Project's results

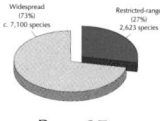

Page 27

- Over 25% of all birds (2,561 species) have *restricted ranges*, being confined to areas of *less than 50,000 km²* (the size of Costa Rica).

- These small areas *overlap to form Endemic Bird Areas* (EBAs), such that the majority of restricted-range species (93% of them) are encompassed by 218 EBAs.

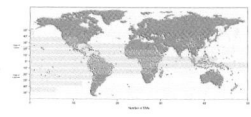

Page 30

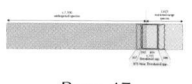

Page 47

- The restricted-range birds include 816 species that are currently classified as threatened—*74% of all threatened bird species*. Most (80%) of the 62 species that have gone extinct in the last 200 years also had restricted ranges.

- EBAs are found around the world, but most (77%) of them are located in the *tropics and subtropics*. The top countries for EBAs are Indonesia, Mexico, Brazil, Peru, Colombia, Papua New Guinea and China, all of which have more than 10 each.

Page 37

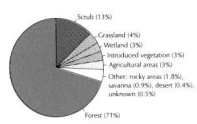

Page 31

- The natural habitat in most EBAs (83%) is *forest*, especially tropical lowland and montane moist forest.

- EBAs vary considerably in *size* (from a few square kilometres to more than 100,000 km²) and in the *numbers* of restricted-range species that they support (from two to 80).

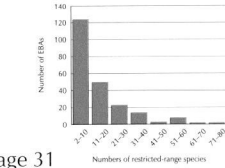

Page 31

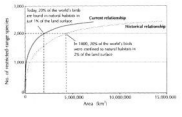

Page 33

- Historically, some 20% of the world's birds were totally confined to EBAs whose area covered 2% of the earth's land surface. Today almost half of the EBAs have lost more than 50% of their key habitats, and *20% of the world's birds can be found in only 1% of the earth's land surface* where these habitats still remain.

- Most EBAs (85%) have one or more *threatened* or extinct restricted-range bird species. Many restricted-range species are at risk—even in EBAs where the habitat remains relatively intact—owing to the intrinsic vulnerability of having a very small range and/or population.

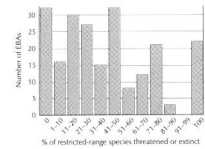

Page 35

Page 51

- The majority of EBAs are important for restricted-range species from *other wildlife groups*. For example, there is a close similarity (an overlap of more than 60%) between the location of EBAs and areas which are similarly important for plants.

What can be done now?

- These findings show that the conservation of a major part of the earth's terrestrial biodiversity can indeed be ensured by focusing conservation resources and actions within a relatively small total area. The *EBAs* of the world are clearly *priorities for conservation action*.

- At the national level, information on EBAs can be used directly in the implementation of conservation agreements, notably the *Convention on Biological Diversity* which among other things requires member states to identify important areas and ecosystems.

- At the local level, representative key sites within EBAs can be targeted, such as in BirdLife's *Important Bird Areas* programme, which makes recommendations for specific conservation action, ranging from the establishment and management of protected areas to the sustainable use of natural resources.

BIODIVERSITY
AND PRIORITY-SETTING

Biodiversity,

or biological diversity, is the total variety of life on earth.

It includes all genes, populations, species and ecosystems and the ecological processes of which they are part. At the ecosystem level, biodiversity underpins the ecological processes which are vital to human life, for example in influencing global climate patterns, in mediating the carbon cycle, in safeguarding watersheds, and in stabilizing soils to prevent desertification. At the species level, components of biodiversity in the form of domesticated and wild animals, plants and micro-organisms provide a vast array of goods and services which are often essential to the survival of humanity as well as being of enormous economic value. Other more wide-reaching but less tangible values may also be ascribed to biodiversity. There is the value of the various components of biodiversity that have yet to be discovered or realized; there is the value attached by many people to the mere fact that biodiversity exists; and there is the value of leaving existing levels of biodiversity to future generations. Taken together, these underscore the immense importance of biodiversity to mankind, and provide compelling arguments for maintaining it.

HOW MUCH DO WE KNOW ABOUT BIODIVERSITY?

Although we have accumulated a great deal of information on biodiversity (see Groombridge 1992 and UNEP 1995 for comprehensive reviews and further references), our knowledge still remains highly incomplete and biased. To date some 1.7 million species, of all forms of life, have been named and described scientifically. This is believed to include a high proportion of the true number of the world's larger terrestrial plants and animals, particularly the so-called higher vertebrates (birds, mammals, reptiles and amphibians), but a far smaller percentage of other groups, especially invertebrates, fungi and micro-organisms, which between them comprise the vast majority of living species. Estimates for the total number of species on earth vary from 10 million to 100 million. Although there is increasing consensus that the true figure is probably at the lower end of this range, this still implies that more than 80% of species have yet to be scientifically described. Even among the best-known taxonomic groups (birds and mammals) new discoveries are still regularly made (see Box 2 on p. 46). Detailed or complete information on distribution is available for only a very small proportion of described species—again, mostly large and conspicuous ones—and there is reliable information on population numbers for even fewer.

Our knowledge of biodiversity is geographically as well as taxonomically biased. Most information is available for terrestrial temperate regions with far less known about other parts of the world, particularly the tropics and aquatic regions. Even within temperate latitudes there are extremely few areas, or even sites, for which anything approaching complete species inventories exist, even if micro-organisms are excluded. Nevertheless, we do know enough to be able to make a number of general observations about the distribution and current status of bio-diversity.

HOW IS BIODIVERSITY DISTRIBUTED?

One of the most important attributes of biodiversity is that it is not evenly distributed. Ultimately this is because each species has its own unique range, largely a product of the interaction between existing ecological conditions and the species' evolutionary history. It should be noted, however, that many species share broadly similar (but usually not identical) distribution patterns.

Ecological effects

The following very general rules determining the distribution of biodiversity appear to apply to terrestrial ecosystems:

- Warmer areas support more species than colder ones.
- Wetter areas support more species than drier ones.
- Less seasonal areas support more species than very seasonal ones.
- Areas with varied topography and climatic conditions support more species than uniform ones.

It is also true that, all other things being equal, larger areas are more diverse than smaller ones.

Globally, perhaps the single most important overall trend is the increase in species diversity with decreasing latitude, so that the number of species in any given area is, on average, far higher in tropical latitudes than in temperate or polar regions. There is also a marked tendency for diversity to be higher in forests than in other terrestrial ecosystems, although there are exceptions to this, notably the extremely high floristic diversity of Mediterranean heath-type vegetation. Tropical moist forests are widely accepted to be the most diverse terrestrial ecosystems.

Evolutionary influences

While the diversity of a given area and the kinds of organisms that can survive there are very largely determined by existing ecological conditions, it is evolutionary history that determines which species actually occur there. Because geographical features present barriers to the dispersal of species (e.g. dry land forms a barrier to most aquatic organisms, while water-bodies present barriers to many terrestrial organisms), each species tends to remain confined to the particular part of the world in which it evolved, even if habitats suitable for it exist elsewhere. For this reason, rain forests in, say, Papua New Guinea and Peru will have very different floras and faunas even though the ecological conditions in them are very similar.

Of course, some species and groups of species are very good at dispersing—and those that in addition have broad habitat tolerances have generally become widespread. However, many species remain confined to small areas, either because they cannot disperse from them, or because they have highly specific habitat requirements, or both. These species are often referred to as endemics (the concept of endemism can in fact be applied at any geographical scale, so that species can be considered endemic to a continent, although in practice the term is usually applied to species with small or restricted ranges). As a general rule, isolated areas support a higher proportion of endemic species than areas which are contiguous with or close to other similar areas; furthermore, the longer an area has been isolated, the higher is the proportion of endemic species likely to be found there. For terrestrial species the most obvious isolated areas are islands, and it is unsurprising that a significant proportion of restricted-range species occur only on them (see Box 1).

Existing biogeographical patterns are complicated by the fact that the landscape itself is not a static entity, but is constantly changing owing to climatic and geological factors. This means that barriers to the dispersal of different species may appear and disappear over time. There are some areas of the world, however, where environmental conditions have stayed predictable such that they have re-

---

Box 1. The special case of islands.

As would be expected from the general rules outlined in this chapter, patterns of diversity on islands are heavily influenced by their degree of isolation (both past and present), by their age and by their size. Generally, islands tend to be poorer in species than equivalent mainland areas, with geologically young islands being particularly depauperate. Truly 'oceanic' islands—those which have never been part of a continent (mostly those resulting from volcanic activity in the middle of oceans)—can become populated with organisms only through colonization. They thus tend to be very poor in groups of species for which water represents an important barrier to dispersal, such as non-flying mammals and amphibians, but relatively richer in groups which can cross such barriers, most notably birds.

mained forested during the cool and arid climatic episodes of the ice ages. These places are often referred to as 'refugia' and have accumulated species over a long time. At the global level the most important mechanisms affecting species distribution are plate tectonics. The break-up of the supercontinent Pangaea 180 million years ago into Gondwanaland and Laurasia, and thence into the continents as they exist today, has largely determined the patterns of distribution of the major groups of terrestrial organisms. Changing sea-levels have affected this by, for example, allowing the continents of North and South America to be successively linked then separated through the Central American isthmus.

Biogeographers now recognize six major biogeographic realms each with a distinctive though not completely separate fauna and flora. These are the Palearctic (Europe, North Africa and northern and western Asia), the Nearctic (North America), the Neotropical (Central and South America), the Afrotropical (Africa south of the Sahara and Arabia), the Indomalayan (India and south-east Asia) and the Australasian (Australia, New Guinea and associated islands). Within these biogeographic realms, many of the species are specialized to particular ecological conditions, leading to groups of species which are characteristic of particular vegetation zones and which share broadly similar distributions.

Human impacts

Natural patterns of distribution have been further influenced by one overwhelmingly important factor: the actions of humans. Mankind has played a major role in decreasing the ranges and populations of many species and, more rarely, in increasing those of others, either deliberately (in the case of domesticated species and some wild species) or accidentally (for example in the case of many weeds and commensal pests, such as rats and mice, and species of disturbed habitats). There is increasingly persuasive evidence that these impacts stretch back for millennia, so that most of the world as it exists today—or at least the terrestrial part of it—has been modified by man. The principal effect of this has undoubtedly been, and continues to be, a progressive loss of biological diversity.

HOW QUICKLY IS BIODIVERSITY BEING LOST?

The extinction of species is perhaps the single most significant measure of the loss of biodiversity. Species extinction is, of course, a natural process. The fossil record strongly suggests that all species have a finite lifespan, with the number of extinct species vastly outnumbering the number of living species.

However, there is evidence that rates of extinction brought about directly or indirectly by human agency greatly exceed background or 'natural' rates of extinction and that these rates are accelerating. It seems incontrovertible that we are heading towards an extinction spasm which, if unchecked, has the potential to be the greatest since the end of the Mesozoic era, 60 million years ago, which saw the extinction of the dinosaurs, plesiosaurs and pterosaurs in what was possibly the aftermath of a single catastrophic event, namely the collision of an asteroid with the earth.

Estimating current extinction rates and predicting future ones are both problematic processes. Because our knowledge of species is incomplete, many estimates are based not on observed or recorded species extinctions, but rather on extrapolations from estimates of habitat loss coupled with assumptions derived from biogeographic theory relating numbers of species to area of habitat. The most widely applied assumption is that a tenfold reduction in area (i.e. loss of 90% of habitat) eventually results in the loss of half the species present. Most quoted global extinction rates have been based on estimates of species richness in tropical forests combined with estimates of actual and projected deforestation rates (on the assumption that the great majority of species are found in tropical forests). Early, very high estimates (11–15% of species lost per decade) have generally been revised downwards, with the most recent estimates indicating perhaps 2–5% of species lost per decade. Taking a conservative estimate of 10 million species on earth this would amount to a potential loss of 20,000–50,000 species per year, the vast majority of which would be invertebrates.

Another attempt to predict extinction rates used data on known extinctions of major animal and plant taxa since 1600, and examined rates at which species had been added to or removed from Red Lists of threatened species (i.e. those most at risk of extinction), concluding that half the planet's 9,600 bird and 4,600 mammal species would be lost within 200–300 years, and half the 2,200–2,600 palm species in 50–100 years (Smith *et al.* 1993). A more recent prediction of avian extinction rates, also comparing two Red Lists but using sounder and more rigorous data, suggested that the time to extinction of half the world's birds will be 800–2,800 years (Crosby *et al.* 1994). Although less pessimistic than the previous study, even this rate of extinction is 100–1,000 times greater than might be expected under natural conditions as illustrated by the fossil record.

There are many potentially important factors which have not been taken into consideration in these global models of extinction rates, and they are generally intended to serve only as very rough indications. There can be no doubt however that, whatever the real rate, the loss of biodiversity is accelerating, being no longer driven by the earth's climatic fluctuations and geological upheavals as in past eras, but instead linked ultimately to rapid human population growth and unsustainable economic activity.

PRIORITY-SETTING FOR CONSERVATION

Just as mankind is responsible for the current loss of species, so we are also capable of taking action to stem this loss. Given that resources are limited and destructive activities are expanding, it is widely recognized that choices must be made, so that attention is focused on those components of biodiversity most in need of conservation action. There are many different ways of addressing this issue, each approach having its own advantages and its own drawbacks.

Single-species approaches

One important approach involves identifying those individual components of biodiversity, usually species, which most merit conservation action. These species are generally either large and charismatic, or highly endangered, or both. A wide range of actions may be undertaken to attempt their conservation, involving protection and sometimes intensive management of habitat and captive breeding/propagation and reintroduction. This approach often finds legal expression in national legislation such as the US Endangered Species Act, which requires that all endangered species occurring in the USA have recovery plans developed for them. A notable number of plant and animal species have undoubtedly been saved from extinction—at least temporarily—in this way (e.g. Whooping Crane *Grus americana* and black-footed ferret *Mustela nigripes*).

However, such approaches are often very expensive and labour-intensive and can accommodate no more than a fraction of the species currently under threat. These may well serve as flagships for conservation, particularly if they are high-profile species such as Arabian oryx *Oryx leucoryx* or white rhinoceros *Ceratotherium simum*, but efforts to conserve them are likely to benefit other species (e.g. through the setting aside of large areas of habitat) only in an incidental rather than in a systematic way.

Area-based approaches

Identifying areas which are important for more than just one species, and then attempting to protect them, might be expected to be a more efficient approach to conservation in the long term. However, there are both practical and theoretical difficulties in identifying areas which are important for biodiversity in this wider sense. One of these is the fact that data on the distribution of the world's species are so incomplete and so heavily biased towards large, conspicuous forms, that decisions have to be made on the basis of partial knowledge. Secondly, when identifying priority areas for biodiversity conservation, the question of geographical scale is fundamentally important; the major reason for this is that diversity generally increases with increasing area but the rate of increase is rarely uniform and varies from place to place (see Box 2). Lastly, the importance of any given area for biodiversity very often cannot easily be quantified in a single measure but rather may need to be seen as a function of several separate attributes, including:

- Its richness—expressed by the number of species present.

- How representative it is—indicated by how well a particular area holds the key habitats and species representative of a wider area.

Box 2. The importance of scale.

The relative apparent diversity (and thereby importance) of different areas will often depend on the scale at which diversity is measured. As an example, one square metre of semi-natural European chalk grassland will contain many more plant species than one square metre of lowland Amazonian rain forest, whereas for an area of one square kilometre this relationship will be reversed. This implies that an area which may appear important at a local level may cease to be so when considered from a regional or global standpoint.

As areas increase in size beyond a certain level, the practical value of assessing and comparing them tends to decrease. This is because large areas may be diverse for different reasons. Such areas may be diverse because they have a large number of different habitats or ecosystems, any individual one of which may be low in diversity, or they may have a small number of highly diverse ecosystems. Approaches to conservation planning will differ in the two cases. In addition, there is a limit to the size of an area which it is realistic to consider protecting or managing for conservation, or which is helpful in indicating priorities. This limit, which varies both in space and time, is determined by political and economic processes outside the control of biology. As an extreme example, identifying South America as the most diverse of the earth's continents gives no guidance on where conservation efforts should be directed as there is no prospect whatever of protecting the entire continent or of abandoning the others.

- Its uniqueness—reflected in the number of species with restricted ranges which it harbours (and particularly in the number of species endemic to the selected area), or in the number of ecosystems of limited extent which are present.

- Its degree of threat—often represented by the number of threatened species present (and particularly by the number of highly threatened species), or by the percentage loss of its natural habitats.

- Its genetic contribution—demonstrated by some calculation of the taxonomic distinctiveness of species present.

- Its population value—as shown by the numbers of individuals of species present (particularly relevant where the area holds key sites which harbour a significant proportion of the species' total population).

Area-based approaches to priority-setting for conservation vary depending on which of these attributes is considered paramount. Some of the advantages and disadvantages of the first three attributes are outlined below. However, none of these priority-setting approaches operates in a vacuum, for most countries in the world already have a more or less extensive protected-area network (see Box 3).

Richness: the megadiversity approach

It is self-evident that areas with high levels of biodiversity will be important for its long-term maintenance. Identifying such areas should therefore provide

Box 3. Finding gaps in protected-area networks.

Many existing protected areas have been established for reasons other than the maintenance of biodiversity—for amenity or recreational value or to protect spectacular landscape features. Even where such areas do have the aim of protecting wild species, they have often been established for large, well-known but not necessarily threatened ones. Expediency has also played a major role in that the areas set aside are often those that do not have immediate or obvious value for other purposes, so that for example montane areas are usually well represented in protected-area networks while lowland areas on soils with high agricultural potential are not. An important part in conservation planning therefore is 'gap analysis', which determines the extent to which biodiversity conservation priorities are already covered in existing protected-area networks (Scott *et al.* 1993). One problem with gap analysis is that there is often no straightforward way of combining different attributes such as the richness, uniqueness and representativeness of different areas in order to assess their importance for biodiversity conservation, and thereby to produce an overall ranking of conservation priorities (see Box 4).

Box 4. Complementarity: a tool for prioritizing areas.

Where detailed data are available, the concept of 'complementarity' has proved to be an interesting development in conservation biology. Complementarity analysis attempts to find the most efficient way, or at least one of the most efficient ways, of including all examples of a particular set of species in a network or system. When applied to conservation problems it is generally used to choose the minimum set of areas which includes at least one population of all representatives of a given group of plants or animals.

Several different computer-based algorithms have been developed to perform complementarity analyses, which may be carried out at any scale. They usually begin by choosing the most diverse area, then the area with the largest number of species not included in the first area and so on until all species are represented. They have been used globally, for example, to determine a set of countries which includes populations of all known swallowtail butterflies (Collins and Morris 1985) and locally to design a reserve network which includes all members of the plant family Proteaceae in Cape Province of South Africa (Rebelo 1994).

Complementarity analyses avoid the need to choose between richness, uniqueness and representativeness in ranking areas in importance for biodiversity, but they themselves have a number of limitations. Firstly, and most important, they presuppose the availability of all relevant biodiversity information for all the areas to be considered. Secondly, although it is relatively straightforward to identify a set of areas which include *all* representatives of a given group (as long as the relevant distributional information is available), in practice the possibility of protecting all such areas is almost always remote. The realistic question usually seeks to know which is the best subset of this set of areas (for example, which are the best six out of twenty given areas, or what is the minimum set of areas which will provide 80% or 95% coverage of a given group of species). Thirdly, it can only target strictly limited subsets of species—such as one family of butterflies or one genus of wasps—becoming inoperably complex the more inclusive it becomes.

valuable guidance in the targeting of conservation efforts. This approach is exemplified at a broad scale by the megadiversity country approach (Mittermeier 1988), which identified a relatively small number of countries with a significant proportion of the world's biodiversity, as measured by known numbers of species. However, approaches such as this which use measurement and comparison of overall known diversity to set priorities do not take into account the degree of overlap between different areas. The closer two areas are geographically, the greater is the proportion of species they are likely to share. This applies particularly when the areas to be compared are determined geopolitically (e.g. are countries or provinces) rather than biogeographically: the ranges of species, on continents at least, very rarely adhere to political boundaries. Areas, particularly geopolitical units, which are adjacent are likely therefore to share a high complement of their wild species. Thus two adjacent and highly diverse countries (e.g. Ecuador and Peru) may share so many of their species that including both of them in a list of highest-priority countries leads on the one hand to redundancy and on the other to possible exclusion of countries which are less diverse but have more distinctive fauna and flora.

Representativeness: the ecosystem approach

An alternative approach which attempts to avoid the problem of overlap uses ecosystems as the basic units for analysis and tries to ensure that representative samples of each ecosystem are protected. This is based on the assumption that the world can be divided into a series of largely discrete ecosystems each of which has its own distinctive species composition and physical structure. By protecting representative samples of each, a high proportion of the world's biodiversity should be protected. This approach is exemplified in the IUCN Systems Reviews carried out in the mid-1980s (IUCN/UNEP 1986a,b,c) and, more recently, by the ecoregions analysis of Dinerstein et al. (1995).

In reality, however, the natural environment cannot always be easily divided into a series of discrete units but in many places seems to form a variable continuum. This being the case, the mapping of boundaries between ecosystems invariably involves a degree of arbitrariness—as does deciding whether any given area is truly representative of some larger ecosystem. In addition, habitat or ecosystem classification systems are highly scale-dependent (see Box 2), such that no one system is appropriate to use at all scales. Very broad-based systems (those at continental or global level) may provide a general overview and highlight major gaps but give little guidance on exactly where conservation activity should be directed, whereas more detailed systems become increasingly site-specific and are of less value in making comparisons and in priority-setting.

Uniqueness: the hotspot approach

A potentially highly efficient approach to identifying conservation priorities is to use knowledge of the distributions of species to identify areas which are particularly rich in narrowly distributed species, such as islands and continental refugia. These areas will by definition contain a high complement of just those species which may be expected by virtue of their small ranges to be most vulnerable to extinction and therefore most in need of conservation action.

A study which emphasized the importance of narrowly distributed species was the botanical 'hotspots' analysis of Myers (1988a, 1990), who identified 18 sites—primarily in tropical forest, but also including Mediterranean vegetation located in the temperate zone—which in total contained over 50,000 endemic species of plants (20% of the world's known plant species) in 746,400 km^2 (0.5% of the world's land surface). This approach has been developed for birds in this study.

IDENTIFYING ENDEMIC BIRD AREAS

BIRDLIFE INTERNATIONAL'S Biodiversity Project began in 1987 with the aim of contributing to the identification of priority areas for biodiversity conservation, drawing upon the expertise of BirdLife's global network of ornithologists. The project has already had a significant impact (Box 1), particularly through the publication of *Putting biodiversity on the map: priority areas for global conservation* (ICBP 1992). However, this is the first time that the scientific basis for the project's results has been published in detail.

It is a phenomenon well known to biologists that certain areas of the world, particularly in tropical regions, support concentrations of animal and plant species with restricted ranges, i.e. species that are found nowhere else on earth. These species are often

---

Box 1. Milestones in the BirdLife Biodiversity Project.

1987 BirdLife International decides to initiate a project to identify key areas for biodiversity conservation, using restricted-range bird species as indicators, and drawing upon years of data-gathering on threatened birds and a worldwide network of ornithological experts.

1988 The project concept and methodology are developed.

1988–1991 The main data-gathering phase. A total of five staff members (plus seven other short-term staff and collaborators) collect more than 50,000 locality records for restricted-range bird species.

1991 Information is collated on other animal and plant groups to investigate the importance of EBAs for non-avian biodiversity.

1991–1992 The first analysis of the distribution patterns of restricted-range bird species is completed. A total of 221 Endemic Bird Areas (EBAs) are identified and a summary of the project results are published in *Putting biodiversity on the map: priority areas for global conservation* (ICBP 1992).

1992–1993 The first drafts documenting the EBAs are prepared and sent out for review to over 350 regional experts.

1993–1997 Several analyses of the Biodiversity Project data are published (see Appendix 5, p. 784).

1993 The selection of sites for the conservation of restricted-range species is adopted as one of the criteria for BirdLife International's Important Bird Areas Programme (see p. 55).

1994 *Putting biodiversity on the map* is awarded the Amsterdam Prize for the Environment 1994 by the Royal Netherlands Academy of Arts and Sciences, a prize made available by the Alfred Heineken Fondsen Foundation. The data gathered on restricted-range species is used to help identify and document many globally threatened species in *Birds to watch 2: the world list of threatened birds* (Collar *et al.* 1994).

1995 A poster entitled *Biodiversity: priority areas for conservation* is produced to advocate the project results for use in the implementation of the Convention on Biological Diversity.

1995–1996 Information on the EBAs of Indonesia is published in the book, *Conserving biodiversity: the Endemic Bird Area approach* (Sujatnika *et al.* 1995), to highlight the outstanding importance of Indonesia for endemic birds. The book is launched by the Indonesian Ministry of Forestry, and presented to President Suharto. The EBA documentation is updated for the rest of the world and the analysis is refined. A final total of 218 EBAs is recognized.

1997 *Endemic Bird Areas of the world: priorities for biodiversity conservation* is completed, including—for the first time—details of the scientific basis for the project's results.

The publication of this book coincides, fittingly, with the 75th anniversary of the founding of the International Council for Bird Preservation—now BirdLife International—and marks a major milestone in BirdLife's mission to *conserve all bird species on earth and their habitats and, through this, to work for the world's biological diversity and the sustainability of human use of natural resources.*

Box 2. Basic principles of the Endemic Bird Area analysis.

A **restricted-range bird species** is a landbird which is judged to have had a breeding range of less than 50,000 km² throughout historical times (since 1800). Some birds which have small ranges today were historically widespread, and are therefore not treated as restricted-range species. Extinct birds which qualify on range size are included.

Range equivalent to size of Costa Rica

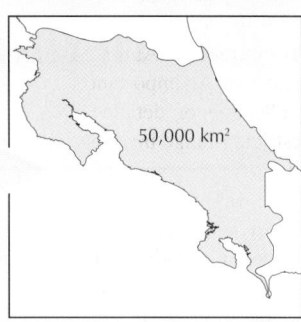

An **Endemic Bird Area (EBA)** is defined as an area which encompasses the over-lapping breeding ranges of restricted-range bird species, such that the complete ranges of two or more restricted-range species are entirely included within the boundary of the EBA. This does not necessarily mean that the complete ranges of *all* of an EBA's restricted-range species are entirely included within the boundary of that single EBA, as some species may be shared between EBAs.

E.g. the Da Lat plateau in Vietnam (EBA 145)

Adjacent areas are identified as **separate EBAs** when more restricted-range bird species are confined to each individual area than are shared between them. EBAs thus reflect the most common patterns of distribution. Widely disjunct records of restricted-range bird species may sometimes be excluded from the EBA (see definition of 'Secondary Area', below).

E.g. Réunion (EBA 101) and Mauritius (EBA 102)

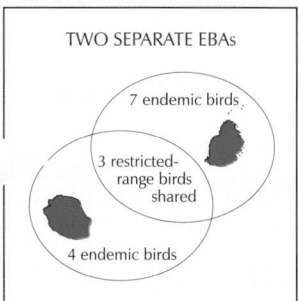

A **Secondary Area** is an area which supports one or more restricted-range bird species, but does not qualify as an EBA because fewer than two species are entirely confined to it. Typical Secondary Areas include single restricted-range species which do not overlap in distribution with any other such species, and places where there are widely disjunct records of one or more restricted-range species.

E.g. Rapa, French Polynesia (Sec. Area s136)

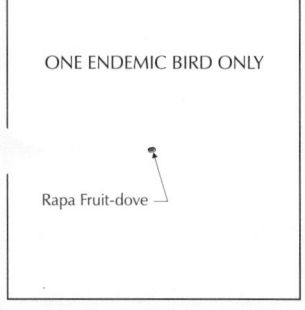

vulnerable to extinction through destruction of their habitats as well as through other threats. The BirdLife Biodiversity Project is the first systematic, global-scale analysis to identify these hotspots—known as Endemic Bird Areas (EBAs)—using restricted-range birds as indicators. An important feature of the project was the collection of detailed data on all of the world's restricted-range bird species, to provide not only the basis for overview analyses at global and regional level, but also more detailed conservation evaluations on a national and local scale.

Two pioneering studies have been particularly important in the development of this project's methodology. Hall and Moreau (1962) collated information on the distribution, ecology and status of 96 restricted-range bird species in sub-Saharan Africa, which they discussed in relation to past climatic and vegetational changes within that continent; they identified several areas with concentrations of such species, and discussed endemism in tropical Africa in relation to other regions of the world. Terborgh and Winter (1983) mapped the distributions of 155 Colombian and Ecuadorian bird species with ranges estimated at less than 50,000 km^2, and used these data to locate areas of concentrated endemism which they were able to demonstrate to be optimal for designation as parks and reserves. Some of these ideas have been incorporated into this study, notably the 50,000-km^2 range-size criterion.

The main stages of the BirdLife Biodiversity Project were:

- To review the distribution of all the world's bird species, in order to make an initial selection of those with restricted ranges.
- To gather all available point-locality records and relevant ecological data for all of these restricted-range species, in order to produce accurate species maps.
- To analyse the data compiled on restricted-range species to identify EBAs, and to determine their boundaries.
- To document these EBAs, including informative texts and accurate maps to show their location.

SELECTION OF RESTRICTED-RANGE BIRD SPECIES

In this study, restricted-range species are defined as all landbirds which have had, throughout historical times (i.e. post-1800, in the period since ornithological recording began), a total global breeding range estimated at below 50,000 km^2 (Box 2). Species with historical ranges estimated to be above this threshold, but which have been reduced to below 50,000 km^2 by habitat loss or other pressures, were not covered because the project has sought to locate natural areas of endemism for birds, which are also

---

Box 3. Taxonomy and nomenclature.

The taxonomy of birds has until recently remained relatively stable. However, the publication of Sibley and Ahlquist (1990) and Sibley and Monroe (1990, 1993) has generated new interest in bird taxonomy in many regions of the world. Moreover, the influence of the phylogenetic species concept (see Cracraft 1983, Zink and McKitrick 1995), and current trends in the application of the biological species concept (see Haffer 1997), are now beginning to lead to many bird taxa being considered full species having formerly been treated as distinct subspecies.

In this project, Sibley and Monroe (1990, 1993) has been used as the basic source for species taxonomy, and for both scientific and English names, because it is the most up-to-date global list—although the family sequence of Morony et al. (1975) (which is based on Peters 1934–1987) has been followed because it is currently more familiar to most ornithologists. The species taxonomy of Andrew (1992) has been used for Indonesia, and Christidis and Boles (1994) for Australia, because they are regarded as the standards in those countries (where most of the restricted-range species are national endemics). In a few other cases we diverge from the species taxonomy of Sibley and Monroe, where there is recent published evidence that this is the most appropriate course. In total, 72 additional species are recognized,

and 20 species new to science since the publication of the Sibley and Monroe list have also been included.

It should be noted that there currently appear to be significant regional differences in the application of the species taxonomy followed, which may affect any comparisons between regions. In particular, many morphologically or vocally distinct Asian and African taxa are lumped as subspecies of widespread species, in contrast to South and Central America where similar taxa are more likely to be treated as full species.

In the next few years, it seems likely that many bird taxa will be elevated from subspecies to full species. Many of these taxa, and most species new to science, will have restricted ranges, and these 'new' species clearly have the potential to alter the analysis presented here. It is the case, however, that the taxa resulting from published changes in species limits (and newly described species) since the publication of Sibley and Monroe (1990) have almost all proved to have distributions which are congruent with other restricted-range species, and have thus had minimal effects on the overall analysis. We predict that large-scale changes in species limits in the future will affect the details of this analysis, but will not lead to the identification of many 'new' areas of endemism.

likely to be important for other unique animals and plants (although it is recognized that many species' ranges will have been severely altered by human impact prior to 1800). Restricted-range landbirds which have become extinct since 1800 were included in the analysis, because they have helped to identify areas which have concentrations of such taxa.

Seabirds were excluded from the analysis because their distributions are determined by different factors to those which affect landbirds and other terrestrial taxa, and they are therefore considered to be best treated as a separate group for conservation purposes.

Estimating range sizes

The estimated range sizes of species were based on their 'extent of occurrence' (see IUCN 1994), defined as the area contained within an imaginary boundary (or boundaries if they have a disjunct distribution) which can be drawn to encompass all the known, inferred or projected sites of present occurrence. Coastlines provide convenient boundaries to small islands, but on larger islands and in continental regions these boundaries were defined on the basis of the habitat requirements and altitudinal range of each species. The area within the boundary (or boundaries) was estimated in order to test whether it was above or below the 50,000-km^2 threshold, and hence whether the species has a restricted range. In the case of species with disjunct distributions, the separate portions of the range were totalled to calculate an overall range size.

The range summaries and distribution maps from standard regional and national ornithological references were used to estimate species' range sizes. For example, reasonably accurate maps were available for most South and Central American bird species in Hilty and Brown (1986), Ridgely and Tudor (1989, 1994), Fjeldså and Krabbe (1990), Howell and Webb (1995a) and other references. All Afrotropical species were mapped by Hall and Moreau (1970) and Snow (1978), although more up-to-date maps have

---

Box 4. The Biodiversity Project database.

The information collected on the restricted-range species and the localities where they occur was entered into two simple databases ('Species' and 'Localities'), and information on the Endemic Bird Areas identified by subsequent analysis of these data was lodged in a third 'Areas' database. The use of these simple flat-file databases (in dBase III+ format) avoided the complex linkages between files and the consequent need for a sophisticated user-interface that would have been made necessary by more complex relational databases. Programmes were written to output information as required. This approach is discussed in more detail by Crosby (1994).

The **Species** database was designed to store information about each of the restricted-range species. These birds are often confined to a limited range of habitat types, often in a narrow altitudinal band, so detailed data were collated on their habitat requirements and altitudinal ranges. Other fields in the database were used to store the data required for the outputs and analyses presented in this book, e.g. on distribution by country and threatened status.

Distributional records were stored in the **Localities** database, including the source reference and full details of each recording locality. The geographical coordinates

cont. opposite

Species database file structure

Field name	Description
Species	Scientific name of the species.
Synonyms	Alternative scientific names.
English	English name.
Family code	Family number from Morony et al. (1975), to enable indexing in taxonomic order.
Sequence	Code for sequence of species within families from Sibley and Monroe (1990, 1993), to enable indexing in taxonomic order.
Taxonomy	To record the few cases where taxonomy used differs from Sibley and Monroe (1990, 1993).
Countries	All countries where the species breeds.
Areas	Codes of EBAs and Secondary Areas where the species breeds.
Habitat	Descriptions of breeding habitats, with references to data-sources.
Altitude	Altitudinal range during breeding season, with references to data-sources.
Threat	Threat classification, initially from Collar and Andrew (1988), updated by Collar et al. (1994).

Localities database file structure

Field name	Description
Species	Scientific name of the species.
Reference	Source reference for locality record.
Locality	Name and description of recording locality.
Country	Name of country.
Coordinates	Geographical coordinates of locality (represented in database by eight fields, used as necessary: degrees, minutes, bearing and decimal coordinates, for both latitude and longitude).
Certainty	Code indicating certainty that coordinates relate to correct locality, as follows:
	A Certain: exact match for locality name in gazetteer used; no possibility of ambiguity.
	B Probable: close match for locality in gazetteer, and/or ambiguity possible but unlikely.
	C Possible: reasonable match in gazetteer, but a worrying ambiguity.
	D Unreliable: only a poor match in gazetteer, and/or unresolved ambiguity.

cont. opposite

now been published for several countries, e.g. Kenya (Lewis and Pomeroy 1989). In Asia and the Pacific, distribution details by island have been published for the Philippines (Dickinson *et al.* 1991), Wallacea (White and Bruce 1986), New Guinea (Beehler *et al.* 1986) and the tropical Pacific (Pratt *et al.* 1987), and distribution maps are available for all species in a few countries—notably China (Cheng Tso-hsin 1987), Australia (Blakers *et al.* 1984) and New Zealand (Bull *et al.* 1985)—but for many species maps are either not available or are of poor quality.

Producing a candidate list

For each region of the world, an initial list of candidate restricted-range species was selected on the basis of published information. Many species have ranges which are clearly below the 50,000-km² threshold, and many are obviously too widespread to meet this criterion. The number of marginal species which were not clearly above or below the threshold varied widely between regions: there were relatively few in

island regions (notable exceptions being Madagascar and New Guinea) and in the Americas, because it was possible to make reasonably accurate initial range-size estimates—but many more in parts of Asia. All of these marginal species were covered in the project until it could be determined whether their ranges were above or below the range-size threshold, either on the basis of the data gathered on them or on the advice of regional experts. The list of restricted-range species continued to be refined throughout the project in the light of new information on distribution and ecology, and to follow taxonomic revisions (see Box 3).

DATA-GATHERING AND SPECIES-MAPPING

The main aim of the project's data-gathering stage was to collect the data required to produce detailed species range maps, at a much finer scale than the maps published in most of the references discussed

---

Box 4 (cont.)

of bird localities were found using gazetteers and a standard series of maps which cover the entire world at a 1:1 million scale, the Operational Navigational Charts (Defense Mapping Agency 1984–1988). The coordinates extracted from these sources have been coded according to their certainty (how certainly the coordinates correspond to the locality) and their accuracy (how closely the coordinates match where the bird species was actually recorded). Note that, for many of the smaller islands, records only refer to presence or absence on the islands, rather than to individual localities within them.

An **Areas** database was developed to store information on EBAs and Secondary Areas for output and further analysis. All of these areas have been assigned a unique code and a name. If possible, an established geographical, political or biogeographical name was chosen for the EBA or SA, but where no existing name was available new names had to be devised, usually based on political or geographical features. Since the project results were first published (ICBP 1992), new information and the comments of reviewers have led to a number of changes to the analysis, which are recorded in the Areas database and detailed in Appendix 4 (p. 781).

Accuracy	Code for accuracy of coordinates, as follows:
	A Believed accurate within 5 km.
	B Believed accurate within 20 km.
	C Coordinates not definitely within 20 km of recording locality.
Record year	Year(s) of records at this locality, with any qualifier (e.g. circa).
Altitude	Minimum and maximum altitudes of records at this locality.
Record type	Code for type of record (e.g. specimen, sight record).
Status	Information on breeding status at this locality, months of records, etc.
Notes	Information on abundance at this locality, names of observers, etc.

Areas database file structure

Field name	Description
Type	Code to indicate whether EBA or SA.
Name	Name of area.
Code	Unique area code.
Countries	All countries in the area.

Area	Estimated area of EBA (areas of SAs were not estimated).
Habitat	Key habitats for restricted-range species breeding in the area.
Altitude	Minimum and maximum altitudes encompassing breeding ranges of all restricted-range species present.
Threats	Main threats to the area and its restricted-range species.
Knowledge	Broad assessment of level of ornithological knowledge of the EBA (good, incomplete or poor) (level of knowledge of SAs was not assessed).
Coordinates	Central geographical coordinates of area (represented in database by eight fields, used as necessary: degrees, minutes, bearing and decimal coordinates, for both latitude and longitude).
Confined	Number of restricted-range species which breed only within the area (and their threat status).
Present	Number of restricted-range species which breed in this area but occur also in other EBA(s) and/or SA(s) (and their threat status).

above. All available point-locality records (with their geographical coordinates) of the species on the candidate list were collated, together with information about the occurrence of these species in relation to habitat—the raw materials required for species-mapping. The ornithological literature is rich in these data: the localities and habitats where species have been recorded are often listed or summarized in publications on ornithological expeditions and surveys, regional works, or in studies of a particular species or group; labels of museum specimens are another invaluable source of data, as they often contain unpublished localities or ecological information. These sources had previously been used to compile comprehensive datasets on the globally threatened birds of Africa (Collar and Stuart 1985) and the Americas (Collar *et al.* 1992).

BirdLife International's Red Data Book Programme has built up a network of contacts throughout the world who are active in the field and are able to provide recent, unpublished records of threatened birds. The Biodiversity Project made full use of the Red Data Book datasets and networks, but a large additional data-gathering exercise was required for those restricted-range species from regions of the world which have not yet been covered in a Red Data Book, and for those African and American restricted-range species which are not threatened. Data were extracted from over 3,000 ornithological references during the project, and additional information was received from many of the people listed in the Acknowledgements (p. 6). Altogether over 50,000 individual records were assembled, and all these data were stored electronically (Box 4).

Range maps were plotted for candidate restricted-range species using point-locality data in a Geographical Information System (GIS) computer mapping package. The GIS builds up range maps by displaying these point data, together with base maps which can include coastlines, contours, political boundaries, rivers and other geographical features. Grid lines were added to preliminary maps, to aid the detection and correction of erroneous records or inaccurate coordinates. These maps were used to help evaluate whether marginal candidate restricted-range species had ranges above or below the 50,000-km^2 threshold once their habitat requirements and altitudinal ranges had been taken into account.

THE ENDEMIC BIRD AREA ANALYSIS

The initial stage in the process of identifying EBAs involved the overlap and comparison of species maps to identify areas with concentrations of restricted-range birds.

- An **Endemic Bird Area (EBA)** is defined as an area which encompasses the overlapping breeding ranges of restricted-range bird species, such that the complete ranges of two or more restricted-range species are entirely included within the boundary of the EBA. This does not necessarily mean that the complete ranges of *all* of an EBA's restricted-range species are entirely included within the boundary of that single EBA, as some species may be shared between EBAs (Box 2).

The sharing of species between two or more areas sometimes made it difficult to decide whether these areas should be grouped together as a single EBA or divided into several separate EBAs. A set of guidelines was devised to deal with these cases, designed to use the most common distributional trends displayed by the restricted-range species to define the EBAs (Box 2). Areas were identified as separate EBAs when more restricted-range species were confined to each individual area than were shared between them; or they were grouped as a single EBA when more species were shared than were unique to any individual area. It should be noted that smaller areas of endemism are thus often nested within EBAs (e.g. a single island within an archipelagic EBA).

In some areas, groups of restricted-range species are found in adjacent vegetation zones, with varying degrees of overlap in habitat requirements and altitudinal range between the two groups. In some of these cases, the division of species between these groups was straightforward, with few (or no) species occurring in both vegetation zones, and the two zones were then treated as separate EBAs. When a significant number of species clearly occurred in both of the adjacent vegetation zones they were grouped in a single EBA.

Some restricted-range species occur outside EBAs, in areas referred to as Secondary Areas; the Secondary Areas support one or more restricted-range species but do not qualify as EBAs because fewer than two species are entirely confined to them (Box 2). Typical Secondary Areas include single restricted-range species which do not overlap in distribution with any other such species, and places where there are widely disjunct records of one or more restricted-range species.

Analysis of complex regions

EBAs are often geographically discrete—as in the case of, for example, oceanic islands or isolated mountain ranges—and are then easily identified from the relevant species distribution maps. In more complex regions (such as the Andes of South America) the multivariate statistical package TWINSPAN (Hill 1979) was used to help identify the EBAs. This

Box 5. The process involved in identifying the boundary of an Endemic Bird Area.

The boundaries of EBAs are defined around the records of restricted-range bird records, but may be refined to take account of the extent of key habitat-types and/or relevant geographical features. In this case, the ranges of four restricted-range species on two mountain ranges are the starting point. The boundary has then been refined to match the 1,000-m contour, as the habitat above this altitude is the key type used by the birds. NB Because the two mountain ranges are separated by a valley, not all species occur in both. However, the smaller mountain range has fewer than two species entirely confined to it, and so does not qualify as an EBA in its own right; neither is it sufficiently disjunct to be treated as a Secondary Area (see Box 2).

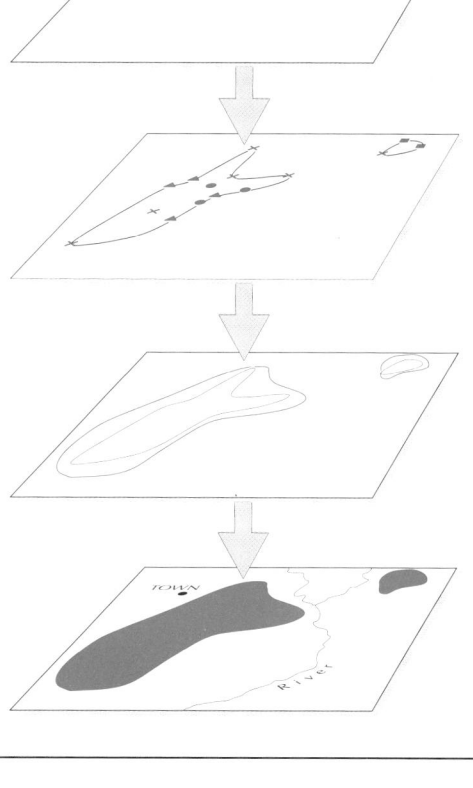

Maps of records
of individual species

Individual species records
overlaid to delineate the
minimum polygon encompassing
the records

EBA boundary is refined using
altitudinal contours, etc. (in this
case, the 1,000-m contour—the
eventual boundary of the EBA)

Final map, showing area of EBA
and geographical features

performs a divisive cluster analysis on multivariate data, in this case distributional data summarized by grid square. It produces a matrix with grid squares in the same EBA grouped on one axis, and the characteristic species of each EBA grouped on the other.

However, the results of the TWINSPAN analyses were often not clear cut and had to be refined through

consideration of the species' habitat requirements and altitudinal ranges, and through consultation with regional experts. The main reason for this was that species from adjacent EBAs were often grouped together in the same grid squares, either because there was a transition from one vegetation zone to another within the boundaries of the grid square, or because of inaccurate coordinates (frequently because the square contained a locality which was used as a base by bird collectors to record specimens or sightings from a relatively wide general area). Another reason is that in these complex regions some restricted-range species often occur in two or more EBAs.

Determining boundaries

The records of the restricted-range species occurring in each EBA were plotted, together with political and geographical features, to provide a guide to the EBA's location and extent. Boundaries to EBAs were defined around the bird records, taking into account the altitudinal ranges and habitat requirements of all the restricted-range species present. A particular geographical feature, such as a coastline or altitudinal contour, could often be used to define accurately the boundaries of EBAs (Box 5). The zones plotted as polygons on vegetation maps sometimes corresponded closely to the EBAs, and could be digitized into the GIS to produce the EBA outlines; this applied particularly to the ecoregions analysis of South America (Dinerstein *et al.* 1995) and the vegetation map of Africa in White (1983). In these cases the areas of the EBAs could be accurately estimated using the GIS. The areas of islands were generally taken from standard references (e.g. Hunter 1994, TAW 1994).

The boundaries of some EBAs could not be clearly defined, often because they lie in poorly known regions (e.g. parts of China) where the distributions and habitat requirements of the birds are not well understood, and an approximate boundary was drawn based on whatever information was available. In such EBAs the habitat requirements of the restricted-range species could usually not be clearly related to a particular geographical feature, or the feature (usually a contour) required to define the boundary was missing from the digital base map. Where boundaries are approximate, the estimated areas of the EBAs are likely to be inaccurate, and in some cases are believed to greatly overestimate the size of the EBAs.

DOCUMENTATION OF ENDEMIC BIRD AREAS

Production of maps

Detailed maps have been produced for all EBAs. These have been designed to show the geographical location of the area as precisely and informatively as is practicable. Political boundaries are shown prominently, including provincial boundaries where appropriate. Most localities and geographical features which are mentioned in the accompanying text are shown on the map, although it has not proved possible to map all the protected areas mentioned because they are often too numerous. Major cities and rivers are included on some maps as an aid to location of the EBA.

The review process

Texts were compiled on all the EBAs and circulated in draft to some 350 regional experts, with the aim that each text would be reviewed by at least two people. Reviewers were asked for their opinions on the most appropriate name for the EBA, whether the species listed did indeed have restricted ranges, and whether any additional restricted-range species had been missed, as well as for their comments on the EBA analysis. They were also asked about the threatened status of the species listed, and this generated a large amount of new information (incorporated in Collar *et al.* 1994). Many reviewers commented on the data on habitat and altitudinal range, and they were asked about the terminology used to describe habitats in the texts, about threats to the EBAs, about important sites for conservation and key protected areas, and about important widespread bird species and other animals and plants which should be mentioned in the text. Many reviewers provided valuable unpublished information and details of important references. This review process refined both the list of restricted-range species covered in the project and the EBA analysis, particularly in many of the more complex regions described earlier, and considerably improved the content and quality of the EBA texts.

GLOBAL ANALYSES

THE ANALYSES presented here are designed to give a broad overview of the data collected on restricted-range species and the Endemic Bird Areas where they occur, and to indicate where there are global patterns and trends which may be of conservation importance. Analyses by political unit are also presented because most conservation action is nationally based.

RESTRICTED-RANGE BIRD SPECIES

How many restricted-range bird species are there?

- *More than a quarter of all the birds of the world have restricted breeding ranges.*

A surprisingly high number—2,623 landbird species, 28% of all landbirds (27% of all birds)—are judged to have had a breeding range of 50,000 km² or less throughout historical times (Figure 1), and therefore qualify as restricted-range species in this study. Of these, 62 are now extinct.

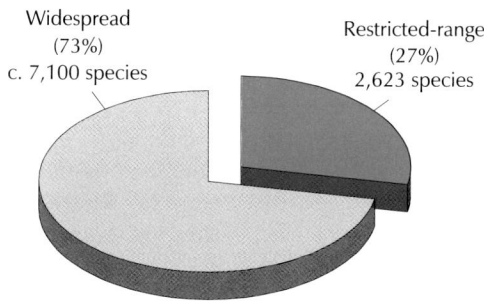

Figure 1. Breeding ranges of the world's bird species.

Where do restricted-range bird species occur?

- *Approximately equal numbers of restricted-range species inhabit islands and continental areas.*

As might be expected, many restricted-range species (53% of the total) occur on islands but almost equal numbers (47%) are found in continental areas. Of the island species, most (69%) occur on oceanic islands with fewer (31%) on continental islands (Figure 2).

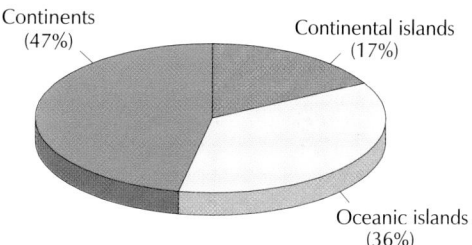

Figure 2. The division between islands and continents of restricted-range landbirds. Continental islands are defined as islands which were once part of continents and which generally lie on a continental shelf less than 200 m below sea-level. Oceanic islands are defined as islands which have never been connected to a continental area by a land-bridge and which are generally volcanic in origin.

What types of birds are restricted-range species?

- *Restricted-range species are very diverse, and include the majority of the landbird families.*

Restricted-range species are found in most landbird families (96 out of the 145 recognized by Morony *et al.* 1975), with some families having significantly higher or lower numbers of such species than might be predicted (Table 1). Those which have unusually high numbers include Drepanididae (Hawaiian honeycreepers: a family which has undergone remarkable adaptive radiation and speciation in an isolated island ecosystem), Zosteropidae (white-eyes: classic small-island colonizers), Paradisaeidae (birds-of-paradise: mostly confined to New Guinea with restricted and/or patchy ranges in the mountains at definite altitudinal zones) and Rhinocryptidae (tapaculos: occurring mainly in the cooler, humid parts of South America at altitudes above 1,000 m).

Table 1. Bird families with significantly high or low numbers of restricted-range species. Families are listed only if more than 50% or fewer than 10% of all their species have restricted ranges.

Family		No. of restricted-range species	Total no. of species	% of family
High numbers of restricted-range species				
Drepanididae	Hawaiian honeycreepers	30	30	100
Mesoenatidae	Mesites	3	3	100
Zosteropidae	White-eyes	79	99	80
Todidae	Todies	4	5	80
Paradisaeidae	Birds-of-paradise	29	44	66
Rhinocryptidae	Tapaculos	19	32	59
Megapodiidae	Megapodes	11	19	58
Tytonidae	Barn owls	9	17	53
Low numbers of restricted-range species				
Hirundinidae	Swallows, martins	8	89	9
Paridae	Tits	5	53	9
Anatidae	Ducks, geese, swans	11	158	7
Ardeidae	Herons, egrets, bitterns	4	66	6
Meropidae	Bee-eaters	1	26	4
Threskiornithidae	Ibises, spoonbills	1	34	3
Dendrocolaptidae	Woodcreepers	0	48	0
Otididae	Bustards	0	25	0
Ciconiidae	Storks	0	19	0
Pteroclididae	Sandgrouse	0	16	0
Gruidae	Cranes	0	15	0
Remizidae	Penduline tits	0	12	0
Recurvirostridae	Avocets, stilts	0	11	0

Other families with significant high numbers of restricted-range species include Columbidae, Psittacidae, Trochilidae, Furnariidae, Formicariidae, Mimidae, Muscicapidae and Meliphagidae. Families with significantly low numbers include Accipitridae, Falconidae, Charadriidae, Rostratulidae, Bucconidae, Picidae, Tyrannidae, Alaudidae, Motacillidae and Ploceidae.

Families were tested at the 95% level for the proportion of restricted-range species being significantly different to the average for all landbirds (28%), using the binomial distribution or normal approximation, as appropriate.

Landbird families which have no restricted-range species (Table 1) tend to have characteristically large species occurring at low densities in open habitats (such as grassland, wetlands and arid areas), and have large breeding ranges; many are nomadic or migratory in their habits.

What habitat-types do restricted-range bird species prefer?

• *Most restricted-range species occur in forest.*

Overall, 71% of all restricted-range species occur in forested habitats with smaller numbers (13%) in 'scrub' habitats (this descriptor often covers dry woodland/forest habitats as well as secondary vegetation). Grassland (4%) and wetland (3%) are relatively much less important (Figure 3).

How many restricted-range bird species are threatened and why?

• *More than half of all restricted-range species qualify as threatened or Near Threatened. The majority of these are affected by habitat loss and alteration.*

A very high proportion of restricted-range species are classified as threatened (31%, compared to 4% for birds which do not have restricted ranges; 11%

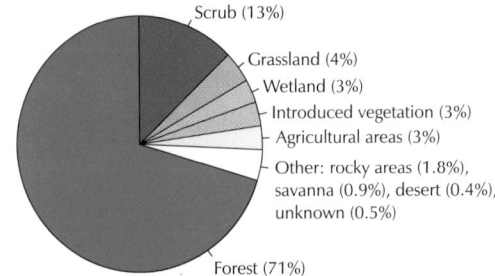

Scrub (13%)
Grassland (4%)
Wetland (3%)
Introduced vegetation (3%)
Agricultural areas (3%)
Other: rocky areas (1.8%), savanna (0.9%), desert (0.4%), unknown (0.5%)
Forest (71%)

Figure 3. Habitats of restricted-range bird species. All species were coded for broad habitat-types used. Equal weight was given where multiple types were allocated.

for all birds) and Near Threatened (19% compared to 5%; 9% overall) (Figure 4). The threatened restricted-range species are divided between the three categories of threat—16% Critical, 22% Endangered and 61% Vulnerable—in similar proportions to those for all threatened species.

Although habitat loss, more specifically loss of forest, is the greatest threat to restricted-range species (affecting 54% of all threatened restricted-range species), many (27%) are judged to be threatened

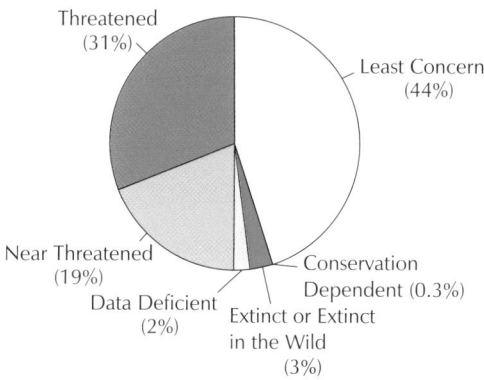

Figure 4. Status of restricted-range bird species.

owing to the intrinsic vulnerability of having very small ranges and/or populations, and smaller numbers are affected by hunting (6%) and introduced species (5%) (Figure 5).

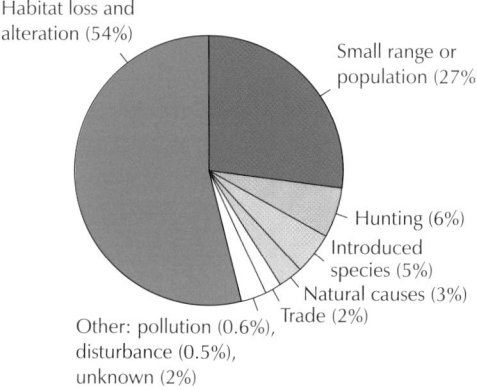

Figure 5. The different threats that act on threatened restricted-range bird species. All species were coded for major threats affecting them. Equal weight was given where multiple types were allocated.

ENDEMIC BIRD AREAS

How many EBAs are there?

- *218 EBAs have been identified, all with at least two restricted-range bird species confined to them.*

Endemic Bird Areas by definition encompass the breeding ranges of two or more restricted-range species. A total of 218 such areas have been identified, covering the ranges of 93% of restricted-range birds (2,451 species, 25% of all birds) and partially covering the ranges of a further 2% (65 species). (The remaining restricted-range species are covered by 138 Secondary Areas, see p. 653; these cover the disjunct ranges of the restricted-range species which also occur in EBAs, as well as the entire ranges of 98,

or 4% of, restricted-range species. A further nine species of unknown provenance are presumed to have restricted breeding ranges; see Appendix 1, p. 724.)

In many EBAs (c.60%) all the restricted-range species have broadly similar habitat requirements and distributions, but in others (c.40%) there are distinct differences in species' distributions related to habitat requirements and to geography; many of these EBAs have smaller areas of finer-scale endemism within their boundaries, such as islands within archipelagos or separate ranges within larger mountain systems.

Where are the EBAs?

- *The tropics are by far the most important zone for EBAs.*

EBAs are scattered around the world but the majority (77%) are situated within the tropics and subtropics, with very few at temperate latitudes (Figure 7). As might be expected with approximately equal numbers of island and continental restricted-range species, there are also approximately equal numbers of island EBAs (105) and continental EBAs (113). Of the island EBAs, 70% are on oceanic islands, with 30% on continental islands. Of the continental EBAs, 42% are largely in montane areas, 35% in lowland areas and 24% embrace both lowland and mountains (Figure 6).

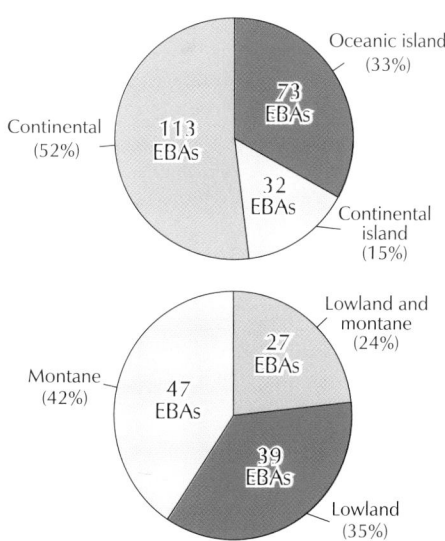

Figure 6. The division between continental and island EBAs, and (for continental areas only) between lowland and montane EBAs. See Figure 2 for island definitions. The altitudinal division between lowland and montane varies between EBAs but is generally c.1,000 m.

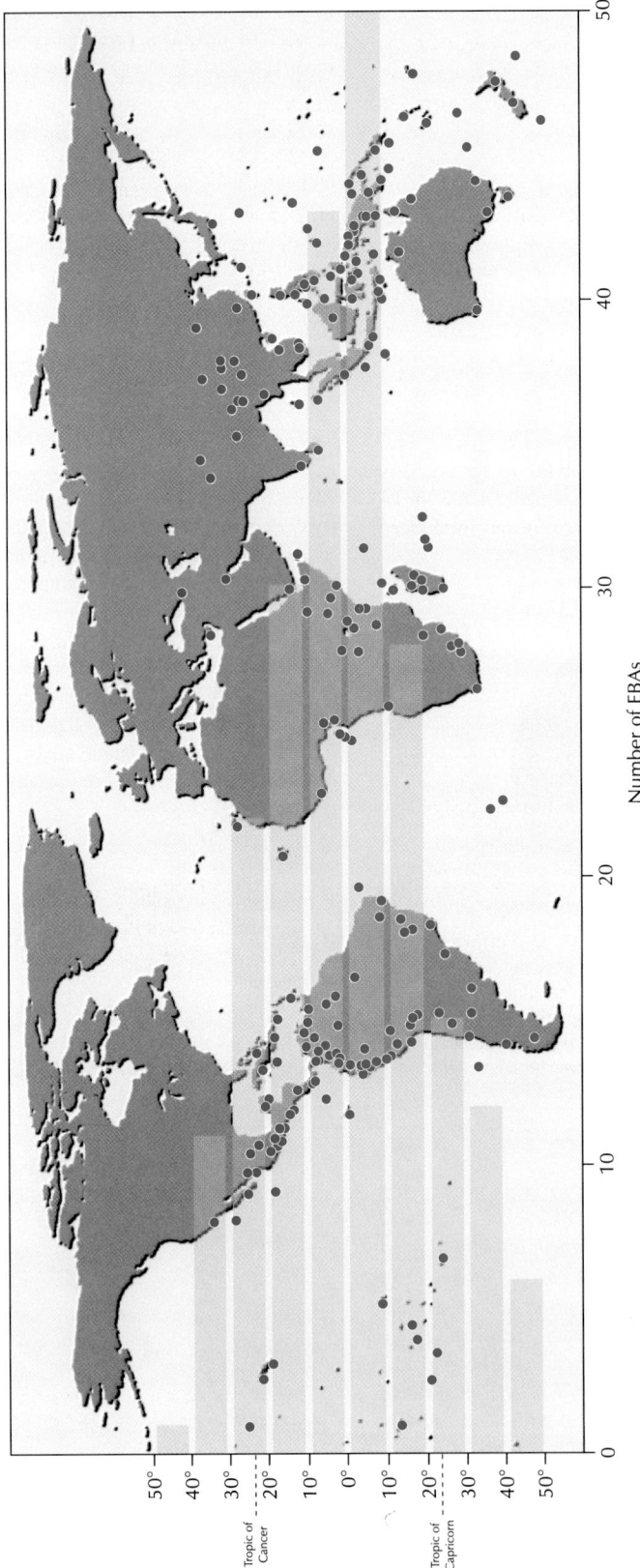

Figure 7. The location and latitudinal distribution of EBAs. Dots indicate the centre of each EBA; histogram shows the frequency of these at 10° intervals.

How unique are the EBAs?

- *Several EBAs are particularly distinct at the generic level, having five or more endemic genera.*

Some of the restricted-range species which occur in EBAs may be the sole representatives of their genera and therefore may be considered as more unique than others—and thus the overall uniqueness of EBAs, based on their complement of restricted-range species, also varies. New Caledonia (EBA 201) and Hispaniola (EBA 028) are especially distinct in having endemic monospecific families (represented by Kagu *Rhynochetos jubatus* and Palmchat *Dulus dominicus* respectively), a degree of evolutionary separation shared with only 13 other (widespread) bird species in the world. Many other EBAs have endemic genera and therefore have particularly unique avifaunas at this taxonomic level; these include Sulawesi in Indonesia (EBA 166) with 12 endemic genera and the Atlantic forest lowlands of Brazil (EBA 075) with 10 (Table 2).

Table 2. EBAs ranked by their numbers of endemic genera. All species within these genera have restricted ranges.

Rank	No. of endemic genera	EBA no. and name	
1	12	166	Sulawesi
2	10	075	Atlantic forest lowlands
3=	9	178	Central Papuan mountains
3=	9	094	East Malagasy wet forests
5	8	020	Costa Rica and Panama highlands
6	7	030	Lesser Antilles
7	6	028	Hispaniola
8=	5	027	Jamaica
8=	5	217	Central Hawaiian islands
8=	5	218	Hawai'i

What are the key habitats in EBAs?

- *The key habitats in EBAs are tropical moist forest.*

With the majority of restricted-range birds being forest species, the key habitat in the majority (83%) of EBAs is forest, mostly tropical lowland forest (32% of all types) and montane moist forest (24% of all types)—although temperate and subalpine forest (18%, but mostly in the tropics, where it is present at high altitudes) and tropical dry forest (15%) are also important (Figure 8). Grassland is the key habitat in only 12 EBAs, wetlands in five and desert in two.

How many restricted-range species do EBAs support and how extensive are they?

- *Most EBAs support 2–10 restricted-range bird species and are under 30,000 km² in size.*

EBAs vary in the number of restricted-range species which they support. The majority (63% of continental EBAs and 50% of island ones) have 2–10 restricted-range species occurring within their boundaries (Figure 9). Several EBAs have outstand-

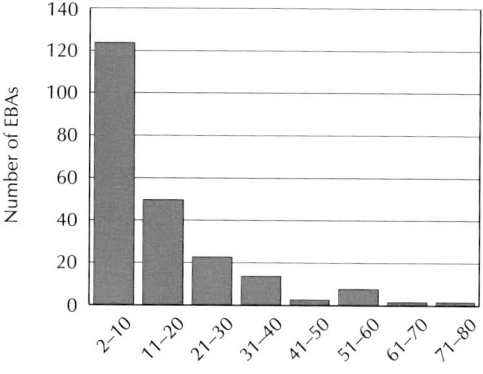

Figure 9. The numbers of restricted-range species in EBAs.

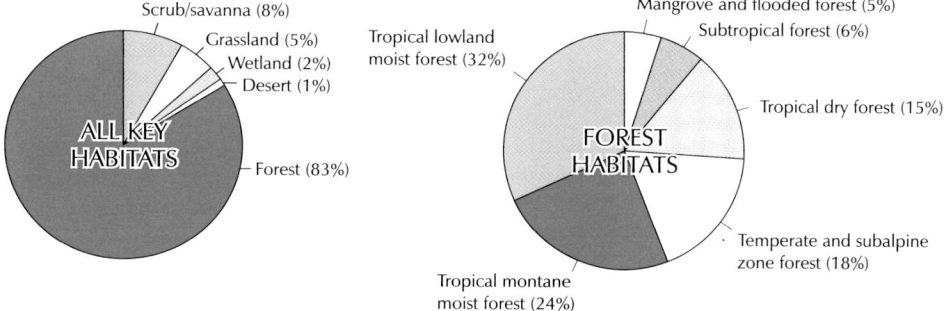

Figure 8. Key habitats of EBAs. All EBAs were coded for the main habitat-types used by restricted-range species and one key habitat-type was selected from these. Where forest was the key type equal weight was given to different forest types where multiple types were allocated.

ing numbers of restricted-range species (Table 3); these include the Solomon group in the Pacific (EBA 198: 79 species, of which 62 are confined to this EBA), the Chocó in Colombia and Ecuador (EBA 041: 62 species, including 51 endemics) and the Atlantic forest lowlands in Brazil (EBA 075: 55 species, including 52 endemics).

The size of EBAs varies considerably, ranging from the tiny Hawaiian island of Laysan (EBA 216) which occupies an area of less than 4 km², to the South-east Chinese mountains (EBA 141) which covers over 600,000 km². Overall, more than 50% of EBAs are of less than 30,000 km² in area. In general, island EBAs are smaller than continental ones: 33% of island EBAs (i.e. 35 EBAs, all but one oceanic) have an area of less than 1,000 km² (there are no continental EBAs this small), and 61% of all island EBAs are under 10,000 km² (only 9% of continental EBAs are in this size range). There are a few, very large, island EBAs, notably Sulawesi in Indonesia (EBA 166) and the Central Papuan mountains (EBA 178) which both have an area estimated at 190,000 km². Small continental EBAs include the Darién highlands (EBA 024) and the Andean ridge-top forests (EBA 047) at under 4,000 km².

Overall, EBAs total c.14,500,000 km². Thus their 2,451 restricted-range species (25% of the world's

birds) were historically totally confined to c.10% of the world's land area (Box 1).

One would expect larger EBAs to have more restricted-range species than smaller ones, and continental EBAs to have more species than island ones (see 'Biodiversity and Priority-setting', pp. 14 and 15). Therefore the outstanding EBAs in this regard are those which have more species than might be predicted for their size, treating continental, continental-island and oceanic-island EBAs separately (Figure 11). These include the Java and Bali forests (EBA 160) with 34 species in 18,000 km², the Banda Sea Islands (EBA 165) with 41 species in 7,100 km², the East Caroline Islands (EBA 192) with 20 species in 580 km² and Laysan island (EBA 216) with five species in only 4 km². EBAs with fewer species than expected include Cyprus (EBA 121) with two species in 9,300 km², the North Island of New Zealand (EBA 206) with five species in 120,000 km² and the South Island of New Zealand (EBA 207) with seven species in 110,000 km². In the case of Cyprus, the degree of endemism is high at the subspecific level, and it has been speculated that further endemic forms may have been lost owing to the great reduction of woodland habitat since human settlement. Many of New Zealand's endemic birds have (or historically had) ranges of more than 50,000 km²

Table 3. EBAs ranked by their numbers of restricted-range species. Where EBAs have the same number of species, higher ranking has been given to those with more species confined to that EBA (if the ranking is by total number of species) or to those with a higher total number of species (if the ranking is by number of species confined to that EBA).

Ranked by total no. of restricted-range species			Ranked by no. of restricted-range species confined to EBA		
Rank	No. of spp.	EBA no. and name	Rank	No. of spp.	EBA no. and name
1.	79	198 Solomon group	1.	62	198 Solomon group
2.	62	041 Chocó	2.	52	075 Atlantic forest lowlands
3.	55	075 Atlantic forest lowlands	3.	51	041 Chocó
4.	55	045 Tumbesian region	4.	49	020 Costa Rica and Panama highlands
5.	54	166 Sulawesi	5.	45	045 Tumbesian region
6.	54	195 New Britain and New Ireland	6.	42	166 Sulawesi
7.	53	178 Central Papuan mountains	7.	39	178 Central Papuan mountains
8.	52	020 Costa Rica and Panama highlands	8.	39	154 Mindanao and the Eastern Visayas
9.	51	154 Mindanao and the Eastern Visayas	9.	36	064 Tepuis
10.	43	171 Northern Moluku	10.	36	106 Albertine Rift mountains
11.	41	165 Banda Sea islands	11.	35	195 New Britain and New Ireland
12.	40	151 Luzon	12.	31	105 Tanzania–Malawi mountains
13.	38	064 Tepuis	13.	28	027 Jamaica
14.	38	158 Sumatra and Peninsula Malaysia	14.	27	086 Cameroon mountains
15.	37	106 Albertine Rift mountains	15.	26	171 Northern Moluku
16.	37	105 Tanzania–Malawi mountains	16.	25	202 Fiji
17.	36	202 Fiji	17.	24	151 Luzon
18.	35	027 Jamaica	18.	24	030 Lesser Antilles
19.	35	164 Timor and Wetar	19.	24	157 Bornean mountains
20.	35	038 Colombian East Andes	20.	23	164 Timor and Wetar
21.	34	030 Lesser Antilles	21.	23	028 Hispaniola
22.	34	028 Hispaniola	22.	23	124 Sri Lanka
23.	34	160 Java and Bali forests	23.	22	201 New Caledonia
24.	31	201 New Caledonia	24.	22	031 Galápagos
25.	30	200 Vanuatu and Temotu	25.	21	076 Atlantic forest mountains

Box 1. Land area occupied by restricted-range species.

Plotted here is the relationship between the numbers of restricted-range species and the land area which they occupy, by taking the smallest and richest EBAs first. Shared restricted-range species are assigned equally between EBAs. For the *historical relationship*, the complete area of the EBA polygon has been used. For the *current relationship*, this area has been reduced according to the estimated habitat loss of the EBA (see Figure 10). For EBAs with severe habitat loss, the area has been reduced by 95%; for major habitat loss, 70%; moderate, 30%; limited, 5%; unquantified/possible, 0%.

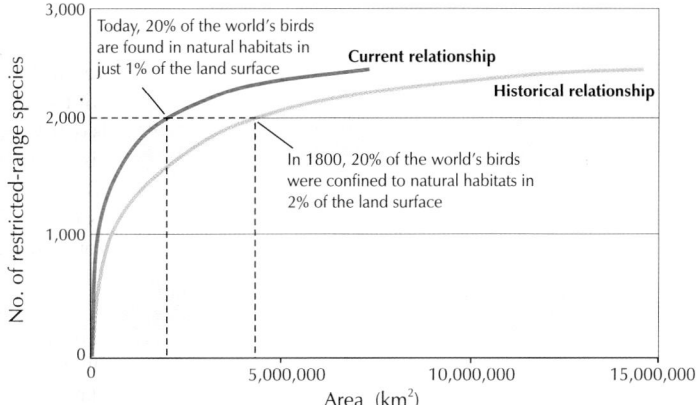

Historically, the world's 2,451 restricted-range bird species (c.25% of the total number of bird species) were confined to c.14,500,000 km² (c.10% of the world's land area)[1] and 2,000 of these (c.20% of all species) were confined to less than 4,000,000 km² (c.2% of the land area).

Today, the same restricted-range species are present in only c.7,300,000 km² of remaining natural habitat (c.5% of the world's land area) and c.20% of those species are found in less than 2,000,000 km² (c.1% of the land area). Many other widespread species will also occur in these same areas.

[1] In *Putting biodiversity on the map* (ICBP 1992) it was estimated that the world's restricted-range birds (25% of all species) were confined to a smaller proportion, 5% (not 10%), of the earth's land surface. This considerable discrepancy relates to differences between that original study and the present one in determining both the boundaries and the size of EBAs (see p. 26). This has resulted in there now being many more large EBAs (particularly in Asia) which have affected the proportion of the world's land surface occupied by 25% of the world's birds, but not the proportion occupied by 20%. This value has been taken as an arbitrary point on the curve before the gradient rapidly declines, and beyond which large increases in area contribute relatively few additional species.

and thus do not qualify as having restricted ranges for this project.

How threatened are EBAs?

- *Most EBAs have lost more than half of their key habitats and have threatened or extinct restricted-range species.*

Nearly half (47%) of all EBAs are estimated to have lost more than 50% of their key habitats, and more than 10% of EBAs have lost over 90% (Figure 10). Overall, the areas of natural habitats within EBAs are estimated to total only c.7,300,000 km². Thus today 25% of the world's birds are found in only c.5% of the land area of the world which has these natural habitats remaining (Box 1).

Most EBAs (85%) have one or more threatened or extinct restricted-range species (Figure 12), and in 23 EBAs all restricted-range species are threatened. The Atlantic slope of Alagoas and Pernambuco (EBA 071) in Brazil is one particularly threatened EBA, with one species already classified Extinct in the Wild and its remaining 12 restricted-range species

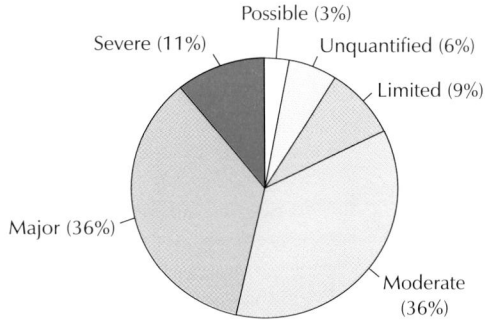

Figure 10. Estimated habitat loss in EBAs. (Severe: >90% of habitat lost. Major: >50% to 90%. Moderate: >10% to 50%. Limited: 0–10%.)

Figure 11. The relationship between numbers of restricted-range bird species and the size of EBAs.

The number of species present in an area is commonly a function of its size, often expressed as $S = cA^z$ where S is species number, A is the area and c and z are constants. An arithmetic plot of species number against area is curved, with the number of species increasing more slowly in larger areas. Species numbers and area are usually plotted on log scales to show a linear relationship between the two:

$$\log_{10}S = z\log_{10}A + \log_{10}c$$

This relationship proves to be significant for the number of restricted-range species and the area of EBAs for the island EBAs (p<0.01) but not for the continental ones. It has been noted for islands that a tenfold increase in area usually results in a doubling of the number of species (equivalent to a linear relationship between the log-species and log-area with a slope of 0.301, i.e. $\log_{10}2$). This is approximately the case for the island EBAs, and outstanding ones in terms of numbers of species per unit area are therefore those with high residual values about the straight lines which show the predicted relationship between species and area.

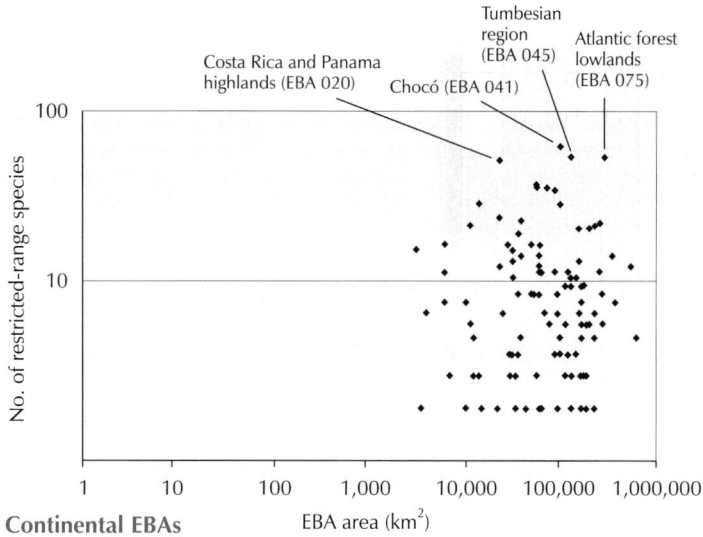

Costa Rica and Panama highlands (EBA 020) Chocó (EBA 041) Tumbesian region (EBA 045) Atlantic forest lowlands (EBA 075)

Continental EBAs   EBA area (km²)

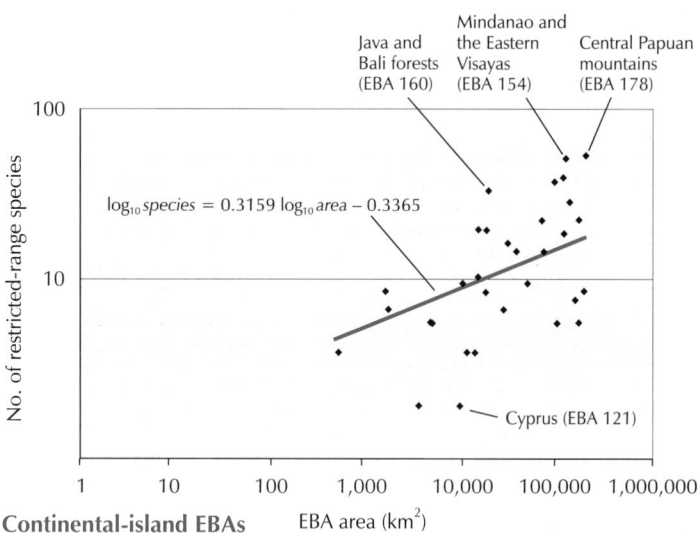

Java and Bali forests (EBA 160) Mindanao and the Eastern Visayas (EBA 154) Central Papuan mountains (EBA 178)

$$\log_{10}species = 0.3159\,\log_{10}area - 0.3365$$

Cyprus (EBA 121)

Continental-island EBAs   EBA area (km²)

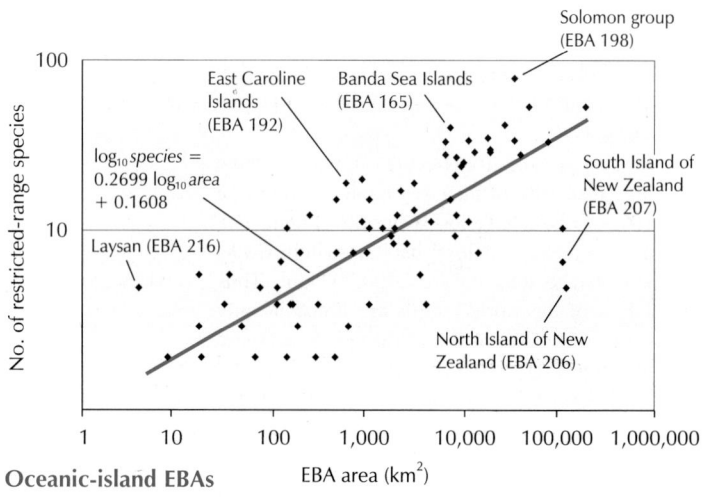

East Caroline Islands (EBA 192) Banda Sea Islands (EBA 165) Solomon group (EBA 198)

$$\log_{10}species = 0.2699\,\log_{10}area + 0.1608$$

Laysan (EBA 216) South Island of New Zealand (EBA 207) North Island of New Zealand (EBA 206)

Oceanic-island EBAs   EBA area (km²)

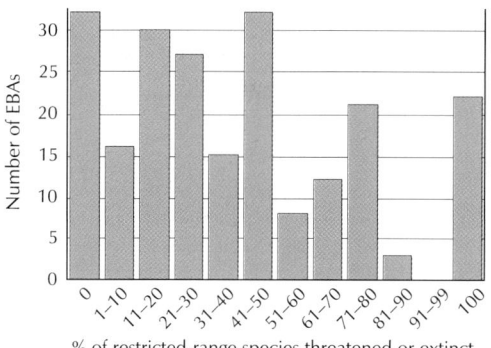

Number of EBAs

% of restricted-range species threatened or extinct

Figure 12. The proportions of restricted-range bird species in EBAs which are threatened or extinct.

all judged to be threatened with extinction. The Atlantic forest lowlands of Brazil (EBA 075) scores highest for the number of threatened restricted-range species (31), for the number which are highly threatened (18) and for the number which are highly threatened and endemic (18). The Central Hawaiian Islands (EBA 217) and Negros and Panay (EBA 152) in the Philippines also score highly for numbers which are highly threatened and endemic (Table 4).

Table 4. EBAs ranked by their numbers of threatened restricted-range species. Under A and B, where units are ranked above others with the same score, this is because weighting has been given either to the threatened species total (in B) or to the degree of endangerment within the species total (in A). Under C, priority where scores are tied has been given to units with higher numbers of endemic species categorized as Vulnerable or as Near Threatened.

A: Ranked by total no. of threatened restricted-range species

	No. of spp.	EBA no. and name
1.	31	075 Atlantic Forest lowlands
2.	22	154 Mindanao and the Eastern Visayas
3.	20	105 Tanzania–Malawi mountains
4.	18	217 Central Hawaiian islands
5.	18	151 Luzon
6.	17	041 Chocó
7.	15	045 Tumbesian region
8.	14	152 Negros and Panay
9.	14	038 Colombian East Andes
10.	14	198 Solomon group
11.	14	094 East Malagasy wet forests
12.	12	071 Atlantic slope of Alagoas and Pernambuco
13.	12	086 Cameroon mountains
14.	11	051 Peruvian High Andes
15.	11	084 Upper Guinea forests
16.	11	106 Albertine Rift mountains
17.	11	130 Eastern Himalayas
18.	9	040 Colombian inter-Andean slopes
19.	9	218 Hawai'i
20.	9	030 Lesser Antilles
21.	9	056 High Andes of Bolivia and Argentina
22.	8	087 Western Angola
23.	8	150 Mindoro
24.	8	100 Granitic Seychelles
25.	8	156 Palawan

B: Ranked by no. of restricted-range species categorized as Critical or Endangered

	No. of spp.	EBA no. and name
1.	18	075 Atlantic Forest lowlands
2.	12	217 Central Hawaiian islands
3.	12	152 Negros and Panay
4.	9	151 Luzon
5.	8	038 Colombian East Andes
6.	7	198 Solomon group
7.	7	051 Peruvian High Andes
8.	6	154 Mindanao and the Eastern Visayas
9.	6	105 Tanzania–Malawi mountains
10.	6	045 Tumbesian region
11.	7	071 Atlantic slope of Alagoas and Pernambuco
12.	6	218 Hawai'i
13.	6	040 Colombian inter-Andean slope
14.	6	150 Mindoro
15.	6	087 Western Angola
16.	5	041 Chocó
17.	5	102 Mauritius
18.	5	212 Marquesas
19.	5	098 Comoros
20.	5	032 Caripe–Paria region
21.	5	037 Nechí lowlands
22.	4	094 East Malagasy wet forests
23.	4	030 Lesser Antilles
24.	4	056 High Andes of Bolivia and Argentina
25.	4	100 Granitic Seychelles

C: Ranked by total no. of species covered by B that are also endemic to the EBA in question

	No. of spp.	EBA no. and name
1.	18	075 Atlantic Forest lowlands
2.	10	217 Central Hawaiian islands
3.	8	152 Negros and Panay
4.	6	105 Tanzania–Malawi mountains
5.	6	045 Tumbesian region
6.	6	198 Solomon group
7.	6	071 Atlantic slope of Alagoas and Pernambuco
8.	5	051 Peruvian High Andes
9.	5	087 Western Angola
10.	5	102 Mauritius
11.	5	212 Marquesas
12.	5	098 Comoros
13.	5	032 Caripe–Paria region
14.	4	154 Mindanao and the Eastern Visayas
15.	4	094 East Malagasy wet forests
16.	4	151 Luzon
17.	4	030 Lesser Antilles
18.	4	038 Colombian East Andes
19.	4	100 Granitic Seychelles
20.	4	201 New Caledonia
21.	4	156 Palawan
22.	4	218 Hawai'i
23.	4	150 Mindoro
24.	4	143 Annamese lowlands
25.	4	040 Colombian inter-Andean slopes

EBAs with severe or major habitat loss have a significantly higher percentage of threatened and extinct species than those with moderate or limited loss (p<0.05). However, it should be noted that the number of EBAs having a combination of severe/major habitat loss and a small proportion (0–20%) of threatened/exinct restricted-range species is fewer than would occur by chance (χ^2 analysis, p<0.05); this is perhaps because habitat loss has been used to infer threatened status of some poorly known species in some of these EBAs.

How well known are the EBAs?

• *The majority of EBAs are judged to be incompletely known.*

In terms of ornithological information (i.e. information relating to the distribution, habitat requirements and altitudinal ranges of restricted-range species), 110 EBAs (50%) are judged to be incompletely known. A further 37 (17%) are considered to be poorly known, while only 71 (33%) are considered well known, with most parts having been sampled by ornithologists (Figure 13).

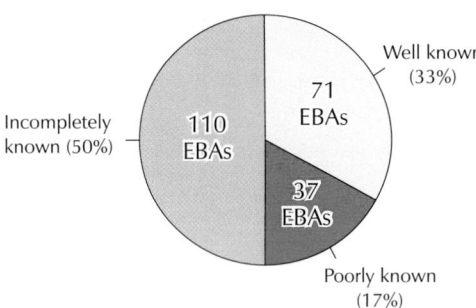

Figure 13. Knowledge of EBAs.

COUNTRIES

Which countries are most important for numbers of restricted-range bird species?

• *Of the 150 countries which have restricted-range species, Indonesia has the most with over 400.*

In total, restricted-range species are found in the majority of the countries of the world (Figure 15)—in 150 out of 231 geopolitical units (as listed in Appendix 2, p. 725). Some countries have exceptionally high numbers of restricted-range species. For example, five South American countries (Venezuela, Colombia, Ecuador, Brazil and Peru), the Philippines and Papua New Guinea each have over 100 restricted-range birds occurring within their territories; Indonesia leads with 403 (Figure 14).

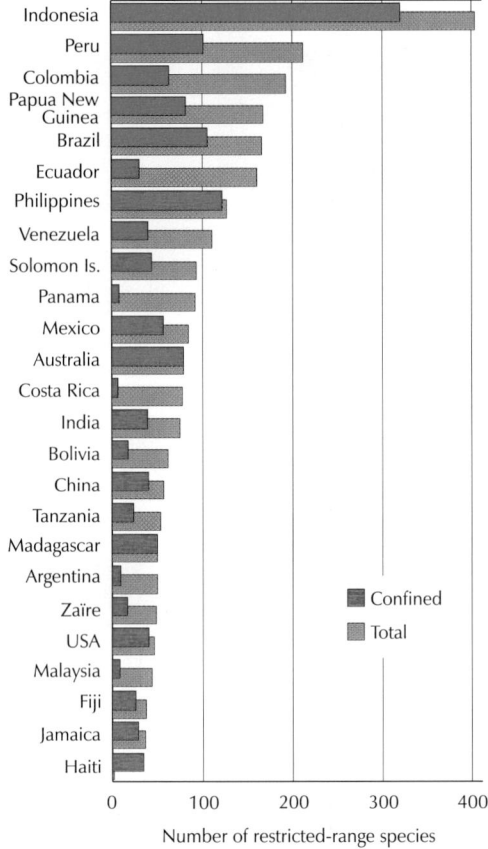

Figure 14. Countries with the highest numbers of restricted-range bird species.

Which countries are most important for numbers of threatened restricted-range bird species?

• *Of 106 countries which have threatened restricted-range species, the Philippines and Indonesia are the most important.*

Threatened restricted-range species are found in 106 geopolitical units; the Philippines leads with 67 threatened restricted-range species, and Indonesia is a close second with 66. A further two countries—Brazil and Colombia—have more than 50 threatened restricted-range spcies (Figure 16).

Such analyses are, of course, inevitably biased against the smaller countries or island nations with smaller avifaunas; few of these appear in this ranked list (a notable exception is French Polynesia at under 4,000 km^2). Nevertheless, many of the tiny countries of the world have their own highly threatened single-island endemics (especially in the Pacific region, e.g. Cook Islands, Northern Mariana Islands, Tonga, Western Samoa). It is important to emphasize that

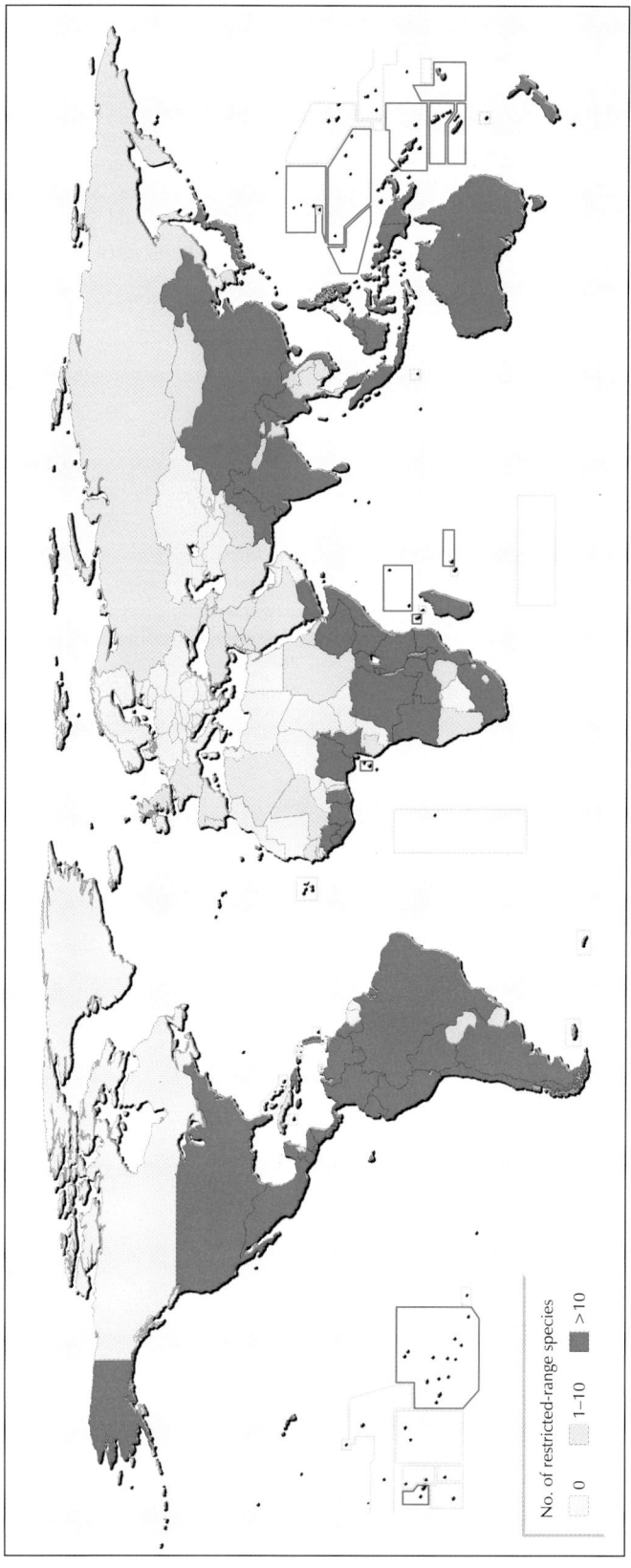

Figure 15. Countries where restricted-range species occur.

No. of restricted-range species

0

1–10

>10

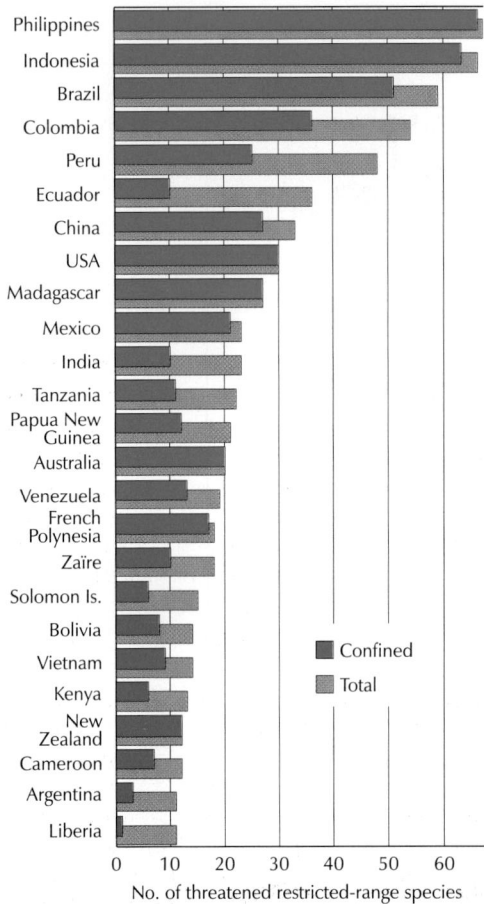

Figure 16. Countries with the highest numbers of threatened restricted-range bird species.

Which countries are most important for numbers of EBAs?

• *Indonesia is the most important country for numbers of EBAs, with 24.*

The top countries for numbers of EBAs are similar to those for numbers of restricted-range species (Figure 17). Indonesia, three South American countries (Colombia, Brazil and Peru), Mexico, China and Papua New Guinea have more than 10 EBAs within their territories. Australia also ranks highly, having eight EBAs (which lie entirely within its borders).

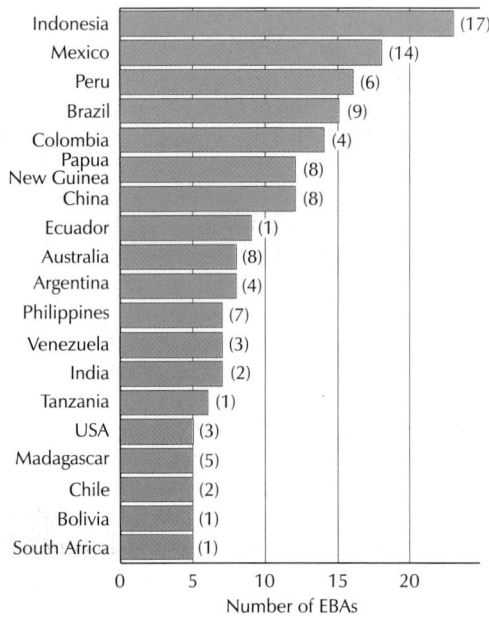

Figure 17. Countries with the highest numbers of EBAs (number of EBAs found entirely within each country's borders is also shown in brackets).

the survival of these species relies solely on conservation action within the EBAs or Secondary Areas of these countries.

THE PRIORITIZATION OF ENDEMIC BIRD AREAS

T AKING their biological importance and current threat levels into account, an overall priority ranking of EBAs has been attempted and is presented in this chapter. This evaluation seeks to select those EBAs with the highest biological importance and current threat level scores, thereby indicating where conservation action will give the best value and return for money and effort. Nevertheless, it is self-evident that all EBAs represent priority areas for conservation and, given that there are increasing data to suggest that rapid species loss can occur at the early stages of human impact (Balmford 1996), it cannot be stressed strongly enough that the targeting of conservation initiatives in *all* EBAs—even those which are not in the top ranks—remains essential.

It is possible to criticize such a numerically guided evaluation as attempted here, but the more detailed data presented in other parts of this book will help users to judge for themselves whether the ranking assigned to the EBAs is appropriate. Before conservation action is taken, additional factors will also need to be considered; these include political will, availability of resources, conservation initiatives already in place, information relating to other animals and plants present, the intactness of remaining habitat, cultural values, logistics, and the chances of success.

BIOLOGICAL IMPORTANCE

A biological importance score for each EBA has been calculated by taking into account the following.

- *The number of restricted-range species occurring in the EBA, and whether or not they are shared with other EBAs.*
In many cases the distribution or population of the restricted-range species which are shared with other EBAs may not be equally divided between the different EBAs; thus the survival of some of these species may depend mainly on conservation action

in one particular EBA—a fact not fully reflected by the isolation index (see 'Calculation', below) assigned to that EBA. In practice the number of shared species comprises only c.20% of the overall total, and in only 12% of EBAs does the eventual biological importance ranking differ from the ranking produced using unadjusted species totals.

- *The taxonomic uniqueness of these species.*
Taxonomy has been taken into account because some families of birds have radiated widely around the world such that they have many closely related genera and species, while other lineages have far fewer members and so perhaps should be valued more highly. It is clear that the method used here to weight for taxonomy using a uniqueness index (see 'Calculation', below) will be affected by the taxonomy followed—in this case Sibley and Monroe (1990, 1993) for species limits and Morony *et al.* (1975) for family ones (see p. 21). The weighting chosen (which results in, e.g., Kagu *Rhynochetos jubatus* being valued 100 times more highly than Seychelles Brush-warbler *Acrocephalus sechellensis*) was arbitrary, though is arguably intuitive. There are sophisticated techniques for determining taxonomic uniqueness using phylogenetic relationships (e.g. May 1990, Vane-Wright *et al.* 1991), but these require an understanding of hierarchical classifications, such as those determined at the genetic level using DNA–DNA hybridization. Species-specific data on molecular sequencing are currently available for only c.10% of all birds (Sibley and Ahlquist 1990), and therefore it was not possible to use these methods in this global study. In only c.25% of EBAs does the incorporation of a weighting for taxonomic uniqueness affect the biological importance ranking.

- *The size of the EBA.*
Area has been taken into account because EBAs vary considerably in size, and larger areas might be expected (purely because of their size) to hold more species than smaller ones—and therefore it may not be appropriate to rank larger areas as relatively more

important (see p. 16). A higher priority has thus been given to EBAs which support an unusually large number of restricted-range species in relation to their size, but a weakness in this adjustment is that the boundaries of some of the continental EBAs have been inferred from incomplete data and will tend to represent the maximum possible extent of the areas. It is therefore possible that a few such EBAs may have been downgraded inappropriately in this exercise. It is also important to note that there may be localized areas of endemism within large EBAs which are critical for the survival of certain restricted-range species but whose importance may not be fully reflected by the overall ranking of the EBA. However, the distribution tables, and text, in individual EBA accounts should draw attention to these places.

Calculation

The calculation of the score is performed as follows.

Biological importance score for EBA =
    score for restricted-range species A
    + score for restricted-range species B
    + score for restricted-range species C, etc.,
where
    Score for each restricted-range species =
        isolation index × uniqueness index
and
    Isolation index =
        1/no. of EBAs in which the species occurs
and
    Uniqueness index =
        $\sqrt{}$ (1/no. of species in the genus ×
        1/no. of genera in the family)

Example. A restricted-range species which is endemic to an EBA scores an isolation index of 1/1 = 1, while one which occurs in two EBAs scores 1/2 = 0.5. Kagu, endemic to New Caledonia, which belongs to a monospecific family, scores a uniqueness index of $\sqrt{}$ (1/1 × 1/1) = 1, while Seychelles Brush-warbler, belonging to a genus with 34 species and a family with 270 genera, scores $\sqrt{}$ (1/34 × 1/270) = 0.01.

Finally, the biological importance scores have been adjusted to take account of the size of the EBA. This has been done by plotting the scores against the area of the EBA using log–log data (see Figure 11, p. 34, and its accompanying text). The relationship between the biological importance score and area is significant for the continental-island and oceanic-island EBAs only (p < 0.01), and in these cases the residual values about a regression line give the relative (i.e. adjusted) biological importance scores for each EBA, treating the continental-island and oceanic-island EBAs separately. For the continental EBAs a comparable residual value is calculated from an average value of the logged scores. EBAs have

been divided into three groups based on whether the adjusted scores are less than would be expected from the log–log plot for the size of the EBA, more than would be expected, or more than twice what would be expected (Table 1).

Table 1. Ranking of EBAs for biological importance.

Biological importance score	Biological importance rank	Number of EBAs
> 2 × expected score	●●●	51
1–2 × expected score	●●	58
< 1 × expected score	●	109

CURRENT THREAT LEVEL

A current threat level score for each EBA has been calculated by taking into account the following.

- *The percentage of the restricted-range species in each EBA which are threatened.*

A percentage value has been taken because the numbers of threatened restricted-range species will tend to increase as the total numbers of restricted-range species increase (therefore combining both a measure of threat and a measure of the biological importance of the area; see also Box 1).

- *The categories of threat of these species.*

Different weighting has been given to species in each of the three different categories of threat, reflecting their different probabilities of going extinct: a 50% chance of extinction within 10 years for species in the 'Critical' category, 20% in 20 years for 'Endangered' and 10% in 100 years for 'Vulnerable' (see p. 679); in other words, over 100 years one would expect all Critical species to have gone extinct, along with c.70% of all Endangered ones and 10% of Vulnerable ones. By weighting the threatened species in this way, the percentage of all restricted-range species (and perhaps of other wildlife) likely to go extinct within each EBA in the next 100 years can be calculated (see 'Calculation', below). An approach such as this assumes that today's conditions prevail, with the status of the restricted-range species remaining unchanged over the 100-year period. This method too relies on the current classification of the status of the world's birds (Collar *et al.* 1994), but the allocation of the Critical category in this assessment is known to have been problematical in some cases, especially for poorly known species where the categories Data Deficient or Vulnerable might also have been appropriate (see pp. 16–21 in Collar *et al.* 1994). In addition, Collar *et al.* (1994) is now somewhat out of date (although officially current in the IUCN Red List; see Baillie and Groombridge 1996), and some EBAs have a few species (newly discovered or elevated to species

Table 2. Ranking of EBAs for current threat level.

Current threat level score (% of the EBA's restricted-range spp. likely to go extinct in next 100 years)	Current threat level rank	Number of EBAs
> 30%	●●●	55
> 5% to 30%	●●	60
0–5%	●	103

project. Overall, taking threatened categories into account has affected the current threat level ranking of 37% of EBAs compared to ranking by the percentage of threatened restricted-range species alone.

Calculation

The calculation of the score is performed as follows.

Current threat level score for the EBA =

$$[(\text{No. of Critical restricted-range species} \times 1)$$
$$+ (\text{No. of Endangered} \quad '' \quad '' \quad \times 0.7)$$
$$+ (\text{No. of Vulnerable} \quad '' \quad '' \quad \times 0.1)]$$
$$\times 100/\text{Total number of extant restricted-range species}$$

EBAs have been divided into three groups based on the proportion of their restricted-range species which are likely to go extinct within the next 100 years (Table 2). These arbitrary divisions were chosen so that the number of EBAs in each group was approximately equal to those produced by dividing EBAs on the basis of their biological importance scores.

OVERALL PRIORITY RANKING

After the assignment of biological importance and current threat level rankings to EBAs, these have been combined to give an overall priority ranking of Critical, Urgent or High to each EBA (Tables 3–4).

Table 3. Numbers of EBAs falling in the different biological importance and threat level ranks, and the method for combining them to give one overall priority ranking.

		Biological importance rank			
		●●●	●●	●	Total
Current threat level rank	●●●	7	15	33	55
	●●	21	16	23	60
	●	23	27	53	103
	Total	51	58	109	218

Overall priority ranking
☐ Critical 76 EBAs
☐ Urgent 62 EBAs
☐ High 80 EBAs

rank) which are classified as 'Not Evaluated'—these species could contribute significantly to the threat level score of the EBA if they were to be classified as Critical or Endangered. Nevertheless the evaluation can easily be repeated periodically in the future as new data (e.g. updated Red Lists) become available. It is also important to note that the more-widespread threatened species which often occur in EBAs (amounting to more than 200 species in total) have not been taken into account. This would require a detailed assessment of range and population overlaps with EBAs which was beyond the scope of this

The method chosen for combining the rankings (Table 3) gives greater emphasis to those EBAs which rank highly for current threat level (and therefore where the immediate extinction risk is greatest) and results in three groups of roughly equal size.

Table 4. The EBAs within each of the three priority categories. No rank ordering is attempted within the categories.

	Biological importance	Current threat level
Critical		
003 Guadalupe Island	•	•••
004 Socorro Island	•••	•••
006 Sierra Madre Occidental and trans-Mexican range	•	•••
009 Sierra Madre del Sur	•	•••
012 Southern Sierra Madre Oriental	•	•••
013 Los Tuxtlas and Uxpanapa	•	•••
023 Darién lowlands	•••	••
025 Cuba	•	•••
027 Jamaica	•••	••
030 Lesser Antilles	•••	••
032 Caripe–Paria region	••	•••
037 Nechí lowlands	••	•••
038 Colombian East Andes	•••	••
040 Colombian inter-Andean slopes	••	•••
042 Northern Central Andes	•	•••
045 Tumbesian region	•••	••
050 Junín puna	•	•••
051 Peruvian high Andes	•••	•••
056 High Andes of Bolivia and Argentina	•••	••
059 Juan Fernández Islands	•	•••
070 North-east Brazilian caatinga	••	•••
071 Atlantic slope of Alagoas and Pernambuco	••	•••
072 Deciduous forests of Bahia	•	•••
074 Deciduous forests of Minas Gerais and Goiás	•	•••
075 Atlantic forest lowlands	•••	•••
077 Argentine Mesopotamian grasslands	•	•••
082 São Tomé	•••	••
084 Upper Guinea forests	•••	•••
086 Cameroon mountains	•••	••
087 Western Angola	••	•••
091 Southern African grasslands	•	•••
094 East Malagasy wet forests	•••	••
095 East Malagasy wetlands	•	•••
096 West Malagasy wetlands	•	•••
098 Comoro Islands	••	•••
100 Granitic Seychelles	••	•••
102 Mauritius	•	•••
103 Rodrigues	••	•••
105 Tanzania–Malawi mountains	•••	••
112 Central Somali coast	•	•••
113 Jubba and Shabeelle valleys	•	•••
114 South Ethiopian highlands	••	•••
115 Central Ethiopian highlands	•	•••
116 North Somali mountains	•	•••
128 Western Himalayas	•••	••

cont.

Table 4. (cont.)	Biological importance	Current threat level
140 Chinese subtropical forests	•	•••
141 South-east Chinese mountains	•	•••
142 Hainan	•	•••
143 Annamese lowlands	•	•••
144 South Vietnamese lowlands	•	•••
147 Ogasawara Islands	•••	••
148 Nansei Shoto	•	•••
150 Mindoro	•	•••
151 Luzon	•••	••
152 Negros and Panay	•	•••
153 Cebu	••	•••
154 Mindanao and the Eastern Visayas	•••	••
155 Sulu archipelago	•••	•••
160 Java and Bali forests	•••	••
167 Sangihe and Talaud	•	•••
181 Cape York	••	•••
183 Eastern Australia	•••	••
184 South-east Australia	•••	••
186 South-west Australia	•••	••
192 East Caroline Islands	•••	••
198 Solomon group	•••	••
204 Lord Howe Island	••	•••
205 Norfolk Island	••	•••
206 North Island of New Zealand	•	•••
209 Chatham Islands	••	•••
211 Rimatara	•	•••
212 Marquesas Islands	•	•••
214 Tuamotu archipelago	•	•••
216 Laysan Island	•••	•••
217 Central Hawaiian Islands	•••	•••
218 Hawai'i	•••	•••
Urgent		
007 Central Mexican marshes	•	••
011 North-east Mexican Gulf slope	•	••
016 Cozumel Island	•••	•
018 North Central American highlands	•••	•
020 Costa Rica and Panama highlands	•••	•
022 Cocos Island	••	••
028 Hispaniola	•••	•
029 Puerto Rico and the Virgin Islands	••	••
031 Galápagos Islands	••	••
034 Cordillera de Mérida	••	••
035 Caribbean Colombia and Venezuela	••	••
036 Santa Marta mountains	•••	•
041 Chocó	••	••
043 Central Andean páramo	••	••
046 Southern Central Andes	•	••
047 Andean ridge-top forests	••	••
048 Marañón valley	•••	•
049 North-east Peruvian cordilleras	•••	•
054 Bolivian and Peruvian lower yungas	••	••
055 Bolivian and Peruvian upper yungas	•••	•
057 Argentine and south Bolivian yungas	•••	•
060 Central Chile	•••	•
062 Southern Patagonia	•••	•
063 Rio Branco gallery forests	•	••
064 Tepuis	•••	•
068 South-east Peruvian lowlands	•••	•

cont.

Table 4. (cont.)

		Biological importance	Current threat level
073	Central Brazilian hills and tablelands	●	●●
076	Atlantic forest mountains	●●●	●
078	Cape Verde Islands	●	●●
079	Tristan Islands	●●	●●
080	Gough Island	●	●●
081	Annobón	●	●●
097	South Malagasy spiny forests	●●●	●
101	Réunion	●	●●
106	Albertine Rift mountains	●●●	●
109	Kenyan mountains	●●	●●
111	East African coastal forests	●	●●
124	Sri Lanka	●	●●
127	Taklimakan Desert	●	●●
130	Eastern Himalayas	●●●	●
131	Assam plains	●	●●
136	Shanxi mountains	●	●●
138	West Sichuan mountains	●	●●
139	Yunnan mountains	●	●●
145	Da Lat plateau	●	●●
146	Izu Islands	●	●●
156	Palawan	●●	●●
157	Bornean mountains	●●●	●
158	Sumatra and Peninsular Malaysia	●●●	●
178	Central Papuan mountains	●●●	●
182	Queensland wet tropics	●●●	●
185	Tasmania	●●	●●
187	North-west Australia	●●●	●
189	Mariana Islands	●●	●●
197	Louisiade archipelago	●●●	●
201	New Caledonia	●●	●●
203	Samoan Islands	●●	●●
207	South Island of New Zealand	●	●●
210	Southern Cook Islands	●	●●
213	Society Islands	●	●●
215	Henderson Island	●	●●

High

		Biological importance	Current threat level
001	California	●●	●
002	Baja California	●	●
005	North-west Mexican Pacific slope	●	●
008	Balsas region and interior Oaxaca	●●	●
010	Northern Sierra Madre Oriental	●	●
014	Isthmus of Tehuantepec	●	●
015	Yucatán peninsula coastal scrub	●	●
017	North Central American Pacific slope	●	●
019	Central American Caribbean slope	●●	●
021	South Central American Pacific slope	●●	●
024	Darién highlands	●●	●
026	Bahamas	●	●
033	Cordillera de la Costa Central	●●	●
039	Colombian inter-Andean valleys	●	●
044	Ecuador–Peru East Andes	●●	●
052	Peru–Chile Pacific slope	●●	●
053	Peruvian East Andean foothills	●●	●
058	Sierras Centrales of Argentina	●	●
061	Chilean temperate forests	●●	●
065	Orinoco–Negro white-sand forests	●●	●

Table 4. (cont.)

		Biological importance	Current threat level
066	Upper Amazon–Napo lowlands	●●	●
067	Amazon flooded forests	●	●
069	Fernando de Noronha	●	●
083	Príncipe	●●	●
085	Cameroon and Gabon lowlands	●	●
088	Cape fynbos	●	●
089	South African forests	●	●
090	Lesotho highlands	●	●
092	South-east African coast	●	●
093	West Malagasy dry forests	●	●
099	Aldabra	●	●
104	Eastern Zimbabwe mountains	●	●
107	Eastern Zaïre lowlands	●	●
108	Serengeti plains	●●	●
110	Pemba	●	●
117	Socotra	●	●
118	South-west Arabian mountains	●●	●
119	Mesopotamian marshes	●	●
120	Madeira and the Canary Islands	●	●
121	Cyprus	●	●
122	Caucasus	●	●
123	Western Ghats	●●	●
125	Andaman Islands	●	●
126	Nicobar Islands	●	●
129	Central Himalayas	●	●
132	Irrawaddy plains	●	●
133	Southern Tibet	●	●
134	Eastern Tibet	●	●
135	Qinghai mountains	●	●
137	Central Sichuan mountains	●●	●
149	Taiwan	●	●
159	Enggano	●	●
161	Javan coastal zone	●	●
162	Northern Nusa Tenggara	●	●
163	Sumba	●	●
164	Timor and Wetar	●●	●
165	Banda Sea Islands	●●	●
166	Sulawesi	●●	●
168	Banggai and Sula Islands	●	●
169	Buru	●●	●
170	Seram	●	●
171	Northern Maluku	●●	●
172	West Papuan lowlands	●	●
173	West Papuan highlands	●●	●
174	Geelvink Islands	●	●
175	North Papuan mountains	●	●
176	North Papuan lowlands	●	●
177	Adelbert and Huon ranges	●	●
179	South Papuan lowlands	●	●
180	Trans-Fly	●	●
188	Christmas Island	●	●
190	Palau	●●	●
191	Yap Islands	●	●
193	Admiralty Islands	●●	●
194	St Matthias Islands	●	●
195	New Britain and New Ireland	●●	●
196	D'Entrecasteaux and Trobriand Islands	●	●
199	Rennell and Bellona	●	●
200	Vanuatu and Temotu	●	●
202	Fiji	●●	●
208	Auckland Islands	●	●

cont.

43

THE CONSERVATION RELEVANCE OF ENDEMIC BIRD AREAS

THE Endemic Bird Area approach is an efficient way of identifying conservation priorities for restricted-range birds, which together amount to more than a quarter of the world's bird species. The value of EBAs as targets for conservation action is further increased because they have a wider relevance beyond the conservation of this subset of bird species alone. We can show that EBAs are effective in identifying areas which are important for the maintenance of avian diversity in general as well as for the diversity of other flora and fauna—this wider role being especially significant given that birds comprise only a very small proportion of the world's biodiversity: c.0.5% of described species and perhaps 0.05% of all species (i.e. both described and undescribed) (see Box 1).

In assessing the conservation relevance of EBAs for birds in general or for biodiversity overall, we have attempted to determine whether the EBA approach misses areas which are judged important by other priority-setting approaches (see pp. 16–18) and, conversely, if it identifies areas which by other criteria would not be considered important. The comparison with other priority-setting approaches must, of course, presuppose that all the world's EBAs have been identified (Box 2).

IMPORTANCE FOR BIRDS IN GENERAL

If, as well as restricted-range species, the more widely distributed bird species (i.e. those with ranges greater than 50,000 km^2) also occurring in EBAs are included, the percentage of the world's bird species found in the small area covered by EBAs (20% of the species in 2% of the earth's land surface, see p. 33) would rise substantially, thereby increasing the im-

---

Box 1. Birds as indicators.

Birds are valuable indicator species for biodiversity conservation for a number of reasons.

- They occupy almost all terrestrial habitats and are widely dispersed in all regions and countries of the world.
- They are the best known and documented major taxonomic group, and the number of species (c.10,000) is manageable, thereby permitting comprehensive and rigorous analyses.
- They are sensitive to environmental disturbance and can be used to monitor potentially harmful changes.
- They have widespread popular appeal and therefore make good flagship species for conservation education and advocacy.

Some of the most detailed studies to date investigating birds as indicators have been carried out in the UK and in the USA.

In the UK, Prendergast et al. (1993) showed that at a small scale (10 km × 10 km) species-rich areas frequently do not coincide for different taxa, and many rare species do not occur in the most species-rich squares. However, a more optimistic picture emerged in this study if the overlap of hotspots for entire groups was considered, e.g. 100% of butterfly species and over 90% of dragonflies, liverworts and aquatic plants occurred in a set of 116 bird hotspots.

In the USA, Dobson et al. (1997) used a complementarity study to identify all the areas (counties, in this case) which contained at least one population of all endangered birds. These areas only contained 30–40% of endangered amphibian, reptile, mammal and plant species, just over 10% of endangered arthropods and only 2% of endangered molluscs. Plants were found generally to be a better predictor of the occurrence of other endangered species: the areas required to conserve all endangered plants would conserve 94% of birds and between 3% and 76% of the other groups. However, the area required for all endangered plants was 10% of the land area of the USA, while that for all endangered birds was only 2%. They decided that, when limitations on the amount of land available were taken into account, birds probably remained the best indicators.

Box 2. Have all the world's EBAs been identified?

Endemic Bird Areas are identified on the basis of the overlapping ranges of restricted-range bird species. As all known restricted-range bird species have been included in the EBA analysis, it is assumed that all significant areas of restricted endemism for birds have been identified as EBAs, although there are limitations in the existing information and difficulties in interpreting the more complex regions.

Since the initial EBA analysis was published (ICBP 1992), it has been modified in the light of new information, in particular a better understanding of the ecological requirements of the restricted-range bird species. Nine EBAs from the original analysis have been split into 18 separate EBAs, and a further 28 of the original EBAs have undergone amalgamation to produce 14 in the present analysis (see Appendix 4, p. 781); further such refinements may be necessary in the future. These changes have not, however, resulted in any areas being added to or dropped from the total area covered by EBAs.

It is possible that some bird species which have been excluded from the EBA analysis are more narrowly distributed than is currently thought and that these should have been included. Conversely, some species which are currently included may turn out to have ranges which are larger than 50,000 km². However, care was taken to refine the candidate list of restricted-range species throughout the project (see p. 23), and during the period 1992–1997 six EBAs were dropped and only two were added owing to a better understanding of range sizes. Any further changes to the EBA analysis resulting from the addition or subtraction of species as their ranges become better known are likely to be minor, as the number of species involved is expected to be relatively small.

The discovery of new restricted-range bird species could significantly affect the EBA analysis. Indeed, any newly discovered species (and many of those taxa elevated to species rank by taxonomic rearrangement) will usually qualify as restricted-range, as the chances of a widespread species remaining still undiscovered are increasingly remote. It is generally acknowledged that the vast majority of bird species have now been discovered and described, so that presently unknown species comprise at most a small percentage of the overall total.

Newly described restricted-range species (1987–1996)

with date of description and relevant EBA or Secondary Area (the breeding range is unknown for three species; see p. 724):

Species	Year	EBA/SA
Roviana Rail *Gallirallus rovianae*	1991	EBA 198
Udzungwa Forest-partridge *Xenoperdix udzungwensis*	1994	EBA 105
El Oro Parakeet *Pyrrhura orcesi*	1988	EBA 045
Bahia Nighthawk *Chordeiles vielliardi*	1994	EBA 070
Itombwe Nightjar *Caprimulgus prigoginei*	1990	EBA 106
Nechisar Nightjar *C. solala*	1995	EBA 114
White-fronted Swift *Cypseloides storeri*	1992	EBA 039
Chiribiquete Emerald *Chlorostilbon olivaresi*	1996	SA s020
Bogotá Sunangel *Heliangelus zusii*	1993	range unknown
Pink-legged Graveteiro *Acrobatornis fonsecai*	1996	EBA 075
Cípo Canastero *Asthenes luizae*	1990	EBA 073
Rondônia Bushbird *Clytoctantes atrogularis*	1990	SA s025
Rio de Janeiro Antwren *Myrmotherula fluminensis*	1988	EBA 075
Long-billed Antwren *Stymphalornis acutirostris*	1995	SA s034
Restinga Antwren *Formicivora littoralis*	1990	EBA 075
Bahia Spinetail *Synallaxis whitneyi*	1995	EBA 076
Cundinamarca Antpitta *Grallaria kaestneri*	1992	EBA 038
Pale-billed Antpitta *G. carrikeri*	1982	EBA 049
Diademed Tapaculo *Scytalopus schulenbergi*	1993	EBA 055
Bahia Tapaculo *S. psychopompus*	1989	EBA 075
Chestnut-bellied Cotinga *oliornis remseni*	1994	EBA 043
Antioquia Bristle-tyrant *Phylloscartes lanyoni*	1988	EBA 037
Alagoas Tyrannulet *P. ceciliae*	1987	EBA 071
Bahia Tyrannulet *P. beckeri*	1995	EBA 076
Restinga Tyrannulet *P. kronei*	1992	EBA 075
Long-tailed Pipit *Anthus longicaudatus*	1996	range unknown
Bulo Burti Bush-shrike *Laniarius liberatus*	1988	EBA 115
Nepal Wren-babbler *Pnoepyga immaculata*	1991	EBA 129
Panay Striped-babbler *Stachyris latistriata*	1990	EBA 152
Cryptic Warbler *Cryptosylvicola randrianasoloi*	1996	EBA 094
Tanimbar Bush-warbler *Cettia carolinae*	1987	EBA 165
Emei Leaf-warbler *Phylloscopus emeiensis*	1995	EBA 140
Hainan Leaf-warbler *P. hainanus*	1993	EBA 142
Sira Tanager *Tangara phillipsi*	1987	EBA 053
Chocó Vireo *Vireo masteri*	1996	EBA 041
Cream-bellied Munia *Lonchura pallidiventer*	1996	range unknown
Kilombero Weaver *Ploceus burnieri*	1990	SA s056

Sources. 1987–1990: Vuilleumier *et al.* (1992), Bahr (1995). 1991–1993: Sibley and Monroe (1993). 1993–1996: sources relating to individual species (see relevant EBA or Secondary Area accounts).

In total, 37 restricted-range species have been newly described during the course of this project, amounting to an average of about three per year. The inclusion of two of these, *Pnoepyga immaculata* and *Phylloscopus hainanus*, resulted in the recognition of two EBAs, the Central Himalayas (EBA 129) and Hainan (EBA 142); the majority of the remainder added to the importance of EBAs which would already have been recognized on the basis of the ranges of previously described restricted-range species. A few species occur singly in new Secondary Areas or are of unknown provenance (but are believed likely to have restricted ranges).

Most changes to the EBA analysis in the future are likely to result from (potentially large) taxonomic changes in recognized species limits. Those which have been incorporated during the course of the project have had a small effect on the EBA analysis (five EBAs added and one dropped, resulting from c.100 taxa being elevated to specific rank or lumped with other taxa following taxonomic changes since Sibley and Monroe 1990), and it is believed that further changes will largely reinforce the patterns which have already been discerned (see p. 21).

portance of EBAs for the conservation of birds in general. However, an exact value cannot be given since no analysis has yet been completed of the occurrence of widespread bird species in EBAs. Nevertheless, we know that EBAs partially encompass the ranges of many widespread threatened species, that they include the key habitats and sites for many more widespread species, and that they cover some of the most species-rich areas in the world.

Threatened species

The most significant wider relevance of EBAs for the conservation of birds in general is their importance for globally threatened species.

One might expect birds with restricted ranges to include a disproportionately high number of threatened species because they are intrinsically more vulnerable to any loss of habitat. This is indeed found to be the case: 74% of bird species currently classified as threatened and 58% of those classified as Near Threatened are included in the restricted-range species identified in this study (Figure 1). Indeed 85% of EBAs support one or more threatened or extinct restricted-range species (see p. 33).

Furthermore, more than 50% of EBAs have been noted to partly cover the ranges of widespread threatened birds (including threatened seabirds), amounting to more than 200 species in total. However, conservation action solely within EBAs is unlikely to be sufficient for the long-term survival of all of these widespread threatened species, and there will be many areas important for these birds which lie outside the boundaries of EBAs.

Many of those restricted-range species which are currently considered to be of least conservation concern are likely to become threatened in the near future given the continuing loss of habitat, especially tropical forest, within many of the EBAs (see Box 3). Deforestation may thus result in a far greater loss of species than the average global figures suggest— and conservation action within EBAs will be crucial to prevent the potential for mass species extinctions.

Key habitats and sites

In general the EBA analysis has been good at representing most of the major forest zones in the tropics and subtropics, and therefore at including the birds which are characteristic of these habitats, but not so good at representing temperate habitats or arid and semi-arid regions. Desert and grassland are particularly poorly represented in EBAs as restricted endemism is not one of their features. These habitats do, however, support characteristic assemblages of relatively widespread species such as bustards (Otididae) and sandgrouse (Pteroclididae) none of which qualify as having a restricted range (see p. 28). In addition, marine habitats and seabirds have been purposefully excluded from the analysis (see p. 22). Areas important for the conservation of these habitats and their birds will therefore be poorly represented in EBAs.

Box 3. Avian endemism and forest loss.

The world's annual overall losses of open and closed forests averaged 15.4 million ha during 1981–1990 (equivalent to 0.8% per year) and appear to be accelerating. Balmford and Long (1994) have integrated these forest data with the Endemic Bird Area analysis (using the ICBP 1992 results) and shown that, on average, countries with large numbers of restricted-range forest birds per unit area are losing their forests faster than countries with low levels of restricted endemism. They suggest that one possibility to explain this disturbing relationship is that long-term isolation of forests surrounded by land suitable for human settlement facilitates deforestation as well as allopatric speciation, both processes being less likely where forests form instead large blocks of continuous habitat. Fjeldså and Lovett (1997) also note that it is of particular interest that the persistence of stable local conditions which promoted the evolution of unique local communities of species may also have enhanced the development of stable human cultures, and that therefore the pressure on nature is often particularly great in the biologically most unique places.

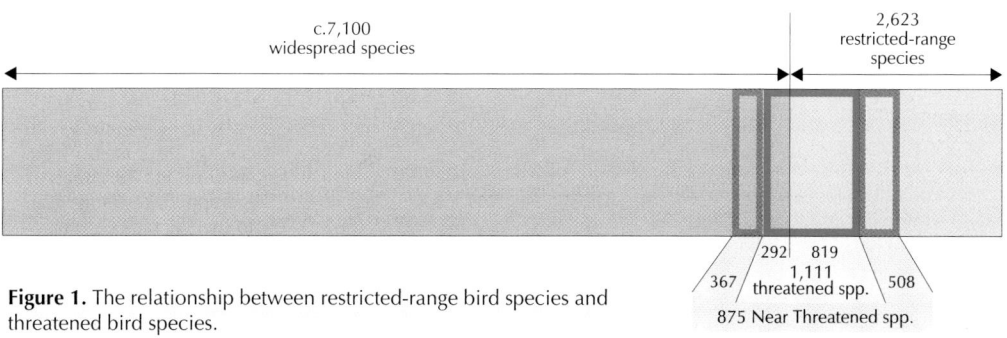

Figure 1. The relationship between restricted-range bird species and threatened bird species.

However, many EBAs do incidentally include sites which are especially important for congregatory species, thereby increasing their overall conservation value. For example, small oceanic island EBAs often include important breeding colonies of seabirds (e.g. the Chatham Islands of New Zealand, EBA 209, and Gough Island in the South Atlantic, EBA 080), EBAs with wetlands may support globally significant populations of waterfowl (e.g. the Assam plains of India, EBA 131, and the South Vietnamese lowlands, EBA 144), and EBAs at strategic points along migratory routes have concentrations of migrants passing through or stopping over (e.g. the south-west Arabian mountains, EBA 118, and the North Central American highlands, EBA 018).

Species richness

Priority-setting exercises for biodiversity conservation often concentrate on areas important for species richness (see p. 17). There are, however, indications in temperate regions (Prendergast *et al.* 1993, Lawton 1996) that some areas which are important for rare species or those with limited distributions are not exceptional for species diversity. This will be true

too for many EBAs, given that a high proportion (48%) of EBAs are on islands, which almost always hold fewer species than equivalent mainland areas, and that many continental EBAs (42%) are in montane regions, which also generally hold fewer species than adjacent lowlands. It is thus likely that some areas of exceptional species diversity will be excluded from the EBA coverage, notably in continental areas of lowland tropical rain forest. However, it should be noted that there are many forest EBAs which include some of the most bird-diverse areas of the world (e.g. along the eastern slope of the Andes at the edge of the Amazon, around the Congo basin, and in south-east Asia and New Guinea).

IMPORTANCE FOR OTHER FLORA AND FAUNA

Just as some important areas for the conservation of birds have been missed through the EBA approach, so it is inevitable that some important areas for other components of biodiversity identified by other priority-setting approaches will also have been missed (see Box 4). The key question, therefore, is do EBAs

---

Box 4. Ecoregions versus EBAs: a comparison between two different priority-setting approaches.

The ecoregions analysis of Latin America and the Caribbean by Dinerstein *et al.* (1995) divides this entire region into five major ecosystem types, 11 main habitat types and 191 ecoregions, with the boundaries between ecoregions being, wherever possible, those generally recognized by conservation planners and biogeographers. This priority-setting study promotes, as a first principle, the maintenance of a representation of all ecosystem and habitat types in regional investment portfolios. In South America, EBAs cover, at least in part, all of the main habitat types but not all ecoregions of the Dinerstein study.

Percentage of South American mainland ecoregions covered by EBAs: 44 South American mainland EBAs versus 89 South American mainland ecoregions.

% coverage by EBAs	No. of ecoregions
0%	7
0–10%	13
10–50%	25
50–90%	21
> 90%	23

Of the 20 ecoregions which have little (< 10%) or no coverage by EBAs, nine are described as tropical moist broadleaf forest (largely in the Amazon basin), two as tropical dry broadleaf forest, seven as grassland, savanna and shrubland, one as flooded grassland, and one as montane grassland.

One might expect the EBAs to fit within the larger-scale patterns set by the ecoregions analysis

and for boundaries to coincide rather than overlap. This is not entirely the case—a comparison within a Geographic Information System of the EBA and ecoregion polygons shows that:

- Particular EBAs overlap with the boundaries of up to 16 ecoregions, but
- If overlaps of less than 10% are discounted, EBAs overlap with the boundaries of a maximum of five ecoregions, and
- If overlaps attributed to the differences in mapping techniques and sources used are ignored, this figure is further reduced to four (16 EBAs show no overlap, 20 overlap with two ecoregions, seven overlap with three ecoregions and only one overlaps with four ecoregions).

Overlaps appear due to three main causes. EBAs may embrace a variety of different vegetation types (distinguished in the ecoregion analysis) such as lowland and montane moist forests, montane forest and páramo, dry forest and xeric scrub, steppe and grassland; although some of the restricted-range bird species of the EBA may be confined to one habitat type, there will be others which utilize more than one, and thus the boundaries of the EBA reflect the commonest patterns of bird distribution. In other instances EBAs embrace more than one mountain range, valley or river system which have broadly similar habitats (again distinguished in the ecoregion analysis). And in a third case the boundaries of ecoregions appear to divide contiguous regions using national boundaries, a distinction not made in the EBA analysis.

---

contain or comprise a significant proportion of sites important for restricted-range species from other groups? Demonstrating this is not straightforward because birds are better known than any other comparable taxonomic group. As knowledge of patterns of distribution in other groups is much less complete, it is difficult to assess how well these patterns are reflected by EBAs. However, much can be inferred from knowledge of the factors which are believed to influence diversity in general.

Patterns of endemism in other animals and plants

Because the basic principles controlling the distribution of species appear to hold for most groups of organisms (see p. 14), we may reasonably expect areas with a significant number of restricted-range species in one taxonomic group to have a significant number in others. However, there are also differences in the factors which control the distribution of different taxonomic groups. For example, some plant species and small animals are confined to small areas of endemism which are simply too small to support viable populations of larger animals such as most birds. The crucial question is thus whether the *similarities* between the factors which control the distribution of birds and those which control that of other groups are more or less important than the *differences*.

Three important ecological attributes of the restricted-range bird species used for the EBA analysis are that they are confined to terrestrial habitats, that they are almost all capable of flight and are therefore potentially good dispersers, and that they are consumers rather than producers (i.e. as opposed to plants) with, ecologically speaking, a generally wide dietary range (unlike, say, a number of insects, very few birds are confined to feeding on only one species of plant or animal). Groups which differ in some or all of these attributes may be expected to differ in their distributions.

Habitat preferences
Birds occur in most of the world's habitats, but there are some where they are not well represented and cannot be expected to act as indicators (see 'Key habitats and sites', above). For example, it would not be expected that the distribution of restricted-range landbirds would give very much information about the distribution of aquatic organisms, particularly marine ones. Similarly, cave ecosystems may be important sites for restricted-range species in a number of groups, especially fish and invertebrates, but would not be expected to be identified in a study of bird distributions.

Dispersal ability
The difference between the dispersal abilities of birds and those of many other groups of terrestrial organisms has a number of implications. Most importantly, birds have colonized most of the world's land areas, including isolated oceanic islands. Many other terrestrial animals are much poorer at dispersing over water and are therefore far less well represented on islands, unless the islands were once part of a continental landmass. Oceanic island EBAs, such as those in the Pacific, have few or no terrestrial mammals (though bats are well represented), amphibians or, to a lesser extent, reptiles. Some plant groups, on the other hand, are very effective at dispersing, notably those with wind-borne seeds, or whose seeds may be carried in the digestive tracts of birds, or those with buoyant water-resistant seeds which may be carried on currents. Many terrestrial invertebrates have also been carried to oceanic islands by the wind or as passengers on floating debris. These plants and invertebrates may show distribution patterns on islands similar to those of birds.

However, it is important to note that although the ability to fly would seem to give birds an ability to disperse freely, there are actually many groups of birds which clearly have a very poor capacity for dispersal. A striking example is the barbets (Capitonidae), which have never succeeded in colonizing eastwards across Wallace's Line from Borneo to Sulawesi or from Bali to Lombok, in each case a sea crossing of just a few tens of kilometres. Other examples are in forest undergrowth birds of the Amazon basin, particularly manakins (Pipridae), woodcreepers (Dendrocolaptidae) and antbirds (Formicariidae), where phenotypic and genotypic differentiation is shown to be frequently correlated with the presence of rivers, indicating that rivers can be significant barriers to gene flow (Capparella 1986).

In general, however, an EBA is likely to contain other restricted-range organisms in that a barrier to bird dispersal is also likely to be a barrier to dispersal for many other organisms. The converse may not necessarily hold: some areas may be important for restricted-range species of other groups and not necessarily for birds, because barriers to dispersal may exist for the other groups even though they do not for birds.

Ecological specialization
Distribution patterns are as much a reflection of the degree of species' ecological specialization as they are of their physical ability to disperse. An example of this lies in the importance of substrate (soil, etc.) in determining the distributions of plants. Limestone and serpentine areas almost always have a highly distinctive flora, very different from that to be found

on adjacent acidic or neutral substrates such as sandstones or volcanic rocks. These differences may be reflected in some components of the fauna, such as soil microfauna and insects which are dependent on particular food plants, but are perhaps less likely to be apparent in vertebrates (although there are some examples of birds which are restricted to forest on limestone outcrops, such as Nava's Wren *H. navai* of Los Tuxtlas and Uxpanapa in Mexico, EBA 013, and Sooty Babbler *Stachyris herberti* of the Annamese lowlands in Vietnam, EBA 143). Overall we may expect some areas which are important for restricted-range plants and invertebrates not to be identified as EBAs.

Congruence between EBAs and areas of endemism for other groups

Many EBAs are isolated from each other. Distinguishing different EBAs in these circumstances is relatively straightforward. In other areas, most notably the Andean Cordillera region of South America, the situation is far more complex. Here a large number of restricted-range bird species with partially overlapping distributions is found, and dividing these areas into a series of separate EBAs requires a good deal of analysis of habitat requirements. A significant test of the effectiveness of EBAs in describing more general patterns of biodiversity is to determine to what extent the precise pattern of EBAs as identified by the present analysis is reflected in known patterns in other groups.

During the first phase of this project, information was assembled from a review of the available literature on patterns of endemism for terrestrial vertebrates, invertebrates and plants (see ICBP 1992, Thirgood and Heath 1994). The results of this work suggest that there is indeed good congruence between global patterns of endemism for different life-forms, supporting work by (e.g.) Simpson and Haffer (1978), Hauge *et al.* (1986), Collar and Stuart (1988) and Gentry (1992). Overall, more than 50% of EBAs showed significant endemism in at least one of these major life-forms, although for 20% of EBAs there were insufficient data to assess levels of endemism for taxa other than birds. However, relative importance was not always perfect. For example, the three richest areas for birds were not the same as the three richest for mammals in continental Africa. More recently, Burgess *et al.* (in press) have found that fewer than half of the most important areas of endemism for birds are also the most important areas for mammals in Afrotropical forests. They note, however, that the data for mammals are far from complete and that these results should only be regarded as preliminary.

The most wide-ranging compilation of information on endemicity to date (other than this present work) has been the Centres of Plant Diversity (CPD) study (WWF/IUCN 1994, 1994–1995, 1997). A comparison between EBAs and CPDs shows good congruence (see Box 5, Figure 2 and Table1).

Box 5. Centres of Plant Diversity versus EBAs: a comparison between similar priority-setting approaches.

The Centres of Plant Diversity study (WWF/IUCN 1994, 1994–1995, 1997) identifies areas with high diversity and/or high levels of endemism for plants. These are defined, for continental regions, as sites with more than 1,000 vascular plants and at least 10% endemism (either to the site or to the phytogeographical region in which the site occurs); and, for islands, as sites with more than 50 endemic species or 10% endemism. However, these criteria were not applied with full rigour, and, as a consequence, some areas have not been chosen using strictly biological criteria (for example boundaries of some CPDs have been determined by the boundaries of protected areas rather than by the limits of distribution of the plants used to define the area). Nevertheless CPDs give a good overview of areas known to be important for plant conservation.

Comparison of CPDs and EBAs shows a good relationship between the two studies (see Figure 2 and Table 1): overall, a total of 70% of CPDs overlap in some way with EBAs, and 60% of EBAs overlap with CPDs. However, only c.10% of CPDs and EBAs match each other, the most common relationship being one of partial overlap. This may be because of

the use of existing protected areas to define the boundaries of CPDs, these often covering broad altitudinal ranges which are likely to be bisected along contours in the EBA analysis in continental areas. However, CPDs which have been entirely missed by the EBA analysis include, most significantly, a suite of sites around the Mediterranean basin, which is an area of larger-scale bird endemism. EBAs which have been missed by the CPD analysis include many small islands and some poorly known areas (e.g. in China), but perhaps more significantly several of the island groups in the Philippines and Indonesia.

In another study, Borchsenius (1997) shows that there is a general correspondence between plant-species endemism in Ecuador and EBAs, the main difference being that bird distributions tend to be wider, and especially to pay less respect to certain latitudinal barriers of importance for plants. There is speculation that where congruence occurs, this is due to ecological factors, whereas unparalleled floristic differences are due to relatively narrow, physical barriers, such as dry inter-Andean valleys.

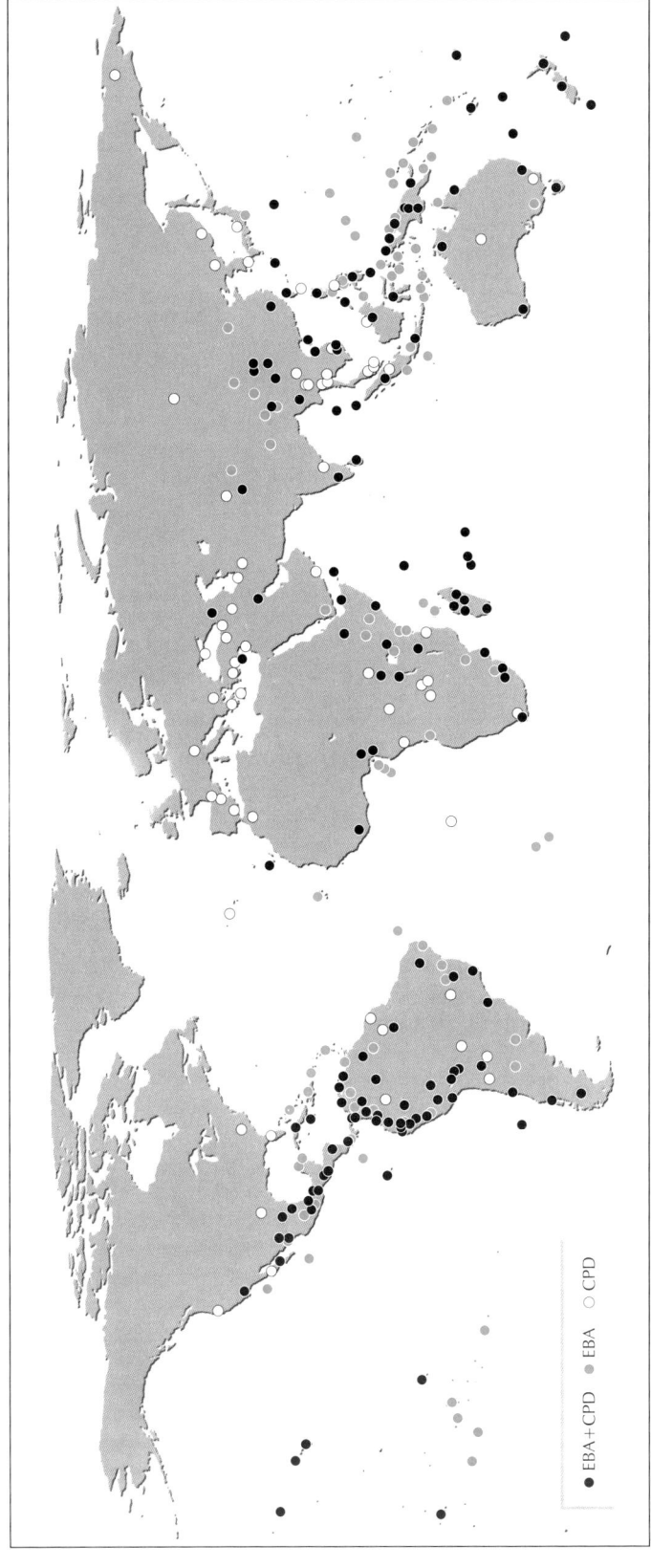

Figure 2. The relationship between Centres of Plant Diversity and EBAs (see Box 5 and Table 1).

Table 1. Relationship between Centres of Plant Diversity and EBAs.	Nature of the relationship	CPD to EBA(s) (numbers)	EBA to CPD(s) (numbers)
	The area matches	23	23
	Area partially overlaps	67	53
	Area is embedded ('nests')	71	16
	Area embraces	8	40
	Area shows no relationship	65 *	86
	Total	234	218

* But 18 show a relationship to a Secondary Area.

CONCLUSIONS

- Conservation within EBAs will always be crucial to maintain avian diversity, as the restricted-range bird species which characterize them occur nowhere else on earth.

- The majority of EBAs are important for reasons in addition to the conservation of restricted-range bird species, notably for the majority of globally threatened bird species and for many restricted-range species from other animal and plant groups.

- The relative importance of EBAs and areas of endemism for other taxonomic groups may not be the same.

- Some areas important for the conservation of biodiversity lie outside the boundaries of EBAs, notably in areas of larger- or smaller-scale endemism.

- Until information on other classes of organism have been collated and analysed to a similar level, EBAs will frequently be one of the best available tools for determining priorities for biodiversity conservation at the global scale.

ENDEMIC BIRD AREAS AS TARGETS FOR CONSERVATION ACTION

THE LAND SURFACE of the earth is almost entirely under undisputed national jurisdiction; the major exception is Antarctica, and the small number of other areas are chiefly islands and some continental borderlands. Conservation efforts aimed at maintenance of terrestrial ecosystems are therefore, in almost all cases, a national responsibility. However, in the past century there has been a growing realization that conservation of biodiversity is ultimately a global concern. This has been reflected in the increasing number of international agreements and treaties concerned with biodiversity conservation to which nations subscribe. The EBA analysis can have considerable input into these, in identifying areas which are important for the conservation of birds, and (as demonstrated in the previous chapter) for other components of biodiversity. However, most EBAs are too large to protect in their entirety and therefore further work needs to be done to identify small areas or sites within them which are more commensurate with practical conservation action. BirdLife has already started to do this in its Important Bird Areas programme (see below).

INTERNATIONAL AGREEMENTS

There are four international agreements to which the EBA analysis could be relevant.

Convention on Wetlands of International Importance especially as Waterfowl Habitat (Ramsar Convention)

The Ramsar Convention was adopted in 1971 and came into force in 1975. By August 1997, the 101 contracting parties (nations) had designated 881 wetlands of international importance. The designation process follows a set of criteria including one based on the 1% flyway population level of waterfowl species and others related to ecological uniqueness. Parties must: maintain the ecological character of Ramsar sites; ensure that any human activities affecting them follow the principle of wise use, so

that the natural properties of the ecosystem are maintained; and develop management plans. There are only a handful of EBAs for which wetlands are an important habitat for restricted-range birds but protection of the key sites in these EBAs under this convention may be possible.

Convention concerning the Protection of the World Cultural and Natural Heritage (World Heritage Convention)

The World Heritage Convention was adopted in 1972 and became effective in 1975, and had 151 contracting parties by August 1997. Parties to the convention designate and protect natural and cultural areas of outstanding universal value. Besides conserving cultural monuments, the convention has become increasingly important to nature conservation by enabling the protection of unique natural sites all over the world through financial and technical assistance. Many sites in EBAs are already protected under this convention (see Box 1) and many more could potentially be considered.

Convention on the Conservation of Migratory Species of Wild Animals (Bonn Convention or CMS)

Aimed at the conservation and effective management of migratory animals, the Bonn Convention was adopted in 1979 and came into force in 1983. By August 1997 the convention had 51 contracting parties. Its concerns are the identification and strict protection of endangered species, the concluding of multilateral agreements for the conservation and management of migratory species that have an unfavourable conservation status or would benefit significantly from international cooperation, and research. The Agreement on the Conservation of African–Eurasian Migratory Waterbirds is the first agreement under the convention to deal specifically with birds, and a similar agreement is envisaged for the Asian–Australasian region. Few restricted-range species are migratory, and the EBA analysis may

---

Box 1. Examples of EBAs, or sites within EBAs, which are protected as World Heritage Sites.

Argentina
Iguazú National Park (EBA 075)

Australia
East Coast Temperate and Subtropical Rainforest
  Parks (EBA 183)
Fraser Island (EBA 183)
Kakadu National Park (EBA 187)
Lord Howe Island Group (EBA 204)
Western Tasmanian Wilderness National Park
  (EBA 185)
Wet tropics of Queensland (EBA 182)

Cameroon
Dja Faunal Reserve (EBA 085)

Ecuador
Galápagos Islands (EBA 031)
Sangay National Park (EBA 043)

Ethiopia
Simien National Park (EBA 115)

Indonesia
Ujung Kulon National Park (EBA 161)

Ivory Coast
Taï National Park (EBA 084)
Mount Nimba Reserve (EBA 084)

Guinea
Mount Nimba Reserve (EBA 084)

Madagascar
Bemaraha Strict Nature Reserve (EBA 093)

Nepal
Sagarmatha National Park (EBA 129)

New Zealand
South West New Zealand (EBA 207)
Tongariro National Park (EBA 206)

Panama
Darién National Park (EBA 023)
La Amistad International Park (EBA 020)

Peru
Huascarán National Park (EBA 051)
Manu National Park (EBA 068)
Río Abiseo (EBAs 049, 051)

Pitcairn Islands (to UK)
Henderson Island (EBA 215)

Seychelles
Vallée de Mai Nature Reserve (EBA 100)
Aldabra Atoll (EBA 099)

St Helena (to UK)
Gough Island (EBA 080)

Sri Lanka
Sinharaja Forest Reserve (EBA 124)

Tanzania
Ngorongoro Conservation Area (EBA 108)
Serengeti National Park (EBA 108)
Kilimanjaro National Park (EBA 109)

Uganda
Bwindi Impenetrable National Park (EBAs 106, 107)
Rwenzori Mountains National Park (EBA 107)

USA
Redwood National Park (EBA 001)
Yosemite National Park (EBA 001)
Hawaii Volcanoes National Park (EBA 218)

Venezuela
Canaima National Park (EBA 064)

Zaïre
Virunga National Park (EBAs 106, 107)
Kahuzi-Biega National Park (EBAs 106, 107)
Okapi Wildlife Reserve (EBA 107)

---

therefore not be particularly significant to this convention. However, there are several EBAs at strategic points along migratory routes, and the birds of these EBAs could benefit from agreements under this convention.

Convention on Biological Diversity (Biodiversity Convention or CBD)

The Biodiversity Convention came into being as a result of the Earth Summit in Rio de Janeiro in 1992 and is the first treaty to deal specifically with the conservation and use of global biodiversity. This convention came into effect in 1993 and now has some 170 contracting parties, making it one of the largest environmental treaties. It has three aims: the conservation of biodiversity; the sustainable use of biodiversity; and the equitable sharing of the benefits arising from the use of biodiversity. These aims are elaborated in a series of 42 articles to which parties to the convention bind themselves to adhere. Of primary concern for the first aim (the conserva-

tion of biodiversity) are Articles 6, 7 and 8. Article 6 deals with general measures for conservation and sustainable use, Article 7 with identification and monitoring, and Article 8 with various measures for *in situ* conservation. Article 7 calls on parties to identify components of biodiversity important for its conservation and sustainable use, drawing attention to an indicative list contained in Annex I to the convention. The first category on this list is 'Ecosystems and habitats: containing high diversity, large numbers of endemic or threatened species, or wilderness; required by migratory species; of social, economic, cultural or scientific importance; or, which are representative, unique or associated with key evolutionary or other biological processes'.

Because this convention is still in its early stages, many parties have yet to begin identifying the important areas and ecosystems set out in Annex I. The information on EBAs presented in this book could be extremely valuable in pointing parties to just such areas (see also Box 2).

Box 2. Biodiversity Conservation Information System.

Decisions about the environment are taken every day at international, national and community levels. However, although the information important for such decisions often exists, it is not always readily accessible. Improved access to data on the status of the world's biodiversity is therefore urgently needed.

The Biodiversity Conservation Information System (BCIS) is being developed to meet this challenge by improving and supporting communication between data-owners and governments, international conventions and organizations concerned with conservation. For example, BCIS will provide information to permit assessment of the extent and types of threats to species, habitats and landscapes, as well as provide feedback on the success of existing conservation and protective measures. This is being made possible by drawing on the extensive data and information already held by the BCIS partners, consisting

in mid-1997 of IUCN The World Conservation Union, BirdLife International, Botanic Gardens Conservation International, TRAFFIC, Wetlands International, the World Conservation Monitoring Centre, Conservation International and The Nature Conservancy. The technological capacities of these partners are currently being improved, and compatible methods of collecting and managing data are being developed in order to facilitate the exchange and analysis of information.

At the national level, BCIS will be a particularly valuable tool for parties to the Convention on Biological Diversity by making its information available to them through the so-called Clearing House Mechanism. It is through this route that the information on EBAs could have considerable impact in helping parties to identify their priority areas for conservation.

BIRDLIFE'S IMPORTANT BIRD AREAS PROGRAMME

In 1993 the selection of sites for the conservation of restricted-range species was adopted as one of the criteria for BirdLife International's Important Bird Areas (IBA) programme. The function of the IBA programme is to identify and protect a network of sites, at a biogeographic scale, critical for the long-term viability of naturally occurring bird populations, across the range of those species for which a site-based approach is appropriate.

IBAs:

- Are places of international significance for the conservation of birds at the global, regional or sub-regional level,
- Are practical tools for conservation,
- Are chosen using standardized, agreed criteria applied with common sense,
- Must, wherever possible, be large enough to support self-sustaining populations of those species for which they are important,
- Must be amenable to conservation and, as far as possible, be delimitable from surrounding areas,
- Will preferably include, where appropriate, existing protected areas,
- Should form part of a wider, integrated approach to conservation that embraces sites, species and habitats.

Criteria for the selection of IBAs have been set in a hierarchy to identify sites of global and regional importance. At a global level, criteria embrace:

- Globally threatened species: sites which regularly hold significant numbers of a globally threatened

species, or other species of global conservation concern.

- Restricted-range species: sites which hold a significant component of the restricted-range species whose breeding distributions define an EBA or a Secondary Area. Sites also have to form one of a set selected to ensure that, as far as possible, all restricted-range species of an EBA or Secondary Area are present in significant numbers in at least one site and, preferably, more.

- Biome-restricted assemblages: sites which hold a significant component of the group of species whose distributions are largely or wholly confined to one biome. Sites also have to form one of a set selected to ensure that, as far as possible, all species restricted to a biome are adequately represented.

- Congregatory species: sites which hold more than 1% of a biogeographic population of a congregatory waterbird species, or more than 1% of the global population of seabird or other species that concentrate in significant numbers, or which meet the criteria of the Ramsar Convention for waterbirds.

The documentation of EBAs has been a major step towards the rational identification of a highly significant suite of Important Bird Areas. Altogether, 2,444 IBAs have already been selected in Europe (Grimmett and Jones 1989), 391 in the Middle East (Evans 1994) and 596 ('Key Areas', for threatened species only) in the Neotropics (Wege and Long 1995). There are programmes currently underway to select sites in Africa, Asia and the Americas, as well as a further review of sites in Europe.

REGIONAL INTRODUCTIONS

THE WORLD has been divided up regionally for presentation of the EBA data. The limits of the chosen regions (see Figure 1) largely reflect biogeography, but some compromises have had to be made; thus the Palearctic and Oriental faunal regions are both split between two of the regions used here.

This chapter presents introductory information region by region. For each there is provided a map displaying all the EBAs which fall within the region, a box of key facts and a table of summary EBA data.

The text presents sections on:

- *Restricted-range species,* with information on where they occur, the types of habitats which they favour, the key sources of information and some of the taxonomic problems encountered in the EBA analysis.

- *Endemic Bird Areas,* with a description of patterns of endemism, some of the characteristics of the EBAs and levels of knowledge.

- *Threats and conservation,* with an indication of habitat loss, other threats to EBAs and their birds, and selected important conservation initiatives.

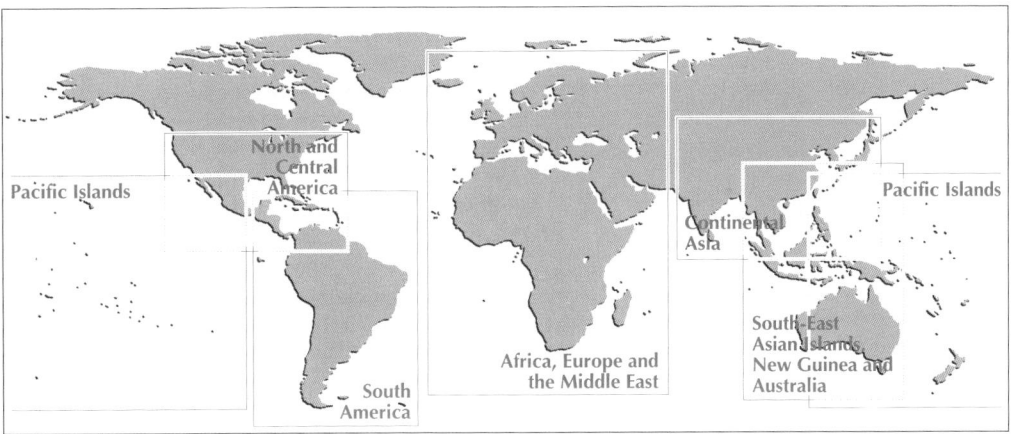

Figure 1. Regional division of the world used in this book. The areas shown correspond to those covered by the regional maps (Figures 2–7).

NORTH AND CENTRAL AMERICA

THIS REGION includes North and Central America through to the Darién lowlands of eastern Panama and north-west Colombia. The Greater and Lesser Antillean islands of the Caribbean are also covered here, as are other islands in the Caribbean Sea such as Cozumel, Providence and San Andrés. On the Pacific side, the islands of Guadalupe,

Socorro and Cocos are included (see Box 1 for key facts).

Restricted-range species

Of the c.200 restricted-range species in the mainland part of this region, only a few are found in North America, the vast majority being associated with

America (Lack 1976), and just four restricted-range bird species are shared between the islands and the continental landmass. The most highly differentiated species include Palmchat *Dulus dominicus*, which is endemic to Hispaniola and is the only member of its family, and several todies (Todidae), an endemic Caribbean family.

Knowledge of birds in this region is, for the most part, good, with a number of excellent regional and national publications documenting in some detail their ecology, distribution and status (e.g. Slud 1964, Monroe 1968, AOU 1983, Bond 1985, Ridgely and Gwynne 1989, Stiles and Skutch 1989, Collar *et al.* 1992, Howell and Webb 1995a, Stotz *et al.* 1996), each benefiting from work by several large, active museums in both North and Central America. However, the region is still in need of major field surveys, with a number of areas in the Greater Antilles and Central America being un- or under-explored ornithologically.

Although only one species from the region has been described as new to science in the last five years (White-fronted Swift *Cypseloides storeri*), species limits have been redefined for many taxa, resulting in numerous new species-level taxa. This is due to the unparalleled attention given to the New World avifauna by taxonomists and field biologists within the region—although it should be noted that this attention has not focused to the same extent on the Caribbean avifauna. As an example of how fluid the taxonomy is within this region, almost 30 species have been added to the North American list since 1995 due to the taxonomic splitting of species (AOU 1995a, 1997). Similarly, Howell and Webb (1995a) considered that, for 15% of the 1,070 species in Mexico and northern Central America, there still remains considerable debate about their taxonomic status.

Endemic Bird Areas

There are only two EBAs in North America: California (EBA 001), which is largely in the USA but extends into northern Baja California, Mexico; and the Northern Sierra Madre Oriental (EBA 010), which is largely in northern Mexico but just overlaps southern Texas, USA. The majority (19) of the EBAs lie solely in (the mainland of) Central America, with a further six covering the Caribbean islands. Three Pacific Ocean islands of the region form three separate EBAs. A total of 17 Secondary Areas, including several on small Caribbean islands, complete the analysis (see Figure 2 for location of EBAs and Secondary Areas, and Table 1 for EBA summary data).

An important feature of the region is the series of mountain chains which effectively separate the Pacific

forests in the mountain ranges of Central America. In the Caribbean, which has over 130 restricted-range species, nearly every island supports at least one restricted-range species, such species having a variety of habitat and altitudinal preferences.

There are no families endemic to the mainland, as Central America forms a land-bridge between North and South America, and thus has avifaunal affinities with both continents. However, very few of the restricted-range species extend out of Central America south into South America. The Greater Antilles have avifaunal similarities with North and Central America, and the Lesser Antilles with South America, but speciation has resulted in an endemic Caribbean avifauna which is quite distinct from that of mainland lowlands from the Gulf/Caribbean lowlands. EBAs occur in the lowlands on both of these slopes, e.g. the North Central American Pacific slope (EBA 017) and the South Central American Pacific slope (EBA 021) on the western side and the Central American Caribbean slope (EBA 019) on the east. There are also EBAs in the higher isolated mountainous areas such as the Costa Rica and Panama highlands (EBA 020) and Darién highlands (EBA 024). The Costa Rica and Panama highlands EBA, although only 23,000 km^2 in size, has 52 restricted-range species confined to it, one of the highest numbers of any of the EBAs identified by the project.

In a few cases a number of smaller islands have been grouped together to form single EBAs, notably the Lesser Antilles (EBA 030), which encompasses the arc of islands from Anguilla south to Grenada and incorporates 12 geopolitical units. Several of these islands support their own single-island endemics; indeed St Lucia (616 km^2) has four species unique to it, but many more restricted-range species are shared between nearby islands, thus making the whole of the Lesser Antilles one EBA.

The topography of mainland Central America is complex, especially in the central Mexican highlands, where it has been difficult to delineate the boundaries of the EBAs precisely. In other highland areas, and on the Caribbean and Pacific slopes in Costa Rica and Panama in particular, poor knowledge of the altitudinal ranges for restricted-range species means that the boundaries of the EBAs involved (e.g. EBAs 020, 021) can only be approximately defined; this problem is exacerbated by the loss of habitat which radically affects species distributions and altitudinal preferences. Similarly, the distributions of birds in the northern portion of the Central American Caribbean slope (EBA 019) are very poorly known, and consequently the EBA is poorly defined in this area.

Threats and conservation

Profound changes during the twentieth century have left this region's natural habitats fragmented and disturbed. Most EBAs have suffered at least moderate habitat loss, with limited loss noted only for the unpopulated and isolated Darién highlands (EBA 024) and Cocos Island (EBA 022).

All the main habitat types have suffered. For example, wetlands have been drained and polluted in the Central Mexican marshes (EBA 007) and Baja California (EBA 002), and forests (tropical dry, humid lowland and humid montane) have been variously altered in the majority of EBAs. Those EBAs whose main habitat is lowland tropical dry forest—such as the North-west Mexican Pacific slope (EBA 005), Balsas region and interior Oaxaca

(EBA 008), North-east Mexican Gulf slope (EBA 011), and North Central American Pacific slope (EBA 017)—are especially vulnerable to habitat loss, being located along the coastal plains of Central America where the human population is at its most dense. Long-standing land use for agriculture has intensified over the past 25 years in this area, especially for cattle-ranching and cash crops (e.g. citrus fruit). Likewise, the predominantly coniferous forest EBAs of the Sierra Madre Occidental and trans-Mexican range (EBA 006) and Northern Sierra Madre Oriental (EBA 010) have lost most of their old-growth forest from logging over the past 50 years, and a similar fate has hit the mainly lowland humid forest EBAs of Los Tuxtlas and Uxpanapa (EBA 013), Central American Caribbean slope (EBA 019) and South Central American Pacific slope (EBA 021).

There are still extensive areas of montane evergreen forest left in some EBAs—the Sierra Madre del Sur (EBA 009), Southern Sierra Madre Oriental (EBA 012), North Central American highlands (EBA 018), Costa Rica and Panama highlands (EBA 020) and Darién highlands (EBA 024)—but even these have been affected by agriculture, especially for coffee and subsistence farming, and logging is increasingly having a severe impact, e.g. in the Southern Sierra Madre Oriental.

The Caribbean EBAs—notably Cuba (EBA 025) and Hispaniola (EBA 028)—have also suffered widespread habitat modification due to cultivation (e.g. of coffee, sugar-cane or bananas) and development for the tourist industry, with introduced predators (e.g. rats, mongooses and cats) being a particular problem for some birds. The Pacific Ocean EBAs of Guadalupe (EBA 003) and Socorro (EBA 004) have suffered from introduced herbivores—goats and sheep—which have caused severe degradation of their natural habitats.

Despite such habitat losses, many of the EBAs have low numbers of threatened species and, overall, only 21% of the region's restricted-range birds are classified as threatened (compared to 31% for all restricted-range bird species). According to the literature, the species in question are almost all numerically strong (N. J. Collar verbally 1997). For example, in the most species-rich mainland EBAs just two of the 20 restricted-range species are threatened in the North Central American highlands (EBA 018), and three of the 53 species in the Costa Rica and Panama highlands (EBA 020). One reason for this is that many of the species have adapted to the extensive habitat degradation, and/or are able to utilize secondary growth and other altered areas. This appears to be the case particularly in those EBAs in which dry forest is the predominant habitat. There are some

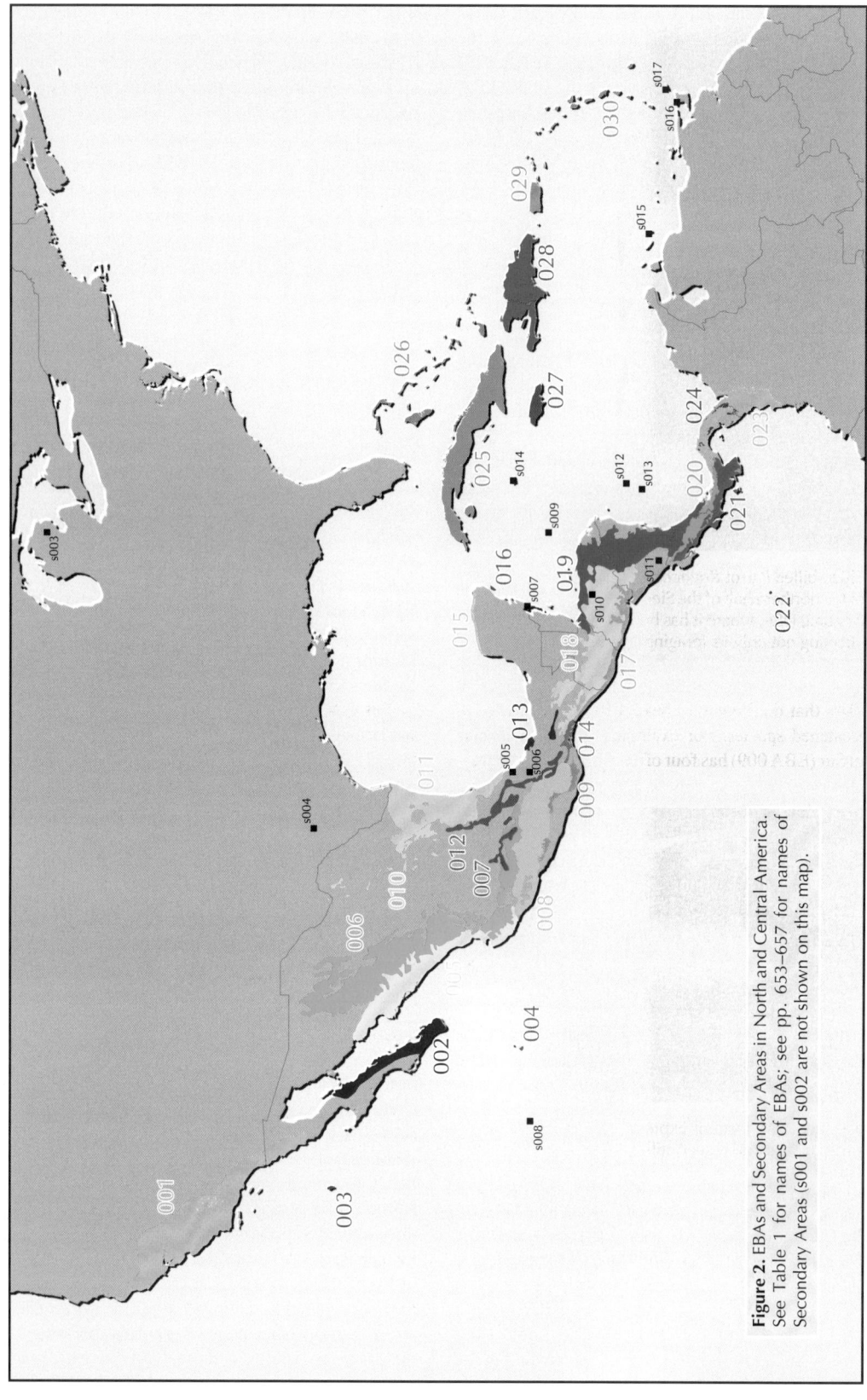

Figure 2. EBAs and Secondary Areas in North and Central America. See Table 1 for names of EBAs; see pp. 653–657 for names of Secondary Areas (s001 and s002 are not shown on this map).

Thick-billed Parrot *Rhynchopsitta pachyrhyncha*, a threatened restricted-range species, breeds in the pine forests of the northern half of the Sierra Madre Occidental (EBA 006), Mexico, though it may have once bred in south-east Arizona, USA, where it has been recently reintroduced. Extensive deforestation has occurred throughout its range affecting not only its foraging options but also, through the selective clearance of old trees, nest-site availability.

EBAs that do, however, have a high proportion of threatened species. For example, the Sierra Madre del Sur (EBA 009) has four of its five restricted-range

This bus—the Jacquot Express—tours local schools on St Lucia in the Lesser Antilles (EBA 030), promoting conservation issues to children, and drawing attention to the St Lucia Amazon (or Jacquot) *Amazona versicolor*. This species has suffered through habitat loss, hurricanes, hunting and trade, but recent action by government and non-government agencies—which has become a model for other Caribbean countries—has reversed the situation, and the nation is now sensitized to the importance of its endemic parrot.

species listed as threatened, and the Sierra Madre Occidental and trans-Mexican range (EBA 006) has three of its seven species so classified. The Lesser Antilles (EBA 030) has the highest total number of threatened restricted-range species in the region (nine), all of them having tiny ranges, being confined to just one or two islands.

There are quite extensive protected-area networks within the countries of mainland Central America, with Costa Rica for example having over 8% of its land area covered by national parks or reserves. However, several EBAs, especially in Mexico, are inadequately protected, and action is urgently required to protect the habitats of their restricted-range birds; this applies particularly to the Sierra Madre Occidental part of the Sierra Madre Occidental and trans-Mexican range (EBA 006) and the Sierra Madre del Sur (EBA 009). There are also many protected areas in the Caribbean EBAs, but some of these are too small and/or do not afford protection sufficiently strict to preserve effectively the wildlife they contain, e.g. in Cuba (EBA 025). Some species, however, e.g. the *Amazona* parrots (see Lesser Antilles, EBA 030), have been the focus of considerable conservation efforts by governments and non-government agencies, and consequently their status has improved.

61

Table 1. EBAs of North and Central America: summary data.

EBA number and name	Countries	Continental/island	Area (km²)	Altitude (m)	Habitat
001 California	Mexico, USA	C	180,000	0–2,000 [L,M]	Scrub (F,W)
002 Baja California	Mexico	C	43,000	0–1,500 [L,M]	Scrub (F,W)
003 Guadalupe Island	Mexico	OI	280	0–1,000 [L]	Forest [5] (S)
004 Socorro Island	Mexico	OI	150	0–1,000 [L]	Forest [4,5] (S)
005 North-west Mexican Pacific slope	Mexico	C	93,000	0–1,200 [L]	Forest [3,4] (S)
006 Sierra Madre Occidental and trans-Mexican range	Mexico	C	230,000	1,200–3,600 [M]	Forest [2,5] (G)
007 Central Mexican marshes	Mexico	C	10,000	1,700–2,500 [M]	Wetland
008 Balsas region and interior Oaxaca	Mexico	C	110,000	0–2,500 [L,M]	Forest [3] (S,D)
009 Sierra Madre del Sur	Mexico	C	12,000	900–3,500 [M]	Forest [2]
010 Northern Sierra Madre Oriental	Mexico, USA	C	15,000	1,500–3,500 [M]	Forest [5] (S)
011 North-east Mexican Gulf slope	Mexico	C	100,000	0–1,200 [L]	Forest [3] (W)
012 Southern Sierra Madre Oriental	Mexico	C	31,000	900–3,500 [M]	Forest [2,5]
013 Los Tuxtlas and Uxpanapa	Mexico	C	14,000	0–1,500 [L,M]	Forest [1,2]
014 Isthmus of Tehuantepec	Mexico	C	6,700	0–1,000 [L]	Forest [3] (S)
015 Yucatán peninsula coastal scrub	Mexico	C	3,400	0–300 [L]	Scrub
016 Cozumel Island	Mexico	CI	490	0–100 [L]	Forest [3,6]
017 North Central American Pacific slope	El Salvador, Guatemala, Honduras, Mexico, Nicaragua	C	30,000	0–1,000 [L]	Forest [3] (S)
018 North Central American highlands	El Salvador, Guatemala, Honduras, Mexico, Nicaragua	C	150,000	500–3,500 [M]	Forest [2,5] (S)
019 Central American Caribbean slope	Costa Rica, Guatemala, Honduras, Nicaragua, Panama	C	120,000	0–1,400 [L]	Forest [1]
020 Costa Rica and Panama highlands	Costa Rica, Panama	C	23,000	1,000–3,800 [M]	Forest [2,5] (G)
021 South Central American Pacific slope	Costa Rica, Panama	C	38,000	0–1,800 [L]	Forest [1,3,6]
022 Cocos Island	Costa Rica	OI	47	0–700 [L]	Forest [1]
023 Darién lowlands	Colombia, Panama	C	61,000	0–1,000 [L]	Forest [1,6]
024 Darién highlands	Colombia, Panama	C	3,000	700–2,300 [M]	Forest [2,5]
025 Cuba	Cuba	OI	110,000	0–1,500 [L]	Forest [3] (S,W)
026 Bahamas	Bahamas, Turks and Caicos Islands (to UK)	OI	14,000	0–60 [L]	Scrub (F)
027 Jamaica	Jamaica	OI	11,000	0–2,000 [L,M]	Forest [1,2,3]
028 Hispaniola	Dominican Republic, Haiti	OI	76,000	0–3,000 [L,M]	Forest [1,2,3]
029 Puerto Rico and the Virgin Islands	Puerto Rico (to USA), Virgin Is. (to USA), Virgin Is. (to UK)	OI	9,400	0–1,200 [L,M]	Forest [1,2,3,5,6]
030 Lesser Antilles	Caribbean *	OI	6,300	0–1,500 [L,M]	Forest [1,2,3,5]

KEY

Habitat

This column names the key habitat of the EBA, followed by any other habitats which are also used by the restricted-range birds (single-letter codes, as below, within parentheses).

Forest (F) Includes both forested areas (generally with a closed canopy) and wooded areas (canopy more open). Primary and secondary forest habitats and forest-edge are all included. Further subdivided as follows.

[1] *Tropical lowland moist forest.* Typically humid forest in the tropics, generally below 1,000 m (varying with geography and topography). Includes types described as lowland and hill evergreen rain forest, moist deciduous forest and wet forest.

[2] *Tropical montane moist forest.* Typically humid forest in the tropics, often above 1,000 m. Includes types described as lower and upper montane evergreen rain forest, mountain forest, montane coniferous forest, cloud forest and mossy forest.

[3] *Tropical dry forest.* Typically dry forest in the tropics at all altitudes. Includes types described as dry deciduous forest, makatea forest, atoll/beach forest, palm forest, thorn or spiny forest and *Acacia* woodland.

[4] *Subtropical forest.* Typically forest in the subtropics or at higher altitudes in tropics.

[5] *Temperate and subalpine zone forest.* Typically forest at higher latitudes, or at higher altitudes at lower latitudes. Includes types described as coniferous and broadleaf forest, *Polylepis* woodland, eucalypt forest, elfin forest and dwarf forest.

[6] *Mangrove and flooded forest.* Typically coastal mangrove forest, swamp forest and flooded forest (including varzea and igapo).

Scrub (S) Any vegetation dominated by shrubs including heathland, moorland, tundra, typical Mediterranean scrub (maquis, fynbos and chaparral) and alpine vegetation. Drier scrub formations are thorn scrub (caatinga), lomas (fog-fed desert formations), arid and cactus scrub, and spinifex associations. Also included are bamboo, fern and sage thickets.

Savanna (V) Extensive tropical vegetation dominated by grasses with a variable amount of tall bushes and/or trees in open formation.

Grassland (G) Includes tussock-grassland, alpine meadows, páramo, steppe and pasture, with limited tree cover.

Wetlands (W) Includes marshes, flooded grassland (wet meadows), reed-beds, bogs, swamps, floodplains and estuaries; also incorporates freshwater bodies and courses of all sizes, and their shores and margins, as well as brackish lakes and lagoons.

Deserts (D) Includes areas where there is an absence of well-developed vegetation.

Rocky areas (R) All rocky terrain such as rocky gorges, rock scree, caves, cliffs, rocky shorelines and beaches.

Habitat loss	Knowledge	Numbers of restricted-range species						Biological importance	Current threat level	Priority	EBA no.
		Confined to the EBA		Present also in other EBAs, SAs		Total					
		Threatened	Total	Threatened	Total	Threatened	Total				
Major	Good	0	6	0	0	0	6	••	•	High	001
Moderate	Incomplete	1	2	0	0	1	2	•	•	High	002
Severe	Good	1	1	0	0	1	1	•	•••	Critical	003
Major	Good	2	3	0	0	2	3	•••	•••	Critical	004
Moderate	Incomplete	1	6	0	1	1	7	•	•	High	005
Major	Incomplete	3	5	0	2	3	7	•	•••	Critical	006
Severe	Good	1	1	0	0	1	1	•	••	Urgent	007
Moderate	Good	0	9	0	1	0	10	••	•	High	008
Major	Incomplete	4	4	0	1	4	5	•	•••	Critical	009
Moderate	Good	1	2	0	0	1	2	•	•	High	010
Major	Good	1	4	0	0	1	4	•	••	Urgent	011
Major	Incomplete	2	3	0	1	2	4	•	•••	Critical	012
Major	Incomplete	2	3	0	0	2	3	•	•••	Critical	013
Moderate	Incomplete	0	2	0	1	0	3	•	•	High	014
Major	Good	0	1	0	1	0	2	•	•	High	015
Moderate	Good	0	3	0	1	0	4	•••	•	Urgent	016
Major	Incomplete	0	3	0	1	0	4	•	•	High	017
Moderate	Incomplete	2	20	0	0	2	20	•••	•	Urgent	018
Moderate	Incomplete	0	7	0	5	0	12	••	•	High	019
Moderate	Good	3	49	0	3	3	52	•••	•	Urgent	020
Major	Good	4	13	0	2	4	15	••	•	High	021
Limited	Good	3	3	0	0	3	3	••	••	Urgent	022
Moderate	Incomplete	3	4	0	9	3	13	•••	••	Critical	023
Limited	Incomplete	0	11	0	5	0	16	••	•	High	024
Major	Good	3	6	0	4	3	10	•	•••	Critical	025
Major	Good	0	3	0	4	0	7	•	•	High	026
Major	Incomplete	3	28	0	7	3	35	•••	••	Critical	027
Severe	Incomplete	6	23	1	11	7	34	•••	•	Urgent	028
Major	Good	3	14	1	10	4	24	••	••	Urgent	029
Major	Incomplete	9	24	0	9	9	33	•••	••	Critical	030

KEY (cont.)

* Antigua and Barbuda, Anguilla (to UK), Netherlands Antilles (to Netherlands), Barbados, Dominica, Grenada, Guadeloupe (to France), St Kitts and Nevis, St Lucia, Martinique (to France), Montserrat (to UK), St Vincent.

Continental/island

C Continent.

CI Continental island (once part of a continent; such islands generally lie on a continental shelf less than 200 m below sea-level).

OI Oceanic island (has never been connected to a continental area by a land-bridge; such islands are generally volcanic in origin).

Altitude

L EBA classified as 'lowland' (generally below c.1,000 m)

M EBA classified as 'montane' (generally above c.1,000 m)

Biological importance See p. 39.

Current threat level See p. 40.

Priority See p. 41.

Habitat loss

Severe   Estimated that >90% of the key habitats (for restricted-range bird species) has been lost (i.e. cleared or severely degraded).

Major   >50% to 90%

Moderate   >10% to 50%

Limited   0–10%

Unquantified   Some of the key habitats known to have been lost, but not possible to quantify as above.

Possible   Some of the key habitats suspected to have been lost.

Knowledge

Good
• Most parts of the EBA have been sampled by ornithologists.
• Habitat requirements and altitudinal ranges of most restricted-range birds generally well understood.
• EBA boundaries usually well-defined.

Incomplete
• Some parts of the EBA have been sampled, but some important gaps in knowledge of restricted-range bird distributions.
• Habitat requirements and altitudinal ranges of some restricted-range birds are well understood, but significant gaps in knowledge for others.
• EBA boundaries approximate, at least in part.

Poor
• EBA seldom visited by ornithologists, or fieldwork concentrated at a few sites or on a few species. Major gaps in knowledge of restricted-range bird distribution.
• Habitat requirements and altitudinal ranges of restricted-range birds generally poorly understood.
• EBA boundaries may be difficult to define.

SOUTH AMERICA

SOUTH AMERICA can be divided into three broad continental regions, namely the Andes (a mountain chain which runs the entire length of the western part of the continent and extends across northern Venezuela as far as the Paria peninsula), the interior and Atlantic lowlands, and the ancient massifs of the Guyana and Brazilian shields and their Atlantic margins. The Pacific Ocean island groups of Galápagos and Juan Fernández, and the Atlantic Ocean islands of Fernando de Noronha, the Falklands and South Georgia are also included in this region (see Box 2 for key facts).

Restricted-range species

The ancient origins of South America, its complex climatic patterns and topography (especially in the Andes), have led to the development of a mosaic of different habitat types, providing conditions for both the radiation and isolation of species. Thus it has by far the largest continental avifauna in the world, with over 3,200 species (roughly a third of the world's total), despite comprising less than 12% of the world's land area. Not surprisingly, it has the highest number of restricted-range species (658) of all the regions in this study.

Restricted-range species can be found at all altitudes and within most habitats, although there are greater concentrations of species within forested habitats and within the upper tropical and subtropical zones (c.1,000–2,500 m). However, they are not distributed evenly through the region. The Andes form a major barrier to the dispersal of lowland and submontane animals and plants, and the mountain ranges themselves are divided by dispersal barriers such as the Marañón, Cauca and Magdalena rivers, and the Táchira depression. Consequently, the Andes and their isolated Pacific and Caribbean slopes are the main centre of speciation, and support the largest concentration of restricted-range birds. In addition, the Atlantic margins of the continent are isolated from the rain forests of the Amazon basin by a relatively arid zone, and, although some species are shared with the Amazon forests, there is a very high level of endemism here, with concentrations of restricted-range birds. In contrast to these areas, there are few restricted-range bird species within the vast expanses of the Amazon basin, other than at the western fringes close to the Andes, where there is a zone of exceptionally high rainfall and one of the highest avian diversity levels of any region of the world. There are also few restricted-range species in interior South America (e.g. the Orinoco basin, Parana–Paraguay lowlands and the Gran Chaco) where most species are more widely distributed than the 50,000-km^2 range-size criterion used in this study.

Knowledge of birds in South America is relatively good, with a number of excellent regional and national publications documenting in some detail their ecology, distribution and status (e.g. Meyer de Schauensee and Phelps 1978, Meyer de Schauensee 1982, Hilty and Brown 1986, Ridgely and Tudor 1989, Fjeldså and Krabbe 1990, Collar *et al.* 1992, Ridgely and Tudor 1994, Stotz *et al.* 1996). However, the continent is still in need of major field surveys, and this is demonstrated by the fact that more than 20 species have been described as new to science from the region (especially Brazil and Colombia) during the past five years (see, e.g., *Cotinga* 1994–1997, 1–7).

The taxonomy of the South American avifauna (indeed that of the whole of the New World) has

Toucan Barbet *Semnornis ramphastinus* is endemic to the wet forests of the Chocó (EBA 041) in Colombia and Ecuador. This area has the highest number of restricted-range bird species (62) of all mainland EBAs, with exceptional diversity and endemism in a wide range of other taxa including plants, reptiles, amphibians and butterflies.

P. Salaman/Proyecto Halcon

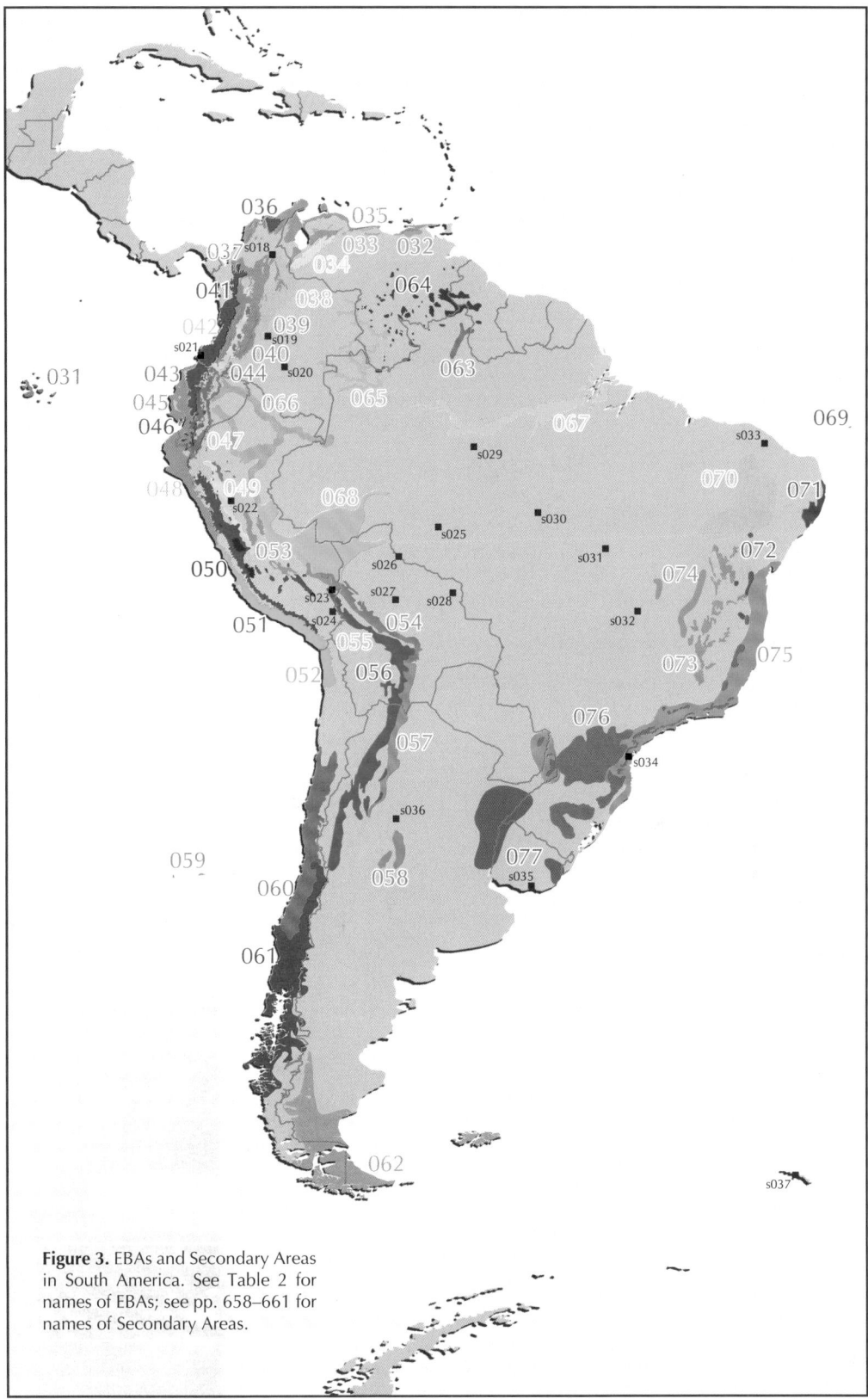

Figure 3. EBAs and Secondary Areas in South America. See Table 2 for names of EBAs; see pp. 658–661 for names of Secondary Areas.

Table 2. EBAs of South America:
summary data.

EBA number and name	Countries	Continental/ island	Area (km²)	Altitude (m)	Habitat
031 Galápagos Islands	Ecuador	OI	8,000	0–1,700 [L,M]	Scrub (F)
032 Caripe–Paria region	Venezuela	C	6,000	400–2,500 [M]	Forest [2]
033 Cordillera de la Costa Central	Venezuela	C	6,200	600–2,500 [M]	Forest [2] (W)
034 Cordillera de Mérida	Venezuela	C	23,000	300–4,000 [L,M]	Forest [1,2,5] (G)
035 Caribbean Colombia and Venezuela	Colombia, Venezuela	C	89,000	0–1,000 [L]	Forest [3,6] (S,D)
036 Santa Marta mountains	Colombia	C	11,000	600–5,200 [L,M]	Forest [1,2,5] (S,G)
037 Nechí lowlands	Colombia	C	58,000	0–1,500 [L]	Forest [1]
038 Colombian East Andes	Colombia, Venezuela	C	85,000	1,000–4,000 [M]	Forest [1,2,5] (G,W)
039 Colombian inter-Andean valleys	Colombia	C	31,000	200–1,700 [L]	Forest [1,3] (S)
040 Colombian inter-Andean slopes	Colombia	C	48,000	1,000–2,500 [M]	Forest [2]
041 Chocó	Colombia, Ecuador	C	100,000	0–3,800 [L,M]	Forest [1,2,5] (G)
042 Northern Central Andes	Colombia, Ecuador	C	36,000	1,500–3,700 [M]	Forest [2,5]
043 Central Andean páramo	Colombia, Ecuador, Peru	C	32,000	2,000–5,000 [M]	Grassland (F,S)
044 Ecuador–Peru East Andes	Colombia, Ecuador, Peru	C	28,000	800–2,200 [L,M]	Forest [1,2]
045 Tumbesian region	Ecuador, Peru	C	130,000	0–3,000 [L,M]	Forest [1,2,3] (S)
046 Southern Central Andes	Ecuador, Peru	C	10,000	1,500–3,500 [M]	Forest [2,5]
047 Andean ridge-top forests	Ecuador, Peru	C	3,800	600–2,500 [M]	Forest [2,5]
048 Marañón valley	Peru	C	11,000	200–3,200 [L,M]	Forest [1,3] (S)
049 North-east Peruvian cordilleras	Peru	C	37,000	1,700–3,800 [M]	Forest [2,5] (S,G)
050 Junín puna	Peru	C	11,000	3,500–5,000 [M]	Grassland (S,W)
051 Peruvian high Andes	Peru	C	100,000	1,500–4,600 [M]	Scrub (F,G)
052 Peru–Chile Pacific slope	Chile, Peru	C	95,000	0–4,000 [M]	Desert (F,S)
053 Peruvian East Andean foothills	Peru	C	32,000	600–2,200 [L,M]	Forest [1,2]
054 Bolivian and Peruvian lower yungas	Bolivia, Peru	C	58,000	400–2,000 [L,M]	Forest [1,2]
055 Bolivian and Peruvian upper yungas	Bolivia, Peru	C	35,000	1,800–3,700 [M]	Forest [2] (S)
056 High Andes of Bolivia and Argentina	Argentina, Bolivia, Peru	C	200,000	1,100–4,600 [M]	Forest [5] (S,G,R)
057 Argentine and south Bolivian yungas	Argentina, Bolivia	C	60,000	800–3,100 [M]	Forest [2]
058 Sierras Centrales of Argentina	Argentina	C	22,000	1,500–2,800 [M]	Grassland (F)
059 Juan Fernández Islands	Chile	OI	180	0–1,300 [L,M]	Forest [5] (S)
060 Central Chile	Chile	C	160,000	0–2,400 [L,M]	Scrub (F)
061 Chilean temperate forests	Argentina, Chile	C	230,000	0–1,500 [L,M]	Forest [5]
062 Southern Patagonia	Argentina, Chile, Falkland Islands (to UK)	C	170,000	0–1,200 [L]	Grassland (S,W,R
063 Rio Branco gallery forests	Brazil, Guyana	C	94,000	0–100 [L]	Forest [1]
064 Tepuis	Brazil, Guyana, Venezuela	C	57,000	600–2,800 [M]	Forest [2,5] (S,V)
065 Orinoco–Negro white-sand forests	Brazil, Colombia, Venezuela	C	62,000	0–500 [L]	Forest [1,6] (S,V)
066 Upper Amazon–Napo lowlands	Brazil, Colombia, Ecuador, Peru	C	130,000	0–600 [L]	Forest [1,6] (S)
067 Amazon flooded forests	Brazil	C	140,000	0–200 [L]	Forest [1,6]
068 South-east Peruvian lowlands	Bolivia, Brazil, Peru	C	260,000	0–800 [L]	Forest [1,6]
069 Fernando de Noronha	Brazil	OI	18	0–60 [L]	Forest [3] (S)
070 North-east Brazilian caatinga	Brazil	C	200,000	0–1,000 [L]	Forest [3] (S)
071 Atlantic slope of Alagoas and Pernambuco	Brazil	C	23,000	0–1,000 [L]	Forest [1]
072 Deciduous forests of Bahia	Brazil	C	10,000	600–1,000 [L]	Forest [3]
073 Central Brazilian hills and tablelands	Brazil	C	67,000	700–2,000 [M]	Savanna (S)
074 Deciduous forests of Minas Gerais and Goiás	Brazil	C	33,000	0–500 [L]	Forest [3]
075 Atlantic forest lowlands	Argentina, Brazil, Paraguay	C	290,000	0–1,700 [L]	Forest [1]
076 Atlantic forest mountains	Argentina, Brazil	C	260,000	500–2,800 [M]	Forest [2]
077 Argentine Mesopotamian grasslands	Argentina, Brazil, Uruguay	C	160,000	0–1,100 [L]	Grassland (W)

KEY See Table 1 (pp. 62–63).

received more attention than has that of any other region, and consequently there have been many recent taxonomic revisions of species and species-groups. However, on the basis of extensive field experience, numerous further species redefinitions and taxonomic splits are suggested in Ridgely and Tudor (1994).

Endemic Bird Areas

A series of 28 EBAs has been identified in the Andes running from east to west along the Caribbean slope (including the Santa Marta mountains: EBA 036), from north to south down the Pacific lowlands, and along their entire length at different altitudes and along various slopes. Thus there are EBAs through-

Habitat loss	Knowledge	Confined to the EBA		Present also in other EBAs, SAs		Total		Biological importance	Current threat level	Priority	EBA no.
		Threatened	Total	Threatened	Total	Threatened	Total				
Moderate	Good	3	22	0	0	3	22	●●	●●	Urgent	031
Major	Good	5	5	1	7	6	12	●●	●●●	Critical	032
Moderate	Incomplete	1	5	1	12	2	17	●●	●	High	033
Moderate	Good	2	10	2	15	4	25	●●	●●	Urgent	034
Moderate	Good	2	11	1	1	3	12	●●	●●	Urgent	035
Major	Good	2	15	1	7	3	22	●●●	●	Urgent	036
Major	Incomplete	2	3	3	9	5	12	●●	●●●	Critical	037
Major	Good	8	14	6	20	14	34	●●●	●●	Critical	038
Major	Good	1	4	0	0	1	4	●	●	High	039
Major	Incomplete	4	5	5	12	9	17	●●	●●●	Critical	040
Major	Incomplete	12	51	5	11	17	62	●●	●●	Urgent	041
Major	Incomplete	3	4	2	5	5	9	●	●●●	Critical	042
Moderate	Good	5	10	0	1	5	11	●●	●●	Urgent	043
Moderate	Good	2	11	1	6	3	17	●●	●	High	044
Severe	Good	14	45	1	10	15	55	●●●	●●	Critical	045
Major	Good	2	5	1	3	3	8	●	●●	Urgent	046
Moderate	Poor	3	6	0	1	3	7	●●	●●	Urgent	047
Major	Incomplete	3	11	2	11	5	22	●●●	●	Urgent	048
Moderate	Incomplete	2	19	0	5	2	24	●●●	●	Urgent	049
Moderate	Good	3	5	0	1	3	6	●	●●●	Critical	050
Moderate	Incomplete	8	20	3	9	11	29	●●●	●●●	Critical	051
Moderate	Good	3	6	0	3	3	9	●●	●	High	052
Moderate	Incomplete	0	6	1	8	1	14	●●	●	High	053
Major	Incomplete	3	7	1	8	4	15	●●	●●	Urgent	054
Moderate	Incomplete	0	15	0	5	0	20	●●●	●	Urgent	055
Major	Incomplete	7	16	2	5	9	21	●●●	●●	Critical	056
Moderate	Incomplete	1	8	0	1	1	9	●●●	●	Urgent	057
Moderate	Good	0	2	0	0	0	2	●	●	High	058
Severe	Good	2	3	0	0	2	3	●	●●●	Critical	059
Major	Incomplete	0	7	0	1	0	8	●●●	●	Urgent	060
Major	Incomplete	0	4	0	1	0	5	●●	●	High	061
Moderate	Incomplete	1	10	0	0	1	10	●●●	●	Urgent	062
Moderate	Incomplete	2	2	0	0	2	2	●	●●	Urgent	063
Limited	Incomplete	2	36	0	2	2	38	●●●	●	Urgent	064
Limited	Incomplete	1	11	0	1	1	12	●●	●	High	065
Moderate	Incomplete	1	10	0	0	1	10	●●	●	High	066
Moderate	Poor	0	4	0	0	0	4	●	●	High	067
Moderate	Incomplete	2	12	0	0	2	12	●●●	●	Urgent	068
Major	Good	1	2	0	0	1	2	●	●	High	069
Major	Incomplete	3	5	1	1	4	6	●●	●●●	Critical	070
Severe	Good	7	7	5	5	12	12	●●	●●●	Critical	071
Severe	Incomplete	2	2	0	0	2	2	●	●●●	Critical	072
Moderate	Incomplete	1	4	1	3	2	7	●	●●	Urgent	073
Severe	Incomplete	1	2	0	0	1	2	●	●●●	Critical	074
Severe	Incomplete	28	52	3	3	31	55	●●●	●●●	Critical	075
Moderate	Good	3	21	0	2	3	23	●●●	●	Urgent	076
Severe	Good	2	3	0	0	2	3	●	●●●	Critical	077

out the central spine of the Andes, in some of the larger Andean intermontane valleys, and on mountain ranges which run parallel to, but separate from, the main range. This makes the Andean region (including their lowland Pacific and Caribbean margins) of utmost importance for conservation. An important concentration of eight EBAs (070–077) is located in the humid and semi-humid tropical Atlantic forests (at the eastern edge of the Brazilian shield) that stretch the length of eastern Brazil (from Alagoas to Rio Grande do Sul), and also extend into eastern Paraguay and Misiones in north-east Argentina. Only five EBAs can be described as Amazonian, two of these being located at the western fringes close to the

<table>
<tbody>
</tbody>
</table>

Box 2. Key facts for South America.

Numbers of:
658 Restricted-range species
195 Threatened restricted-range species
47 EBAs
20 Secondary Areas
12 Countries with EBAs

EBAs with high numbers of restricted-range species
- Chocó (EBA 041), 62 species
- Tumbesian region (EBA 045), 55 species
- Atlantic forest lowlands (EBA 075), 55 species

EBAs which are especially distinct at the generic level
- Atlantic forest lowlands (EBA 075),
  11 endemic genera

EBAs with high numbers of threatened restricted-range species
- Atlantic forest lowlands (EBA 075), 31 species
- Chocó (EBA 041), 17 species
- Tumbesian region (EBA 045), 15 species

EBAs with high numbers of Critical and Endangered endemic species
- Atlantic forest lowlands (EBA 075), 18 species
- Tumbesian region (EBA 045), 6 species
- Atlantic slope of Alagoas and Pernambuco (EBA 071), 6 species

Examples of EBAs critically in need of conservation action
- Tumbesian region (EBA 045)
- Atlantic slope of Alagoas and Pernambuco (EBA 071)
- Atlantic forest lowlands (EBA 075)

Countries with high numbers of restricted-range species
- Peru, 211 species
- Colombia, 192 species (some of these species are covered under the North and Central American region)
- Brazil, 164 species

Countries with high numbers of threatened restricted-range species
- Brazil, 59 species
- Colombia, 54 species (some of these species are covered under the North and Central American region)
- Peru, 48 species

of Amazonian birds, complete the analysis (see Figure 3 for location of EBAs and Secondary Areas, and Table 2 for EBA summary data).

The continental EBAs range in size from relatively small areas such as the Andean ridge-top forests (EBA 047, 3,800 km^2) and the Caripe–Paria region (EBA 032, 6,000 km^2), to the vast Atlantic forest areas (EBA 075, 290,000 km^2, and EBA 076, 260,000 km^2) and the South-east Peruvian lowlands (EBA 086, 260,000 km^2). They are distributed relatively evenly between lowland and montane elevations (16 EBAs are primarily lowland, 18 primarily montane, and 13 cover both lowland and montane zones).

It is unsurprising that the predominant habitat-type of South America's EBAs is humid forest, which ranges from the wet, pluvial forests of the Chocó (EBA 041), the Upper Amazon–Napo lowlands (EBA 066) and the South-east Peruvian lowlands (068), to the relatively stunted and species-poor white-sand forests of the upper Orinoco–Negro (EBA 065) and the semi-tropical forests that characterize the southern and western extension of the Atlantic lowland forests (EBA 075) in eastern Paraguay and northern Brazil.

Dry deciduous forest can be found in Caribbean Colombia and Venezuela (EBA 035), but also in the Tumbesian region (EBA 045), the Marañón valley (EBA 048), Bahia (EBA 072) and Minas Gerais and Goiás (EBA 074). With even less rainfall, the dry forest of north-west Peru grades into the desert vegetation of the Peru–Chile Pacific slope (EBA 052). Subtropical or temperate forest, characterized by 'southern pine' *Araucaria* and *Nothofagus* forest, can be found in southern Chile (EBA 061). Semi-open and open lowland habitats are well represented in Southern Patagonia (EBA 062), Mediterranean matorral scrub in Central Chile (EBA 060), caatinga in North-east Brazil (EBA 070), and wet grassland or monte in the Argentine Mesopotamian grasslands (EBA 077).

Montane habitats are extremely important in some EBAs, such as in the Santa Marta mountains (EBA 036) which in fact cover all life-zones including tropical to temperate forest. Stunted ridge-top forest is important for some Andean birds (e.g. in EBA 047), and treeline elfin forest and (above the treeline) páramo (comprising tussocky grassland, scrub, open rocky areas, etc.) defines the Central Andes (EBA 043). Particularly important for some restricted-range and threatened birds are the semi-humid, isolated forest patches comprising *Polylepis*, *Gynoxys*, *Escallonia* and *Weinmannia* trees/bushes (e.g. in the Peruvian high Andes, EBA 051). Where páramo defines the vegetation above the treeline in the northern Andes, puna defines it in the southern

Andes (EBAs 066, 068). The Sierras Centrales of Argentina (EBA 058), Southern Patagonia (EBA 062 in part) and Tepuis (EBA 064) complete the mainland EBAs in South America. Island EBAs cover the Galápagos Islands (EBA 031), Juan Fernández Islands (EBA 059), Fernando de Noronha (EBA 069, the smallest EBA in the region at only 18 km^2) and the Falkland Islands (EBA 062 in part). A total of 20 Secondary Areas, many covering the isolated ranges

Andes, and is especially important in the Junín EBA (050) in southern Peru. In some parts of the Andes, for example in Peru and Bolivia, local conditions have led to the development of a particularly complex mosaic of different habitat types. In such areas, some EBAs overlap geographically, but as their species have completely different habitat requirements (such as wet subtropical or temperate forest, puna, páramo, cloud forest and *Polylepis* woodland) the EBAs can be divided on the basis of these preferences. For example, the north-east Peruvian cordilleras (EBA 049) primarily comprise humid montane forest, whereas the adjacent Peruvian high Andes (EBA 051) are characterized by arid and semi-arid vegetation. The Junín puna (EBA 050) is surrounded by the Peruvian high Andes, but differs due to the presence of puna grassland, scrub, marshland and open water.

Knowledge of EBAs is incomplete in many areas because of complex biogeography, the inaccessibility of some areas, and the complicating factor of widespread habitat destruction. For example, in the Chocó (EBA 041) it has not been possible to divide the EBA further into lowland and montane areas owing to an incomplete knowledge of the precise altitudinal ranges of the species involved. Similarly, the distributions of Amazonian birds are generally incompletely or poorly known, so the boundaries and areas of the EBAs can only be approximately defined. Two EBAs are particularly poorly known, namely the Andean ridge-top forests in Ecuador and Peru (EBA 047), and the Amazon flooded forests in Brazil (EBA 067), and further information would help to refine the EBA analysis.

Threats and conservation

A long history of human colonization and its associated economic, social and political factors, especially in the twentieth century, has brought about serious changes to the South American environment. The forests are being felled, the grasslands cultivated, wetlands drained and pristine habitats increasingly fragmented and disturbed. Throughout the Americas the primary threat to birds (and thus EBAs) is this destruction and disturbance (or alteration) of the habitats on which their existence depends. In the Andean region, eight of the 28 EBAs are considered of critical importance for conservation action, with the Tumbesian region (EBA 045) standing out in particular. Some of the original great forests, such as those of eastern Brazil, are functionally gone. Being one of the first parts of the continent to be colonized by Europeans, these Atlantic forests have been reduced to an estimated 2–5% of their original forest cover (Oliver and Santos 1991), and mass species

extinctions are likely unless urgent action is taken. Six of the eight EBAs in this region are considered of critical importance for conservation action. The Atlantic forest lowlands (EBA 075) is possibly the most important EBA in South America: it has especially high numbers of restricted-range species (59), endemic genera (11), and threatened restricted-range species (32, of which 18 are considered Critical or Endangered). The Atlantic slope of Alagoas and Pernambuco (EBA 071) also has a particularly high number of species (7) classified as Critical or Endangered.

Although the Amazon basin is not rich in restricted-range species, extensive deforestation there could disrupt climatic patterns over the continent and threaten the integrity of many Andean EBAs. Even within this vast region, there is a criss-cross of highways, and steadily the cleared margins of these roads swell to meet one another, isolating a growing number of forest fragments between them. Currently more devastating has been the conversion of the complex of open-country habitats in central South America (e.g. Sierras Centrales of Argentina, EBA 058; southern Patagonia, EBA 062; central Brazilian hills and tablelands, EBA 073; Argentine Mesopotamian grasslands, EBA 077) into planted pines, soya beans and sugar-cane, interspersed with citrus groves, overgrazed pasture and other crops (Stotz *et al.* 1996).

South America has a well-developed protected-area network covering approximately 4.8% of terrestrial habitats (e.g. IUCN 1992b, Harcourt and Sayer 1996), although this network does not adequately embrace all areas of high biodiversity conservation value. Specific sites within South American EBAs and elsewhere have been identified as part of an analysis which has documented the 499 most important sites ('Key Areas') currently known for threatened species in the continent (Wege and Long 1995). If adequately protected, these Key Areas would help ensure the conservation of almost all of the region's threatened species and are perhaps the most efficient areas currently known in which to target conservation initiatives, whether these be direct protection or field surveys. However, only some 44% of Key Areas currently have any form of protected status, and just 22% are national parks, strict nature reserves or biosphere reserves (IUCN categories I, II and IX). In addition, many of these protected areas remain under threat and, in many, habitat degradation, uncontrolled hunting, etc., continue unchecked, suggesting that effective management of activities undertaken within them is still required if their effectiveness for biodiversity conservation is to be ensured.

THIS REGION covers all of continental Africa plus Europe and the Middle East. Islands in the Atlantic Ocean are included, west as far as the Azores and south to Tristan da Cunha, as well as islands in the Indian Ocean east as far as the Mascarenes and south to Kerguelen and the Crozet Islands. Most of these islands are in small, isolated archipelagos, with the notable exception of the large continental island of Madagascar (see Box 3 for key facts).

Restricted-range species

Like the world's other tropical and subtropical regions, sub-Saharan Africa has a high bird-species diversity, although total numbers are lower than in the Neotropics or tropical Asia. This relatively high diversity is reflected in the number of restricted-range species (408), the third (equal) highest of all of the regions (note that few of these species are from Europe or the Middle East). A little more than half of the restricted-range species (59%) occur in continental regions, with somewhat fewer (41%) on islands. Of the continental species, the majority occur in montane, largely forest, habitats (66%), as opposed to lowland ones (34%). Some restricted-range species are associated with grassland, scrub and open, rocky areas.

Hall and Moreau (1970) and Snow (1978) published detailed point-locality maps for the resident species of the Afrotropical region. More up-to-date atlases have been produced for several African countries, for example Kenya (Lewis and Pomeroy 1989) and several provinces of South Africa (e.g. Tarboton *et al.* 1987; see also Harrison *et al.* 1997, which appeared too late to be used in this project). Information for the Palearctic region is generally good (e.g. Cramp *et al.* 1977–1994), as is that for the island distribution of birds, e.g. Cape Verdes (Hazevoet 1995), Madagascar (Langrand 1990) and the Mascarenes (Diamond 1987). It was therefore relatively straightforward to select candidate species for this region and to judge which have restricted ranges. For islands, these included all endemics apart from those on Madagascar, where about half (c.50 species) were excluded from the project because their historical ranges were estimated to be larger than 50,000 km^2 (notably those which formerly occurred throughout the eastern coastal rain forests).

There are major gaps in knowledge of the avifaunas of some countries, for example Angola, Mozambique, Ethiopia, Somalia and Zaïre. The limited recent ornithological work in these poorly known countries has led to the description of several new species, such as Bulo Burti Bush-shrike *Laniarius liberatus* from Somalia (Smith *et al.* 1991b) and Itombwe Nightjar

---

Box 3. Key facts for Africa, Europe and the Middle East.

Numbers of:
408 Restricted-range species
180 Threatened restricted-range species
45 EBAs
33 Secondary Areas
48 Countries with EBAs

EBAs with high numbers of restricted-range species
- Tanzania–Malawi mountains (EBA 105), 37 species
- Albertine Rift mountains (EBA 106), 37 species
- Cameroon mountains (EBA 086), 29 species

EBAs which are especially distinct at the generic level
- East Malagasy wet forests (EBA 094), 9 endemic genera

EBAs with high numbers of threatened restricted-range species
- Tanzania–Malawi mountains (EBA 105), 20 species
- East Malagasy wet forests (EBA 094), 14 species
- Cameroon mountains (EBA 086), 12 species

EBAs with high numbers of Critical and Endangered endemic species
- Tanzania–Malawi mountains (EBA 105), 6 species
- Western Angola (EBA 087), 5 species
- Comoro Islands (EBA 098), 5 species
- Mauritius (EBA 102), 5 species

Examples of EBAs critically in need of conservation action
- Western Angola (EBA 087)
- Comoro Islands (EBA 098)
- South Ethiopian highlands (EBA 114)

Countries with high numbers of restricted-range species
- Tanzania, 52 species
- Madagascar, 49 species
- Zaïre, 47 species

Countries with high numbers of threatened restricted-range species
- Madagascar, 27 species
- Tanzania, 22 species
- Zaïre, 18 species

Caprimulgus prigoginei from Zaïre (Louette 1990). New species continue to be described even from some of the better known countries, such as Kilombero Weaver *Ploceus burnieri* from Tanzania (Baker and Baker 1990) and Long-tailed Pipit *Anthus longicaudatus* from South Africa (Liversidge 1996).

As in other regions of the world, Sibley and Monroe (1990, 1993) has been followed as the standard taxonomic work. However, Collar *et al.* (1994) diverged from this list for a number of African taxa, generally following Dowsett and Dowsett-Lemaire (1993), Dowsett and Forbes-Watson (1993) and the advice of regional experts; these taxonomic amendments have been followed in this analysis.

Endemic Bird Areas

Africa is generally less complex biogeographically than the tropical Americas or the Oriental region, and most EBAs are discrete, having few shared restricted-range species. However, there are several immediately adjacent pairs of EBAs, usually one montane and one lowland, e.g. the Cameroon mountains (EBA 086) and the Cameroon and Gabon lowlands (EBA 085). Not surprisingly, many of the region's EBAs (21) are in sub-Saharan Africa, only six falling within Europe and the Middle East. Levels of endemism are high on almost all of the African islands especially in relation to their size, and most are included within 13 island EBAs. A further five EBAs cover much of Madagascar, and 33 Secondary Areas complete the analysis (see Figure 4 for location of EBAs and Secondary Areas, and Table 3 for EBA summary data).

The wide range of tropical and subtropical vegetation types found in Africa were documented and mapped in detail by White (1983). Many of these vegetation types, and their characteristic flora and fauna, are well represented within the African EBAs and Secondary Areas. For example, almost all of the disjunct mountain ranges included in White's Afromontane regional centre of endemism are coincident with the Cameroon mountains (EBA 086), Lesotho highlands (EBA 090), South African grasslands (EBA 091), Eastern Zimbabwe mountains (EBA 104), Tanzania–Malawi mountains (EBA 105), Albertine Rift mountains (EBA 106), Kenyan mountains (EBA 109), South Ethiopian highlands (EBA 114), Central Ethiopian highlands (EBA 115), North Somali mountains (EBA 116) and Mount Kulal (Secondary Area s062). Several of the restricted-range species of Western Angola (EBA 087) and one from the Upper Guinea forest (EBA 084) occur in Afromontane habitats, and those of the South African forests (EBA 089) occur in both Afromontane and White's Tongaland–Pondoland regional mosaic habitats. The Afromontane EBAs include those with the highest totals of restricted-range species in the region.

It should be noted that a compromise has been made to the EBA analysis in the case of the Taita hills and Mt Kasigau in southern Kenya. The three taxa which are endemic to these mountains are here treated as species following Collar *et al.* (1994), although Sibley and Monroe (1990, 1993), Dowsett

and Forbes-Watson (1993) and Zimmerman *et al.* (1996) consider them to be forms of more widespread species. Because of the disputed taxonomic status of these forms, these mountains are treated as part of the Tanzania–Malawi mountains (EBA 105) rather than as a separate EBA in their own right.

The characteristic fauna and flora of the lowland rain forests of White's Guineo-Congolian regional centre of endemism are well represented by the Upper Guinea forests (EBA 084), Cameroon–Gabon lowlands (EBA 085) and Eastern Zaïre lowlands (EBA 107). The northern and southern sections of White's Zanzibar–Inhambane regional mosaic are included in the East African coastal forests (EBA 111) and South-east African coast (EBA 092) respectively; the restricted-range species in the former are mainly confined to forest, but in the latter they occur in non-forest habitats. The Serengeti plains (EBA 108), the Central Somali coast (EBA 112), the Jubba and Shabeele valleys (EBA 113) and several Secondary Areas—North-east Uganda (s060), North Kenyan short-grass plains (s061), Northern Ethiopia (s063) and North-west Somalia (s064)—lie within White's Somalia–Masai regional centre of endemism, where the restricted-range species occur in a variety of semi-arid non-forest habitats. The Cape regional centre of endemism is also an EBA—the Cape fynbos (EBA 088)—but is far less important for endemic birds (and other animals) than it is for endemic plants.

There are several important vegetation zones defined by White which do not include any EBAs, although most contain one or more Secondary Areas. These cover the Lake Victoria regional mosaic which includes the Dry woodlands west of Lake Victoria (Secondary Area s057), and the Sahara and Sahel regional transition zones, as well as the following regional centres of endemism: the Zambesian which includes Southern Zambia (Secondary Area s051) and North-west Zambia (s052); the Sudanian which includes the Upper Niger valley (s040); and the Karoo–Namib which includes the Namibian escarpment (s045), Namib desert (s046) and Karoo (s047).

Like the Cape regional centre of endemism, the Mediterranean region of southern Europe, North Africa and the Middle East is exceptionally rich in narrowly endemic plants, but is only covered by EBAs and Secondary Areas in Cyprus (EBA 121), the North Algerian mountains (Secondary Area s039), Corsican mountains (s068), and the Levantine mountains of Syria, Lebanon, Israel and Jordan (s067). Other European EBAs cover Madeira and the Canary Islands (EBA 120), and the subalpine and alpine zones of the Caucasus mountains (EBA 122). Middle Eastern EBAs cover the island of Socotra (EBA 117), which lies off the horn of Africa, the South-west

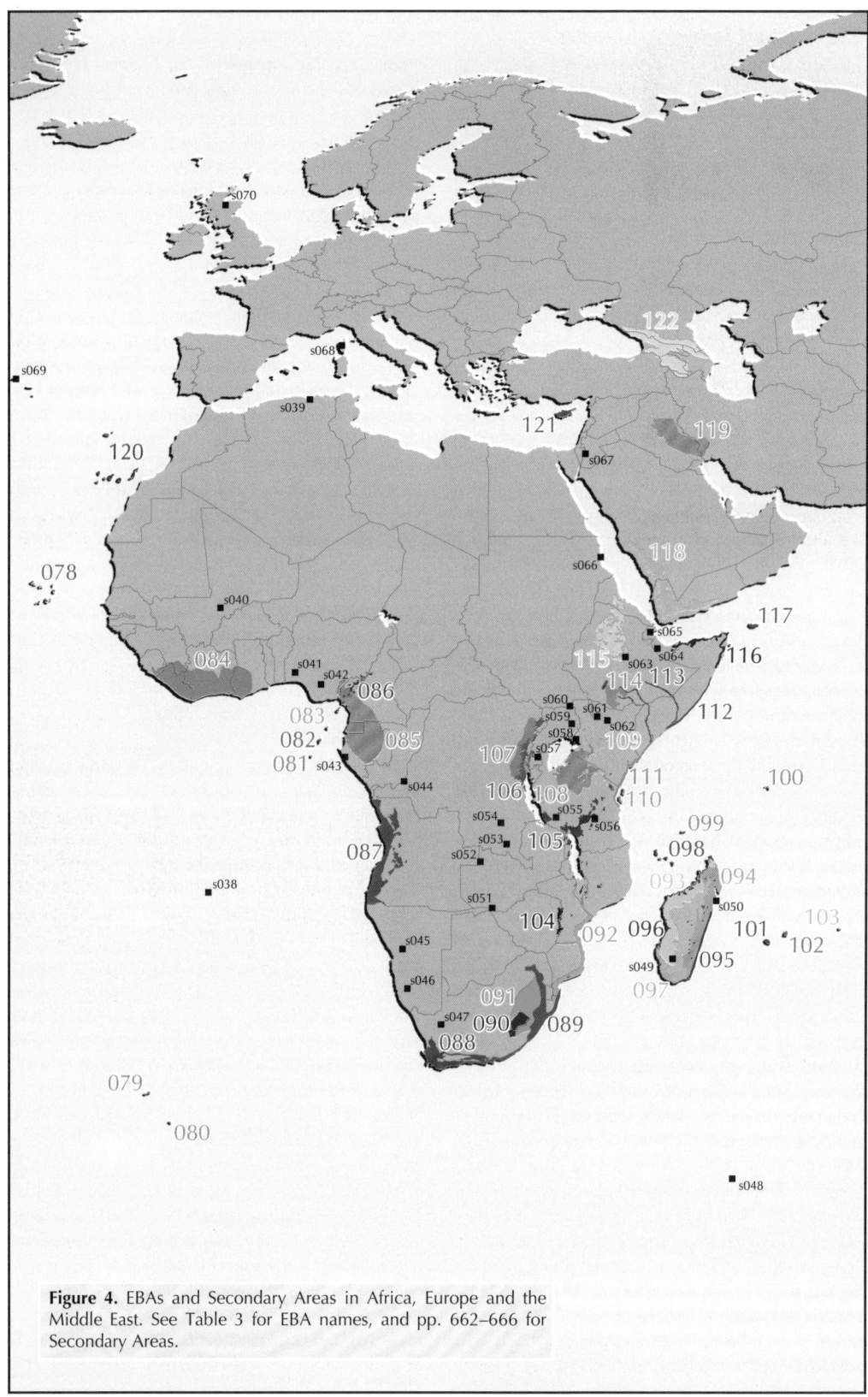

Figure 4. EBAs and Secondary Areas in Africa, Europe and the Middle East. See Table 3 for EBA names, and pp. 662–666 for Secondary Areas.

Verreaux's sifaka *Propithecus verreauxi* is found in the West Malagasy dry forests (EBA 093) and the South Malagasy spiny forests (EBA 097).

Arabian mountains (EBA 118) and the Mesopotamian marshes of Iraq and Iran (EBA 119).

Knowledge of many of the EBAs is still judged to be incomplete. For example, São Tomé (EBA 082) had been little studied ornithologically until recently when four endemic bird species were rediscovered after 50 years without records (Atkinson *et al.* 1991), while information for the tiny island of Annobón (EBA 081), also in the Gulf of Guinea, comes from a brief visit in 1989, the first by an ornithologist in 30 years (Harrison 1990). Ornithological exploration remains incomplete in Madagascar, where a new species (and genus) of passerine, Cryptic Warbler *Cryptosylvicola randrianasoloi*, was discovered only in 1992, and subsequently revealed to have a relatively broad distribution in the East Malagasy wet forests (EBA 094) (Goodman *et al.* 1996).

Threats and conservation

Many countries in Africa are experiencing rapid human population growth, with associated pressures on natural habitats. In some EBAs a high proportion of the key habitats for the restricted-range species has already been lost, for example in the Upper Guinea forests (EBA 084), the East African coastal forests (EBA 111) and several of the Indian Ocean island EBAs such as the Comoros (EBA 098), Mauritius (EBA 102) and Rodrigues (EBA 103). In some EBAs habitat loss is localized: in the Albertine Rift mountains (EBA 106), for example, much of the forest has been lost from the densely populated countries of Rwanda and Burundi, but in eastern Zaïre large areas

of montane forest remain intact, although the lower-altitude transitional forests are being rapidly cleared.

The EBAs with highest numbers of threatened restricted-range species are the Afromontane Tanzania–Malawi mountains (EBA 105) and Cameroon mountains (EBA 086), and the East Malagasy wet forests (EBA 094), which all have high overall totals of restricted-range species. The threatened species in these EBAs are usually the forest birds with particularly small ranges, which are therefore the most vulnerable to any habitat loss.

Introduced species are a serious problem on many of the island EBAs, for example on Aldabra (EBA 099) where it is thought that predation by rats was the main cause of the (presumed) extinction of Aldabra Warbler *Nesillas aldabrana*, and in the Granitic Seychelles (EBA 100) where many populations of restricted-range birds have become extinct from at least one island in the group.

The protected areas of Africa are documented in IUCN (1992c), which is used as the standard reference for this region. However, IUCN (1992c) only lists a small proportion of the forest reserves in most African countries. Although these reserves were designated to protect natural resources, rather than specifically for wildlife conservation, they are vitally important for the protection of the key habitats in many EBAs. Collar and Stuart (1988) documented key forests for the conservation of threatened birds in Africa, many of which are mentioned in the relevant EBA and Secondary Area accounts. The current

One of the most characteristic plants of the South Malagasy spiny forests (EBA 097) are the Didiereaceae (an endemic family).

Table 3. EBAs of Africa, Europe and the Middle East: summary data.

EBA number and name	Countries	Continental/island	Area (km²)	Altitude (m)	Habitat
078 Cape Verde Islands	Cape Verde	OI	4,000	0–2,800[L]	Scrub (R)
079 Tristan Islands	St Helena (to UK)	OI	110	0–2,000[L]	Grassland (S,R)
080 Gough Island	St Helena (to UK)	OI	65	0–900[L]	Grassland (S)
081 Annobón	Equatorial Guinea	OI	17	0–600[L]	Forest[1]
082 São Tomé	São Tomé e Príncipe	OI	860	0–2,000[L,M]	Forest[1,2]
083 Príncipe	São Tomé e Príncipe	OI	140	0–900[L]	Forest[1]
084 Upper Guinea forests	Ghana, Guinea, Ivory Coast, Liberia, Sierra Leone	C	340,000	0–1,000[L]	Forest[1]
085 Cameroon and Gabon lowlands	Cameroon, Equatorial Guinea, Gabon, Nigeria	C	280,000	0–1,000[L]	Forest[1]
086 Cameroon mountains	Cameroon, Equatorial Guinea, Nigeria	C	14,000	800–3,000[M]	Forest[2] (S)
087 Western Angola	Angola, Namibia	C	150,000	0–2,000[L,M]	Forest[1,2] (S,G)
088 Cape fynbos	South Africa	C	110,000	0–1,500[L,M]	Scrub (R)
089 South African forests	Mozambique, South Africa, Swaziland	C	91,000	0–1,900[L,M]	Forest[4] (S)
090 Lesotho highlands	Lesotho, South Africa	C	30,000	1,000–3,000[M]	Grassland (S,R)
091 Southern African grasslands	Lesotho, South Africa	C	110,000	1,700–2,400[M]	Grassland
092 South-east African coast	Malawi, Mozambique, South Africa, Swaziland, Zimbabwe	C	87,000	0–200[L]	Forest[3] (S)
093 West Malagasy dry forests	Madagascar	CI	150,000	0–800[L]	Forest[3]
094 East Malagasy wet forests	Madagascar	CI	160,000	0–2,000[L,M]	Forest[1,2]
095 East Malagasy wetlands	Madagascar	CI	17,000	0–2,700[L,M]	Wetland (R)
096 West Malagasy wetlands	Madagascar	CI	26,000	0–1,500[L]	Wetland (F,R)
097 South Malagasy spiny forests	Madagascar	CI	46,000	0–500[L]	Forest[3] (S)
098 Comoro Islands	Comoros, Mayotte (to France)	OI	2,200	0–2,600[L,M]	Forest[1,2] (S)
099 Aldabra	Seychelles	OI	160	0–20[L]	Scrub (F)
100 Granitic Seychelles	Seychelles	OI	240	0–900[L]	Forest[1,3]
101 Réunion	Réunion (to France)	OI	2,500	0–3,000[L,M]	Forest[1,2] (S)
102 Mauritius	Mauritius	OI	1,900	0–800[L]	Forest[1,5]
103 Rodrigues	Mauritius	OI	110	0–300[L]	Forest[1]
104 Eastern Zimbabwe mountains	Mozambique, Zimbabwe	C	12,000	800–2,400[M]	Forest[2]
105 Tanzania–Malawi mountains	Kenya, Malawi, Mozambique, Tanzania, Zambia	C	72,000	200–3,000[L,M]	Forest[1,2] (S,G)
106 Albertine Rift mountains	Burundi, Rwanda, Tanzania, Uganda, Zaïre	C	56,000	1,000–4,300[M]	Forest[2] (S)
107 Eastern Zaïre lowlands	Uganda, Zaïre	C	75,000	700–1,800[L,M]	Forest[1,2]
108 Serengeti plains	Kenya, Tanzania	C	160,000	1,000–2,200[L,M]	Scrub (V,G)
109 Kenyan mountains	Kenya, Tanzania, Uganda	C	48,000	900–4,400[M]	Forest[2] (S,G)
110 Pemba	Tanzania	OI	1,000	0–100[L]	Forest[1]
111 East African coastal forests	Kenya, Somalia, Tanzania	C	25,000	0–500[L]	Forest[1,3] (S)
112 Central Somali coast	Somalia	C	15,000	0–60[L]	Grassland
113 Jubba and Shabeelle valleys	Ethiopia, Kenya, Somalia	C	35,000	0–800[L]	Forest[3] (S,W)
114 South Ethiopian highlands	Ethiopia	C	37,000	1,000–2,000[M]	Savanna (F,S,G)
115 Central Ethiopian highlands	Eritrea, Ethiopia	C	120,000	1,300–3,300[M]	Scrub (R)
116 North Somali mountains	Somalia	C	32,000	300–2,100[L,M]	Forest[4] (S,R)
117 Socotra	Yemen	OI	3,500	0–1,500[L]	Scrub (R,D)
118 South-west Arabian mountains	Sauda Arabia, Yemen	C	150,000	1,200–3,600[M]	Forest[4] (S,R)
119 Mesopotamian marshes	Iran, Iraq	C	130,000	0–100[L]	Wetland
120 Madeira and the Canary Islands	Portugal, Spain	OI	8,000	0–3,700[L,M]	Forest[4] (S,R)
121 Cyprus	Cyprus	CI	9,300	0–1,800[L,M]	Forest[5] (S)
122 Caucasus	Armenia, Azerbaijan, Georgia, Iran, Turkey, Russia	C	170,000	1,200–4,000[M]	Grassland (F,S)

KEY See Table 1 (pp. 62–63).

Important Bird Areas (IBA) Programme of BirdLife International's African Partnership is preparing inventories of sites for threatened, restricted-range, biome-restricted and congregatory bird species (already complete in Ethiopia: EWNHS 1996), and will work for the conservation of this network of sites. There are already several very important conservation initiatives within African EBAs; examples of these are described in the EBA accounts for the Cameroon mountains (EBA 086), the East Usambara

Habitat loss	Knowledge	Confined to the EBA		Present also in other EBAs, SAs		Total		Biological importance	Current threat level	Priority	EBA no.
		Threatened	Total	Threatened	Total	Threatened	Total				
Severe	Incomplete	2	4	0	0	2	4	●	●●	Urgent	078
Moderate	Good	3	4	0	0	3	4	●●	●●	Urgent	079
Possible	Good	2	2	0	0	2	2	●	●●	Urgent	080
Limited	Poor	2	2	0	1	2	3	●	●●	Urgent	081
Limited	Incomplete	7	16	1	5	8	21	●●●	●●	Critical	082
Moderate	Incomplete	1	6	1	5	2	11	●●	●	High	083
Major	Incomplete	11	15	0	0	11	15	●●●	●●●	Critical	084
Moderate	Poor	1	5	1	1	2	6	●	●	High	085
Major	Incomplete	10	27	2	2	12	29	●●●	●●	Critical	086
Unquantified	Poor	7	13	1	1	8	14	●●	●●●	Critical	087
Moderate	Good	0	6	0	0	0	6	●	●	High	088
Possible	Good	0	7	0	0	0	7	●	●	High	089
Moderate	Incomplete	0	3	0	0	0	3	●	●	High	090
Major	Good	3	3	0	0	3	3	●	●●●	Critical	091
Unquantified	Incomplete	0	4	0	0	0	4	●	●	High	092
Major	Incomplete	3	3	1	5	4	8	●	●	High	093
Major	Incomplete	13	20	1	3	14	23	●●●	●●	Critical	094
Major	Incomplete	3	6	0	2	3	8	●	●●●	Critical	095
Moderate	Incomplete	5	5	0	2	5	7	●	●●●	Critical	096
Moderate	Incomplete	2	8	0	2	2	10	●●●	●	Urgent	097
Major	Incomplete	6	16	0	2	6	18	●●	●●●	Critical	098
Limited	Good	0	1	0	2	0	3	●	●	High	099
Major	Good	8	11	0	0	8	11	●●	●●●	Critical	100
Moderate	Incomplete	1	4	0	3	1	7	●	●●	Urgent	101
Severe	Good	7	7	0	3	7	10	●	●●●	Critical	102
Severe	Incomplete	2	2	0	0	2	2	●●	●●●	Critical	103
Moderate	Incomplete	0	2	1	1	1	3	●	●	High	104
Moderate	Incomplete	16	31	4	6	20	37	●●●	●●	Critical	105
Moderate	Incomplete	10	36	1	1	11	37	●●●	●	Urgent	106
Moderate	Poor	3	6	0	0	3	6	●	●	High	107
Moderate	Incomplete	1	5	1	1	2	6	●●	●	High	108
Moderate	Good	3	8	0	1	3	9	●●	●●	Urgent	109
Major	Incomplete	0	4	0	0	0	4	●	●	High	110
Major	Incomplete	2	3	3	4	5	7	●	●●	Urgent	111
Possible	Poor	1	2	0	0	1	2	●	●●●	Critical	112
Unquantified	Poor	2	4	0	0	2	4	●	●●●	Critical	113
Unquantified	Poor	4	5	0	0	4	5	●●	●●●	Critical	114
Unquantified	Poor	3	4	0	0	3	4	●	●●●	Critical	115
Unquantified	Poor	3	3	0	0	3	3	●	●●●	Critical	116
Major	Incomplete	3	6	0	0	3	6	●	●	High	117
Moderate	Incomplete	2	7	0	0	2	7	●●	●	High	118
Major	Incomplete	0	2	0	0	0	2	●	●	High	119
Major	Good	2	8	0	1	2	9	●	●	High	120
Major	Good	0	2	0	0	0	2	●	●	High	121
Major	Incomplete	0	3	0	0	0	3	●	●	High	122

Mountains in Tanzania (EBA 105) and the East African coastal forests (EBA 111).

An IBA inventory is also available for the Middle East (Evans 1994), and information and action are further advanced in Europe: an IBA inventory has already been published (Grimmett and Jones 1989) and is being updated (Heath et al. in prep.), the status of all birds has been reviewed (Tucker and Heath 1994), and detailed action plans for threatened species are available (Heredia et al. 1996).

CONTINENTAL ASIA

THIS REGION covers the eastern Palearctic and much of the Oriental region (but not Peninsular Malaysia, the Philippines and Indonesia, which are included with New Guinea and Australia in a separate region, see p. 81). Continental Asia is characterized by numerous mountains, most notably the Himalayas and other ranges around the margins of the high-altitude Qinghai–Tibetan plateau, which include the highest mountain peaks in the world (see Box 4 for key facts).

Restricted-range species

This is one of the richer regions of the world in overall bird species diversity, but the total number of restricted-range species (203) is relatively low. However, this may underestimate the importance of localized endemism in Asia for two reasons. The first is that there appear to be many species which have relatively small ranges but which narrowly fail to meet the 50,000-km² range-size criterion, notably in the Himalayas and mountains of south-west China. Secondly, much of the work on species taxonomy in this region took place during a period when the trend was to treat morphologically distinct allopatric and parapatric taxa as subspecies of relatively widespread species, an approach which is followed in most of the major avifaunal works which cover the region (e.g. King *et al.* 1975, Ripley 1982, Smythies 1986, Ali and Ripley 1987, Cheng Tso-hsin 1987, Boonsong and Round 1991, Inskipp and Inskipp 1991, Roberts 1991). There are, for example, c.46 subspecies of bird endemic to Hainan according to Cheng Tso-hsin (1987) and Howard and Moore (1991), several of which are very distinct and may be better treated as full species (Olsson *et al.* 1993). Many of the restricted-range species are associated with the montane forests and other habitats of the

Edwards's Pheasant *Lophura edwardsi* is endemic to the Annamese lowlands (EBA 143) in Vietnam where it was feared extinct in the wild until recently refound.

> ### Box 4. Key facts for continental Asia.
>
> Numbers of:
> - 203 Restricted-range species
> - 88 Threatened restricted-range species
> - 27 EBAs
> - 23 Secondary Areas
> - 13 Countries with EBAs
>
> **EBAs with high numbers of restricted-range species**
> - Sri Lanka (EBA 124), 23 species
> - Eastern Himalayas (EBA 130), 22 species
> - Taiwan (EBA 149), 15 species
>
> **EBAs with high numbers of threatened restricted-range species**
> - Eastern Himalayas (EBA 130), 11 species
> - Annamese lowlands (EBA 143), 7 species
> - Sri Lanka (EBA 124), 6 species
>
> **EBAs with high numbers of Critical and Endangered endemic species**
> - Annamese lowlands (EBA 143), 4 species
>
> **Examples of EBAs critically in need of conservation action**
> - Chinese subtropical forests (EBA 140)
> - Annamese lowlands (EBA 143)
> - Nansei Shoto (EBA 148)
>
> **Countries with high numbers of restricted-range species**
> - India, 74 species
> - China, 56 species
>
> **Countries with high numbers of threatened restricted-range species**
> - China, 33 species
> - India, 23 species
> - Vietnam, 14 species

Himalayas and south-west China, but there are also significant numbers in tropical and subtropical forests in southern and south-east Asia. Very few occur in the temperate, boreal and arctic habitats in northern Asia.

Parts of the continent have historically been inaccessible, for political as well as for logistical reasons, and as a consequence the region's avifauna is relatively poorly known. Many of the restricted-range species are known by a handful of records, and their habitat requirements are not fully understood—notably Vaurie's Nightjar *Caprimulgus centralasicus* (from China) and Rusty-throated Wren-babbler *Spelaeornis badeigularis* (India), both known only by the type specimens, and Himalayan Quail *Ophrysia superciliosa* (India; not recorded during the twentieth century). Several restricted-range species have only been described in the past 20 years, including Okinawa Rail *Gallirallus okinawae* (from Nansei

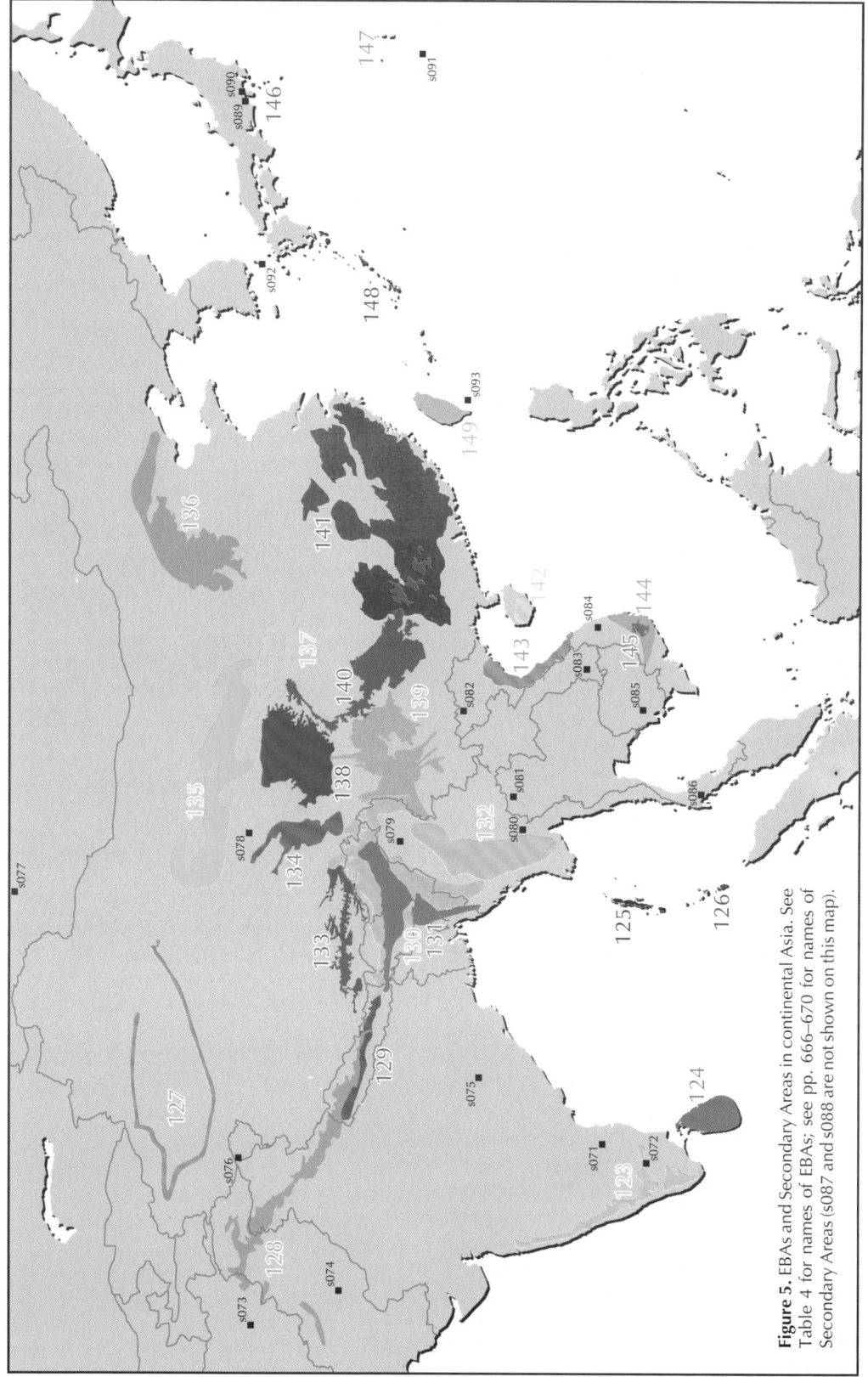

Figure 5. EBAs and Secondary Areas in continental Asia. See Table 4 for names of EBAs; see pp. 666–670 for names of Secondary Areas (s087 and s088 are not shown on this map).

Table 4. EBAs of continental Asia: summary data.

EBA number and name	Countries	Continental/ island	Area (km²)	Altitude (m)	Habitat
123 Western Ghats	India	C	61,000	0–2,600 [L,M]	Forest [1,2] (G)
124 Sri Lanka	Sri Lanka	CI	66,000	0–2,400 [L,M]	Forest [1,2,3]
125 Andaman Islands	India, Myanmar	OI	8,200	0–700 [L]	Forest [1,6]
126 Nicobar Islands	India	OI	1,800	0–600 [L]	Forest [1]
127 Taklimakan Desert	China	C	60,000	900–1,300 [L]	Desert (S)
128 Western Himalayas	Afghanistan, India, Nepal, Pakistan	C	130,000	1,500–3,600 [M]	Forest [5] (G)
129 Central Himalayas	Nepal	C	56,000	1,500–3,300 [M]	Forest [5] (S)
130 Eastern Himalayas	Bangladesh, Bhutan, China, India, Myanmar, Nepal	C	220,000	300–4,000 [M]	Forest [4,5]
131 Assam plains	Bangladesh, India, Nepal	C	126,000	0–1,000 [L]	Grassland (S,W)
132 Irrawaddy plains	Myanmar	C	160,000	0–1,000 [L]	Forest [3] (S)
133 Southern Tibet	China, India	C	63,000	2,700–5,000 [M]	Forest [5] (S,G)
134 Eastern Tibet	China	C	65,000	3,600–4,600 [M]	Forest [5] (S,R)
135 Qinghai mountains	China	C	230,000	1,800–3,500 [M]	Scrub (G,R)
136 Shanxi mountains	China	C	180,000	1,300–2,800 [M]	Forest [5]
137 Central Sichuan mountains	China	C	140,000	1,500–3,700 [M]	Forest [5] (S)
138 West Sichuan mountains	China	C	180,000	2,700–4,900 [M]	Forest [5] (S,G,R)
139 Yunnan mountains	China, Myanmar	C	190,000	1,500–4,000 [M]	Forest [5] (S)
140 Chinese subtropical forests	China	C	160,000	300–2,200 [L,M]	Forest [4]
141 South-east Chinese mountains	China	C	610,000	300–1,900 [L,M]	Forest [4]
142 Hainan	China	CI	13,000	600–1,800 [L,M]	Forest [1,2]
143 Annamese lowlands	Laos, Vietnam	C	51,000	0–1,000 [L]	Forest [1]
144 South Vietnamese lowlands	Vietnam	C	30,000	0–1,000 [L]	Forest [1]
145 Da Lat plateau	Vietnam	C	6,000	800–2,400 [M]	Forest [2,4]
146 Izu Islands	Japan	OI	300	0–800 [L]	Forest [4]
147 Ogasawara Islands	Japan	OI	73	0–400 [L]	Forest [4]
148 Nansei Shoto	Japan	OI	4,500	0–1,900 [L,M]	Forest [4,5]
149 Taiwan	Taiwan	CI	36,000	0–3,900 [L,M]	Forest [4,5]

KEY See Table 1 (pp. 62–63).

Shoto in Japan), Nepal Wren-babbler *Pnoepyga immaculata* and (from China) Emei Leaf-warbler *Phylloscopus emeiensis*, Hainan Leaf-warbler *P. hainanus* and Sillem's Mountain-finch *Leucosticte sillemi*. Several have recently been rediscovered after several decades without any records, including Orange-necked Partridge *Arborophila davidi* (Vietnam), Jerdon's Courser *Rhinoptilus bitorquatus* (India), Gurney's Pitta *Pitta gurneyi* (Thailand), Grey-crowned Crocias *Crocias langbianis* (Vietnam), Tibetan Babax *Babax koslowi* and Tibetan Bunting *Emberiza koslowi* (China) and White-browed Nuthatch *Sitta victoriae* (Myanmar).

Endemic Bird Areas

The distribution of EBAs in continental Asia is related to the region's complex topography and climatic patterns. Six EBAs are located in the Indian subcontinent and Myanmar, 10 in China and three in south-east Asia; the remaining eight cover islands. There are also 23 Secondary Areas completing the analysis (see Figure 5 for location of EBAs and Secondary Areas, and Table 4 for EBA summary data).

Several EBAs lie around the margins of the Qinghai–Tibetan plateau, including the Western Himalayas (EBA 128), Central Himalayas (EBA 129), Eastern Himalayas (EBA 130), Yunnan mountains (EBA 139) and Central Sichuan mountains (EBA 137). Temperate-zone forest is the most important habitat for the restricted-range species in all of these EBAs, although some of the species of the Eastern Himalayas breed in the subtropical zone. Other EBAs in this region include the West Sichuan mountains (EBA 138), where the restricted-range birds occur in subalpine forests and alpine habitats above the treeline, and Eastern Tibet (EBA 134). Southern Tibet (EBA 133) and the Qinghai mountains (EBA 135), which lie in relatively arid regions on the edge of the Qinghai–Tibetan plateau. Many of the restricted-range species on the mountainous island of Taiwan (EBA 149) have affinities with Himalayan species and are found in temperate-zone forest.

The natural vegetation of much of south-east China is subtropical forest, and this region has been subdivided into two EBAs, the Chinese subtropical forests (EBA 140) and the South-east Chinese mountains (EBA 141). However, habitats in this part of

		Numbers of restricted-range species									
		Confined to the EBA		Present also in other EBAs, SAs		Total					
Habitat loss	Knowledge	Threatened	Total	Threatened	Total	Threatened	Total	Biological importance	Current threat level	Priority	EBA no.
Major	Good	0	16	1	1	1	17	●●	●	High	123
Major	Good	6	23	0	0	6	23	●	●●	Urgent	124
Moderate	Incomplete	2	8	0	4	2	12	●	●	High	125
Moderate	Incomplete	2	5	0	4	2	9	●	●—	High	126
Unquantified	Poor	2	2	0	0	2	2	●	●●	Urgent	127
Moderate	Good	4	11	0	0	4	11	●●●	●●	Critical	128
Moderate	Good	0	2	0	1	0	3	●	●	High	129
Moderate	Incomplete	10	19	1	3	11	22	●●●	●	Urgent	130
Major	Incomplete	3	3	0	0	3	3	●	●●	Urgent	131
Major	Incomplete	1	2	0	0	1	2	●	●	High	132
Unquantified	Incomplete	1	2	0	0	1	2	●	●	High	133
Unquantified	Poor	0	2	0	0	0	2	●	●	High	134
Unquantified	Incomplete	0	2	0	0	0	2	●	●	High	135
Severe	Incomplete	2	2	0	0	2	2	●	●●	Urgent	136
Major	Incomplete	5	10	0	1	5	11	●●	●	High	137
Major	Incomplete	3	3	0	0	3	3	●	●●	Urgent	138
Major	Incomplete	2	3	0	0	2	3	●	●●	Urgent	139
Severe	Poor	4	5	0	0	4	5	●	●●●	Critical	140
Severe	Incomplete	4	4	1	1	5	5	●	●●●	Critical	141
Severe	Incomplete	2	2	2	2	4	4	●	●●●	Critical	142
Severe	Incomplete	5	5	2	4	7	9	●	●●●	Critical	143
Major	Poor	2	2	0	1	2	3	●	●●●	Critical	144
Moderate	Incomplete	3	4	3	4	6	8	●	●●	Urgent	145
Major	Good	2	2	0	1	2	3	●	●●	Urgent	146
Major	Good	1	1	0	0	1	1	●●●	●●	Critical	147
Major	Good	5	7	0	3	5	10	●	●●●	Critical	148
Major	Good	0	14	0	1	0	15	●	●	High	149

China were greatly affected by human activity in the past, and there are important gaps in ornithological knowledge here, so it has only been possible to define approximate boundaries to both EBAs. As a result, both the mapped extent and estimated areas of these EBAs almost certainly represent substantial over-estimates of their true sizes. For similar reasons, the areas of several other EBAs in this region have probably also been overestimated, notably the East-ern Himalayas (EBA 130), Irrawaddy plains, (EBA 132), Eastern Tibet (EBA 134), Qinghai mountains (EBA 135), West Sichuan mountains (EBA 138) and Yunnan mountains (EBA 139).

In south-east Asia, there are two lowland rain forest EBAs—the Annamese lowlands (EBA 143) and the South Vietnamese lowlands (EBA 144)—and two in isolated areas of tropical montane forest—the island of Hainan (EBA 142) and Vietnam's Da Lat plateau (EBA 145). The Western Ghats (EBA 123) and Sri Lanka (EBA 124) represent areas of moist habitat isolated by relatively dry regions in the rest of the Indian peninsula; they both include tropi-cal rain forest in the lowlands, and subtropical hill forest, temperate-zone forest and montane grassland

at higher altitudes. Two EBAs are in the floodplains of major rivers, the Assam plains (EBA 131) and the Irrawaddy plains (EBA 132), and one in the Taklimakan desert (EBA 127) in western China.

The remaining island EBAs are the Andaman Islands (EBA 125) and Nicobar Islands (EBA 126), where the native vegetation is largely tropical rain forest, and the Japanese islands of Izu (EBA 146), where temperate forest is the key habitat, and the Ogasawara Islands (EBA 147) and Nansei Shoto (EBA 148), where subtropical forest is important.

A particular feature of the EBAs in this region is the relatively small numbers of restricted-range spe-cies which they hold; only eight EBAs support ten or more, and the highest total is just 23 (Sri Lanka, EBA 124). It is interesting to speculate about the effects that the splitting of morphologically distinct allopatric and parapatric taxa into full species would have on the EBA analysis for this region (see above). Many of the 'new' species resulting from such taxonomic reassessments would have restricted ranges, but a high proportion of these taxa are known to occur in existing EBAs, so this would simply increase the species totals for these EBAs. In a few cases, however, new Secondary Areas would result or existing Secondary Areas would be upgraded into EBAs. An example is the Indus plains (Secondary Area s074), which would qualify as an EBA if Rufous-vented Prinia *Prinia burnesii* were split into two species following Morony *et al.* (1975)—who unfortunately did not publish justification for this taxonomic treatment. It is also possible that some EBAs would be subdivided into two or more EBAs. For example, the mountain ranges south of the Brahmaputra river have an avifauna distinct from the rest of the Eastern Himalayas (EBA 130), and a small number of taxonomic revisions (such as the separation of the two forms of Wedge-billed Wren-babbler *Sphenocichla humei* proposed by P. Rasmussen verbally to N. J. Collar 1997) could justify their treatment as a separate EBA.

Some of the EBAs have been well studied—e.g. the Western Ghats (EBA 123) and Sri Lanka (EBA 124)—but most have not been fully explored ornithologically, although the recent activities of travelling birdwatchers have added significantly to knowledge of some of these areas (see, e.g., Olsson 1995).

Threats and conservation
China and India have by far the largest human populations of any nations in the world, and many of the other countries in the region are currently experiencing a period of rapid growth in both their human populations and their economies. The consequent demands for land and resources are putting increasing pressure on remaining areas of natural habitat. Forest is particularly under pressure from unsustainable commercial logging, clearance for agricultural land or development projects, felling for fuelwood and animal fodder, overgrazing, burning and conversion to plantations (Smil 1984, 1993, Collins *et al.* 1991). As forest is by far the most important habitat for restricted-range species, it is unsurprising that the principal threat to the these birds is forest loss and fragmentation.

China, India and Vietnam have the most threatened restricted-range species, and the Annamese lowlands (EBA 143) is notable both for its total number of threatened species and for the high number of Critical and Endangered species unique to it. Some EBAs support important populations of more widespread threatened species, notably the Assam plains (EBA 131) and South Vietnamese lowlands (EBA 144).

Some poorly known areas have recently been targeted for survey work by BirdLife International and others, for example the Vietnamese EBAs (143–145) (see Robson *et al.* 1991, 1993a,b, Eames *et al.* 1992, 1994, 1995a, Eames and Nguyen Cu 1994,

Lambert *et al.* 1994, Eames 1995) and the Nicobar Islands (Sankaran 1993a,b, 1995). The results of surveys completed in 1997 in the Annamitic mountains of Vietnam and Laos (Robson 1997) could significantly modify the EBA analysis. Two new taxa discovered on Ngoc Linh, the highest peak of the Kontum plateau (Secondary Area s084) are both likely to be described as new species (J. C. Eames verbally 1997), and the Black-hooded Laughingthrush *Garrulax milleti*, previously known only from the Da Lat plateau (EBA 145), has been found across the border in Laos—the net effect of which will probably be to create a new EBA (incorporating Secondary Area s084). Further field surveys are required in many EBAs, to determine the distributions and habitat requirements of the restricted-range birds and other wildlife, and to identify the pressures they face and hence the most appropriate actions required for their conservation.

The location and extent of the Central Sichuan mountains (EBA 137) closely matches the current distribution of giant panda *Ailuropoda melanoleuca*, for which Wolong is a reserve. Like the EBA's 10 restricted-range bird species, giant panda occurs in temperate-zone forest with a bamboo understorey.

There are protected areas in most, if not all, of the EBAs in this region. Some EBAs, such as the Western Ghats (EBA 123) and Central Sichuan mountains (EBA 137), have networks of reserves which include extensive areas of the key habitats for the restricted-range species. In a few, such as Eastern Tibet (EBA 134), the area of habitat covered by protected areas is very small. However, in many EBAs the information available on the habitat types represented within the protected areas, and the occurrence of restricted-range species in these areas, is too limited to allow a full evaluation of the adequacy of the existing networks. Surveys of these and potential protected areas are required to establish the basis for future planning for the conservation of these EBAs and their unique plant and animal life.

SOUTH-EAST ASIAN ISLANDS, NEW GUINEA AND AUSTRALIA

THIS REGION embraces the Philippines, Peninsular Malaysia and the Greater Sunda islands of Sumatra, Borneo, Java and Bali, the Lesser Sundas, the Moluccas, Sulawesi (which are all part of the Oriental region; see also p. 76), New Guinea (but note that Papua New Guinean islands are covered under the Pacific Islands region, p. 87), Christmas Island and Australia.

There is a notable discontinuity between the flora and fauna of the Oriental and Australasian faunal regions, as they originated from different continental shelves (the Sunda and Sahul shelves respectively). Two imaginary lines divide up this region on the basis of biogeography: Wallace's (or Weber's) Line follows the eastern edge of the Sunda Shelf, which lies between Bali and the Lesser Sunda island of Lombok and between Borneo and Sulawesi; Lydekker's Line follows the edge of the Sahul Shelf, which lies between New Guinea and Australia and the oceanic islands of the Moluccas and Lesser Sundas to the west (and represents the eastern boundary of the Oriental faunal region). The area between the Sunda and Sahul shelves is known as Wallacea, and is a zone of transition between the Oriental and Australasian faunas (see Beehler *et al.* 1986, White and Bruce 1986).

Many of the islands of this region are mountainous and rugged as a result of volcanic activity and the uplifting of sedimentary deposits, and Sumatra, Java, the Lesser Sundas and Papua New Guinea include some of the most actively volcanic areas in the world (see Box 5 for key facts).

Restricted-range species

The predominantly insular character and mountainous terrain of this region have resulted in much localized speciation, and hence there are many restricted-range species: 636, the second highest total, after South America, of all the regions. There are a number of distinctive families (largely) endemic to the region, such as the megapodes (Megapodiidae) and birds-of-paradise (Paradisaeidae), and these include many restricted-range species.

Most of the restricted-range species are forest birds occurring in a variety of different types, including tropical lowland and montane evergreen and semi-evergreen rain forest in Malaysia, Indonesia, the Philippines and Papua New Guinea, deciduous monsoon forest in parts of Indonesia, particularly the Lesser Sundas, where the Australian rain-shadow results in seasonal rainfall (see Whitmore 1984, WWF/IUCN 1994–1995), and tropical, subtropical and temperate forest in Australia.

Box 5. Key facts for the south-East Asian Islands, New Guinea and Australia.

Numbers of:
636 Restricted-range species
160 Threatened restricted-range species
 39 EBAs
 28 Secondary Areas
  7 Countries with EBAs

EBAs with high numbers of restricted-range species
- Sulawesi (EBA 166), 54 species
- Central Papuan mountains (EBA 178), 53 species
- Mindanao and the Eastern Visayas (EBA 154), 51 species

EBAs which are especially distinct at the generic level
- Sulawesi (EBA 166), 12 endemic genera
- Central Papuan mountains (EBA 178), 9 endemic genera

EBAs with high numbers of threatened restricted-range species
- Mindanao and the Eastern Visayas (EBA 154), 22 species
- Luzon (EBA 151), 18 species
- Negros and Panay (EBA 152), 14 species

EBAs with high numbers of Critical and Endangered endemic species
- Negros and Panay (EBA 152), 8 species
- Mindoro (EBA 150), 4 species
- Luzon (EBA 151), 4 species
- Mindanao and the Eastern Visayas (EBA 154), 4 species
- Palawan (EBA 156), 4 species

Examples of EBAs critically in need of conservation action
- Mindoro (EBA 150)
- Negros and Panay (EBA 152)
- Sulu archipelago (EBA 155)
- Sangihe and Talaud (EBA 167)

Countries with high numbers of restricted-range species
- Indonesia, 403 species
- Papua New Guinea, 167 (some of these species are covered under the Pacific Islands region)
- Philippines, 126

Countries with high numbers of threatened restricted-range species
- Indonesia, 66 species
- Papua New Guinea, 21 species (some of these species are covered under the Pacific Islands region)
- Australia, 20 species

Within the region, knowledge of the distribution and ecology of birds varies from relatively comprehensive in Australia, where data are available from an atlas project (Blakers *et al.* 1984), to highly incomplete in parts of Indonesia, New Guinea and the Philippines, although there are several good reviews of the available information (e.g. Medway and Wells 1976, Smythies 1981, Coates 1985, 1990, Beehler *et al.* 1986, White and Bruce 1986, van Marle and Voous 1988, Dickinson *et al.* 1991, Andrews 1992, MacKinnon and Phillipps 1993; see also Coates and Bishop 1997 which was published too late to be used in this project).

In some of the region's least-known parts, notably New Guinea, it is difficult to determine whether some species truly have restricted ranges. Thus many appear to be very scarce and/or to have disjunct distributions, but this may reflect incomplete knowledge rather than genuine distributional patterns. For example, Papuan Hawk-owl *Uroglaux dimorpha* (excluded from the analysis) is so far known by just a handful of scattered records in the West and North Papuan lowlands, Yapen and the south-east, but probably occurs all through these areas (Coates

Giant 'klinkii pines' *Araucaria hunsteinii* in the Central Papuan mountains (EBA 178). This EBA's particularly distinct avifauna includes four genera of birds-of-paradise.

1985). On the other hand, Obscure Berrypecker *Melanocharis arfakiana* (included) is known from only two specimens, over 1,000 km apart but with several additional (unconfirmed) sightings, and may occupy a narrow altitudinal belt due to competition with congeners (Coates 1990).

The species taxonomy used deviates from Sibley and Monroe (1990, 1993) for Indonesia (following Andrew 1992) and Australia (Christidis and Boles 1994), because these alternative works are the standard within those countries. Particularly on the numerous islands of Indonesia and the Philippines, the region generally has many distinctive allopatric taxa which are currently treated as subspecies but which are potential candidates for species status in the light of current trends in taxonomy (see, e.g., Haffer 1992).

Endemic Bird Areas

Virtually the whole of the Philippines (seven EBAs), Indonesia (23 EBAs; one shared with Peninsular Malaysia, one with Brunei and East Malaysia, and seven with Papua New Guinea) and mainland Papua New Guinea (eight EBAs; seven shared with Indonesia) are included in EBAs. A further seven EBAs are located in Australia and one on Christmas Island. A total of 28 Secondary Areas completes the analysis (see Figure 6 for location of EBAs and Secondary Areas, and Table 5 for EBA summary data).

In the Greater Sunda islands and the Malayan Peninsula, there are characteristic avifaunas in both the lowland and montane forests (Wells 1985), but most of the Sundaic lowland endemics are too widespread to be considered as restricted-range species and there are therefore no lowland EBAs (although lowland forest in this area is of cardinal conservation importance because of its rapid and extensive clearance, leading to some of its characteristic species being listed as globally threatened). However, the Sundaic montane endemics include many species which are confined to relatively small areas of forest on just one or two of the major islands and therefore have restricted ranges; three Sundaic montane EBAs—the Bornean mountains (EBA 157), Sumatra and Peninsular Malaysia (EBA 158) and the Java and Bali forests (EBA 160)—cover the entire Sundaic montane region.

In Australia there are avifaunas characteristic of both forest and drier habitats (see Keast 1961, Cracraft 1986), but the endemic desert-adapted species are generally widely distributed (although a few qualify as having restricted ranges which are covered by Secondary Areas). The Australian EBAs are situated in the isolated areas of wetter forest, woodland or scrubland around the periphery of the continent. Most of these EBAs are large, e.g. South-east Australia (EBA 184) at 380,000 km^2, but the restricted-

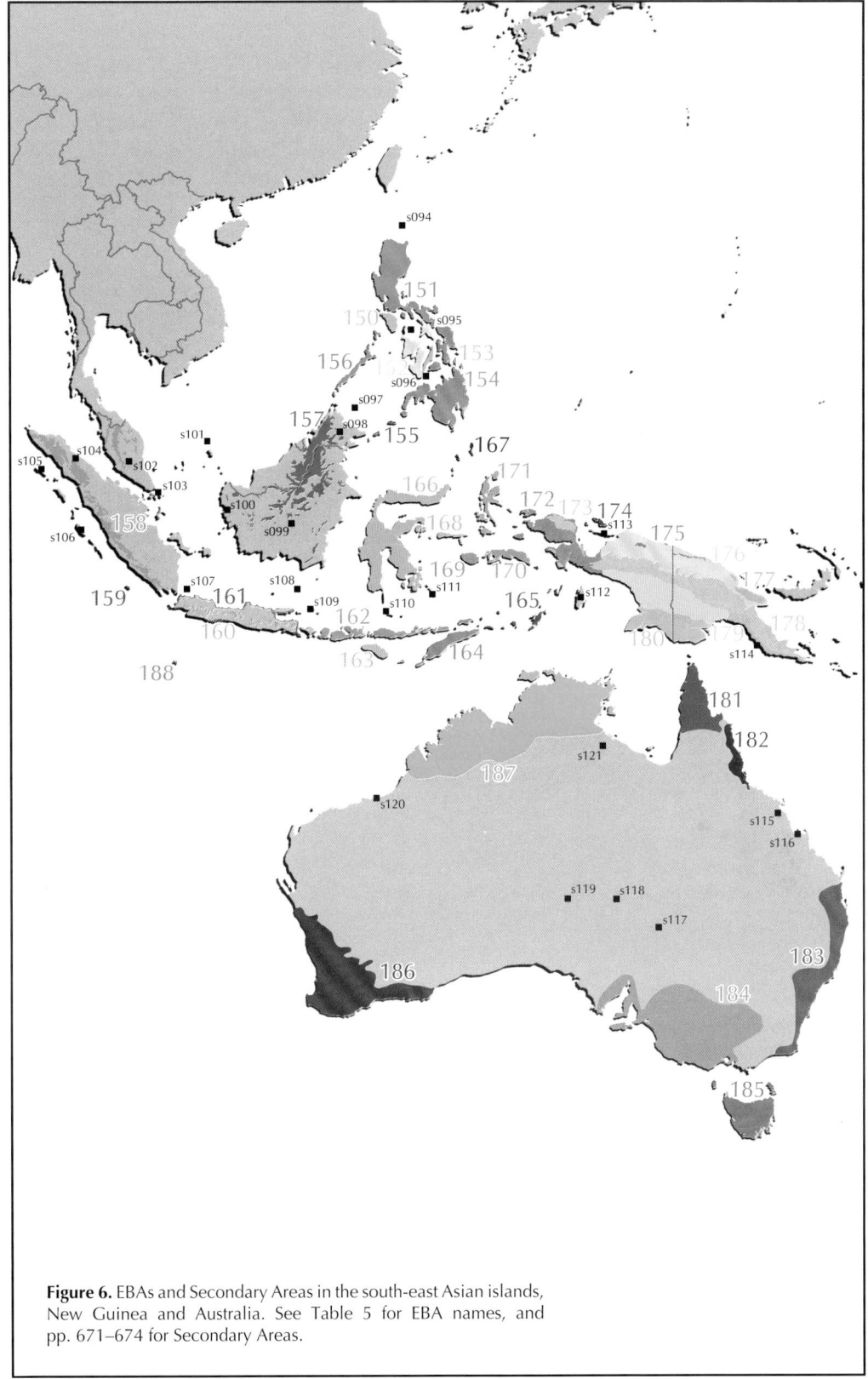

Figure 6. EBAs and Secondary Areas in the south-east Asian islands, New Guinea and Australia. See Table 5 for EBA names, and pp. 671–674 for Secondary Areas.

Table 5. EBAs of South-east Asian islands,
New Guinea and Australia: summary data.

EBA number and name	Countries	Continental/ island	Area (km²)	Altitude (m)	Habitat
150 Mindoro	Philippines	CI	9,800	0–2,000 [L,M]	Forest [1,2]
151 Luzon	Philippines	CI	110,000	0–2,700 [L,M]	Forest [1,2]
152 Negros and Panay	Philippines	CI	29,000	0–2,000 [L,M]	Forest [1,2]
153 Cebu	Philippines	CI	4,500	0–1,000 [L]	Forest [1] (S)
154 Mindanao and the Eastern Visayas	Philippines	CI	120,000	0–2,700 [L,M]	Forest [1,2]
155 Sulu archipelago	Philippines	CI	1,500	0–700 [L]	Forest [1]
156 Palawan	Philippines	CI	14,000	0–2,000 [L,M]	Forest [1,2]
157 Bornean mountains	Brunei, Indonesia, Malaysia	CI	130,000	500–3,700 [L,M]	Forest [1,2]
158 Sumatra and Peninsular Malaysia	Indonesia, Malaysia	CI	89,000	500–3,500 [L,M]	Forest [1,2]
159 Enggano	Indonesia	OI	450	0–300 [L]	Forest [1]
160 Java and Bali forests	Indonesia	CI	18,000	0–3,000 [L,M]	Forest [1,2,3]
161 Javan coastal zone	Indonesia	CI	11,000	0–0 [L]	Wetland (F,S,G)
162 Northern Nusa Tenggara	Indonesia	OI	39,000	0–2,400 [L,M]	Forest [1,2,3]
163 Sumba	Indonesia	OI	11,000	0–1,200 [L,M]	Forest [1,2,3] (G)
164 Timor and Wetar	Indonesia	OI	34,000	0–2,600 [L,M]	Forest [1,2,3] (S)
165 Banda Sea Islands	Indonesia	OI	7,100	0–850 [L]	Forest [1,3,6] (S)
166 Sulawesi	Indonesia	OI	190,000	0–3,400 [L,M]	Forest [1,2] (S)
167 Sangihe and Talaud	Indonesia	OI	1,700	0–1,700 [L,M]	Forest [1,2]
168 Banggai and Sula Islands	Indonesia	OI	7,200	0–1,600 [L,M]	Forest [1,2]
169 Buru	Indonesia	OI	8,300	0–2,000 [L,M]	Forest [1,2,3]
170 Seram	Indonesia	OI	19,000	0–3,000 [L,M]	Forest [1,2]
171 Northern Maluku	Indonesia	OI	27,000	0–2,000 [L,M]	Forest [1,2,6]
172 West Papuan lowlands	Indonesia	CI	110,000	0–1,000 [L]	Forest [1,6]
173 West Papuan highlands	Indonesia	CI	17,000	1,000–3,000 [M]	Forest [2] (G)
174 Geelvink Islands	Indonesia	OI	3,000	0–1,000 [L]	Forest [1,6]
175 North Papuan mountains	Indonesia, Papua New Guinea	CI	4,700	1,000–2,200 [M]	Forest [2]
176 North Papuan lowlands	Indonesia, Papua New Guinea	CI	180,000	0–1,000 [L]	Forest [1,6]
177 Adelbert and Huon ranges	Papua New Guinea	CI	14,000	1,000–4,100 [M]	Forest [2,5] (G)
178 Central Papuan mountains	Indonesia, Papua New Guinea	CI	190,000	1,000–4,600 [M]	Forest [2,5] (G)
179 South Papuan lowlands	Indonesia, Papua New Guinea	CI	160,000	0–1,000 [L]	Forest [1,6]
180 Trans-Fly	Indonesia, Papua New Guinea	CI	94,000	0–90 [L]	Wetland (F,V)
181 Cape York	Australia	C	99,000	0–500 [L]	Forest [1,3,6]
182 Queensland wet tropics	Australia	C	32,000	0–1,600 [L,M]	Forest [1,2]
183 Eastern Australia	Australia	C	160,000	0–1,200 [L,M]	Forest [4,5] (S)
184 South-east Australia	Australia	C	380,000	0–1000 [L]	Forest [5]
185 Tasmania	Australia	CI	68,000	0–1,600 [L]	Forest [5] (S)
186 South-west Australia	Australia	C	280,000	0–400 [L]	Forest [5] (S)
187 North-west Australia	Australia	C	560,000	0–1,000 [L]	Forest [1,3,6] (S,V)
188 Christmas Island	Christmas Island (to Australia)	OI	140	0–300 [L]	Forest [1]

KEY See Table 1 (pp. 62–63).

range species are confined to smaller areas of specialized habitat within these areas—such as the four south-east Australian restricted-range species which favour mallee (a particularly distinct, semi-arid woodland of multi-stemmed eucalypts).

There is much sharing of species between EBAs in this region, especially between the smaller islands in the Moluccas and Lesser Sundas. This has caused some difficulties in the analysis, notably in the Banda Sea islands (EBA 165) where several different interpretations are possible. In this case, it has been considered most appropriate to include the widely scattered islands and island groups within a single EBA, and to highlight in the relevant EBA account the fact that the Tanimbar and Kai island groups each have several of their own endemic species.

Some of the larger islands in the region support groups of both lowland and montane restricted-range species, so Luzon (EBA 151), Mindanao and the Eastern Visayas (EBA 154) and Sulawesi (EBA 166) were formerly divided into separate lowland and montane EBAs (ICBP 1992). Because there are restricted-range species on all of these islands which occur in both lowland and montane habitats or at intermediate altitudes, with some species too poorly known to be confidently allocated to either a lowland or montane EBA, they are all here treated as single EBAs (see Appendices 3 and 4, pp. 779 and 781).

Several of the EBAs in this region are notable for their taxonomic uniqueness, especially Sulawesi (EBA 166) with 12 endemic genera, the Central Papuan mountains (EBA 178) with nine, and the

Habitat loss	Knowledge	Confined to the EBA		Present also in other EBAs, SAs		Total		Biological importance	Current threat level	Priority	EBA no.
		Threatened	Total	Threatened	Total	Threatened	Total				
Severe	Incomplete	5	5	3	5	8	10	●	●●●	Critical	150
Major	Incomplete	11	24	7	16	18	40	●●●	●●	Critical	151
Severe	Incomplete	10	10	4	7	14	17	●	●●●	Critical	152
Severe	Incomplete	2	2	0	0	2	2	●●	●●●	Critical	153
Major	Incomplete	19	39	3	12	22	51	●●●	●●	Critical	154
Major	Incomplete	3	4	2	5	5	9	●●●	●●●	Critical	155
Moderate	Incomplete	7	17	1	3	8	20	●●	●●	Urgent	156
Limited	Incomplete	0	24	0	5	0	29	●●●	●	Urgent	157
Moderate	Incomplete	6	20	1	18	7	38	●●●	●	Urgent	158
Limited	Incomplete	0	2	0	0	0	2	●	●	High	159
Severe	Good	6	20	0	14	6	34	●●●	●●	Critical	160
Severe	Incomplete	1	1	0	2	1	3	●	●	High	161
Major	Incomplete	3	17	0	12	3	29	●	●	High	162
Major	Incomplete	4	7	0	5	4	12	●	●	High	163
Major	Poor	5	23	0	12	5	35	●●	●	High	164
Unquantified	Poor	1	18	0	23	1	41	●●	●	High	165
Moderate	Incomplete	5	42	1	12	6	54	●●	●	High	166
Major	Poor	4	5	1	5	5	10	●	●●●	Critical	167
Moderate	Incomplete	2	8	1	8	3	16	●	●	High	168
Limited	Incomplete	5	10	1	18	6	28	●●	●	High	169
Limited	Incomplete	4	14	1	16	5	30	●	●	High	170
Limited	Incomplete	5	26	1	17	6	43	●●	●	High	171
Moderate	Poor	2	9	0	10	2	19	●	●	High	172
Limited	Poor	1	9	0	11	1	20	●●	●	High	173
Major	Poor	3	10	0	4	3	14	●	●	High	174
Possible	Poor	0	3	0	3	0	6	●	●	High	175
Limited	Poor	1	5	0	4	1	9	●	●	High	176
Unquantified	Poor	2	6	0	5	2	11	●	●	High	177
Moderate	Poor	5	39	0	14	5	53	●●●	●	Urgent	178
Limited	Poor	0	3	0	3	0	6	●	●	High	179
Moderate	Poor	1	3	0	3	1	6	●	●	High	180
Moderate	Incomplete	2	3	0	2	2	5	●●	●●●	Critical	181
Moderate	Good	0	13	0	3	0	16	●●●	●	Urgent	182
Moderate	Good	3	9	0	1	3	10	●●●	●●	Critical	183
Major	Good	3	6	1	1	4	7	●●●	●●	Critical	184
Moderate	Good	3	14	0	0	3	14	●●	●●	Urgent	185
Major	Good	3	7	1	1	4	8	●●●	●●	Critical	186
Moderate	Incomplete	1	12	0	1	1	13	●●●	●	Urgent	187
Moderate	Good	1	2	0	0	1	2	●	●	High	188

Bornean mountains (EBA 157) and Northern Maluku (EBA 171), both with four.

Most of the larger islands in the Moluccas and Lesser Sundas in Indonesia have only ever been visited a few times by ornithologists, and the avifaunas of many of the small islands remain virtually unknown (White and Bruce 1986). For example, the island of Wetar (part of EBA 164) has three single-island endemic species but has apparently only been visited once by ornithologists since 1910, and then only for a few hours (Robson 1990).

Threats and conservation

Since the early 1970s the forests of this region have been the world's primary source for tropical timber. The impact of logging varies according to the tech-

niques used and levels of harvesting, but, in addition to the direct loss and degradation of habitat, increased access to once-remote areas leads to colonization and shifting cultivation and further detrimental effects. As the human population grows, traditional sustainable agricultural practices are often replaced by more destructive slash-and-burn ones, resulting in vast areas of land becoming degraded in some parts of the region. For example, grassland, bamboo and other types of scrub, and weed-infested landscapes have replaced much of the original forest cover in southern and central Borneo, in the New Guinea uplands, the Philippines and in the Lesser Sunda islands. In the Philippines, it is feared that virtually all primary forest outside protected areas will be lost by the end of the twentieth century, mainly as a result of commercial logging followed by conversion to oil-palm plantations and other crops. If the current rates of deforestation continue, little primary lowland forest is expected to remain in 20 years time in some parts of Malaysia and Indonesia (apart from Kalimantan and Irian Jaya) (Collins et al. 1991, WWF/IUCN 1994–1995).

The main threat to the EBAs of this region is therefore habitat loss. Several EBAs in the Philippines and Indonesia have already suffered extensive forest loss. An extreme example is Cebu (EBA 153), more than 99% of which is deforested: half the forest bird species formerly resident on the island have gone (39 species lost altogether, including four restricted-range species and a further five endemic subspecies (Brooks et al. 1995b; see also Dutson et al. 1993). Examples of other EBAs which have lost much of their original forest cover are Negros and Panay (EBA 152), Mindoro (EBA 150) and the Sulu archipelago (EBA 155) in the Philippines, and Sangihe and Talaud (EBA 167) in Indonesia.

Indonesia has the world's largest programme of voluntary assisted migration (transmigration). Since the early 1900s at least 2.5 million people have been moved from the crowded and environmentally degraded islands of Java, Madura, Bali and Lombok to new settlements in the less densely populated islands of Sumatra, Kalimantan, Sulawesi, Maluku and Irian Jaya. Although the actual deforested area arising from these programmes is small relative to the total forest estate, associated road developments open up formerly undisturbed areas, and requirements for fuelwood and building materials place additional pressure on surrounding areas of forest (WWF/IUCN 1994–1995; see also Whitten et al. 1987a). Another threat to biodiversity from transmigration is the possibility of introduced species outcompeting native ones, as the regions of Maluku and Irian Jaya have quite different species assemblages from those of Java. For example, macaques Macaca could cause an ecological disaster if they became established on New Guinea, potentially outcompeting fruit-eating birds which have evolved in the absence of primates.

There is considerable variation in the protected-area coverage of EBAs in this region. Apart from in Australia, management of protected areas is often constrained by insufficient trained personnel and an absence of clearly and accurately defined boundaries, and many of the legally designated protected areas are not, in practice, under complete protection. Local people can often play a vital role in managing the areas they utilize, and on which they may depend for survival, and thus management is increasingly concerned with improving the welfare of local inhabitants and developing buffer zones around reserves (WWF/IUCN 1994–1995).

In Indonesia, large sections of some EBAs are included in protected areas, for example Sumatra and Peninsular Malaysia (EBA 158), while others have very limited (or no) official protection, notably several of the EBAs in the Moluccas (see MacKinnon in press). Recognizing the importance of Indonesia for both restricted-range and globally threatened birds, BirdLife International established a country programme there in 1992, in collaboration with the Directorate General of Forest Protection and Nature Conservation. This programme has focused particularly on the EBAs in the Moluccas and Lesser Sundas. Ornithological surveys have been completed in several EBAs, including Sumba (EBA 163), Tanimbar (in EBA 165), Buru (EBA 169) and Halmahera (in EBA 171), and detailed recommendations have been made regarding the gazetting of proposed protected areas.

In the Philippines, the government has recently passed its National Integrated Protected Areas System (NIPAS) legislation, which is designed to completely redevelop the protected-area system of the country. The Haribon Foundation (the BirdLife Partner organization in the Philippines) is working in collaboration with the Department of Environment and Natural Resources on a project (funded by the Darwin Initiative of the UK Department of the Environment) to identify key sites for threatened and restricted-range species within the country's seven EBAs. Through this project, the Haribon–BirdLife programme is helping to ensure that the most appropriate sites within the EBAs are selected as reserves, as well as providing some of the background material needed for designating them under the NIPAS Act.

In Papua New Guinea, 97% of all land is owned according to customary tenure, and only a very small proportion is therefore contained within reserves on state property. Rather, Papua New Guinea has attempted to develop protected areas on customary land through Wildlife Management Areas, with landowners being responsible for deciding boundaries, the rules and their development. There has been a recent study to identify areas worthy of conservation through the compilation of current biological knowledge (including data on restricted-range birds from this project) and an attempt to map areas of high biodiversity and endemism, areas of scant knowledge and areas of significant habitat-types (Beehler 1993, Osborne 1995).

In Australia, where there is already an extensive protected-area network, a framework for setting priorities in the national reserves system is being developed through the Interim Biogeographic Regionalisation of Australia (IBRA) and Conservation Planning Attributes (CPA) (Thackway and Cresswell 1995). Altogether 80 IBRAs are currently recognized, of which 28 correspond with or are included within the seven Australian EBAs. The major attributes used to delineate IBRA boundaries include climate, geology, landform, vegetation, flora and fauna and land-use, while the identification of deficiencies in the current reserve system and priorities for action are derived from four CPAs, including

the existing reservation of each IBRA, the level of bias within protected areas (i.e. how comprehensively the existing protected areas sample the known environmental heterogeneity), constraints and limitations, and opportunities for alternative conservation management measures. This approach will help to identify important gaps in the system.

PACIFIC ISLANDS

THE PACIFIC ISLANDS as defined here comprise Micronesia, the Bismarck archipelago, the east Papuan islands, Melanesia, central and eastern Polynesia, Lord Howe and Norfolk Islands, New Zealand and associated islands, and the Hawaiian Islands.

Most of the islands are oceanic in origin, never having been connected to a continental area by land. Many are tiny and extremely low-lying—such as the coral atolls (motus) of the Tuamotu archipelago (less than 10 km² in size on average and mostly below 7 m in altitude), where the volcanic remnants of former high islands are now completely submerged—but some are of considerable size and altitude, e.g. Hawai'i (more than 10,000 km²), which is a relatively young volcanic island, little eroded and rising to over 4,000 m. Others are raised islands (sometimes called makatea islands) characterized by rocky coralline (limestone) substrates, e.g. the Rock Islands of Palau, Rennell in the Solomon Islands, Makatea in the Tuamotu archipelago, and Henderson in the Pitcairns, and a few are (at least in part) continental in origin, often containing a complex of volcanic and limestone substrates, such as the ancient island of New Caledonia (see Box 6 for key facts).

Restricted-range species

Overall, the Pacific islands have a relatively depauperate land avifauna, chiefly as a result of their small size and great isolation resulting in poorer prospects for continental birds reaching them (but also because of the numerous extinctions which they have suffered: see 'Threats', below). Nevertheless, a high proportion of the total Pacific land avifauna is included in this analysis, resulting in the third (equal) highest number of restricted-range species in total—408—of all the regions.

Restricted-range species are found on nearly all island groups. The majority occur in forest although many utilize other habitats including gardens and secondary vegetation, possibly as a result of being adapted to a cyclone-prone environment, although a

Box 6. Key facts for the Pacific Islands.

Numbers of:
408 Restricted-range species
127 Threatened restricted-range species
30 EBAs
17 Secondary Areas
15 Countries with EBAs

EBAs with high numbers of restricted-range species
- Solomon group (EBA 198), 79 species
- New Britain and New Ireland (EBA 195), 54 species
- Fiji (EBA 202), 36 species

EBAs which are especially distinct at the generic level
- Central Hawaiian Islands (EBA 217), 5 endemic genera
- Hawai'i (EBA 218), 5 endemic genera

EBAs with high numbers of threatened restricted-range species
- Central Hawaiian islands (EBA 217), 18 species
- Solomon group (EBA 198), 14 species
- Hawai'i (EBA 218), 9 species

EBAs with high numbers of Critical and Endangered endemic species
- Central Hawaiian islands (EBA 217), 10 species
- Solomon group (EBA 198), 6 species
- Marquesas (EBA 212), 5 species

Examples of EBAs critically in need of conservation action
- East Caroline Islands (EBA 192)
- Solomon group (EBA 198)
- Marquesas Islands (EBA 212)

Countries with high numbers of restricted-range species
- Solomon Islands, 92 species
- Fiji, 36 species

Countries with high numbers of threatened restricted-range species
- French Polynesia, 18 species
- Solomon Islands, 15 species
- New Zealand, 12 species

Table 6. EBAs of Pacific islands: summary data.

EBA number and name	Countries	Continental/island	Area (km²)	Altitude (m)	Habitat
189 Mariana Islands	Guam (to USA), Northern Mariana Islands (to USA)	OI	1,000	0–900[L]	Forest[1]
190 Palau	Palau	OI	460	0–200[L]	Forest[1,6]
191 Yap Islands	Micronesia	OI	120	0–100[L]	Forest[1,6]
192 East Caroline Islands	Micronesia	OI	580	0–700[L]	Forest[1,2,6]
193 Admiralty Islands	Papua New Guinea	OI	2,000	0–700[L]	Forest[1]
194 St Matthias Islands	Papua New Guinea	OI	460	0–1,000[L]	Forest[1]
195 New Britain and New Ireland	Papua New Guinea	OI	48,000	0–2,200[L,M]	Forest[1,2]
196 D'Entrecasteaux and Trobriand Islands	Papua New Guinea	CI	3,400	0–2,200[L,M]	Forest[1,2]
197 Louisiade archipelago	Papua New Guinea	CI	1,600	0–1,000[L]	Forest[1]
198 Solomon group	Papua New Guinea, Solomon Is.	OI	34,000	0–2,000[L,M]	Forest[1,2]
199 Rennell and Bellona	Solomon Islands	OI	850	0–100[L]	Forest[1]
200 Vanuatu and Temotu	Solomon Islands, Vanuatu	OI	13,000	0–1,800[L,M]	Forest[1,2]
201 New Caledonia	New Caledonia (to France)	OI	19,000	0–1,600[L,M]	Forest[1,2,3] (S,V)
202 Fiji	Fiji	OI	18,000	0–1,300[L,M]	Forest[1,2]
203 Samoan Islands	American Samoa (to USA), Western Samoa	OI	3,000	0–1,800[L,M]	Forest[1,2]
204 Lord Howe Island	Australia	OI	17	0–800[L]	Forest[1]
205 Norfolk Island	Norfolk Island (to Australia)	OI	35	0–300[L,M]	Forest[1]
206 North Island of New Zealand	New Zealand	OI	120,000	0–2,000[L,M]	Forest[5] (W)
207 South Island of New Zealand	New Zealand	OI	110,000	0–2,500[L,M]	Forest[5] (S,W)
208 Auckland Islands	New Zealand	OI	610	0–600[L]	Forest[5] (S,G)
209 Chatham Islands	New Zealand	OI	970	0–200[L]	Forest[5] (S,G,R)
210 Southern Cook Islands	Cook Islands (to New Zealand)	OI	190	0–600[L]	Forest[1,2,3]
211 Rimatara	French Polynesia (to France)	OI	8	0–80[L]	Forest[3]
212 Marquesas Islands	French Polynesia (to France)	OI	1,000	0–1,200[L,M]	Forest[2,3]
213 Society Islands	French Polynesia (to France)	OI	1,400	0–2,200[L,M]	Forest[2,3]
214 Tuamotu archipelago	French Polynesia (to France)	OI	690	0–100[L]	Forest[3] (S)
215 Henderson Island	Pitcairn Islands (to UK)	OI	31	0–30[L]	Forest[3] (S)
216 Laysan Island	USA	OI	4	0–10[L]	Scrub (G,W)
217 Central Hawaiian Islands	USA	OI	6,300	0–3,000[L,M]	Forest[2,3] (W)
218 Hawai'i	USA	OI	10,000	0–3,100[L,M]	Forest[2,3]

KEY See Table 1 (pp. 62–63).

wide range of habitat tolerance is a general phenomenon exhibited by many (of the surviving) oceanic-island landbirds.

The great remoteness of many Pacific islands has led to the evolution of a large number of highly distinctive species, notably the Hawaiian honeycreepers (an endemic Hawaiian family) and the Kagu *Rhynochetos jubatus* (a monospecific family endemic to New Caledonia). Other species which are of similarly obscure origin, representing a very early colonization, include Silktail *Lamprolia victoria* from Fiji and Tooth-billed Pigeon *Didunculus strigirostris* from Western Samoa. Some genera are particularly well represented in the region, e.g. white-eyes *Zosterops*, and *Acrocephalus* warblers, both being classic small-island colonizers.

The most substantial contribution to the ornithology of Micronesia, Melanesia and Polynesia has been several expeditions—collectively called the Whitney South Seas Expedition—carried out over nearly 20 years from 1920. A high proportion of the islands in the region were visited and a large series of bird skins was deposited in the American Museum of Natural History, forming the basis our knowledge of bird distribution today. The results of this extended work were published in *American Museum Novitates*, chiefly by Mayr and Amadon, and summarized in Mayr (1945). This book and Pratt *et al.* (1987) are the most comprehensive bird guides to many parts of this region.

The taxonomy of the majority of Pacific island birds has not received the same attention as some other areas of the world and, as a consequence, many allopatric island subspecies may well come to be treated as full species if modern taxonomic trends are extended to the region. On the other hand some species which are recognized by Sibley and Monroe (1990, 1993) show introgression and are regarded as conspecific with other species by some experts. For example, Polynesian Imperial-pigeon *Ducula aurorae* (from the Society Islands and Tuamotu archipelago) approaches populations of the widespread Pacific Pigeon *D. pacifica* in morphological characteristics, and is thus included in the latter by Holyoak

Habitat loss	Knowledge	Numbers of restricted-range species						Biological importance	Current threat level	Priority	EBA no.
		Confined to the EBA		Present also in other EBAs, SAs		Total					
		Threatened	Total	Threatened	Total	Threatened	Total				
Moderate	Good	5	7	1	5	6	12	••	••	Urgent	189
Moderate	Incomplete	0	10	1	6	1	16	••	•	High	190
Major	Incomplete	1	3	0	4	1	7	•	•	High	191
Moderate	Incomplete	4	11	0	7	4	18	•••	••	Critical	192
Limited	Poor	3	6	0	7	3	13	••	•	High	193
Possible	Poor	0	2	0	6	0	8	•	•	High	194
Moderate	Poor	2	35	1	19	3	54	••	•	High	195
Unquantified	Poor	1	2	0	0	1	2	•	•	High	196
Moderate	Poor	0	5	0	2	0	7	•••	•	Urgent	197
Moderate	Poor	13	61	1	17	14	78	•••	••	Critical	198
Limited	Poor	0	5	0	7	0	12	•	•	High	199
Moderate	Poor	6	15	0	15	6	30	•	•	High	200
Major	Poor	8	22	0	9	8	31	••	••	Urgent	201
Major	Incomplete	5	24	0	11	5	35	••	•	High	202
Major	Incomplete	5	11	0	9	5	20	••	••	Urgent	203
Limited	Good	2	2	0	0	2	2	••	•••	Critical	204
Major	Good	3	3	0	0	3	3	••	•••	Critical	205
Major	Good	2	3	0	0	2	3	•	•••	Critical	206
Moderate	Good	4	6	0	0	4	6	•	••	Urgent	207
Moderate	Good	1	1	0	1	1	2	•	•	High	208
Moderate	Good	4	5	0	0	4	5	••	•••	Critical	209
Moderate	Incomplete	4	6	0	1	4	7	•	••	Urgent	210
Major	Incomplete	1	2	0	0	1	2	•	•••	Critical	211
Major	Incomplete	7	10	0	0	7	10	•	•••	Critical	212
Major	Incomplete	3	5	2	3	5	8	•	••	Urgent	213
Moderate	Poor	4	6	2	2	6	8	•	•••	Critical	214
Limited	Good	3	4	0	0	3	4	•	••	Urgent	215
Possible	Good	2	2	0	0	2	2	•••	••	Critical	216
Major	Good	14	15	4	8	18	23	•••	•••	Critical	217
Major	Good	5	7	4	8	9	15	•••	•••	Critical	218

and Thibault (in prep.). Likewise, the *Acrocephalus* warblers of the Marquesas, Society and Tuamotu Islands are treated as three separate species by Sibley and Monroe (1990, 1993), but show intermediate characteristics that imply gene-flow between archipelagos.

Endemic Bird Areas

The vast majority of the islands of this region are included in 30 EBAs, including four in Micronesia, nine in the Bismarck archipelago and Melanesia, eight in central and eastern Polynesia, one each on Lord Howe and Norfolk Islands, four in New Zealand, and three in the Hawaiian islands. A further 17 Secondary Areas cover additional islands (see Figure 7 for location of EBAs and Secondary Areas, and Table 6 for EBA summary data).

The patterns of endemism shown by the EBA analysis are not necessarily 'natural'; rather they reflect fragmented surviving avifaunas, the result of man's influence over several thousand years (see 'Threats', below). In most cases the EBA analysis

reflects well-known patterns of endemism. An exception to this is New Zealand, which has a mainland area of over 250,000 km², and many of its endemic birds have (or historically had) ranges of more than 50,000 km² thus failing to qualify as having restricted ranges for this project. The EBA analysis therefore results in a rather artificial division of mainland New Zealand into two EBAs (EBAs 206, 207), based on North and South Islands, which together constitute a larger and better-known centre of endemism.

There are several other larger areas of endemism in the region, especially in Micronesia, Melanesia and central Polynesia, and a few restricted-range species are shared within these larger groupings. Conversely, some species have tiny ranges and are confined to single islands within EBAs. Thus smaller nested areas of endemism are also a common feature, e.g. the main islands of the East Caroline Islands (EBA 192) each have (or had) their own endemics (three on Truk, five on Pohnpei and two on Kosrae), and New Georgia in the Solomon group (EBA 198) has 10 endemic species, some of them occurring on

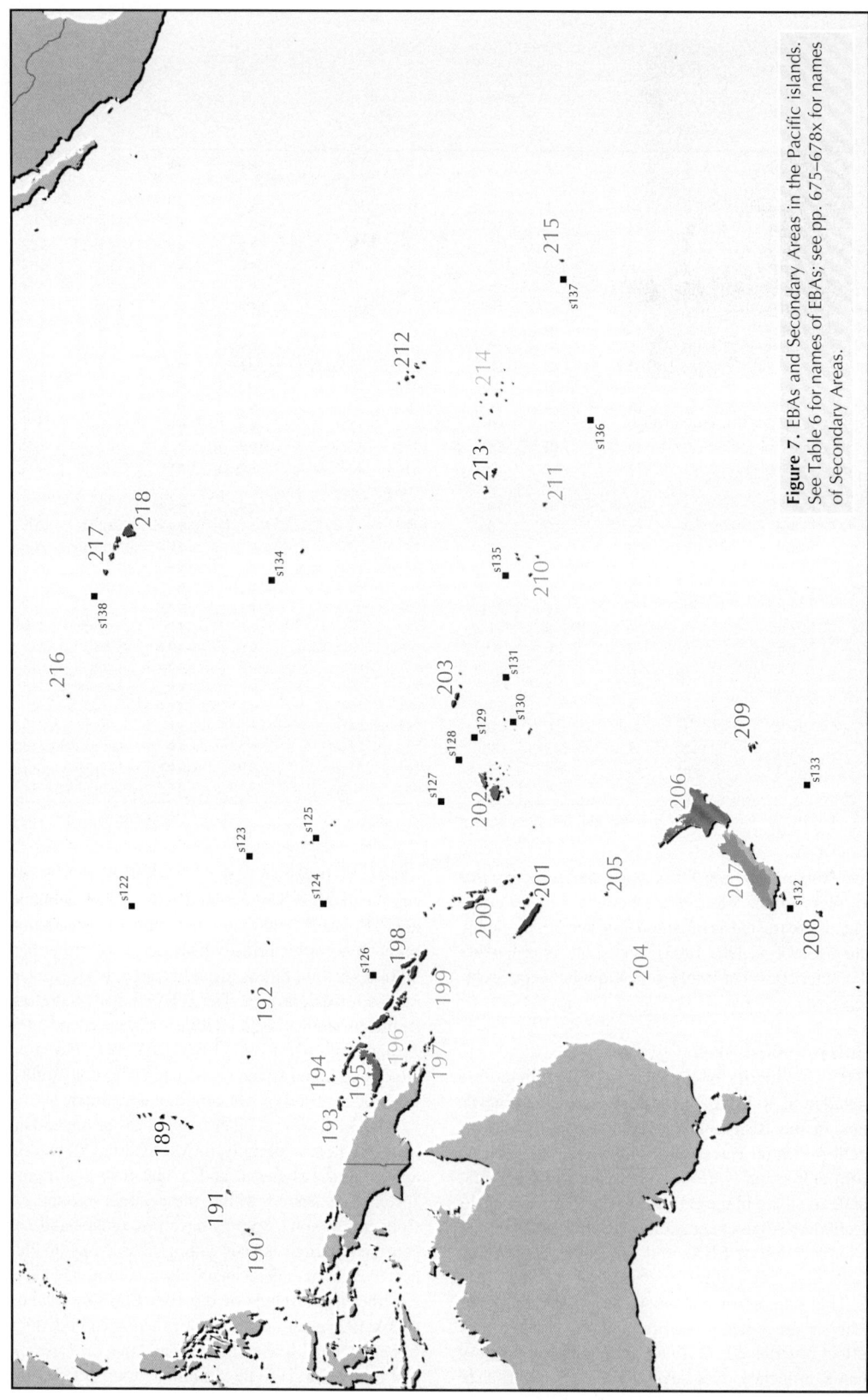

Figure 7. EBAs and Secondary Areas in the Pacific islands. See Table 6 for names of EBAs; see pp. 675–678x for names of Secondary Areas.

The Rock Islands of Palau (EBA 190). The forests here are particularly important as a haven for several restricted-range bird species, and beaches provide safe nesting sites for the threatened Micronesian Scrubfowl *Megapodius laperouse*, although tourism is causing increasing disturbance.

H. D. Pratt

single islands within the group. Overall, the Solomon group (EBA 198), centred on the political Solomon Islands (but including Bougainville, and excluding Rennell and Temotu), has the greatest number of restricted-range species (79) of all the world's EBAs; New Britain and New Ireland (EBA 195) with 54 species and Fiji (EBA 202) with 36 species also rank highly in global terms.

There are many small-island Secondary Areas, perhaps because highly disjunct ranges are commoner (or easier to distinguish) in an island—rather than in a continental—region. Several islands have single-island endemics, e.g. Nauru (Secondary Area s124) and Rapa (s136), and some islands share restricted-range species with two EBAs, with no clear affinity with one of these EBAs over the other, e.g. Wallis and Futuna (s128) and Niue (s131).

Several of the world's smallest EBAs lie in the Pacific region, including the islands of Laysan (EBA 261, 4 km²) and Rimatara (EBA 211, 8 km²). As most restricted-range species are forest-dependent, forest is the key habitat in nearly all EBAs, mostly tropical lowland and montane forest, but also tropical dry forest and mangroves and, in the New Zealand EBAs, temperate forest. There is some habitat specialization and altitudinal zonation of birds on the higher Pacific islands, but this is not sufficient to warrant the splitting of EBAs into lowland and montane groups as has been done on some larger islands in other regions and continental areas. In the Hawaiian EBAs (EBAs 217, 218) many of the restricted-range birds are found above 500 m, although originally they are likely to have occurred in the lowlands too.

Several EBAs are poorly known ornithologically, e.g. the Bismarck archipelago, consisting of the Admiralty Islands (EBA 193), St Matthias Islands (EBA 194) and New Britain and New Ireland (EBA 195); the east Papuan islands, consisting of D'Entrecasteaux and Trobriand Islands (EBA 196),

and the Louisiade archipelago (EBA 197); Melanesia, consisting of the Solomon group (EBA 198), Rennell and Bellona (EBA 199), Vanuatu and Temotu (EBA 200) and New Caledonia (EBA 201); and the Tuamotu archipelago (EBA 214) in French Polynesia.

Threats and conservation

Many Pacific bird species (especially flightless ones) have been locally extirpated from islands or have even become globally extinct since colonization by Polynesians, owing not only to habitat loss and hunting but also to the effects of introduced mammalian predators (Pacific rat *Rattus exulans*, dogs and pigs). These losses are relatively well documented historically and paleontologically in New Zealand, the Hawaiian Islands and eastern Polynesia (e.g. Steadman 1989, Johnson and Stattersfield 1990, Bell 1991, Milberg and Tyrberg 1993, Pratt 1994), but are likely to be region-wide. On islands where the prehistoric fauna has been investigated, the richest

K. D. Bishop

Kagu *Rhynochetos jubatus*, endemic to New Caledonia (EBA 201), is an exceptional bird, being the sole representative of its family. Its eggs are eaten by introduced wild pigs, chicks are killed by dogs, cats and rats, and adults are hunted.

examples have been found to have held three to four times more landbird species than are present today. For example, most or all islands in Polynesia supported one to four endemic species of flightless rail of different size, virtually all now extinct; there are known survivors on Guam in the Mariana Islands (EBA 189), on the New Georgia group in the Solomon group (EBA 198) and on Henderson (EBA 215), a poor remnant of an amazingly diverse group of birds, which once may have had some 2,000 members in the region (Steadman 1995).

Further declines followed European contact, less than 300 years ago, with the concomitant spread of brown rat *Rattus norvegicus*, black rat *R. rattus* (the most pernicious threat to birds: Atkinson 1985; see also Moors *et al.* 1992) and cats to many islands, as well as mustelids to New Zealand (EBAs 206, 207), mongoose *Herpestes auropunctatus* to Fiji and Hawai'i (EBAs 202, 217, 218) and brown tree snake *Boiga irregularis* to Guam (EBA 189 in part). Other introduced species which have had a significant effect, either directly or indirectly, are browsing and grazing animals (e.g. goats, cattle, sheep), competitors (e.g. Common Myna *Acridotheres tristis* in the Cook Islands, EBA 210), avian diseases (e.g. avian malaria and pox carried by *Culex* mosquitoes in Hawai'i, EBAs 217, 218) and aggressive weedy plants (e.g. the Neotropical tree *Miconia calvescens* on Tahiti, EBA 213). Since 1800, nine species have become extinct on Hawai'i (EBA 218) and four on Lord Howe (EBA 204), largely as a result of these introductions. Since the 1980s, two species have become extinct from Guam (EBA 189 in part) and a further seven have become locally extinct, as a result of predation by the introduced brown tree snake.

In addition to the legacy of introduced species, a major current threat to the EBAs and to their surviving birds is forest loss: beach and atoll forest is cleared and replaced with plantations (where coconut and breadfruit are usually dominant) and tourist developments; lowland forest is logged or cleared and replaced with exotic trees (e.g. pine and eucalyptus) and agriculture; and fire destroys large areas of native forest leading to the spread of impoverished man-made grassland, fernland and scrub, which is usually unsuitable for native birds (e.g. on the leeward sides of the Hawaiian Islands, EBAs 217, 218, on Viti Levu and Vanua Levu in Fiji, EBA 202, in southern Guam, EBA 189, and in the Marquesas, EBA 212). Forest damage through hurricanes (e.g. in Western Samoa, EBA 203, in 1990–1991, and in the

central Hawaiian Islands, EBA 217, in 1992) can also be extensive and especially serious in areas which are already fragmented and degraded. Even where habitats remain relatively intact (e.g. on Rennell, EBA 199, and Henderson, EBA 215) or have been restored (e.g. Laysan, EBA 216), species are classified as threatened because of their tiny ranges and populations, which render them permanently vulnerable to chance events such as introductions and hurricanes.

Overall, a high proportion of the Pacific region's avifauna (c.14%) is currently considered threatened with extinction (Stattersfield in press) and yet terrestrial conservation programmes are absent or weakly advanced in many EBAs. The Central Hawaiian islands (EBA 217) stand out for having the highest number of threatened restricted-range species (18), including 10 Critical and Endangered endemics. The majority of the other EBAs, many of them tiny, also have threatened restricted-range species.

Most Pacific EBAs are very poorly protected by state-owned reserves (less than 5% of their land area: ICBP 1992) with the exception of Lord Howe and Norfolk Islands (EBAs 204, 205), New Zealand (EBAs 206–209), Hawai'i (EBAs 216–218) and Henderson (EBA 215). Most land elsewhere in the Pacific is communally owned by indigenous groups who are (or were) highly dependent on subsistence agriculture. On many islands, cultural traditions attach particular significance to some species and sites, and have thereby played an important role in protecting certain natural resources (although these traditions are commonly now being lost or replaced). Conservation efforts, if they are to succeed, must operate within this framework of customary land ownership and traditional practice, and pay particular attention to the needs of local people, encouraging local community participation in all facets of conservation and management (see, e.g., Gilman 1997). Encouraging examples of such initiatives can be found in the Solomon group (EBA 198), Vanuatu (EBA 200) and Fiji (EBA 202), but many EBAs are critically in need of (more) conservation action.

There have been some major conservation programmes in the region targeted at individual species, and many have involved intensive rat control, notably in New Zealand (EBAs 206, 207) but also in the Cook Islands (EBA 210) and Society Islands (EBA 213). These may serve as models of management that can be applied to other critically threatened bird species, where introduced species are the key factor in their demise.

ENDEMIC BIRD AREAS

Interpretation of a sample EBA account

General characteristics describes the location of the EBA, its boundaries, and its relationship to other nearby EBAs and gives information on relevant physical features (e.g. topography) and biological features (e.g. vegetation). For regional information on such general characteristics, see pp. 57–92.

Distribution patterns table (optional) shows complex distribution patterns (by mountain, island or other area) of restricted-range bird species within the EBA. Species are ordered geographically so that these patterns can be clearly seen. Smaller areas of endemism within the EBA are also then apparent, as are those areas which are most important for numbers of restricted-range bird species.

Header with summary information (see opposite).

Region within which the EBA falls (see p. 57).

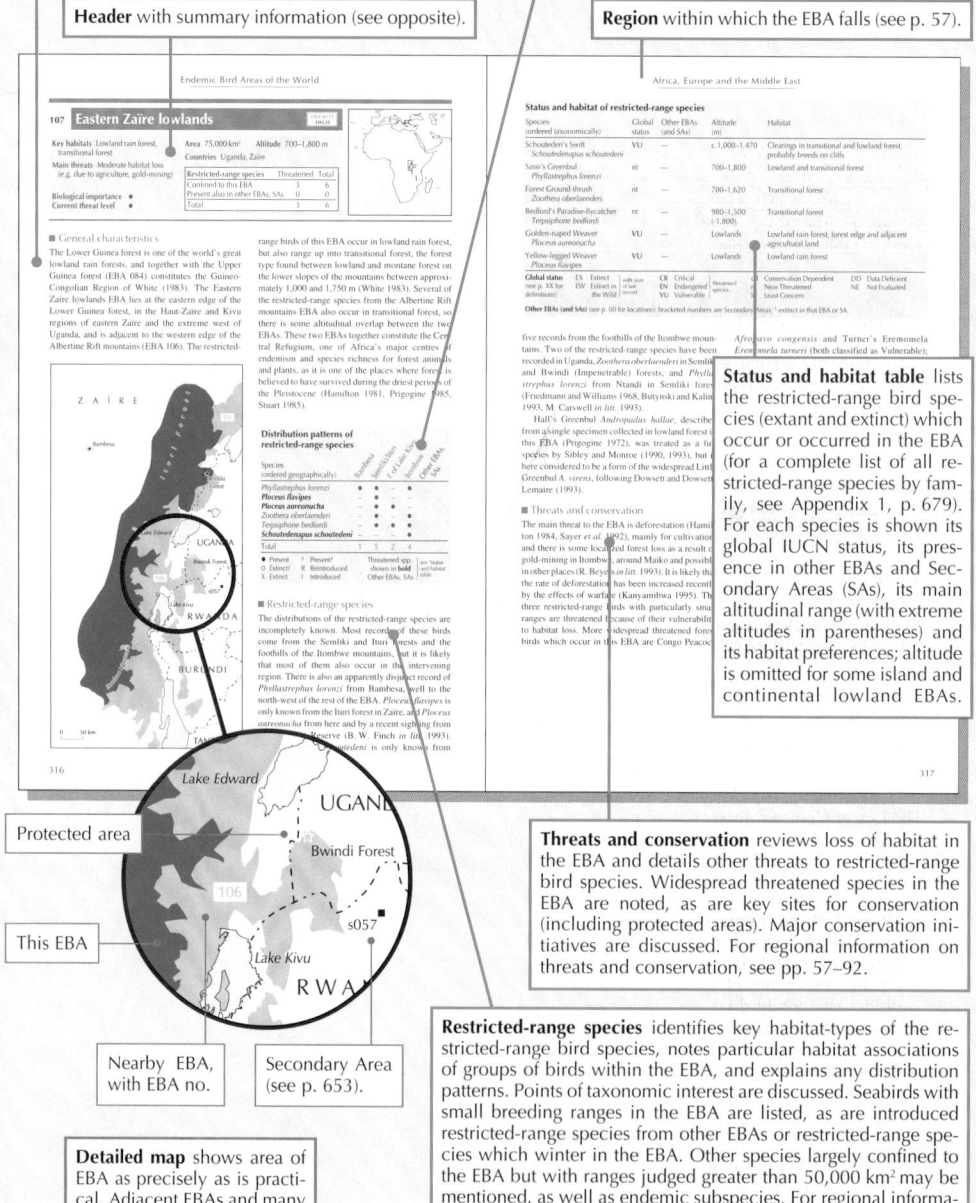

Status and habitat table lists the restricted-range bird species (extant and extinct) which occur or occurred in the EBA (for a complete list of all restricted-range species by family, see Appendix 1, p. 679). For each species is shown its global IUCN status, its presence in other EBAs and Secondary Areas (SAs), its main altitudinal range (with extreme altitudes in parentheses) and its habitat preferences; altitude is omitted for some island and continental lowland EBAs.

Protected area

This EBA

Nearby EBA, with EBA no.

Secondary Area (see p. 653).

Detailed map shows area of EBA as precisely as is practical. Adjacent EBAs and many of the geographical features mentioned in the text are included.

Threats and conservation reviews loss of habitat in the EBA and details other threats to restricted-range bird species. Widespread threatened species in the EBA are noted, as are key sites for conservation (including protected areas). Major conservation initiatives are discussed. For regional information on threats and conservation, see pp. 57–92.

Restricted-range species identifies key habitat-types of the restricted-range bird species, notes particular habitat associations of groups of birds within the EBA, and explains any distribution patterns. Points of taxonomic interest are discussed. Seabirds with small breeding ranges in the EBA are listed, as are introduced restricted-range species from other EBAs or restricted-range species which winter in the EBA. Other species largely confined to the EBA but with ranges judged greater than 50,000 km² may be mentioned, as well as endemic subspecies. For regional information on restricted-range species, see pp. 57–92.

Habitat associations table (optional, not shown in this example) groups species by key habitats, e.g. lowland forest, alpine grassland.

Interpretation of the account header for an EBA

Each EBA's header provides summary information for it. See Tables 1–6 in 'Regional Introductions' (p. 57–92), for easy comparison between EBAs—and for additional information on how each EBA has been coded for type (island/continent, lowland/montane), for forest (six different categories) and for level of knowledge (well known, poorly known and incompletely known). All these data have been used in the global analysis (see p. 27).

Main threats to restricted-range bird species. Always indicates extent of habitat loss in the EBA (severe, major, moderate, limited, possible or unquantified: see p. 63 for definitions), usually with examples. Other threats (e.g. introduced species, cage-bird trade) may also be listed.

Area of EBA (in km², to three significant figures). Usually estimated from the GIS or, where a complete island or island group comprises an EBA, taken from published sources (see p. 26).

Main altitudinal range used by the restricted-range bird species. Rounded down for lowest range or up for highest range to nearest 100 m, or to nearest 10 m for ranges <100 m. See 'Altitude' column in the EBA's 'Status and habitat' table for more detail (for some island EBAs where no altitudes are given in that table, the altitude in the header is from sea-level to the island's highest point, rounded down to nearest 100 m). NB Lower limits are often difficult to determine because of seasonal altitudinal migration and differences in topography resulting in habitats typical of higher regions occurring locally at altitudes lower than might be expected.

Key habitats of restricted-range bird species. See key on p. 62 for main types recognized, also habitat column in the EBA's 'Status and habitat' table for more detail.

Number and name of EBA (see Appendix 3, p. 779, for EBA numbering system used in previous publications).

Priority ranking for conservation action—Critical, Urgent or High—assigned to the EBA, based on its biological importance and current threat level (see p. 41).

---

107 Eastern Zaïre lowlands

PRIORITY HIGH

Key habitats Lowland rain forest, transitional forest

Area 75,000 km² **Altitude** 700–1,800 m

Countries Uganda, Zaïre

Main threats Moderate habitat loss (e.g. due to agriculture, gold-mining)

Restricted-range species	Threatened	Total
Confined to this EBA	3	6
Present also in other EBAs, SAs	0	0
Total	3	6

Biological importance •
Current threat level •

■ General characteristics

The Lower Guinea forest is one of the world's great lo... i... ...sts, ...geth... ...with... ...e Uppe...

range birds of this EBA occur in lowland rain forest, but also range up into transitional forest, the forest type ...und between l...lan... ...mont... ...fores... on

---

One of three **current threat level** ranks is assigned to the EBA, based on the percentage of its restricted-range bird species which are threatened, and the categories of threat of these species (see p. 40).

Countries covered by the EBA. The geopolitical units included, the names assigned to them, and their political affinities are those recognized by the International Standards Organisation. See Appendix 2 (p. 725) for a complete list of EBAs, Secondary Areas and restricted-range bird species by country.

Location of the EBA within one of the six regions into which the world has been divided (see p. 57). The box around the EBA covers the same area as that of the detailed EBA map. For regional maps showing all EBAs, see Figures 2–7, pp. 60–90.

Summary table giving numbers of restricted-range bird species confined to this EBA, numbers present also in other EBAs and Secondary Areas, and whether or not they are threatened. Only extant species are included.

One of three **biological importance** ranks is assigned to the EBA, based on its number of restricted-range bird species (and whether they are shared with other EBAs), the taxonomic uniqueness of those species, and the size of the EBA (see p. 39).

001 California

Key habitats Mediterranean scrub (chaparral), montane coniferous and deciduous forest, wetlands

Main threats Major habitat loss (e.g. due to agriculture, urbanization)

Biological importance ● ●
Current threat level ●

Area 180,000 km² **Altitude** 0–2,000 m

Countries Mexico, USA

Restricted-range species	Threatened	Total
Confined to this EBA	0	6
Present also in other EBAs, SAs	0	0
Total	0	6

■ General characteristics

The boundaries of this EBA run from south-west Oregon (USA) through the coastal valleys and foothills of the Sierra Nevada mountains of California to north-west Baja California (Mexico). The 2,000-m contour has been used as the upper limit of the EBA, as the breeding ranges of all the restricted-range species lie between this altitude and sea-level.

The climate is Mediterranean, characterized by cool, wet winters and dry, warm or hot summers. General vegetation types include montane coniferous forest, oak forest, mixed evergreen forest, chaparral (a dense scrub 1–3 m high with many endemic plant species), coastal scrubland, grassland and riparian habitats. Overall, nearly 50% of plant species are endemic to this region (WWF/IUCN 1997).

■ Restricted-range species

All the restricted-range species occur in chaparral and/or coniferous–oak forest, apart from *Agelaius tricolor*, which nests in large colonies in marshes.

This is a large EBA and the restricted-range species are not found throughout. Of the two most restricted species, *Selasphorus sasin* breeds in a narrow coastal strip from south-west Oregon through California and winters south to Mexico, with non-migratory populations on some of the offshore islands and much of the southern Californian coast. *Pica nuttalli* is only found in the coastal valleys and foothills of central California. The remaining species are more widespread in California and north-west Baja California, but are still judged to have breeding ranges of less than 50,000 km² and so qualify as restricted-range.

Two other species, Anna's Hummingbird *Calypte anna* and Wrentit *Chamaea fasciata*, are also largely confined to this region, but are judged to exceed the range limit, and have therefore been excluded. California Gnatcatcher *Polioptila californica*, sometimes considered conspecific with the widespread Black-tailed Gnatcatcher *P. melanura*, occurs in Baja California as well as in southern California and has also been excluded on range size.

There are many subspecies in this region which are clearly delimited and are candidates for elevation to full species rank in the near future (K. L. Garrett *in litt.* 1997). Examples are Bell's Sage Sparrow *Amphispiza (belli) belli*, which is found in coastal sage scrub and chaparral from north-west California to north-west Baja California, and Santa Cruz Jay *Aphelocoma (coerulescens) insularis* (already treated as a species by some authorities), which is restricted to Santa Cruz Island in the Channel Islands.

■ Threats and conservation

California is the most heavily populated state of the USA, and the extent and character of the natural vegetation almost throughout this region have changed dramatically in the last two centuries, a process which has included the loss, fragmentation and degradation of many wetlands and riparian and

Status and habitat of restricted-range species

Species (ordered taxonomically)	Global status	Other EBAs (and SAs)	Altitude (m)	Habitat
Allen's Hummingbird *Selasphorus sasin*	lc	—	0–250	Chaparral, coastal sage thickets, gallery forest, pine forest, urban parks, residential areas
Nuttall's Woodpecker *Picoides nuttallii*	lc	—	0–1,800	Gallery forest, pine–oak forest, chaparral
California Thrasher *Toxostoma redivivum*	lc	—	0–1,700	Arid lowland scrub, riparian thickets, chaparral
Tricoloured Blackbird *Agelaius tricolor*	lc	—	0–1,050	Freshwater marshes, wet meadows, farmland
Lawrence's Goldfinch *Carduelis lawrencei*	lc	—	0–2,000	Gallery forest, oak forest, chaparral
Yellow-billed Magpie *Pica nuttalli*	lc	—	0–550	Oak forest, scrub, savanna

Global status (see p. 679 for definitions)
EX Extinct ⎫ with year
EW Extinct in ⎬ of last
    the Wild ⎭ record

CR Critical   ⎫ threatened
EN Endangered ⎬ species
VU Vulnerable ⎭

cd Conservation Dependent
nt Near Threatened
lc Least Concern

DD Data Deficient
NE Not Evaluated

Other EBAs (and SAs) (see p. 60 for locations): bracketed numbers are Secondary Areas; ˣ extinct in that EBA or SA.

coniferous woodlands. For example, there has been a 91% loss of wetlands (due to filling and draining for urban and agricultural growth), an 89% loss of riparian woodland (due to agricultural and urban development, and river canalization and diversions), a >90% loss of native perennial grassland (through urbanization, conversion to agriculture and a conversion to non-native annual grassland mediated by overgrazing), and a >30% loss of the most diverse conifer forests (through conversion to less diverse forest–scrub, montane chaparral, and clear-felled areas (WWF/IUCN 1997).

Despite the destruction, the EBA's restricted-range species are relatively common within their remaining habitat, and none is considered threatened. There is, however, one very high-profile, non-restricted-range, threatened species which occurs in this EBA: California Condor *Gymnogyps californianus* (classified as Critical), historically widespread but having declined rapidly throughout the twentieth century owing to direct persecution and accidental lead ingestion from carcasses, so that in the mid-1980s the remaining eight wild birds were captured to join other zoo-held stock in a captive-breeding recovery programme. In April 1997 the total population stood at 118 birds, of which 92 are in captivity at the San Diego Wild Animal Park and World Center for Birds of Prey, and 26 are in the wild, including five in northern Arizona, 17 near Cuyama valley in the Santa Barbara County region, and four in the Ventana Wilderness Area at Big Sur (L. F. Kiff *in litt.* 1997). Another much publicized bird is Spotted Owl *Strix occidentalis* (classified as Near Threatened), which relies on mature coniferous and mixed coniferous–oak forest along the Pacific coast of Canada, USA (including in this EBA) and Mexico.

There are many protected areas in this region (estimated to cover c.11%). Of particular note is Yosemite National Park (3,083 km²) in the Sierra Nevada, one of the most visited national parks in the USA, although the great majority of this park's land is above 2,000 m. Others include the Channel Islands National Park (1,001 km²), various coastal sage habitat reserves in Orange and San Diego counties, and Redwood National Park (424 km²), which is a World Heritage Site.

002 Baja California

PRIORITY
HIGH

Key habitats Arid scrub, wetlands, pine–oak forest

Main threats Moderate habitat loss (e.g. due to agriculture, grazing)

Biological importance ●

Current threat level ●

Area 43,000 km² **Altitude** 0–1,500 m

Countries Mexico

Restricted-range species	Threatened	Total
Confined to this EBA	1	2
Present also in other EBAs, SAs	0	0
Total	1	2

■ General characteristics

The EBA is located in the southern half of the Baja California peninsula, and falls within the Mexican states of Baja California Norte and (principally) Baja California Sur. The main mountain range of the EBA is the Sierra de la Giganta/Sierra Victoria (rising to c.1,700 m) along the eastern side of the peninsula, with the less extensive Cape Mountains in the Sierra de San Lázaro (to 2,400 m) in southern Baja California Sur.

With low rainfall and high mean annual temperatures, especially in the summer months, the dominant vegetation is arid and desert scrub on the west coast, dry forest on the eastern slopes, and coniferous forests and pine–oak forests confined to the higher altitudes of the mountains. The peninsula is very important floristically: 25% of its 2,700 plant species are endemic, as are 20 genera (Rzedowski 1993).

■ Restricted-range species

Two subspecies of *Geothlypis beldingi* are recognized: the nominate form is restricted to southern Baja California Sur and *goldmani* to central Baja California Sur. This species is confined to freshwater marsh areas, especially those fringed with generous vegetation cover, whereas *Hylocharis xantusii* is found in a variety of habitats.

There are potentially more restricted-range species occurring in this EBA. Baird's Junco *Junco bairdi*, which is confined to the Cape Mountains is traditionally (and here) considered conspecific with the widespread Yellow-eyed Junco *J. phaeonotus*, but is treated as a full species by Howell and Webb (1995a); it is a fairly common resident of arid to semi-arid oak and pine–oak forest at 1,200–1,900 m. Cape Pygmy-owl *Glaucidium hoskinsii*, which is endemic to the Sierra de San Lázaro and probably also Sierra de la Giganta, is usually treated under Mountain Pygmy-owl *G. gnoma*, but is considered to be an allospecies by Howell and Webb (1995a). It inhabits pine and pine–oak forest at 1,500–2,100 m and deciduous forest down to 500 m in winter. Conversely, a subspecies of American Robin, San Lucas Robin *Turdus migratorius confinis*, which is also endemic to the mountain pine forests of Sierra de San Lázaro, has been treated by some authorities as a distinct species, but is now considered a subspecies by all modern checklists and guides to the region.

■ Threats and conservation

Large areas of the EBA are uninhabited but southern Baja California is becoming ever more popular for tourism and recreational activities. The arid scrub desert on the western side of the EBA is being damaged by off-road vehicles, and illegal logging of boojum trees *Idria columnaris*, while the dry forests on the eastern side are threatened by agricultural expansion and grazing (Dinerstein *et al.* 1995).

U S A

001

Baja California Norte

M E X I C O

006

Baja California Sur

G U L F   O F   C A L I F O R N I A

005

Sierra de la Giganta

P A C I F I C

Sierra de San Lázaro

Cabo San Lucas SAN JOSÉ

O C E A N

0   100 km

Status and habitat of restricted-range species

Species (ordered taxonomically)	Global status	Other EBAs (and SAs)	Altitude (m)	Habitat
Xantus's Hummingbird *Hylocharis xantusii*	lc	—	0–1,500	Arid lowland and montane scrub, open forest, forest edge, pine-oak forest
Belding's Yellowthroat *Geothlypis beldingi*	VU	—	0–500	Freshwater (possibly saltwater/brackish) marshes

Global status (see p. 679 for definitions)	EX Extinct EW Extinct in the Wild } with year of last record	CR Critical EN Endangered VU Vulnerable } threatened species	cd Conservation Dependent nt Near Threatened lc Least Concern	DD Data Deficient NE Not Evaluated

Other EBAs (and SAs) (see p. 60 for locations): bracketed numbers are Secondary Areas; ˣ extinct in that EBA or SA.

Oak forests in the Sierra Victoria of southern Baja are home to Xantus's Hummingbird *Hylocharis xantusii*.

S. N. G. Howell and S. Webb

Geothlypis beldingi is treated as threatened because the nominate race apparently survives at only one small marsh near San José, while *goldmani* remains common at just a handful of localities owing to the loss of its preferred habitat through drainage and drought.

The EBA does not have any protected areas. Although the El Vizcaíno Biosphere Reserve, one of the world's largest protected areas (more than 25,000 km²), is nearby in north-west Baja California Sur, the reserve falls outside the range of both *Hylocharis xantusii* and *Geothlypis beldingi*.

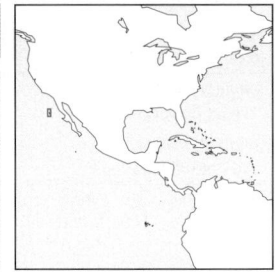

003 Guadalupe Island

PRIORITY
CRITICAL

Key habitats Oak, pine and cypress forest, introduced scrub

Main threats Severe habitat loss (e.g. due to overgrazing by feral goats), introduced species

Biological importance ● ● ●
Current threat level ● ● ●

Area 280 km² **Altitude** 0–1,000 m

Countries Mexico

Restricted-range species	Threatened	Total
Confined to this EBA	1	1
Present also in other EBAs, SAs	0	0
Total	1	1

■ General characteristics

Guadalupe Island is the westernmost territory of Mexico, located c.280 km west of northern Baja California Norte state and 250 km south of San Diego (USA). It is an oceanic volcanic island with a rugged topography, which is highest in its northern and north-central parts. This northern end rises to a sharp ridge that drops off abruptly on the west side, but less so to the east, and widens to a plateau in the centre,

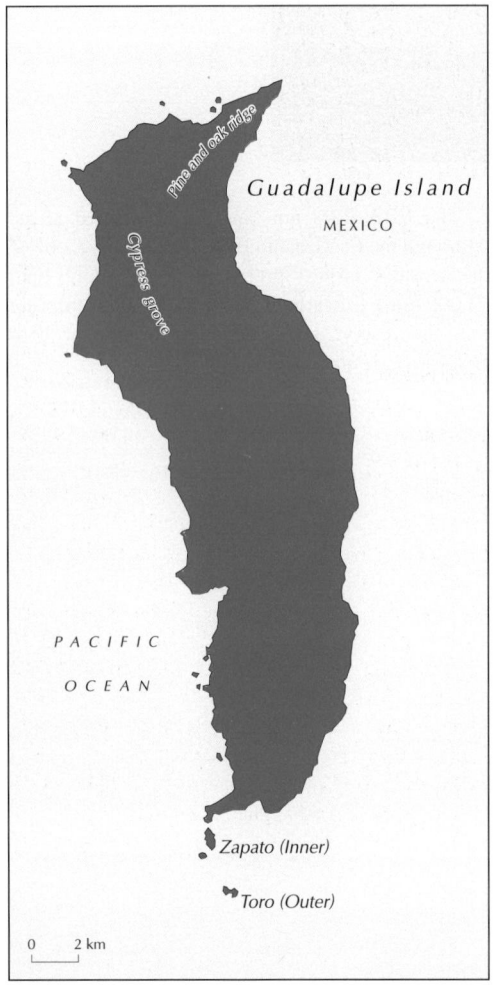

Guadalupe Island
MEXICO

Pine and oak ridge

Cypress grove

PACIFIC

OCEAN

Zapato (Inner)

Toro (Outer)

0   2 km

with land from there gradually descending to the south. Close to the island's southern tip are two islets known as Zapato (Inner) and Toro (Outer) Islet.

The island's climate is one of dry, hot summers with cold winters. Abundant shrubs and forest once covered most of the island. These forests were especially prevalent at higher altitudes in the north and included cypress *Cupressus guadalupensis*, pines *Pinus radiata* var. *binata*, oaks *Quercus tomentella* and fan palms *Erythea edulis*, with more open and scrubby habitats at lower altitudes (Howell and Cade 1953).

■ Restricted-range species

Both the two restricted-range species are often treated as subspecies of more widespread taxa: *Polyborus lutosus* may be a race of Crested Caracara *P. plancus*, and *Junco insularis* has been considered a subspecies of Dark-eyed Junco *J. hyemalas*, but differences in voice, morphology and plumage indicate that the junco's specific status, at least, is justified (Howell and Cade 1953, Mirsky 1976, Howell and Webb 1995a).

■ Threats and conservation

Today little is left of the once-abundant vegetation. Virtually all of the native shrubs have gone, so that only vertical cliffs inaccessible to feral goats now hold the last patches. The forests are also greatly reduced in size and, because the understorey is absent in those remaining, there is no regeneration. The total extent of remaining forest includes a small area of oaks and pines on the northern ridge of the island, and a cypress grove (c.1 km in length in 1988) on the north-central plateau.

This lack of vegetation and predation by introduced cats has had a catastrophic effect on Guadalupe's birds, although *Polyborus lutosus* became extinct about 1900 as a result of heavy persecution, mainly by shooting, often when birds gathered at water-holes (del Hoyo *et al.* 1994). Of the island's six endemic landbird subspecies, three have been lost: Northern Flicker *Colaptes auratus rufipileus* (although there were sightings possibly relating to

Status and habitat of restricted-range species

Species (ordered taxonomically)	Global status	Other EBAs (and SAs)	Altitude (m)	Habitat
Guadalupe Caracara *Polyborus lutosus*	EX (c.1900)	—	0–500	Open and semi-open country
Guadalupe Junco *Junco insularis*	CR	—	0–1,000	Pine, pine-oak and cypress forest, a few pairs in *Nicotiana* scrub

Global status (see p. 679 for definitions)	EX Extinct EW Extinct in the Wild	with year of last record	CR Critical EN Endangered VU Vulnerable	threatened species	cd Conservation Dependent nt Near Threatened lc Least Concern	DD Data Deficient NE Not Evaluated	

Other EBAs (and SAs) (see p. 60 for locations): bracketed numbers are Secondary Areas; [X] extinct in that EBA or SA.

Feral goats have rendered most of Guadalupe barren.

S. N. G. Howell and S. Webb

this subspecies in 1988: Howell and Webb 1992a), Bewick's Wren *Thryomanes bewickii brevicauda* and Rufous-sided Towhee *Pipilo erythrophthalmus consobrinus*. Of all the endemic subspecies, only the local Rock Wren *Salpinctes obsoletus guadeloupensis* survives in good numbers (Jehl and Everett 1985).

Junco insularis has been found during the twentieth century mostly in the remaining forest patches in the northern half of the island but, in 1988, a group of four or five were found in stands of tobacco *Nicotiana glauca* shrubs on the beach, suggesting some level of adaptability (Collar *et al.* 1992). There have been various population estimates put forward for the species, and altogether these indicate a steep decline and fewer than 100 individuals in the late 1980s (hence the species' threat classification as Critical).

The island also held the only known breeding colonies of the seabird, Guadalupe Storm-petrel *Oceanodroma macrodactyla*, which was discovered in 1885 and has not been sighted since 1912 (Collar *et al.* 1992). The little information collected on the species in this period suggests that its major nesting area was along the steep north-east ridge, where it made burrows in the soft soil under the pines and oaks (Jehl and Everett 1985). The main cause of the storm-petrel's demise was presumably heavy predation by cats, and the reduced availability of nesting areas through goats causing forest loss (Jehl 1972). There are very faint hopes that the species could still persist as, although searches for it have been carried out, a thorough survey of the entire island during the breeding season has not been made since 1906.

Removal of goats from the island is needed to help the vegetation regenerate and provide habitat for the birds, especially the junco (Collar *et al.* 1992). Nearly 35,000 goats were removed in 1970 and 1971, but current numbers are conservatively estimated at 10,000 individuals and unless they are completely eradicated the junco is doomed (P. Sweet *in litt.* 1996). This EBA is embraced entirely within the Isla Guadalupe Special Biosphere Reserve.

004 Socorro Island

PRIORITY CRITICAL

Key habitats Semi-deciduous forest, arid scrub

Main threats Major habitat loss (e.g. due to overgrazing by sheep), introduced species

Biological importance ● ● ●
Current threat level ● ● ●

Area 150 km²   **Altitude** 0–1,000 m
Countries Mexico

Restricted-range species	Threatened	Total
Confined to this EBA	2	3
Present also in other EBAs, SAs	0	0
Total	2	3

■ General characteristics

Socorro, politically part of Mexico, is the largest and most diverse of four volcanic oceanic islands that comprise the Revillagigedo Islands, each rising independently from the ocean floor (see also Secondary Area s008). The islands are located c.450 km south-south-west of Cabo San Lucas in Baja California, and 640 km west from the mainland state of Colima (Brattstrom 1990, Rodríguez-Estrella *et al.* 1996).

Socorro consists of one high central volcanic peak, Cerro Evermann (1,130 m), and has a mainly undulating landscape with small hills, but there are also steep slopes, dry canyons and flatter areas at mid-elevation. The natural vegetation of the west,

south and east sides of the island below 600 m consists predominantly of a thick mass of the shrub *Croton masoni* and the cactus *Opuntia engelmanni*. The north side of the island and all the higher elevations have semi-deciduous forest, including trees such as *Prunus capuli*, *Ficus continifolia*, *Guettarda insularis*, *Ilex socorrensis* and *Bumelia socorrensis*, and some bromeliads and orchids (Brattstrom and Howell 1956).

■ Restricted-range species

The nine native terrestrial landbirds are all endemic to Socorro, one (*Mimodes*) to genus level, three to species level, and five to subspecies. Of the four

Status and habitat of restricted-range species

Species (ordered taxonomically)	Global status	Other EBAs (and SAs)	Altitude (m)	Habitat
Socorro Dove *Zenaida graysoni*	EW (1972)	—	>500	Arid lowland scrub, semi-deciduous forest
Socorro Parakeet *Aratinga brevipes*[1]	VU	—	550–910	Semi-deciduous forest
Socorro Wren *Thryomanes sissonii*	nt	—	0–1,000	Arid lowland scrub, semi-deciduous forest
Socorro Mockingbird *Mimodes graysoni*	EN	—	300–900	Semi-deciduous forest, arid lowland scrub

Global status
(see p. 679 for definitions)

EX Extinct
EW Extinct in the Wild } with year of last record

CR Critical
EN Endangered } threatened species
VU Vulnerable

cd Conservation Dependent
nt Near Threatened
lc Least Concern
DD Data Deficient
NE Not Evaluated

Other EBAs (and SAs)
(see p. 60 for locations)

Bracketed numbers are Secondary Areas.
ˣ Extinct in that EBA or SA.

Notes
[1] Taxonomy follows Collar *et al.* (1992) and Howell and Webb (1995a).

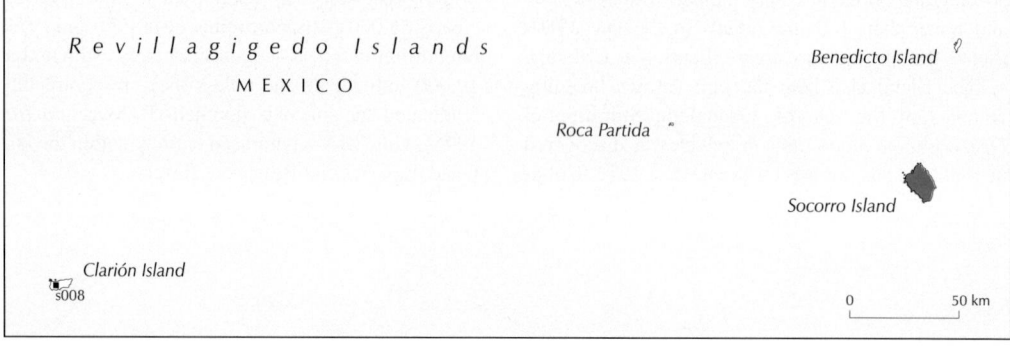

Revillagigedo Islands
MEXICO

Benedicto Island

Roca Partida

Socorro Island

Clarión Island
s008

0   50 km

restricted-range species, there are some differences in habitat and altitudinal requirements. *Aratinga brevipes* is found in the forests mostly above 550 m (Rodríguez-Estrella *et al.* 1992), whereas *Thryomanes sissonii* appears to prefer shrubby habitat at lower elevations. *Zenaida graysoni* was found all over the island when first discovered in 1867, but principally in the forests with a good understorey.

Interestingly, *Mimodes graysoni* was found by different ornithologists to be commoner in either the shrub or the forest habitats, suggesting that seasonal movements might take place. However, recent surveys have found it principally in forest and shrubby ravines at elevations above 600 m, appearing to prefer a relatively unbroken, shrubby ground cover and moderately dense trees for nesting (Castellanos and Rodríguez-Estrella 1993, Martínez-Gómez and Curry 1996).

A recent census estimated the population of Socorro Mockingbird *Mimodes graysoni* to be only c.350 individuals. Habitat destruction by sheep is thought to be the primary reason for its decline.

■ Threats and conservation

Socorro's flora and fauna have declined drastically owing to the introduction of sheep and cats. Sheep proliferated after their release in 1869 (Brattstrom 1990), and their overgrazing has caused accelerated erosion and has produced extensive savannas that were probably not present before their arrival. Trees are now absent over large parts of the southern end of the island (Martínez-Gómez and Curry 1996, Rodríguez-Estrella *et al.* 1996). Cats probably arrived on Socorro in the late 1950s after the establishment of a military base (Veitch 1989). Their

abundance and distribution are poorly understood but evidence of their presence has been found from areas at all altitudes on the island (Martínez-Gómez and Curry 1996).

Habitat destruction by sheep is thought to be the primary reason for the decline of *Mimodes graysoni*, which is currently the most threatened bird species on the island, with a provisional estimate of c.350 individuals (Martínez-Gómez and Curry 1996). Recent surveys found that the grassy areas on the south side of the island no longer support the species, and that forests which had overgrazed understoreys held no birds or far fewer than did areas less affected by sheep. However, the widespread Northern Mockingbird *Mimus polyglottos*, which became established on the island in 1978, favours these areas (Rodríguez-Estrella *et al.* 1996).

The arrival of the cats almost certainly caused the extinction of the tame and ground-nesting *Zenaida graysoni*, the last sighting being apparently in 1972 when several birds were shot (Velasco-Murgía 1982). However, c.200 individuals are kept in captivity (Collar *et al.* 1992), hence its status Extinct in the Wild.

Aratinga brevipes is also classified as threatened: a recent study indicated a population of only 400–500 birds although numbers appear to be stable (Rodríguez-Estrella *et al.* 1992).

Socorro is also the stronghold of the threatened seabird, Townsend's Shearwater *Puffinus auricularis* (classified as Vulnerable), endemic as a breeder to the Revillagigedo Islands. Its population was estimated to be 1,000 pairs in 1981, with feral cats now known to be causing substantial losses (Collar *et al.* 1992, R. L. Curry verbally 1994).

Socorro needs an immediate programme to eradicate sheep and cats (Santaella and Sada 1991, Castellanos and Rodríguez-Estrella 1993, Martínez-Gómez and Curry 1996, Rodríguez-Estrella *et al.* 1996) in order to avert the eventual extinctions of at least *Mimodes graysoni* and *Puffinus auricularis*, and to allow for the restocking of *Zenaida graysoni*. Encouragingly, the Revillagigedo Islands and surrounding waters were declared a Biosphere Reserve in 1994, indicating that the Mexican government acknowledges the great importance of these islands to biodiversity conservation.

005 North-west Mexican Pacific slope

PRIORITY HIGH

Key habitats Deciduous and semi-deciduous forest, thorn scrub

Main threats Moderate habitat loss (e.g. due to rising human population, agriculture)

Biological importance ●

Current threat level ●

Area 93,000 km²   **Altitude** 0–1,200 m

Countries Mexico

Restricted-range species	Threatened	Total
Confined to this EBA	1	6
Present also in other EBAs, SAs	0	1
Total	1	7

■ General characteristics

This EBA comprises the coastal plain in the north of Mexico from the mouth of the Colorado river (at the head of the Gulf of California), south through the states of Sonora, Sinaloa, Nayarit, Jalisco and Colima; it also includes the Tres Marías islands located some 150 km off the coast of Nayarit. The upper limit of the EBA is c.1,200 m and within these altitudes there is a variety of habitats, the main ones being tropical deciduous (dry) forest, thorn forest, thorn scrub,

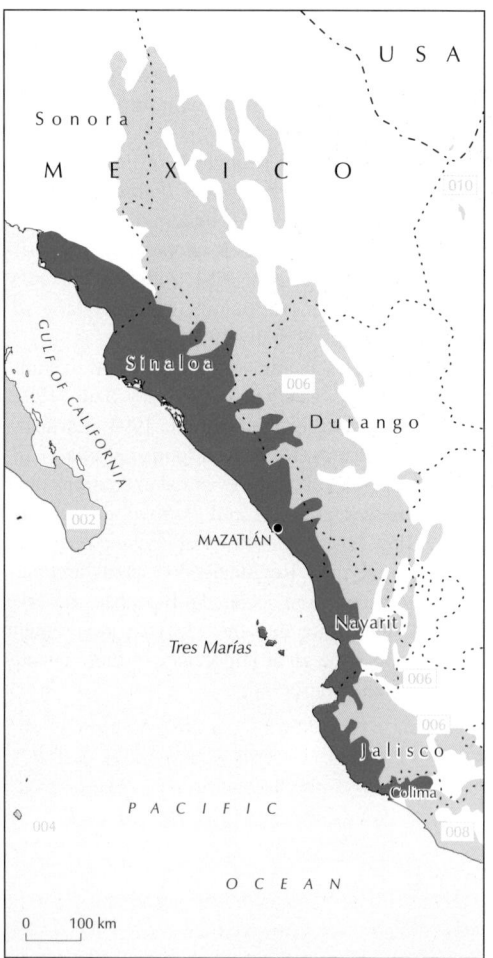

semi-humid subtropical forest and mangroves. Immediately inland of the EBA lies the Sierra Madre Occidental and trans-Mexican range (EBA 006), while the southern end abuts the western end of the Balsas region (EBA 008 in part).

■ Restricted-range species

Most of the EBA's restricted-range species occur throughout it, but there are some variations in this pattern. *Cyanocorax beecheii* and *C. sanblasianus* have nearly allopatric ranges with perhaps a small zone of overlap in the region of San Blas in central Nayarit. Indeed the southern part of the range of *C. sanblasianus* in Michoacán and Guerrero falls outside the boundaries of this EBA as none of the other species occurs this far south. Only *Forpus cyanopygius* and *Turdus graysoni* occur on the Tres Marías islands, and the status of *T. graysoni* on mainland Mexico is unclear as it has been recorded on the Nayarit coastal plain opposite the Tres Marías islands between December and June (Howell and Webb 1995a) but, apparently, not in other months.

There are few differences in the general habitat requirements of the species, as the majority are found in tropical deciduous forest. However, *Thalurania ridgwayi* prefers more humid forest than the other restricted-range species of the EBA, and so tends to occur in shaded barrancas within the foothills of the coastal plain which are patchily distributed within Nayarit, Jalisco and Colima states. Although described originally as a new species, it was treated as a subspecies of Crowned Woodnymph *T. colombica* until a revision of the taxa by Escalante-Pliego and Peterson (1992) showed that it was better treated as a distinct species.

■ Threats and conservation

The dry forests of western Mexico have largely been ignored as a key habitat for biodiversity conservation, with no comprehensive plan to conserve them (Ceballos and García 1995). Much of the coastal plain within this EBA is densely populated and consequently the dry forests in particular have been heavily degraded; many of the more humid forests in

Status and habitat of restricted-range species

Species (ordered taxonomically)	Global status	Other EBAs (and SAs)	Altitude (m)	Habitat
Rufous-bellied Chachalaca *Ortalis wagleri*	lc	—	0–1,000	Tropical dry deciduous thorn forest, semi-deciduous and secondary growth
Mexican Parrotlet *Forpus cyanopygius*	lc	—	0–1,400	Tropical deciduous, secondary and thorn forest, open country
Mexican Woodnymph *Thalurania ridgwayi*	VU	—	250–1,200	Humid forest, secondary and tropical deciduous forest, shaded coffee plantations
Grayson's Thrush *Turdus graysoni*	nt	—	0–600	Tropical deciduous forest, forest edge, and plantations
San Blas Jay *Cyanocorax sanblasianus*	lc	008	0–1,200	Tropical deciduous forest, mangrove, secondary growth
Purplish-backed Jay *Cyanocorax beecheii*	lc	—	0–600	Tropical deciduous forest, arid thorn scrub, mangrove
Sinaloa Crow *Corvus sinaloae*	lc	—	0–1,000	Tropical deciduous and secondary forest, pastures/ agricultural areas

Global status (see p. 679 for definitions)	EX Extinct EW Extinct in the Wild	} with year of last record	CR Critical EN Endangered VU Vulnerable	} threatened species	cd Conservation Dependent nt Near Threatened lc Least Concern	DD Data Deficient NE Not Evaluated

Other EBAs (and SAs) (see p. 60 for locations): bracketed numbers are Secondary Areas; ˣ extinct in that EBA or SA.

The Chamela–Cuixmala Biosphere Reserve was established in 1994 in recognition of the importance of these dry forests.

A. Challenger

the barrancas of the foothills have been turned over to coffee production.

Fortunately, most of the restricted-range species seem tolerant of degraded habitat and so only *Thalurania ridgwayi* is currently classified as threatened (Vulnerable). It is apparently locally common within its shaded barranca habitat, but it may well prove to be threatened by habitat destruction when its range and the causes of its patchy distribution are better understood (Collar *et al.* 1994).

Two widespread but threatened species also occur in this EBA: Yellow-headed Parrot *Amazona oratrix* (Endangered) occurs in the southern part of the EBA, with an important population (the endemic race *tresmariae*) on the Tres Marías islands; and

Black-capped Vireo *Vireo atricapillus* (Endangered) winters partly within this EBA.

There are few protected areas in the EBA, but encouragingly a new Biosphere Reserve, Chamela–Cuixmala (covering 131 km²), was decreed in 1994 to safeguard dry forests of western Mexico. There are three other large protected areas in the region, embracing mainly highland and humid forests: Cerro San Juan Special Biosphere Reserve, Nayarit (270 km²); Sierra de Manantlán Biosphere Reserve, Jalisco-Colima (1,396 km²); and Nevados de Colima, Jalisco–Colima (222 km²). The seven Key Areas for threatened birds identified by Wege and Long (1995) in this EBA cover the above protected areas and three other sites, including the Tres Marías islands.

006 Sierra Madre Occidental and trans-Mexican range

PRIORITY
CRITICAL

Key habitats Pine and pine–oak forest, montane evergreen forest, alpine grassland

Main threats Major habitat loss (e.g. due to logging for timber)

Biological importance ● ● ●
Current threat level ● ● ●

Area 230,000 km² **Altitude** 1,200–3,600 m

Countries Mexico

Restricted-range species	Threatened	Total
Confined to this EBA	3	5
Present also in other EBAs, SAs	0	2
Total	3	7

■ General characteristics

The Sierra Madre Occidental is the longest continuous mountain range in Mexico, passing north to south through the states of Sonora, Chihuahua, Sinaloa, Durango, Nayarit, Zacatecas, Jalisco and Michoacán. The trans-Mexican volcanic range, which also forms part of this EBA, runs from the southern end of the Sierra Madre Occidental eastwards along the southern edge of the Mexico plateau, from the states of Michoacán and Colima in the west to Puebla in the east; it has several of the highest peaks in Mexico, such as the volcanoes of Pico de Orizaba (5,650 m), Popacatapetl (5,450 m), and Ixtaccíhuatl (5,280 m).

The Sierra Madre Occidental and the western end of the trans-Mexican range, around Sierra de Manantlán and Nevados de Colima, lie adjacent to the North-west Mexican Pacific slope (EBA 005). The southern side of the trans-Mexican volcanic range lies alongside the Balsas region (EBA 008 in part), and at its eastern end abuts the Sierra Madre Oriental (EBA 012).

The EBA is characterized by temperate forests: with increasing altitude from 1,500 to 3,000 m these are of mature pine–oak, pine, and fir. The dominant species are mainly pine *Pinus* but also spruce *Abies*, firs *Pseudotsuga*, oaks *Quercus*, *Arbutus* and *Populus*. In humid canyons below 2,000 m the main

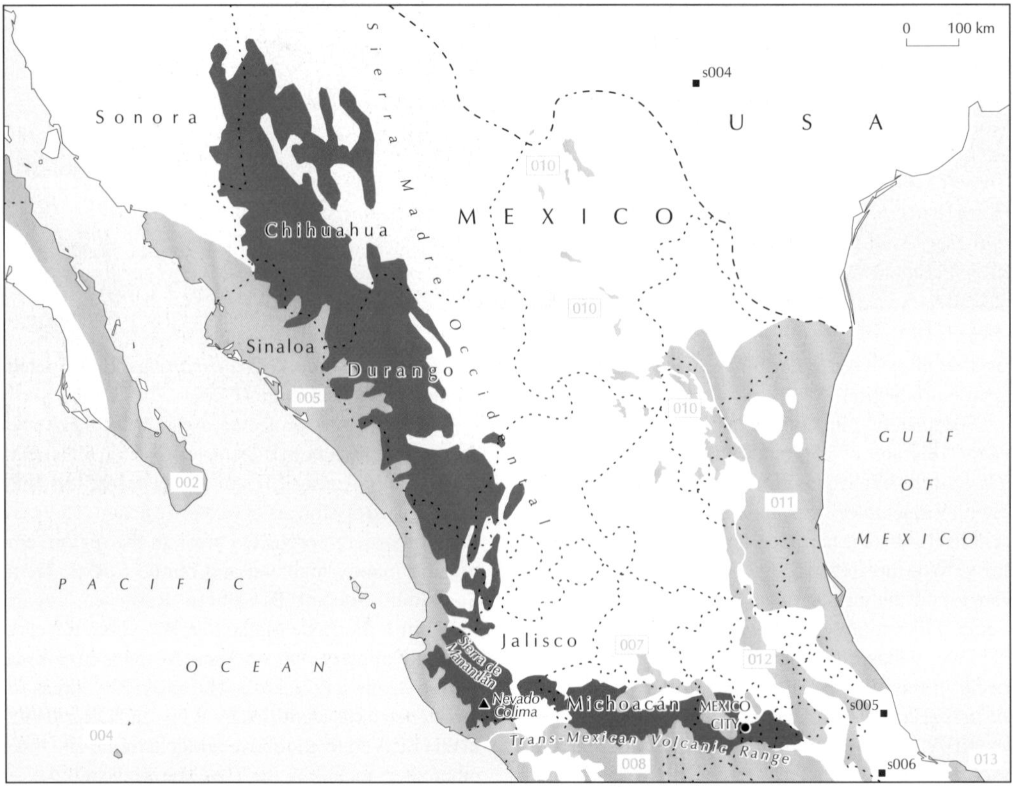

Status and habitat of restricted-range species

Species (ordered taxonomically)	Global status	Other EBAs (and SAs)	Altitude (m)	Habitat
Thick-billed Parrot *Rhynchopsitta pachyrhyncha*	EN	—	1,200–3,600	Mature pine and pine–oak forest
White-fronted Swift *Cypseloides storeri*	DD	009	1,500–2,500	Montane evergreen forest
Imperial Woodpecker *Campephilus imperialis*	CR	—	1,920–3,050	Mature pine forest with open grassy areas
Grey-barred Wren *Campylorhynchus megalopterus*	lc	012	2,100–3,000	Pine and pine–oak forest, forest edge
Sierra Madre Sparrow *Xenospiza baileyi*	EN	—	2,200–3,000	Bunch-grassland, usually near pine forest
Green-striped Brush-finch *Atlapetes virenticeps*	lc	—	1,800–3,500	Montane evergreen and pine–oak forest
Tufted Jay *Cyanocorax dickeyi*	nt	—	1,500–2,100	Montane evergreen and pine–oak forest

Global status (see p. 679 for definitions)	EX	Extinct	with year of last record	CR	Critical	threatened species	cd	Conservation Dependent	DD	Data Deficient
	EW	Extinct in the Wild		EN	Endangered		nt	Near Threatened	NE	Not Evaluated
				VU	Vulnerable		lc	Least Concern		

Other EBAs (and SAs) (see p. 60 for locations): bracketed numbers are Secondary Areas; ˣ extinct in that EBA or SA.

habitat is evergreen and semi-evergreen forest. There are also extensive areas of alpine tundra, consisting of bunch-grass (zacatón) near the higher volcanoes of the trans-Mexican range.

■ Restricted-range species

All the restricted-range species are forest birds, apart from *Xenospiza baileyi*, which favours marsh and bunch-grass, but is normally in areas with some pines. This species and *Atlapetes virenticeps* are found in both the Sierra Madre Occidental and the trans-Mexican range, whereas *Rhynchopsitta pachyrhyncha* (but see below), *Campephilus imperialis* and *Cyanocorax dickeyi* are mainly in the Sierra Madre Occidental, with *C. dickeyi* being especially restricted (canyon forests in western Durango only, though it is apparently common there). Within this EBA *Campylorhynchus megalopterus* is present only in the trans-Mexican range, though it is found also in the Oaxaca highlands (EBA 012). Little is known of the status of the recently described *Cypseloides storeri*, which has been recorded in this EBA only from a couple of records in Michoacán and Jalisco, and from the type-locality in the Sierra Madre del Sur of Guerrero (EBA 009).

Eared Quetzal *Euptilotis neoxenus* is not included as a restricted-range species—though, like *Rhynchopsitta pachyrhyncha* and *Campephilus imperialis*, it is confined to the Sierra Madre Occidental—because its habitat and altitudinal preferences are more varied than these species and it is therefore judged to have a range larger than 50,000 km². *Campephilus imperialis* shows the most precise preferences, being a specialist of old-growth pine forests (trees commonly 15–

Imperial Woodpecker *Campephilus imperialis*, once confined to this EBA, is now almost certainly extinct.

20 m to the lowest limb) with many dead branches, usually intermixed with grassy areas on flat mountain-tops, and with almost all records coming from 1,920–3,050 m (Collar *et al.* 1992). *Rhynchopsitta pachyrhyncha* prefers temperate conifer forests with abundant cones, but breeding has been confirmed

of south-east Arizona (Collar *et al.* 1992); the species makes irruptive movements, especially in winter, travelling (at least formerly) northwards to south-east Arizona and south-west New Mexico (USA) and south to Nayarit and the trans-Mexican range.

Much of the main wintering area of Colima Warbler *Vermivora crissalis* (an endemic breeder of the Sierra Madre Oriental, EBA 010) falls within the present EBA in the centre and west of the trans-Mexican range.

■ Threats and conservation

Several of the restricted-range species are threatened, due in part to the almost complete destruction of old-growth pine forest within the EBA. For example, old-growth clearance for timber and wood pulp threatens the survival of *Rhynchopsitta pachyrhyncha* by destroying food sources and nest-sites; because it is nomadic in response to variations in cone abundance, it requires substantial areas of pine in different, but adjacent, parts of its range if it is to be secure.

Lack of any extensive continuous tracts of old-growth forest has been the major cause of the now probable extinction of *Campephilus imperialis*, the largest woodpecker in the world (although it is officially classified as Critical). It was previously thought not to have been recorded with certainty since 1958 (Collar *et al.* 1992), but recent surveys have uncovered reliable reports of a pair in February 1993 and a lone individual as recently as March 1995 (Lammertink *et al.* 1996). However, the handful of remaining birds must be forced to wander over huge areas in the last remnants of their forest, and, with no

D. C. Wege

Imperial Woodpecker *Campephilus imperialis* was the largest woodpecker in the world. Here, specimens are compared with Pileated Woodpecker *Dryocopus pileatus* and Lineated Woodpecker *D. lineatus* (the sheet of paper is 29.5 cm long).

only in the northern half of the Sierra Madre Occidental (in Chihuahua and Durango states) though it may have once bred in the Chiracahua mountains

J. M. Lammertink

Tufted Jay *Cyanocorax dickeyi* is confined to the central portion of this EBA, being restricted to forest, often in canyons, on the Pacific slope. There is no formal protection of forest within the range of this species.

J. M. Lammertink

Thick-billed Parrot *Rhynchopsitta pachyrhyncha* is threatened by the removal of old-growth forest throughout the EBA. A number of priority sites for the conservation of this (and other restricted-range) species have recently been identified, but all need formal protection.

suitable breeding area to support a viable population, the species is effectively extinct (Lammertink 1996, Lammertink *et al.* 1996). These same surveys also found *Euptilotis neoxenus* (see 'Restricted-range species', above) in many new localities in Durango

and Nayarit, often within degraded, secondary pine forest, and the species is clearly not as threatened as was thought previously (e.g. Endangered in Collar *et al.* 1994).

Xenospiza baileyi has been seen in recent years only in a few localities near Mexico City in the trans-Mexican range. However, at only one of these sites, El Capulín–La Cima, is it regularly recorded, and there have been problems with burning and cattle-grazing of its bunch-grass habitat there (Collar *et al.* 1992). The species has not been seen in the Sierra Madre Occidental part of the EBA since 1951, in spite of searches in 1994 in the Sierra Huicholes near to Bolaños (Lammertink and Rojas Tomé 1995), one of only a handful of historical localities for the species from the Sierra Madre Occidental.

There are a number of protected areas in the trans-Mexican range, but, apart from La Michilía Biosphere Reserve (350 km^2) in south-east Durango, there are no protected areas within the Sierra Madre Occidental, and therefore *Rhynchopsitta pachyrhyncha* and *Cyanocorax dickeyi* remain unprotected. Lammertink *et al.* (1996) identified three old-growth forests which are priority areas for conservation: El Carricito del Huichol, northern Jalisco (149 km^2); Las Bufas, central-west Durango (147–206 km^2); Sierra Tabsco–Río Bavispe, northern Sonora (512 km^2). They also conclude that besides these three sites where complete protection is needed, there are zones of regenerating forest which are important for breeding *R. pachyrhyncha*, and in which a total ban on the exploitation of dead trees is urgently required: Mesa las Guacamayas, northern Chihuahua (29 km^2); Cebadilla–Yahuirachic, central Chihuahua (351 km^2); and Cócono–Ciénaga de la Vaca, north-west Durango (1,521 km^2).

007 Central Mexican marshes

PRIORITY
URGENT

Key habitats Lake and river marshes

Main threats Severe habitat loss (e.g. due to drainage, water extraction)

Biological importance ● ○ ○
Current threat level ● ● ○

Area 10,000 km² **Altitude** 1,700–2,500 m

Countries Mexico

Restricted-range species	Threatened	Total
Confined to this EBA	1	1
Present also in other EBAs, SAs	0	0
Total	1	1

■ General characteristics

This EBA consists of a small number of lake and river marshes, mainly in the Lerma drainage, in the Mexican states of Guanajuato, Michoacán and México. The river drainage falls within the southern end of the Mexican plateau and also in the zone where the plateau merges with the trans-Mexican volcanic range, thus overlapping with the Sierra Madre Occidental and trans-Mexican range (EBA 006), whose restricted-range species are, however, confined primarily to forest habitats.

Around the lake shores and river marshes the habitat comprises cattails and other reedy vegetation, mainly *Typha* and *Scirpus*, and to a lesser extent *Heleocharis* and *Cyperus*, all of which form dense stands often more than 2 m tall.

■ Restricted-range species

This area is designated an EBA because it has one extant and one extinct restricted-range species, both marsh birds. *Quiscalus palustris* was last recorded in 1910 (Dickerman 1965), and was a resident endemic in marshes at the headwaters of the Lerma river, around Mexico City. Little is known of the species,

but it is thought to have been a colonial breeder, nesting in reedbeds (Hardy 1965).

A subspecies of Yellow Rail *Coturnicops noveboracensis goldmani* is also endemic to the marshes of the Lerma valley. It prefers sedge marshes in ungrazed areas with vegetation less than 0.5 m tall (Hardy and Dickerman 1965). This race may, however, be extinct as it has not been sighted since 1964, but it is skulking and hard to see unless flushed by chance.

■ Threats and conservation

The marshes of this EBA have been greatly reduced in size, most having been drained and planted with crops. Water extraction is an additional threat to both lakes and marshes, with the headwaters of the Lerma now supplying México City and Toluca. Thus the water level of the large lakes in the north and west of the EBA (Yuriria, Pátzcuaro and Cuitzeo) in Guanajuato and Michoacán states is falling and affecting the marsh-edge and cattail habitat. The situation is exacerbated because these lakes are old, and are becoming shallower through natural build-up of organic material. The destruction of the marshes is

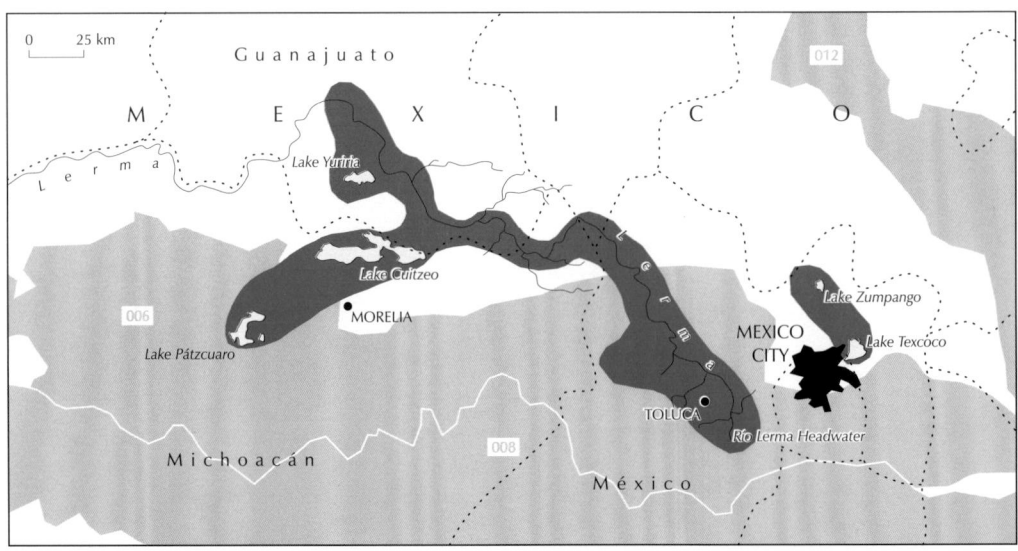

Status and habitat of restricted-range species

Species (ordered taxonomically)	Global status	Other EBAs (and SAs)	Altitude (m)	Habitat
Black-polled Yellowthroat *Geothlypis speciosa*	VU	—	1,750–2,500	Freshwater upland marshes
Slender-billed Grackle *Quiscalus palustris*	EX (1910)	—	c.2,000	Freshwater upland marshes

Global status (see p. 679 for definitions)	EX Extinct EW Extinct in the Wild } with year of last record	CR Critical EN Endangered } threatened species VU Vulnerable	cd Conservation Dependent nt Near Threatened lc Least Concern	DD Data Deficient NE Not Evaluated

Other EBAs (and SAs) (see p. 60 for locations): bracketed numbers are Secondary Areas; ˣ extinct in that EBA or SA.

the most likely reason for the demise of *Quiscalus palustris*, and for the threatened status of *Geothlypis speciosa*.

Four Key Areas have been identified by Wege and Long (1995) for the protection of *G. speciosa*: the three lakes listed above and the region of the upper Lerma around Lerma da Villada, San Mateo Atenco and San Pedro Techuchuco. The best populations of the species appear to be at Lago Cuitzeo, where it is apparently quite abundant (in the 1980s,

three times as numerous as Common Yellowthroat *G. trichas*), and on the upper Lerma, where it has been described as fairly common. However, the population has not been censused in either area in the 1990s, and the marsh habitat probably continues to decline. Drainage in the upper Lerma has left the marshes highly fragmented, and the effect of this on yellowthroat populations is unknown. There are no protected areas within this EBA, and no conservation measures for the yellowthroat are known.

008 Balsas region and interior Oaxaca

PRIORITY HIGH

Key habitats Dry forest, arid scrub, cactus desert

Main threats Moderate habitat loss (e.g. due to agricultural intensification)

Biological importance ● ●
Current threat level ●

Area 110,000 km²   **Altitude** 0–2,500 m

Countries Mexico

Restricted-range species	Threatened	Total
Confined to this EBA	0	9
Present also in other EBAs, SAs	0	1
Total	0	10

■ General characteristics

The catchment area of the Balsas river delimits this Mexican EBA and for this purpose extends from Colima state in the west to interior Oaxaca in the east, and to Puebla and Morelos states in the north. The trans-Mexican volcanic range (EBA 006 in part) lies adjacent to the northern boundary of this EBA, and the interior slopes of the Sierra Madre del Sur of Guerrero and the Sierras de Yucuyacua and Mia-huatlán in Oaxaca (EBA 009) abut its southern boundary. The altitude varies from sea-level (though most of the EBA is above c.300 m) up to 2,500 m (especially on some of the mountain slopes in the interior of Oaxaca state).

There is a marked dry season of five to eight months in this region, and low annual average rainfall (Rzedowski 1978). The vegetation is consequently dominated by tropical dry deciduous forest, especially at lower altitudes. These dry forests have been noted for their high levels of regional and local endemism in a wide range of taxa, especially cacti (Dinerstein et al. 1995). Other habitats include arid scrub and, at higher altitudes, especially in the interior of Oaxaca, arid oak scrub.

■ Restricted-range species

All of the restricted-range bird species occur in the dry deciduous and arid scrub habitats, but there are some clear differences in their distributions: *Philortyx fasciatus* and *Aimophila humeralis* are confined to the western and central parts of the Balsas drainage and do not occur in Oaxaca; conversely, *A. notosticta*

Distribution patterns of restricted-range species

Species (ordered geographically)	SW Jalisco, Colima	E Michoacán, W Guerrero	E Guerrero, S Puebla	Oaxaca state
Philortyx fasciatus	●	●	●	–
Melanerpes hypopolius	●	●	●	–
Cynanthus sordidus	–	●	●	●
Xenotriccus mexicanus	–	●	●	●
Aimophila humeralis	–	●	●	●
Calothorax pulcher	–	–	●	●
Pipilo albicollis	–	–	●	●
Aimophila notosticta	–	–	●	●
Aimophila mystacalis	–	–	●	●
Campylorhynchus jocosus	–	–	●	●
Total	2	5	10	8

● Present   ? Present?   Threatened spp.   ⎫ see 'Status
○ Extinct?   R Reintroduced   shown in **bold**   ⎬ and habitat'
X Extinct   I Introduced   Other EBAs, SAs   ⎭ table

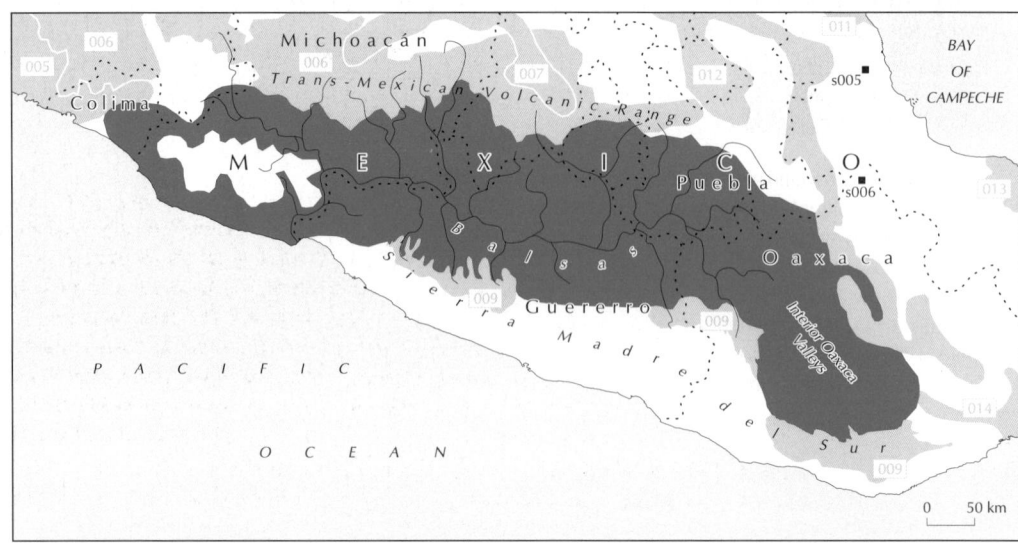

Status and habitat of restricted-range species

Species (ordered taxonomically)	Global status	Other EBAs (and SAs)	Altitude (m)	Habitat
Banded Quail *Philortyx fasciatus*	lc	—	0–1,500	Arid lowland, arid montane and second-growth scrub, tropical deciduous forest, thorn forest
Dusky Hummingbird *Cynanthus sordidus*	lc	—	900–2,200	Arid montane scrub, gallery forest, secondary growth
Beautiful Hummingbird *Calothorax pulcher*	lc	—	1,000–2,200	Arid montane scrub
Grey-breasted Woodpecker *Melanerpes hypopolius*	lc	—	900–1,800	Arid montane scrub, gallery forest, cactus desert
Pileated Flycatcher *Xenotriccus mexicanus*	nt	—	900–2,000	Arid montane scrub, mesquite within arid scrub
Bridled Sparrow *Aimophila mystacalis*	lc	—	900–1,800	Arid montane scrub, thorn forest, cactus scrub
Black-chested Sparrow *Aimophila humeralis*	lc	—	300–1,500	Arid lowland and arid montane scrub
Oaxaca Sparrow *Aimophila notosticta*	nt	—	c.1,850	Arid montane and oak scrub
White-throated Towhee *Pipilo albicollis*	lc	—	1,000–2,500	Arid montane and oak scrub, arid pine–oak forest
San Blas Jay *Cyanocorax sanblasianus*	lc	005	0–1,200	Tropical deciduous forest, mangrove, secondary growth

Global status (see p. 679 for definitions)	EX Extinct EW Extinct in the Wild	} with year of last record	CR Critical EN Endangered VU Vulnerable	} threatened species	cd Conservation Dependent nt Near Threatened lc Least Concern	DD Data Deficient NE Not Evaluated

Other EBAs (and SAs) (see p. 60 for locations): bracketed numbers are Secondary Areas; ˣ extinct in that EBA or SA.

Tehuacan valley, in Puebla state, is renowned for its high levels of plant diversity and endemism.

and *A. mysticalis* are found mainly in interior Oaxaca.

Another possible addition to this EBA is Balsas Screech-owl *Otus seductus*, confined to the western and central Balsas region. It was listed as a species by Sibley and Monroe (1990), but was later treated as a subspecies of the widespread Western Screech-owl *O. kennicottii* (Sibley and Monroe 1993). Most of the ranges of Slaty Vireo *Vireo brevipennis* and Dwarf Vireo *V. nelsoni* are confined to this EBA, but neither is treated as a restricted-range species because each is judged to breed over an area greater than 50,000 km².

■ Threats and conservation

The largest remaining dry forests north of the equator, of which this EBA holds a significant amount, are found in western Mexico (Ceballos and García 1995). Most have been affected by human activity; this EBA is no exception, with agricultural expansion, intensive cultivation for export crops, conversion for cattle-ranching, coffee and citrus plantations posing threats to wildlife (Dinerstein *et al.* 1995). There are very few protected areas within the EBA, but none of the restricted-range species is currently considered threatened as all of them are fairly common in their appropriate habitats (Howell and Webb 1995a).

009 Sierra Madre del Sur

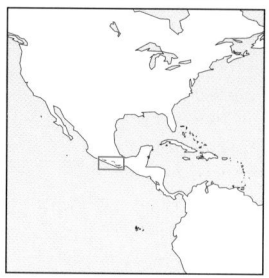

Key habitats Montane forest, cloud forest, lower montane forest

Main threats Major habitat loss (e.g. due to agricultural expansion, timber extraction)

Biological importance ● ● ●
Current threat level ● ● ●

Area 12,000 km² **Altitude** 900–3,500 m

Countries Mexico

Restricted-range species	Threatened	Total
Confined to this EBA	4	4
Present also in other EBAs, SAs	0	1
Total	4	5

■ General characteristics

Several mountain ranges in southern Oaxaca and southern Guerrero states of Mexico together form the Sierra Madre del Sur. The isolated Sierra de Miahuatlán in southern Oaxaca is the easternmost part of the Sierra Madre del Sur. To the west and further inland the Sierra de Yucuyacua straddles the Oaxaca and Guerrero state boundaries. The Sierra de Atoyac continues through Guerrero to the Balsas valley, which marks the western limits of the EBA. Inland and on the lower Gulf slopes of these mountain ranges lie the arid lands of the Balsas region and interior Oaxaca (EBA 008).

The principal habitats of the EBA are various types of humid montane and lower montane forests. The dominant vegetation is lower montane (semi-deciduous) forest from 600 to 1,400 m, humid montane and cloud forest on the wettest slopes between 1,400 and 2,500 m, pine–oak forest at 2,500–3,000 m, and fir forest at altitudes above 3,000 m (Navarro 1992). On drier exposed slopes the vegetation is more arid, with oak scrub predominant. The montane forest found partly within this EBA represents some of the world's most diverse and complex subtropical mixed hardwood–conifer forests (WWF/IUCN 1997).

■ Restricted-range species

The restricted-range birds are found mainly in humid montane forest consisting of many evergreen tree species, especially oaks, with variable amounts of pine at higher altitudes. Because the altitudinal ranges of particular forest types vary according to the local topography and climate, the restricted-range species appear to show quite wide altitudinal preferences.

Lophornis brachylopha is still known from only a single 25-km stretch of the Atoyac–Paraíso–Puerto el Gallo road in the Sierra de Atoyac (north-west of Acapulco), and is likely to be confined to the Sierra Madre del Sur within Guerrero. The species has been found to be common only seasonally, which suggests that it may undergo altitudinal movements to an unknown area and habitat. The Sierra de Atoyac is also the type-locality of the recently described *Cypseloides storeri* (Navarro *et al.* 1992), which has subsequently been recorded also in Michoacán and Jalisco in the trans-Mexican range (EBA 006 in part); little information is available on this bird, and its status as a resident within the Sierra Madre del Sur is unknown.

Of the remaining restricted-range birds, the two *Eupherusa* species are allopatric, *E. poliocerca* be-

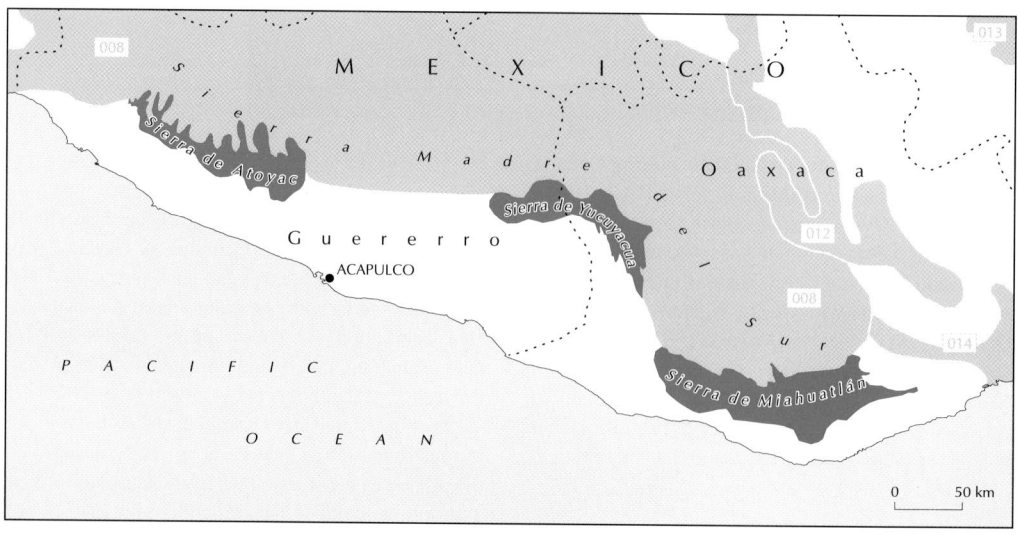

Status and habitat of restricted-range species

Species (ordered taxonomically)	Global status	Other EBAs (and SAs)	Altitude (m)	Habitat
White-fronted Swift *Cypseloides storeri*	DD	006	1,500–2,500	Montane evergreen forest
Short-crested Coquette *Lophornis brachylopha*	EN	—	900–1,800	Semi-deciduous and montane evergreen forest, forest edge
White-tailed Hummingbird *Eupherusa poliocerca*	EN	—	915–2,440	Montane evergreen, semi-deciduous forest, tropical deciduous forest and forest edge
Oaxaca Hummingbird *Eupherusa cyanophrys*	EN	—	1,300–2,500	Montane evergreen, semi-deciduous and tropical deciduous forest, forest edge
White-throated Jay *Cyanolyca mirabilis*	EN	—	1,525–3,500	Humid pine–oak and montane evergreen forest

Global status (see p. 679 for definitions)   EX   Extinct   EW   Extinct in the Wild } with year of last record   CR   Critical   EN   Endangered   VU   Vulnerable } threatened species   cd   Conservation Dependent   nt   Near Threatened   lc   Least Concern   DD   Data Deficient   NE   Not Evaluated

Other EBAs (and SAs) (see p. 60 for locations): bracketed numbers are Secondary Areas; ˣ extinct in that EBA or SA.

ing confined to the Sierras de Atoyac and Yucuyacua, *E. cyanophrys* to the Sierra de Miahuatlán. *Cyanolyca mirabilis* is the only restricted-range species to be found in all three sierras.

■ Threats and conservation

Many of the forests of these mountains are being cleared for large-scale agricultural expansion or for timber, and it has been suggested that all are in danger of complete destruction (Navarro 1992). The lower montane forest is being cleared for corn, fruit (notably citrus fruits in the Sierra de Miahuatlán: Dinerstein *et al.* 1995) and coffee; the cloud forests below 1,800 m are being destroyed for coffee plantations; and the pine, oak and fir forests are being cut

for lumber (Navarro 1992). With habitat destruction continuing rapidly, all four of the restricted-range species confined to this EBA are considered to be highly threatened.

There is just one protected area within this EBA, Omiltemi State Ecological Park (96 km²) lying in the Sierra de Atoyac c.20 km west of Chilpancingo in Guerrero; it supports populations of *Eupherusa poliocerca* and *Cyanolyca mirabilis* (ICBP 1992, Navarro and Escalante Pliego 1993). The other two threatened species remain unprotected, and at least two new protected areas need to be created in the Sierras de Atoyac and Miahuatlán to support these birds in reserves.

010 Northern Sierra Madre Oriental

PRIORITY
HIGH

Key habitats Mixed coniferous forest, thorn scrub

Main threats Moderate habitat loss (e.g. due to fire, logging, agriculture)

Biological importance ● ● ●
Current threat level ● ● ●

Area 15,000 km² **Altitude** 1,500–3,500 m

Countries Mexico, USA

Restricted-range species	Threatened	Total
Confined to this EBA	1	2
Present also in other EBAs, SAs	0	0
Total	1	2

■ General characteristics

This highland EBA extends from the Chisos mountains of southern Texas in USA, south-eastwards along the north-east edge of the arid central-northern Mexican plateau in Coahuila state to the northern part of the Sierra Madre Oriental in Nuevo León and Tamaulipas states. To the east lies the extensive coastal plain of the North-east Mexican Gulf slope (EBA 011), while the southern end of the EBA marks the beginning of the Southern Sierra Madre Oriental (EBA 012).

The lowest altitude of the Sierra Madre Oriental EBA marks the upper limit of desert scrub, which predominates on the Mexican plateau to the west. The main vegetation types in the EBA between 1,800 and 2,500 m are oak scrub, pine–*Yucca*–juniper scrub, or pine–oak–*Arbutus* forest, and above this altitude coniferous forest with firs *Abies* and several *Pinus* species. In degraded areas, scrub ('chapparal') is the main habitat covering the slopes.

■ Restricted-range species

The EBA's two restricted-range species overlap in the northern part of the Sierra Madre Oriental, which encompasses the entire range of *Rhynchopsitta terrisi*. The breeding range of *Vermivora crissalis* extends the EBA further north. Lanning *et al.* (1990) showed that *V. crissalis* was present in most areas of open pine–oak forest where the average height of the trees reached 8 m and where there was a good understorey

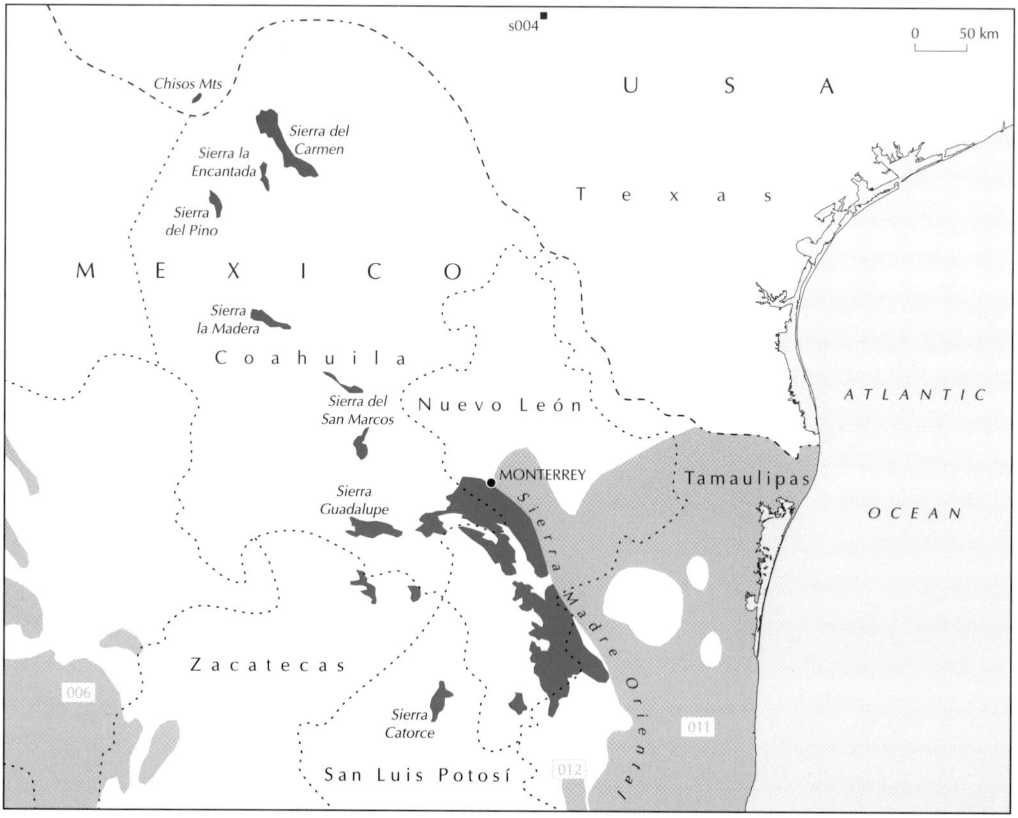

s004

0   50 km

U   S   A

Chisos Mts

Sierra del
Carmen

Sierra la
Encantada

Sierra
del Pino

T e x a s

M   E   X   I   C   O

Sierra
la Madera

C o a h u i l a

Sierra del
San Marcos

N u e v o   L e ó n

ATLANTIC

MONTERREY

Sierra
Guadalupe

Tamaulipas

OCEAN

Z a c a t e c a s

Sierra
Madre
Oriental

006

011

Sierra
Catorce

S a n   L u i s   P o t o s í

012

Status and habitat of restricted-range species

Species (ordered taxonomically)	Global status	Other EBAs (and SAs)	Altitude (m)	Habitat
Maroon-fronted Parrot *Rhynchopsitta terrisi*	VU	—	1,500–3,500	Mixed conifer forest, pine and pine–oak forest
Colima Warbler *Vermivora crissalis*	nt	—	1,500–2,500	Pine–oak forest and chaparral with well-developed shrub understorey

Global status (see p. 679 for definitions)	EX Extinct EW Extinct in the Wild	} with year of last record	CR Critical EN Endangered VU Vulnerable	} threatened species	cd Conservation Dependent nt Near Threatened lc Least Concern	DD Data Deficient NE Not Evaluated

Other EBAs (and SAs) (see p. 60 for locations): bracketed numbers are Secondary Areas; ˣ extinct in that EBA or SA.

The forests around Monterrey are now part of a local initiative to safeguard them from logging.

of shrubs and ground vegetation. The species winters out of the EBA principally in oak–conifer forests of central Mexico (EBA 012) and humid to semi-humid montane forests of the Pacific slope of western Mexico (EBAs 005, 006) (Lanning *et al.* 1990, Howell and Webb 1995a).

The prime habitat of *Rhynchopsitta terrisi* is mixed conifer forest, mostly at higher elevations although, interestingly, the species nests exclusively in holes in limestone cliffs, there being few trees of sufficient size to offer nest-holes.

■ Threats and conservation

The mixed-conifer forests of this EBA are being destroyed by fire, logging and clearance for agriculture. This habitat destruction is the reason for *Rhynchopsitta terrisi*, which has a relatively circumscribed range, being judged to be threatened. The largest single observation since 1978, and perhaps ever, was made in October 1994 when 1,480 birds were seen (E. Enkerlin *in litt.* 1995). A significant portion of the southern half of this EBA, and indeed the range of *R. terrisi*, is covered by the Cumbres de Monterrey National Park (2,465 km²), which em-

braces the highland pine forests near Monterrey City. The national park is one of the largest designated protected areas in Mexico, but unfortunately is poorly administered. A working group is investigating how to give effective protection to the park, and an initial proposal includes reducing its size to c.1,500 km² in order to focus on the area of highest conservation value (E. Enkerlin *in litt.* 1995). Another promising conservation initiative for the parrot is the creation of the El Taray Sanctuary (3.6 km²) to protect the largest-known nesting cliff of the species—holding c.100 pairs which is roughly a quarter of the total breeding population currently known (Snyder and Enkerlin 1996, *World Birdwatch* 1996, 18: 4).

The northern part of the EBA from the Chisos mountains to western Coahuila state encompasses the southern end of the breeding range of Black-capped Vireo *Vireo atricapillus* (classified as Endangered). This species has suffered a substantial contraction of its US breeding range owing to habitat loss and near-total nest-parasitism by Brown-headed Cowbird *Molothrus ater*, although numbers in Coahuila (in this EBA) remain disputed (Collar *et al.* 1992, Collar *et al.* 1994).

011 North-east Mexican Gulf slope

PRIORITY
URGENT

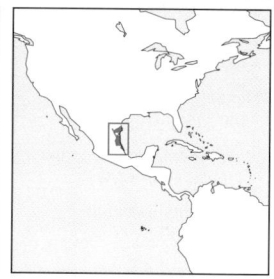

Key habitats Deciduous forest, wetlands

Main threats Major habitat loss (e.g. due to cattle-ranching)

Biological importance ● ○ ○
Current threat level ● ● ○

Area 100,000 km² **Altitude** 0–1,200 m

Countries Mexico

Restricted-range species	Threatened	Total
Confined to this EBA	1	4
Present also in other EBAs, SAs	0	0
Total	1	4

■ General characteristics

This EBA embraces the Gulf of Mexico coastal plain of north-east Mexico in the states of Tamaulipas and northern Veracruz, and adjacent Nuevo León and San Luis Potosí; the plain is widest in the north and narrows markedly southwards. The landward boundaries of the EBA are the Bravo river to the north, the edge of the foothills of the Mexican plateau and the Northern Sierra Madre Oriental (EBA 010) to the west, and the Southern Sierra Madre Oriental (EBA 012) to the south.

There is a wide variety of vegetation types in this EBA, but tropical deciduous forest and scrub predominates, with semi-evergreen forest in humid canyons, and extensive coastal lagoons.

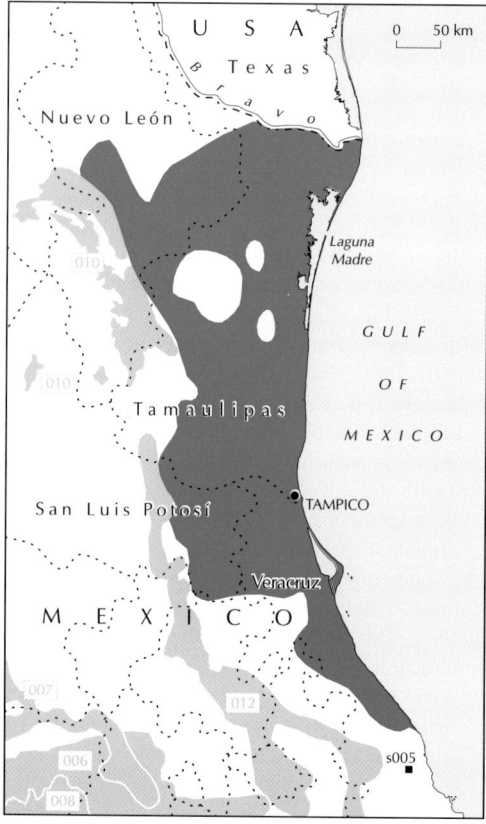

■ Restricted-range species

All four restricted-range species of the EBA are confined to it. *Geothlypis flavovelata* is restricted to freshwater marshes and reedbeds, but the other three occupy a variety of mainly forest habitats though they occur widely also in open country and agricultural land.

■ Threats and conservation

The natural habitats present within this EBA have been heavily modified in this now largely agricultural region where cattle-ranching is the predominant activity. Extensive areas of deciduous and semi-deciduous forest have become rare, and are mainly confined to the foothills on the western side of the EBA.

All of the restricted-range species appear to be able to persist in degraded lands. However, *Amazona viridigenalis* is considered threatened because it has gone from being a common and widespread species a few decades ago to being a generally rare bird today. The reason for this decline is a combination of extensive habitat loss and overexploitation for the cage-bird trade. The current wild population is judged to be 3,000–6,500 birds, and illegal trade continues, with no adequate protection of its habitat (E. C. Enkerlin *in litt.* 1994).

Part of the range of the Atlantic lowland race *magna* of the widespread Yellow-headed Amazon *Amazona oratrix* (classified as Endangered) is found within this EBA. The species, which is the most popular and sought-after amazon in trade, co-occurs with *A. viridigenalis* at four sites listed by Wege and Long (1995) as Key Areas for the protection of threatened species: Los Colorados Ranch (8 km²), a privately owned ranch of southern Tamaulipas, where, although 80–85% of the land is cleared for cattle pasture, many large trees remain and both threatened *Amazona* species breed, with more than 100 nests found there during a recently completed five-year study (Enkerlin 1995); Soto La Marina/La Pesca, lying at sea-level in eastern Tamaulipas, holding small but stable populations of both the threatened *Amazona*; Río el Naranjo, centred on Las Abritas

Status and habitat of restricted-range species

Species (ordered taxonomically)	Global status	Other EBAs (and SAs)	Altitude (m)	Habitat
Green-cheeked Amazon *Amazona viridigenalis* [1]	EN	—	0–1,000	Tropical deciduous/semi-deciduous forest and forest edge, semi-open country with scattered trees
Crimson-collared Grosbeak *Rhodothraupis celaeno*	lc	—	0–1,200	Tropical deciduous and gallery forest, secondary growth
Altamira Yellowthroat *Geothlypis flavovelata*	nt	—	0–500	Freshwater marshes, reedbeds
Tamaulipas Crow *Corvus imparatus*	lc	—	0–800	Tropical deciduous and secondary forest, pastures/agricultural areas

Global status (see p. 679 for definitions)
EX Extinct ⎫
EW Extinct in the Wild ⎬ with year of last record
CR Critical ⎫
EN Endangered ⎬ threatened species
VU Vulnerable ⎭

cd Conservation Dependent
nt Near Threatened
lc Least Concern
DD Data Deficient
NE Not Evaluated

Other EBAs (and SAs) (see p. 60 for locations)
Bracketed numbers are Secondary Areas.
ˣ Extinct in that EBA or SA.

Notes
[1] Introduced to Puerto Rico (EBA 029).

village in north-central San Luis Potosí, consisting mainly of humid oak–sweetgum forest, where *A. viridigenalis* nests but *A. oratrix* is probably only an uncommon resident; and the El Cielo Biosphere Reserve (1,445 km²), centred on the Rancho Rinconada and the Río Frío districts, and located on the lower Atlantic slopes of southern Tamaulipas.

The latter reserve holds one of the most extensive tracts of pristine deciduous and semi-deciduous forest, as well as montane forest at higher altitudes. Both threatened *Amazona* occur, as well as the widespread Military Macaw *Ara militaris* (Vulnerable), as do the other restricted-range species inhabiting woodlands.

012 Southern Sierra Madre Oriental

PRIORITY
CRITICAL

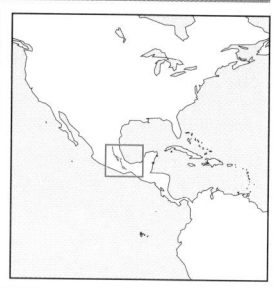

Key habitats Montane forest, pine–oak forest

Main threats Major habitat loss (e.g. due to logging, agricultural expansion)

Biological importance ● ○ ○
Current threat level ● ● ●

Area 31,000 km² **Altitude** 900–3,500 m

Countries Mexico

Restricted-range species	Threatened	Total
Confined to this EBA	2	3
Present also in other EBAs, SAs	0	1
Total	2	4

■ General characteristics

This EBA includes a number of mountain ranges of eastern Mexico, principally within the Sierra Madre Oriental and the Sierra Madre de Oaxaca. The northern end of the EBA begins in the Sierra Madre Oriental from southern Tamaulipas and eastern San Luis Potosí southwards through Hidalgo, Puebla and Veracruz states. South from there it runs through Oaxaca state (where the many sierras such as Juárez, Aloapaneca and Zempoaltepec are often referred to as the Sierra Madre de Oaxaca) in a north-west to south-east direction until it ends near the Isthmus of Tehuantepec in eastern Oaxaca. The northern end of the EBA lies south of the extreme southern end of the

Northern Sierra Madre Oriental (EBA 010) and the upper limits of the North-east Mexican Gulf slope (EBA 011). In Puebla and Veracruz the topography is very complicated and it is there that the EBA lies next to the eastern end of the trans-Mexican range (EBA 006 in part).

The predominant habitats of this EBA are pine and pine–oak forest, with humid evergreen montane forest (including cloud forest) in the wettest parts of the EBA. The Sierra de Oaxaca appears to have high levels of plant endemism especially in the evergreen montane forests such as the Sierra de Juárez in north Oaxaca (Lorence and Mendoza 1989).

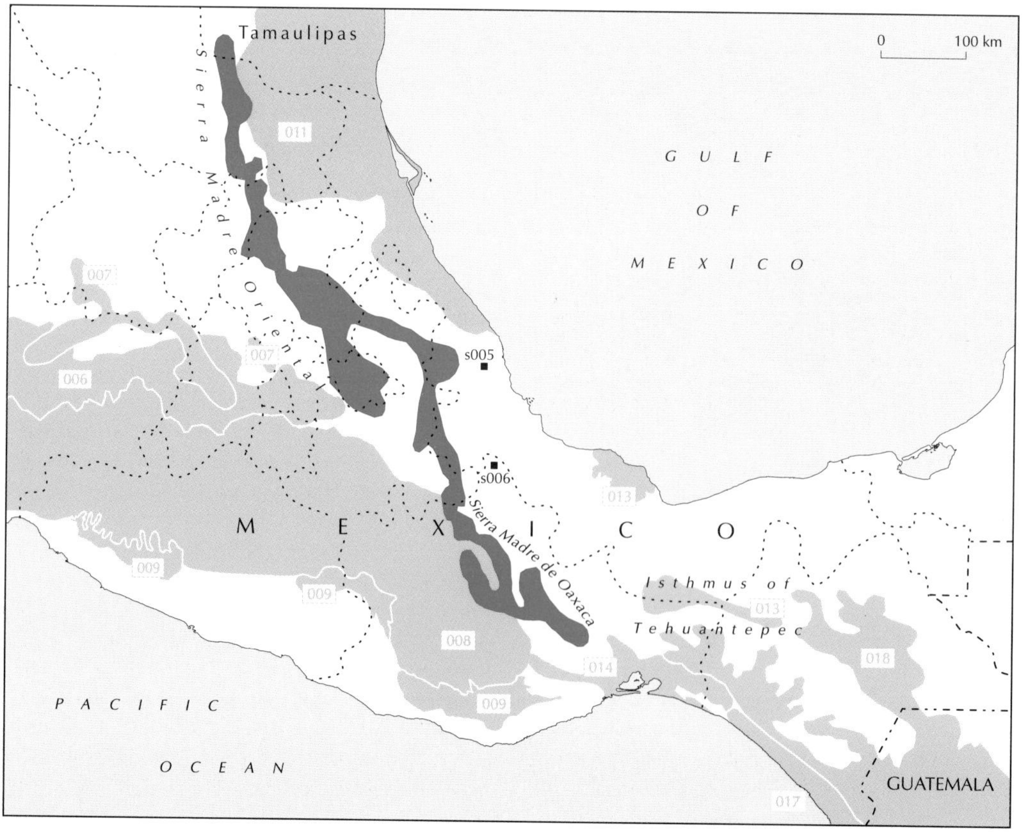

Status and habitat of restricted-range species

Species (ordered taxonomically)	Global status	Other EBAs (and SAs)	Altitude (m)	Habitat
Bearded Wood-partridge *Dendrortyx barbatus*	CR	—	1,220–2,135	Montane evergreen and pine–oak forest
Grey-barred Wren *Campylorhynchus megalopterus*	lc	006	2,100–3,000	Pine and pine–oak forest, forest edge
Dwarf Jay *Cyanolyca nana*	EN	—	2,000–3,500	Pine–oak, pine and montane evergreen forest
Tamaulipas Pygmy-owl *Glaucidium sanchezi* [1]	NE	—	900–2,100	Subtropical, humid evergreen (inc. pine–evergreen and montane evergreen) and semi-deciduous forest

Global status (see p. 679 for definitions)				
EX	Extinct	with year of last record	cd	Conservation Dependent
EW	Extinct in the Wild		nt	Near Threatened
CR	Critical	threatened species	lc	Least Concern
EN	Endangered		DD	Data Deficient
VU	Vulnerable		NE	Not Evaluated

Other EBAs (and SAs) (see p. 60 for locations) Bracketed numbers are Secondary Areas. [x] Extinct in that EBA or SA.

Notes [1] Taxonomy follows Howell and Robbins (1995).

■ Restricted-range species

All of the restricted-range birds are forest species, with humid montane forest being a particularly important habitat, though there are some marked distributional differences between the species. *Glaucidium sanchezi* is currently known only from the forests of southern Tamaulipas and eastern San Luis Potosí at the northern end of the EBA, but it has been suggested that it should be looked for in intervening areas between there and central Veracruz (Howell and Robbins 1995, Howell and Webb 1995a).

Bearded Wood-partridge *Dendrortyx barbatus* is currently known from just a couple of sites in the central portion of this EBA where, due to the widespread destruction of montane forest, it is considered critically threatened.

Dendrortyx barbatus overlaps with *G. sanchezi* in eastern San Luis Potosí (e.g. Cerro San Antonio) and with the other species in Puebla and Veracruz, which marks the northern part of the range of *Cyanolyca nana*, a bird also found in Sierras Aloapaneca and Zempoaltepec in Oaxaca. *Campylorhynchus megalo-*

pterus is found in the mountains of western Veracruz and Oaxaca but is also present in the trans-Mexican range (EBA 006).

Glaucidium sanchezi was traditionally considered a subspecies of Least Pygmy-owl *G. minutissimum* until a recent taxonomic review based on plumage, morphology and vocalizations recommended the complex be split into six species (Howell and Robbins 1995), and this course is followed here.

■ Threats and conservation

The majority of the forests of this EBA have already been lost or degraded, and today this destruction continues through logging, agricultural expansion, firewood-gathering, road and associated tourist developments, sheep-ranching and overgrazing, as well as intensive urbanization (Dinerstein *et al.* 1995).

This habitat destruction is the main reason for the threatened status of *Dendrortyx barbatus* and *Cyanolyca nana*. Several Key Areas for these birds have been identified by Wege and Long (1995), but they have not been recorded at most sites for more than 20 years, being known with certainty to occur in only a couple. Cerro San Felipe in the Sierra Aloapaneca is the only current site for *C. nana*, in spite of many bird surveys in parts of its former range (A. T. Peterson *in litt.* 1995). Coatepec in Veracruz (Gómez de Silva and Aguilar Rodríguez 1994), and Tlanchinol in Hidalgo (Howell and Webb 1992b) are the only two localities where *D. barbatus* has been seen in the past 10 years.

There are some protected areas within the EBA, but notably few in the Oaxacan part, a region which holds some of the most diverse and extensive of Mexico's remaining montane forests. Encouragingly, this gap is now recognized, and initiatives to create a protected area in the Cuasimulco area of the Sierra de Juárez are under way (e.g. Salas *et al.* 1994).

013 Los Tuxtlas and Uxpanapa

PRIORITY
CRITICAL

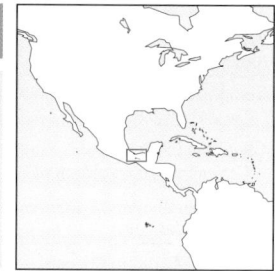

Key habitats Lowland and montane evergreen forest

Main threats Major habitat loss (e.g. due to logging, agricultural expansion)

Biological importance ● ● ●
Current threat level ● ● ●

Area 14,000 km²   **Altitude** 0–1,500 m

Countries Mexico

Restricted-range species	Threatened	Total
Confined to this EBA	2	3
Present also in other EBAs, SAs	0	0
Total	2	3

■ General characteristics

The Sierra Los Tuxtlas are mountains located near the coast of the Gulf of Mexico in the Mexican state of Veracruz. It is an area of intense volcanic activity with many peaks, including Volcán San Martín Tuxtla at 1,700 m and Volcán Santa Marta at 1,650 m (Dirzo and García 1992). From Sierra Los Tuxtlas, the EBA probably spreads south-east into the Gulf slope of the Isthmus of Tehuantepec in the Uxpanapa region of extreme eastern Veracruz and eastern Oaxaca, and in the El Ocote region of western Chiapas.

The principal habitat of the EBA is tropical rain forest, which is at its northern limits for eastern Mexico. The forest can be divided into lower montane and montane types, especially on the slopes of Volcán San Martín Tuxtla and Volcán Santa Marta (Andrle 1967). In the lowlands of Uxpanapa and El Ocote there are distinct zones of tropical rain forest found on limestone karst, a prominent characteristic of these areas being large rocky outcrops in other-

Pasture for cattle dominates the lowlands of southern Veracruz around Volcán Santa Marta.

wise flat terrain. The EBA encompasses two areas (notably the Uxpanapa region) of the three in eastern Mexico which receive unusually high rainfall and which have pronounced levels of plant endemism

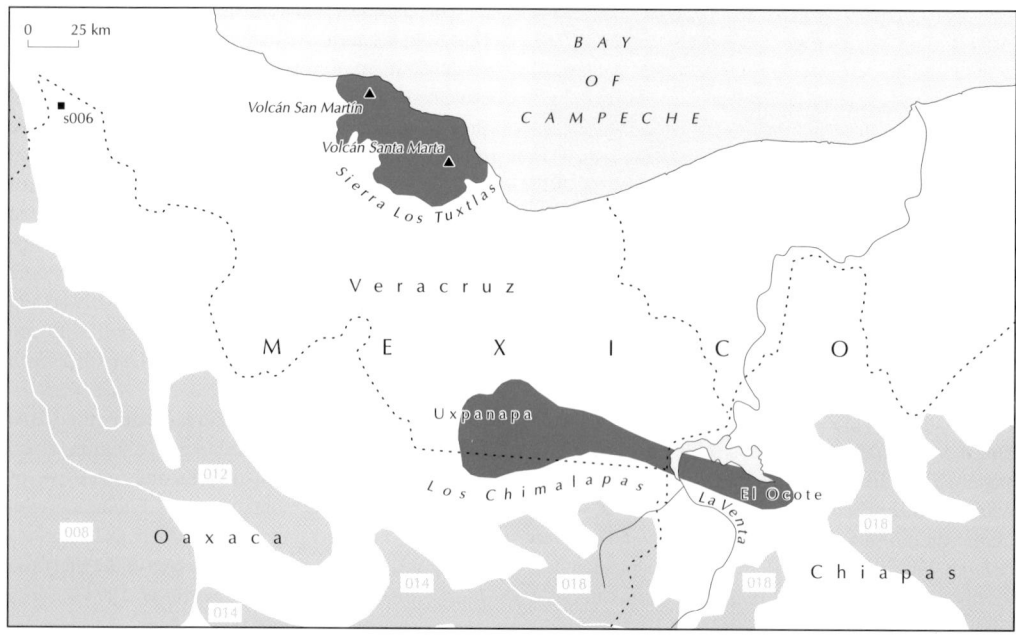

Status and habitat of restricted-range species

Species (ordered taxonomically)	Global status	Other EBAs (and SAs)	Altitude (m)	Habitat
Veracruz Quail-dove *Geotrygon carrikeri*[1]	EN	—	350–1,500	Tropical lowland evergreen and montane evergreen forest
Long-tailed Sabrewing *Campylopterus excellens*	nt	—	0–1,200	Tropical lowland evergreen and montane evergreen forest, forest edge, plantations
Nava's Wren *Hylorchilus navai*[2]	VU	—	75–800	Limestone outcrops in primary lowland evergreen forest

Global status (see p. 679 for definitions)	EX Extinct EW Extinct in the Wild	with year of last record	cd Conservation Dependent	Other EBAs (and SAs) (see p. 60 for locations)	Bracketed numbers are Secondary Areas. [X] Extinct in that EBA or SA.
	CR Critical EN Endangered VU Vulnerable	threatened species	nt Near Threatened lc Least Concern DD Data Deficient NE Not Evaluated	Notes	[1] Taxonomy follows Peterson (1993). [2] Taxonomy follows Atkinson *et al.* (1993).

and species diversity (Wendt 1993, WWF/IUCN 1997).

■ Restricted-range species

This region has been identified as an EBA since the previous analysis (ICBP 1992) owing to the recent recognition of *Geotrygon carrikeri* and *Hylorchilus navai* as full species. *G. carrikeri* was previously regarded as a well-marked and isolated subspecies of the widespread Purplish-backed Quail-dove *G. lawrenci* of Costa Rica and Panama, but its larger size, paler plumage and possibly different calls and egg colour, as well as the fact that its breeding range lies more than 1,500 km from that of the nominate form, together indicate that it is better treated as a species (Peterson 1993, Howell and Webb 1995a). It is confined to the Los Tuxtlas region, occurring on both of the main volcanoes. *H. navai* was originally described as a subspecies of Sumichrast's Wren *H. sumichrasti* (see Atkinson *et al.* 1993 and Secondary Area s006). It was poorly known until the 1980s when populations were found in the northern part of the Uxpanapa region, mainly in the Coatzacoalcos drainage of eastern Veracruz, in neighbouring Oaxaca and in western Chiapas along the La Venta canyon (Collar *et al.* 1992, Whittingham and Atkinson 1996). Its range lies within the forests on karst limestone outcrops in the central zone of the Isthmus of Tehuantepec.

Campylopterus excellens is probably found throughout the EBA (i.e. in the intervening lowland area between Sierra Los Tuxtlas and the Uxpanapa and El Ocote regions), but most records are from the Sierra Los Tuxtlas with a few in the Uxpanapa region and just one from western Chiapas in the El Ocote region (Howell and Webb 1995a). The bird is, however, very similar to the widespread Wedge-tailed Sabrewing *C. curvipennis* (with which it is often

considered conspecific), and so may well be overlooked. In Sierra Los Tuxtlas it is a fairly common member of the understorey avifauna, also occurring there in degraded habitats such as forest edge and overgrown orchards (Winker *et al.* 1992).

■ Threats and conservation

The EBA has suffered from extensive deforestation especially in Veracruz. A recent study estimated that 86% of the original forest area of Volcán San Martín in the Sierra Los Tuxtlas had been lost by 1986 (Dirzo and García 1992). Flatter areas on the karst limestone areas are being cleared, mainly for cattle-grazing and agriculture, leaving isolated forest fragments on the main rock outcrops. Much forest within the immediate range of *Hylorchilus navai* has presumably been destroyed by the creation of a reservoir, Lake Malpaso, in western Chiapas. Both *Geotrygon carrikeri* and *H. navai* are considered threatened owing to the large-scale habitat destruction in the region.

In spite of the serious habitat loss which has occurred within the EBA there do exist a number of protected areas which give some security to the region's remaining forests, including Santa Marta Biosphere Reserve (546 km²) and Los Tuxtlas Biological Station (6 km²), the latter the best-studied forest site in Mexico (Dirzo and García 1992). Additionally, La Venta river in western Chiapas, where *Hylorchilus navai* has been recorded, lies within the El Ocote Ecological Reserve (c.480 km²). In the Uxpanapa area, the Los Chimalapas–Uxpanapa Biosphere Reserve has been proposed (8,000 km²), covering a relatively undisturbed transect through lowland rain forest in Uxpanapa to extensive montane forest in the Chimalapas mountains to the south (Wendt 1993).

014 Isthmus of Tehuantepec

PRIORITY HIGH

Key habitats Dry forest, arid scrub

Main threat Moderate habitat loss (e.g. due to road-building)

Biological importance ● ○ ○
Current threat level ● ○ ○

Area 6,700 km² **Altitude** 0–1,000 m

Countries Mexico

Restricted-range species	Threatened	Total
Confined to this EBA	0	2
Present also in other EBAs, SAs	0	1
Total	0	3

■ General characteristics

The Isthmus de Tehuantepec is the part of southern Mexico in the states of eastern Veracruz, eastern Oaxaca and south-west Chiapas where the continental landmass constricts to its minimum width, the distance between the Pacific and Atlantic Oceans being only 210 km. This EBA covers the Pacific Ocean/Gulf of Tehuantepec side of the isthmus in south-east Oaxaca and south-west Chiapas, including the coastal plain (the Plains of Tehuantepec) and the low-lying hills and isolated peaks to 1,000 m altitude.

The western boundary of the EBA is marked by the basin of the Tehuantepec river, and the eastern end lies along the coastal plain near Tonala, which also marks the northern end of the North Central American Pacific slope (EBA 017). The landward northern boundary of the EBA falls along the Sierra

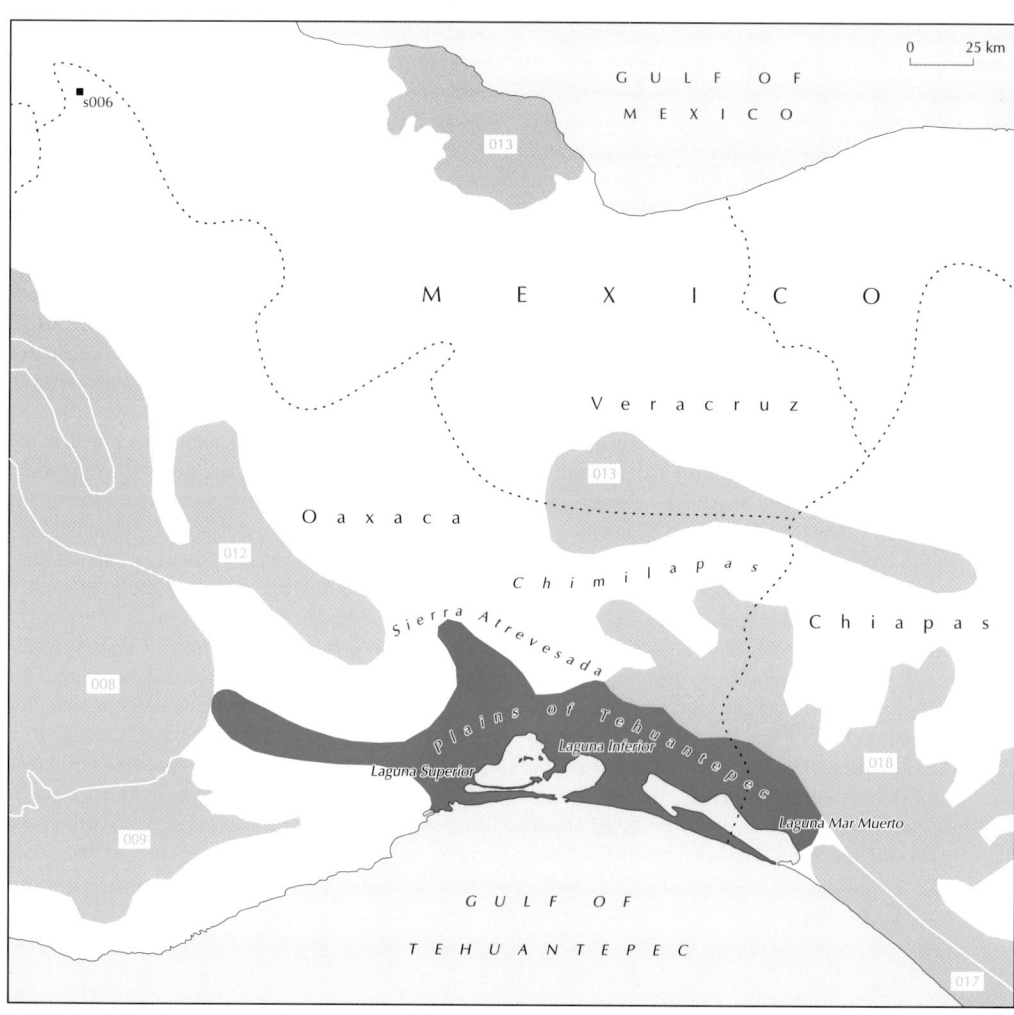

Status and habitat of restricted-range species

Species (ordered taxonomically)	Global status	Other EBAs (and SAs)	Altitude (m)	Habitat
Pacific Parakeet *Aratinga strenua*	lc	017	0–1,500	Tropical deciduous, gallery, pine–oak and secondary forest, arid scrub
Cinnamon-tailed Sparrow *Aimophila sumichrasti*	nt	—	0–900	Arid lowland scrub, edge of and openings within tropical deciduous forest
Rose-bellied Bunting *Passerina rositae*	nt	—	150–800	Tropical deciduous forest, semi-deciduous gallery forest, arid scrub

Global status (see p. 679 for definitions)	EX Extinct EW Extinct in the Wild ⎱with year ⎰of last ⎱record	CR Critical EN Endangered VU Vulnerable ⎱threatened ⎰species	cd Conservation Dependent nt Near Threatened lc Least Concern	DD Data Deficient NE Not Evaluated

Other EBAs (and SAs) (see p. 60 for locations): bracketed numbers are Secondary Areas; ˣ extinct in that EBA or SA.

Atrevesada, a small, low-lying range stretching for 50 km, and the Sierra Madre de Chiapas, which is the western end of the North Central American highlands (EBA 018). The southern coastal side falls alongside several large coastal lagoons, including Lagunas Superior, Inferior and Mar Muerto.

The main habitats in the coastal plain of this EBA are deciduous forest, semi-deciduous gallery forest and arid scrub, in the foothills also arid pine–oak forest.

■ Restricted-range species

Two of this EBA's three restricted-range bird species are confined to it, while *Aratinga strenua* occurs also further south in Central America (EBA 017). *A. strenua* is very closely related to the widespread Green Parakeet *A. holochlora*, and Binford (1989) prefers to treat them as conspecific because there are two specimens known with measurements intermediate between the two taxa.

The habitat requirements of *Aratinga strenua* and *Aimophila sumichrasti* are quite similar, both species preferring open areas in tropical deciduous forest and arid tropical scrub from sea-level to 1,000 m. *Passerina rositae* inhabits the riparian forest and denser portions of tropical deciduous forest, mainly from 200 to 500 m elevation (Binford 1989).

■ Threats and conservation

The Pan-American Highway runs through the entire length of the EBA. Consequently the dry forests are quite fragmented and many of them are degraded or secondary. However, none of the restricted-range species is currently considered threatened, as, although *Passerina rositae* and *Aimophila sumichrasti* clearly have very small ranges, both are considered to be common in their appropriate habitats, including areas altered by man (Binford 1989, Howell and Webb 1995a).

The Chiapan part of the EBA is almost entirely covered by La Sepultura Biosphere Reserve, which was designated by presidential decree as recently as 1995. It comprises five core areas totalling 138 km² and a buffer area of 1,536 km² (A. Flamenco *in litt.* 1995).

015 Yucatán peninsula coastal scrub

PRIORITY
HIGH

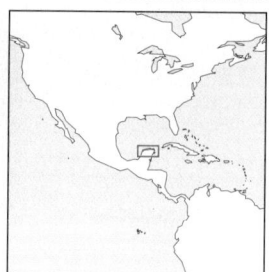

| Key habitats | Coastal dune scrub | Area 3,400 km² | Altitude 0–300 m |

Key habitats Coastal dune scrub

Main threats Major habitat loss (e.g. due to coconut plantations, tourist development)

Biological importance ● ● ●
Current threat level ● ● ●

Area 3,400 km² **Altitude** 0–300 m

Countries Mexico

Restricted-range species	Threatened	Total
Confined to this EBA	0	1
Present also in other EBAs, SAs	0	1
Total	0	2

■ General characteristics

The large peninsula of Yucatán juts northwards into the Gulf of Mexico and Caribbean Sea. Being a flat, sedimentary, limestone, shallow-soiled shelf, it is geologically and topographically distinct from adjacent mainland Central America, which is formed mainly along a core of mountains, igneous in origin. This EBA comprises only a small, narrow coastal strip of the northern end of the peninsula mainly in the Mexican states of Yucatán and Quintana Roo, but also extreme north-west Campeche.

The habitat of the EBA is coastal dune scrub (often termed 'thorn forest') on a calcareous sand bar, which is usually separated from the limestone bedrock of the mainland by mangrove swamps, lagoons or sawgrass savanna. Typically the dune scrub varies in width from 70 to 2,000 m and the landward lagoons and swamps can be up to 3 km wide (Ornat and Lynch 1990). The area is coincident with the lowest rainfall in the Yucatán peninsula, being 450 mm per year (Ornat *et al.* 1989). According to Standley (1930), 17% of the peninsula's flora

Status and habitat of restricted-range species

Species (ordered taxonomically)	Global status	Other EBAs (and SAs)	Altitude (m)	Habitat
Mexican Sheartail *Doricha eliza*	lc	(s005)	0–300	Coastal dune scrub
Yucatán Wren *Campylorhynchus yucatanicus*	lc	—	Sea-level	Coastal dune scrub

Global status (see p. 679 for definitions)	EX	Extinct	} with year of last record	**CR**	Critical	} threatened species	**cd**	Conservation Dependent	**DD**	Data Deficient
	EW	Extinct in the Wild		**EN**	Endangered		**nt**	Near Threatened	**NE**	Not Evaluated
				VU	Vulnerable		**lc**	Least Concern		

Other EBAs (and SAs) (see p. 60 for locations): bracketed numbers are Secondary Areas; ˣ extinct in that EBA or SA.

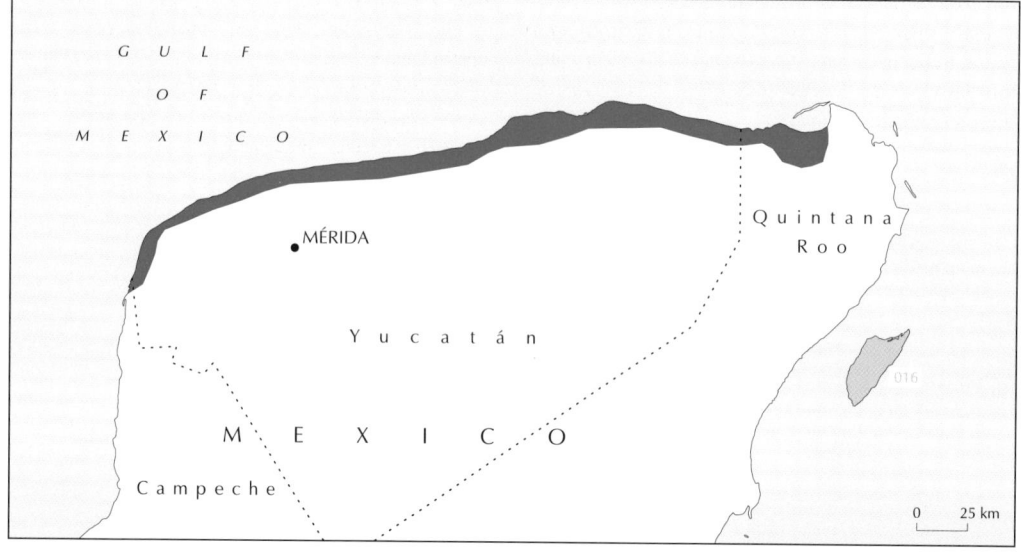

This idyllic beach scene (at Río Lagartos), with coconut palms fringing the coastal dune scrub, is not typical everywhere on the coast of the Yucatán because of development for tourism.

D. C. Wege

is endemic, and its northern portion (relating at least in part to this EBA) has been noted as the area with the most pronounced levels of endemism (Rzedowski and Calderón de Rzedowski 1989).

■ Restricted-range species

The two restricted-range bird species of the EBA share broadly similar ranges and habitats. *Doricha eliza* has a wider distribution, occurring along the north Yucatán coast east as far as north-east Quintana Roo, whereas *Campylorhynchus yucatanicus* does not reach Quintana Roo. Interestingly, there is also a small and disjunct population of *D. eliza* in Central Veracruz state near Veracruz City (s005; see map p. 112). Both species are resident and considered common to fairly common (Howell and Webb 1995a).

The Yucatán peninsula as a whole has nearly 20 bird species which are endemic to it, and in the original EBA analysis presented in ICBP (1992) much of the peninsula was included as an EBA. Most of these Yucatán peninsula endemics have now been found to occupy ranges larger than 50,000 km^2 and this EBA is one of two smaller EBAs resulting from the rationalization, the other being Cozumel (EBA 016).

■ Threats and conservation

Ornat and Lynch (1990) report that over the past century perhaps half of the original extent of the coastal dune scrub habitat of the peninsula has been destroyed or severely degraded by commercial cultivation of coconut palms or through development for tourism. However, they note that the northern part, which refers to this EBA, has suffered less from tourist development than has the Quintana Roo coast, and sizeable areas of native scrub still remain. Additionally, there are abandoned coconut plantations, now with regenerating vegetation, which support the bird species of the area (Ornat and Lynch 1990). For these reasons neither *D. eliza* or *C. yucatanicus* are currently considered as threatened.

Extensive portions of this EBA are included within two special Biosphere Reserves. Celustún (591 km^2) is located in north-west Campeche and adjacent north-west Yucatán, while Río Lagartos (478 km^2) lies principally along the north Yucatán coast. Both areas were designated to protect the nesting sites of Greater Flamingo *Phoenicopterus ruber* and waterbird feeding areas, but also support extensive areas of the coastal dune scrub important for the restricted-range species.

016 Cozumel Island

PRIORITY
URGENT

Key habitats Dry forest, mangroves

Main threats Moderate habitat loss (e.g. due to tourist development)

Biological importance ● ● ●
Current threat level ● ○ ○

Area 490 km² **Altitude** 0–100 m

Countries Mexico

Restricted-range species	Threatened	Total
Confined to this EBA	0	3
Present also in other EBAs, SAs	0	1
Total	0	4

■ General characteristics

The coralline limestone island of Cozumel is located in the Caribbean c.18 km off the north-east coast of Mexico's Yucatán peninsula. Although close to the mainland, the island is separated from it by waters c.1,000 m deep (the Canal de Cozumel), and so is usually classified as being oceanic (Martínez-Morales 1996), though not in this study.

Cozumel has a warm, humid climate and the main vegetation is coastal mangrove forest (which covers c.7% of the land surface, especially in the north and south), tropical deciduous forest (c.13% of the area, mainly occurring immediately inland of the mangrove and littoral zone) and tropical semi-deciduous forest (c.60%, principally in the centre of the island). Vegetation of the semi-deciduous forest is 8–20 m tall, and includes few epiphytes and vines; the de-

ciduous forest is up to 8–12 m high; the mangroves, in which the main tree species include *Rhizophora mangle, Laguncularia racemosa, Conocarpus erectus* and *Avicennia germinans*, reach 10 m tall (Téllez-Valdés *et al.* 1989).

Cozumel lies within the area in Mexico most frequently hit by hurricanes, and altogether 20 struck the island between 1971 and 1995 (Martínez-Morales 1996).

■ Restricted-range species

The restricted-range birds are found in all the island's forest types, as well as forest edge and secondary scrub habitats, but *Vireo bairdi* and *V. magister* occur more commonly in the mangroves and coastal tropical deciduous forest than do the other species.

Cozumel is only a small part of the range of *V. magister*, which is found mainly along the east Yucatán coast of Mexico and Belize, including small islands and cays, and on the Honduras Bay Islands (Secondary Area s014).

There is one specimen of *Chlorostilbon forficatus* from Isla Mujeres, 60 km north of Cozumel, suggesting that it may be a rare visitor there. It was formerly considered a subspecies of the widespread Fork-tailed Hummingbird *C. canivetii* until Howell (1993) revised the taxonomy of that species-complex for north Central America; his treatment of *forficatus* as a full species has been generally accepted (e.g. AOU 1995b, Stiles 1996, C. G. Sibley *in litt.* 1996).

As well as its three endemic bird species, Cozumel has 15 endemic subspecies, including Cozumel Curassow *Crax rubra griscomi*, and a form of the House Wren *Troglodytes aedon beani* which is possibly better treated as a full species (e.g. Howell and Webb 1995a).

■ Threats and conservation

Relatively undisturbed areas of forest still remain on Cozumel, although mangroves and tropical deciduous forest have been affected by coastal developments for the burgeoning tourist industry. The last major hurricane in 1988 probably adversely affected numbers of some of the bird species and subspecies

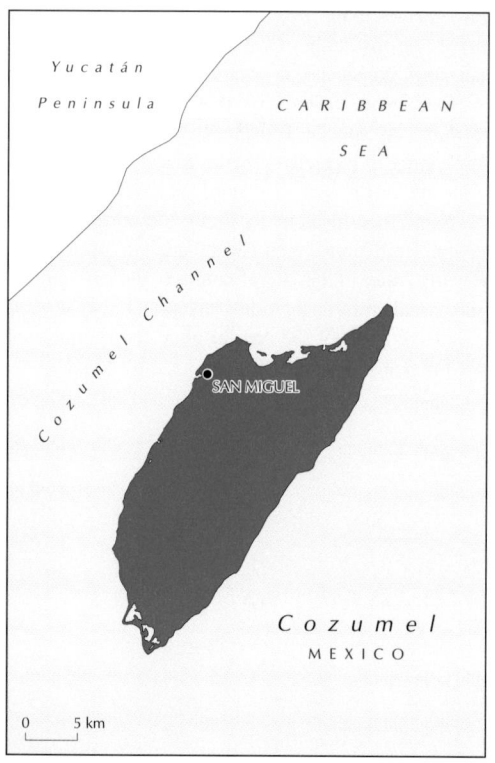

Yucatán Peninsula

CARIBBEAN SEA

Cozumel Channel

SAN MIGUEL

Cozumel

MEXICO

0   5 km

Status and habitat of restricted-range species

Species (ordered taxonomically)	Global status	Other EBAs (and SAs)	Habitat
Cozumel Emerald *Chlorostilbon forficatus*[1]	lc	—	Tropical deciduous forest, semi-deciduous forest, secondary forest
Cozumel Thrasher *Toxostoma guttatum*	nt	—	Tropical deciduous and semi-deciduous forest edge
Cozumel Vireo secondary forest *Vireo bairdi*	lc	—	Mangroves, tropical deciduous forest, semi-deciduous forest,
Yucatán Vireo *Vireo magister*	lc	(s007,s014)	Mangroves, tropical deciduous forest, secondary growth

Global status (see p. 679 for definitions)						Other EBAs (and SAs) (see p. 60 for locations) Notes
	EX	Extinct	with year of last record	cd	Conservation Dependent	Bracketed numbers are Secondary Areas.
	EW	Extinct in the Wild		nt	Near Threatened	ˣ Extinct in that EBA or SA.
	CR	Critical	threatened species	lc	Least Concern	[1] Taxonomy follows Howell (1993).
	EN	Endangered		DD	Data Deficient	
	VU	Vulnerable		NE	Not Evaluated	

Mangroves on Cozumel have been reduced owing to coastal development for tourism, but extensive areas remain in the south.

as they were found to be unobtrusive in the years that followed, e.g. *Toxostoma guttatum*.

Cozumel Curassow *Crax rubra griscomi* was assessed as Critical in 1994 by Strahl *et al.* (1994).

Recent studies on this cracid have confirmed its continued existence, and the estimated population has been put in the low hundreds (Martínez-Morales 1996).

017 North Central American Pacific slope PRIORITY HIGH

Key habitats Dry forest, scrub

Main threats Major habitat loss (e.g. due to agriculture, cattle-ranching)

Biological importance ● ● ●
Current threat level ● ● ●

Area 30,000 km^2 Altitude 0–1,000 m
Countries El Salvador, Guatemala, Honduras, Mexico, Nicaragua

Restricted-range species	Threatened	Total
Confined to this EBA	0	3
Present also in other EBAs, SAs	0	1
Total	0	4

■ General characteristics

The narrow strip of the Pacific coastal plain and adjoining foothills of Chiapas state (Mexico), Guatemala, El Salvador, southern Honduras and north-west Nicaragua form this EBA, on the Pacific slope of the Sierra Madre mountains. The coastal plain of the Isthmus of Tehuantepec (EBA 014) is located at its northern end, and the highlands of the Sierra Madre de Chiapas and Guatemala (which are part of the North Central American highlands, EBA 018) run parallel to it.

There are a variety of habitats in the EBA, including mangroves along much of the coastline, semi-evergreen humid forest, tropical deciduous forest and thorn woodland.

■ Restricted-range species

All the restricted-range species inhabit tropical deciduous and semi-evergreen humid forest, but they show different distributions, with *Campylorhynchus chiapensis* being found only in the northern part of

the EBA in Chiapas, while the remaining species occur throughout it. The southern range of *Ortalis leucogastra* is taken as northern Nicaragua. Some authors, however, consider the isolated population of *Ortalis* in the Nicoya peninsula of Costa Rica to be this species, but Delacour and Amadon (1973) and Stiles and Skutch (1989) place this population under the widespread Plain Chachalaca *O. vetula*.

There are two subspecies of *Amazilia cyanura*, which are as distinct from each other as are many recognized species of hummingbird. *A. c. guatemalae* is confined to south-east Chiapas and Guatemala where it ranges from 100 to 1,800 m, while the nominate form occurs in eastern El Salvador, southern Honduras and north-west Nicaragua from sea-level to 1,200 m (Howell and Webb 1995a). However, the species may well be shown to be an altitudinal migrant breeding only below 1,000 m. There are also a couple of records of the nominate race from central Honduras, which suggests that it might have a larger range stretching further north into the interior of

Status and habitat of restricted-range species

Species (ordered taxonomically)	Global status	Other EBAs (and SAs)	Altitude (m)	Habitat
White-bellied Chachalaca *Ortalis leucogastra*	lc	—	0–800	Tropical deciduous and gallery forest, deciduous forest edge, secondary growth, scrub
Pacific Parakeet *Aratinga strenua*	lc	014	0–1,500	Tropical deciduous, gallery and secondary forest, arid scrub
Blue-tailed Hummingbird *Amazilia cyanura*	lc	—	100–1,800	Secondary and tropical deciduous forest, tropical lowland evergreen forest edge, scrub
Giant Wren *Campylorhynchus chiapensis*	lc	—	0–300	Tropical lowland evergreen forest edge, secondary growth, scrub, agricultural areas

Global status (see p. 679 for definitions)	EX Extinct EW Extinct in the Wild	} with year of last record	CR Critical EN Endangered VU Vulnerable	} threatened species	cd Conservation Dependent nt Near Threatened lc Least Concern	DD Data Deficient NE Not Evaluated

Other EBAs (and SAs) (see p. 60 for locations): bracketed numbers are Secondary Areas; ^{X} extinct in that EBA or SA.

A. Challenger

The foothills of this region have more extensive areas of dry forest remaining than the flatter coastal plain which is now mainly under cultivation.

Honduras. *A. c. guatemalae* probably overlaps with some of the species occurring around 1,000–1,500 m on the Pacific slope in the Sierra Madre of Chiapas, Mexico and Sierra Madre of Guatemala (North Central American highlands, EBA 018, in part).

■ Threats and conservation

Much of the coastal plain of this EBA is under cultivation, especially banana, cocoa and coffee plantations and cattle-ranching. None of the species is, however, considered to be threatened, as they have all been found in degraded habitats and appear to be fairly common.

There are a number of protected areas that embrace, at least in part, the distributions of the restricted-range species: La Encrucijada Natural and Typical Biotope Reserve (20 km²), Mexico; Monterrico Biotope Reserve (28 km²), Guatemala; El Imposible National Park (39 km²) and Barra de Santiago Wildlife Refuge, El Salvador (22 km²); Volcán Cosiguina National Nature Reserve (124 km²), Estero Real National Nature Reserve (387 km²) and Padre Ramos Nature Reserve (48 km²), Nicaragua.

018 North Central American highlands

PRIORITY
URGENT

Key habitats Montane forest, pine–oak forest, deciduous forest, scrub

Main threats Moderate habitat loss (e.g. due to logging, agricultural expansion for coffee)

Biological importance ● ● ●
Current threat level ● ○ ○

Area 150,000 km² **Altitude** 500-3,500 m
Countries El Salvador, Guatemala, Honduras, Mexico, Nicaragua

Restricted-range species	Threatened	Total
Confined to this EBA	2	20
Present also in other EBAs, SAs	0	0
Total	2	20

■ General characteristics

This EBA includes the mountains of south-east Mexico (east of the Isthmus of Tehuantepec, EBA 014), Guatemala, El Salvador, Honduras and north-central Nicaragua. The topography is especially complex in central Guatemala, with several volcanoes rising above 4,000 m. Some of the mountain ranges, such as the Sierra Madre de Chiapas, run parallel to the Pacific coast and so lie adjacent to the North Central American Pacific slope (EBA 017).

The principal habitats are various types of humid montane and lower montane forest: at 600–1,400 m lower montane (semi-deciduous) forest; at 1,400–2,500 m humid montane forest and (on the wettest slopes) cloud forest, both dominated by evergreen oaks; at 2,500–3,000 m pine–oak and cypress forests; and above 3,000 m fir forest dominates. In parts receiving less rain there are more deciduous formations, such as tropical deciduous forest and oak

A. Challenger

Much of the forest in the Central Highlands of Guatemala and Chiapas, Mexico, is under pressure from agriculture.

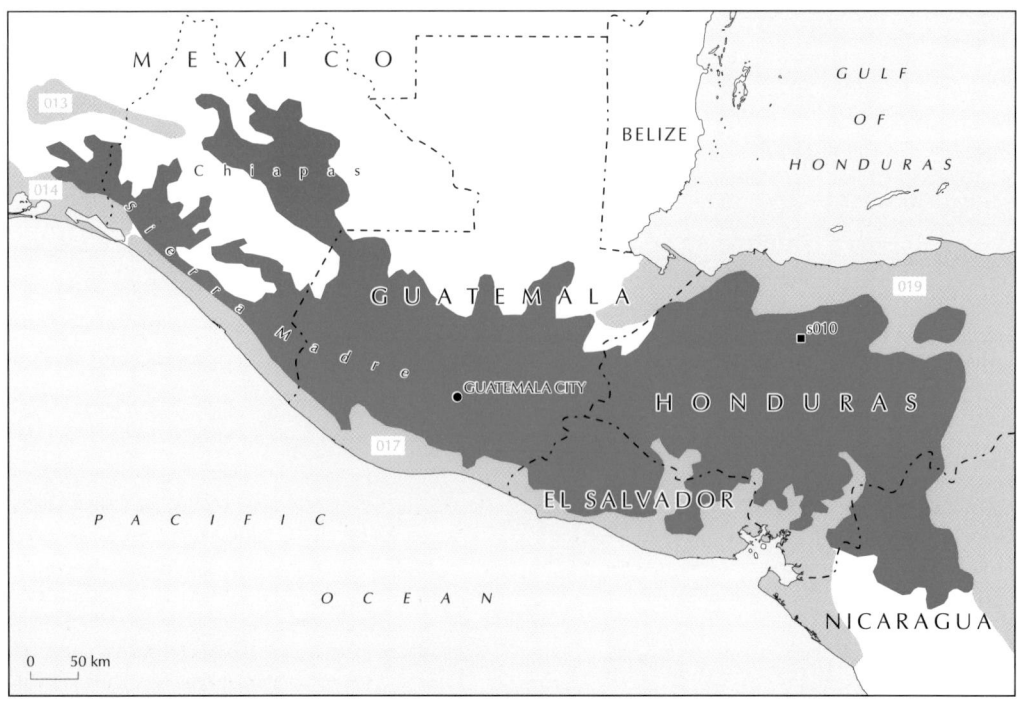

Status and habitat of restricted-range species

Species (ordered taxonomically)	Global status	Other EBAs (and SAs)	Altitude (m)	Habitat
Atitlán Grebe *Podilymbus gigas*	EX (1987)	—	1,500	Freshwater lakes and ponds with open water and reedbeds
Horned Guan *Oreophasis derbianus*	VU	—	2,000–3,000	Montane evergreen forest
Ocellated Quail *Cyrtonyx ocellatus*	nt	—	1,000–3,000	Grassy understorey of open pine–oak and pine forest
Santa Barbara Screech-owl *Otus barbarus*	nt	—	1,800–2,500	Montane evergreen and pine–oak forest
Fulvous Owl *Strix fulvescens*	lc	—	1,200–3,000	Montane evergreen and pine–oak forest
Rufous Sabrewing *Campylopterus rufus*	lc	—	(50–) 900–2,000	Montane evergreen and lower montane forest, secondary forest, forest edge, agricultural areas
Green-throated Mountain-gem *Lampornis viridipallens*	lc	—	1,400–2,200	Montane evergreen and pine–oak forest, forest edge
Green-breasted Mountain-gem *Lampornis sybillae*	lc	—	1400–2200	Montane evergreen forest, pine–oak forest, forest edge
Slender Sheartail *Doricha enicura*	lc	—	1,000–2,200	Montane evergreen forest edge, humid and semi-arid second-growth scrub
Wine-throated Hummingbird *Atthis ellioti*	lc	—	1,500–3,500	Pine–oak forest, montane evergreen forest edge, second-growth scrub
Blue-throated Motmot *Aspatha gularis*	lc	—	1,500–3,000	Montane evergreen and pine–oak forest, secondary growth
Belted Flycatcher *Xenotriccus callizonus*	nt	—	1,200–2,000	Tropical deciduous and semi-deciduous forest, esp. with oaks
Black-capped Swallow *Notiochelidon pileata*	lc	—	1,000–3,000	Pine–oak, montane evergreen and secondary forest, forest edge, cultivated land, open areas
Rufous-browed Wren *Troglodytes rufociliatus*	lc	—	1,700–3,500	Montane evergreen and pine–oak forest, forest edge and clearings
Blue-and-white Mockingbird *Melanotis hypoleucus*	lc	—	1,000–3,000	Montane evergreen forest edge, pine–oak forest, secondary growth, oak scrub
Rufous-collared Robin *Turdus rufitorques*	lc	—	1,500–3,350	Pine, pine–oak and secondary forest, forest edge, pasture and clearings
Azure-rumped Tanager *Tangara cabanisi*	EN	—	1,000–1,700	Montane evergreen and lower montane forest
Pink-headed Warbler *Ergaticus versicolor*	nt	—	1,800–3,500	Pine–oak and montane evergreen forest, secondary growth
Bar-winged Oriole *Icterus maculialatus*	lc	—	500–1,800	Pine–oak forest, semi-deciduous forest esp. with oaks, arid and semi-arid oak scrub and secondary growth
Black-capped Siskin *Carduelis atriceps*	nt	—	2,000–3,500	Pine and pine–oak forest edge, second-growth scrub, pasture with scattered pines
Bushy-crested Jay *Cyanocorax melanocyaneus*	lc	—	600–2,450	Arid to semi-humid forest and edge, pine–oak forest, secondary growth

Global status (see p. 679 for definitions)
EX Extinct — with year of last record
EW Extinct in the Wild — with year of last record
CR Critical — threatened species
EN Endangered — threatened species
VU Vulnerable — threatened species
cd Conservation Dependent
nt Near Threatened
lc Least Concern
DD Data Deficient
NE Not Evaluated

Other EBAs (and SAs) (see p. 60 for locations): bracketed numbers are Secondary Areas; [x] extinct in that EBA or SA.

scrub. The montane forests of north Central America are noted for high levels of plant endemism (Breedlove 1981, Rzedowski and Calderón de Rzedowski 1989).

■ Restricted-range species

With 20 extant restricted-range species, these highlands hold more than any other of the north Central American and Mexican EBAs. The majority of the birds are found above 1,500 m in the pine–oak and montane forests, some (e.g. *Atthis ellioti*, *Melanotis hypoleucus*, *Cyanocorax melanocyanea*) being associated with forest edge, secondary growth and scrub areas. *Xenotriccus callizonus* and *Icterus maculialatus*, which occur mainly in semi-deciduous forest,

Horned Guan *Oreophasis derbianus* is the only species in its genus and is one of the most striking birds of Central America.

N. Arlott

are found in drier inter-montane areas of the EBA down to 500 m (but do not occur in the North Central American Pacific slope [EBA 017]).

Most species are distributed throughout the EBA but *Oreophasis derbianus*, *Otus barbarus*, *Tangara cabanisi*, *Ergaticus versicolor* and *Carduelis atriceps* occur only in the western part (Mexico and Guatemala). *Podilymbus gigas* has the most restricted distribution being endemic to Lake Atitlán in southwest Guatemala. The two mountain-gems are allospecies, both confined to this EBA, *Lampornis viridipallens* being found from Mexico to eastern Honduras, *L. sybillae* in interior eastern Honduras to north-central Nicaragua.

■ Threats and conservation

The pine–oak forest within this EBA is disappearing rapidly through logging, firewood-gathering, uncontrolled burning, agricultural expansion and bark-beetle epidemics that are exacerbated by degradation from logging, grazing and burning. The montane forests are especially affected at 1,000–1,800 m by the growing of coffee without shade trees and by firewood-gathering. New roads continue to open up areas for further human exploitation (Dinerstein *et al.* 1995). The current civil war in Chiapas has caused accelerated deforestation of pine–oak areas in the Altos de Chiapas (P. J. Bubb *in litt.* 1997).

Two of the restricted-range species are considered threatened, and a further five Near Threatened. Most restricted-range species are found in degraded forest, hence the low number threat-listed in relation to the high number confined to this EBA. However, *Oreophasis derbianus* is threatened by a combination of extensive and intensifying deforestation and continuing hunting pressure (Collar *et al.* 1992). *Tangara cabanisi* is restricted to a small part of this EBA in the Sierra Madre de Chiapas and adjacent

Guatemala, principally on its Pacific slope at 1,000–1,700 m; it is threatened because its habitat is prime land for coffee cultivation (Heath and Long 1991).

The winter quarters of the threatened restricted-range Golden-cheeked Warbler *Dendroica chrysoparia* fall within the highlands of this EBA (it breeds in Edwards plateau, Secondary Area 006)—but there are few records, probably due to the paucity of observers, especially in Guatemala, El Salvador and Honduras; the only area with regular sightings (46 during 1990–1992) is around San Cristóbal de las Casas in central Chiapas, Mexico (Vidal *et al.* 1994). Atitlán Grebe *Podilymbus gigas*, estimated to have a population of 210 in 1973, apparently became extinct on Lake Atitlán during the 1980s, owing probably to replacement by or hybridization with the widespread Pied-billed Grebe *P. podiceps*.

Wege and Long (1995) identified 14 Key Areas for this EBA's threatened restricted-range species (two endemics and one wintering) (see also Barker 1990). More surveys are needed in most of these areas, such as those identified for *Dendroica chrysoparia* (e.g. Volcán de San Salvador, El Salvador; La Esperanza and Cerro Cantoral, Honduras) where the records are over 20 years old, and those for *Oreophasis derbianus* along the volcano peaks in Guatemala and south-east Chiapas. Several Key Areas are protected, including, in Mexico, the El Triunfo Biosphere Reserve and Lagunas de Montebello National Park; and, in Guatemala, Sierra de las Minas Biosphere Reserve and Atitlán National Park. El Triunfo is especially important as it holds a significant proportion of the range of *Tangara cabanisi* and important populations of *O. derbianus*, as well as the enigmatic Resplendent Quetzal *Pharomachrus mocinno*—and indeed most of the restricted-range species of this EBA.

019 Central American Caribbean slope

PRIORITY HIGH

Key habitats Tropical lowland and foothill evergreen forest

Main threats Moderate habitat loss (e.g. due to banana plantations, cattle-ranching, logging)

Biological importance ● ●
Current threat level ●

Area 120,000 km²   **Altitude** 0–1,400 m
Countries Costa Rica, Guatemala, Honduras, Nicaragua, Panama

Restricted-range species	Threatened	Total
Confined to this EBA	0	7
Present also in other EBAs, SAs	0	5
Total	0	12

■ General characteristics

This EBA, encompassing the Caribbean slope from eastern Guatemala to western Panama, is characterized by lowland and foothill tropical evergreen forest from sea-level to c.1,350 m and thus overlaps altitudinally with the lowest parts of the Costa Rica and Panama highlands (EBA 020). The centre of the EBA extends from the Sula valley in western Honduras, along the coast and rivers of northern and eastern Honduras, across the broad coastal plain of eastern Nicaragua (the Costa de Mosquitos, but excluding the pine savanna of Mosquitia in both Honduras and Nicaragua), throughout northern Costa Rica, and in a narrowing strip down through eastern Costa Rica to the north coast of western Panama around Laguna de Chiriquí. A single record of a restricted-range species extends the EBA west to the Motagua river area of easternmost Guatemala. In Honduras and Nicaragua, the known distributions of the restricted-range species delineate a more discrete area, but this is more likely to reflect observer bias than to be a real biogeographic distinction between the lowland and foothill forests (see below).

■ Restricted-range species

Most species occupy tropical forest, forest borders and secondary growth (the exception being *Oryzoborus nuttingi*), and occur primarily below 1,000 m, some perhaps undertaking seasonal altitudinal migrations.

MEXICO

BELIZE

CARIBBEAN

SEA

Motagua

Sula

s010

GUATEMALA

HONDURAS

Olancho

Mosquitia

EL SALVADOR

Costa de Mosquitos

s012

s013

NICARAGUA

s011

PACIFIC

OCEAN

COSTA

RICA

Laguna de Chiriquí

Escudo I.

0   100 km

PANAMA

Status and habitat of restricted-range species

Species (ordered taxonomically)	Global status	Other EBAs (and SAs)	Altitude (m)	Habitat
Purplish-backed Quail-dove *Geotrygon lawrencii*	lc	021,023	350–1,500	Tropical lowland evergreen and montane evergreen forest
Lattice-tailed Trogon *Trogon clathratus*	lc	—	150–1,350	Tropical lowland evergreen forest, forest edge, secondary growth
Stripe-cheeked Woodpecker *Piculus callopterus*	lc	023	300–900	Tropical lowland evergreen forest, forest edge, open woodland, secondary growth
Streak-crowned Antvireo *Dysithamnus striaticeps*	lc	—	0–800	Tropical lowland evergreen forest, tall secondary growth
Black-crowned Antpitta *Pittasoma michleri*	lc	023	300–1,050	Tropical lowland evergreen forest, tall secondary growth
Snowy Cotinga *Carpodectes nitidus*	lc	—	0–750	Tropical lowland evergreen forest and secondary growth
Grey-headed Piprites *Piprites griseiceps*	nt	—	100–900	Tropical lowland evergreen forest, secondary growth
Tawny-chested Flycatcher *Aphanotriccus capitalis*	nt	—	0–1,050	Tropical lowland evergreen and secondary forest, forest edges
Black-throated Wren *Thryothorus atrogularis*	lc	—	0–1,100	Tropical lowland evergreen forest edge, secondary forest, forest gaps, abandoned clearings
Nicaraguan Seed-finch *Oryzoborus nuttingi*	lc	—	0–900	Riparian thickets, freshwater marshes, second-growth scrub, grassy areas, agricultural areas
Black-and-yellow Tanager *Chrysothlypis chrysomelas*	lc	023	400–1,200	Tropical lowland evergreen and montane evergreen forest, forest edge, adjacent tall secondary growth
Sulphur-rumped Tanager *Heterospingus rubrifrons*	lc	023	0–900	Tropical lowland evergreen forest, adjacent secondary growth, forest edge

Global status (see p. 679 for definitions)	EX Extinct ⎫ with year EW Extinct in ⎬ of last the Wild ⎭ record	CR Critical ⎫ EN Endangered ⎬ threatened VU Vulnerable ⎭ species	cd Conservation Dependent nt Near Threatened lc Least Concern	DD Data Deficient NE Not Evaluated

Other EBAs (and SAs) (see p. 60 for locations): bracketed numbers are Secondary Areas; ˣ extinct in that EBA or SA.

Just three of the restricted-range species extend the range of the EBA west into Honduras: *Carpodectes nitidus* occurs east of the Sula valley in western Honduras, *Dysithamnus striaticeps* is found in and east of the Olancho region of eastern Honduras, and *Piprites griseiceps* has been recorded once in easternmost Guatemala and once in northern Honduras (Howell and Webb 1995a). However, the species recorded from Guatemala and Honduras (and those within Nicaragua) are known from very few localities, suggesting that the Caribbean slope forests in these countries require further surveys. *Piculus callopterus* is primarily a bird of the Darién lowlands (EBA 023) east of the Panama Canal, though there is an old record from the Caribbean slope in Veraguas province (Ridgely and Gwynne 1989).

An additional restricted-range species, the Bare-necked Umbrellabird *Cephalopterus glabricollis*, migrates seasonally into the Caribbean lowland forests of Costa Rica and Panama from its breeding grounds in the Costa Rica and Panama highlands (EBA 020) (Collar *et al.* 1992, Wege 1993). A number of other highland species may also make such altitudinal movements, although current knowledge is scant. The Escudo Hummingbird *Amazilia*

(*tzacatl*) *handleyi* was described as a distinct species (Wetmore 1963), and is probably still best considered as such, but has been excluded here, following Sibley and Monroe (1990, 1993); if recognized as a full species it should be considered Vulnerable by virtue of its minute range, being endemic to the tiny island of Escudo de Veraguas off Bocas del Toro, Panama (Wetmore 1963). The Panama form *hypophaeus* of Yellow-throated Bush-tanager *Chlorospingus flavigularis* (perhaps also best considered a full species) is primarily confined to the Caribbean slope of central and western Panama (thus in this EBA), although it has been recorded in western San Blas, and locally on the Pacific slope (Ridgely and Gwynne 1989). Both the Critically Endangered Honduran Emerald *Amazilia luciae* (from the dry thorn forests of northern Honduras, Secondary Area s010), and the Nicaraguan Grackle *Quiscalus nicaraguensis* (from the marshes around Lake Nicaragua, Secondary Area s011) are lone species whose ranges fall outside the boundaries of this EBA, although geographically they are in close proximity. Rufous-winged Woodpecker *Piculus simplex* occurs throughout the EBA but has a range larger than 50,000 km², and can be found locally on the Pacific

La Selva Protection Zone in Costa Rica, one of the EBA's few protected areas to support lowland tropical forest.

J. Lowen

slope in western Panama and southern Costa Rica (Ridgely and Gwynne 1989, Stiles and Skutch 1989).

■ Threats and conservation

The region as a whole, but especially Costa Rica, has suffered widespread deforestation (Stiles and Skutch 1989), and although Nicaragua's Costa de Mosquitos area has the largest remaining tract of wet forest in Central America (IUCN 1992a), this too is being reduced by continued deforestation (Harcourt and Sayer 1996). Specific and severe threats to the area include banana plantation and cattle ranch expansion, logging, clearance and refugee settlements (in Nicaragua), with exploitation of parrots and other wildlife also a problem (Dinerstein et al. 1995).

None of the restricted-range species is considered to be threatened, although the EBA is extremely important for the widespread threatened Great Green Macaw *Ara ambigua* (classified as Vulnerable; incorrectly lumped with Military Macaw *A. militaris* in Collar *et al.* 1994) and non-breeding populations of the threatened (Vulnerable) Three-wattled Bellbird *Procnias tricarunculata* and *Cephalopterus glabricollis* (Collar *et al.* 1994). The contiguous Braulio Carillo National Park and La Selva Protection Zone has been identified as a Key Area for threatened birds (for *C. glabricollis*) (Wege and Long 1995).

Other protected areas in the EBA include Pico Bonito National Park and Olancho Forest Reserve (Honduras), Río Indio Maíz Biological Reserve and Bosawas National Natural Resource Reserve (Nicaragua), and Tortuguero National Park/Protection Zone (Costa Rica) (IUCN 1992a).

137

020 Costa Rica and Panama highlands

PRIORITY URGENT

Key habitats Montane evergreen forest, elfin forest, páramo

Main threats Moderate habitat loss (e.g. due to logging, cultivation)

Biological importance ● ● ●
Current threat level ● ○ ○

Area 23,000 km² **Altitude** 1,000–3,800 m

Countries Costa Rica, Panama

Restricted-range species	Threatened	Total
Confined to this EBA	3	49
Present also in other EBAs, SAs	0	3
Total	3	52

■ General characteristics

This species-rich EBA extends over both Caribbean and Pacific slopes from the mountainous region of Costa Rica (the northern boundary abuts Lago de Nicaragua on the Nicaragua border) through western Panama to just west of the Panama Canal. Also part of the EBA but isolated from this main mountain chain is Cerro Hoya, at the southern tip of the Azuero peninsula. East of the Panama Canal, the continuation of the main Costa Rica–Panama mountains forms the Darién highlands (EBA 024).

The EBA is centred on the foothills and highlands above c.1,000 m with the upper altitudinal limit extending to the mountain-tops, which reach a maximum height of c.3,800 m. The region is dominated by montane evergreen forest, and at higher altitudes by cloud forest and elfin forest with páramo vegetation above the treeline on the highest mountains.

■ Restricted-range species

This EBA has a particularly distinct avifauna including eight endemic genera—*Panterpe*, *Elvira*, *Phainoptila*, *Thryorchilus*, *Pezopetes*, *Pselliophorus*, *Acanthidops* and *Zeledonia*.

Most of the EBA's restricted-range species are forest-dependent, with others occurring in secondary and forest-edge habitats, bamboo thickets and páramo. All the species have their centres of distribution above c.1,000 m, although a number occur below this, and therefore overlap altitudinally with the higher parts of the adjacent Central American Caribbean slope (EBA 019) and South Central American Pacific slope (EBA 021). With the vegetation zones being relatively compressed (and at lower altitudes) on the lower mountains of northern Costa Rica, the altitudinal ranges given in the 'Status and habitat' table may appear artificially large, but the zone of overlap with adjacent lowland and foothill EBA species is probably relatively small at any one locality during a particular season.

A number of species such as *Selasphorus ardens* and *Pselliophorus luteoviridis* have extremely small ranges even within the EBA, although the majority of birds are more widespread. Recent exploration of Cerro Hoya at the southern end of the Azuero peninsula resulted in the discovery of a new population of *Selasphorus* hummingbird, possibly representing a disjunct colony of *S. ardens* (Engleman

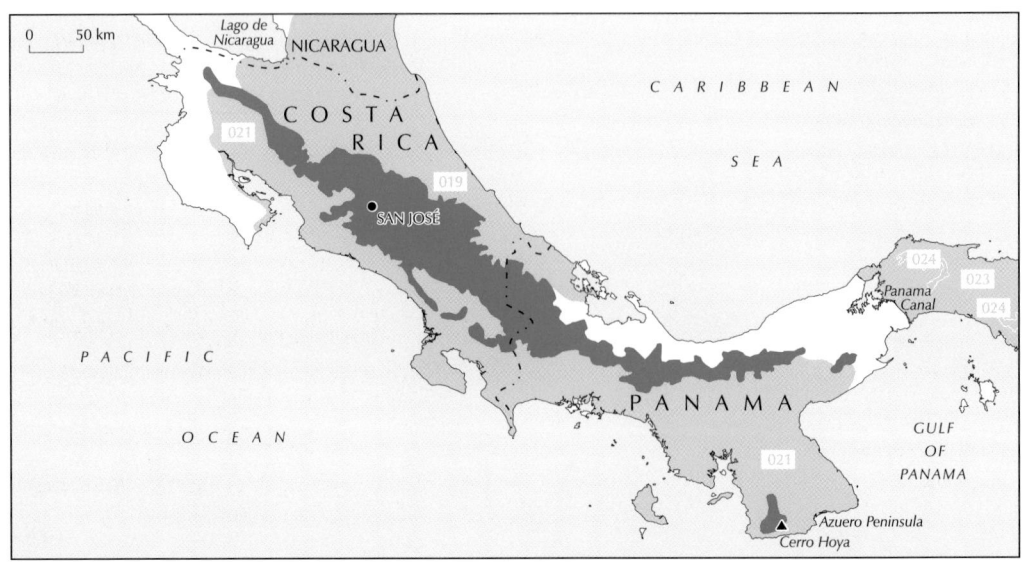

Status and habitat of restricted-range species

Species (ordered taxonomically)	Global status	Other EBAs (and SAs)	Altitude (m)	Habitat
Black Guan *Chamaepetes unicolor*	nt	—	900–2,250	Montane evergreen forest, forest edge, secondary growth
Black-breasted Wood-quail *Odontophorus leucolaemus*	nt	—	700–1,850	Montane evergreen forest
Buff-fronted Quail-dove *Geotrygon costaricensis*	lc	—	1,000–3,000	Montane evergreen forest
Rufous-breasted Quail-dove *Geotrygon chiriquensis*	lc	—	600–2,500	Montane evergreen forest
Sulphur-winged Parakeet *Pyrrhura hoffmanni*	lc	—	700–3,000	Montane evergreen forest, secondary growth
Red-fronted Parrotlet *Touit costaricensis*	nt	—	500–3,000	Montane evergreen forest
Bare-shanked Screech-owl *Otus clarkii*	lc	024	900–2,330	Montane evergreen forest, cloud forest, forest edge
Dusky Nightjar *Caprimulgus saturatus*	lc	—	1,500	Montane evergreen forest, open forest and secondary forest edge
Fiery-throated Hummingbird *Panterpe insignis*	lc	—	1,000–3,800	Montane evergreen forest edge, páramo grassland, secondary growth, clearings
Black-bellied Hummingbird *Eupherusa nigriventris*	lc	—	900–2,000	Montane evergreen forest, forest edge
White-tailed Emerald *Elvira chionura*	lc	—	750–2,000	Montane evergreen forest, forest edge
Coppery-headed Emerald *Elvira cupreiceps*	lc	—	300–1,500	Montane evergreen forest, forest edge
White-bellied Mountain-gem *Lampornis hemileucus*	lc	—	700–1,400	Montane evergreen forest, forest edge
Magenta-throated Woodstar *Philodice bryantae*	nt	—	700–1,850	Montane evergreen forest edge, secondary growth, clearings, shrubby areas
Volcano Hummingbird *Selasphorus flammula*	lc	—	900–2,450	Páramo grassland, montane evergreen forest edge, secondary growth
Scintillant Hummingbird *Selasphorus scintilla*	lc	—	900–2,100	Montane evergreen forest edge, scrubby pastures, young secondary growth
Glow-throated Hummingbird *Selasphorus ardens*	VU	—	750–1,850	Montane evergreen forest edge, secondary growth, clearings
Orange-bellied Trogon *Trogon aurantiiventris*	lc	—	600–1,850	Montane evergreen forest, forest edge, secondary growth
Prong-billed Barbet *Semnornis frantzii*	lc	—	500–2,450	Montane evergreen forest, old secondary growth, clearings with large trees
Ruddy Treerunner *Margarornis rubiginosus*	lc	—	>1,200	Montane evergreen forest, forest edge, clearings
Streak-breasted Treehunter *Thripadectes rufobrunneus*	lc	—	700–3,000	Montane evergreen forest, mature secondary growth
Silvery-fronted Tapaculo *Scytalopus argentifrons*	lc	—	1,000–2,450	Montane evergreen forest, adjacent secondary growth, bamboo thickets
Bare-necked Umbrellabird *Cephalopterus glabricollis*	VU	—	800–2,000	Tropical lowland evergreen and montane evergreen forest, sometimes adjacent tall secondary growth
Dark Pewee *Contopus lugubris*	lc	—	1,200–2,250	Montane evergreen forest and edge, clearings, open woodland, secondary growth
Ochraceous Pewee *Contopus ochraceus*	nt	—	2,200–3,000	Montane evergreen forest, oak forest, forest edge, tall secondary growth
Black-capped Flycatcher *Empidonax atriceps*	lc	—	1,850–3,300	Montane evergreen forest, oak forest, forest edge, secondary growth
Golden-bellied Flycatcher *Myiodynastes hemichrysus*	lc	—	700–2,300	Montane evergreen forest, forest edge, usually near water

cont.

Status and habitat of restricted-range species (cont.)

Species (ordered taxonomically)	Global status	Other EBAs (and SAs)	Altitude (m)	Habitat
Long-tailed Silky-flycatcher *Ptilogonys caudatus*	lc	—	>1,200	Montane evergreen forest, secondary forest, forest edge
Black-and-yellow Silky-flycatcher *Phainoptila melanoxantha*	lc	—	>1,200	Montane evergreen forest, adjacent secondary growth, forest edge
Ochraceous Wren *Troglodytes ochraceus*	lc	—	750–3,000	Montane evergreen forest, forest edge, tall secondary growth
Timberline Wren *Thryorchilus browni*	lc	—	2,400–3,600	Elfin forest, montane evergreen forest edge, bamboo thicket, secondary growth
Black-faced Solitaire *Myadestes melanops*	lc	—	750–2,750	Montane evergreen forest
Black-billed Nightingale-thrush *Catharus gracilirostris*	lc	—	2,150–3,500	Montane evergreen, oak and elfin forest, secondary growth, clearings, forest edge shrubbery
Sooty Thrush *Turdus nigrescens*	lc	—	>2,000	Montane evergreen forest edge, semi-humid/humid montane scrub, páramo, pasture, low secondary growth
Volcano Junco *Junco vulcani*	lc	—	>2,100	Semi-humid/humid montane scrub, páramo grassland, secondary growth, pastures
Large-footed Finch *Pezopetes capitalis*	lc	—	2,100–3,350	Montane evergreen forest edge, semi-humid/humid montane and second-growth scrub, forest edge, bamboo thicket
Yellow-thighed Finch *Pselliophorus tibialis*	lc	—	>1,200	Montane evergreen and secondary forest, forest edge, bamboo thicket
Yellow-green Finch *Pselliophorus luteoviridis*	VU	—	1,200–1,800	Montane evergreen forest, forest edge, usually near water
Sooty-faced Finch *Lysurus crassirostris*	lc	024	600–3,100	Montane evergreen forest, forest edge
Peg-billed Finch *Acanthidops bairdii*	nt	—	>1,500	Montane evergreen forest edge, forest openings, secondary growth, bamboo
Black-thighed Grosbeak *Pheucticus tibialis*	lc	—	750–2,600	Montane evergreen forest edge, pasture with trees, secondary growth
Sooty-capped Bush-tanager *Chlorospingus pileatus*	lc	—	>1,600	Montane evergreen and elfin forest, tall secondary growth
Blue-and-gold Tanager *Bangsia arcaei*	nt	024	300–1,500	Tropical lowland evergreen and montane evergreen forest, forest edge and gaps
Golden-browed Chlorophonia *Chlorophonia callophrys*	lc	—	>900	Montane evergreen forest, forest edge, secondary growth, clearings with trees
Spangle-cheeked Tanager *Tangara dowii*	lc	—	800–3,200	Montane evergreen forest, secondary growth, clearings with some trees
Slaty Flower-piercer *Diglossa plumbea*	lc	—	>1,200	Montane evergreen forest edge, semi-humid/humid montane scrub, second-growth scrub, páramo grassland
Flame-throated Warbler *Parula gutturalis*	lc	—	>1,400	Montane evergreen forest, forest edge, clearings
Collared Whitestart *Myioborus torquatus*	lc	—	>1,050	Montane evergreen, secondary and elfin forest, humid forest edge, secondary growth, thicket
Black-cheeked Warbler *Basileuterus melanogenys*	lc	—	>1,350	Elfin, montane evergreen and secondary forest, scrub
Wrenthrush *Zeledonia coronata*	lc	—	1,050–2,500	Montane evergreen and elfin forest
Yellow-winged Vireo *Vireo carmioli*	lc	—	1,500	Montane evergreen forest, humid forest edge, open woodland
Silvery-throated Jay *Cyanolyca argentigula*	lc	—	1,500–3,200	Montane evergreen and humid oak forest, forest edge, secondary growth

Global status (see p. 679 for definitions)	EX Extinct EW Extinct in the Wild	} with year of last record	CR Critical EN Endangered VU Vulnerable	} threatened species	cd Conservation Dependent nt Near Threatened lc Least Concern	DD Data Deficient NE Not Evaluated

Other EBAs (and SAs) (see p. 60 for locations): bracketed numbers are Secondary Areas; [x] extinct in that EBA or SA.

Montane forest in Braulio Carillo National Park, Costa Rica. Unlike neighbouring Panama, most of the remaining habitat in this EBA is reasonably well protected in Costa Rica.

1994), and it seems likely that, with further work, more highland EBA species will be found there. *Cephalopterus glabricollis* breeds in this EBA, but outside the breeding season birds undertake an altitudinal migration downslope to the Central American Caribbean slope (EBA 019).

Volcano Hummingbird *Selasphorus flammula* is characteristic of the higher reaches of this EBA and occurs right up onto the páramo.

■ Threats and conservation

There has been widespread destruction of the highland forests in this region, primarily as a result of burning, logging and other conversion leading to intensive agricultural use (Dinerstein *et al.* 1995). With more than half of Costa Rica's forest having been destroyed since 1940, and a rate of deforestation currently running at 3% per year, it is anticipated that the majority of the remaining highland forest will eventually be found only within existing pro-

tected areas (Stiles and Skutch 1989). In Panama, to the east of Chiriquí province, only isolated patches of forest are left within the EBA, and it is likely that some of the restricted-range species formerly present there will now have disappeared from the area (W. J. Adsett *in litt.* 1993).

Three of the restricted-range species are considered threatened: *Cephalopterus glabricollis*, principally because of its reliance on both lowland and highland forest at different times in its annual cycle; *Pselliophorus luteoviridis*, due to its minute range in an area lacking any formal protection (Collar *et al.* 1994); and *Selasphorus ardens*, also due to its minute range which, however, is now thought to include Cerro Hoya National Park (Wege and Long 1995). This EBA is the main breeding stronghold for the widespread, threatened (Vulnerable) Three-wattled Bellbird *Procnias tricarunculata*, and also for the Resplendent Quetzal *Pharomachrus mocinno* (Near Threatened).

In Costa Rica the remaining forest is now reasonably well protected within the existing protected-area system. However, apart from La Amistad International Park (and adjacent reserves), highland forest in Panama is afforded little protection. Nine Key Areas for threatened birds have been identified within the EBA (four in Costa Rica and five in Panama): Rincón de la Vieja National Park, Braulio Carillo National Park, Monteverde Biological Reserve, La Selva Protection Zone, La Amistad International Park, Volcán Barú National Park, Cerro Hoya National Park, La Fortuna Water Production Reserve and Fortuna Forest Reserve; six of these areas are formally protected (Wege and Long 1995).

021 South Central American Pacific slope

PRIORITY
HIGH

Key habitats Tropical lowland evergreen forest, dry forest, mangroves

Main threats Major habitat loss (e.g. due to logging, shrimp farms)

Biological importance ● ●
Current threat level ●

Area 38,000 km² **Altitude** 0–1,800 m
Countries Costa Rica, Panama

Restricted-range species	Threatened	Total
Confined to this EBA	4	13
Present also in other EBAs, SAs	0	2
Total	4	15

■ General characteristics

This EBA embraces the Pacific slope lowlands and foothills from northern Costa Rica on the slopes of the Cordillera de Guanacaste, south along the coast including the Osa and Burica peninsulas, and east along the coast of Panama including and to just east of the Azuero peninsula; also the Panamanian islands of Coiba and Cebaco. The boundary of the EBA overlaps altitudinally with that of the Costa Rica and Panama highlands (EBA 020), and the poorly known altitudinal migrations of the restricted-range species tend to confuse this separation.

The primary vegetation types are seasonal dry to moist forests in the north-west, which merge with the wetter forest around the Golfo Dulce and Osa peninsula; there is a pronounced dry season on the Pacific slope of Panama, again resulting in dry to moist forest. Areas of mangrove swamp are found in all suitable coastal situations.

■ Restricted-range species

The majority of the species on the Pacific slope are found in lowland and foothill evergreen forest, although some clearly show a preference for more open areas of secondary growth. Most of the restricted-range species are relatively widespread within the EBA, although the centre of abundance is the area of wetter forest around the Golfo Dulce and Osa peninsula (known to support over 50% of this EBA's restricted-range species). The exceptions to this are the two (threatened) birds (*Amazilia boucardi* and *Carpodectes antoniae*, essentially confined to areas of mangrove), *Cranioleuca dissita* (occurs only on Coiba island, also a stronghold for *Leptotila battyi*: Ridgely and Gwynne 1989), and *Habia atrimaxillaris* (see below). The other threatened and Near Threatened birds also tend to have more limited distributions within the EBA (see below; Ridgely and Gwynne 1989, Stiles and Skutch 1989). *Geotrygon lawrencii* is primarily confined to the foothills of the Central American Caribbean slope (EBA 019) and the Darién lowlands (EBA 023) of eastern Panama, although it has been recorded from the Pacific slope in Veraguas province (Ridgely and Gwynne 1989).

A subspecies of Painted Parakeet, *Pyrrhura picta eisenmanni* (discovered in 1979), is endemic to the Azuero peninsula (Delgado 1985). The Garden Emerald *Chlorostilbon assimilis* occurs in open areas

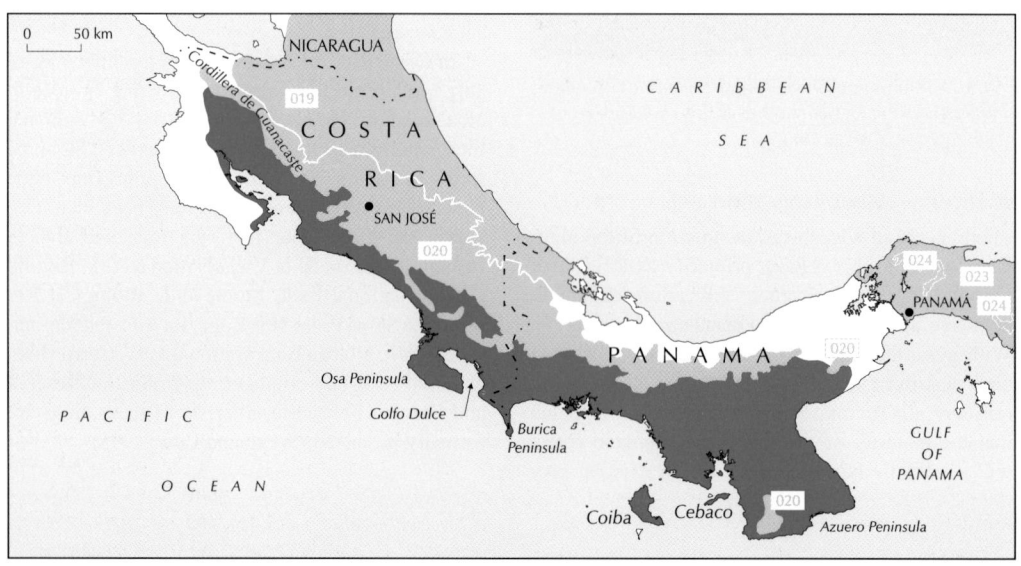

Status and habitat of restricted-range species

Species (ordered taxonomically)	Global status	Other EBAs (and SAs)	Altitude (m)	Habitat
Brown-backed Dove *Leptotila battyi*	nt	—	0–750	Tropical lowland evergreen forest, wooded swamps
Purplish-backed Quail-dove *Geotrygon lawrencii*	lc	019,023	350–1,500	Tropical lowland evergreen and montane evergreen forest
White-crested Coquette *Lophornis adorabilis*	lc	—	300–1,220	Tropical lowland evergreen forest edge, secondary growth, open woodland
Charming Hummingbird *Amazilia decora*	lc	—	0–1,200	Tropical lowland evergreen forest edge, secondary growth, open woodland
Mangrove Hummingbird *Amazilia boucardi*	VU	—	Sea-level	Mangrove forest
Baird's Trogon *Trogon bairdii*	nt	—	0–1,200	Tropical lowland evergreen forest, tall secondary growth
Fiery-billed Aracari *Pteroglossus frantzii*	lc	—	0–1,500	Tropical lowland evergreen forest, secondary forest, forest edge, clearings
Golden-naped Woodpecker *Melanerpes chrysauchen*	lc	037	0–1,500	Tropical lowland evergreen forest edge, secondary growth
Coiba Spinetail *Cranioleuca dissita*	nt	—	Lowlands	Tropical deciduous forest, forest edge
Black-hooded Antshrike *Thamnophilus bridgesi*	lc	—	0–1,100	Tropical lowland evergreen forest edge, gallery, secondary and mangrove forest, scrub
Turquoise Cotinga *Cotinga ridgwayi*	VU	—	0–1,830	Tropical lowland evergreen forest, secondary growth
Yellow-billed Cotinga *Carpodectes antoniae*	VU	—	0–760	Mangrove and adjacent forest, clearings, tropical lowland evergreen forest
Riverside Wren *Thryothorus semibadius*	lc	—	0–1,200	Tropical lowland evergreen forest edge, thicket, usually near water
Black-cheeked Ant-tanager *Habia atrimaxillaris*	VU	—	Lowlands	Tropical lowland evergreen forest, secondary growth
Spot-crowned Euphonia *Euphonia imitans*	lc	—	0–1,400	Tropical lowland evergreen forest, forest clearing, tall secondary growth

Global status (see p. 679 for definitions)	EX Extinct EW Extinct in the Wild	} with year of last record	CR Critical EN Endangered VU Vulnerable	} threatened species	cd Conservation Dependent nt Near Threatened lc Least Concern	DD Data Deficient NE Not Evaluated

Other EBAs (and SAs) (see p. 60 for locations): bracketed numbers are Secondary Areas; ˣ extinct in that EBA or SA.

throughout this EBA, but is also found locally on the Caribbean slope and as far east as Darién province (Ridgely and Gwynne 1989), and is not therefore considered a restricted-range species.

■ Threats and conservation

Widespread and extensive destruction of forest (including major stands of mangroves) throughout this Pacific region has caused a serious decline in the extent of available habitat, leading to those species with the most specific habitat needs or the most restricted ranges being considered threatened; increasing threat is also posed to a number of the other endemics present. *Amazilia boucardi* and *Carpodectes antoniae* are both essentially confined to the now much depleted and seriously threatened areas of mangrove, although *C. antoniae* has the additional seasonal requirement for nearby areas of humid forest. *Habia atrimaxillaris* is restricted to the lowlands in a small area of southern Costa Rica around the Golfo Dulce and Osa peninsula where, due to forest loss, it may well become confined to the Corcovado National Park (Collar *et al.* 1994). *Cotinga ridgwayi* inhabits the dwindling lowland and foothill forests in central and southern Costa Rica, and westernmost Panama.

Eleven Key Areas for threatened birds have been identified in this EBA (only one of which is in Panama), including five that are formally protected: Carara Biological Reserve, Golfo Dulce Forest Reserve, Corcovado National Park, Río Tivives Protection Zone and Golfito Faunal Refuge (Wege and Long 1995). Other protected areas in the EBA include Palo Verde National Park (Costa Rica) and Coiba National Park, Sarigua National Park and Montuoso Forest Reserve (Panama) (IUCN 1992a)— but this EBA, and in particular its threatened species, remain inadequately covered by protected areas.

022 Cocos Island

PRIORITY
URGENT

Key habitats Tropical lowland evergreen forest	**Area** 47 km²	**Altitude** 0–700 m
	Countries Costa Rica	

Main threats Limited habitat loss (e.g. due to grazing and browsing), introduced species

Biological importance ● ● ○
Current threat level ● ● ○

Restricted-range species	Threatened	Total
Confined to this EBA	3	3
Present also in other EBAs, SAs	0	0
Total	3	3

■ General characteristics

Cocos Island is a forest-covered volcanic island in the eastern Pacific Ocean, some 500 km south of Puntarenas in Costa Rica of which it is politically a part. It is the point of land nearest to the Galápagos Islands, which lie 630 km to the south-west.

The island comprises primarily a dense forested plateau (at 400–700 m) rising steeply through wooded ravines from sea-level. Closed-canopy forest (cloud forest at 500 m and above) covers c.95% of the island and remains largely undisturbed, although there are some areas of second-growth forest and cleared land. *Hibiscus* scrub is found along the relatively flat, narrow coastal strip, and other habitats present include *Annona* swamp.

■ Restricted-range species

Three of the four resident landbirds are endemic to the island, all three being distributed throughout in varying abundances: the widespread (non-endemic) Yellow Warbler *Dendroica petechia* is also resident (Slud 1967). All available habitat types appear to be used by the three endemics, but thickets of *Hibiscus* seem to be favoured. *Coccyzus ferrugineus* is widespread but the least common of the native landbirds on Cocos Island, although population data are not

available and it seems likely that the species is under-recorded in the interior forests (Slud 1967, Stiles and Skutch 1989). *Pinaroloxias inornata*, the only Darwin's finch (Geospizini) occurring outside of the Galápagos Islands (EBA 031), occupies every available habitat, being abundant in the *Hibiscus* thickets along the coast but sparser in the wet highland forest (Smith and Sweatman 1976, Stiles and Skutch 1989). *Nesotriccus ridgwayi* is common throughout the forest and other habitats including *Hibiscus* scrub, *Annona* swamp and wooded ravines (Sherry 1985, Stiles and Skutch 1989).

■ Threats and conservation

All three restricted-range species in this EBA are classified as Vulnerable by virtue of their exceptionally small ranges. Although Cocos Island is, in its entirety, a national park (and still covered in forest), it has been the subject of general disturbance from increasing ecotourism, but more importantly, overgrazing and browsing caused by introduced (and now feral) deer, pigs and goats, and predation of the native avifauna by introduced cats and rats (T. W. Sherry *in litt.* 1985). The impact of these threats on the avifauna is essentially unknown, and studies are clearly needed.

Status and habitat of restricted-range species

Species (ordered taxonomically)	Global status	Other EBAs (and SAs)	Altitude (m)	Habitat
Cocos Cuckoo *Coccyzus ferrugineus*	VU	—	0–700	Tropical lowland evergreen forest, secondary growth, scrub, open country
Cocos Flycatcher *Nesotriccus ridgwayi*	VU	—	0–700	Tropical lowland evergreen forest, forest undergrowth, secondary growth, scrub
Cocos Finch *Pinaroloxias inornata*	VU	—	0–700	Tropical lowland evergreen forest, secondary growth, scrub, open country

Global status (see p. 679 for definitions)
EX Extinct
EW Extinct in the Wild
} with year of last record

CR Critical
EN Endangered
VU Vulnerable
} threatened species

cd Conservation Dependent
nt Near Threatened
lc Least Concern

DD Data Deficient
NE Not Evaluated

Other EBAs (and SAs) (see p. 60 for locations): bracketed numbers are Secondary Areas; ˣ extinct in that EBA or SA.

023 Darién lowlands

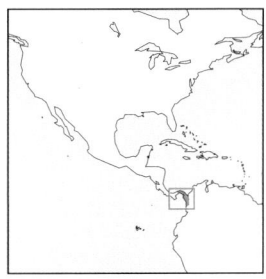

Key habitats Tropical lowland evergreen forest, swamp forest

Main threats Moderate habitat loss (e.g. due to logging, pasture, banana plantations)

Biological importance ● ● ●
Current threat level ● ●

Area 61,000 km² **Altitude** 0–1,000 m

Countries Colombia, Panama

Restricted-range species	Threatened	Total
Confined to this EBA	3	4
Present also in other EBAs, SAs	0	9
Total	3	13

■ General characteristics

The Darién lowlands EBA embraces lowlands and foothills (below c.1,000 m) of eastern Panama and northernmost Colombia: in Panama from the canal area east through Colón, Panamá and Darién provinces, and in Colombia the Urabá lowlands along the Atrato river (west of the West Andes), terminating in the northern Chocó just south of the Serranía de Baudó. The Darién highlands (EBA 024) is divided altitudinally from this lowland area (see below), and the Chocó (EBA 041) is south of but adjacent to it.

The primary vegetation is wet and humid lowland forest, with extensive areas of wetland and swamp forest in the Urabá lowlands.

■ Restricted-range species

Most of the restricted-range species in this EBA occur in humid forest (or disturbed forest) habitats, primarily below 800 m. However, as some birds do occur up to c.1,000 m there is some altitudinal overlap with species endemic to the Darién highlands EBA, which mainly occur above 700–800 m. *Chrysothlypis chrysomelas* is the most dramatic example of this overlap, although it is essentially a lowland form (see EBA 024 for examples of highland species regularly found below 1,000 m). Many of the birds in this EBA are shared with adjacent areas such as the Central American Pacific and Caribbean slopes (EBAs 017 and 019) and the Nechí

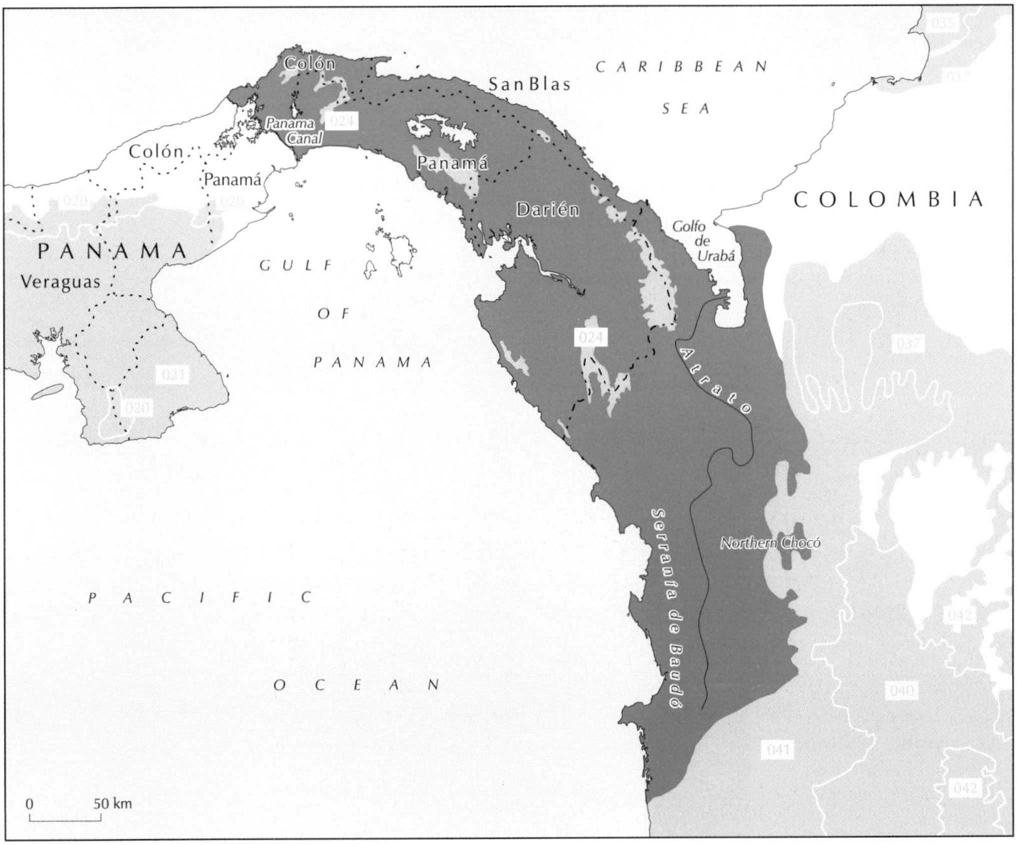

145

Status and habitat of restricted-range species

Species (ordered taxonomically)	Global status	Other EBAs (and SAs)	Altitude (m)	Habitat
Chocó Tinamou *Crypturellus kerriae*	VU	—	300–800	Tropical lowland evergreen forest
Purplish-backed Quail-dove *Geotrygon lawrencii*	lc	019,021	350–1,500	Tropical lowland evergreen and montane evergreen forest
Dusky-backed Jacamar *Brachygalba salmoni*	lc	037	Lowlands to 600	Tropical lowland evergreen and secondary forest edge, tall secondary growth, near streams
Sooty-capped Puffbird *Bucco noanamae*	nt	041	Lowlands to 100	Tropical lowland evergreen forest, scrub
Stripe-cheeked Woodpecker *Piculus callopterus*	lc	019	300–900	Tropical lowland evergreen forest, forest edge, open woodland, secondary growth
Speckled Antshrike *Xenornis setifrons*	VU	—	150–600	Tropical lowland evergreen forest
Black-crowned Antpitta *Pittasoma michleri*	lc	019	300–1,050	Tropical lowland evergreen forest, tall secondary growth
Black-billed Flycatcher *Aphanotriccus audax*	nt	037	0–600	Tropical lowland evergreen forest, secondary growth
Black-and-yellow Tanager *Chrysothlypis chrysomelas*	lc	019	400–1,200	Tropical lowland evergreen and montane evergreen forest, forest edge, adjacent tall secondary growth
Sulphur-rumped Tanager *Heterospingus rubrifrons*	lc	019	0–900	Tropical lowland evergreen forest, adjacent secondary growth, forest edge
Viridian Dacnis *Dacnis viguieri*	nt	—	Lowlands to 700	Tropical lowland evergreen forest, forest edge
Baudó Oropendola *Psarocolius cassini*	EN	—	100–365	Tropical lowland evergreen forest, probably humid forest edge
Black Oropendola *Gymnostinops guatimozinus*	lc	037	0–800	Tropical lowland evergreen forest, river-edge forest, forest edge, logged forest

Global status (see p. 679 for definitions)	EX Extinct	} with year of last record	CR Critical	} threatened species	cd Conservation Dependent	DD Data Deficient
	EW Extinct in the Wild		EN Endangered		nt Near Threatened	NE Not Evaluated
			VU Vulnerable		lc Least Concern	

Other EBAs (and SAs) (see p. 60 for locations): bracketed numbers are Secondary Areas; ˣ extinct in that EBA or SA.

lowlands (EBA 037). Only one species, *Bucco noanamae*, is shared with the Chocó EBA to the south. *Piculus callopterus* is essentially confined to the present EBA, although there is an old record of it from the Caribbean slope in Veraguas province (Ridgely and Gwynne 1989).

D. C. Wege

Tropical lowland evergreen forest near Nusagandi, within Panama's Comarca Kuna Yala Indigenous Reserve.

Forest clearance for pasture is a threat to the birds of this EBA; that shown here is advancing towards the Comarca Kuna Yala Indigenous Reserve, Panama.

D. C. Wege

Distribution patterns of restricted-range species

Species (ordered geographically)	Cent. Panama	E Darién, Urabá lowlands	N Chocó	Other EBAs, SAs
Geotrygon lawrencii	●	●	–	●
Piculus callopterus	●	●	–	●
Chrysothlypis chrysomelas	●	●	–	●
Heterospingus rubrifrons	●	●	–	●
Xenornis setifrons	●	●	●	–
Pittasoma michleri	●	●	●	●
Aphanotriccus audax	●	●	●	●
Gymnostinops guatimozinas	?	●	●	●
Crypturellus kerriae	–	●	●	–
Dacnis viguieri	–	●	●	–
Psarocolius cassini	–	●	●	–
Brachygalba salmoni	–	●	–	●
Bucco noanamae	–	●	●	●
Total	7	13	8	

● Present	? Present?	Threatened spp. shown in **bold**	see 'Status and habitat' table
O Extinct?	R Reintroduced		
X Extinct	I Introduced	Other EBAs, SAs	

■ Threats and conservation

Forest in Colón and western Darién provinces is disappearing following road-building projects during the 1970s and 1980s (W. J. Adsett *in litt.* 1993). Logging has been extensive in the swamp forest of the Urabá lowlands, the cleared areas then being converted to pasture or banana plantations (L. M. Renjifo *in litt.* 1993). The Serranía de Baudó also faces serious deforestation as a result of road-building programmes and logging activities (Collar *et al.* 1994). A number of potentially damaging projects have been proposed for the area, such as the connection of the Pan-American highway through Darién (through either Los Katios or Utría National Parks), and the building of an inter-oceanic channel using the Atrato and Truando rivers (L. G. Olarte *in*

litt. 1993, L. M. Renjifo *in litt.* 1993, W. J. Adsett verbally 1996): both of these projects would have a severe impact on the biodiversity of the area.

Three threatened species occur in the EBA. *Xenornis setifrons* appears to have specific habitat requirements (Whitney and Rosenberg 1993) and, at least on Cerro Azul–Cerro Jefe (within Chagres National Park), it is being directly threatened by habitat loss (W. J. Adsett verbally 1994). The other two species, *Crypturellus kerriae* and *Psarocolius cassini*, are both poorly known, and the Colombian portions of their ranges are under great pressure from road construction, settlement and timber extraction. The widespread Northern Screamer *Chauna chavaria* (Near Threatened; restricted to the wetlands of northern Colombia and north-west Venezuela) is abundant in Los Katios National Park, which may be a stronghold for it (L. M. Renjifo *in litt.* 1993).

Eight Key Areas for threatened birds have been identified within this EBA (five in Panama and three in Colombia): all of the Panamanian areas are formally protected (three within Darién National Park, the others in Chagres National Park and the Comarca Kuna Yala Indigenous Reserve), and Ensenada Utría National Park protects a portion of one Colombian Key Area (Wege and Long 1995). In Panama, many areas in the EBA are under Indian (e.g. Kuna) control, and are thus protected conservation areas (e.g. the Atlantic coast forest in Colón province, and Comarca Kuna Yala Indigenous Reserve in San Blas) (IUCN 1992a, W. J. Adsett *in litt.* 1993). Other protected areas in the EBA include (in Panama) Soberanía and Portobelo National Parks, Canglón and Chepigana Forest Reserves, and Alto de Darién Protection Forest, and (in Colombia) Los Katios National Park (IUCN 1992a).

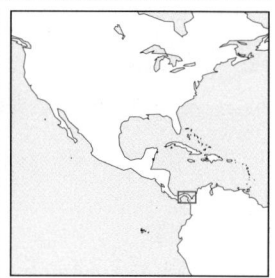

024 Darién highlands

PRIORITY
HIGH

Key habitats Montane evergreen forest, elfin forest

Main threats Limited habitat loss (e.g. due to gold-mining)

Biological importance ● ● ○
Current threat level ● ○ ○

Area 3,000 km²   **Altitude** 700–2,300 m

Countries Colombia, Panama

Restricted-range species	Threatened	Total
Confined to this EBA	0	11
Present also in other EBAs, SAs	0	5
Total	0	16

■ General characteristics

Embracing the highlands that rise from the Darién lowlands (EBA 023), this EBA includes the serranías of central and eastern Panama (east of the Panama Canal, and including Cerro Jefe–Cerro Azul, Cerro Brewster, Cerro Bruja, Serranía de Majé, Serranía de Jungurudó, Serranía del Sapo and Serranía del Darién) and those that form the border between Panama and Colombia (e.g. Serranía de Pirre, Alturas de Nique, Altos de Quía, Serranía de Tacarcuna). The EBA extends from 700 m to c.2,300 m, between which altitudes the principal vegetation types range from subtropical to cloud and elfin forest. The continuation of these mountains west of the Panama Canal forms the Costa Rica and Panama highlands (EBA 020).

■ Restricted-range species

All the restricted-range species are confined to forest habitats, primarily above 700–800 m. *Bangsia arcaei* is found primarily above 700 m in this part of its range, but occurs at lower altitudes further west

(W. J. Adsett *in litt.* 1993). At the lower elevations these birds overlap with species endemic to the Darién lowlands (EBA 023), some of which occur up to 800–900 m, but are nevertheless principally low-altitude in their distributions.

Although a number of the species are widespread within the EBA, and four occur in other nearby EBAs, the mountains along the Colombian border (Cerros Tacarcuna and Malí, Cerro Pirre, Alturas de Nique and Altos de Quía) support six species (*Odontophorus dialeucos*, *Margarornis bellulus*, *Scytalopus panamensis*, *Myadestes coloratus*, *Tangara fucosa* and *Basileuterus ignotus*) which are totally confined to various combinations of these mountains. A further two species (*Geothalsia bella* and *Chlorospingus inornatus*) are found also on Cerro Sapo. The predominance of species endemic to the mountains at the eastern end of this EBA highlights the importance of this area for conservation.

A bird, previously reported as *Scytalopus vicinior*, recorded from Cerro Pirre and thus disjunct from that

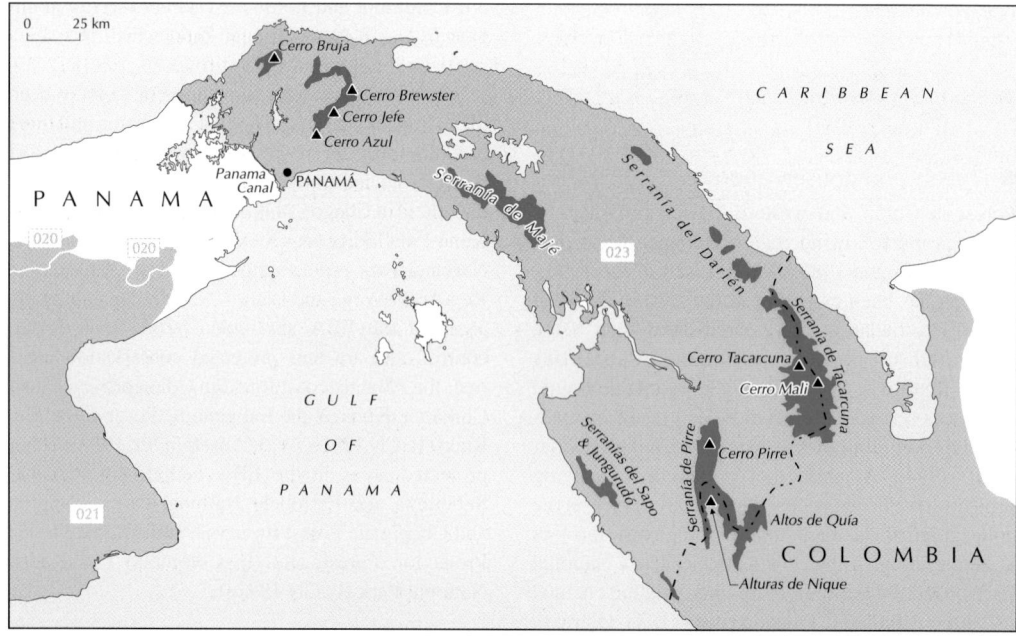

Status and habitat of restricted-range species

Species (ordered taxonomically)	Global status	Other EBAs (and SAs)	Altitude (m)	Habitat
Tacarcuna Wood-quail *Odontophorus dialeucos*	nt	—	1,050–1,500	Montane evergreen forest
Russet-crowned Quail-dove *Geotrygon goldmani*	nt	—	750–1,600	Montane evergreen forest, cloud forest
Bare-shanked Screech-owl *Otus clarkii*	lc	020	900–2,330	Montane evergreen forest, cloud forest, forest edge
Violet-capped Hummingbird *Goldmania violiceps*	lc	—	Usually >1,000	Montane evergreen forest, elfin forest, forest edge
Rufous-cheeked Hummingbird *Goethalsia bella*	nt	—	600–1,500	Montane evergreen forest, forest edge
Beautiful Treerunner *Margarornis bellulus*	nt	—	Usually >1,350	Montane evergreen and elfin forest, cloud forest
Tacarcuna Tapaculo *Scytalopus panamensis*	lc	—	1,020–1,800	Montane evergreen forest
Nariño Tapaculo *S. vicinior*	lc	041	750–1,800	Montane evergreen forest, forest edge
Varied Solitaire *Myadestes coloratus*	lc	—	>900	Montane evergreen forest, cloud forest
Sooty-faced Finch *Lysurus crassirostris*	lc	020	600–1,850	Montane evergreen forest, forest edge
Tacarcuna Bush-tanager *Chlorospingus tacarcunae*	lc	—	750–1,500	Montane evergreen and elfin forest, forest edge
Pirre Bush-tanager *C. inornatus*	lc	—	780–1,560	Montane evergreen and elfin forest, forest edge
Blue-and-gold Tanager *Bangsia arcaei*	nt	020	700–1,500	Tropical lowland evergreen and montane evergreen forest, forest edge and gap
Yellow-collared Chlorophonia *Chlorophonia flavirostris*	lc	041	1,200	Montane evergreen and tropical lowland evergreen forest, forest edge, secondary growth
Green-naped Tanager *Tangara fucosa*	nt	—	Usually >1,350	Montane evergreen and elfin forest, forest edge
Pirre Warbler *Basileuterus ignotus*	nt	—	1,200–1,650	Montane evergreen and elfin forest, forest edge

Global status (see p. 679 for definitions)
EX Extinct — with year of last record
EW Extinct in the Wild — with year of last record
CR Critical — threatened species
EN Endangered — threatened species
VU Vulnerable — threatened species
cd Conservation Dependent
nt Near Threatened
lc Least Concern
DD Data Deficient
NE Not Evaluated

Other EBAs (and SAs) (see p. 60 for locations): bracketed numbers are Secondary Areas; [X] extinct in that EBA or SA.

species' main range in the Chocó (EBA 041), appears not to be referable to *vicinior* (based on vocalization and morphology: Wetmore 1972, Fjeldså and Krabbe 1990), and may thus represent a new, Vulnerable, single-mountain endemic (see below).

■ Threats and conservation

None of the restricted-range species is currently considered threatened, due in part to the relatively pristine state of the highland forests (especially those in Darién) which in turn is a result of their inaccessibility and formal protection (Ridgely and Gwynne 1989). However, close examination of the distributions of species endemic to the mountains on the Panama–Colombia border suggests that those confined to higher elevations should be considered Vulnerable on range-size alone (estimated at less than 100 km^2); such species include *Odontophorus dialeucos*, *Margarornis bellulus*, *Scytalopus panamensis* and *Basileuterus ignotus* (Wege 1996). These species are inherently at risk from any habitat loss or degradation within their small ranges, as is happening locally from mining operations (especially for gold). More specifically, some of the western sections of the area (e.g. around Cerros Jefe and Bruja) have been partially deforested despite being in national parks, and the proposed Pan-American Highway link through Darién could have further highly detrimental effects on the forest (W. J. Adsett *in litt.* 1993, Dinerstein *et al.* 1995).

In Panama, the extensive Darién National Park (a Biosphere Reserve and World Heritage Site) protects most of the important highlands in Darién province, with Los Katíos National Park in Colombia protecting the adjacent and contiguous part of Cerro Tacarcuna ridge (IUCN 1992a). Alto de Darién Forest Reserve covers the Serranía del Darién, and further west the Chagres National Park embraces the Cerro Azul–Cerro Jefe highland ridge, although habitat loss on the lower slopes of the ridge has opened up the montane forest to the damaging effects of wind (W. J. Adsett verbally 1994).

025 Cuba

PRIORITY
CRITICAL

Key habitats Dry forest, pine forest, arid scrub, wetlands	**Area** 110,000 km²	**Altitude** 0–1,500 m

Countries Cuba

Main threats Major habitat loss (e.g. due to cultivation, pasture), introduced species

Biological importance ● ● ●
Current threat level ● ● ●

Restricted-range species	Threatened	Total
Confined to this EBA	3	6
Present also in other EBAs, SAs	0	4
Total	3	10

■ General characteristics

This EBA encompasses Cuba itself (the largest island in the Caribbean) and surrounding smaller islands and cays (from where many subspecies of birds have been described: Garrido 1992), including the Isla de la Juventud (formerly Isla de Pinos) off the south-west coast.

On Cuba, four main mountain ranges dominate an otherwise lowland landscape of arid scrub, savanna, and forest, with extensive wetlands on the Zapata peninsula. Forest can be divided into several different types including lowland and montane rain forest, cloud forest, and drier seasonal (deciduous) forest, which was once very widespread in the lowlands. Coniferous forest is restricted to the eastern and western ends of the island where it is the dominant vegetation type (Harcourt and Sayer 1996).

Recent survey work has shown that, as well as being significant for restricted-range birds, Cuban forests are extremely important wintering areas for Neotropical species, equal to the richest sites that have been surveyed elsewhere in the Caribbean and Mexico (Wallace 1995; see also Wallace *et al.* 1996).

■ Restricted-range birds

In total, 25 species are endemic to Cuba, but only six of these are judged to have historical ranges of less than 50,000 km². All ten of the restricted-range species are reliant on wooded or scrubland areas, mostly in the lowlands, but their patterns of distribution vary: *Teretistris fernandinae* is confined to western Cuba (east to Matanzas and south-west Las Villas provinces) and Isla de la Juventud; *Polioptila lembeyei* is most numerous in southern Cuba (Oriente); *Dendroica pityophila* is confined to Pinar del Río and north-east Oriente; *Corvus palmarum* is very local; *Mimus gundlachii* and *Vireo crassirostris* occur on cays off northern Cuba; *Teretistris fornsi* occurs largely in eastern Cuba; *Torreornis inexpectata* is restricted to three isolated and subspecifically distinct populations in Matanzas (Zapata swamp only), Camagüey (Cayo Coco only) and Oriente; and *Cyanolimnas cerverai* and *Ferminia cerverai* are confined to the Zapata swamp. Another Near Threatened restricted-range species, Bahama Swallow *Tachycineta cyaneoviridis*, from the Bahama Islands (EBA 016), winters in eastern Cuba.

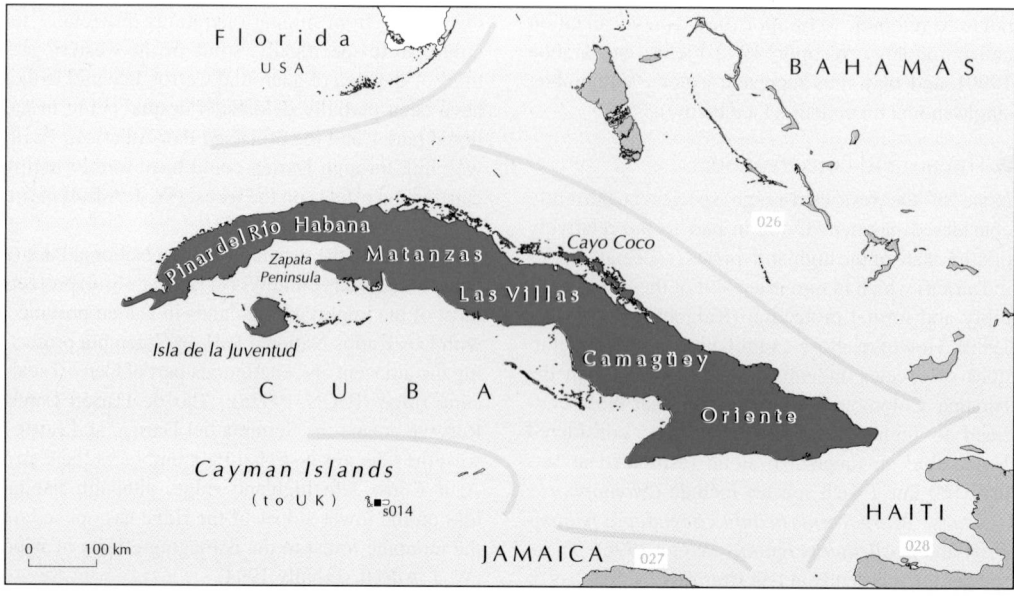

Status and habitat of restricted-range species

Species (ordered taxonomically)	Global status	Other EBAs (and SAs)	Altitude (m)	Habitat
Zapata Rail *Cyanolimnas cerverai*	CR	—	Sea-level	Freshwater marshes, dense bush-covered swamp
Cuban Macaw *Ara tricolor*[1]	EX (c.1855)	—	No data	Forest, forest edge, open country, palm groves
Zapata Wren *Ferminia cerverai*	CR	—	Sea-level	Freshwater marshes, savanna-like habitat with grasses, rushes, scattered bushes and low trees
Bahama Mockingbird *Mimus gundlachii*	lc	026,027	Sea-level	Rain and dry forest edge, arid and second-growth scrub
Cuban Gnatcatcher *Polioptila lembeyei*	nt	—	Sea-level	Arid scrub
Cuban Sparrow *Torreornis inexpectata*	EN	—	Sea-level	Arid scrub, mangroves, dry forest
Olive-capped Warbler *Dendroica pityophila*	lc	026	All	Pine forest
Yellow-headed Warbler *Teretistris fernandinae*	lc	—	0–500	Rain forest, dry forest, scrubby thickets
Oriente Warbler *Teretistris fornsi*	lc	—	0–1,500	Rain forest, dry forest, pine forest, arid scrub
Thick-billed Vireo *Vireo crassirostris*	lc	026,028 (s012,s014)	Sea-level	Dry forest, arid scrub, mangroves
Palm Crow *Corvus palmarum*	nt	028	All	Rain forest, pine forest, arid scrub, swamps

Global status (see p. 679 for definitions)	EX Extinct EW Extinct in the Wild	} with year of last record	cd Conservation Dependent nt Near Threatened	**Other EBAs (and SAs)** (see p. 60 for locations)	Bracketed numbers are Secondary Areas. x Extinct in that EBA or SA.
	CR Critical EN Endangered VU Vulnerable	} threatened species	lc Least Concern DD Data Deficient NE Not Evaluated	**Notes**	[1] Taxonomy follows Walters (1995).

■ Threats and conservation

Much of Cuba's native vegetation has been converted to cultivation and pasture for cattle, with only 15–20% of land remaining in its natural state (Perera and Rosabal 1986). Today, expansion of cacao, coffee and tobacco production are serious threats to rain forest, while logging, charcoal production and slash-and-burn agriculture destroy dry forest. In the Zapata swamp, dry-season burning, draining, agricultural expansion and introduced predators such as mongooses and rats are problems (Dinerstein *et al.* 1995), and the two species endemic to this region are consequently rated as Critical.

Several of the widespread Cuban endemics are also very rare today as a result of loss and disturbance of wooded habitats and, for some species, hunting: these are Gundlach's Hawk *Accipiter gundlachii* (Endangered), Blue-headed Quail-dove *Starnoenas cyanocephala* (Endangered), Cuban Parakeet *Aratinga euops* (Vulnerable), Bee Hummingbird *Calypte helenae* (Near Threatened, the world's smallest bird), Fernandina's Flicker *Colaptes fernandinae* (Endangered), Giant Kingbird *Tyrannus cubensis* (Endangered) and Cuban Solitaire *Myadestes elisabeth* (Near Threatened). In addition there are a number of widespread, non-endemic rare species

which also occur: West Indian Whistling-duck *Dendrocygna arborea* (Vulnerable), Piping Plover *Charadrius melodus* (Vulnerable; winter only), Plain Pigeon *Columba inornata* (Endangered; the highest known population, 100 pairs, is in Cuba), Grey-headed Quail-dove *Geotrygon caniceps* (Near Threatened), Cuban Parrot *Amazona leucocephala* (Near Threatened) and Bachman's Warbler *Vermivora bachmani* (Critical, possibly extinct; winters only in Cuba, last unconfirmed sighting anywhere being in 1988). Black-capped Petrel *Pterodroma hasitata*, a seabird that breeds on islands in the Caribbean including Cuba, is also threatened (Endangered).

Ivory-billed Woodpecker *Campephilus principalis*, once widespread in virgin forest in the USA and Cuba, appears to be extinct, having last been recorded in Cuba in 1987 or 1988, possibly 1991 (Lammertink and Estrada 1995).

Some 12% of the total land area of Cuba falls within 200 or so conservation units (including, in the Zapata swamp area, the 14.8 km² Santo Tomás Faunal Refuge), but few of these afford strict protection (logging occurs in some: J. M. Lammertink *in litt.* 1993) and some reserves appear to be too small for effective preservation of the wildlife they contain (Santana 1991).

026 Bahamas

PRIORITY
HIGH

Key habitats Arid scrub, pine forest, dry forest

Main threats Major habitat loss (e.g. due to tourist development, recreational use, firewood-gathering)

Biological importance ● ● ●
Current threat level ● ● ●

Area 14,000 km²   **Altitude** 0–60 m
Countries Bahamas, Turks and Caicos Islands (to UK)

Restricted-range species	Threatened	Total
Confined to this EBA	0	3
Present also in other EBAs, SAs	0	4
Total	0	7

■ General characteristics

This EBA comprises some 13 sizeable islands or island groups, and hundreds of smaller islets and cays, covering the political units of the Bahamas and the Turks and Caicos Islands (a UK dependent territory), c.80 km east of the state of Florida (USA).

The islands are low-lying, either swampy or covered in dense vegetation which is mainly coppice and arid scrub, with extensive Caribbean pine *Pinus caribaea* forest on the northern islands and drier forest in the south; mangrove communities commonly fringe sheltered coasts. The smaller cays support strand vegetation, occasionally with a dense growth of cacti (Brudenell-Bruce 1975, Buden 1987).

■ Restricted-range species

All the restricted-range species occur in forest or scrub, but there is no consistent pattern of distribution between the islands: three species breed on the northern islands only (including two which are dependent on pine forest) and one on the southern islands only. For some species on some islands, breeding is very probable but not proved.

Kirtland's Warbler *Dendroica kirtlandii*, a threatened (Vulnerable) restricted-range species which breeds in Michigan jack pine scrub in the USA (Secondary Area s003), winters in this EBA. An additional 18 species of landbird have one or more subspecies endemic to the Bahamas (Buden 1987).

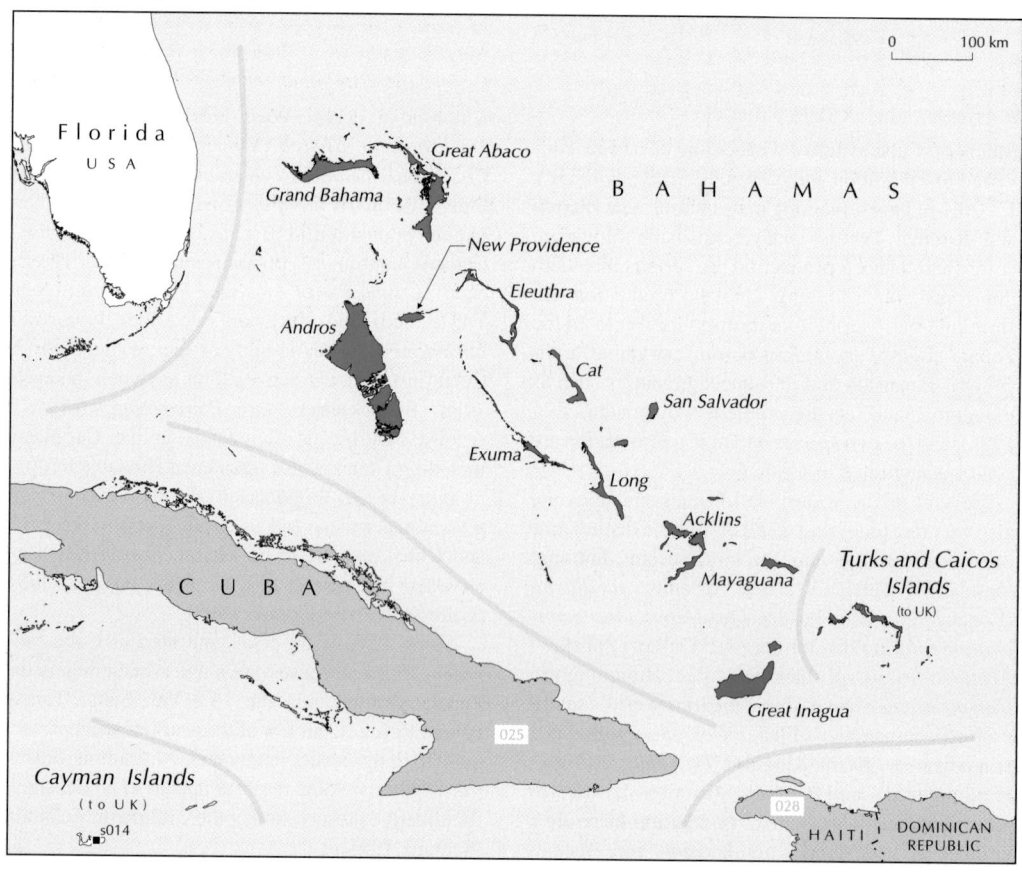

Status and habitat of restricted-range species

Species (ordered taxonomically)	Global status	Other EBAs (and SAs)	Habitat
Brace's Emerald *Chlorostilbon bracei*[1]	EX (1877)	—	Arid scrub
Bahama Woodstar *Calliphlox evelynae*	lc	—	Mixed pine forest, scrubby forest, arid scrub, open clearings, gardens
Bahama Swallow *Tachycineta cyaneoviridis*	nt	—	Pine forest (nesting); open and partly open areas, e.g. marshes and old fields (feeding)
Bahama Mockingbird *Mimus gundlachii*	lc	025,027	Dry forest edge, arid and second-growth scrub
Pearly-eyed Thrasher *Margarops fuscatus*	lc	028,029, 030 (s015)	Most forest types, arid scrub
Olive-capped Warbler *Dendroica pityophila*	lc	025	Pine forest
Bahama Yellowthroat *Geothlypis rostrata*	lc	—	Arid scrub
Thick-billed Vireo *Vireo crassirostris*	lc	025,028 (s012,s014)	Dry forest, mangroves, arid scrub

Global status (see p. 679 for definitions)
EX Extinct — with year of last record
EW Extinct in the Wild — with year of last record
CR Critical — threatened species
EN Endangered — threatened species
VU Vulnerable — threatened species
cd Conservation Dependent
nt Near Threatened
lc Least Concern
DD Data Deficient
NE Not Evaluated

Other EBAs (and SAs) (see p. 60 for locations) Bracketed numbers are Secondary Areas. [X] Extinct in that EBA or SA.

Notes [1] Known only from the type specimen (Graves and Olson 1987).

■ Threats and conservation

The vegetation of the main islands of the EBA has been heavily modified, with forests facing threats from tourism development, heavy recreational use, and firewood-gathering (Dinerstein *et al*. 1995). Changes in climate since the last glaciation have been proposed as a major cause of vertebrate extinction in the Bahamas and elsewhere in the West Indies, and may have contributed to the decline of *Chlorostilbon bracei* (see Graves and Olson 1987).

One species which has suffered particularly is *Tachycineta cyaneoviridis*. Its breeding range is normally limited to the four pine-forested islands in the north where nesting occurs in natural cavities and old woodpecker holes; mid-twentieth-century clear-cutting as well as the continuing agricultural and other development probably caused a significant decline in its numbers, but cessation of logging suggests that its declining population may have levelled off (Smith and Smith 1989; see also Allen 1996), hence its Near Threatened status.

Other widespread threatened species (all Vulnerable) in this EBA include West Indian Whistling-duck *Dendrocygna arborea* (the 200–300 birds that feed overnight on Hog Cay are the subject of a radio-tracking study of habitat use and breeding biology: Staus 1994) and Piping Plover *Charadrius melodus* (wintering records from the Bahamas only). There are several protected areas in the EBA, notably Inagua National Park (750 km²).

Distribution patterns of restricted-range species

Species (ordered geographically)	Grand Bahama	Great Abaco	Andros	New Providence	Eleuthra	Cat	San Salvador	Exuma	Long	Acklins	Mayaguana	Great Inagua	Turks and Caicos	Other EBAs, SAs
Dendroica pityophila	•	•	–	–	–	–	–	–	–	–	–	–	–	•
Tachycineta cyaneoviridis	•	•	•	•	W	–	W	W	–	–	–	W	–	–
Geothlypis rostrata	•	•	•	•	•	•	–	–	–	–	–	–	–	–
Calliphlox evelynae	•	•	•	•	•	•	•	•	•	•	•	•	•	–
Mimus gundlachii	•	•	•	•	•	•	•	•	•	•?	•?	•?	•	○
Vireo crassirostris	•	•	•	•	•	•	•	•	•	•?	•?	•?	•?	○
Chlorostilbon bracei	–	–	–	X	–	–	–	–	–	–	–	–	–	–
Margarops fuscatus	–	–	–	–	W	W	•	•	•	•?	•?	•?	•	○
Total	6	6	5	5	4	4	4	4	4	4	4	4	4	

- • Breeds
- ○ Extinct?
- X Extinct
- •? Probably breeds
- W Winter visitor (non-breeding)
- Threatened spp. shown in **bold** / Other EBAs, SAs } see 'Status and habitat' table

027 Jamaica

Key habitats Lowland and montane rain forest, limestone forest

Main threats Major habitat loss (e.g. due to coffee and pine plantations, hurricanes), hunting

Biological importance ● ● ●
Current threat level ● ●

Area 11,000 km² **Altitude** 0–2,000 m

Countries Jamaica

Restricted-range species	Threatened	Total
Confined to this EBA	3	28
Present also in other EBAs, SAs	0	7
Total	3	35

■ General characteristics

Jamaica, the third largest island in the Caribbean, is dominated by an extensive cordillera (c.80% of the island is hilly or mountainous) which includes the John Crow Mountains (reaching more than 1,000 m in altitude) near the eastern coast, the Blue Mountains (with a highest point of 2,256 m), and a series of lower limestone hills (including the Cockpit Country) in the west.

The island was once almost entirely covered by forest, of which there are four main types whose distribution is determined by the rainfall pattern: dry (deciduous) limestone forest on southern lowlands and hills; intermediate limestone forest in the central uplands, wet and very wet limestone forest in the Cockpit Country and John Crow Mountains (mainly between 30 and 750 m); and rain forest (lowlands largely cleared, but montane forest remains in the higher parts of the Blue Mountains).

As well as being significant for restricted-range species, Jamaica is an important refuge for migratory birds. Thus, during the northern winter the native avifauna is almost doubled (to c.250 species) by long-distance migrants from North and Central America.

■ Restricted-range species

Jamaica has the highest number of endemic species of any Caribbean island, and a very distinct avifauna with five endemic genera—*Pseudoscops*, *Trochilus*, *Loxipasser*, *Euneornis* and *Nesopsar*.

All the restricted-range species occur in forest (mostly in rain forest, although a few favour forest on limestone) and, although most species occur in both the lowlands and mountains, many are altitudinal migrants which breed only in the mid- to high-level forests. Most species, like *Trochilus polytmus*, Jamaica's national bird, are quite widely distributed, but

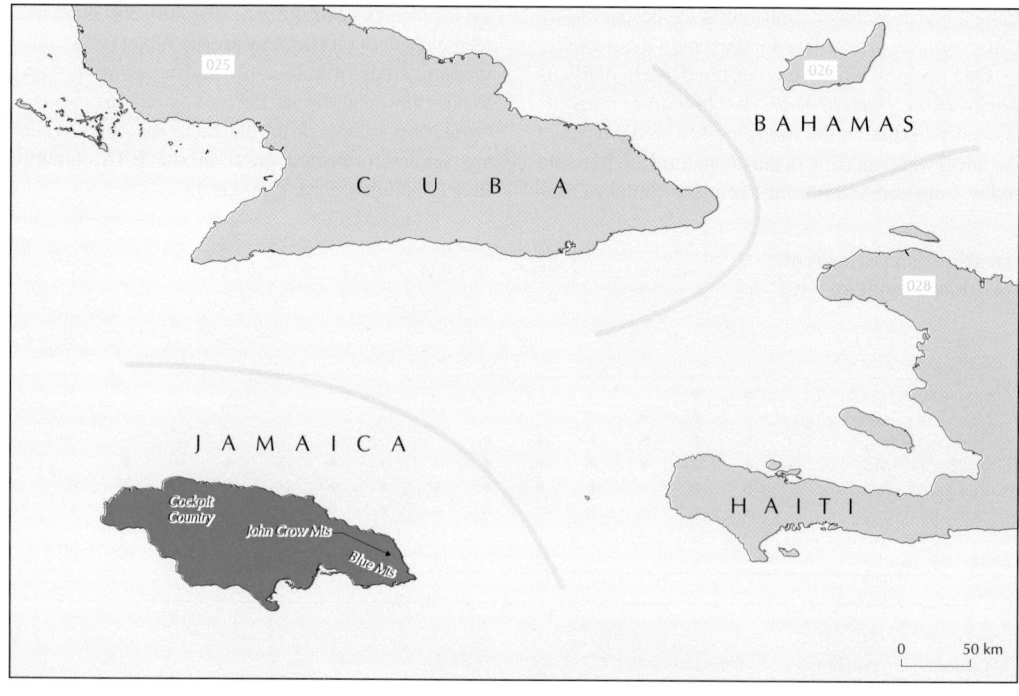

Status and habitat of restricted-range species

Species (ordered taxonomically)	Global status	Other EBAs (and SAs)	Altitude (m)	Habitat
Ring-tailed Pigeon *Columba caribaea*	CR	—	150–2,000	Rain forest, wet limestone forest
Crested Quail-dove *Geotrygon versicolor*	nt	—	200–2,000	Rain forest, wet limestone forest
Yellow-billed Amazon *Amazona collaria*	nt	—	100–1,300	Intermediate and wet limestone forest, cultivation
Black-billed Amazon *Amazona agilis*	VU	—	100–800	Intermediate and wet limestone forest, cultivation
Chestnut-bellied Cuckoo *Hyetornis pluvialis*	lc	—	300–1,800	Rain forest, intermediate and wet limestone forest, forest edge
Jamaican Lizard-cuckoo *Saurothera vetula*	lc	—	0–1,200	All forest types, forest edge
Jamaican Owl *Pseudoscops grammicus*	lc	—	0–600	All forest types, forest edge, plantations, gardens
Jamaican Pauraque *Siphonorhis americanus*	CR	—	Sea-level	Possibly dry forest and scrub
Jamaican Mango *Anthracothorax mango*	lc	—	0–500	Limestone forest, forest edge, mangroves, gardens
Red-billed Streamertail *Trochilus polytmus*[1]	lc	—	0–2,000	All forest types, gardens, cultivation, parks
Black-billed Streamertail *Trochilus scitulus*[1]	lc	—	0–1,800	Wet limestone forest, plantations, gardens
Vervain Hummingbird *Mellisuga minima*	lc	028	0–2,000	All forest types, forest edge, scrub, gardens, cultivation
Jamaican Tody *Todus todus*	lc	—	0–2,000	All forest types, forest edge, plantations
Jamaican Woodpecker *Melanerpes radiolatus*	lc	—	0–2,000	All forest types, gardens at edge of forest, plantations
Jamaican Becard *Pachyramphus niger*	lc	—	0–1,800	All forest types, pastures with large trees
Jamaican Elaenia *Myiopagis cotta*	lc	—	0–2,000	All forest types, forest edge
Greater Antillean Elaenia *Elaenia fallax*	lc	028	500–2,000	Rain forest, forest edge
Jamaican Pewee *Contopus pallidus*[2]	lc	—	300–2,000	All forest types, forest edge, coffee plantations
Sad Flycatcher *Myiarchus barbirostris*	lc	—	0–2,000	All forest types, secondary forest, forest edge, mangroves
Rufous-tailed Flycatcher *Myiarchus validus*	lc	—	0–2,000	All forest types, secondary forest, forest edge
Stolid Flycatcher *Myiarchus stolidus*	lc	028	0–700	Dry and intermediate forest, forest edge, mangroves, scrub
Golden Swallow *Tachycineta euchrysea*	nt	028	0–2,000	Rain forest (nesting); limestone forest, canefields, open country (feeding)
Bahama Mockingbird *Mimus gundlachii*	lc	025,026	0–200	Arid and second-growth scrub, dry limestone forest
Rufous-throated Solitaire *Myadestes genibarbis*	lc	028,030	0–2,000	Rain forest, intermediate and wet limestone forest
White-chinned Thrush *Turdus aurantius*	lc	—	0–1,800	All forest types, gardens near to forest edge, cultivation, plantations
White-eyed Thrush *Turdus jamaicensis*	lc	—	0–1,800	Rain forest, intermediate and wet limestone forest
Yellow-shouldered Grassquit *Loxipasser anoxanthus*	lc	—	0–1,800	All forest types, forest edge

cont.

Status and habitat of restricted-range species (cont.)

Species (ordered taxonomically)	Global status	Other EBAs (and SAs)	Altitude (m)	Habitat
Jamaican Euphonia *Euphonia jamaica*	lc	—	0–1,800	All habitats inc. forest, gardens, open areas with large trees, cultivation
Orangequit *Euneornis campestris*	lc	—	0–1,800	Rain forest, intermediate and wet limestone forest, forest edge
Arrowhead Warbler *Dendroica pharetra*	lc	—	50–2,200	Rain forest, intermediate and wet limestone forest, forest edge
Jamaican Vireo *Vireo modestus*	lc	—	0–1,800	All forest types, forest edge, scrub
Blue Mountain Vireo *Vireo osburni*	nt	—	500–2,200	Rain forest, wet limestone forest
Jamaican Oriole *Icterus leucopteryx*	lc	(s013,s014)	0–1,800	All habitats inc. forest, mangroves, gardens, cultivation, plantations
Jamaican Blackbird *Nesopsar nigrimus*	nt	—	500–2,200	Rain forest, wet limestone forest
Jamaican Crow *Corvus jamaicensis*	lc	—	0–1,200	Intermediate and wet limestone forest, plantations

Global status (see p. 679 for definitions): EX Extinct, EW Extinct in the Wild (with year of last record), CR Critical, EN Endangered, VU Vulnerable (threatened species), cd Conservation Dependent, nt Near Threatened, lc Least Concern, DD Data Deficient, NE Not Evaluated

Other EBAs (and SAs) (see p. 60 for locations): Bracketed numbers are Secondary Areas. X Extinct in that EBA or SA.

Notes: [1] Taxonomy follows Schuchmann (1978). [2] Taxonomy follows Reynard et al. (1993).

its congener *T. scitulus* (which is treated here as a separate species, following Schuchmann 1978) is one exception, being restricted to the eastern end of the island.

The subspecific status of Jamaican Parakeet *Aratinga nana nana* and Jamaican Tanager *Spindalis zena nigricephala* is questionable and both may prove to be full species (C. Levy *in litt.* 1993), although they have not been treated as such here.

■ Threats and conservation

Jamaica's lowlands have been mostly cleared for agriculture and overall some 75% of the original forest has been lost (Haynes *et al.* 1989). Remaining forest is largely secondary in nature and it is only the montane forest in the most remote, inaccessible and steep part of the island that has survived undisturbed. The last 10–20 years has seen a resurgence in the growth and profitability of coffee (for example, the world-famous Blue Mountain variety), which has led to the loss of much secondary growth, potentially good habitat for some birds. Modern methods of cultivation rely heavily on chemical fertilizers, insecticides and often herbicides, and these could pose widespread problems for wildlife. Other current threats are the establishment of plantations (mostly of Caribbean pine *Pinus caribaea*), removal of trees for charcoal-burning, deliberate fires, small-scale farming, clearance for development, firewood-gathering and heavy recreational use (see, e.g. Dinerstein *et al.* 1995; also Eyre 1987).

Periodic hurricanes are a serious threat to remaining forest areas. For example, in 1988 Hurricane Gilbert (one of the most powerful ever recorded) caused widespread damage, with 43% of trees in the John Crow mountains either toppled or with crowns broken (Varty 1991). The montane nectar-feeders and fruit-/seedeaters are especially vulnerable to damage caused by hurricanes, particularly as most lowland forest (which might provide temporary refuge) is already cleared (Wunderle *et al.* 1992).

Despite these conservation problems, only three restricted-range species have been identified as threatened, although five more are classified as Near Threatened. The three threatened species suffer from habitat loss (as do the other endemics) but additional dangers compound this effect. Thus, constant hunting pressure on *Columba caribaea* has contributed to the great reduction in its numbers and range over the past 150 years, and it is now judged to be Critical. Introduced rats and mongooses are the most likely cause of the disappearance of *Siphonorhis americanus*, also Critical; this bird was last recorded in 1863 and is so little known that its habitat preferences are still uncertain, but there are recent unconfirmed reports of caprimulgids that do not fit any other known species on the island, and it is therefore not treated as extinct. Poaching for food and trapping for the local bird trade is a further problem for *Amazona agilis*, although recent information indicates a healthy and numerous populations in the Cockpit Country (C. Levy *in litt.* 1997). The recent discovery on

Parrots on Jamaica, such as the Yellow-billed Amazon *Amazona collaria* shown here, suffer from the loss of forest, from poaching for food and from trapping for the local bird trade.

BirdLife

Jamaica of Shiny Cowbird *Molothrus bonariensis*, a brood parasite, may put the populations of some of the endemic species at risk (C. Levy *in litt*. 1993) (e.g. see Puerto Rico and the Virgin Islands, EBA 029, for a similar problem there).

Three widespread threatened birds also occur on the island: West Indian Whistling Duck *Dendrocygna arborea* (Vulnerable), Piping Plover *Charadrius melodus* (Vulnerable; winter only) and Plain Pigeon *Columba inornata* (Endangered). Jamaican Petrel *Pterodroma caribbaea* (Critical), a seabird which was once an abundant breeder in the forests of the Blue and John Crow mountains, was killed off by introduced mongooses and human exploitation, but it may conceivably still survive.

With a growing population, easier transport and economic hardships, there is increasing pressure to cultivate the higher, still-forested mountain slopes. To protect the natural vegetation and wildlife, and the largest watershed in the island, the Blue Mountain and John Crow National Park has recently been set up, extending over nearly 800 km². This is part of a system of protected areas comprising some 40 or more legally designated forest reserves throughout the island, although the long-term security and therefore value of these is uncertain, as the reserves are unmanaged and unmonitored, and neither hunting nor habitat destruction are controlled (C. Levy *in litt*. 1993, A. and R. Sutton *in litt*. 1993).

028 Hispaniola

	PRIORITY URGENT

Key habitats Lowland and montane rain forest, dry forest, pine forest

Main threats Severe habitat loss (e.g. due to shifting agriculture, sugar-cane plantations), hunting

Biological importance ● ● ●
Current threat level ●

Area 76,000 km² **Altitude** 0–3,000 m

Countries Dominican Republic, Haiti

Restricted-range species	Threatened	Total
Confined to this EBA	6	23
Present also in other EBAs, SAs	1	11
Total	7	34

■ General characteristics

Hispaniola lies between Cuba (EBA 025) and Puerto Rico (EBA 029), and the EBA also includes the smaller offshore islands such as Gonâve, Tortue, Beata and Saona. Politically the region is divided between Haiti for the western third and the Dominican Republic for the eastern two-thirds.

The variation in altitude and climate is reflected in a range of vegetation types, including dry forest (usually 40–500 m, but up to 1,000 m in some areas), semi-deciduous forest (400–900 m, transitional between the dry and rain/cloud forests), rain forest (<500 m), cloud forest (600–2,300 m), pine forest (of *Pinus occidentalis*, a fire-adapted endemic species predominating over much of the Cordillera Central and the higher reaches of Sierra de Bahoruco/Massif de la Selle) and mangroves in many coastal areas. Savannas include small natural savannas in dry and pine forest, and large and abundant man-made livestock pastures (Harcourt and Sayer 1996, A. Schubert, T. V. Mora and D. A. S. Nuñez *in litt.* 1994).

■ Restricted-range species

Hispaniola has a particularly distinct avifauna with six endemic genera—*Calyptophilus, Dulus*, (the sole representative of its family) *Microligea, Nesoctites, Phaenicophilus* and *Xenoligea*.

All the restricted-range species occur in forest,

often in rain, dry and pine forest. Of these, some 40% occupy forest ecosystems exclusively, and the others live mainly in forest, but temporarily use surrounding open habitat (scrub, savanna or agricultural land). About a third of the species occur in lower areas up to c.1,000 m, another third (notably *Turdus swalesi* and *Xenoligea montana*) are confined to the higher mountains, and the remainder can be found over a broad band of altitudes (A. Schubert, T. V. Mora and D. A. S. Nuñez *in litt.* 1994).

All species which are endemic to the island are included as having restricted ranges because it is assumed that, historically, appropriate habitat amounted to less than 50,000 km². Most species are widely distributed, apart from *Margarops fuscatus* (Beata Island only in this EBA), *Phaenicophilus poliocephalus* (southern peninsula of Haiti) and *Vireo crassirostris* (Tortue Island only in this EBA).

Hispaniolan Crossbill *Loxia leucoptera megaplaga*, an isolated form of a widespread Eurasian and North American bird, is sometimes recognized as a distinct species (e.g. Ottenwalder 1992).

■ Threats and conservation

Between 1630 and the 1880s the lowland forests of Hispaniola were converted to sugar-cane plantations, and after this time, following the abolition of slavery, destruction of montane forest took place as

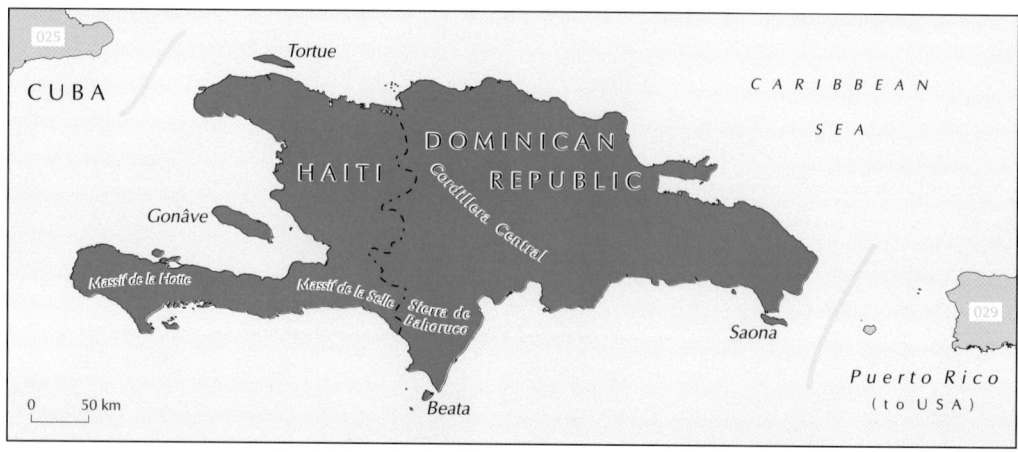

Status and habitat of restricted-range species

Species (ordered taxonomically)	Global status	Other EBAs (and SAs)	Altitude (m)	Habitat
Hispaniolan Hawk *Buteo ridgwayi*	EN	—	0–1,000	Rain forest, pine forest, plantations, forest edge/open areas for hunting
Hispaniolan Parakeet *Aratinga chloroptera*	VU	029	0–2,000	Rain forest, dry forest, pine forest, plantations, agricultural areas for feeding
Hispaniolan Amazon *Amazona ventralis*[1]	nt	—	0–1,500	Rain forest, dry forest, pine forest, forages in cultivated land
Rufous-breasted Cuckoo *Hyetornis rufigularis*	VU	—	0–1,000	Dry forest, rain forest
Hispaniolan Lizard-cuckoo *Saurothera longirostris*	lc	—	0–2,000	Dry forest, rain forest, pine forest, plantations
Ashy-faced Owl *Tyto glaucops*	lc	—	0–2,000	Dry forest, rain forest, scrub, savanna
Least Poorwill *Siphonorhis brewsteri*	nt	—	0–800	Dry forest, savanna
Antillean Mango *Anthracothorax dominicus*	lc	029	0–1,000	Dry forest, savanna, plantations, agricultural areas
Hispaniolan Emerald *Chlorostilbon swainsonii*	lc	—	800–2,400	Rain forest, pine forest, scrub for feeding
Vervain Hummingbird *Mellisuga minima*	lc	027	0–2,400	Dry forest, rain forest edge, pine forest, savanna, plantations, agricultural areas
Hispaniolan Trogon *Priotelus roseigaster*	nt	—	500–3,000	Rain forest, dry forest, pine forest
Narrow-billed Tody *Todus angustirostris*	nt	—	1,000–2,400	Rain forest, pine forest, scrub for feeding
Broad-billed Tody *Todus subulatus*	lc	—	0–1,000	Dry forest, rain forest edge, scrub
Antillean Piculet *Nesoctites micromegas*	nt	—	0–1,200	Rain forest, dry forest, mangroves, plantations
Hispaniolan Woodpecker *Melanerpes striatus*	lc	—	0–2,400	All habitats inc. rain forest, dry forest, pine forest, mangroves, scrub, savanna, agriculture, urban areas
Hispaniolan Pewee *Contopus hispaniolensis*[2]	lc	—	0–1,500+	Pine forest, rain forest, dry forest, mangroves, plantations
Greater Antillean Elaenia *Elaenia fallax*	lc	027	1,500–2,000	Pine forest, rain forest
Stolid Flycatcher *Myiarchus stolidus*	lc	027	0–1,800	Dry forest, rain forest edge, mangroves
Golden Swallow *Tachycineta euchrysea*	nt	027	800–2,000	Rain forest, pine forest (nesting); canefields, open country (feeding)
Palmchat *Dulus dominicus*	lc	—	0–1,500	Dry forest, rain forest edge, savanna, agriculture, urban areas; nests mainly in Hispaniolan royal palms
Pearly-eyed Thrasher *Margarops fuscatus*	lc	026,029, 030 (s015)	0–100	Dry forest
Rufous-throated Solitaire *Myadestes genibarbis*	lc	027,030	1,000–1,800	Rain forest, pine forest
La Selle Thrush *Turdus swalesi*	VU	—	1,500–2,100	Rain forest, pine forest
Black-crowned Palm-tanager *Phaenicophilus palmarum*	lc	—	0–2,000	All habitats inc. rain forest, dry forest, pine forest, scrub, savanna, plantations, agriculture, urban areas
Grey-crowned Palm-tanager *Phaenicophilus poliocephalus*	lc	—	0–2,400	Rain forest, mangroves
Chat-tanager *Calyptophilus frugivorus*	VU	—	(Lowlands–) 1,500–2,200	Rain forest, dry forest, pine forest, lowland thickets (rare), scrub (Gonâve Island)
Antillean Euphonia *Euphonia musica*	lc	029,030	0–2,000	Rain forest, dry forest
Green-tailed Warbler *Microligea palustris*	lc	—	0–2,000	Dry forest, rain forest

cont.

Status and habitat of restricted-range species (cont.)

Species (ordered taxonomically)	Global status	Other EBAs (and SAs)	Altitude (m)	Habitat
White-winged Warbler *Xenoligea montana*	VU	—	1,300–1,800	Rain forest, pine forest
Thick-billed Vireo *Vireo crassirostris*	lc	025,026 (s012,s014)	Sea-level	Dry forest, mangroves, scrub
Flat-billed Vireo *Vireo nanus*	lc	—	0–1,800	Dry forest, rain forest
Antillean Siskin *Carduelis dominicensis*	lc	—	500–3,000	Rain forest, pine forest, agricultural areas
Palm Crow *Corvus palmarum*	nt	025	0–2,000	Dry forest, pine forest
White-necked Crow *Corvus leucognaphalus*	VU	029[x]	0–1,000	Rain forest, dry forest, pine forest, plantations, agricultural areas

Global status (see p. 679 for definitions)	EX Extinct	} with year of last record	cd Conservation Dependent	Other EBAs (and SAs) (see p. 60 for locations)	Bracketed numbers are Secondary Areas. [x] Extinct in that EBA or SA.
	EW Extinct in the Wild		nt Near Threatened		
	CR Critical	} threatened species	lc Least Concern	Notes	[1] Introduced to Puerto Rico and the Virgin Islands (EBA 029).
	EN Endangered		DD Data Deficient		
	VU Vulnerable		NE Not Evaluated		[2] Taxonomy follows Reynard *et al.* (1993).

many freed slaves established themselves in the mountains (Harcourt and Sayer 1996).

Today Haiti is one of the most environmentally degraded and densely populated countries in the world, with forest cover of less than 1.5%, the largest remaining blocks being in the Massifs de La Hotte and de La Selle (Paryski *et al.* 1989). The Dominican Republic has c.10% of its land forested, but the rain and cloud forests which remain are in danger of further loss, mainly due to shifting (slash-and-burn) agriculture, with what little forest that there is left being very dispersed through the country; dry forests have been altered considerably by charcoal production and there are only a few pristine areas left; pine forests face fewer threats because they are located mainly at higher elevations and are less affected by fires (Schubert 1993). Even the pine forests have, however, been devastated by indiscriminate logging and clear-cutting, and the reforestation with exotic pine species does not necessarily provide good bird habitat (Ottenwalder 1992).

Continuing habitat loss has resulted in seven of Hispaniola's endemic species being considered threatened (though none critically so) and in seven more being classified as Near Threatened. Hunting has also contributed to the decline of *Buteo ridgwayi*, *Aratinga chloroptera* (shot to protect crops, and trapped for use as a house pet and for international trade), *Hyetornis rufigularis* (shot for its medicinal value) and *Corvus leucognaphalus* (shot to protect crops and for food).

As well as its many threatened restricted-range species, two more-widespread threatened species also occur on Hispaniola: West Indian Whistling-duck *Dendrocygna arborea* (Vulnerable) and Plain Pigeon *Columba inornata* (Endangered). Black-capped Petrel *Pterodroma hasitata*, a seabird which

breeds on islands in the Caribbean (including in small colonies on cliffs and in undisturbed montane forests in this EBA), is also threatened (Endangered); the clearance of vegetation by grazing, logging and fires is reducing the quality of nesting habitat and increasing the birds' susceptibility to predators.

There are many protected areas in the Dominican Republic (a network of 22 areas amounting to c.16% of the land surface), but these do not include all the major ecosystems, with many being under-represented or absent altogether (particularly montane forest), and only two national parks having management plans. In addition, several Hispaniolan parks and reserves are small (under 75 km^2), and thus have a limited prospect of overcoming threats from development and of achieving their primary goal of the long-term maintenance of biological diversity. In Haiti there are only two small national parks with any significant forest fragments, La Viste (20 km^2) and Macaya (55 km^2) (IUCN 1992a, J. A. Ottenwalder *in litt.* 1993).

To address these problems the wildlife service in the Dominican Republic has recently identified gaps in the representation of ecosystems within the nation's protected-area system: 15 new areas have been proposed for protected status including six with cloud forest, four with lowland rain forest and four with dry or semi-deciduous forest (Schubert 1993).

Important sites in this EBA include Los Haitises National Park (recently extended to 1,600 km^2), which has wet limestone forest with a wide array of lowland species (including *Buteo ridgwayi* and *Hyetornis rufigularis*), although there is some cutting of trees and some agriculture. Sierra de Bahoruco National Park (800 km^2) and Jaragua National Park (1,374 km^2) both protect threatened species (J. W. Wiley *in litt.* 1993).

029   Puerto Rico and the Virgin Islands   PRIORITY URGENT

Key habitats Lowland and montane rain forest, dry forest, mangroves

Main threats Major habitat loss (e.g. due to coffee plantations, hurricanes), introduced species

Biological importance ● ●

Current threat level ● ●

Area 9,400 km²   **Altitude** 0–1,200 m

Countries Puerto Rico (to USA), Virgin Islands (to UK and USA)

Restricted-range species	Threatened	Total
Confined to this EBA	3	14
Present also in other EBAs, SAs	1	10
Total	4	24

■ General characteristics

The main part of this EBA is formed by Puerto Rico and its offshore islands (e.g. Mona, Vieques, Culebra) which are a self-governing commonwealth in association with the USA. The land is mountainous and was originally almost completely forested. Because of variations in climate, topography and soils, the forests are diverse and include mangroves, wet and dry coastal forest, wet and dry limestone forest in the west, rain forest in the Cordillera Central and Sierra de Luquillo, and elfin forest on a few summits.

The Virgin Islands comprise two dependent territories, of the UK (main islands Anegada, Tortola and Virgin Gorda) and USA (St Thomas, St John and St Croix), and consists of c.100 small islands and cays with dry scrub forest, mostly heavily modified by man.

■ Restricted-range species

Nearly all the restricted-range species are forest birds, present in a variety of forest types and man-modified habitats, with the exception of *Amazona vittata* (now confined to rain forest), *Caprimulgus noctitherus* (dry limestone forest) and *Dendroica angelae* (upper montane and elfin forest). All species occur on Puerto Rico apart from *Loxigilla noctis*, which, in this EBA, is only found on St John in the US Virgin Islands. Three species are confined to Puerto Rico and the Virgin Islands: *Otus nudipes*, *Melanerpes portoricensis* (now extinct on St Thomas) and

Puerto Rican Amazon *Amazona vittata* had declined to just 13 birds in the 1970s because of deforestation and hunting, but a conservation programme has helped it to recover to c.40 birds.

Status and habitat of restricted-range species

Species (ordered taxonomically)	Global status	Other EBAs (and SAs)	Altitude (m)	Habitat
Bridled Quail-dove *Geotrygon mystacea*	nt	030	0–700	Dry forest, rain forest
Hispaniolan Parakeet *Aratinga chloroptera*[1]	VU	028	No data	Rain forest, dry forest
Puerto Rican Amazon *Amazona vittata*	CR	—	200–900	Rain forest; historically mangroves
Puerto Rican Lizard-cuckoo *Saurothera vieilloti*	lc	—	0–800	Dry forest, rain forest, coffee plantations
Puerto Rican Screech-owl *Otus nudipes*	lc	—	0–900	Rain forest, dry forest
Puerto Rican Nightjar *Caprimulgus noctitherus*	CR	—	Sea-level	Dry limestone forest
Antillean Mango *Anthracothorax dominicus*	lc	028	0–1,200	Rain forest, dry forest, secondary forest, gardens, scrub
Green Mango *Anthracothorax viridis*	lc	—	0–900	Rain forest, secondary forest, forest edges, coffee plantations
Green-throated Carib *Eulampis holosericeus*	lc	030	0–900	Rain forest, dry forest, secondary forest, second-growth scrub, plantations, gardens
Antillean Crested Hummingbird *Orthorhyncus cristatus*	lc	030	Lowlands	Rain forest, secondary forest, second-growth scrub, forest edge, adjacent plantations
Puerto Rican Emerald *Chlorostilbon maugaeus*	lc	—	0–1,000	Rain forest, dry forest, secondary forest, mangroves, second-growth scrub, coffee plantations
Puerto Rican Tody *Todus mexicanus*	lc	—	0–1,000	Rain forest, dry forest, secondary forest, coffee plantations, scrub
Puerto Rican Woodpecker *Melanerpes portoricensis*	lc	—	0–1,000	Rain forest, dry forest, secondary forest, mangroves, coffee and coconut plantations
Lesser Antillean Pewee *Contopus latirostris*	lc	030	0–900	Rain forest, dry forest, adjacent plantations
Puerto Rican Flycatcher *Myiarchus antillarum*	lc	—	0–800	Dry forest, rain forest, mangroves, scrub
Pearly-eyed Thrasher *Margarops fuscatus*	lc	026,028, 030 (s015)	0–1,000	Rain forest, dry forest, secondary forest, scrub
Puerto Rican Bullfinch *Loxigilla portoricensis*	lc	030[X]	0–1,000	Rain forest, dry forest, secondary forest, possibly mangroves, coffee plantations
Lesser Antillean Bullfinch *Loxigilla noctis*	lc	030	Sea-level	Rain forest, dry forest
Puerto Rican Tanager *Nesospingus speculiferus*	lc	—	200–1,200	Rain forest, locally in secondary growth
Antillean Euphonia *Euphonia musica*	lc	028,030	0–1,200	Rain forest, dry forest, secondary forest, forest edge, scrub
Adelaide's Warbler *Dendroica adelaidae*	lc	030	0–800	Rain forest, dry forest, scrub
Elfin-woods Warbler *Dendroica angelae*	nt	—	650–1,050	Elfin forest, rain forest
Puerto Rican Vireo *Vireo latimeri*	lc	—	0–900	Dry forest, rain forest, secondary forest, scrub, coffee plantations
Yellow-shouldered Blackbird *Agelaius xanthomus*	EN	—	Sea-level	Mangroves, cactus scrub, pasture/agricultural land, riparian thickets, plantations, cliffs
White-necked Crow *Corvus leucognaphalus*[2]	VU	028	0–1,200	Rain forest, dry forest, secondary forest, mangroves

Global status (see p. 679 for definitions)

EX Extinct ⎫ with year
EW Extinct in ⎬ of last
      the Wild ⎭ record
CR Critical ⎫
EN Endangered ⎬ threatened species
VU Vulnerable ⎭

cd Conservation Dependent
nt Near Threatened
lc Least Concern
DD Data Deficient
NE Not Evaluated

Other EBAs (and SAs) (see p. 60 for locations)
Bracketed numbers are Secondary Areas.   [X] Extinct in that EBA or SA.

Notes
[1] Possibly extinct in this EBA (e.g. Forshaw and Cooper 1981), but small numbers still in south-west Puerto Rico (J. A. Colon *in litt.* 1993).
[2] Extinct in this EBA (1960s).

Myiarchus antillarum. Five further species occur on Puerto Rico and the Virgin Islands and elsewhere: *Geotrygon mystacea*, *Anthracothorax dominicus*, *Eulampis holosericeus*, *Orthorhyncus cristatus* and *Margarops fuscatus*. Many restricted-range species are shared with Hispaniola (EBA 028) to the west and the Lesser Antilles (EBA 030) to the east.

Hispaniolan Parrot *Amazona ventralis*, a restricted-range species from Hispaniola (EBA 028), and Green-checked Amazon *A. viridigenalis*, a restricted-range species from Mexico (EBA 011), have been introduced to Puerto Rico, but this is outside their natural historical range so they have not been included as restricted-range species of this EBA.

■ Threats and conservation

Natural succession has been slowly reforesting Puerto Rico since industry replaced agriculture as the economic base in the late 1940s (Wadsworth 1950, Birdsey and Weaver 1982). Data from 1978 indicated 37% of the island to be covered in woody vegetation, but this comprised 32% secondary growth, 5% native trees used for shade in coffee plantations and less than 1% virgin forest (Harcourt and Sayer 1996). Secondary forest is used by some restricted-range birds, and coffee plantations in the central mountains provide an important refuge for some species (Brash 1987), but hurricanes are a continual threat to small remnant populations (Wiley 1985).

Storms may, however, have positive long-term effects. Thus, because of deforestation, hunting and nest-robbing, *Amazona vittata* had a population of just 13 in the early 1970s, confined to the Luquillo mountains; but the mountain forests (which are older, undisturbed and not highly productive) may not be optimal habitat. Hurricane damage in 1989 reduced parrot numbers by half but may have stimu-

lated production of buds, fruit and seeds, resulting in increased clutch sizes and numbers of nests of the survivors, as well as forcing them to disperse to the lowlands, which may have led them to discover new nesting sites (Meyers *et al.* 1993). These effects—along with a conservation programme, involving artificial nest-sites, control of predators and competitors, and captive breeding—probably helped the parrot's recovery to c.40 birds by 1996.

Two further restricted-range species are judged to be threatened: *Caprimulgus noctitherus* is at risk from loss of its specialized habitat (c.100 km^2) and from introduced predators such as mongooses, rats and cats, while *Agelaius xanthomus* is under pressure from a range of threats, most notably brood-parasitism by Shiny Cowbirds *Molothrus bonariensis*, loss of mangroves and introduced predators—although the Mona Island population is reasonably healthy and not threatened by cowbirds (J. M. Wunderle *in litt.* 1996). A population decline has recently been noted in *Vireo latimeri* in Guánica Forest, also attributable to parasitism by *M. bonariensis* (Faaborg *et al.* 1997).

Widespread threatened species which occur in this EBA include West Indian Whistling-duck *Dendrocygna arborea* (Vulnerable), Piping Plover *Charadrius melodus* (Vulnerable, winter only), Plain Pigeon *Columba inornata* (Endangered) and Red Siskin *Carduelis cucullata* (Endangered, the population here derived from escaped cage-birds).

Forest is present in over 20 protected areas on Puerto Rico including two Biosphere Reserves: the Luquillo Forest (rain forest, also known as the Caribbean National Forest, 113 km^2) in the north-east and the Guánica State Forest (dry limestone forest, 40 km^2) in the south-west. Private lands also contain large, mature tracts of secondary forest.

030 Lesser Antilles

Key habitats Lowland and montane rain forest, dry forest, elfin forest

Main threats Major habitat loss (e.g. due to plantations, tourist development), introduced species

Biological importance ● ● ●
Current threat level ● ● ○

Area 6,300 km² **Altitude** 0–1,500 m

Countries 12 (see 'General characteristics')

Restricted-range species	Threatened	Total
Confined to this EBA	9	24
Present also in other EBAs, SAs	0	9
Total	9	33

■ General characteristics

This EBA comprises those islands of the Lesser Antilles which stretch in an arc from the Greater Antilles (EBAs 025–029) to the north-eastern part of South America (i.e. it excludes the east–west chain of Lesser Antillean islands which lies off the north coast of Venezuela). Adjacent to the north of the EBA are

the Virgin Islands (part of EBA 029), and Trinidad and Tobago lie to the south (Secondary Areas s016 and s017). Politically, the Lesser Antillean EBA includes the UK dependent territories of Anguilla and Montserrat, the French overseas départements of Guadeloupe and Martinique (St Barthelemy and the northern part of St Martin are dependencies of

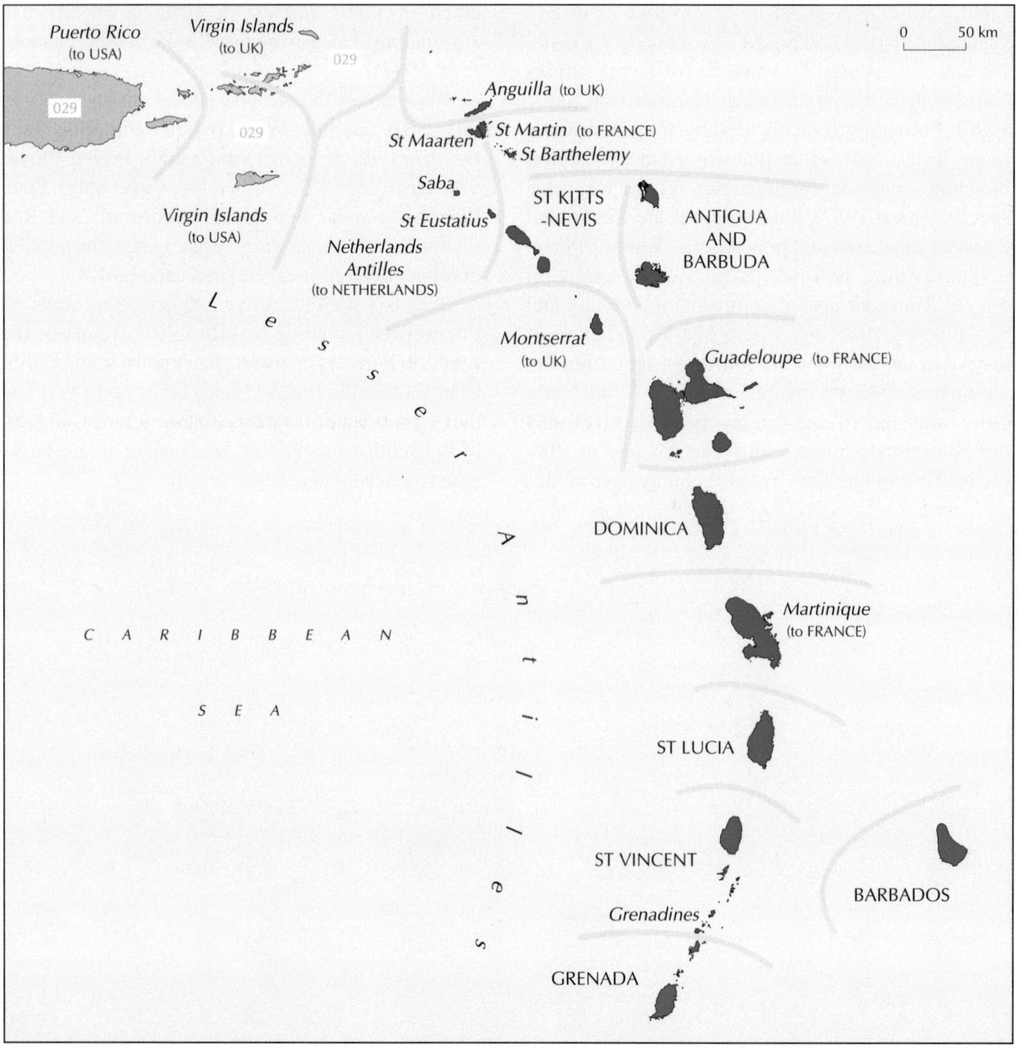

Puerto Rico (to USA)

Virgin Islands (to UK)

029

029

029

Anguilla (to UK)

St Maarten

St Martin (to FRANCE)

St Barthelemy

Saba

ST KITTS -NEVIS

Virgin Islands (to USA)

St Eustatius

Netherlands Antilles (to NETHERLANDS)

ANTIGUA AND BARBUDA

L e s s e r

Montserrat (to UK)

Guadeloupe (to FRANCE)

C A R I B B E A N

S E A

A n t i l l e s

DOMINICA

Martinique (to FRANCE)

ST LUCIA

ST VINCENT

Grenadines

BARBADOS

GRENADA

0   50 km

Status and habitat of restricted-range species

Species (ordered taxonomically)	Global status	Other EBAs (and SAs)	Altitude (m)	Habitat
Grenada Dove *Leptotila wellsi*	CR	—	0–500	Dry forest
Bridled Quail-dove *Geotrygon mystacea*	nt	029	0–800	Dry forest, rain forest
St Lucia Amazon *Amazona versicolor*	VU	—	0–1,000	Rain forest
Red-necked Amazon *Amazona arausiaca*	VU	—	0–1,200	Rain forest
St Vincent Amazon *Amazona guildingii*	VU	—	0–1,000	Rain forest
Imperial Amazon *Amazona imperialis*	VU	—	0–1,400	Rain forest
Lesser Antillean Swift *Chaetura martinica*	lc	—	0–1,500	Rain forest
Purple-throated Carib *Eulampis jugularis*	lc	—	0–1,500	Rain forest, dry forest, secondary forest, adjacent plantations
Green-throated Carib *Eulampis holosericeus*	lc	029	0–1,200	Rain forest, dry forest, secondary forest, second-growth scrub, plantations, gardens
Antillean Crested Hummingbird *Orthorhyncus cristatus*	lc	029	0–1,500	Rain forest, secondary forest, second-growth scrub, forest edge, adjacent plantations
Blue-headed Hummingbird *Cyanophaia bicolor*	lc	—	0–900	Rain forest, montane thicket, elfin forest, secondary forest
Guadeloupe Woodpecker *Melanerpes herminieri*	nt	—	0–1,000	Rain forest, dry forest, secondary forest, mangroves
Lesser Antillean Pewee *Contopus latirostris*	lc	029	0–1,000	Rain forest, dry forest, adjacent plantations, mangroves
Grenada Flycatcher *Myiarchus nugator*	lc	—	0–900	Rain forest, secondary forest
Lesser Antillean Flycatcher *Myiarchus oberi*	lc	—	0–900	Rain forest, adjacent plantations
Brown Trembler *Cinclocerthia ruficauda*	lc	—	0–1,200	Rain forest, dry forest, secondary forest
Grey Trembler *Cinclocerthia gutturalis*	lc	—	0–1,200	Rain forest, dry forest, secondary forest
White-breasted Thrasher *Ramphocinclus brachyurus*	EN	—	0–300	Dry forest
Scaly-breasted Thrasher *Margarops fuscus*	lc	—	0–1,000	Rain forest, dry forest
Pearly-eyed Thrasher *Margarops fuscatus*	lc	026,028, 029 (s015)	0–1,000	Arid scrub, rain forest, dry forest, secondary forest
Forest Thrush *Cichlherminia lherminieri*	nt	—	0–1,000	Rain forest, secondary forest
Rufous-throated Solitaire *Myadestes genibarbis*	lc	027,028	0–1,800	Rain forest, montane thickets
Puerto Rican Bullfinch *Loxigilla portoricensis*[1]	lc	029	0–1,000	Rain forest, dry forest, secondary forest, possibly
Lesser Antillean Bullfinch *Loxigilla noctis*	lc	029	0–1,500	Rain forest, elfin forest, dry forest, secondary forest, adjacent plantations, gardens
St Lucia Black Finch *Melanospiza richardsoni*	nt	—	0–1,000	Rain forest edge, dry forest, dry scrub, secondary growth, plantations
Antillean Euphonia *Euphonia musica*	lc	028,029	0–900	Rain forest, dry forest, forest edge, secondary forest, scrub
Lesser Antillean Tanager *Tangara cucullata*	lc	—	0–900	Rain forest, dry forest, secondary forest

cont.

Status and habitat of restricted-range species (cont.)

Species (ordered taxonomically)	Global status	Other EBAs (and SAs)	Altitude (m)	Habitat
Adelaide's Warbler *Dendroica adelaidae*	lc	029	0–800	Rain forest, dry forest, arid scrub
Plumbeous Warbler *Dendroica plumbea*	lc	—	0–1,500	Rain forest, elfin forest, dry forest
Whistling Warbler *Catharopeza bishopi*	VU	—	300–1,100	Rain forest, montane thickets, elfin forest
Semper's Warbler *Leucopeza semperi*	CR	—	400–900	Rain forest, montane thickets, elfin forest
Montserrat Oriole *Icterus oberi*	nt	—	100–1,000	Rain forest
Martinique Oriole *Icterus bonana*	EN	—	0–700	Dry forest, rain forest, mangroves, secondary forest, plantations
St Lucia Oriole *Icterus laudabilis*	nt	—	0–1,000	Rain forest, dry forest, secondary forest, plantations

Global status (see p. 679 for definitions)

EX	Extinct	} with year of last record
EW	Extinct in the Wild	
CR	Critical	} threatened species
EN	Endangered	
VU	Vulnerable	

cd	Conservation Dependent	
nt	Near Threatened	
lc	Least Concern	
DD	Data Deficient	
NE	Not Evaluated	

Other EBAs (and SAs) (see p. 60 for locations)
Bracketed numbers are Secondary Areas.
X Extinct in that EBA or SA.

Notes [1] Extinct in this EBA (1926).

Guadeloupe), the northern Netherlands Antilles (southern part of St Maarten, Saba and St Eustatius), and the independent territories of St Kitts–Nevis, Antigua and Barbuda, Dominica, St Lucia, St Vincent (including some of the Grenadines), Barbados, and Grenada (including the rest of the Grenadines).

The EBA's main islands are volcanic and mountainous, while the outlying ones are composed mostly of limestone and are of low relief. Volcanoes on four islands (Montserrat, Guadeloupe, Martinique and St Vincent) have erupted during the twentieth century. The more mountainous islands of Guadaloupe, Dominica, Martinique, St Lucia and St Vincent have a rich variety of habitats ranging from rain forest (including lowland and lower montane types), with montane thicket, palm brake and elfin forest along summits, to dry forest and mangroves in the lowlands.

In addition to its restricted-range birds, this EBA is important for many North American migrants and for seabirds, with many of the smaller, uninhabited islands having large and varied seabird breeding populations (see van Halewyn and Norton 1984).

■ Restricted-range species

This EBA has a particularly distinct avifauna, including seven endemic genera—*Catharopeza, Cichlherminia, Cinclocerthia, Cyanophaia, Leucopeza, Melanospiza* and *Ramphocinclus*.

Most restricted-range species occur over a wide altitudinal range and in many habitats including dry and rain forest, and, less frequently, montane thickets and elfin forest of the uplands. A few species show more specific habitat requirements: examples are *Leptotila wellsi* and *Ramphocinclus brachyurus*

which are confined to the dry forest of the lowlands, and *Catharopeza bishopi* and *Leucopeza semperi* which occur in montane habitats only.

The pattern of distribution between the EBA's islands varies considerably, with only a small number of restricted-range species occurring widely (i.e. on half or more of the islands); there is, nevertheless, sufficient distributional overlap (more sharing than not) for the islands all to be included within a single EBA—though several islands have their own endemic species and are therefore important centres of endemism in their own right: Montserrat (one endemic species), Guadeloupe (one), Dominica (two), Martinique (one), St Lucia (four), St Vincent (two) and Grenada (one). The numbers of restricted-range species occurring on the islands also vary considerably, the three islands with the most being St Lucia (20), Dominica (18) and Martinique (16).

■ Threats and conservation

The islands have suffered large-scale disturbance and destruction of forest ecosystems, mainly as a part of agricultural development. Thus some of the lower-lying limestone islands, such as Antigua and Barbados, have lost most of their natural vegetation, while on the more mountainous islands forest remnants are generally in high and inaccessible areas. Clearance for banana plantations continues on all the mountainous islands, and alteration of habitats for tourist developments (e.g. golf courses) is also a threat.

All the single-island endemics are considered threatened or Near Threatened chiefly as a result of habitat loss, but hunting, trade, brood parasitism and introduced species have all contributed to their de-

Distribution patterns of restricted-range species

Species (ordered geographically)	Anguilla	St Martin, Barthélemy	N. Antilles	St Kitts & Nevis	Barbuda	Antigua	Montserrat	Guadeloupe	Dominica	Martinique	St Lucia	St Vincent	Barbados	Grenadines	Grenada	Other EBAs, SAs
Margarops fuscatus	•	•	•	•	•	•	•	•	•	•	•	–	–	–	–	•
Loxigilla noctis	•	•	•	•	•	•	•	•	•	•	•	•	•	–	•	•
Eulampis holosericeus	•	•	•	•	•	•	•	•	•	•	•	•	•	•	•	•
Orthorhynchus cristatus	•	•	•	•	•	•	•	•	•	•	•	•	•	•	•	•
Euphonia musica	–	•	•	–	•	•	•	•	•	•	–	–	–	–	o	•
Geotrygon mystacea	–	–	•	–	X	•	•	•	o	•	•	–	–	–	–	•
Cinclocerthia ruficauda	–	–	•	•	–	•	•	•	•	–	–	–	–	–	–	–
Eulampis jugularis	–	–	•	•	–	•	•	•	•	•	–	–	–	–	–	–
Margarops fuscus	–	–	•	–	•	•	•	•	•	•	•	•	–	•	o	–
Loxigilla portoricensis	–	–	–	X	–	–	–	–	–	–	–	–	–	–	–	•
Myiarchus oberi	–	–	–	•	•	–	•	•	•	•	–	–	–	–	–	–
Dendroica adelaidae	–	–	–	–	•	–	–	–	–	•	–	–	–	–	–	•
Icterus oberi	–	–	–	–	–	–	•	–	–	–	–	–	–	–	–	–
Cichlherminia lherminieri	–	–	–	–	–	–	•	•	•	–	–	–	–	–	–	–
Melanerpes herminieri	–	–	–	–	–	–	–	•	–	–	–	–	–	–	–	–
Dendroica plumbea	–	–	–	–	–	–	–	•	•	–	–	–	–	–	–	–
Contopus latirostris	–	–	–	–	–	–	–	•	•	•	•	–	–	–	–	•
Chaetura martinica	–	–	–	–	–	–	–	•	•	•	•	–	–	–	–	–
Amazona arausiaca	–	–	–	–	–	–	–	–	•	–	–	–	–	–	–	–
Amazona imperialis	–	–	–	–	–	–	–	–	•	–	–	–	–	–	–	–
Cyanophaia bicolor	–	–	–	–	–	–	–	–	•	•	–	–	–	–	–	–
Myadestes genibarbis	–	–	–	–	–	–	–	–	•	•	•	–	–	–	–	o
Icterus bonana	–	–	–	–	–	–	–	–	–	•	–	–	–	–	–	–
Cinclocerthia gutturalis	–	–	–	–	–	–	–	–	–	•	•	–	–	–	–	–
Ramphocinclus brachyurus	–	–	–	–	–	–	–	–	–	•	•	–	–	–	–	–
Amazona versicolor	–	–	–	–	–	–	–	–	–	–	•	–	–	–	–	–
Melanospiza richardsoni	–	–	–	–	–	–	–	–	–	–	•	–	–	–	–	–
Leucopeza semperi	–	–	–	–	–	–	–	–	–	–	o	–	–	–	–	–
Icterus laudabilis	–	–	–	–	–	–	–	–	–	–	•	–	–	–	–	–
Amazona guildingii	–	–	–	–	–	–	–	–	–	–	–	•	–	–	–	–
Catharopeza bishopi	–	–	–	–	–	–	–	–	–	–	–	•	–	–	–	–
Myiarchus nugator	–	–	–	–	–	–	–	–	–	–	–	•	–	•	–	–
Tangara cucullata	–	–	–	–	–	–	–	–	–	–	–	•	–	•	•	–
Leptotila wellsi	–	–	–	–	–	–	–	–	–	–	–	–	–	–	•	–
Total	4	5	9	7	8	8	12	15	18	16	20	13	4	4	8	

- • Present
- o Extinct?
- X Extinct
- ? Present?
- R Reintroduced
- I Introduced

Threatened spp. shown in **bold**
Other EBAs, SAs } see 'Status and habitat' table

cline. The *Amazona* parrots, in particular, have been the focus of considerable conservation efforts by government and non-government agencies, and consequently their status has improved. *Leptotila wellsi* remains Critical on Grenada (c.75 birds in 1992), being greatly threatened by chronic and continuing habitat alteration and destruction (plantations, construction developments, agriculture), possibly compounded by predation of fledglings by introduced mongooses. Likewise *Ramphocinclus brachyurus* has been reduced by habitat destruction and introduced predators to near-extinction in two dry forest areas on the islands of Martinique (15–40 pairs) and St Lucia (c.50 pairs). *Leucopeza semperi* is very possibly extinct on St Lucia, there being just a handful of records since the 1920s, and it is likely that its disappearance is related to the introduction of the mongoose, with habitat loss inevitably playing a part too. *Icterus bonana* is present in most habitat types

throughout Martinique, but has suffered severe levels of brood-parasitism from the recently established Shiny Cowbird *Molothrus bonariensis*.

The widespread, but threatened (Vulnerable), West Indian Whistling-duck *Dendrocygna arborea* occurs on St Kitts and Nevis, and on Antigua and Barbuda, where hunting and commercial development of coastal wetlands are threats. The threatened (Endangered) seabird, Black-capped Petrel *Pterodroma hasitata*, was known in this EBA from Martinique and Guadeloupe, and is still reported from Dominica.

Protected areas of particular note within the EBA are: Guadeloupe National Park (173 km²); Morne Trois Pitons National Park (69 km²) and Syndicate Forest Reserve/Parrot Sanctuary on Dominica; Martinique Regional Nature Park (702 km²); the Parrot Sanctuary (15 km²) on St Lucia; St Vincent Parrot Reserve (44 km²); and the Levera and Grand Etang National Parks on Grenada.

167

031 Galápagos Islands

PRIORITY
URGENT

Key habitats Arid scrub, mangroves, deciduous and montane forest

Main threats Moderate habitat loss (e.g. due to overgrazing, fires), introduced species

Biological importance ● ● ○
Current threat level ● ● ○

Area 8,000 km²   **Altitude** 0–1,700 m

Countries Ecuador

Restricted-range species	Threatened	Total
Confined to this EBA	3	22
Present also in other EBAs, SAs	0	0
Total	3	22

■ General characteristics

The Galápagos Islands are widely known for their historical role in the development of the theory of natural selection and evolution. This volcanic archipelago, still one of the most active volcanic areas in the world, straddles the equator, some 960 km west of mainland Ecuador, to which it belongs politically. In all there are 13 islands of more than 10 km² (with Isabela the largest at 4,590 km²), and over 40 islets that have official names (with many small rocks and islets as yet unnamed). Most islands are below 900 m in elevation, although Isabela (1,710 m) and Fernandina (1,490 m) are considerably higher.

Marine iguana *Amblyrhynchus cristatus*, one of the numerous taxa endemic to this important and unique archipelago.

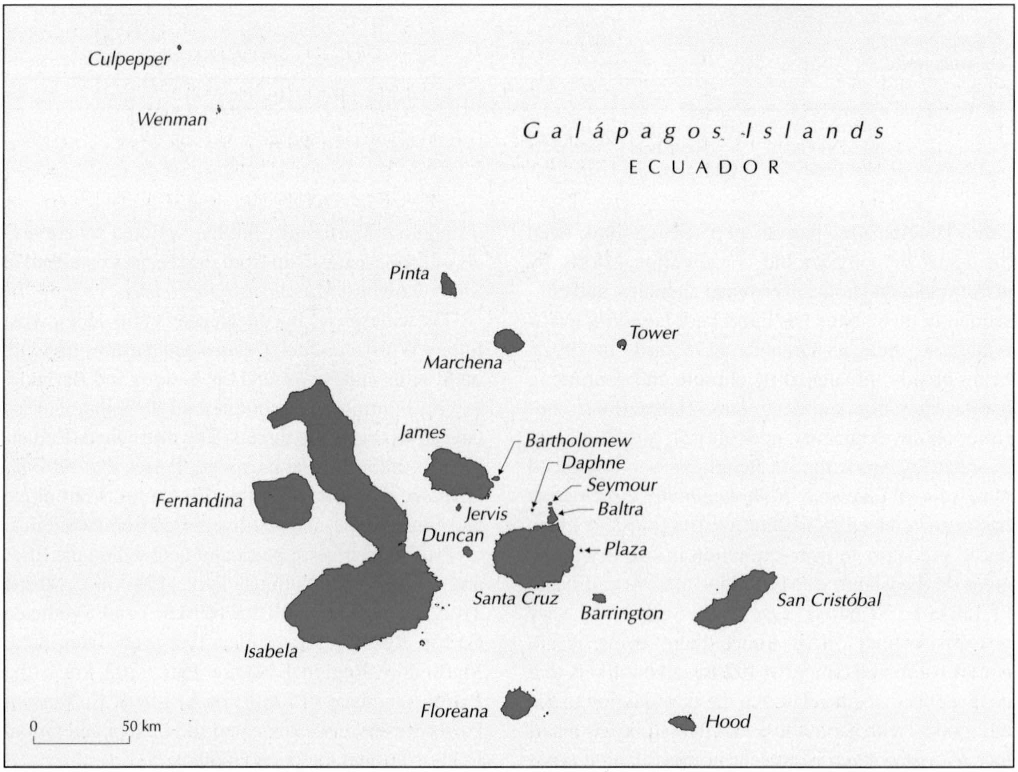

A. and J. Fitter

Culpepper

Wenman

Galápagos Islands
ECUADOR

Pinta

Marchena

Tower

James

Bartholomew
Daphne
Seymour
Baltra

Fernandina

Jervis
Duncan

Plaza

Santa Cruz
Barrington

San Cristóbal

Isabela

Floreana

Hood

0   50 km

Status and habitat of restricted-range species

Species (ordered taxonomically)	Global status	Other EBAs (and SAs)	Altitude (m)	Habitat
Galápagos Heron *Butorides sundevalli*	lc	—	Coastal	Freshwater and saltwater/brackish marshes, mangrove forest, rocky coasts
Galápagos Hawk *Buteo galapagoensis*	VU	—	Lowlands, highlands	Tropical deciduous forest, arid lowland scrub, semi-desert, lava flows
Galápagos Rail *Laterallus spilonotus*	nt	—	Usually >500	Montane evergreen forest, deep thickets, dense grass; historically mangrove, possibly freshwater marshes
Galápagos Dove *Zenaida galapagoensis*	lc	—	Lowlands	Tropical deciduous forest, arid rocky lowland scrub, arid and transitional zones
Large-billed Flycatcher *Myiarchus magnirostris*	lc	—	Lowlands, highlands	Tropical deciduous forest, arid lowland scrub up to pampa zone
Galápagos Mockingbird *Nesomimus parvulus*	lc	—	Lowlands	Arid lowland scrub, tropical deciduous forest, arid and transitional zones, open country
Floreana Mockingbird *Nesomimus trifasciatus*	EN	—	Lowlands	Arid lowland scrub, tropical deciduous forest, arid and transitional zones, open country
Hood Mockingbird *Nesomimus macdonaldi*	lc	—	Lowlands	Arid lowland scrub, tropical deciduous forest, arid and transitional zones, open country
San Cristóbal Mockingbird *Nesomimus melanotis*	lc	—	Lowlands	Arid lowland scrub, tropical deciduous forest, arid and transitional zones, open country
Large Ground-finch *Geospiza magnirostris*	lc	—	Mainly lowlands	Arid lowland scrub, tropical deciduous forest, arid and transitional zones
Medium Ground-finch *Geospiza fortis*	lc	—	Mainly lowlands	Arid lowland scrub, tropical deciduous forest, arid and transitional zones
Small Ground-finch *Geospiza fuliginosa*	lc	—	Mainly lowlands	Arid lowland scrub, tropical deciduous forest, arid and transitional zones
Sharp-beaked Ground-finch *Geospiza difficilis*	lc	—	Mainly lowlands	Arid lowland scrub, tropical deciduous forest, arid humid scrub
Common Cactus-finch *Geospiza scandens*	lc	—	Mainly lowlands	Arid lowland scrub, tropical deciduous forest, and transitional zones, cactus forest
Large Cactus-finch *Geospiza conirostris*	lc	—	Mainly lowlands	Arid lowland scrub, tropical deciduous forest, arid and transitional zones, cactus forest
Vegetarian Finch *Camarhynchus crassirostris*	lc	—	Mainly lowlands	Tropical deciduous forest, montane evergreen forest, arid and transitional zones, humid scrub
Large Tree-finch *Camarhynchus psittacula*	lc	—	Mainly highlands	Montane evergreen and tropical deciduous forest, *Scalesia* zone, humid scrub
Medium Tree-finch *Camarhynchus pauper*	nt	—	Mainly highlands	Montane evergreen and tropical deciduous forest, *Scalesia* zone, humid scrub
Small Tree-finch *Camarhynchus parvulus*	lc	—	Mainly highlands	Tropical deciduous forest, arid lowland scrub, transitional and *Scalesia* zones, humid scrub
Woodpecker Finch *Camarhynchus pallidus*	lc	—	Mainly highlands	Arid lowland scrub, tropical deciduous forest, *Scalesia* zone, cactus forest
Mangrove Finch *Camarhynchus heliobates*	EN	—	Coastal	Dense mangrove forest
Warbler Finch *Certhidea olivacea*	lc	—	Mainly highlands	Arid lowland scrub, tropical deciduous and montane evergreen forest, transitional and *Scalesia* zones, humid scrub

Global status (see p. 679 for definitions): EX Extinct, EW Extinct in the Wild (with year of last record); CR Critical, EN Endangered, VU Vulnerable (threatened species); cd Conservation Dependent, nt Near Threatened, lc Least Concern; DD Data Deficient, NE Not Evaluated

Other EBAs (and SAs) (see p. 65 for locations): bracketed numbers are Secondary Areas; ˣ extinct in that EBA or SA.

The vegetation of the islands has been divided into various zones: the littoral or coastal zone, which includes beaches, lagoons and mangroves; the arid zone, just inland from the coast, which is the most extensive habitat type on the islands with the greatest number of endemics, characterized by deciduous trees and shrubs; the transition zone, intermediate in character between the arid zone and the *Scalesia* zone, but dominated by different species, resulting in a diverse, mainly deciduous dense forest; the *Scalesia*

Distribution patterns of restricted-range species

Species (ordered geographically)	Culpepper	Wenman	Fernandina	Isabela	Pinta	Marchena	Tower	James, Bartholomew, Jervis	Duncan	Baltra	Santa Cruz, Daphne, Plaza, Seymour	Floreana & Islands	Barrington	San Cristóbal	Hood	Other EBAs, SAs
Nesominus parvulus	●	●	●	●	●	●	●	●	?	●	●	—	●	—	—	—
Geospiza difficilis	●	●	●	○	●	—	●	—	—	—	○	○	—	○	—	—
Geospiza conirostris	●	●	—	—	?	—	●	—	—	—	—	?	—	—	●	—
Butorides sundevalli	●	●	●	●	●	●	●	●	●	●	●	●	●	●	●	—
Zenaida galapagoensis	?	?	●	●	●	?	●	●	?	?	●	●	●	●	●	—
Certhidia olivacea	●	●	●	●	●	●	●	●	●	●	●	●	●	●	●	—
Camarhynchus parvulus	—	?	●	●	●	●	—	●	●	●	●	●	—	●	—	—
Geospiza magnirostris	—	●	?	●	●	—	●	●	●	—	●	○	○	○	—	—
Myiarchus magnirostris	—	?	●	●	●	●	?	●	●	●	●	●	●	—	●	—
Camarhynchus heliobates	—	—	●	●	—	—	—	—	—	—	—	—	—	—	—	—
Camarhynchus crassirostris	—	—	●	●	●	●	—	●	?	—	●	●	—	●	—	—
Laterallus spilonotus	—	—	●	●	—	●	—	●	—	●	●	●	—	●	—	—
Camarhynchus pallidus	—	—	●	●	?	●	—	●	—	●	—	●	?	?	●	—
Camarhynchus psittacula	—	—	●	●	●	●	—	●	?	?	●	●	?	?	—	—
Buteo galapagoensis	—	—	●	●	●	●	—	●	●	X	●	X	●	X	●	—
Geospiza fortis	—	—	●	●	●	●	●	●	●	●	●	●	●	●	○	—
Geospiza fuliginosa	—	—	●	●	●	●	●	●	●	●	●	●	●	●	●	—
Geospiza scandens	—	—	—	●	●	●	—	●	○	●	●	●	●	—	—	—
Camarhynchus pauper	—	—	—	—	—	—	—	—	—	—	—	●	—	—	—	—
Nesomimus trifasciatus	—	—	—	—	—	—	—	—	—	—	—	●	—	—	—	—
Nesomimus melanotis	—	—	—	—	—	—	—	—	—	—	—	—	—	●	—	—
Nesomimus macdonaldi	—	—	—	—	—	—	—	—	—	—	—	—	—	—	●	—
Total	5	6	15	17	15	11	8	16	10	9	16	14	11	14	9	

● Present ? Present?
○ Extinct? R Reintroduced
X Extinct I Introduced

Threatened spp. shown in **bold**
Other EBAs, SAs
see 'Status and habitat' table

J. P. Croxall

A. and J. Fitter

J. P. Croxall

Galápagos Hawk *Buteo galapagoensis* (top left), Medium Ground-finch *Geospiza fortis* (bottom left) and Galápagos Mockingbird *Nesomimus parvulus* (above)—three characteristic birds endemic to the Galápagos Islands.

zone, comprising lush evergreen cloud forest dominated by *Scalesia pedunculata*; and the open pampa zone consisting largely of ferns, grasses and sedges (Jackson 1985).

The archipelago's native biota demonstrates remarkable adaptive radiation. Both flora and fauna display a high degree of endemism, as would be expected in such an isolated tropical archipelago.

Destruction of the native vegetation by feral goats is a significant threat to endemic wildlife, such as giant tortoise *Geochelone elephantopus*.

A. and J. Fitter

■ Restricted-range species

The restricted-range birds of the Galápagos are all endemic to the archipelago, and occupy most of the vegetation (and thus altitudinal) zones outlined above. Thirteen of the 22 endemics are known collectively as Darwin's finches (sometimes recognized as the separate subtribe Geospizini, with a fourteenth species on Cocos Island, EBA 022). The four *Nesomimus* mockingbirds constitute the next largest group of endemic species, and are indeed an endemic genus, all four species occurring in the littoral and arid zones. There are only four single-island endemics in Galápagos, these being *Camarhynchus pauper* and *Nesomimus trifasciatus* (on Floreana and satellites), *N. melanotis* (on San Cristóbal) and *N. macdonaldi* (on Hood), the remaining species generally being found on three or more islands (Harris 1982).

Six seabirds—Galápagos Penguin *Spheniscus mendiculus*, Waved Albatross *Diomedea irrorata* (also on Isla de la Plata), Galápagos Petrel *Pterodroma phaeopygia*, Galápagos Cormorant *Phalacrocorax harrisi*, Lava Gull *Larus fuliginosus* and Swallow-tailed Gull *Creagrus furcatus*—are endemic breeders to the islands, but are not included in the EBA analysis. White-vented Storm-petrel *Oceanites gracilis* is known to breed only in this EBA and on Isla Chungungo off Chile.

■ Threats and conservation

The islands' wildlife is threatened as a result of various human activities: overgrazing by domestic and feral livestock, predation by exotic species, fires started by man, and poaching (Dinerstein *et al.* 1995).

Three of the endemic landbirds are presently considered threatened, all for slightly different reasons. *Buteo galapagoensis* occupies c.130 breeding territories (but exhibits cooperative polyandry), and has declined due to human persecution, and partly from a reduction in prey items (caused by introduced predators). *Nesomimus trifasciatus* now occurs only on Floreana's two satellite islands, where the population stands at c.300 birds and thus requires constant management. *Camarhynchus heliobates* is very poorly known, occurring on Fernandina and Isabela in an area of mangrove totalling some 5 km^2 (Collar *et al.* 1992).

Additionally, four of the endemic seabirds are considered to be threatened: *Spheniscus mendiculus* (classified as Vulnerable), *Pterodroma phaeopygia* (Critical), *Phalocrocorax harrisi* (Vulnerable) and *Larus fuliginosus* (Vulnerable); *Oceanites gracilis* is classified as Data Deficient (Collar *et al.* 1994). *Diomedea irrorata* should also be considered threatened and is treated as such in Croxall and Gales (in press).

The entire Galápagos archipelago is formally protected as a national park and Biosphere Reserve (IUCN 1992a), and as a World Heritage Site. However, with so many island-adapted endemics, constant vigilance needs to be exercised by the large number of tourists and resident scientists to prevent the accidental introduction of further alien species (especially predators) to islands where the native flora and fauna would probably be unable to compete. Efforts to eradicate existing alien species could only benefit the vulnerable native flora and fauna.

032 Caripe–Paria region

Key habitats Montane evergreen forest

Main threats Major habitat loss (e.g. due to cultivation, pasture)

Biological importance ● ● ○
Current threat level ● ● ●

Area 6,000 km² **Altitude** 400–2,500 m
Countries Venezuela

Restricted-range species	Threatened	Total
Confined to this EBA	5	5
Present also in other EBAs, SAs	1	7
Total	6	12

■ General characteristics

The region comprises two disjunct mountain ranges in northern Venezuela, separated by the San Juan river: the coastal and low-lying mountains of the central and eastern Paria peninsula, and, further inland, the Cordillera de Caripe. Cerro Peonía lies at the western end of the Cordillera de Caripe, Cerro Turumiquire (the highest peak) in the middle, and Cerro Negro and Los Cumbres de San Bonifacio at the eastern end. The large Paria peninsula projects east from the mainland towards Trinidad (Secondary Area s016), and at 400–1,300 m supports lower and upper montane evergreen forest (rich in epiphytes, bromeliads, ferns and *Heliconia* spp.) with elfin forest on the peaks. These forest types are at lower altitudes than on the adjacent Cordillera de Caripe. Oilbird *Steatornis caripensis*, which nests in this area (and from which its specific name derives), is a major seed disperser and crucial to the biodiversity of these forests (A. Grajal *in litt*. 1993).

■ Restricted-range species

All the restricted-range species occur in the now much-reduced montane evergreen forest, a number being forest-edge specialists and occurring also in secondary habitats. The species are primarily found above 400 m, the altitude at which lower montane forest is present on the Paria peninsula, but the same

C. J. Sharpe

Humid montane forest on the Caribbean slope of the eastern Paria peninsula, inside the national park.

Status and habitat of restricted-range species

Species (ordered taxonomically)	Global status	Other EBAs (and SAs)	Altitude (m)	Habitat
Tepui Parrotlet *Nannopsittaca panychlora*	lc	064	750–1,850	Montane evergreen forest
White-tailed Sabrewing *Campylopterus ensipennis*	VU	(s017)	460–1,830	Montane evergreen forest, clearings
Green-tailed Emerald *Chlorostilbon alice*	lc	033,034	750–1,800	Montane evergreen forest edge, secondary and tropical lowland evergreen forest, plantations
Scissor-tailed Hummingbird *Hylonympha macrocerca*	CR	—	800–1,200	Montane evergreen forest, forest edge
White-tipped Quetzal *Pharomachrus fulgidus*	lc	033,036	900–2,500	Montane evergreen forest, forest edge, secondary growth
White-throated Barbtail *Premnoplex tatei*	EN	—	800–2,400	Montane evergreen forest, forest edge
Guttulated Foliage-gleaner *Syndactyla guttulata*	lc	033	800–2,100	Montane evergreen and secondary forest
Handsome Fruiteater *Pipreola formosa*	lc	033	800–2,200	Montane evergreen forest, forest edge
Fulvous-headed Tanager *Thlypopsis fulviceps*	lc	033,034,038	750–2,300	Secondary and montane evergreen forest, forest edge, thickets, bamboo
Venezuelan Flower-piercer *Diglossa venezuelensis*	CR	—	1,525–2,450	Montane evergreen forest edge, secondary forest, second-growth scrub
Paria Whitestart *Myioborus pariae*	CR	—	800–1,150	Montane evergreen forest, forest edge
Grey-headed Warbler *Basileuterus griseiceps*	CR	—	1,200–2,440	Montane evergreen forest, possibly secondary forest

Global status (see p. 679 for definitions)
EX Extinct — with year of last record
EW Extinct in the Wild
CR Critical — threatened species
EN Endangered
VU Vulnerable
cd Conservation Dependent
nt Near Threatened
lc Least Concern
DD Data Deficient
NE Not Evaluated

Other EBAs (and SAs) (see p. 65 for locations): bracketed numbers are Secondary Areas; [x] extinct in that EBA or SA.

species occur at higher altitudes on the Cordillera de Caripe. This is best demonstrated by the two subspecies of *Premnoplex tatei*, the Paria form being found up to 1,200 m, and the Caripe one occurring from 1,200 m upwards.

Distribution patterns of restricted-range species

Species (ordered geographically)	Cordillera de Caripe	Paria peninsula	Other EBAs, SAs
Basileuterus griseiceps	●	–	–
Chlorostilbon alice	●	–	○
Syndactyla guttulata	●	–	○
Thlypopsis fulviceps	●	–	○
Premnoplex tatei	●	●	–
Diglossa venezuelensis	●	●	–
Nannopsittaca panychlora	●	●	○
Campylopterus ensipennis	●	●	○
Pharomachrus fulgidus	●	●	○
Pipreola formosa	●	●	○
Hylonympha macrocerca	–	●	–
Myioborus pariae	–	●	–
Total	10	8	

● Present
○ Extinct?
X Extinct
? Present?
R Reintroduced
I Introduced
Threatened spp. shown in **bold** — see 'Status and habitat' table
Other EBAs, SAs

Over half of the restricted-range species in this EBA occur also in the adjacent Cordillera de la Costa Central (EBA 033). Ten species are present in the Cordillera de Caripe, and eight occur in the Paria peninsula. Just one species is found solely in the Cordillera de Caripe, and two are confined to the peninsula—but an additional two are endemic to both areas, and thus these two centres of endemism are combined into a single EBA. The number of Andean-derived bird species in the various coastal mountain ranges decreases eastwards, so leaving the peninsula relatively impoverished (Bond *et al.* 1989).

Cracraft (1985) described the Caripe–Paria region as including 45 endemic subspecies, 13 of which are confined to the Paria peninsula. One restricted-range form, Caracas Tapaculo *Scytalopus* (*latebricola*) *caracae*, which occurs on Cerro Turumiquire, has recently been recognised as specifically distinct (Ridgley and Tudor 1994, though it is not so treated here), and with further work other taxa may be raised to species level.

■ Threats and conservation

The Cordillera de Caripe is under severe human pressure which, through widespread clearance for

Coffee harvest from a small shade-tolerant plantation. Removal of the understorey is a threat to a number of species in this EBA.

understorey for coffee) have reduced the park's humid montane forest to a small percentage of its former extent. On the Paria peninsula, although the national park embraces most of the remaining forest, changes in agricultural practices have led to increased forest degradation (Wege and Long 1995). The Paria peninsula is just south of an enormous natural gas field, with a pipeline and a major refinery planned for the middle of the peninsula (C. J. Sharpe *in litt.* 1997). This project, which is proceeding apace, is still in urgent need of an impact assessment, the recommendations from which must be followed to prevent an environmental disaster.

Each of the six species (largely) confined to this EBA are considered threatened (four are classified as Critical), and five Key Areas for their conservation were recently identified (Wege and Long 1995). *Hylonympha macrocerca* and *Myioborus pariae* are found at only a handful of localities on the Paria peninsula (the most important being Cerro Humo), and *Basileuterus griseiceps* is confined to the Cordillera de Caripe where it is severely threatened by almost total deforestation and currently known only from the El Guácharo National Park area, primarily around Cerro Negro (Boesman and Curson 1995). The other three species are more widespread within the EBA, *Campylopterus ensipennis* being found also on Tobago (Secondary Area s017).

Both the Paria peninsula and El Guácharo National Parks offer formal protection to the restricted-range (and threatened) species, but habitat destruction is still occurring at a frightening rate within them.

agriculture and pasture, has resulted in extensive degradation of the montane forest such that little remains undisturbed. Even in El Guácharo National Park the agricultural practices of local campesinos (forest clearance, repeated burning and removal of

033 | Cordillera de la Costa Central

PRIORITY HIGH

Key habitats Montane evergreen forest, wetlands

Main threats Moderate habitat loss (e.g. due to settlement)

Biological importance ● ●
Current threat level ●

Area 6,200 km² **Altitude** 600–2,500 m

Countries Venezuela

Restricted-range species	Threatened	Total
Confined to this EBA	1	5
Present also in other EBAs, SAs	1	12
Total	2	17

■ General characteristics

The Cordillera de la Costa Central extends from Carabobo state to Laguna de Tacarigua in Miranda state, along the north coast of Venezuela. In the west, the main cordillera terminates at the Yaracuy river. The EBA also embraces the parallel southern chain, the Cadena del Interior, as well as the Sierra de Aroa to the west of the Yaracuy around San Felipe (and north of the Cojedes headwaters that form the northern boundary of the Cordillera de Mérida, EBA 034), and also some of the isolated higher peaks in Lara and Falcón states (e.g. Cerro Cerrón and Sierra de San Luis).

The isolated mountains and ranges that characterize this EBA support montane evergreen forests that have long been isolated by drier surrounding lowlands from one another and from larger blocks of moist forest to the south (e.g. the Andes and Orinoco basin) (Dinerstein *et al.* 1995). The forests, which range from 600 to 2,500 m, include deciduous to evergreen and elfin forest (Huber and Alarcón 1988).

■ Restricted-range species

The birds in this EBA are primarily reliant on montane evergreen forest and forest-edge habitats (mostly above 750 m), although secondary vegetation and coffee plantations also feature as important for a

Distribution patterns of restricted-range species

Species (ordered geographically)	Cordillera de la Costa	Sierra de Aroa	Sierra de San Luis	Cerro Cerrón	Other EBAs, SAs
Laterallus levraudi	●	–	–	–	–
Synallaxis castanea	●	–	–	–	–
Phylloscartes venezuelanus	●	–	–	–	–
Pyrrhura hoematotis	●	–	–	–	●
Cypseloides phelpsi	●	–	–	–	●
Grallaria excelsa	●	–	–	–	●
Thlypopsis fulviceps	●	–	–	–	●
Pauxi pauxi	●	●	–	–	●
Sternoclyta cyanopectus	●	●	–	–	●
Pharomachrus fulgidus	●	●	–	–	●
Syndactyla guttulata	●	●	–	–	●
Chamaeza turdina	●	●	–	–	–
Grallaricula loricata	●	●	–	–	–
Pipreola formosa	●	●	–	–	●
Tangara rufigenis	●	●	–	–	–
Odontophorus columbianus	●	–	–	–	●
Chlorostilbon alice	●	●	●	●	●
Total	17	9	1	1	

● Present ? Present? Threatened spp. shown in **bold** } see 'Status and habitat' table
○ Extinct? R Reintroduced Other EBAs, SAs
X Extinct I Introduced

number of species. Apart from *Laterallus levraudi* which appears to be confined to wetland habitats at lower elevations (Collar *et al.* 1992), all of the restricted-range species occurring in the area are

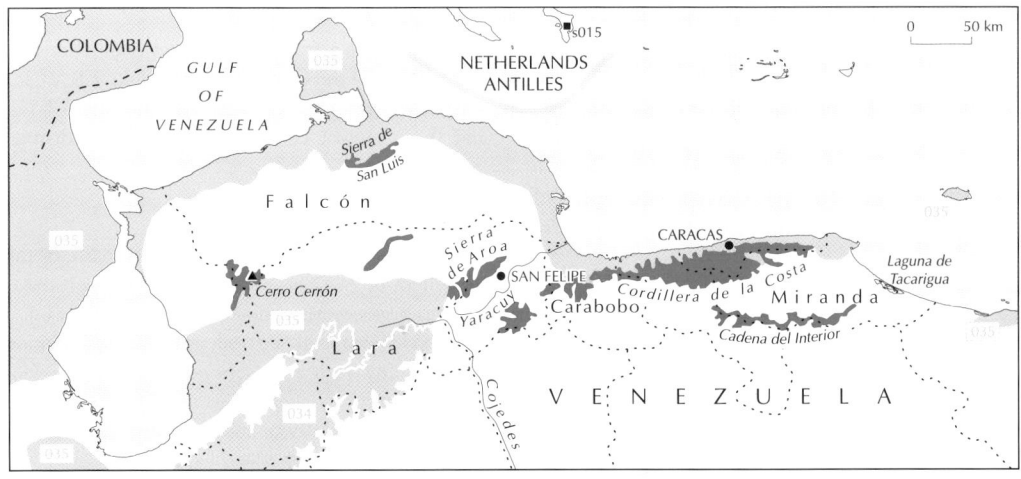

Status and habitat of restricted-range species

Species (ordered taxonomically)	Global status	Other EBAs (and SAs)	Altitude (m)	Habitat
Northern Helmeted Curassow *Pauxi pauxi*	EN	034,038	900–1,800	Montane evergreen forest
Venezuelan Wood-quail *Odontophorus columbianus*	nt	038	1,300–2,400	Montane evergreen forest, forest edge
Rusty-flanked Crake *Laterallus levraudi*	VU	—	Lowlands to 600+	Freshwater marshes, lakes, lagoons, swamps, marshy meadows, rarely dry grassland
Red-eared Parakeet *Pyrrhura hoematotis*	lc	034	1,200–2,000	Montane evergreen and secondary forest, savanna woodland
Tepui Swift *Cypseloides phelpsi*	lc	064	400–1,400	Montane evergreen and tropical lowland evergreen forest, cliffs, rocky canyons, waterfalls
Green-tailed Emerald *Chlorostilbon alice*	lc	032,034	750–1,800	Montane evergreen forest edge, secondary and tropical lowland evergreen forest, plantations
Violet-chested Hummingbird *Sternoclyta cyanopectus*	lc	034	<1,900	Montane evergreen forest, lowland evergreen forest, old secondary forest, coffee plantations
White-tipped Quetzal *Pharomachrus fulgidus*	lc	032,036	900–2,500	Montane evergreen forest, forest edge, secondary growth
Black-throated Spinetail *Synallaxis castanea*	lc	—	1,300–2,200	Montane evergreen and secondary forest, forest edge, clearings, bamboo thickets
Guttulated Foliage-gleaner *Syndactyla guttulata*	lc	032	800–2,100	Montane evergreen and secondary forest
Schwartz's Antthrush *Chamaeza turdina*	lc	040	1,400–2,600	Montane evergreen forest
Great Antpitta *Grallaria excelsa*	nt	034,038	1,700–2,300	Montane evergreen forest
Scallop-breasted Antpitta *Grallaricula loricata*	nt	—	1,440–2,100	Montane evergreen forest
Handsome Fruiteater *Pipreola formosa*	lc	032	800–2,200	Montane evergreen forest, forest edge
Venezuelan Bristle-tyrant *Phylloscartes venezuelanus*	nt	—	850–1,400	Montane evergreen forest, forest edge
Fulvous-headed Tanager *Thlypopsis fulviceps*	lc	032,034,038	750–2,300	Secondary and montane evergreen forest, forest edge, thickets, bamboo
Rufous-cheeked Tanager *Tangara rufigenis*	lc	—	900–2,050	Montane evergreen forest, forest edge

Global status (see p. 679 for definitions)	EX Extinct ⎫ EW Extinct in ⎬ the Wild ⎭ with year of last record	CR Critical ⎫ EN Endangered ⎬ threatened VU Vulnerable ⎭ species	cd Conservation Dependent nt Near Threatened lc Least Concern	DD Data Deficient NE Not Evaluated

Other EBAs (and SAs) (see p. 65 for locations): bracketed numbers are Secondary Areas; [X] extinct in that EBA or SA.

found in the main coastal range; 10 species are present in the adjacent but disjunct Sierra de Aroa, and only *Chlorostilbon alice* occurs on Cerro Cerrón and the Sierra de San Luis. *Cypseloides phelpsi*, essentially a bird of the Tepuis (EBA 064), is known in the present region from just one record (possibly of a vagrant) at Rancho Grande in Aragua state (Meyer de Schauensee and Phelps 1978).

One restricted-range form, Caracas Tapaculo *Scytalopus* (*latebricola*) *caracae*, which occurs throughout this portion of the Cordillera, has recently been recognized as a species (Ridgley and Tudor 1994, though it is not so treated here), and further work may raise other taxa to species level. Rufous-lored Tyrannulet *Phylloscartes flaviventris*, for ex-

ample, is known from two disjunct populations, in this EBA (and the Cordillera de Mérida, EBA 034) and the Peruvian East Andean foothills (EBA 053), and these almost certainly represent two distinct species (Ridgely and Tudor 1994).

■ Threats and conservation

There is still extensive forest cover in parts of the Cordillera de la Costa Central, although deforestation has been severe around Caracas, and many other areas have been badly degraded (Huber and Alarcón 1988). Being such a densely populated area, widespread hunting threatens most species of large bird (A. Grajal *in litt.* 1993), and pollution and drainage threaten most of the wetland habitats.

Sunrise over montane evergreen forest in Guatopo National Park, a 'Key Area' for threatened bird species and home to many of the restricted-range species in this EBA.

D. C. Wege

Just two of the restricted-range species are presently considered threatened: *Pauxi pauxi*, due to excessive hunting (and, to a lesser extent, deforestation); and *Laterallus levraudi*, due to the loss of wetland habitats (Collar *et al*. 1992). Two widespread threatened species also occur in this EBA: Red Siskin *Carduelis cucullata* (classified as Endangered) and Yellow-faced Siskin *Carduelis yarrellii* (Vulnerable). Six Key Areas have been identified for the conservation of these threatened species (both restricted-range and widespread): four of the areas (San Esteban, Henri Pittier, Guatopo and Laguna de Tacarigua) are currently designated as national parks (Wege and Long 1995). Other protected areas within this EBA include Pico Codazzi National Monument and Sierra de San Luis, Yurubi, El Avila and Macarao National Parks, although El Avila is under severe threat from an influx to the park of landless people, now estimated at c.100,000 (M. L. Goodwin *in litt*. 1993), and Laguna de Tacarigua National Park, which is known to have supported a population of *Laterallus levraudi*, is under severe pressure from tourist-related development (Wege and Long 1995).

034 Cordillera de Mérida

PRIORITY
URGENT

Key habitats Tropical lowland to montane evergreen forest, páramo

Main threats Moderate habitat loss (e.g. due to logging, cultivation, grazing, mining)

Biological importance ● ● ○
Current threat level ● ● ○

Area 23,000 km²   **Altitude** 300–4,000 m

Countries Venezuela

Restricted-range species	Threatened	Total
Confined to this EBA	2	10
Present also in other EBAs, SAs	2	15
Total	4	25

■ General characteristics

The Cordillera de Mérida is situated in north-west Venezuela, primarily in the states of Táchira, Mérida, Barinas, Trujillo, Portuguesa and Lara. The south-west end of the cordillera abuts the East Andes (EBA 038) on the border with Colombia, but is separated from them by the Táchira depression (i.e. the Torbes and Quinimari valleys). The mountains run from south-west to north-east where they terminate at Barquisimeto, the point at which the cordillera is separated from the Cordillera de la Costa Central (EBA 033) by the headwaters of the Cojedes. The EBA is centred on the high peaks of the Sierra de la Culata and Sierra Nevada, around the city of Mérida.

This area includes the full complement of altitudinal zones from the tropical lowlands, through subtropical and temperate zones, to páramo areas on the highest peaks, and the vegetation types thus vary from lowland forest up to elfin forest near the treeline, with páramo scrub and grassland above this.

D. C. Wege

A species of *Espeletia* in flower. These large Compositae are characteristic of the páramo in this EBA.

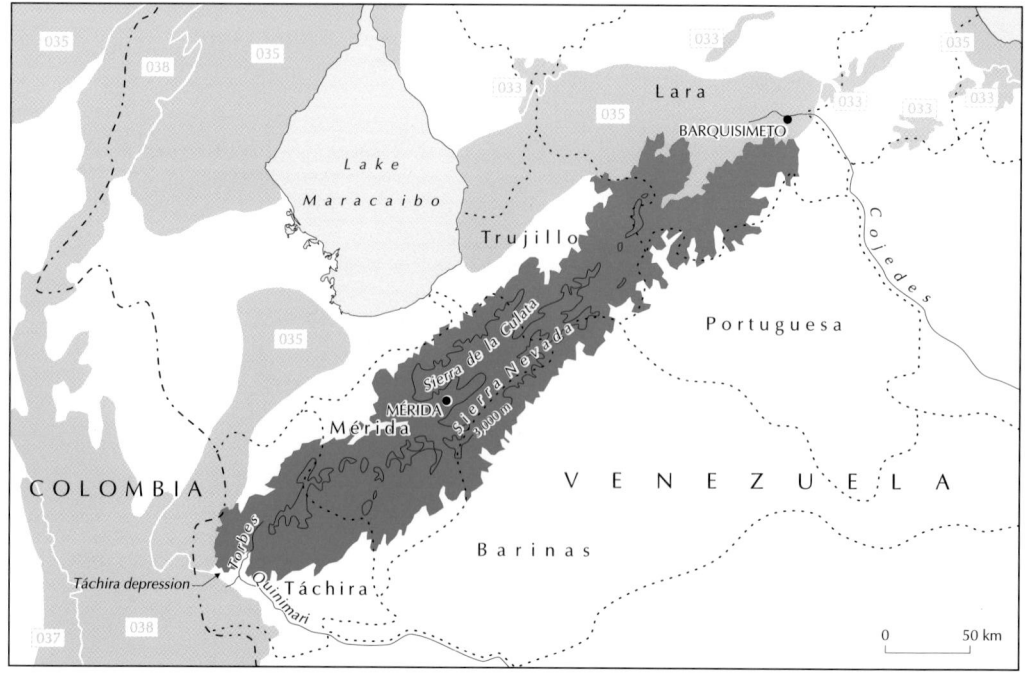

Status and habitat of restricted-range species

Species (ordered taxonomically)	Global status	Other EBAs (and SAs)	Altitude (m)	Habitat
Northern Helmeted Curassow *Pauxi pauxi*	EN	033,038	1,000–1,500	Montane evergreen forest
Red-eared Parakeet *Pyrrhura hoematotis*	lc	033	1,200–2,000	Montane evergreen and secondary forest, savanna woodland
Rose-headed Parakeet *Pyrrhura rhodocephala*	nt	—	800–3,050	Montane evergreen, elfin and secondary forest, páramo
Rusty-faced Parrot *Hapalopsittaca amazonina*	EN	038, 042	2,200–3,000	Montane evergreen forest
Narrow-tailed Emerald *Chlorostilbon stenura*	lc	038	1,000–3,000	Montane evergreen forest edge, secondary growth, scrub
Green-tailed Emerald *Chlorostilbon alice*	lc	032,033	750–1,800	Montane evergreen forest edge, secondary and tropical lowland evergreen forest, plantations
Short-tailed Emerald *Chlorostilbon poortmani*	lc	038	1,000–2,400	Montane evergreen and tropical lowland evergreen forest edge, secondary growth, woodland, scrub
Táchira Emerald *Amazilia distans*	EN	—	300–800	Secondary growth, coffee plantations, possibly tropical lowland evergreen forest
Violet-chested Hummingbird *Sternoclyta cyanopectus*	lc	033	<1,900	Montane evergreen, tropical lowland evergreen and old secondary forest, coffee plantations
Golden-bellied Starfrontlet *Coeligena bonapartei*	lc	038	1,400–3,200	Montane evergreen and elfin forest, forest edge
Orange-throated Sunangel *Heliangelus mavors*	lc	038	2,000–3,200	Montane evergreen, elfin and secondary forest, forest edge, scrub
Mérida Sunangel *Heliangelus spencei*	lc	—	2,000–3,600	Montane evergreen and elfin forest, forest edge
Coppery-bellied Puffleg *Eriocnemis cupreoventris*	lc	038	1,950–3,000	Elfin and montane evergreen forest, forest edge, scrub
Bearded Helmetcrest *Oxypogon guerinii*	lc	036,038,043	3,200–5,200	Páramo grassland, *Espeletia* stands, *Polylepis* scrub
Ochre-browed Thistletail *Schizoeaca coryi*	lc	—	3,000–4,100	Páramo grassland and scrub, elfin forest, *Espeletia* stands
Great Antpitta *Grallaria excelsa*	nt	033,038	1,700–2,300	Montane evergreen forest
Grey-naped Antpitta *Grallaria griseonucha*	lc	—	2,300–2,800	Montane evergreen forest
Mérida Wren *Cistothorus meridae*	lc	—	3,000–4,100	Marshes and boggy areas in páramo, páramo grassland, shrubs inc. *Espeletia*
Moustached Brush-finch *Atlapetes albofrenatus*	lc	038	1,500–2,500	Montane evergreen forest and forest edge, secondary growth, thickets
Grey-capped Hemispingus *Hemispingus reyi*	lc	—	1,900–3,200	Montane evergreen and elfin forest, forest edge, clearings, scrub
Slaty-backed Hemispingus *Hemispingus goeringi*	VU	—	2,600–3,200	Elfin forest and edge, bamboo
Fulvous-headed Tanager *Thlypopsis fulviceps*	lc	032,033,038	750–2,300	Secondary and montane evergreen forest, forest edge, thickets, bamboo
Mérida Flower-piercer *Diglossa gloriosa*	lc	—	2,500–4,150	Semi-humid/humid montane and páramo scrub, elfin forest, montane evergreen forest edge
White-fronted Whitestart *Myioborus albifrons*	lc	—	2,200–4,000	Montane evergreen and elfin forest, forest edge
Grey-throated Warbler *Basileuterus cinereicollis*	nt	038	800–2,100	Montane evergreen forest undergrowth, forest edge, secondary growth

Global status (see p. 679 for definitions) — EX Extinct, EW Extinct in the Wild (with year of last record); CR Critical, EN Endangered, VU Vulnerable (threatened species); cd Conservation Dependent, nt Near Threatened, lc Least Concern; DD Data Deficient, NE Not Evaluated

Other EBAs (and SAs) (see p. 65 for locations): bracketed numbers are Secondary Areas; ˣ extinct in that EBA or SA.

A typical, rather barren páramo scene above the treeline. Three of the EBA's restricted-range bird species are associated with this habitat.

and grassland, bamboo and *Espeletia* stands. Only one species is confined to the tropical lowland forest, and of those restricted to the tropical and subtropical zones the majority are found in other EBAs, confirming that this is primarily an EBA of highland, upper subtropical to páramo habitats (see 'Habitat associations' table), with distributions of the species often being centred on the highest peaks surrounding the city of Mérida.

Most of the species which are shared between this and other EBAs occur in the adjacent East Andes (EBA 038), although many are clearly differentiated at the subspecific level due to the isolation of the cordillera from the main Andean chain: *Coeligena bonapartei eos*, for example, is especially distinct

■ Restricted-range species

Most species occupy montane evergreen forest or its edges as well as secondary habitats, although some of the birds at lower altitudes are found in more open woodland and savanna. At higher altitudes, the birds tend to be associated with elfin forest, páramo scrub

Habitat associations of restricted-range species

Tropical forest	
Amazilia distans	*Chlorostilbon stenura*
	Coeligena bonapartei
Tropical/subtropical forest	*Heliangelus mavors*
Pauxi pauxi	*Heliangelus spencei*
Pyrrhura hoematotis	*Eriocnemis cupreoventris*
Chlorostilbon alice	*Hemispingus reyi*
Chlorostilbon poortmani	
Sternoclyta cyanopectus	**Temperate forest**
Thylopsis fulviceps	*Grallaria griseonucha*
Basileuterus cinereicollis	**Hemispingus goeringi**
	Diglossa gloriosa
Subtropical forest	*Myioborus albifrons*
Grallaria excelsa	
Atlapetes albofrenatus	**Páramo**
	Oxypogon guerinii
Subtropical/temperate forest	*Schizoeaca coryi*
	Cistothorus meridae
Pyrrhura rhodocephala	
Hapalopsittaca amazonia	

Threatened species (Critical, Endangered, Vulnerable) are shown in **bold**; see 'Status and habitat' table.

Sierra de la Culata National Park, one of the EBA's few (mainly high-altitude) protected areas.

Cultivation in the Sierra Nevada, both commercial and subsistence, has already been at the expense of large tracts of páramo and temperate forest.

D. C. Wege

(J. Fjeldså *in litt.* 1993). Similarly, *Pyrrhura hoematotis* is apparently known in this EBA from just one record representing the subspecies *immarginata*, the nominate form being confined to the Cordillera de la Costa Central (EBA 033) (Meyer de Schauensee and Phelps 1978). Rufous-lored Tyrannulet *Phylloscartes flaviventris* is known from two disjunct populations in this EBA (together with the Cordillera de la Costa Central, EBA 033) and in the Peruvian East Andean foothills (EBA 053), these almost certainly being two distinct species (Ridgely and Tudor 1994). The distributions of species at the south-westernmost end of this EBA are poorly known: *Amazilia distans* is known from just five (apparent) observations since its discovery in 1954, all from the area around the Táchira depression. On the East Andes side of this area (just c.30 km distant), three tropical/subtropical restricted-range species, Venezuelan Wood-quail *Odontophorus columbianus*, Táchira Antpitta *Grallaria chthonia* and Hooded Antpitta *Grallaricula cucullata*, are known only from records along the Chiquito river, but should perhaps be searched for within the cordillera.

Amethyst-throated Sunangel *Heliangelus* (*amethysticollis*) *clarissae* is treated here as a subspecies but has sometimes been considered a separate species, in which event it would be shared between this EBA and the East Andes (EBA 038) (Fjeldså and Krabbe 1990, J. Fjeldså *in litt.* 1993).

■ Threats and conservation

Some large tracts of forest still remain in a number of places, but deforestation has been severe elsewhere, with logging continuing to expand to higher areas. A major threat is the clearance of forests on the eastern slope of the EBA (e.g. in western Barinas state) for extensive cattle-ranching. The areas affected are public land (and some old coffee haciendas), with thousands of hectares cleared every year for this activity (C. J. Sharpe *in litt.* 1997). Agricultural colonization represents a significant threat, although many areas of páramo and temperate forest have already been cleared for cultivation, both commercial and subsistence (D. C. Wege). Mining concessions for zinc, copper and lead are being requested in Páramos del Batallón y La Negra National Park (M. L. Goodwin *in litt.* 1993), and may well have a detrimental impact in other areas. Proposals for road construction form potential threats to several national parks (C. J. Sharpe *in litt.* 1997).

This EBA is home to four threatened species. *Amazilia distans* is essentially a tropical species, but is so poorly known that the threats to it are difficult to assess. Both *Hapalopsittaca amazonina* and *Hemispingus goeringi* are birds of the treeline, and have suffered from the widespread loss of suitable habitat within their ranges. *Pauxi pauxi*, here as in other EBAs, faces the combined threats of hunting and loss of its subtropical forest habitat, which is poorly protected within this EBA. Five Key Areas for these threatened species were recently identified by Wege and Long (1995), three of which (Páramos del Batallón y La Negra, Sierras de la Culata y Nevada, and Yacambú) are currently designated as national parks. At present, only the higher zones of the Cordillera de Mérida are protected by the Páramos del Batallón y La Negra, Sierra Nevada and Sierra de la Culata National Parks (IUCN 1992a), although these appear to be inadequate to conserve the full complement of restricted-range species occurring at the various altitudes through the EBA. Yacambú National Park, at the north-east end of the cordillera, is one of the few protected tracts of tropical and subtropical forest in the EBA.

035 Caribbean Colombia and Venezuela `PRIORITY URGENT`

Key habitats Tropical dry forest, arid scrub, thorn scrub, mangroves

Main threats Moderate habitat loss (e.g. due to overgrazing, wood-cutting, development)

Biological importance ● ● ○
Current threat level ● ● ○

Area 89,000 km²   **Altitude** 0–1,000 m

Countries Colombia, Venezuela

Restricted-range species	Threatened	Total
Confined to this EBA	2	11
Present also in other EBAs, SAs	1	1
Total	3	12

■ General characteristics

This EBA embraces the lowlands of northernmost Colombia and north-west and coastal northern Venezuela, and as such extends from Bolívar and Atlántico departments, around the base of the Santa Marta mountains (EBA 036) and through the Guajira peninsula, Maracaibo lowlands and north Venezuelan coastal plain (and the Paraguaná peninsula) to the Araya peninsula; it also includes La Tortuga, Margarita and associated islands. The boundary of the EBA coincides almost exactly with the southern limit of the south Caribbean dry zone inside which the annual rainfall is less than 1,000 mm (Sugden 1982). However, the EBA does extend slightly beyond the dry zone and includes the seasonally dry forest and woodlands of Norte de Santander and César departments in Colombia (Forero 1989).

The vegetation types within this zone (from sea-level to 1,000 m) have been classified as desert (including cactus scrub), thorn scrub, dry forest (deciduous and evergreen), riparian associations and mangroves (Sugden 1982, L. M. Renjifo *in litt.* 1993).

C. J. Sharpe

A typical area of desert cactus scrub on the Caribbean coastal plain of western Venezuela. This is one of very few EBAs in which desert is a key habitat for restricted-range birds.

■ Restricted-range species

Most of the restricted-range birds in this EBA occur primarily in the lowland dry-zone vegetation associations described above, the exceptions being *Rallus*

wetmorei and *Lepidopyga lilliae*, which are confined to small areas of mangrove swamp in Venezuela and Colombia respectively. Also, *Micropanyptila furcata* and a subspecies (*venezuelensis*) of the relatively

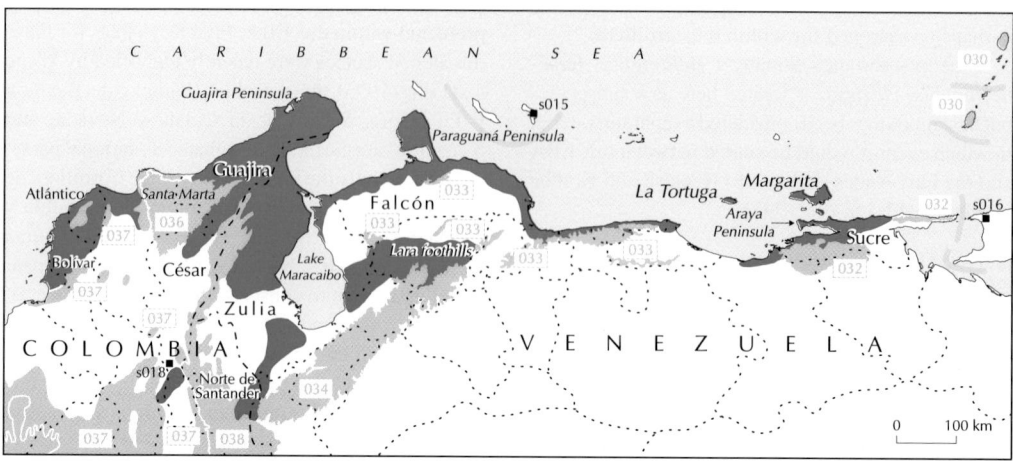

Status and habitat of restricted-range species

Species (ordered taxonomically)	Global status	Other EBAs (and SAs)	Altitude (m)	Habitat
Plain-flanked Rail *Rallus wetmorei*	EN	—	Coastal	Saltwater/brackish marshes, mangrove forest
Yellow-shouldered Amazon *Amazona barbadensis*	VU	(s015)	0–100	Arid lowland and thorn scrub, tropical deciduous forest
Pygmy Swift *Tachornis furcata*	lc	—	0–500	Tropical lowland evergreen forest, secondary growth, open country
Sapphire-bellied Hummingbird *Lepidopyga lilliae*	CR	—	Coastal	Mangrove forest
Buffy Hummingbird *Leucippus fallax*	lc	—	0–800	Thorn scrub in semi-desert, arid lowland scrub, tropical deciduous forest and mangrove forest edge
Chestnut Piculet *Picumnus cinnamomeus*	lc	—	0–300	Tropical deciduous and mangrove forest, dry forest edge, arid lowland scrub
White-whiskered Spinetail *Synallaxis candei*	lc	—	Lowlands to 300	Arid lowland and thorn scrub, cactus, tropical deciduous forest, saltflats
Black-backed Antshrike *Sakesphorus melanonotus*	lc	—	Lowlands to 500	Tropical deciduous and dry thorn forest, riparian woodland, semi-arid scrub
Maracaibo Tody-flycatcher *Todirostrum viridanum*	nt	—	Lowlands to 100	Tropical deciduous and gallery forest, semi-arid woodland, arid lowland scrub, thickets
Slender-billed Tyrannulet *Inezia tenuirostris*	lc	—	Lowlands to 600	Tropical deciduous forest, dry thorn woodland, arid lowland scrub
Tocuyo Sparrow *Arremonops tocuyensis*	lc	—	0–1,100	Tropical deciduous forest, arid lowland scrub, thickets
Vermilion Cardinal *Cardinalis phoeniceus*	lc	—	0–300	Arid lowland scrub, thorn thickets, cactus

Global status (see p. 679 for definitions)	EX	Extinct	with year of last record	CR	Critical	threatened species	cd	Conservation Dependent	DD	Data Deficient
	EW	Extinct in the Wild		EN	Endangered		nt	Near Threatened	NE	Not Evaluated
				VU	Vulnerable		lc	Least Concern		

Other EBAs (and SAs) (see p. 65 for locations): bracketed numbers are Secondary Areas; ˣ extinct in that EBA or SA.

wide-ranging *Picumnus cinnamomeus* occur in humid forest south of Lago de Maracaibo (Meyer de Schauensee and Phelps 1978, Ryan *et al.* 1995).

The Guajira peninsula and the north-west Venezuelan lowlands (primarily Falcón) are of critical importance for the restricted-range species (see 'Distribution patterns' table). *Sakesphorus melanonotus* was, historically, confined to this EBA, but has recently been found at up to 1,500 m on the slopes of the Santa Marta mountains (EBA 036) (L. G. Olarte

Distribution patterns of restricted-range species

Species (ordered geographically)	N Colombian lowlands	Guajira peninsula	Maracaibo lowlands	NW Venezuelan lowlands	Paraguaná peninsula	Lara foothills	NE Venezuelan coastal lowlands & islands	Other EBAs, SAs
Lepidopyga lilliae	●	—	—	—	—	—	—	—
Picumnus cinnamomeus	●	●	●	●	—	—	—	—
Sakesphorus melanonotus	●	●	●	●	—	—	—	—
Synallaxis candei	●	●	●	●	●	●	—	—
Inezia tenuirostris	●	●	—	●	●	●	—	—
Arremonops tocuyensis	—	●	—	●	●	●	—	—
Cardinalis phoeniceus	—	●	—	●	—	—	●	—
Leucippus fallax	—	●	—	●	●	●	●	—
Micropanyptila furcata	—	—	●	—	—	—	—	—
Rallus wetmorei	—	—	—	●	—	—	—	—
Todirostrum viridanum	—	—	—	●	—	—	—	—
Amazona barbadensis	—	—	—	●	●	●	●	●
Total	5	7	4	10	5	5	3	

●	Present	?	Present?	Threatened spp. shown in **bold**	see 'Status and habitat' table
O	Extinct?	R	Reintroduced	Other EBAs, SAs	
X	Extinct	I	Introduced		

in litt. 1993), almost certainly due to the clearance of forest and the expansion of dry scrub up the slopes. *Amazona barbadensis* is the EBA's only restricted-range species to have a known long-standing population outside its boundaries, being present on Bonaire and previously on Aruba in the Netherlands Antilles (Secondary Area s015).

Yellow-shouldered Amazon *Amazona barbadensis*, a threatened species typical of the desert vegetation in this EBA, is widely exploited for the pet trade.

Chestnut-winged Chachalaca *Ortalis garrula* is endemic to this general region, being found within the Colombian portion of this EBA, but is distributed further south within the Nechí lowlands (EBA 037) so does not qualify as a restricted-range species.

■ Threats and conservation

Large expanses of the characteristic vegetation of this EBA still remain (but are unprotected) in both Colombia and Venezuela (Huber and Alarcón 1988,

Forero 1989). Substantial areas of habitat have, nevertheless, been destroyed, especially in north-west Venezuela (principally around Lago de Maracaibo). Overgrazing is preventing regeneration and causing a problem in Guajira in Colombia (Sugden 1982, Huber and Alarcón 1988). Overgrazing by goats and firewood-gathering by local people are resulting in severe pressure on the Araya peninsula, and burgeoning tourism, development pressures and pollution are threatening habitats elsewhere in Venezuela (Wege and Long 1995). Large-scale open-cast coal-mining poses a substantial threat to parts of this EBA in Colombia (L. M. Renjifo *in litt.* 1993).

Rallus wetmorei is restricted to brackish lagoons and mangroves along a small stretch of Venezuela's north coast, where its habitat is severely threatened by house and road construction and associated pollution. Similarly, *Lepidopyga lilliae* is confined to mangroves along the north coast of Colombia, where urbanization and pollution have caused the death of large areas of mangrove and continue to put pressure on remaining stands. *Amazona barbadensis* has suffered from habitat loss, but more significantly from widespread exploitation for the pet trade (Collar *et al.* 1992, 1994). However, conservation action has been able to double its population (now some 1,500 birds) at its stronghold on Isla de Margarita (C. J. Sharpe *in litt.* 1997). The widespread Red Siskin *Carduelis cucullata* (classified as Endangered) also occurs in the deciduous forest and dry scrub of this zone, where it too is threatened by the pet trade. Ten Key Areas (eight in Venezuela and two in Colombia) have been identified for the threatened birds in this EBA (Wege and Long 1995).

The xeric vegetation that characterizes this EBA is currently not covered within the protected-area network, which has primarily focused on the coastal wetland sites, e.g. Isla de Salamanca National Park in Colombia, and Morrocoy National Park (and the adjacent Cuare Faunal Refuge) and the coastal portions of San Esteban and Henri Pittier National Parks in Venezuela (IUCN 1992a), although even these protected areas face severe threats as outlined above.

036 Santa Marta mountains

Key habitats Tropical lowland through to montane evergreen forest, páramo scrub and grassland

Main threats Major habitat loss (e.g. due to agriculture, logging, burning)

Biological importance ● ● ●
Current threat level ●

Area 11,000 km² **Altitude** 600–5,200 m

Countries Colombia

Restricted-range species	Threatened	Total
Confined to this EBA	2	15
Present also in other EBAs, SAs	1	7
Total	3	22

■ General characteristics

The Sierra Nevada de Santa Marta is an isolated mountain massif in northernmost Colombia, close to the Venezuelan border and astride the Magdalena, César and Guajira department boundaries. This glaciated granitic massif, totally isolated from the adjacent Sierra de Perijá (EBA 038 in part), comprises the highest peaks in Colombia, rising directly from the shores of the Caribbean up to 5,800 m. Originally covering all life-zones from tropical to temperate forest, and including páramo scrub and grassland (Norton 1975, Ridgely and Tudor 1989), very little original vegetation now remains unaltered, in spite of the area being a national park (see 'Threats and conservation', below). Santa Marta is adjacent to portions of Caribbean Colombia and Venezuela (EBA 035), and the boundaries between these two EBAs are becoming poorly defined due to the increasing degradation of the mountain vegetation and resultant encroachment of secondary scrub (see below).

■ Restricted-range species

Most of the restricted-range birds occupy relatively wide altitudinal bands between the tropical and temperate zones, where they inhabit humid forest,

Santa Marta Parakeets *Pyrrhura viridicata*. Less than 5,000 individuals remain in what little forest persists.

forest edge and a number of other associated habitats. Just three species, *Crax alberti*, *Anthocephala floriceps* and *Chlorostilbon russatus* are restricted to tropical-zone forest (from lowlands to 1,700 m), and two others, *Oxypogon guerinii* and *Troglodytes monticola*, are confined to treeline scrub and grass-

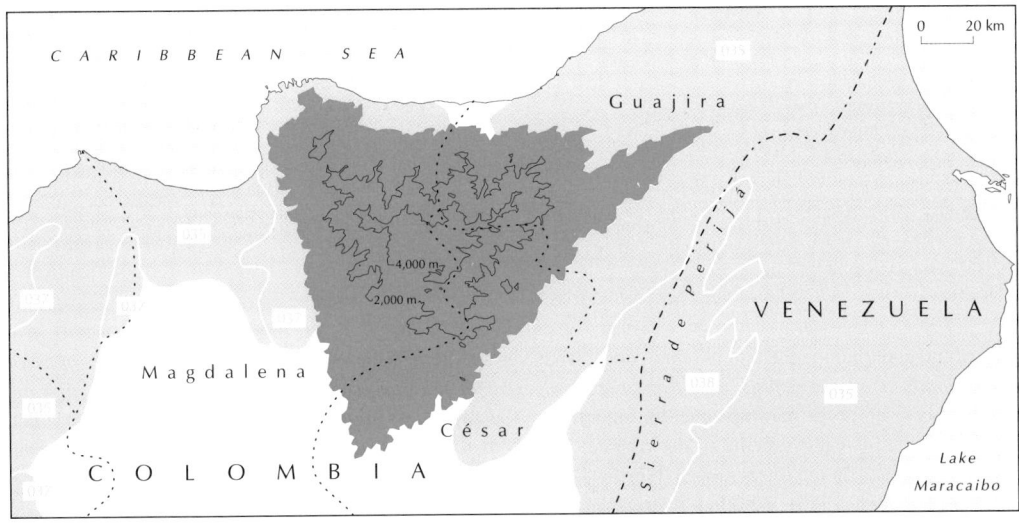

Endemic Bird Areas of the World

Status and habitat of restricted-range species

Species (ordered taxonomically)	Global status	Other EBAs (and SAs)	Altitude (m)	Habitat
Blue-billed Curassow *Crax alberti*	CR	037	Lowlands to 1,200	Tropical lowland evergreen forest, possibly also montane evergreen forest
Black-fronted Wood-quail *Odontophorus atrifrons*	nt	038	1,200–2,700	Montane evergreen forest
Santa Marta Parakeet *Pyrrhura viridicata*	VU	—	2,000–2,500	Montane evergreen forest, forest edge, scrub
Santa Marta Sabrewing *Campylopterus phainopeplus*	nt	—	1,200–4,500	Montane evergreen and secondary forest, forest edge, scrub, plantations
Coppery Emerald *Chlorostilbon russatus*	lc	038	600–1,700	Montane evergreen forest edge, second-growth scrub, agricultural land
Blossomcrown *Anthocephala floriceps*	nt	040	600–1,700	Montane evergreen forest, older secondary growth
White-tailed Starfrontlet *Coeligena phalerata*	lc	—	1,400–3,300	Montane evergreen and elfin forest, forest edge, scrub
Black-backed Thornbill *Ramphomicron dorsale*	lc	—	2,000–4,500	Montane evergreen and elfin forest and forest edge, páramo grassland
Bearded Helmetcrest *Oxypogon guerinii*	lc	034,038,043	3,200–5,200	Páramo grassland, *Espeletia* stands, *Polylepis* scrub
Santa Marta Woodstar *Acestrura astreans*	lc	—	800–2,800	Humid forest, forest edge, scrub
White-tipped Quetzal *Pharomachrus fulgidus*	lc	032,033	900–2,500	Montane evergreen forest, forest edge, secondary growth
Rusty-headed Spinetail *Synallaxis fuscorufa*	nt	—	2,000–3,000	Montane evergreen forest edge, second-growth scrub, overgrown clearings
Streak-capped Spinetail *Cranioleuca hellmayri*	lc	—	1,600–3,000	Montane evergreen forest, forest edge, tall secondary growth
Santa Marta Antpitta *Grallaria bangsi*	nt	—	1,200–2,400	Montane evergreen forest, tall secondary growth
Santa Marta Bush-tyrant *Myiotheretes pernix*	VU	—	2,100–2,900	Montane evergreen forest edge, secondary growth edge, scrub
Santa Marta Wren *Troglodytes monticola*	lc	—	3,200–4,600	Elfin forest, treeline scrub, páramo grassland
Santa Marta Brush-finch *Atlapetes melanocephalus*	lc	—	1,500–3,200	Montane evergreen forest edge, secondary forest, clearings, scrub
Santa Marta Mountain-tanager *Anisognathus melanogenys*	lc	—	1,500–3,200	Montane evergreen forest edge, secondary growth
Yellow-crowned Whitestart *Myioborus flavivertex*	lc	—	1,500–3,000	Montane evergreen, secondary and elfin forest and forest edge
Santa Marta Warbler *Basileuterus basilicus*	nt	—	2,300–3,000	Montane evergreen, elfin forest and secondary forest and forest edge
White-lored Warbler *Basileuterus conspicillatus*	nt	—	750–2,200	Montane evergreen forest and secondary forest
Rufous-browed Conebill *Conirostrum rufum*	lc	038	2,650–3,400	Elfin forest, forest edge, secondary growth, semi-humid/humid montane scrub

Global status (see p. 679 for definitions): EX Extinct, EW Extinct in the Wild (with year of last record); CR Critical, EN Endangered, VU Vulnerable (threatened species); cd Conservation Dependent, nt Near Threatened, lc Least Concern; DD Data Deficient, NE Not Evaluated

Other EBAs (and SAs) (see p. 65 for locations): bracketed numbers are Secondary Areas; ˣ extinct in that EBA or SA.

land of the upper temperate and páramo zones. Both *Campylopterus phainopeplus* and *Ramphomicron dorsale* occur up to the páramo zone, but undertake seasonal altitudinal movements to the tropical and subtropical zones on the lower slopes (Norton 1975, Hilty and Brown 1986). Another restricted-range species, Black-backed Antshrike *Sakesphorus melanonotus*, is considered endemic to the adjacent Caribbean Colombia and Venezuela (EBA 035) but has recently started to colonize the higher slopes of the sierra due to widespread forest clearance and the resultant spread of drier secondary vegetation.

186

Although the Santa Marta massif was present before the Andes rose, most of the species confined to it are recent divergences, and there are a large number of endemic subspecies present, reflecting the recent colonization and differentiation from the main Andean chain; the exceptions are *Pyrrhura viridicata* and *Coeligena phalerata*, both of which are relict species (Fjeldså and Krabbe 1990, J. Fjeldså *in litt.* 1993). One endemic taxon, the Santa Marta Tapaculo *Scytalopus (femoralis) sanctaemartae*, occurring in the undergrowth of montane forest between 1,350 and 1,700 m, is considered here to be a subspecies but has recently been recognized as a distinct species by Ridgely and Tudor (1994) and may even qualify as threatened.

■ Threats and conservation

The Santa Marta mountains are seriously threatened by agricultural expansion, logging and burning (Dinerstein *et al.* 1995). The south-east slope of the sierra has been extensively deforested, and the western slopes have also suffered, primarily from clearance for illegal marijuana plantations (especially during the 1980s) which have subsequently been sprayed with herbicide by the government (L. G. Olarte *in litt.* 1993, L. M. Renjifo *in litt.* 1993). Only the forest on the northern slope is still relatively intact, although active clearance continues, and only 15% of the sierra's original vegetation remains unaltered (L. G. Olarte *in litt.* 1993, L. M. Renjifo *in litt.* 1993).

Due to this extensive deforestation, two of the endemics are now considered threatened and several more are classified as Near Threatened. *Pyrrhura viridicata* is thought to have a population of fewer than 5,000 individuals, now confined to less than 200 km² of remaining habitat. Similarly, *Myiotheretes pernix* is uncommon within a limited altitudinal range where the available habitat is much reduced in extent (Collar *et al.* 1994).

P. Boesman

The northern slope of the Sierra Nevada de Santa Marta is the only part of the massif where forest remains largely intact. Although formally protected within a national park, only 15% of the sierra's original habitats remain unaltered.

This EBA is formally protected within the Sierra Nevada de Santa Marta National Park (covering some 3,830 km²), the Sierra Nevada de Santa Marta Biosphere Reserve (embracing a further 3,480 km²) and Tayrona National Park (IUCN 1992a). However, as is demonstrated by the devastating loss of natural vegetation, these formal designations have done little to protect the birds of this EBA.

037 Nechí lowlands

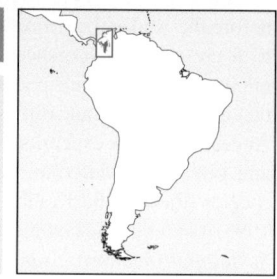

Key habitats Tropical lowland evergreen forest

Main threats Major habitat loss (e.g. due to agriculture)

Biological importance ● ● ●
Current threat level ● ● ●

Area 58,000 km²   **Altitude** 0–1,500 m

Countries Colombia

Restricted-range species	Threatened	Total
Confined to this EBA	2	3
Present also in other EBAs, SAs	3	9
Total	5	12

■ General characteristics

The Nechí lowlands embrace the moist forest region at the northern end of the Colombian Andes, and are centred on the Nechí, Cauca and Sinú rivers. The moist forest, and hence the EBA, lies in the region having 1,500–4,000 mm of rain per year, and runs in a band across the northern end of the West and Central Andes (just into the Cauca valley), including the Serranía de San Lucas, and down the western slope of the East Andes to c.5°N in the Magdalena valley (i.e. north-west Cundinamarca department). Isolated patches of moist forest extend the EBA northwards into the drier lowlands of Caribbean

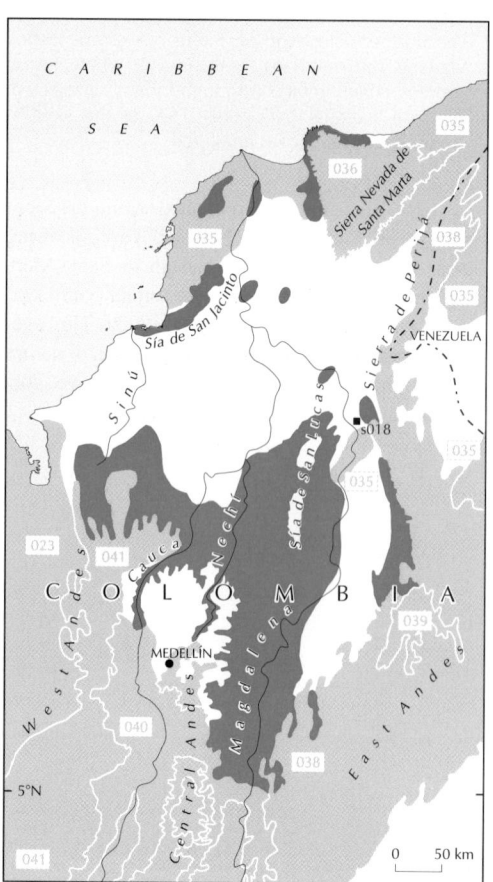

Colombia and Venezuela (EBA 035, characterized by less than 1,000 mm of rain per year); these are found along the western slope of the (southern) Sierra de Perijá, the northern and western slopes of the Sierra Nevada de Santa Marta, and the Serranía de San Jacinto (Haffer 1967, 1975).

■ Restricted-range species

The restricted-range birds of this EBA are primarily dependent on moist tropical forest and associated forest-edge and secondary-growth habitats in the lowlands and foothills up to c.1,500 m.

Most of the species (many of which occur in other moist/wet forest EBAs) are widespread within the core area of moist forest north of the West and Central Andes, and in the broad Magdalena valley. However, three of the threatened birds are poorly known, with even their distributions being incompletely documented (see 'Threats and conservation', below). Only four of the EBA's species occur also in the more isolated moist forest patches of the Caribbean lowlands: *Crax alberti*, *Brachygalba salmoni* and *Aphanotriccus audax* have all been found in the Serranía de San Jacinto (*C. alberti* also in the Santa Marta mountains, EBA 036), and *Aphanotriccus audax* is known from the foothills at the southern end of the Sierra de Perijá (Hilty and Brown 1986).

Chestnut-winged Chachalaca *Ortalis garrula* is endemic to this general region, being found in the drier portions of this EBA (and the adjacent Caribbean Colombia and Venezuela EBA), but occupies too wide an area to qualify as a restricted-range species.

■ Threats and conservation

This area has been subjected to extensive deforestation although some large areas of moist forest apparently still survive (Forero 1989). The middle and lower Magdalena and Cauca valleys have been heavily deforested since the nineteenth century (for agriculture), and clearance of the floodplain and foothills of the middle Magdalena valley has been almost total since the 1950s (Collar *et al.* 1992).

Five species (two of which are endemic to this EBA) are presently thought to be threatened, all of

Status and habitat of restricted-range species

Species (ordered taxonomically)	Global status	Other EBAs (and SAs)	Altitude (m)	Habitat
Blue-billed Curassow *Crax alberti*	CR	036	Lowlands to 1,200	Tropical lowland evergreen forest, possibly also montane evergreen forest
Chestnut-bellied Hummingbird *Amazilia castaneiventris*	EN	038	850–2,045	Presumably forest or woodland
White-eyed Trogon *Trogon comptus*	lc	041	Lowlands to 1,800	Tropical lowland evergreen and montane evergreen forest, forest edge
Dusky-backed Jacamar *Brachygalba salmoni*	lc	023	Lowlands to 600	Tropical lowland evergreen and secondary forest edge, tall secondary growth, near streams
White-mantled Barbet *Capito hypoleucus*	EN	—	200–1,500	Tropical lowland evergreen forest
Golden-naped Woodpecker *Melanerpes chrysauchen*	lc	021	0–1,500	Tropical lowland evergreen forest edge, secondary growth
Recurve-billed Bushbird *Clytoctantes alixii*	EN	038	180–1,200	Tropical lowland evergreen forest, forest edge, secondary growth, thickets
Antioquia Bristle-tyrant *Phylloscartes lanyoni*	EN	—	450–750	Possibly tropical lowland evergreen forest, tall secondary growth, clearings
Black-billed Flycatcher *Aphanotriccus audax*	nt	023	0–600	Tropical lowland evergreen forest, secondary growth
Scarlet-and-white Tanager *Chrysothlypis salmoni*	lc	041	Lowlands to 1,100	Secondary and tropical lowland evergreen forest, forest edge, scrub
Sooty Ant-tanager *Habia gutturalis*	nt	—	100–1,100	Secondary and tropical lowland evergreen forest, forest edge
Black Oropendola *Gymnostinops guatimozinus*	lc	023	0–800	Tropical lowland evergreen forest, river-edge forest, forest edge, logged forest

Global status (see p. 679 for definitions): EX Extinct, EW Extinct in the Wild (with year of last record); CR Critical, EN Endangered, VU Vulnerable (threatened species); cd Conservation Dependent, nt Near Threatened, lc Least Concern; DD Data Deficient, NE Not Evaluated

Other EBAs (and SAs) (see p. 65 for locations): bracketed numbers are Secondary Areas; ˣ extinct in that EBA or SA.

them primarily through extensive habitat destruction, with *Crax alberti* doubtless also hunted (it is now thought to be extinct throughout most of its range, hence its Critical status) and *Amazilia castaneiventris* (recorded once from c.150 m on the Serranía de San Lucas), *Clytoctantes alixii* and *Phylloscartes lanyoni* all very poorly known (Collar *et al.* 1992).

Seven Key Areas have been identified for the threatened birds in this EBA, including Serranías de San Jacinto and San Lucas, Paramillo National Park, Puerto Valdivia, Punchina Dam, Río Claro and La Victoria. However, the only protected areas within the EBA are Paramillo National Park (covering some characteristic habitat within Córdoba and Antioquia departments at the northern end of the West Andes) and the Punchina and La Victoria watershed reserves (IUCN 1992a, Wege and Long 1995), although it is not known how many of the restricted-range species benefit from their protection.

038 Colombian East Andes

PRIORITY
CRITICAL

Key habitats Tropical montane and foothill evergreen forest, elfin forest, páramo, wetlands

Main threats Major habitat loss (e.g. due to logging, agriculture, drainage)

Biological importance ● ● ●
Current threat level ● ● ▪

Area 85,000 km² **Altitude** 1,000–4,000 m

Countries Colombia, Venezuela

Restricted-range species	Threatened	Total
Confined to this EBA	8	14
Present also in other EBAs, SAs	6	20
Total	14	34

■ General characteristics

The East Andes run almost the length of Colombia, taking in the Sierra de Perijá which sits astride the border with Venezuela, the Páramo de Tamá which extends just into Venezuela where the East Andes abuts the Cordillera de Mérida (EBA 034; the two being separated by the Táchira depression, i.e. the Torbes and Quinimari valleys), and the main Andean chain to just north of Neiva near the head of the

Magdalena valley. The head of the Magdalena valley and the southernmost end of the East Andes south of Neiva form part of the Colombian inter-Andean slopes (EBA 040).

Covering a wide altitudinal range, this EBA supports diverse vegetation including large expanses of páramo, dry temperate scrub and woodland, humid elfin forest and humid subtropical forest typical of lower mountain slopes. The western slope, between 1,500 and 2,500 m, historically supported humid subtropical and temperate oak–Lauraceae forest, with oak-dominated forest characteristic of higher altitudes. Also on the western slope are areas of upper tropical, dense, dry *Acacia* scrub and numerous bushy canyons (Wege and Long 1995). The Bogotá and Ubaté savannas (at 2,600 m), Laguna de Tota and a number of other high-altitude lakes once supported a diverse range of wetland and marsh habitats that have now all but been destroyed (see 'Threats and conservation', below).

■ Restricted-range species

The restricted-range birds occupy the full range of habitat-types from the upper tropical to temperate and páramo zones: the lakes and marshland of the central plateau (and páramo fens) are inhabited by the threatened *Rallus semiplumbeus* and *Cistothorus apolinari*, and were home to *Podiceps andinus* before its recent extinction (Collar *et al.* 1992); the páramo zone (and the ecotone with elfin forest) is inhabited by *Chalcostigma heteropogon*, *Oxypogon guerinii* and *Schizoeaca perijana*; and the majority of the remaining species can be found in humid forest or open/secondary habitats. The lakes and marshland of the central plateau (and páramo fens) form a severely threatened ecosystem and a well-defined smaller area of endemism; as well as its wetland specialists, it harbours endemic subspecies such as Yellow-billed Pintail *Anas georgica nicefori*, Ruddy Duck *Oxyura jamaicensis andina*, Spot-flanked Gallinule *Gallinula melanops bogotensis*, Bearded Tachuri *Polystictus pectoralis bogotensis* and Yellow-hooded Blackbird *Agelaius icterocephalus bogotensis* (Fjeldså and Krabbe 1990, Collar and Wege 1995).

Status and habitat of restricted-range species

Species (ordered taxonomically)	Global status	Other EBAs (and SAs)	Altitude (m)	Habitat
Colombian Grebe *Podiceps andinus*	EX (1977)	—	2,500–3,100	Freshwater lakes and ponds with tall marginal reeds and extensive shallows
Northern Helmeted Curassow *Pauxi pauxi*	EN	033,034	900–1,800	Montane evergreen forest
Black-fronted Wood-quail *Odontophorus atrifrons*	nt	036	1,200–2,700	Montane evergreen forest
Gorgeted Wood-quail *Odontophorus strophium*	EN	—	1,750–2,050	Montane evergreen forest
Venezuelan Wood-quail *Odontophorus columbianus*	nt	033	1,300–2,400	Montane evergreen forest, forest edge
Bogotá Rail *Rallus semiplumbeus*	EN	—	2,100–4,000	Freshwater marshes, reedbeds, flooded grassland, fens in páramo
Flame-winged Parakeet *Pyrrhura calliptera*	VU	—	1,850–3,400	Montane evergreen and elfin forest, forest edge
Rusty-faced Parrot *Hapalopsittaca amazonina*	EN	034, 042	2,200–3,000	Montane evergreen forest
Coppery Emerald *Chlorostilbon russatus*	lc	036	600–2,600	Montane evergreen forest edge, second-growth scrub, agricultural land
Narrow-tailed Emerald *Chlorostilbon stenura*	lc	034	1,000–3,000	Montane evergreen forest edge, secondary growth, scrub
Short-tailed Emerald *Chlorostilbon poortmani*	lc	034	1,000–2,400	Montane evergreen and tropical lowland evergreen forest edge, secondary growth, woodland, scrub
Chestnut-bellied Hummingbird *Amazilia castaneiventris*	EN	037	850–2,045	Presumably forest or woodland
Black Inca *Coeligena prunellei*	VU	—	1,650–2,500	Montane evergreen forest, forest edge, flowering shrubs
Golden-bellied Starfrontlet *Coeligena bonapartei*	lc	034	1,400–3,200	Montane evergreen and elfin forest, forest edge
Blue-throated Starfrontlet *Coeligena helianthea*	lc	—	1,900–3,000	Montane evergreen and elfin forest, forest edge, semi-humid/humid montane scrub, flowering shrubs
Orange-throated Sunangel *Heliangelus mavors*	lc	034	2,000–3,200	Montane evergreen, elfin and secondary forest, forest edge, scrub
Coppery-bellied Puffleg *Eriocnemis cupreoventris*	lc	034	1,950–3,000	Elfin and montane evergreen forest, forest edge, scrub
Perijá Metaltail *Metallura iracunda*	nt	—	1,850–3,100	Elfin forest, forest edge, scrub
Bronze-tailed Thornbill *Chalcostigma heteropogon*	lc	—	2,900–3,500	Elfin forest/páramo ecotone, shrubs, cliffs and rocky outcrops
Bearded Helmetcrest *Oxypogon guerinii*	lc	034,036,043	3,200–5,200	Páramo grassland, *Espeletia* stands, *Polylepis* scrub
Perijá Thistletail *Schizoeaca perijana*	nt	—	3,000–3,400	Páramo grassland, forest edge, scrub
Silvery-throated Spinetail *Synallaxis subpudica*	lc	—	2,000–3,200	Montane evergreen and secondary forest edge, hedgerows, overgrown clearings
Recurve-billed Bushbird *Clytoctantes alixii*	EN	037	180–1,200	Tropical lowland evergreen forest, forest edge, secondary growth, thickets
Great Antpitta *Grallaria excelsa*	nt	033,034	1,700–2,300	Montane evergreen forest
Táchira Antpitta *Grallaria chthonia*	VU	—	1,800–2,100	Montane evergreen forest
Cundinamarca Antpitta *Grallaria kaestneri*	VU	—	1,800–2,300	Montane evergreen forest, tall secondary growth
Hooded Antpitta *Grallaricula cucullata*	VU	040	1,500–2,700	Montane evergreen forest

cont.

Status and habitat of restricted-range species (cont.)

Species (ordered taxonomically)	Global status	Other EBAs (and SAs)	Altitude (m)	Habitat
Apolinar's Wren *Cistothorus apolinari*	EN	—	2,500–4,000	Páramo grassland, marshland, marshy meadows, reedbeds
Niceforo's Wren *Thryothorus nicefori*	CR	—	c.1,100	Arid montane/thorn scrub
Moustached Brush-finch *Atlapetes albofrenatus*	lc	034	1,500–2,500	Montane evergreen forest and forest edge, secondary growth, thickets
Fulvous-headed Tanager *Thlypopsis fulviceps*	lc	032,033,034	750–2,300	Secondary and montane evergreen forest, forest edge, thickets, bamboo
Turquoise Dacnis *Dacnis hartlaubi*	VU	040,041	1,350–2,200	Montane evergreen forest edge, secondary forest, clearings
Grey-throated Warbler *Basileuterus cinereicollis*	nt	034	800–2,100	Montane evergreen forest undergrowth, forest edge, secondary growth
Rufous-browed Conebill *Conirostrum rufum*	lc	036	2,650–3,400	Elfin forest, humid forest edge, secondary growth, semi-humid/humid montane scrub
Mountain Grackle *Macroagelaius subalaris*	nt	—	1,950–3,100	Montane evergreen forest, forest edge

Global status (see p. 679 for definitions)
EX Extinct
EW Extinct in the Wild — with year of last record
CR Critical
EN Endangered
VU Vulnerable — threatened species
cd Conservation Dependent
nt Near Threatened
lc Least Concern
DD Data Deficient
NE Not Evaluated

Other EBAs (and SAs) (see p. 65 for locations): bracketed numbers are Secondary Areas; [x] extinct in that EBA or SA.

The most interesting distributional patterns shown by species in this EBA belong to the suite of species known only from the Páramo de Tamá massif on the Colombia–Venezuela border: *Grallaria chthonia* is known only from Hacienda La Providencia near the source of the Chiquita river on the Venezuelan side of this massif; *Grallaricula cucullata* is found in the Colombian inter-Andean slopes (EBA 040), but within the East Andes is known only from the Páramo de Tamá in Venezuela, as a distinct subspecies *venezuelana*; and *Odontophorus columbianus* is primarily confined to the Cordillera de la Costa Central (EBA 033), with a disjunct population known from the Chiquita river in the present EBA (Meyer de Schauensee and Phelps 1978, Collar *et al.* 1992). The area either side of the Táchira depression warrants further research, as the distributions of species in this region where the East Andes and Cordillera de Mérida (EBA 034) meet are poorly understood; Táchira Emerald *Amazilia distans*, for example, is known from just five (apparent) observations since its discovery in 1954, in an area which in places is just c.30 km distant from the Páramo de Tamá (and therefore perhaps occurring in this EBA too). Both *Metallura iracunda* and *Schizoeaca perijana* are endemic to the Sierra de Perijá at the northernmost end of the EBA, and *Clytoctantes alixii* and *Grallaria excelsa* are present only in the sierra and adjacent EBAs. *Grallaria kaestneri* and *Thryothorus nicefori* are presently known from just one locality each, on opposite slopes of the East Andes. Distributions at the south-westernmost end of the EBA (where the

East Andes join the Central Andean chain) are poorly known, and restricted-range species from this EBA (e.g. *Chlorostilbon poortmani*) at times overlap with those from the inter-Andean slopes (EBA 040).

Amethyst-throated Sunangel *Heliangelus amethysticollis clarissae*, which has sometimes been considered a separate species, is confined to this EBA and the Cordillera de Mérida (EBA 034) (Fjeldså and Krabbe 1990, J. Fjeldså *in litt.* 1993).

■ Threats and conservation

The forests and marshlands of the Colombian East Andes have been subjected to extensive degradation (Forero 1989, Collar *et al.* 1992), with progressive deforestation on the lower slopes, i.e. the lower montane humid forest (Wege and Long 1995). On the western slopes, the humid subtropical and temperate (primarily oak) forest at 1,500–2,500 m has been largely cleared for intensive crop cultivation and pastureland, although important fragments do still remain (see below). Even the dense, dry *Acacia* scrub that was the dominant vegetation along the Fonce river in the upper tropical zone on the western slope has been lost to widespread agriculture such as coffee plantations, pasture and arable. On the eastern side, the forest that once surrounded Laguna de Tota (at c.3,000 m) is now almost totally gone, and the fringing wetland habitat is extensively reduced. Introduced fish, intensive agriculture, pollution and sediment run-off have caused serious problems to the lake community. Most of the lakes on the Bogotá and Ubaté savannas have been subjected to similar prob-

Distribution patterns of restricted-range species

Species (ordered geographically)	Sierra de Perijá	E. Andes (inc. Páramo de Tamá)	E. Andes of Bogotá	Other EBAs, SAs
Metallura iracunda	●	–	–	–
Schizoeaca perijana	●	–	–	–
Clytoctantes alixii	●	–	–	●
Grallaria excelsa	●	–	–	●
Coeligena helianthea	●	●	–	–
Pauxi pauxi	●	●	–	●
Odontophorus atrifrons	●	●	–	●
Chlorostilbon russatus	●	●	–	●
Coeligena bonapartei	●	●	–	●
Thlypopsis fulviceps	●	●	–	●
Basileuterus cinereicollis	●	●	–	–
Podiceps andinus	–	X	–	–
Odontophorus strophium	–	●	–	–
Rallus semiplumbeus	–	●	–	–
Pyrrhura calliptera	–	●	–	–
Amazilia castaneiventris	–	●	–	–
Coeligena prunellei	–	●	–	–
Chalcostigma heteropogon	–	●	–	–
Synallaxis subpudica	–	●	–	–
Grallaria kaestneri	–	●	–	–
Cistothorus apolinari	–	●	–	–
Thryothorus nicefori	–	●	–	–
Macroagelaius subalaris	–	●	–	–
Odontophorus columbianus	–	●	–	●
Chlorostilbon stenura	–	●	–	●
Heliangelus mavors	–	●	–	●
Eriocnemis cupreoventris	–	●	–	●
Oxypogon guerinii	–	●	–	●
Grallaria chthonia	–	●	–	–
Grallaricula cucullata	–	●	–	●
Atlapetes albofrenatus	–	●	–	●
Dacnis hartlaubi	–	●	–	●
Conirostrum rufum	–	●	–	●
Hapalopsittaca amazonina	–	●	●	●
Chlorostilbon poortmani	–	●	●	●
Total	11	30	2	

● Present   ? Present?   Threatened spp. shown in **bold**   Other EBAs, SAs } see 'Status and habitat' table
O Extinct?   R Reintroduced
X Extinct   I Introduced

future is uncertain, particularly as there are Venezuelan government proposals for coal-mining within its boundaries (C. J. Sharpe *in litt.* 1997).

Fourteen of the restricted-range birds in this area are threatened (and a further seven are Near Threatened), primarily due to the extensive loss of forest cover and the destruction of wetland habitats throughout the mountain chain. The severe degradation of the marshes and lake ecosystems is shown by the fact that *Podiceps andinus* is now considered extinct (300 individuals were reported on Laguna de Tota as recently as 1968), with the endemic subspecies of Yellow-billed Pintail *Anas georgica nicefori* almost certainly gone (Fjeldså and Krabbe 1990). A number of the threatened birds are very poorly known, with three species (see 'Restricted-range species', above) recorded from just one locality (these include *Grallaria chthonia*, which has not been recorded since 1956) and *Amazilia castaneiventris* known from only five localities and just one record since the 1960s (Collar *et al.* 1992). The widespread but threatened Yellow-eared Parrot *Ognorhynchus icterotis* and Red Siskin *Carduelis cucullata* also occur in this EBA, and similarly are threatened due to loss of their forest habitat—and also, in the case of *C. cucullata*, by the cage-bird trade.

Nine of the 24 Key Areas for the threatened birds in this EBA (Wege and Long 1995) currently have some form of protected status. In Venezuela, two important protected areas (which correspond to the two Key Areas in that country) are the Sierra de Perijá and El Tamá National Parks, the latter being contiguous with Tamá National Park in Colombia. Other important protected areas in Colombia (which are primarily centred on the higher-altitude sites) include: Chingaza National Park (and the adjacent Río Blanco–Olivares Forest Reserve and Carpanta Biological Reserve), El Cocuy National Park, Pisba National Park and Sumapaz National Park (Hernández Camacho *et al.* undated). The Guanentá–Alto Río Fonce Fauna and Flora Sanctuary on the western slope of the East Andes protects the only sizeable forest tract remaining in the area (humid subtropical and temperate oak forest).

lems. The potential exploitation of coal concessions threatens the subtropical forest in a portion of Venezuela's El Tamá National Park. The Sierra de Perijá is being rapidly deforested on the Venezuelan side: from the bottom up for cattle-ranching, and from the top down for narcotics cultivation. There is no active management of Sierra de Perijá National Park and its

039 Colombian inter-Andean valleys

PRIORITY HIGH

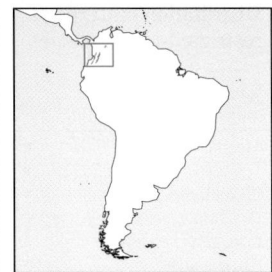

Key habitats Tropical lowland dry forest, lowland evergreen forest, arid scrub

Main threats Major habitat loss (e.g. due to agricultural expansion)

Biological importance ● ● ○
Current threat level ● ○ ○

Area 31,000km² **Altitude** 200–1,700 m

Countries Colombia

Restricted-range species	Threatened	Total
Confined to this EBA	1	4
Present also in other EBAs, SAs	0	0
Total	1	4

■ General characteristics

This EBA is situated in Colombia between the main Andean ranges, embracing the Patía valley (which separates the Central and West Andes south of Popayán), the Cauca valley, and the west side and head of the Magdalena valley. At the head of the Magdalena valley, the EBA extends onto the southernmost end of the East Andes. The EBA thus includes: the eastern slope of the West Andes (in both the Patía and Cauca valleys); the western slope of the Central Andes; the eastern slope of the Central Andes; the head of the Magdalena valley (see above); and it extends onto the Pacific slope of the West Andes in the dry Dagua and Calima valleys (and thus dovetails with the Chocó, EBA 041). At the northern end of the Magdalena valley the EBA includes the isolated Suárez and Chicamocha valleys which dovetail with the East Andes (EBA 038).

These Andean valleys are primarily 200–1,700 m above sea-level, and as such their natural vegetation comprises open woodland, dry forest and arid scrub; much of the area has, however, now been converted to agricultural land with little natural vegetation remaining (see 'Threats and Conservation', below). The EBA abuts the Colombian inter-Andean slopes (EBA 040), though that region lies at higher elevations (chiefly 1,200–2,600 m) and within a more humid vegetation zone.

■ Restricted-range species

Of the restricted-range species, the requirements of *Cypseloides lemosi* are essentially unknown, al-

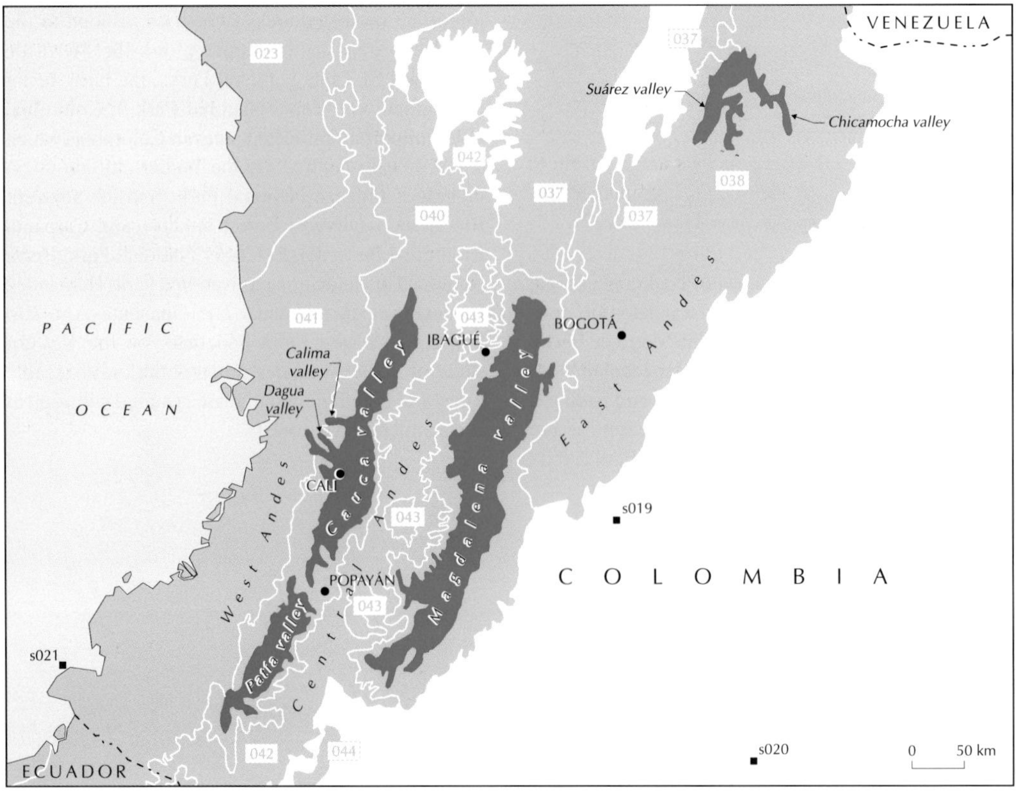

VENEZUELA

023

037

Suárez valley

Chicamocha valley

042

037

038

040

037

041

043

Calima valley

Dagua valley

PACIFIC

OCEAN

IBAGUÉ

BOGOTÁ

East Andes

Cauca valley

West Andes

Central Andes

Magdalena valley

CALI

043

s019

POPAYÁN

043

COLOMBIA

s021

Patía valley

042

044

s020

0   50 km

ECUADOR

Status and habitat of restricted-range species

Species (ordered taxonomically)	Global status	Other EBAs (and SAs)	Altitude (m)	Habitat
White-chested Swift *Cypseloides lemosi*	VU	—	1,000–1,300	Secondary forest, grassland, scrub, rocky areas
Greyish Piculet *Picumnus granadensis*	lc	—	600–2,100	Tropical deciduous and secondary forest, tropical lowland evergreen forest edge, scrub
Apical Flycatcher *Myiarchus apicalis*	lc	—	400–1,700 (–2,500)	Tropical deciduous, secondary and gallery forest, tropical lowland evergreen forest edge, arid scrub
Velvet-fronted Euphonia *Euphonia concinna*	lc	—	200–1,100	Tropical deciduous and secondary forest, agricultural land, near water

Global status (see p. 679 for definitions)	EX Extinct EW Extinct in the Wild ⎱ with year of last record	CR Critical EN Endangered VU Vulnerable ⎱ threatened species	cd Conservation Dependent nt Near Threatened lc Least Concern	DD Data Deficient NE Not Evaluated

Other EBAs (and SAs) (see p. 65 for locations): bracketed numbers are Secondary Areas; ˣ extinct in that EBA or SA.

though most observations have historically been made over dry non-forest areas at the head of the Cauca valley (Collar *et al.* 1992). Both *Myiarchus apicalis* and *Euphonia concinna* rely on the dry, more open vegetation characteristic of the valley bottoms and dry side valleys, with *Picumnus granadensis* also able to exist in some more humid situations. The clearance of humid forest on the slopes of the Andes in this area has led to the expansion of dry secondary forest up-slope from this EBA, and consequently some of the endemics in this area are starting to occur at similar altitudes to the endemics in the adjacent but higher-altitude Colombian inter-Andean slopes (EBA 040). This is the case with *Myiarchus apicalis*, which primarily occurs below 1,700 m but has recently been found in a number of areas up to 2,500 m (Ridgely and Tudor 1994).

All four restricted-range species are endemic to the EBA: *Euphonia concinna* is confined to the Magdalena valley, *Cypseloides lemosi* to the Cauca valley (although recent sightings suggest that it also occurs in neighbouring Ecuador: B. M. Whitney *in litt.* 1991, S. N. G. Howell *in litt.* 1996) and *Picumnus granadensis* to the Cauca and Pacific slope valleys; *Myiarchus apicalis* has the broadest distribution, being found in the Magdalena, Cauca and Pacific slope valleys. Both *Picumnus granadensis* and *Myiarchus apicalis* occur in the dry Dagua and Calima valleys on the Pacific slope of the West Andes, where they undoubtedly exist alongside the humid forest species typical of the Chocó (EBA 041). However, these two species are not considered shared with the Chocó due to their different habitat preferences.

■ Threats and conservation

All three valleys (Cauca, Magdalena and Patía), and the mountain slopes that bound them, have been severely deforested during past decades due primarily to the expansion of agriculture. However, although *Cypseloides lemosi* is considered threatened (possibly because of agrochemical applications in the area in which it remains poorly known), the other three endemics in the area are apparently adapted to scrub and secondary growth (which is expanding as a result of forest clearance and subsequent abandonment), so have not suffered from the deforestation in the same way that the subtropical humid forest species have done on the inter-Andean slopes (see EBA 040). Nevertheless, very little original vegetation remains, and the EBA species are essentially unprotected within the formal protected-area system.

040 Colombian inter-Andean slopes

PRIORITY
CRITICAL

Key habitats Tropical montane
evergreen forest

Main threats Major habitat loss (e.g.
due to human colonization,
clearance for plantations)

Biological importance ● ● ●
Current threat level ● ● ●

Area 48,000 km²   **Altitude** 1,000–2,500 m

Countries Colombia

Restricted-range species	Threatened	Total
Confined to this EBA	4	5
Present also in other EBAs, SAs	5	12
Total	9	17

■ General characteristics

Lying within the Andes of Colombia, this EBA
embraces the slopes of the Patía, Cauca and
Magdalena valleys. At the head of the Magdalena
valley it extends on both slopes onto the southernmost
end of the East Andes (south of EBA 038). It extends
across the Central Andes at a low narrow point
(between Manizales and Medellín at c.5°40′N) to the
eastern slope of the Central Andes, thus embracing
most of the western side of the Magdalena valley and
Central Andean foothills. Although traditionally regarded as two separate centres of endemism (the

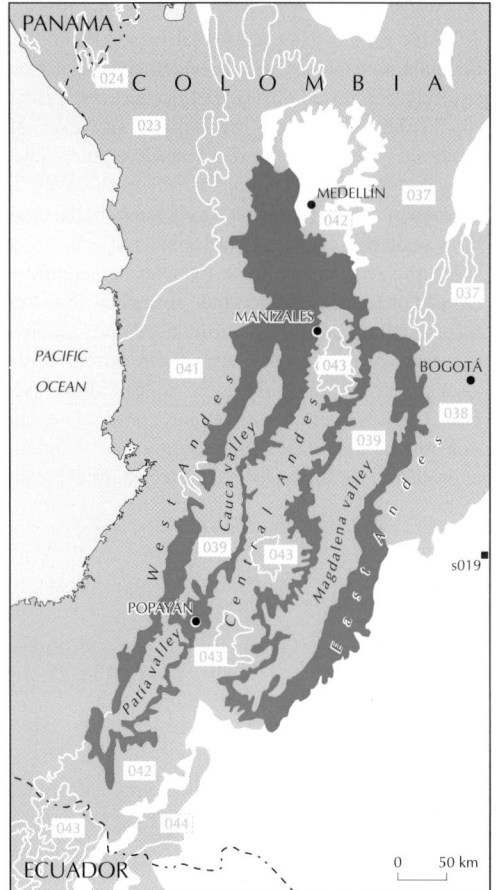

P. G. W. Salaman

Severe deforestation in this EBA over centuries of
human colonization has resulted in a patchwork of
pasture and commercial plantations—and just a few
remnant patches of forest.

Cauca and Magdalena centres), many of the restricted-range species occur in both valley systems,
and they are thus considered here to comprise a
single EBA.

The EBA is characterized by the mid-elevation
(subtropical) evergreen forests of the Andean foothills at 1,000–2,500 m. The species confined to the
drier vegetation of the valley floors (Colombian
inter-Andean valleys, EBA 039) may overlap
altitudinally with some of those from the humid
forest, especially where clearance has resulted in dry
scrub spreading up the valley sides. Also adjacent is
the North Central Andes (EBA 042), whose species

Status and habitat of restricted-range species

Species (ordered taxonomically)	Global status	Other EBAs (and SAs)	Altitude (m)	Habitat
Black Tinamou *Tinamus osgoodi*	DD	053,054	1,500–2,100	Montane evergreen forest
Cauca Guan *Penelope perspicax*	EN	—	900–2,150	Montane evergreen forest
Chestnut Wood-quail *Odontophorus hyperythrus*	nt	042	1,600–2,700	Montane evergreen forest, forest edge, secondary growth
Tolima Dove *Leptotila conoveri*	EN	—	1,600–2,250	Forest edge, possibly secondary forest
Blossomcrown *Anthocephala floriceps*	nt	036	1,200–2,300	Montane evergreen forest, older secondary growth
Rufous-vented Whitetip *Urosticte ruficrissa*	lc	044	1,350–2,300	Montane evergreen forest, forest edge, scrub
Schwartz's Antthrush *Chamaeza turdina*	lc	033	1,400–2,600	Montane evergreen forest
Moustached Antpitta *Grallaria alleni*	EN	—	2,000–2,130	Montane evergreen forest
Hooded Antpitta *Grallaricula cucullata*	VU	038	1,500–2,700	Montane evergreen forest
Black-chested Fruiteater *Pipreola lubomirskii*	nt	044	1,500–2,300	Montane evergreen forest
Yellow-headed Manakin *Chloropipo flavicapilla*	nt	041,044	1,200–2,400	Montane evergreen forest, tall secondary growth
Yellow-headed Brush-finch *Atlapetes flaviceps*	EN	—	1,300–2,255	Montane evergreen forest edge, clearings, scrub
Dusky-headed Brush-finch *Atlapetes fuscoolivaceus*	nt	—	1,600–2,400	Montane evergreen forest edge, second-growth scrub, clearings
Black-and-gold Tanager *Bangsia melanochlamys*	EN	041	1,000–2,285	Montane evergreen and secondary forest, forest edge
Multicoloured Tanager *Chlorochrysa nitidissima*	VU	041	1,300–2,195	Montane evergreen forest and forest edge, secondary growth
Turquoise Dacnis *Dacnis hartlaubi*	VU	038,041	1,350–2,200	Montane evergreen forest edge, secondary forest, clearings
Red-bellied Grackle *Hypopyrrhus pyrohypogaster*	EN	041	800–2,400	Montane evergreen forest, forest edge, humid scrub

Global status (see p. 679 for definitions)
EX Extinct
EW Extinct in the Wild
} with year of last record
CR Critical
EN Endangered
VU Vulnerable
} threatened species
cd Conservation Dependent
nt Near Threatened
lc Least Concern
DD Data Deficient
NE Not Evaluated

Other EBAs (and SAs) (see p. 65 for locations): bracketed numbers are Secondary Areas; ˣ extinct in that EBA or SA.

sometimes overlap altitudinally with species on the slopes of the Central Andes, although the birds of the North Central Andes generally occupy higher areas (2,000–3,600 m) and are confined to humid upper montane forest and cloud forest.

■ Restricted-range species

The species primarily occupy humid foothill and lower montane forest with associated edge and secondary vegetation, mainly at c.1,200–2,500 m.

A number of species from this EBA are also found on the Pacific slope of the West Andes within the Chocó (EBA 041). *Penelope perspicax* occurs in just a few low passes and is thus regarded as confined to the inter-Andean area, much as the species found in

(presumably the same) low passes on the eastern side of the West Andes are taken to be restricted to the Chocó (see EBA 041). *Bangsia melanochlamys* is primarily a bird of the Pacific slope of the West Andes (EBA 041), but is known from a disjunct population on the northern and western slopes of the Central Andes in Antioquia department (where it has however been recorded from very few localities, and not since 1948) (Collar *et al.* 1992). *Tinamus osgoodi* has a curious distribution: the subspecies *hershkovitzi* is known from just two localities within this EBA (one is the Cueva de los Guácharos National Park), and the only other population lies c.2,000 km south in the Peruvian East Andean foothills (EBA 053).

N. Arlott

Multicoloured Tanager *Chlorochrysa nitidissima*, a threatened and formerly common species, is now confined to remnant patches of montane evergreen forest.

Birds which are almost certainly *Grallaria alleni* have been seen and tape-recorded in the Cordillera de Guacamayo in Ecuador (P. Coopmans *in litt.* 1995), which would extend the species' range into the North Central Andes (EBA 042). A specimen of Black Inca *Coeligena prunellei* from Salento in the Central Andes (Collar *et al.* 1992) is now suspected to be in error (A. J. Negret *in litt.* 1994), and the species has therefore been omitted from consideration for this EBA (it is thus confined to the Colombian East Andes, EBA 038).

■ Threats and conservation

Both the Cauca and Magdalena valleys (and the mountain slopes bounding them) have been severely deforested over a long history of human colonization, and the area is now characterized by remnant (often secondary) forest patches, pasture, coffee, banana plantations, etc. (Collar *et al.* 1992, Wege and Long 1995). In the Cauca valley at the northern end of the West Andes, extensive forest destruction for pasture has confined remaining forest to ridge crests and isolated patches, with humid subtropical forest almost totally gone from the middle part of the valley (e.g. in the Quindío watershed). Similarly, at the northernmost end of the Central Andes, forest destruction has been near-complete, with extensive clearance around Medellín leaving just remnant patches of primary and old secondary growth (among coffee and *Pinus patulla* plantations) in urgent need of protection. At the head of the Magdalena valley, forest has given way to coffee, bananas and sugar-cane, with the western slope of the southernmost East Andes (e.g. Cueva de los Guácharos National Park) increasingly threatened by human encroachment and opium production (Wege and Long 1995).

The widespread (though localized) destruction of natural vegetation in this EBA has resulted in all but two of the restricted-range species being considered either threatened (nine species) or Near Threatened (five species), with one species classified as Data Deficient. The widespread (though localized) but threatened Yellow-eared Parrot *Ognorhynchus icterotis* (classified as Critical) and Golden-plumed Parakeet *Leptosittaca branickii* (Vulnerable) also occur in this EBA, and similarly are threatened almost exclusively by forest loss.

Sixteen Key Areas for the threatened birds have been identified in this EBA, including important protected areas such as Los Nevados, Cueva de los Guácharos and Munchique National Parks, Ucumarí Regional Park, Alto Quindío Acaime Natural Reserve and Cañon del Quindío Natural Reserve, Bosque de Yotoco Reserve and Tambito Nature Reserve (Wege and Long 1995). With such widespread forest destruction, the value of these areas cannot be over-stated as critically important sites for conservation.

041 Chocó

PRIORITY URGENT

Key habitats Tropical lowland and montane evergreen forest, páramo

Main threats Major habitat loss (e.g. due to logging, human settlement, agriculture, grazing)

Biological importance ● ●
Current threat level ● ●

Area 100,000 km²   **Altitude** 0–3,800 m

Countries Colombia, Ecuador

Restricted-range species	Threatened	Total
Confined to this EBA	12	51
Present also in other EBAs, SAs	5	11
Total	17	62

■ General characteristics

This EBA traverses the length of western Colombia and Ecuador, although the majority of the ranges of its restricted-range species terminate north of

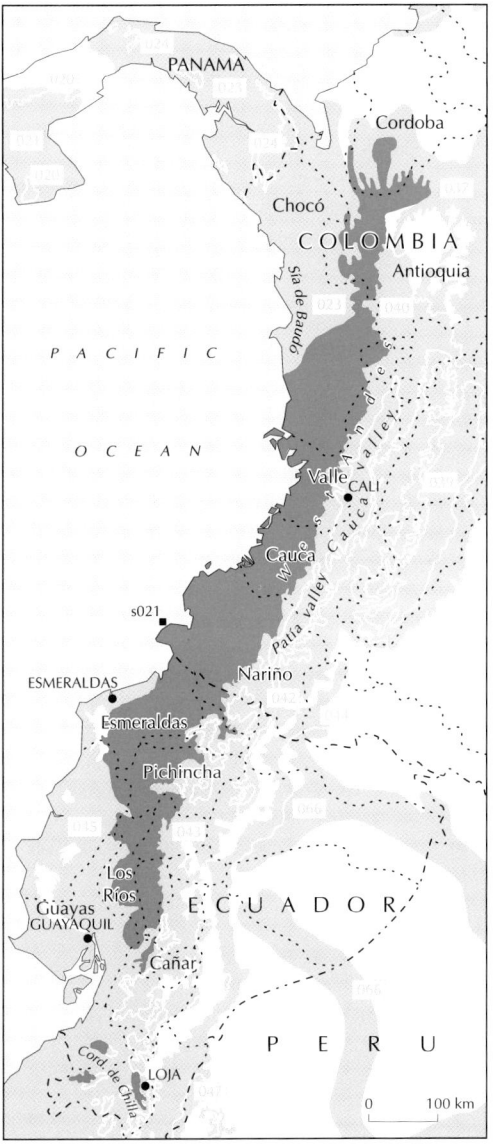

Guayaquil at c.2°S. The area comprises the Pacific slope of the Colombian West Andes, the Pacific slope of the Andes in Nariño department (southernmost Colombia), and south into Ecuador where it incorporates the westernmost volcanic peaks and Pacific slope of the Andes south to Cañar province. A few species occur in the Cordillera de Chilla. Some geographical overlap with the North Central Andes (EBA 042) may occur in parts of northern Ecuador, although the species endemic to that EBA all inhabit higher altitudes (primarily above 2,500 m). In the lowlands, the EBA extends throughout the Chocó from the southern end of the Serranía de Baudó (where it abuts the Darién lowlands, EBA 023), south along the Andean foothills and through the Pacific coast lowlands into northern Esmeraldas province, and from there along the base of the Andes in Pichincha, Los Ríos, and northern Guayas provinces of Ecuador.

The EBA is characterized by wet forest, and indeed, with up to 16,000 mm of rain per year in some places, this is probably the wettest place on earth. The major vegetation zones of the Pacific slope vary considerably according to local climatic and altitudinal conditions. Lowland tropical wet forest is found in the Pacific lowlands and lower foothills (0–1,000 m) in areas with high rainfall (4,000–8,000 mm/ year). Super-wet (pluvial) forest occurs in a limited zone (with an excess of 8,000 mm/year rainfall) between the dominant wet lowland and foothill forests. Subtropical forest replaces the tropical forest between 1,000 and 2,300 m in a zone of lower rainfall (2,000–6,000 mm/year) but with very high humidity. From 2,000 m towards the treeline at c.3,200 m, temperate Andean humid forest persists, trees becoming increasingly stunted with altitude and eventually giving way to wet grassland or páramo, which is characterized by stands of tall composites like *Espeletia* and *Puya*, and isolated, small dense patches of *Polylepis*-dominated woodland in sheltered areas (Salaman 1994).

The Chocó has one of the world's richest lowland biotas, with exceptional richness and endemism in a wide range of taxa including plants, reptiles, amphib-

Status and habitat of restricted-range species

Species (ordered taxonomically)	Global status	Other EBAs (and SAs)	Altitude (m)	Habitat
Berlepsch's Tinamou *Crypturellus berlepschi*	lc	—	<500(–900)	Tropical lowland evergreen forest edge, secondary forest, esp. dense secondary growth
Plumbeous Forest-falcon *Micrastur plumbeus*	EN	—	0–1,400	Tropical lowland evergreen forest
Baudó Guan *Penelope ortoni*	VU	—	Lowlands to 1,500	Montane evergreen and tropical lowland evergreen forest
Dark-backed Wood-quail *Odontophorus melanonotus*	nt	—	1,200–1,500	Montane evergreen forest
Dusky Pigeon *Columba goodsoni*	lc	—	Lowlands to 1,000	Tropical lowland evergreen and montane evergreen forest
Rose-faced Parrot *Pionopsitta pulchra*	lc	—	Lowlands to 2,100	Tropical lowland evergreen and montane evergreen forest, tall secondary growth
Banded Ground-cuckoo *Neomorphus radiolosus*	EN	—	450–1,525	Tropical lowland evergreen forest
Colombian Screech-owl *Otus colombianus*[1]	nt	—	1,250–2,130	Montane evergreen forest
Chocó Poorwill *Nyctiphrynus rosenbergi*[2]	nt	—	Lowlands to 900	Tropical lowland evergreen forest
Purple-chested Hummingbird *Amazilia rosenbergi*	lc	—	Lowlands to 400	Tropical lowland evergreen forest edge, secondary forest, scrub
Empress Brilliant *Heliodoxa imperatrix*	lc	—	400–1,800	Montane evergreen and tropical lowland evergreen forest, forest edge, secondary growth
Brown Inca *Coeligena wilsoni*	lc	—	700–1,900	Montane evergreen forest, forest edge
Velvet-purple Coronet *Boissonneaua jardini*	lc	—	350–2,200	Montane evergreen and secondary forest, forest edge
Gorgeted Sunangel *Heliangelus strophianus*	lc	—	1,200–2,800	Montane evergreen and secondary forest, forest edge, thickets
Turquoise-throated Puffleg *Eriocnemis godini*	CR	—	2,100–2,300	Montane evergreen forest, possibly arid woodland
Colourful Puffleg *Eriocnemis mirabilis*	VU	—	2,195–2,440	Montane evergreen and secondary forest, forest edge and clearings
Hoary Puffleg *Haplophaedia lugens*	nt	—	1,200–2,500	Montane evergreen forest, forest edge, occasionally scrub
Purple-bibbed Whitetip *Urosticte benjamini*	lc	—	700–1,500	Montane evergreen forest, forest edge, flowering shrubs
Violet-tailed Sylph *Aglaiocercus coelestis*	lc	—	(300–) 900–2,100	Montane evergreen forest, forest edge, shrubs
White-eyed Trogon *Trogon comptus*	lc	037	Lowlands to 1,800	Tropical lowland evergreen and montane evergreen forest, forest edge
Sooty-capped Puffbird *Bucco noanamae*	nt	023	Lowlands to 100	Tropical lowland evergreen forest, scrub, secondary growth, plantations
Orange-fronted Barbet *Capito squamatus*	nt	—	Lowlands to 1,500	Tropical lowland evergreen forest, forest edge, secondary growth
Five-coloured Barbet *Capito quinticolor*	VU	—	Lowlands to 100	Tropical lowland evergreen forest, forest edge, tall secondary growth
Toucan Barbet *Semnornis ramphastinus*	nt	—	1,000–2,400	Montane evergreen forest, forest edge
Plate-billed Mountain-toucan *Andigena laminirostris*	nt	—	Usually 1,000–3,200	Montane evergreen forest, forest edge
Chocó Toucan *Ramphastos brevis*	lc	—	Lowlands to 1,000	Tropical lowland evergreen forest, forest edge
Chocó Woodpecker *Veniliornis chocoensis*	nt	—	Lowlands to 1,000	Tropical lowland evergreen forest, forest edge

cont.

Status and habitat of restricted-range species (cont.)

Species (ordered taxonomically)	Global status	Other EBAs (and SAs)	Altitude (m)	Habitat
Lita Woodpecker *Piculus litae*	lc	—	Lowlands	Tropical lowland evergreen forest, open woodland, secondary growth
Fulvous-dotted Treerunner *Margarornis stellatus*	lc	—	1,200–2,200	Montane evergreen and elfin forest
Uniform Treehunter *Thripadectes ignobilis*	lc	—	700–1,700	Montane evergreen and tropical lowland evergreen forest and forest undergrowth
Bicoloured Antvireo *Dysithamnus occidentalis*	VU	044	900–2,200	Montane evergreen and tropical lowland evergreen forest, esp. around gaps
Stub-tailed Antbird *Myrmeciza berlepschi*	lc	—	Lowlands to 650	Tropical lowland evergreen forest
Rufous-crowned Antpitta *Pittasoma rufopileatum*	lc	—	Lowlands to 1,100	Tropical lowland evergreen forest
Yellow-breasted Antpitta *Grallaria flavotincta*	lc	—	1,300–2,350	Montane evergreen forest, forest edge and dense undergrowth
Nariño Tapaculo *Scytalopus vicinior*	lc	024	750–1,800	Montane evergreen forest, forest edge
Orange-breasted Fruiteater *Pipreola jucunda*	lc	—	600–1,700	Montane evergreen forest, secondary growth
Long-wattled Umbrellabird *Cephalopterus penduliger*	VU	—	500–1,400	Montane evergreen forest, forest edge and clearings
Club-winged Manakin *Machaeropterus deliciosus*	lc	—	400–1,500	Montane evergreen and secondary forest
Yellow-headed Manakin *Chloropipo flavicapilla*	nt	040,044	1,200–2,400	Montane evergreen forest, tall secondary growth
Black Solitaire *Entomodestes coracinus*	lc	—	450–1,900	Montane evergreen and tropical lowland evergreen forest, forest edge
Tanager-finch *Oreothraupis arremonops*	VU	—	1,200–2,600	Montane evergreen forest floor
Dusky Bush-tanager *Chlorospingus semifuscus*	lc	—	700–2,750	Montane evergreen forest, forest edge, secondary growth, clearings
Yellow-green Bush-tanager *Chlorospingus flavovirens*	VU	—	500–1,100	Montane evergreen forest, forest edge and clearings
Scarlet-and-white Tanager *Chrysothlypis salmoni*	lc	037	Lowlands to 1,100	Secondary and tropical lowland evergreen forest, forest edge, scrub
Crested Ant-tanager *Habia cristata*	lc	—	700–2,100	Tropical lowland evergreen and montane evergreen forest, forest edge
Black-and-gold Tanager *Bangsia melanochlamys*	EN	040	1,000–2,285	Montane evergreen and secondary forest, forest edge
Golden-chested Tanager *Bangsia rothschildi*	lc	—	150–1,500	Tropical lowland evergreen and montane evergreen forest, forest edge
Moss-backed Tanager *Bangsia edwardsi*	lc	—	500–2,100	Montane evergreen and tropical lowland evergreen forest, forest edge, secondary growth, clearings
Gold-ringed Tanager *Bangsia aureocincta*	VU	—	1,600–2,195	Montane evergreen forest
Black-chinned Mountain-tanager *Anisognathus notabilis*	lc	—	800–2,750	Montane evergreen forest, forest edge
Purplish-mantled Tanager *Iridosornis porphyrocephala*	nt	—	1,500–2,200	Montane evergreen forest, forest edge, secondary growth
Yellow-collared Chlorophonia *Chlorophonia flavirostris*	lc	024	100–1,900	Montane evergreen and tropical lowland evergreen forest, forest edge, secondary growth
Glistening-green Tanager *Chlorochrysa phoenicotis*	lc	—	1,100–2,400	Montane evergreen forest, forest edge, secondary growth, clearings
Multicoloured Tanager *Chlorochrysa nitidissima*	VU	040	1,300–2,195	Montane evergreen forest and forest edge, secondary growth

cont.

Status and habitat of restricted-range species (cont.)

Species (ordered taxonomically)	Global status	Other EBAs (and SAs)	Altitude (m)	Habitat
Blue-whiskered Tanager Tangara johannae	nt	—	0–1,500	Tropical lowland evergreen forest, forest edge, secondary growth
Turquoise Dacnis Dacnis hartlaubi	VU	038,040	1,350–2,200	Montane evergreen forest edge, secondary forest, clearings
Scarlet-breasted Dacnis Dacnis berlepschi	VU	—	0–1,200	Tropical lowland evergreen forest, forest edge, tall secondary growth
Chestnut-bellied Flower-piercer Diglossa gloriosissima	nt	—	3,000–3,800	Elfin forest, forest edge, semi-humid/humid montane scrub, páramo grassland
Indigo Flower-piercer Diglossopis indigotica	lc	—	1,000–2,200	Montane evergreen and secondary forest, forest edge, secondary growth
Chocó Vireo Vireo masteri[3]	VU	—	1,200–1,600	Montane evergreen forest or cloud forest
Red-bellied Grackle Hypopyrrhus pyrohypogaster	EN	040	800–2,400	Montane evergreen forest, forest edge, humid scrub
Beautiful Jay Cyanolyca pulchra	nt	—	900–2,300	Montane evergreen forest, forest edge

Global status (see p. 679 for definitions)

EX Extinct ⎱ with year
EW Extinct in ⎰ of last
 the Wild ⎰ record

CR Critical ⎱
EN Endangered ⎰ threatened
VU Vulnerable ⎰ species

cd Conservation
 Dependent
nt Near Threatened
lc Least Concern
DD Data Deficient
NE Not Evaluated

Other EBAs (and SAs) (see p. 65 for locations)
Bracketed numbers are Secondary Areas.   ˣ Extinct in that EBA or SA.

Notes
[1] Taxonomy follows Fitzpatrick and O'Neill (1986).
[2] Taxonomy follows Robbins and Ridgely (1992).
[3] New species, following Salaman and Stiles (1996).

ians and butterflies (Dinerstein et al. 1995). In the case of plants, over 10% (8,000–9,000) of species recorded from the Neotropics have been found from the narrow band of pluvial forest that runs through the Chocó; it has been suggested that 25% of these species are endemic to the area (Salaman 1994).

■ Restricted-range species

The Chocó EBA supports the largest number of restricted-range birds of any EBA in the Americas, over 50 species being endemic to the area. A large number of birds are confined to the tropical lowland and lower subtropical foothill forests, with the remainder primarily found in the subtropical zone; only a few species occur in the high-altitude temperate areas. This bias is primarily due to the West Andes of Colombia having an average ridge height of c.2,000 m, with relatively few mountain peaks above this (Hilty and Brown 1986). The birds restricted to the subtropical zone and above are almost invariably found on the disjunct peaks of the Colombian West Andes (e.g. Paramillo, Páramo Frontino, Cerro Tatamá, Cerro Munchique), and further south in southern Colombia and northern Ecuador (e.g. Nevado Cumbal, Volcán Chiles, Cotacachi, Pichincha).

With relatively little known about the precise distributions, altitudinal movements and ecological requirements of the restricted-range birds, it is not currently possible to further divide this EBA. It does, however, seem likely that the ranges of tropical

foothill and lowland species are associated with the band of pluvial forest that runs through the centre of the Chocó region (Hilty and Brown 1986); also, (in Colombia) forest composition changes strikingly from lowland to montane at 1,000–1,500 m (L. G. Olarte in litt. 1993), and this may form the natural boundary between distinct groups of tropical lowland and higher Pacific slope birds.

Five species—Otus colombianus, Aglaiocercus coelestis, Semnornis ramphastinus, Habia cristata and Iridosornis porphyrocephala—although regarded as confined to the EBA, occur locally on the eastern slope of the West Andes (in the Cauca valley), primarily near low wet passes (Hilty and Brown 1986), much as Cauca Guan Penelope perspicax does from the opposite direction (see EBA 040, where local distributions of species are discussed). A similar situation exists with Greyish Piculet Picumnus granadensis and Apical Flycatcher Myiarchus apicalis, which occur in the dry Dagua and Calima valleys on the Pacific slope. Both of these species are primarily dry forest, woodland or scrub birds, and are thus considered endemic to the inter-Andean valleys (EBA 039), rather than being shared with the more humid forest species of the Chocó. Bangsia melanochlamys is known from a disjunct population on the northern and western slopes of the North Central Andes (EBA 042) in Antioquia department, where, however, it has been recorded from very few localities, and not since 1948 (Collar et al. 1992). In northern Ecuador (e.g. in the Bilsa area), Haplo-

Habitat associations of restricted-range species

Lowland tropical forest	Bangsia rothschildi
Crypturellus berlepschi	Bangsia edwardsi
Micrastur plumbeus	Chlorophonia flavirostris
Columba goodsoni	Tangara johannae
Nyctiphrynus rosenbergi	
Amazilia rosenbergi	Subtropical forest
Bucco noanamae	Otus colombianus
Capito quinticolor	Heliangelus strophianus
Ramphastos brevis	Haplophaedia lugens
Veniliornis chocoensis	Semnornis ramphastinus
Piculus litae	Margarornis stellatus
Myrmeciza berlepschi	**Dysithamnus occidentalis**
Pittasoma rufopileatum	Grallaria flavotincta
Dacnis berlepschi	Chloropipo flavicapilla
	Chlorospingus semifuscus
Lowland tropical and	**Bangsia melanochlamys**
lower subtropical forest	**Bangsia aureocincta**
Penelope ortoni	Anisognathus notabilis
Odontophorus	Iridosornis
melanonotus	porphyrocephala
Pionopsitta pulchra	Chlorochrysa phoenicotis
Neomorphus radiolosus	**Chlorochrysa nitidissima**
Heliodoxa imperatrix	**Dacnis hartlaubi**
Coeligena wilsoni	Diglossopis indigotica
Boissonneaua jardini	**Vireo masteri**
Urosticte benjamini	**Hypopyrrhus**
Aglaiocercus coelestis	**pyrohypogaster**
Trogon comptus	Cyanolyca pulchra
Capito squamatus	
Thripadectes ignobilis	Upper subtropical/lower
Scytalopus vicinior	temperate forest
Pipreola jucunda	**Eriocnemis godini**
Cephalopterus penduliger	**Eriocnemis mirabilis**
Machaeropterus	**Oreothraupis arremonops**
deliciosus	
Entomodestes coracinus	Subtropical and/or
Chlorospingus flavovirens	temperate forest/páramo
Chrysothlypis salmoni	Andigena laminirostris
Habia cristata	Diglossa gloriosissima

Threatened species (Critical, Endangered, Vulnerable) are shown in **bold**; see 'Status and habitat' table.

phaedia lugens and *Cephalopterus penduliger* (and possibly other species) have been recorded at the same localities as species characteristic of the Tumbesian region (EBA 045), namely Grey-backed Hawk *Leucopternis occidentalis*, Rufous-headed Chachalaca *Ortalis erythroptera* and Slaty Becard *Pachyramphus spodiurus* (Wege and Long 1995). The extent to which these species (and thus the two EBAs) overlap is unknown.

■ Threats and conservation

Unplanned colonization following the completion of roads and massive logging concessions are major threats to the Chocó forests. Since 1960, over 40% of the forest area has been cleared or heavily degraded, and deforestation rates are accelerating (Salaman 1994). Currently, intensive logging, human settle-

ment, cattle-grazing, mining, wildlife exploitation, and coca and palm cultivation all threaten the region, with forest destruction most severe in the coastal plain and foothills below c.2,000 m. Over the next 5–10 years the region faces threats from national development projects including dams, roads, sea ports, pipelines and military installations (Dinerstein *et al.* 1995, Wege and Long 1995).

A total of 16 of the restricted-range species are presently thought to be threatened (with a further 14 Near Threatened), primarily due to the widespread destruction of forest throughout the region. A number of species are extremely poorly known or localized: *Eriocnemis godini*, for example, is known from just one locality in Pichincha province of Ecuador, where it is possibly extinct; *Neomorphus radiolosus* is genuinely localized, being recorded from very few localities; *Eriocnemis mirabilis* is known only from within the boundary of Munchique National Park in Colombia; *Micrastur plumbeus* has recently (since c.1960) been recorded from fewer than five localities; *Vireo masteri* is currently known from just two localities; and the two *Dacnis* species are patchily distributed, occur at low densities and, though poorly known, appear to be genuinely rare (Collar *et al.* 1994, Salaman and Stiles 1996). Compounding the effects of habitat destruction is hunting pressure which appears to be having a significant negative impact on *Penelope ortoni* and *Cephalopterus penduliger* (the latter species is also captured for the pet trade). Additional, more widespread threatened species that occur within the EBA include Yellow-eared Parrot *Ognorhynchus icterotis* (classified as Critical) and Brown Wood-rail *Aramides wolfi* (Vulnerable).

Seventeen Key Areas were recently identified for the EBA's threatened species (10 in Colombia and seven in Ecuador), with at least 10 currently having some form of protected status (Wege and Long 1995). In Colombia, the most important protected areas include Paramillo, Las Orquideas, Tatamá, Los Farallones and Munchique National Parks, Tambito Nature Reserve, Río Ñambi Community Nature Reserve and La Planada Nature Reserve. In Ecuador, protected areas include the Awa Forest Reserve Zone, Jatun Sacha Bilsa Biological Reserve, Mindo Nambillo Protection Forest and the Río Palenque Scientific Centre. Total coverage remains, however, relatively small, with very little lowland and foothill forest (below c.1,000 m) represented in these primarily montane protected areas, leaving perhaps the most important portion of this EBA insufficiently protected and exposed to yet further degradation.

042 Northern Central Andes

PRIORITY
CRITICAL

Key habitats Tropical montane evergreen forest, elfin forest

Main threats Major habitat loss (e.g. due to cultivation, grazing)

Biological importance ● ● ●
Current threat level ● ● ●

Area 36,000 km² **Altitude** 1,500–3,700 m

Countries Colombia, Ecuador

Restricted-range species	Threatened	Total
Confined to this EBA	3	4
Present also in other EBAs, SAs	2	5
Total	5	9

■ General characteristics

This EBA embraces all the mountains above c.2,500 m throughout the Central Andean chain of Colombia and northern Ecuador, to south of the equator at around Ambato (c.1°30′S). In Colombia, the Central Andes has a main ridge-line at c.3,000 m with isolated peaks (and massifs) reaching greater altitudes throughout; consequently, the EBA is concentrated around a number of disjunct areas, namely Nevados del Huila, Ruiz and Tolima, Volcán Puracé, Nevados de Cumbal and Chiles. In Ecuador, the EBA extends south to include the Cotacachi and Cayambe mountains, the mountains either side of the central valley (and Quito) and south to Cotopaxi, terminating at the break in the mountains caused by the Napo and Pastaza rivers. The Southern Central Andes (EBA 046) lies adjacent to the south.

The primary habitat is tropical upper montane evergreen forest and elfin forest. The Central Andean páramo (EBA 043) abuts these forest areas on all the same mountain massifs, but lies at higher altitudes. In a number of areas the Northern Central Andes is adjacent to (and may overlap with) the Ecuador–Peru East Andes (EBA 044), though that is a lower-altitude region.

■ Restricted-range species

Most of the restricted-range birds occur at 2,000–3,650 m, where they are all dependent on montane and cloud forest. All nine restricted-range species are found in various combinations on the highland massifs mentioned above. The ranges of three species continue south of the Napo in the montane forests of the Southern Central Andes (EBA 046).

Hapalopsittaca fuertesi is apparently confined to the Nevados del Tolima, Quindío and Santa Isabel, whereas the closely related *H. amazonina* is primarily a bird of the Andes in Venezuela (EBA 034), and the East Andes of Colombia (EBA 038), although the subspecies *velezi* is known from the Nevado del Ruiz near Manizales in this EBA and birds have recently been recorded in the northern Andes of Ecuador (R. Williams verbally 1997). Records of *Hapalopsittaca* parrots at the head of the Magdalena valley (on the east slope of the Central Andes in this EBA, and on the west slope of the East Andes, EBA 038) may also refer to *H. a. velezi*, although confirmation is needed (Collar *et al.* 1992). *Grallaria gigantea* has been recorded at a number of localities on the east slope of this EBA, with just two records extending its range south to the Southern Central Andes (EBA 046) (Collar *et al.* 1992, Krabbe *et al.* 1994). *G. milleri* is confined to the Nevado del Tolima–Ruiz area where it had gone unrecorded since 1942 until 1994 when rediscovered in the Ucumarí Regional

(map)

```
0    50 km

              COLOMBIA
        023
              040      037
                  MANIZALES
                    Nev. Ruiz
PACIFIC       Nev. Quindío
        041       Nev. Tolima
OCEAN
              039      039
                           038
          Nevado del Huila
        POPAYÁN
              039    Volcán Puracé
s021
              Nev. Cumbal
045
  Volcán Chiles       044
041
  Volcán Cotacachi
Volcán Pichincha  Volcán Cayambe
  QUITO         Cord. de Guacamayo
Cotopaxi  043      066
              Napo      PERU
       ECUADOR
```

Status and habitat of restricted-range species

Species (ordered taxonomically)	Global status	Other EBAs (and SAs)	Altitude (m)	Habitat
Chestnut Wood-quail Odontophorus hyperythrus	nt	040	1,600–2,700	Montane evergreen forest, forest edge, secondary growth
Rusty-faced Parrot Hapalopsittaca amazonina	EN	034,038	2,200–3,200	Montane evergreen forest
Fuertes's Parrot H. fuertesi	CR	—	3,100–3,650	Montane evergreen forest
Black-thighed Puffleg Eriocnemis derbyi	nt	—	(2,500–) 2,900–3,600	Secondary forest, forest edge
Giant Antpitta Grallaria gigantea	VU	046	1,200–3,000	Montane evergreen forest, secondary woodland, adjacent overgrown usually muddy clearings
Bicoloured Antpitta Grallaria rufocinerea	EN	—	2,100–3,150	Montane evergreen forest
Brown-banded Antpitta Grallaria milleri	EN	—	2,745–3,140	Montane evergreen forest
Crescent-faced Antpitta Grallaricula lineifrons	nt	046	2,900–3,400	Montane evergreen and elfin forest, adjacent secondary woodland
White-rimmed Brush-finch Atlapetes leucopis	nt	046	2,100–3,100	Montane evergreen, elfin and secondary forest, forest edge, undergrowth near water, secondary scrub

Global status (see p. 679 for definitions) EX Extinct, EW Extinct in the Wild } with year of last record; CR Critical, EN Endangered, VU Vulnerable } threatened species; cd Conservation Dependent, nt Near Threatened, lc Least Concern; DD Data Deficient, NE Not Evaluated

Other EBAs (and SAs) (see p. 65 for locations): bracketed numbers are Secondary Areas; ˣ extinct in that EBA or SA.

Park (*Cotinga* 1995, 3: 8–9). Birds which are almost certainly Moustached Antpitta *G. alleni* have been seen and tape-recorded in this EBA in Ecuador's Cordillera de Guacamayo (P. Coopmans *in litt.* 1995), and this would extend the range of the species currently treated as endemic to the Colombian inter-Andean slopes (EBA 040).

■ Threats and conservation

The upper montane forests in this EBA (especially in the 2,000–3,200 m zone) have been subjected to widespread and severe deforestation during this and previous centuries to the extent that most, if not all, of the forest has been cleared in many areas . The forests continue to be felled as a result of agricultural expansion (including clearance for pasture), and further degradation is projected to continue (Collar *et al*. 1992, 1994). The poor state of the forest in this EBA is reflected by the fact that all of the restricted-range birds are considered either threatened or Near Threatened. The widespread (though localized) but threatened Yellow-eared Parrot *Ognorhynchus icterotis* (classified as Critical) and Golden-plumed Parakeet *Leptosittaca branickii* (Vulnerable) also occur in this EBA.

A number of Key Areas for the threatened birds have been identified in this EBA, including (in Colombia) Los Nevados National Park, Puracé National Park, Ucumarí Regional Park, Río Blanco Watershed Reserve, Alto Quindío Acaime Natural Reserve and Cañón del Quindío Natural Reserve (Wege and Long 1995). A number of other notable protected areas cover the montane forests of the EBA (many of these being the same areas protecting the Central Andean páramos) with Las Hermosas and Nevado del Huila National Parks (in Colombia), and Cayambe–Coca Ecological Reserve (in Ecuador) standing out as of primary importance (IUCN 1992a).

Distribution patterns of restricted-range species

Species (ordered geographically)	N Cent. Andes, Colombia	Nevados del Ruiz, Quindío & Tolima	Volcán Puracé-Nevado del Huila	S Andes, Colombia	N Andes, Ecuador	Other EBAs, SAs
Odontophorus hyperythrus	●	●	●	–	–	○
Grallaria rufocinerea	●	●	●	●	–	–
Hapalopsittaca fuertesi	–	●	–	–	–	–
Grallaria milleri	–	●	–	–	–	–
Hapalopsittaca amazonina	–	●	–	–	●	○
Eriocnemis derbyi	–	●	●	●	●	–
Grallaricula lineifrons	–	●	●	●	–	○
Atlapetes leucopis	–	–	●	●	–	○
Grallaria gigantea	–	–	●	–	●	○
Total	2	6	6	3	3	

● Present
○ Extinct?
X Extinct
? Present?
R Reintroduced
I Introduced
Threatened spp. shown in **bold**
Other EBAs, SAs } see 'Status and habitat' table

043 Central Andean páramo

PRIORITY
URGENT

Key habitats Páramo, grassland, scrub, *Polylepis* woodland, elfin forest

Main threats Moderate habitat loss (e.g. due to burning, grazing, cultivation)

Biological importance ● ●
Current threat level ● ●

Area 32,000 km² **Altitude** 2,000–5,000 m

Countries Colombia, Ecuador, Peru

Restricted-range species	Threatened	Total
Confined to this EBA	5	10
Present also in other EBAs, SAs	0	1
Total	5	11

■ General characteristics

The Central Andean páramo EBA includes all the mountains higher than c.2,000 m throughout the central Andean chain of Colombia, Ecuador and extreme northern Peru. In Colombia, the Central Andes have a main ridge-line at c.3,000 m with isolated peaks and massifs reaching greater elevations throughout the range. The EBA is split into a number of disjunct areas, namely Nevados del Ruiz, Quindío, Tolima, Huila, Cumbal and Chiles, and Volcán Puracé. In Ecuador, the volcanic mountains average continuously higher than in Colombia, and

the Central Andean páramo, which follows the main eastern ridge of mountains, is also more continuous, becoming disjunct again in southern Ecuador and just across the border in northernmost Peru. In northern Peru, the EBA terminates at Cerro Chinguela in the upper Huancabamba drainage in Piura department. The Central Andean páramo is at higher altitudes and embraces habitats different from those of the Central Andes humid cloud forest (EBAs 042 and 046).

The EBA extends from 2,000 to 5,000 m and supports major vegetation types such as humid elfin forest (especially *Escallonia* and *Weinmannia*), *Polylepis* woodland and scrub, páramo scrub and grassland (Fjeldså and Krabbe 1990). Páramo occurs above the treeline, and is thus restricted to high peaks and mountain ranges (in Costa Rica and Panama, and from Venezuela south to Ecuador, then patchily south to northern Bolivia). It supports plants and animals displaying remarkable adaptations to the extreme conditions of high altitudes (cold, wind and high levels of exposure to the sun), and often comprises humid grassy habitats, sometimes with heather-like vegetation, ferns, etc. In some areas the páramo supports a scattered vegetation of large composites of the genus *Espeletia* up to 10 m tall (Fjeldså and Krabbe 1990).

■ Restricted-range species

All the restricted-range species are confined to temperate-zone elfin forest, *Polylepis* woodland, páramo scrub and grassland, or the páramo–forest ecotone, primarily above 2,500 m. There are a number of more limited distributions shown by the species in this EBA: *Bolborhynchus ferrugineifrons* is endemic to the páramo areas in central and southern Colombia; *Oxypogon guerinii* appears to be confined, in this EBA, to the Nevado del Ruiz in Colombia where it exists as a distinct subspecies *strubelii*; *Eriocnemis nigrivestis* is known only from the Volcán Pichincha area in northern Ecuador; *Metallura baroni* is endemic to the highlands in Azuay province of Ecuador; and *M. odomae* is confined to southernmost Ecuador and Cerro Chinguela in Peru. The remaining

Status and habitat of restricted-range species

Species (ordered taxonomically)	Global status	Other EBAs (and SAs)	Altitude (m)	Habitat
Carunculated Caracara *Phalcoboenus carunculatus*	lc	—	3,000–4,000	Páramo grassland, second-growth scrub, agricultural land, open grassy and bushy pasture
Rufous-fronted Parakeet *Bolborhynchus ferrugineifrons*	EN	—	3,200–4,000	Semi-humid/humid montane scrub, elfin forest, moist grassland, *Espeletia* stands
Black-breasted Puffleg *Eriocnemis nigrivestis*	CR	—	2,400–4,300	Elfin and montane evergreen forest, grassland with patches of stunted humid forest
Violet-throated Metaltail *Metallura baroni*	VU	—	(1,900–) 3,100–3,650	Elfin forest, forest edge, open *Polylepis* woodland, semi-humid/humid montane scrub
Neblina Metaltail *Metallura odomae*	nt	—	(2,750–) 2,850–3,350	Elfin forest, forest edge, scrub
Bearded Helmetcrest *Oxypogon guerinii*	lc	034,036,038	3,200–5,200	Páramo grassland, *Espeletia* stands, *Polylepis* scrub
Stout-billed Cinclodes *Cinclodes excelsior*[1]	lc	—	3,300–5,000	Páramo grassland, semi-humid/humid montane scrub
Mouse-coloured Thistletail *Schizoeaca griseomurina*	lc	—	2,100–3,350	Páramo grassland, tangled undergrowth, shrubs, mossy trees
Chestnut-bellied Cotinga *Doliornis remseni*[2]	VU	—	2,500–3,500	*Escallonia* and *Weinmannia* elfin woodland
Black-backed Bush-tanager *Urothraupis stolzmanni*	lc	—	2,750–4,000	Elfin forest, humid páramo scrub
Masked Mountain-tanager *Buthraupis wetmorei*	VU	—	2,900–3,650	Elfin forest, páramo scrub near treeline

Global status (see p. 679 for definitions)

EX	Extinct } with year	cd	Conservation Dependent
EW	Extinct in } of last the Wild } record		
		nt	Near Threatened
CR	Critical } threatened species	lc	Least Concern
EN	Endangered }	DD	Data Deficient
VU	Vulnerable }	NE	Not Evaluated

Other EBAs (and SAs) (see p. 65 for locations)
Bracketed numbers are Secondary Areas.   [x] Extinct in that EBA or SA.

Notes
[1] Taxonomy follows Fjeldså and Krabbe (1990).
[2] New species, following Robbins *et al.* (1994).

birds are found in various combinations of the EBA's highland massifs, with just four species present in northernmost Peru. *Cinclodes excelsior*, which is found on the Nevados del Ruiz and Nevado, and then from Nariño (Colombia) south to Azuay (Ecuador), is here considered distinct from *C. aricomae*, which is a threatened species confined to the Peruvian high Andes (EBA 051) (Collar *et al.* 1992, 1994: also Fjeldså and Krabbe 1990, Ridgely and Tudor 1994).

■ Threats and conservation

The Central Andean páramo is threatened by frequent burning, grazing and conversion for agriculture (e.g. potato cultivation). Above c.3,200 m the vegetation has in many areas suffered through burning and overgrazing (e.g. in Los Nevados National Park, Colombia), although large tracts do remain more or less intact. Below this level, deforestation has been generally widespread and thorough (e.g. on Volcán Pichincha, Ecuador), although in eastern Ecuador this zone is more intact than in many other areas (Collar *et al.* 1992, Wege and Long 1995).

Habitat destruction is responsible for the categorization of five restricted-range species as threatened (Collar *et al.* 1994). For these species and for the widespread but equally threatened White-tailed Shrike-tyrant *Agriornis andicola* (classified as Vulnerable), 12 Key Areas for conservation were identified by Wege and Long (1995)—two of these in Colombia, nine in Ecuador and one in Peru.

A number of protected areas cover the highlands (and to a certain extent the Key Areas) of this EBA, with Los Nevados, Las Hermosas, Nevado del Huila and Puracé National Parks (in Colombia) and Sangay, Cotopaxi and Podocarpus National Parks and Cayambe–Coca Ecological Reserve (in Ecuador) standing out as of primary importance (IUCN 1992a, Wege and Long 1995). Unfortunately, though, formal protection does not appear to have prevented habitat destruction in many of these areas, and the species within them should not necessarily be considered safeguarded.

044 Ecuador–Peru East Andes

PRIORITY
HIGH

Key habitats Tropical montane and lowland evergreen forest

Main threats Moderate habitat loss (e.g. due to agriculture, pasture, logging)

Biological importance ●●

Current threat level ●

Area 28,000 km² **Altitude** 800–2,200 m

Countries Colombia, Ecuador, Peru

Restricted-range species	Threatened	Total
Confined to this EBA	2	11
Present also in other EBAs, SAs	1	6
Total	3	17

■ General characteristics

This foothill and lower mountain slope EBA stretches the entire length of Ecuador, from southernmost Colombia in Nariño department, along the eastern slopes of the Andes in Ecuador, embracing the Cordilleras Cutucú and del Condor, south into Peru around Huancabamba, then discontinuously across the northern end of the Cordillera Colán and along the eastern slope of the northern Cordillera Oriental (in Amazonas, Loreto and San Martín departments).

The native vegetation of this EBA is tall, upper tropical and subtropical/lower temperate zone evergreen forest (primarily c.800–2,000 m).

The EBA is adjacent to a number of other areas, and its restricted-range species may at times overlap with those from these areas: the Central Andean forests (EBAs 042, 046) are primarily at higher altitude (1,500–3,200 m) and the vegetation is cloud forest; the Andean ridgetop forests (EBA 047) of south-east Ecuador and northern Peru are at 1,000–2,450 m, with the restricted-range species present only in the stunted forest on the ridgetops; and the North-east Peruvian cordilleras (EBA 049) are primarily higher at 1,900–3,700 m.

■ Restricted-range species

All of the restricted-range birds are confined to humid or wet forest, the more stunted forest near the tops of ridges (e.g. *Campylopterus villaviscensio*), or secondary growth near primary forest, all between c.800 and c.2,200 m. *Heliodoxa gularis* is found at lower altitudes than most of the other species, but on current evidence appears to be associated solely with the East Andes, although Hilty and Brown (1986) suggest that it may have been recorded at Letitia in the Colombian Amazon. *Zimmerius cinereicapillus* is known from very few records in Napo department of Ecuador, primarily at 600–800 m, although within the Peruvian portion of its range it is clearly an eastern slope foothill species rather than a lowland Amazonian bird (Ridgely and Tudor 1994). *Tangara argyrofenges* is essentially a bird of the Bolivian yungas with (apparently) disjunct populations in the East Andean foothills (EBA 053) of Junín department and in the southern, Peruvian portion of the present EBA.

■ Threats and conservation

Many of the moist montane and foothill forests of the northern portion of the Andes are under intense threat from conversion for agriculture and cattle pasture, mining operations and logging (Dinerstein *et al.* 1995). Widespread destruction of the forest is being caused by peasant farmers and tea and coffee grow-

Status and habitat of restricted-range species

Species (ordered taxonomically)	Global status	Other EBAs (and SAs)	Altitude (m)	Habitat
White-necked Parakeet *Pyrrhura albipectus*	VU	—	c.900–2,000	Montane evergreen forest
Cinnamon Screech-owl *Otus petersoni*[1]	lc	—	1,900–2,600	Montane evergreen forest
Napo Sabrewing *Campylopterus villaviscensio*	nt	—	1,050–1,500	Montane evergreen and elfin forest, secondary growth
Ecuadorian Piedtail *Phlogophilus hemileucurus*	nt	—	800–1,500	Montane evergreen forest
Pink-throated Brilliant *Heliodoxa gularis*	nt	—	900–1,050	Tropical lowland evergreen forest, possibly montane evergreen forest, forest edge
Rufous-vented Whitetip *Urosticte ruficrissa*	lc	040	1,350–2,300	Montane evergreen forest, forest edge, scrub
Coppery-chested Jacamar *Galbula pastazae*	VU	—	1,000–2,100	Montane evergreen forest
Speckle-chested Piculet *Picumnus steindachneri*	nt	—	1,100–1,900	Montane evergreen forest
Equatorial Greytail *Xenerpestes singularis*	nt	—	1,000–1,700	Montane evergreen forest
Bicoloured Antvireo *Dysithamnus occidentalis*	VU	041	900–2,200	Montane evergreen and tropical lowland evergreen forest, esp. around gaps
Peruvian Antpitta *Grallaricula peruviana*	nt	—	1,680–2,100	Montane evergreen forest
Black-chested Fruiteater *Pipreola lubomirskii*	nt	040	1,500–2,300	Montane evergreen forest
Masked Fruiteater *Pipreola pulchra*	lc	—	1,500–2,200	Montane evergreen forest, forest
Yellow-headed Manakin *Chloropipo flavicapilla*	nt	040,041	1,200–2,400	Montane evergreen forest, tall secondary growth
Red-billed Tyrannulet *Zimmerius cinereicapillus*	lc	053	750–1,200	Tropical lowland evergreen and montane evergreen forest
Ecuadorian Tyrannulet *Phylloscartes gualaquizae*	lc	—	800–1,200	Montane evergreen forest
Straw-backed Tanager *Tangara argyrofenges*	lc	053,054	1,200–2,700	Montane evergreen forest, forest edge

Global status (see p. 679 for definitions)	EX Extinct EW Extinct in the Wild } with year of last record CR Critical EN Endangered } threatened species VU Vulnerable	cd Conservation Dependent nt Near Threatened lc Least Concern DD Data Deficient NE Not Evaluated	**Other EBAs (and SAs)** (see p. 65 for locations) **Notes**	Bracketed numbers are Secondary Areas. ˣ Extinct in that EBA or SA. [1] Taxonomy follows Fitzpatrick and O'Neill (1986).

ers at appropriate elevations all along the eastern slope of the Andes (Collar *et al.* 1992). Specific threats to the forest in this EBA include the cultivation of naranjilla by an increasing human population at c.1,000 m and above in the Volcán Sumaco area of Napo province in Ecuador; in the northernmost portion of the EBA, plans to construct a highway beside the Tumaco–Orito oil pipeline threaten the otherwise pristine forests in eastern Nariño department of Colombia (Wege and Long 1995).

As a consequence of these threats, three restricted-range species are currently considered threatened, and two further more-widespread threatened birds occur in the EBA, Spot-winged Parrotlet *Touit*

stictoptera (classified as Vulnerable) and Little Woodstar *Acestrura bombus* (Endangered). Eight Key Areas for the conservation of these birds were identified (El Carmen in Colombia, the others in Ecuador) by Wege and Long (1995).

A number of protected areas cover parts of this EBA, such as (in Ecuador) Podocarpus and Sangay National Parks, Cayambe–Coca Ecological Reserve, Sumaco Protection Forest and Cordillera de Cutucú Protection Forest (each of which has been identified as a Key Area for threatened birds), although it should be noted that some of these areas cover altitudinal ranges extending significantly beyond the EBA.

045 Tumbesian region

Key habitats Tropical lowland to montane evergreen forest, deciduous forest, arid lowland scrub

Main threats Severe habitat loss (e.g. due to cultivation, grazing, logging)

Biological importance ● ● ●
Current threat level ● ● ○

Area 130,000 km²   **Altitude** 0–3,000 m

Countries Ecuador, Peru

Restricted-range species	Threatened	Total
Confined to this EBA	14	45
Present also in other EBAs, SAs	1	10
Total	15	55

■ General characteristics

This EBA lies in west Ecuador and north-west Peru, an area often called the Tumbesian centre (after Tumbes department of Peru). It primarily is centred

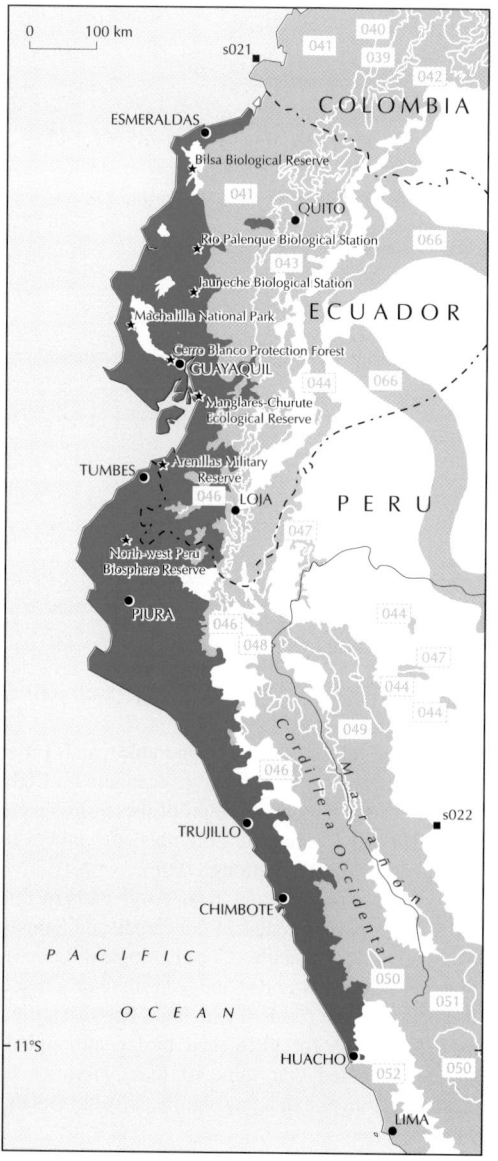

R. G. Pople/Project Ortalis

Pacific Royal Flycatcher *Onychorhynchus occidentalis*: like so many species in this EBA, this enigmatic bird now has little habitat left in which to survive.

on El Oro and Azuay provinces in south-west Ecuador, and Tumbes and Piura departments in north-west Peru, but it extends in patches northwards along the coast of Ecuador in Guayas, Los Ríos, Manabí and even Esmeraldas provinces, and runs southwards in Peru along the narrow coastal strip to northernmost Lima department (at c.11°S), where it adjoins the Peru–Chile Pacific slope (EBA 052). The Tumbesian region lies adjacent to a number of Andean EBAs, and the Tumbesian restricted-range species overlap with the Andean birds at some sites where the habitat is humid enough to support the latter; of the Andean EBAs, only the Peru–Chile Pacific slope (EBA 052) and the arid Marañón valley (EBA 048) are considered to share restricted-range species with the Tumbesian region.

The EBA covers a large area, embracing altitudes from sea-level to 3,000 m (but primarily below 2,000 m). The vegetation in this region is extremely diverse, with a large number of distinct habitat types (at least 18: Best and Kessler 1995) in an area which has remained climatically stable for long periods due to the influence of the adjacent ocean currents (J. Fjeldså *in litt.* 1993). Thus habitats range from arid scrub and desert, through deciduous tropical thorn-

Status and habitat of restricted-range species

Species (ordered taxonomically)	Global status	Other EBAs (and SAs)	Altitude (m)	Habitat
Pale-browed Tinamou *Crypturellus transfasciatus*	nt	—	0–1,500	Tropical deciduous forest, semi-evergreen (occasionally evergreen) forest, scrub
Grey-backed Hawk *Leucopternis occidentalis*	EN	—	0–1,400 (–2,100)	Tropical lowland evergreen and tropical deciduous forest
Rufous-headed Chachalaca *Ortalis erythroptera*	VU	—	0–1,950	Dry tropical deciduous forest, possibly gallery forest
White-winged Guan *Penelope albipennis*	CR	—	0–800	Dry tropical deciduous forest, (formerly) mangroves
Ecuadorian Ground-dove *Columbina buckleyi*	lc	—	0–900	Tropical deciduous forest, forest edge, secondary growth, arid lowland scrub
Ochre-bellied Dove *Leptotila ochraceiventris*	VU	—	0–1,700 (–2,625)	Tropical deciduous and tropical lowland evergreen forest, scrub
Red-masked Parakeet *Aratinga erythrogenys*	nt	—	0–800	Dry tropical deciduous and gallery forest, scrub, desert, agricultural land
El Oro Parakeet *Pyrrhura orcesi*	VU	—	(50–) 300–1,300	Montane evergreen forest
Pacific Parrotlet *Forpus coelestis*	lc	—	0–1,500	Tropical deciduous, gallery and secondary forest, arid lowland scrub, agricultural land
Grey-cheeked Parakeet *Brotogeris pyrrhopterus*	nt	—	0–1,300	Tropical deciduous and gallery forest, possibly secondary forest, agricultural land
Scrub Nightjar *Caprimulgus anthonyi*	lc	048	0–800	Dry tropical deciduous forest, arid lowland scrub, mesquite, secondary growth
Tumbes Hummingbird *Leucippus baeri*	lc	—	0–1,300	Arid lowland scrub, dry tropical deciduous forest
Short-tailed Woodstar *Myrmia micrura*	lc	—	0–800 (–2,000)	Arid lowland scrub, dry tropical deciduous forest
Esmeraldas Woodstar *Acestrura berlepschi*	EN	—	0–150	Lowland evergreen forest, secondary growth
Ecuadorian Piculet *Picumnus sclateri*	lc	—	0–1,400	Dry tropical deciduous forest, arid thorn scrub
Coastal Miner *Geositta peruviana*	lc	052	0–400	Sandy, rocky deserts, arid lowland scrub
Surf Cinclodes *Cinclodes taczanowskii*	lc	052	0–100 (–370)	Rocky coasts and beaches
Blackish-headed Spinetail *Synallaxis tithys*	VU	—	0–1,100	Dry tropical deciduous forest, scrub
Necklaced Spinetail *Synallaxis stictothorax*	lc	048	0–200	Arid lowland scrub, dry deciduous forest
Rufous-necked Foliage-gleaner *Syndactyla ruficollis*	VU	—	400–2,900	Montane evergreen and tropical deciduous forest
Henna-hooded Foliage-gleaner *Hylocryptus erythrocephalus*	VU	—	400–1,800	Tropical deciduous, evergreen and semi-evergreen forest
Chapman's Antshrike *Thamnophilus zarumae*[1]	lc	—	400–2,620	Secondary growth, scrub, humid forest, dry deciduous forest
Collared Antshrike *Sakesphorus bernardi*	lc	048	<1,500	Dry tropical deciduous forest, arid lowland scrub, riparian thickets
Grey-headed Antbird *Myrmeciza griseiceps*	EN	—	600–2,900	Montane evergreen and tropical deciduous forest, bamboo
Scrub Antpitta *Grallaria watkinsi*	lc	—	550–1,800	Dry tropical deciduous forest, forest edge, scrub
Elegant Crescent-chest *Melanopareia elegans*[2]	lc	—	0–2,000	Dry tropical deciduous forest, arid scrub, riparian bamboo
Slaty Becard *Pachyramphus spodiurus*	nt	048	0–750	Tropical deciduous and semi-evergreen bamboo

cont.

Status and habitat of restricted-range species (cont.)

Species (ordered taxonomically)	Global status	Other EBAs (and SAs)	Altitude (m)	Habitat
Pacific Elaenia *Myiopagis subplacens*	lc	—	0–1,700	Tropical deciduous, semi-evergreen and gallery bamboo
Grey-and-white Tyrannulet *Pseudelaenia leucospodia*	lc	—	0–300	Arid lowland scrub, riparian thickets
Pacific Royal Flycatcher *Onychorhynchus occidentalis*[3]	VU	—	0–900	Dry tropical deciduous and tropical lowland evergreen forest
Grey-breasted Flycatcher *Lathrotriccus griseipectus*	VU	048	0–700 (–1,750)	Tropical lowland evergreen forest, seasonally in tropical deciduous forest
Piura Chat-tyrant *Ochthoeca piurae*	nt	—	1,500–2,800	Arid montane scrub, riparian thickets
Tumbes Tyrant *Ochthoeca salvini*	nt	—	c.0–200	Gallery and dry tropical deciduous forest, riparian thickets, arid lowland scrub
Rufous Flycatcher *Myiarchus semirufus*	lc	—	<200	Arid lowland scrub, gallery forest, arid woodland
Sooty-crowned Flycatcher *Myiarchus phaeocephalus*	lc	048	<c.1,500	Dry tropical deciduous and gallery forest, arid scrub
Baird's Flycatcher *Myiodynastes bairdii*	lc	—	Lowlands to 1,000	Dry tropical deciduous, gallery and secondary forest, arid scrub
Peruvian Plantcutter *Phytotoma raimondii*	CR	—	0–550	Arid lowland scrub, riparian thickets
Superciliated Wren *Thryothorus superciliaris*	lc	—	0–1,200	Dry tropical deciduous, mangrove and gallery forest, arid lowland scrub, tropical lowland evergreen forest edge, farmland
Plumbeous-backed Thrush *Turdus reevei*	lc	—	0–1,500	Tropical deciduous, semi-evergreen and gallery forest, montane evergreen forest edge, scrub
Ecuadorian Thrush *Turdus maculirostris*	lc	—	0–1,600	Tropical deciduous and semi-evergreen forest, forest edge, clearings
Tumbes Sparrow *Aimophila stolzmanni*	lc	—	0–1,950	Arid lowland scrub, dry tropical deciduous forest, cactus
Black-capped Sparrow *Arremon abeillei*	lc	048	0–800	Tropical deciduous, gallery and semi-evergreen
Bay-crowned Brush-finch *Atlapetes seebohmi*	lc	—	800–2,500	Tropical deciduous forest, montane evergreen forest edge, arid scrub
White-headed Brush-finch *Atlapetes albiceps*	lc	—	0–1,200	Dry tropical deciduous and gallery forest, arid scrub, riparian thickets
Pale-headed Brush-finch *Atlapetes pallidiceps*	CR	—	1,500–2,100	Semi-humid/humid montane scrub, semi-evergreen forest, agricultural land
Crimson Finch-tanager *Rhodospingus cruentus*	lc	—	0–800	Dry tropical deciduous forest, tropical lowland evergreen forest edge, arid scrub, grassland
Cinereous Finch *Piezorhina cinerea*	lc	—	0–300	Arid lowland scrub and woodland
Sulphur-throated Finch *Sicalis taczanowskii*	lc	—	0–200	Arid lowland scrub and grassland
Drab Seedeater *Sporophila simplex*	lc	052	0–1,800	Arid lowland and montane scrub, *Acacia*, riparian thickets, agricultural land
Black-cowled Saltator *Saltator nigriceps*	lc	—	800–2,400	Tropical deciduous and gallery forest, forest edge, secondary growth, scrub
Grey-and-gold Warbler *Basileuterus fraseri*	lc	—	0–2,100	Tropical deciduous, tropical lowland evergreen and gallery forest, scrub
Three-banded Warbler *Basileuterus trifasciatus*	lc	—	1,200–3,050	Montane evergreen and secondary forest, forest edge, near streams
White-edged Oriole *Icterus graceannae*	lc	—	0–800	Dry tropical deciduous and gallery forest, arid scrub, riparian thickets

cont.

Status and habitat of restricted-range species (cont.)

Species (ordered taxonomically)	Global status	Other EBAs (and SAs)	Altitude (m)	Habitat
Saffron Siskin *Carduelis siemiradzkii*	VU	—	0–750	Tropical deciduous and secondary forest, second-growth scrub and arid scrub
White-tailed Jay *Cyanocorax mystacalis*	lc	—	0–1,200	Tropical deciduous, semi-deciduous and gallery forest, secondary growth, scrub

Global status (see p. 679 for definitions)

EX	Extinct ⎫ with year	cd	Conservation
EW	Extinct in ⎬ of last		Dependent
	the Wild ⎭ record	nt	Near Threatened
CR	Critical ⎫	lc	Least Concern
EN	Endangered ⎬ threatened species	DD	Data Deficient
VU	Vulnerable ⎭	NE	Not Evaluated

Other EBAs (and SAs) (see p. 65 for locations)
Bracketed numbers are Secondary Areas.   ˣ Extinct in that EBA or SA.

Notes
[1] Taxonomy follows Parker *et al.* (1995); evaluated as a species for threatened status by Collar *et al.* (1992, 1994).
[2] Taxonomy follows Meyer de Schauensee (1982) and Ridgely and Tudor (1994).
[3] Treated as a species by Collar *et al.* (1992, 1994).

forest and deciduous *Ceiba trichistandra* forest, then, depending on altitude and humidity, semi-evergreen *Ceiba pentandra* forest, semi-evergreen lowland and premontane tall forest, moist lowland forest, humid pre-montane and lower montane cloud forest, deciduous to semi-evergreen inter-montane scrub, etc. (Best and Kessler 1995).

The forests of the Tumbesian region represent one of the richest and most threatened biotic sites on earth. A number of endemic floras and faunas converge in this region, and the forests thus feature large concentrations of species and high levels of endemism in many groups of organisms (Best and Kessler 1995).

■ Restricted-range species

The result of such a diversity of vegetation types is a specialized and distinctive endemic avifauna, which can broadly be split into five groups depending on their preferred habitat types. The EBA is characterized by species dependent on deciduous forest (including *Acacia* thorn-forest and *Ceiba trichistandra*-dominated forest, up to 1,400 m) for at least part of the year. Many other species also occur in semi-evergreen

Ceiba pentandra forest, the higher elevations usually resulting from birds ranging into humid montane evergreen forest, although similar evergreen forest does occur at lower altitudes (Best and Kessler 1995). The precise ecological requirements of many of the restricted-range species have not been deter-

Habitat associations of restricted-range species

Deciduous to evergreen
Ortalis erythroptera
Leptotila ochraceiventris
Aratinga erythrogenys
Synallaxis tithys   ·
Grallaria watkinsi
Thamnophilus zarumae
Onychorhynchus occidentalis

Semi-evergreen/ evergreen
Leucopternis occidentalis
Pyrrhura orcesi
Acestrura berlepschi
Syndactyla ruficollis
Hylocryptus erythrocephalus
Myrmeciza griseiceps
Lathrotriccus griseipectus
Saltator nigriceps
Basileuterus trifasciatus

Deciduous/semi-evergreen
Crypturellus transfasciatus
Columbina buckleyi
Brotogeris pyrrhopterus
Pachyramphus spodiurus
Myiopagis subplacens
Turdus maculirostris
Turdus reevei
Arremon abeillei
Atlapetes pallidiceps
Basileuterus fraseri
Cyanocorax mystacalis

Deciduous forest/arid scrub
Penelope albipennis
Forpus coelestis
Caprimulgus anthonyi
Leucippus baeri
Myrmia micrura
Picumnus sclateri
Synallaxis stictothorax
Sakesphorus bernardi
Melanopareia elegans
Myiarchus phaeocephalus
Myiodynastes bairdii
Ochthoeca piurae
Ochthoeca salvini
Thryothorus superciliaris
Aimophila stolzmanni
Atlapetes albiceps
Atlapetes seebohmi
Rhodospingus cruentus
Sporophila simplex
Icterus graceannae
Carduelis siemiradzkii

Arid scrub/desert
Cinclodes taczanowskii
Geositta peruviana
Myiarchus semirufus
Pseudelaenia leucospodia
Phytotoma raimondii
Piezorhina cinerea
Sicalis taczanowskii

Threatened species (Critical, Endangered, Vulnerable) are shown in **bold**; see 'Status and habitat' table.

R. G. Pople/Project Ortalis

An understorey specialist, Henna-hooded Foliage-gleaner *Hylocryptus erythrocephalus* suffers from widespread habitat degradation caused by grazing.

mined, and it is probable that there will be some future reclassification of species between habitats. For example, some species move seasonally into the dry deciduous forest zone, although the birds may actually be confined to the more humid elements (e.g. along watercourses) within this forest type. Similarly, the altitudinal distribution of species is poorly understood, with some birds apparently undertaking seasonal migrations between habitat types (Parker *et al.* 1995).

Plumbeous-backed Thrush *Turdus reevei* is found throughout the EBA in most habitats and so is not considered threatened.

The main distributional trends of the restricted-range species are, unsurprisingly, determined by their habitat preferences. The species found in northern Ecuador (Esmeraldas province) are primarily those reliant on evergreen forest, and those that reach La Libertad department or further south in Peru (to northern Lima department, or are shared with the Peru–Chile Pacific slope, EBA 052) are all deciduous forest/arid scrub/desert species. A number of species are confined to the arid scrub and desert habitats of coastal Peru and south-west Ecuador, but although they are characteristic of this arid vegetation and possibly constitute a discrete area of endemism, most of them are found overlapping ecologically and geographically with deciduous forest/arid scrub birds. Similarly, some of the dry deciduous forest species also occupy the arid scrub

found in southern Guayas province and Isla Puna, south-west Ecuador, and on the coastal plain of Tumbes and Piura departments in north-west Peru. Of the species shared with the Peru–Chile Pacific slope EBA, *Geositta peruviana* and *Cinclodes taczanowskii* are essentially coastal species that have radiated from southern Patagonia (J. Fjeldså *in litt.* 1993); *C. taczanowskii*, confined to the littoral zone, is described as the most maritime of all passerine birds (Ridgely and Tudor 1994). The threatened Ochraceous Attila *Attila torridus* is not a restricted-range species, but is essentially confined to the humid and semi-humid forests of the Tumbesian region (its range extends into south-west Colombia) (Collar *et al.* 1992, 1994).

■ Threats and conservation

The Tumbesian region is one of the most important and threatened of all EBAs. Less than 5% of the area remains forested: the landscape is a patchwork of cropland, only occasionally punctuated by small forest patches which are often confined to steep slopes that cannot be cultivated. Most forest types have suffered catastrophic losses since the 1950s. At only a handful of sites does the forest stretch unbroken for more than a few kilometres, but even then the forest, especially the understorey, is often degraded. The more arid vegetation, although affected by grazing and agriculture in valley bottoms, remains in a reasonable state within the region as a whole.

The Tumbesian avifauna is affected by five primary threats: most important is deforestation and understorey degradation, but also of significance is hunting, trade and tiny range sizes. The most severely endangered species are those which suffer a combination of these threats such as *Penelope albipennis* which is imperilled by both habitat destruction and hunting, compounded by its tiny range and population (Collar *et al.* 1992, Best and Kessler 1995). Due primarily to the widespread destruction and degradation of the characteristic forests, 15 of the restricted-range birds are considered threatened. Only one of these species, *Phytotoma raimondii*, is confined to the desert zone, where it is under threat from the loss (through irrigated agriculture) of its riverine thicket habitat (Collar *et al.* 1992). *Atlapetes pallidiceps* (classified as Critical) has not been seen since 1969 and may already be extinct (Collar *et al.* 1994).

Various initiatives have prioritized the remnant forest blocks in this EBA in terms of their conservation importance: Best and Kessler (1995) documented 15 priority sites for habitat conservation and 30 sites for bird conservation, while Wege and Long (1995) detailed 43 Key Areas for the threatened birds in the region. These assessments are complementary,

Cerro Blanco Protected Forest, close to Guayaquil, is one of the few protected areas in this critically important EBA: the reserve supports populations of at least nine threatened bird species (including the widespread Great Green Macaw *Ara ambigua* shown here as the reserve's emblem).

C. Kennedy/Project Ortalis

and they present clear recommendations for conservation action that is urgently needed if a number of species are to survive in the long term, given the continued loss of habitat and the current inadequacy of forest protection. Protected-area coverage in this EBA, while prolonging the survival of a number of forest patches, does not presently ensure the survival of all the threatened birds, many of which require large, relatively undisturbed tracts incorporating a number of forest types (Collar *et al.* 1992). However, Machalilla National Park (Ecuador) and the North-

west Peru Biosphere Reserve support the largest remaining forest fragments within the EBA, and consequently stand out as being critically important for many threatened species (see also Parker *et al.* 1995). Smaller, but extremely important reserves currently include Jatun Sacha Bilsa Biological Reserve, Río Palenque Scientific Centre, Jauneche Biological Research Station, Cerro Blanco Protected Forest, Manglares–Churute Ecological Reserve and Arenillas Military Reserve, all of which are in Ecuador (Wege and Long 1995).

046 Southern Central Andes

PRIORITY
URGENT

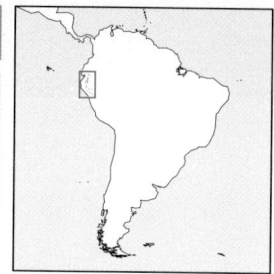

| Key habitats Tropical montane evergreen and cloud forest | Area 10,000 km² | Altitude 1,500–3,500 m |

Main threats Major habitat loss (e.g. due to logging, cultivation, grazing)

Countries Ecuador, Peru

Restricted-range species	Threatened	Total
Confined to this EBA	2	5
Present also in other EBAs, SAs	1	3
Total	3	8

Biological importance ● ○ ○
Current threat level ● ● ○

■ General characteristics

The scattered montane cloud forests of southern Ecuador and northern Peru run from the Volcán Sangay area of Ecuador (c.2°S) to northern Ancash department in Peru (c.8°S), embracing the humid forest between c.1,500 and 3,500 m in the main Andean chain (especially on the eastern slope), but also including a few areas in the Eastern Andes of Ecuador and east of the Marañón valley in Peru. This EBA overlaps with a number of others, but is separated from them on vegetational and altitudinal criteria. For example, the evergreen cloud forests in this EBA are found below the high-altitude Central Andean páramo (EBA 043), which lies mainly further north and comprises species of the temperate-zone elfin forests and paramó. Some of the EBA cloud forest patches are adjacent to but at higher altitudes (i.e. above c.2,000 m) than the Ecuador–Peru East Andes (EBA 044), and some lie near the northern end of the Peruvian high Andes (EBA 051), which is a region of drier vegetation. The Southern Central Andes, due to its patchy nature, only covers c.10,000 km², with the vegetation varying from wet, epiphyte-clad temperate cloud forest to drier cloud forest, and secondary woodland.

■ Restricted-range species

All the restricted-range species in this EBA rely on humid montane forest or cloud forest, with some also using associated secondary woodland, and natural clearings, largely between 1,500 and 3,500 m.

Penelope barbata, *Coeligena iris* and *Heliangelus viola* are widespread within this EBA, the latter two species extending its boundaries into the Cordillera Central, east of the Marañón river. The remaining species, however, have more restricted ranges. For example, the three species shared with the North Central Andes are of particularly limited distribution within the EBA—*Grallaria gigantea* is known from just two specimens collected (in 1938) at El Tambo in Loja province of Ecuador, *Grallaricula lineifrons* from just two localities in Cañar and Loja provinces, and *Atlapetes leucopis* from the eastern slope south only to Azuay province of Ecuador—and the other two species, *Hapalopsittaca pyrrhops* and *Myiophobus lintoni*, are found south to Cerro Chinguela in Piura province of northern Peru. The southern portion of Ecuador and adjacent northern Peru is biogeographically complex, and the birds in this EBA may at times overlap with species from neighbouring EBAs (see above), especially where the patchy montane forests splice into, for example, elfin forest and páramo (as is the case within the range of *Hapalopsittaca pyrrhops*).

The 'Chusquea' Tapaculo *Scytalopus* sp. nov. has yet to be described, but is wholly confined to this EBA (J. Fjeldså *in litt.* 1995).

Status and habitat of restricted-range species

Species (ordered taxonomically)	Global status	Other EBAs (and SAs)	Altitude (m)	Habitat
Bearded Guan *Penelope barbata*	VU	—	1,500–3,000	Montane evergreen forest
Red-faced Parrot *Hapalopsittaca pyrrhops*	EN	—	2,500–3,500	Montane evergreen forest, wet epiphyte-clad temperate forest up to dwarf and elfin forest
Rainbow Starfrontlet *Coeligena iris*	lc	—	1,500–3,500	Montane evergreen, elfin and secondary forest, forest edge, humid montane scrub, gardens, riparian scrub
Purple-throated Sunangel *Heliangelus viola*	lc	—	2,150–3,050	Montane evergreen and secondary forest, forest edge, thickets
Giant Antpitta *Grallaria gigantea*	VU	042	1,200–3,000	Montane evergreen forest, secondary woodland, adjacent overgrown usually muddy clearings
Crescent-faced Antpitta *Grallaricula lineifrons*	nt	042	2,900–3,400	Montane evergreen and elfin forest, adjacent secondary woodland
Orange-banded Flycatcher *Myiophobus lintoni*	nt	—	2,250–2,800	Montane evergreen forest, secondary woodland
White-rimmed Brush-finch *Atlapetes leucopis*	nt	042	2,100–3,100	Montane evergreen, elfin and secondary forest, forest edge, undergrowth near water, second-growth scrub

Global status (see p. 679 for definitions)

EX   Extinct
EW   Extinct in the Wild } with year of last record

CR   Critical
EN   Endangered } threatened species
VU   Vulnerable

cd   Conservation Dependent
nt   Near Threatened
lc   Least Concern

DD   Data Deficient
NE   Not Evaluated

Other EBAs (and SAs) (see p. 65 for locations): bracketed numbers are Secondary Areas; [x] extinct in that EBA or SA.

■ Threats and conservation

The cloud forest habitats within this EBA have been heavily degraded (Collar *et al.* 1992). Forest tracts are still being actively felled, and some areas with dense populations of Indian farmers have suffered from the combination of forest loss and understorey grazing by livestock; this situation is one which holds true in both Ecuador and Peru (Wege and Long 1995).

Three of the restricted-range species in this area are considered threatened by the widespread destruction of habitat that is occurring, and *Penelope barbata* faces the additional threat of being a target for hunters (Collar *et al.* 1992). The more-widespread Golden-plumed Parakeet *Leptosittaca branickii* (classified as Vulnerable) is a fourth threatened species present in the EBA. Eleven Key Areas for the conservation of these threatened birds were identi-

fied by Wege and Long (1995), five being in Ecuador and the remainder in Peru.

The large Podocarpus National Park in Ecuador protects areas of suitable cloud forest for at least five of the EBA's restricted-range species, but it is itself under threat from habitat destruction (Collar *et al.* 1992). Huashapamba Protection Forest supports populations of at least four of the restricted-range species (including *Penelope barbata* and *Hapalopsittaca pyrrhops*) (Wege and Long 1995) and, also in Ecuador, the Cajas National Recreation Area and Río Mazan Cloud Forest Reserve are important. All of these Ecuadorian protected areas were identified as Key Areas for threatened birds. However, none of the Key Areas in Peru is formally protected, and the few very small parks that do exist appear inadequate for the conservation of the five restricted-range species that penetrate Peruvian territory.

047 Andean ridge-top forests

Key habitats Tropical montane and foothill evergreen forest, elfin forest

Main threats Moderate habitat loss (e.g. due to cultivation)

Biological importance ● ●
Current threat level ● ●

Area 3,800 km² **Altitude** 600–2,500 m

Countries Ecuador, Peru

Restricted-range species	Threatened	Total
Confined to this EBA	3	6
Present also in other EBAs, SAs	0	1
Total	3	7

■ General characteristics

This poorly explored EBA includes various mountain ridge-tops: those of the Cordillera del Condor on the border of south-east Ecuador and northern Peru, and in northern Peru the isolated Cordillera de Colán, the northernmost end of the Cordillera Oriental, and the isolated mountains east of the Mayo river (on the San Martín–Loreto department boundary); the range of one endemic species extends the boundaries of the EBA east of the Cordillera del Condor into the middle Marañón valley in Peru's northern Amazonas department. Distributionally, the species defining the EBA are poorly known, so the boundaries of the area cannot be more precisely delineated than the various mountain ranges described above. Though separated by habitat preferences, the ridge-top forest restricted-range species overlap with the ranges of some of the restricted-range species from the North-east Peruvian cordilleras (EBA 049) in the northernmost part of the Cordillera Oriental and the Cordillera de Colán.

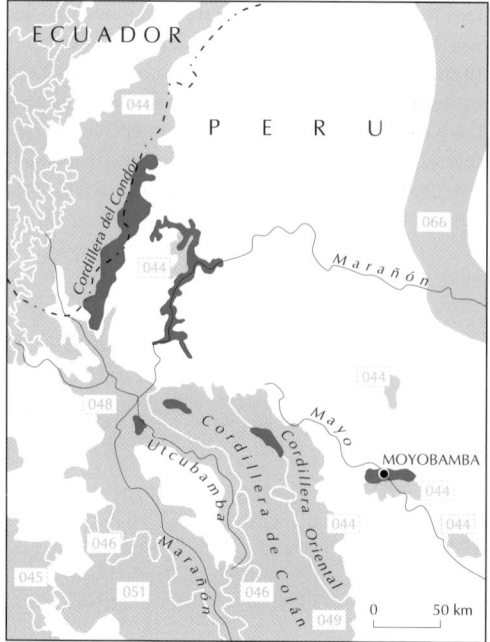

Native vegetation of this EBA is the humid, often stunted evergreen forest on ridge-tops (ridge spurs projecting from the main mountain chain), primarily between 1,000 and 2,450 m. The highly specialized stunted elfin or cloud forest on such ridges is generally the result of the drenching afforded by the moisture-laden prevailing easterly winds, the exposed nature of the situation and, quite often, outcrops of mineral-poor soil (Collar *et al.* 1992).

■ Restricted-range species

Most of the restricted-range species occur in humid, subtropical to lower temperate zone, stunted ridge-top forest, with forest edge and bushy areas adjacent to forest also being inhabited by some of the birds. *Wetmorethraupis sterrhopteron* has a distribution slightly disjunct from the other species, and occurs lower down, at 600–800 m, where it inhabits mature humid forest on mountain slopes; however, it is probably best treated in this EBA due to suspected sympatry with other endemics on the Cordillera del Condor (Collar *et al.* 1992, T. A. Parker *in litt.* 1991).

This area of southernmost Ecuador and northern Peru has only recently been explored; thus, five of the six endemics have been discovered since 1975, and *Wetmorethraupis sterrhopteron* was first found in 1963 (Collar *et al.* 1992; also Fitzpatrick *et al.* 1977, Graves *et al.* 1983). Because of the general paucity of distributional information, the limits of the various species in this group, and how they relate to those species in the North-east Peruvian cordilleras, is poorly known. However, the North-east Peruvian cordillera birds appear to be confined to the main mountain range at slightly higher altitudes (1,900–3,700 m), with the restricted-range species from this EBA (*Xenoglaux loweryi*, *Grallaricula ochraceifrons*, *Hemitriccus cinnamomeipectus* and *Henicorhina leucoptera*) overlapping with them but restricted to the stunted, lower-altitude forest on the ridge spurs.

■ Threats and conservation

Vegetation in this EBA is generally in a reasonable state, although deforestation is increasing, with areas adjacent to the EBA having suffered particularly

Status and habitat of restricted-range species

Species (ordered taxonomically)	Global status	Other EBAs (and SAs)	Altitude (m)	Habitat
Long-whiskered Owlet *Xenoglaux loweryi*	nt	—	1,900–2,350	Elfin forest, esp. along exposed ridges
Royal Sunangel *Heliangelus regalis*	VU	—	1,450–2,200	Elfin forest, humid ridgetop forest, forest edge and adjacent bushy slopes
Ash-throated Antwren *Herpsilochmus parkeri*	VU	—	c.1,350	Montane evergreen forest
Ochre-fronted Antpitta *Grallaricula ochraceifrons*	nt	—	1,890–1,980	Montane evergreen and humid stunted forest
Cinnamon-breasted Tody-tyrant *Hemitriccus cinnamomeipectus*	nt	—	1,700–2,200	Montane evergreen forest and esp. elfin forest along exposed ridges
Bar-winged Wood-wren *Henicorhina leucoptera*	nt	049	1,350–2,450	Elfin forest, esp. along exposed ridges
Orange-throated Tanager *Wetmorethraupis sterrhopteron*	EN	—	600–1,000	Tropical lowland evergreen forest

Global status (see p. 679 for definitions)
EX Extinct
EW Extinct in the Wild } with year of last record
CR Critical
EN Endangered
VU Vulnerable } threatened species
cd Conservation Dependent
nt Near Threatened
lc Least Concern
DD Data Deficient
NE Not Evaluated

Other EBAs (and SAs) (see p. 65 for locations): bracketed numbers are Secondary Areas; ˣ extinct in that EBA or SA.

badly in recent decades (Collar *et al.* 1992). Recent surveys of the northern end of the Cordillera de Colán (within the EBA) found an alarmingly high deforestation rate, with most of the forest in this area already gone, and what remains being rapidly cleared for cash-crops, particularly marijuana and coffee (Barnes *et al.* 1995).

The threatened Royal Sunangel *Heliangelus regalis* epitomizes this EBA in being poorly known.

Three of the endemics are considered threatened, partly due to the uncertain status of the habitat in many of the areas, where even limited deforestation potentially threatens species with such restricted ranges and specific needs. All the ridge-top areas are of critical importance, especially those projecting from the northern part of the Cordillera Oriental and the isolated Cordillera de Colán (which are the only known localities for *Xenoglaux loweryi* and *Grallaricula ochraceifrons*) and the area east of the Mayo river (the only known area for *Herpsilochmus parkeri*). Another more-widespread threatened bird known from this EBA is Military Macaw *Ara militaris* (Vulnerable).

Nine Key Areas have been identified in this EBA for the conservation of threatened species, two in the Cordillera del Condor in Ecuador and the remainder in Peru. None of these Key Areas is currently protected, and the EBA as a whole remains one of the most biologically important but least protected EBAs in the Americas (IUCN 1992a, Wege and Long 1995).

048 Marañón valley

Key habitats Dry tropical deciduous forest, arid and riparian scrub, gallery forest

Main threats Major habitat loss (e.g. due to cultivation, grazing, logging)

Biological importance ● ● ●
Current threat level ● ○ ○

Area 11,000 km² **Altitude** 200–3,200 m
Countries Peru

Restricted-range species	Threatened	Total
Confined to this EBA	3	11
Present also in other EBAs, SAs	2	11
Total	5	22

■ General characteristics

The Marañón valley in north-west Peru (Cajamarca, Amazonas and La Libertad departments) is one of the most important biogeographic boundaries in the Andes, and is itself a discrete area of endemism. The EBA includes the Marañón river primarily from north-east Ancash/south-east La Libertad departments, north to the confluence of the Chinchipe and Utcubamba, the lower parts of these valleys (nearly into Ecuador in the case of the Chinchipe), and to the Chamaya. Thus defined, the Marañón drainage embraces a relatively small area, primarily from the valley floor up to c.2,000 m, although some re-

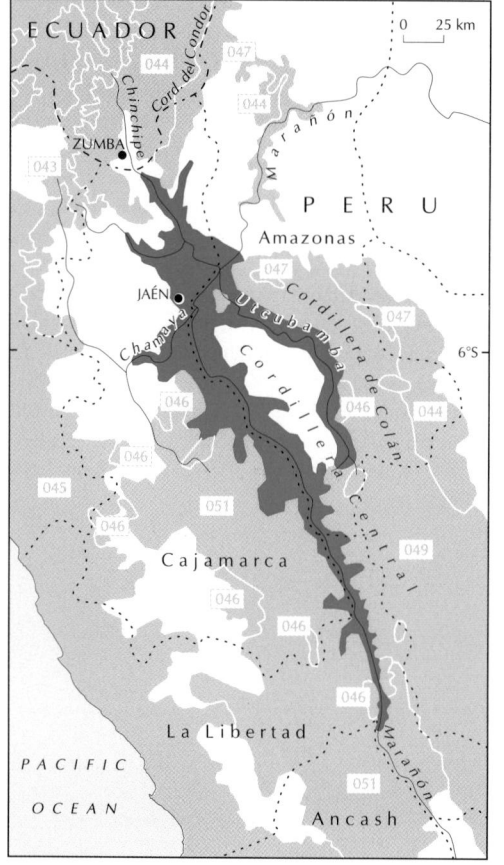

A typical area of cactus-dominated desert scrub in the northern Marañón valley.

stricted-range species occur higher into temperate zones, where they extend into the Peruvian high Andes (EBA 051).

The Marañón is in a rain shadow created by mountains to the east (the Cordilleras Central, del Condor and de Colán). The resultant arid tropical and subtropical vegetation is (as far as is known, for the region has been under cultivation for a long time) characterized by desert scrub including cactus–*Prosopis* desert, dense herbaceous scrub with small *Acacia* and cacti, seasonally dry forest dominated by *Ceiba* with *Acacia* and *Prosopis* admixed, and riparian forests comprising *Salix* and *Schinus* (Collar *et al.* 1992, Wege and Long 1995). Some of the areas within the upper Marañón are characterized by more

Status and habitat of restricted-range species

Species (ordered taxonomically)	Global status	Other EBAs (and SAs)	Altitude (m)	Habitat
Peruvian Pigeon *Columba oenops*	VU	—	900–2,300	Tropical deciduous and gallery forest
Yellow-faced Parrotlet *Forpus xanthops*	VU	—	600–1,800	Tropical deciduous and gallery forest, arid montane and desert scrub, riparian vegetation
Scrub Nightjar *Caprimulgus anthonyi*	lc	045	200–800	Arid scrub, mesquite woodland, secondary growth
Spot-throated Hummingbird *Leucippus taczanowskii*	lc	051	300–2,900	Arid lowland and montane scrub, dry tropical deciduous forest
Purple-backed Sunbeam *Aglaeactis aliciae*	VU	—	3,000–3,200	Semi-humid/humid montane scrub, slopes with open areas and some trees
Grey-bellied Comet *Taphrolesbia griseiventris*	VU	051	2,750–3,170	Arid montane scrub, forest edge, thickets, agricultural land
Marañón Spinetail *Synallaxis maranonica*	lc	—	Lowlands to 1,500	Gallery and secondary forest, forest edge, riparian thickets
Necklaced Spinetail *Synallaxis stictothorax*	lc	045	c.200	Arid lowland scrub, dry deciduous forest
Great Spinetail *Siptornopsis hypochondriacus*	nt	—	2,000–3,000	Arid montane and humid scrub, dry woodland
Chestnut-backed Thornbird *Phacellodomus dorsalis*	nt	—	2,000–2,700	Arid montane/thorn scrub
Collared Antshrike *Sakesphorus bernardi*	lc	045	<1,500	Dry tropical deciduous forest, arid lowland scrub, riparian thickets
Marañón Crescent-chest *Melanopareia maranonica*[1]	nt	—	200–750	Dry tropical deciduous forest, arid lowland scrub, riparian thickets
Slaty Becard *Pachyramphus spodiurus*	nt	045	Lowlands	Dry forest, tropical deciduous and semi-evergreen forest
Grey-breasted Flycatcher *Lathrotriccus griseipectus*	VU	045	200–700 (–1,750)	Dry forest, tropical deciduous and evergreen forest
Sooty-crowned Flycatcher *Myiarchus phaeocephalus*	lc	045	<c.1,500	Dry tropical deciduous and gallery forest, arid scrub
Marañón Thrush *Turdus maranonicus*	lc	—	600–2,200	Dry tropical deciduous and gallery forest, arid scrub
Black-capped Sparrow *Arremon abeillei*	lc	045	200–800	Tropical deciduous, gallery and semi-evergreen forest, secondary growth, arid scrub
Rufous-backed Inca-finch *Incaspiza personata*	lc	051	2,200–3,400	Arid montane scrub, cactus
Grey-winged Inca-finch *Incaspiza ortizi*	nt	051	1,800–2,300	Arid montane scrub
Buff-bridled Inca-finch *Incaspiza laeta*	lc	—	1,400–3,000	Arid montane scrub, dry tropical deciduous forest
Little Inca-finch *Incaspiza watkinsi*	nt	—	500–900	Arid lowland scrub, terrestrial bromeliads
Buff-bellied Tanager *Thlypopsis inornata*	lc	—	450–2,000	Semi-humid/humid montane and arid montane scrub, forest edge, thickets, savanna

Global status (see p. 679 for definitions)	EX Extinct EW Extinct in the Wild	} with year of last record	cd Conservation Dependent nt Near Threatened lc Least Concern DD Data Deficient NE Not Evaluated	**Other EBAs (and SAs)** (see p. 65 for locations)	Bracketed numbers are Secondary Areas. ˣ Extinct in that EBA or SA.
	CR Critical EN Endangered VU Vulnerable	} threatened species		**Notes**	[1] Taxonomy follows Meyer de Schauensee (1970) and Ridgely and Tudor (1994).

humid vegetation (J. Fjeldså *in litt.* 1993). Temperate zone vegetation comprises shrubs and *Alnus* and *Eucalyptus* trees, but also open *Acacia* woodland, grass and thorny montane shrubbery (Collar *et al.* 1992, Wege and Long 1995).

■ Restricted-range species

Most restricted-range species appear to inhabit the dry forest and scrub, the riparian forest obviously being an additional important component for the avifauna. With similar vegetation types in the

A. J. Begazo

Yellow-faced Parrotlet *Forpus xanthops* survives in the relatively intact desert vegetation, but is threatened by trapping for the pet trade.

maranonicus and *Thlypopsis inornata* are found throughout the Marañón; *Synallaxis maranonica*, *Melanopareia maranonica* and *Incaspiza watkinsi* are primarily confined to the northern part; and *Aglaeactis aliciae*, *Siptornopsis hypochondriacus*, *Phacellodomus dorsalis* and *Incaspiza laeta* are essentially southern Marañón species. *Melanopareia maranonica* and a number of other northern Marañón species have recently been found in southernmost Ecuador in the Zumba region of Zamora–Chinchipe (Ridgely and Tudor 1994, Williams *et al.* 1997), suggesting that this EBA may extend further up the Chinchipe into Ecuador.

■ Threats and conservation

The Marañón drainage has been under cultivation for a long time, and has progressively deteriorated, much of the original riparian and dry forest habitat now being lost (Collar *et al.* 1992). The spread of oil palms, cattle ranching and logging are all serious threats, and oil extraction is a potential future problem (Dinerstein *et al.* 1995). Most forest around Huancabamba, for example, has been totally cleared for agriculture, and little forest remains on the Cordillera de Colán due to clearance for cattle-grazing and drug cash crops (Wege and Long 1995).

Five of the EBA's restricted-range species are considered threatened. Confined to the area are two arid-vegetation species found throughout the valley—*Columba oenops* (threatened by hunting) and *Forpus xanthops* (threatened by the pet trade)—and *Aglaeactis aliciae*, a poorly known bird of montane shrubbery in the upper Marañón (Collar *et al.* 1994, Begazo 1996). *Lathrotriccus griseipectus* is threatened within its main range in the Tumbesian region as well as here, and *Taphrolesbia griseiventris* is extremely poorly known and found at very few localities (including one in the Peruvian high Andes, EBA 051) (Collar *et al.* 1992, 1994). A further six species are considered Near Threatened. The widespread but threatened (Endangered) Little Woodstar *Acestrura bombus* has also been recorded (Collar *et al.* 1992).

Nine Key Areas have been identified for the threatened species in the EBA, and the Cordillera de Colán stands out as critically important (Wege and Long 1995). Unfortunately, none of the Key Areas (indeed no area within the EBA) currently has any form of protected status (IUCN 1992a), suggesting an urgent need for conservation measures.

Tumbesian region (EBA 045), these two EBAs have clear avifaunal similarities (e.g. seven restricted-range species are shared between them), although the far larger Tumbesian region is substantially more diverse both floristically and avifaunally. There is a broad range of altitudinal distributions shown by the species in this EBA, although in general the birds restricted to the upper Marañón tend to occur at higher altitudes, and will at times be found alongside Peruvian high Andes species (EBA 051). There is also a real possibility that some species (e.g. *Columba oenops*) may undertake seasonal altitudinal movements upslope into the deciduous forest (Collar *et al.* 1992).

The restricted-range species in this EBA can be split into two groups: those concentrated within the northern, lower portion of the Marañón valley (in the vicinity of Jaén and northwards, i.e. north of 6°S); and those primarily to the south in the upper Marañón. The birds shared with the Tumbesian region are all northern, lower Marañón species, and those shared with the Peruvian high Andes are all from the southern, upper Marañón. Of species confined to the valley, *Columba oenops*, *Forpus xanthops*, *Turdus*

049 North-east Peruvian cordilleras

Key habitats Tropical montane evergreen forest, cloud and elfin forest, páramo scrub and grassland

Main threats Moderate habitat loss (e.g. due to grazing, cultivation)

Biological importance ● ● ●
Current threat level ●

Area 37,000 km²   **Altitude** 1,700–3,800 m
Countries Peru

Restricted-range species	Threatened	Total
Confined to this EBA	2	19
Present also in other EBAs, SAs	0	5
Total	2	24

■ General characteristics

This EBA comprises mainly the Cordillera Central which forms the easternmost chain of high Andean mountains in Peru. The EBA starts in the north at the isolated Cordillera de Colán, and runs the length of the Cordillera Central which is separated from the Cordillera Occidental by the Marañón valley; the Cordilleras Central and Occidental join just south of the Cordillera Carpish, and, although the EBA is centred on the Cordillera Central north of the 'Huallaga bend' in Huánuco (J. Fjeldså *in litt.* 1993),

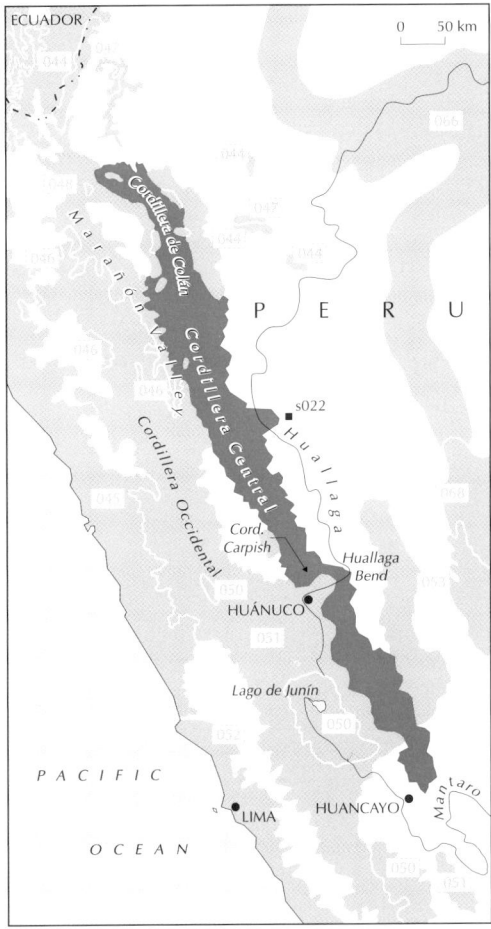

some of the restricted-range species occur south along the mountains east of Lago de Junín and south to Huancayo (c.12°S), the biogeographic division in the mountains at this point apparently being the Mantaro river. On the Cordillera de Colán, this EBA overlaps with the Andean ridge-top forests (EBA 047), although there is a general altitudinal and ecological separation of species.

In the north of the EBA, many of the mountain slopes are open country with fields, pasture and shrubs, and isolated woodlots of *Alnus* admixed with thorny *Rubus* thickets (Collar *et al.* 1992). Lush, epiphyte-laden evergreen cloud forest is the primary vegetation type along the Cordillera Central, dominant genera being *Clusia*, *Escallonia*, *Clethra*, *Gynoxys* and *Weinmannia*, with *Chusquea* bamboo thickets being common higher up. Stunted elfin forest occurs at the higher altitudes adjacent to the páramo, but is present down to 2,000 m or lower in the cool local climate of the Cordillera de Colán (Barnes *et al.* 1995).

■ Restricted-range species

The habitat in this area is quite diverse, and in many places forms an intricate mosaic of vegetation types, with the restricted-range species occupying most habitats, but all reliant (at least in part) on humid forest, and concentrated altitudinally between 1,700 and 3,800 m.

The distributions of most of the restricted-range birds are concentrated north of the Huallaga bend, with just a few species crossing this gap. However, there is usually differentiation of sister taxa in this section of the EBA, with, for example, the two *Metallura* and *Schizoeaca* species split either side of the gap (J. Fjeldså *in litt.* 1993). Other species show even more disjunct distributions across this gap, *Hapalopsittaca melanotis*, for example, being found north of Huánuco and then in the Upper Bolivian yungas (EBA 055). There is also a distributional gap for several species in southern Pasco (central Peru), where there is often no cloud cover and humidity is low (J. Fjeldså *in litt.* 1993), thus presumably affecting the vegetation. The EBA's two threatened spe-

Status and habitat of restricted-range species

Species (ordered taxonomically)	Global status	Other EBAs (and SAs)	Altitude (m)	Habitat
Black-winged Parrot *Hapalopsittaca melanotis*	lc	055	2,000–3,400	Montane evergreen forest
Coppery Metaltail *Metallura theresiae*	lc	—	3,100–3,550	Elfin forest, forest edge, scrub near boggy grassland
Fire-throated Metaltail *Metallura eupogon*	lc	—	3,000–3,400	Elfin forest, forest edge, scrub
Marvellous Spatuletail *Loddigesia mirabilis*	VU	—	2,100–2,800	Semi-humid/humid montane scrub, montane evergreen forest edge, secondary growth, scrub
Yellow-browed Toucanet *Aulacorhynchus huallagae*	nt	—	2,000–2,600	Montane evergreen forest
Eye-ringed Thistletail *Schizoeaca palpebralis*	lc	—	2,100–3,300	Páramo grassland, tangled undergrowth, shrubs, mossy trees
Vilcabamba Thistletail *Schizoeaca vilcabambae*	lc	—	2,800–3,500	Páramo grassland, elfin forest, tangled undergrowth, shrubs, mossy trees
Russet-mantled Softtail *Thripophaga berlepschi*	nt	—	2,450–3,350	Elfin forest
Pale-billed Antpitta *Grallaria carrikeri*	lc	—	2,350–2,900	Montane evergreen forest, bamboo thickets
Rusty-tinged Antpitta *Grallaria przewalskii*	lc	—	2,200–2,750	Montane evergreen forest edge, secondary forest, bamboo
Bay Antpitta *Grallaria capitalis*	lc	—	2,600–3,000	Montane evergreen forest edge, secondary forest, bamboo
Chestnut Antpitta *Grallaria blakei*	nt	—	2,150–2,475	Montane evergreen forest
Large-footed Tapaculo *Scytalopus macropus*	lc	—	2,400–3,500	Montane evergreen forest, thickets, mossy vegetation, rocks along streams
Bay-vented Cotinga *Doliornis sclateri*	lc	—	2,500–3,450	*Escallonia* and *Weinmannia* elfin forest
Inca Flycatcher *Leptopogon taczanowskii*	lc	—	1,700–2,800	Montane evergreen forest, forest edge
Peruvian Tyrannulet *Zimmerius viridiflavus*	lc	—	1,000–2,500	Montane evergreen forest, forest edge, secondary growth, plantations
Unstreaked Tit-tyrant *Uromyias agraphia*	lc	—	2,700–3,100	Elfin forest, low bamboo thickets, bamboo-covered landslides
Rufous-bellied Bush-tyrant *Myiotheretes fuscorufus*	nt	055	1,900–2,900	Montane evergreen forest, forest edge, adjacent secondary woodland
Bar-winged Wood-wren *Henicorhina leucoptera*	nt	047	1,350–2,450	Elfin forest, esp. along exposed ridges
Rufous-browed Hemispingus *Hemispingus rufosuperciliaris*	nt	—	2,500–3,350	Elfin forest, *Chusquea* bamboo thickets
Golden-backed Mountain-tanager *Buthraupis aureodorsalis*	VU	—	3,050–3,500	Elfin forest, esp. on ridges near the treeline
Golden-collared Tanager *Iridosornis jelskii*	lc	055	3,000–3,600	Elfin forest, forest edge, scrub, bamboo
Yellow-scarfed Tanager *Iridosornis reinhardti*	lc	055	2,050–3,500	Montane evergreen and elfin forest, forest edge, scrub
Pardusco *Nephelornis oneillei*	lc	—	3,000–3,800	Elfin forest, humid forest edge, scrub

Global status (see p. 679 for definitions) — EX Extinct, EW Extinct in the Wild } with year of last record; CR Critical, EN Endangered, VU Vulnerable } threatened species; cd Conservation Dependent, nt Near Threatened, lc Least Concern; DD Data Deficient, NE Not Evaluated

Other EBAs (and SAs) (see p. 65 for locations): bracketed numbers are Secondary Areas; ˣ extinct in that EBA or SA.

Marvellous Spatuletail *Loddigesia mirabilis* is the only species in its genus, and is rare within a small area in the north of this EBA. Like a number of species in the EBA it is under pressure from habitat loss.

N. Arlott

cies have particularly restricted ranges (see 'Threats and conservation', below).

■ Threats and conservation

Deforestation in the area is particularly widespread on the mountain slopes in the Marañón drainage, but in the Huallaga valley it is worst below 2,000 m. The cloud forest as a whole is relatively pristine, although elfin forest is readily approached from the páramo, and is clearly vulnerable to grazing and burning (Collar *et al*. 1992). However, the Huallaga valley, especially the upper reaches, has recently been taken over by coca growers, and it seems likely that forest at all altitudes will have suffered (M. A. Plenge *in litt*. 1993). Recent surveys of the northern end of the Cordillera de Colán found an alarmingly high deforestation rate, with most of the forest in this area already gone, and what remains being rapidly cleared

for cash crops, particularly marijuana and coffee (Barnes *et al*. 1995).

Two of the species in this EBA are considered threatened, *Loddigesia mirabilis* primarily due to its restricted range within which it is rare and under pressure from habitat loss, and *Buthraupis aureo-dorsalis* because of its confinement to such a small area of elfin forest within which it too is rare (Collar *et al*. 1994). With the recent discovery of habitat loss in the northern Cordillera de Colán, the status of some of the six Near Threatened species in this EBA should be reassessed. Of the nine Key Areas identified for threatened birds in this EBA, the recently established Río Abiseo National Park is the only significant protected area harbouring populations of a number of this EBA's threatened and Near Threatened species (Collar *et al*. 1992, Wege and Long 1995).

050 Junín puna

| Key habitats | Puna grassland and scrub, lake-side marshland, open water | Area | 11,000 km² | Altitude | 3,500–5,000 m |

Key habitats Puna grassland and scrub, lake-side marshland, open water

Area 11,000 km² **Altitude** 3,500–5,000 m

Countries Peru

Main threats Moderate habitat loss (e.g. due to pollution, drainage)

Biological importance ● ○ ○
Current threat level ● ● ●

Restricted-range species	Threatened	Total
Confined to this EBA	3	5
Present also in other EBAs, SAs	0	1
Total	3	6

■ General characteristics

The Junín puna EBA covers two discrete areas of central Peru. Although the puna zone of the Peruvian Andes extends throughout the central and southern parts of the country, the restricted-range species which define the extent of this EBA are apparently confined to the areas around Lago de Junín (in the Junín department) and central Huancavelica department (there are records of just one species outside this immediate area in adjacent Lima and Pasco departments). The altitudinal limits of the puna are c.3,500–5,000 m, Lago de Junín being at 4,080 m. The climatically seasonal vegetation comprises tussocky grassland, some scrub and open rocky areas, with bogs and mires interspersed (often below glaciers); there are also some areas of woodland (Fjeldså and Krabbe 1990).

■ Restricted-range species

Of the five birds confined to the EBA, *Podiceps taczanowskii*, *Laterallus tuerosi* and *Geositta saxicolina* are restricted to the area around Lago de Junín, the first two species being confined to the open water, submerged vegetation and surrounding marshland of the lake itself, while *G. saxicolina* is found in typical puna vegetation. The remaining two endemics also occur in the Junín area: *Cinclodes palliatus* is found additionally to the south in central Huancavelica, inhabiting the mineral-rich *Distichia* bogs of the upper puna zone; *Oreotrochilus melanogaster* occurs there too, with a population also in Ancash (north of Junín), inhabiting puna grassland at lower altitudes (Fjeldså and Krabbe 1990). *Asthenes virgata* occurs in this EBA as a disjunct population from that in the Peruvian high Andes (EBA 051) (J. Fjeldså *in litt.* 1993).

Very few puna zone species have restricted ranges: however, although the puna seems quite uniform on casual observation, it is sufficiently complex to result in the patchy distributions of many birds (Fjeldså and Krabbe 1990). The local and patchy distributions of the birds in this EBA appear to reflect requirements that are only satisfied locally. The area around Lago de Junín was ice-free during the last glacial periods (the surrounding areas above c.4,000 m were generally covered in ice: Fjeldså 1992), and was presumably a refuge for the restricted-range species, three of which have not subsequently dispersed out of this immediate area (J. Fjeldså *in litt.* 1993).

■ Threats and conservation

Pollution and man-made changes in the water-level at Lago de Junín are factors that appear to be having adverse effects on the two lake endemics, and consequently both species are considered threatened. *Cinclodes palliatus* appears to have very specific habitat needs (though their precise nature remains unknown), and although not threatened from habitat destruction, the bird has a small and declining popu-

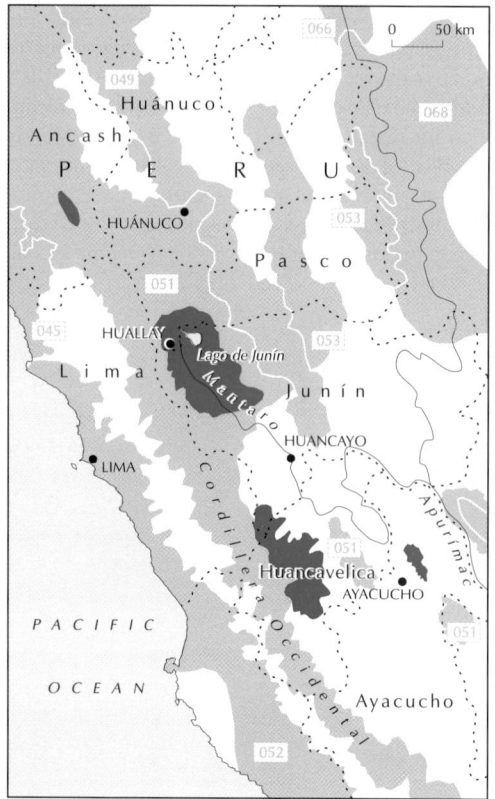

Status and habitat of restricted-range species

Species (ordered taxonomically)	Global status	Other EBAs (and SAs)	Altitude (m)	Habitat
Junín Grebe *Podiceps taczanowskii*	CR	—	4,080	Open freshwater lakes and ponds with submerged vegetation
Junín Rail *Laterallus tuerosi*[1]	EN	—	4,080	*Juncus* zone fringing marshes
Black-breasted Hillstar *Oreotrochilus melanogaster*	lc	—	3,700–4,800	Puna grassland, rocky slopes
Dark-winged Miner *Geositta saxicolina*	lc	—	4,000–4,900	Puna grassland, stony hills with sparse vegetation
White-bellied Cinclodes *Cinclodes palliatus*	VU	—	4,400–5,000	Puna grassland, mineral-rich bogs, rocky outcrops and slopes below glaciers
Junín Canastero *Asthenes virgata*	lc	051	3,300–4,300	Puna grassland, scrub, forest edge, rocky areas, forest, woodland

Global status (see p. 679 for definitions)

EX Extinct — with year of last record
EW Extinct in the Wild — with year of last record
CR Critical — threatened species
EN Endangered — threatened species
VU Vulnerable — threatened species

cd Conservation Dependent
nt Near Threatened
lc Least Concern
DD Data Deficient
NE Not Evaluated

Other EBAs (and SAs) (see p. 65 for locations) Bracketed numbers are Secondary Areas. X Extinct in that EBA or SA.

Notes [1] Taxonomy follows Collar *et al.* (1992, 1994).

Puna habitat such as this—tussocky grassland, open rocky areas and wetlands—is characteristic of the EBA and is relatively free from human intervention. Elsewhere, pollution and man-made changes in water-levels are having adverse effects on the restricted-range species.

D. J. Brooks

lation which would be vulnerable should mining commence within its range (Collar *et al.* 1992, 1994). Pale-tailed Canastero *Asthenes huancavelicae* (classified as Vulnerable) is a more widespread threatened species found in this general area.

Four Key Areas—Lago de Junín, Marcapomacocha, Pampa Pucacocha and Yauli—have been identified for the conservation of these four threatened species (Wege and Long 1995). Lago de Junín is a national reserve (at which all three threatened restricted-range birds have been recorded), although this has had little effect in preventing pollution and water-level changes (Valqui 1994, Wege and Long 1995). The Huayllay National Sanctuary may also protect some of the species in this EBA (IUCN 1992a).

051 Peruvian high Andes

PRIORITY
CRITICAL

| Key habitats | Arid and semi-humid montane scrub, grassland, *Polylepis* woodland | **Area** 100,000 km² | **Altitude** 1,500–4,600 m |

Countries Peru

Main threats Moderate habitat loss (e.g. due to cultivation, burning)

Biological importance ● ● ●
Current threat level ● ● ●

Restricted-range species	Threatened	Total
Confined to this EBA	8	20
Present also in other EBAs, SAs	3	9
Total	11	29

■ General characteristics

This EBA includes a large proportion of the high Andes in Peru from the border with Ecuador in the north to the Chilean and Bolivian border in the south. It includes the mountains west of the Marañón valley such as the Cordilleras Blanca and Negra, and the highlands around Lago de Junín. The area extends southwards from Junín in two separate forks, the first running along the continuous western side of the Andes (the Cordillera Occidental), the other on the eastern side of the Andes in Cuzco and Puno departments. This latter area includes the disjunct cordilleras north of the Apurímac river (i.e. Vilcabamba, Vilcanota and Carabaya), and some areas just south of the river in north-east Apurímac. This is a complex area biogeographically, and as such is in close prox-

imity to a number of other EBAs: it surrounds the Junín puna (EBA 050), which is at slightly higher elevation and is in a different habitat zone; around Junín and northwards it runs alongside the North-east Peruvian cordilleras (EBA 049), from which it differs in vegetation; in the south-east it adjoins the Peruvian East Andean foothills (EBA 053), which embrace humid forest at lower altitudes; and to the north it continues with a different suite of species as the more humid forests of the South Central Andes (EBA 046).

The habitat in this EBA primarily comprises arid and semi-arid vegetation in the subtropical and temperate zone, and in many areas is best described as dense arid montane scrub and shrubby forest with cacti, *Puya* and other terrestrial bromeliads. The landscape is dry and rocky: the hills are often covered in open *Acacia* woodland, grass and thorny scrub interspersed with areas of stony ground, and at higher altitudes there are *Alnus* thickets and *Gynoxys* shrubs. In semi-humid areas (such as canyons), mixed woodlands of *Polylepis*, *Weinmannia*, *Gynoxys* and *Escallonia* often occur in isolated patches in a mosaic with more open areas (Fjeldså and Krabbe 1990). Other patches of mixed woodland (with bushy undergrowth at its edges) are dominated by *Oreopanax*, *Myrcianthes* and *Escallonia*, and *Podocarpus* forest grows in some areas. In cultivated regions a mosaic of habitats has resulted, with small tuber (potato) and barley fields, and heavily grazed patches of pasture interspersed with natural vegetation, a landscape that has not changed much for at least a century (Collar *et al.* 1992).

■ Restricted-range species

Almost all the restricted-range species are concentrated above 2,000 m in the subtropical and temperate zones, where they inhabit the full range of arid to semi-humid habitats described above. There are no clear altitudinal or habitat trends within this suite of birds, but there are a number of interesting distributional patterns: one group of species is confined to the north-west cordilleras (Blanca and Negra), and a second, larger group is restricted to the south-east

Status and habitat of restricted-range species

Species (ordered taxonomically)	Global status	Other EBAs (and SAs)	Altitude (m)	Habitat
Taczanowski's Tinamou *Nothoprocta taczanowskii*	VU	—	2,750–4,000	Arid montane scrub, grassland, open woodland, rocky slopes, humid woodland edge
Kalinowski's Tinamou *Nothoprocta kalinowskii*	CR	—	c.3,000–4,575	Arid montane scrub, possibly agricultural land
Spot-throated Hummingbird *Leucippus taczanowskii*	lc	048	300–2,900	Arid montane scrub, dry tropical deciduous forest
White-tufted Sunbeam *Aglaeactis castelnaudii*	lc	—	3,100–4,200	Semi-humid/humid montane scrub, elfin forest, *Polylepis* and *Escallonia* woodland
Olivaceous Thornbill *Chalcostigma olivaceum*	lc	056	3,150–4,500	Puna and páramo grassland with composite scrub, *Polylepis–Gynoxys* forest edge
Grey-bellied Comet *Taphrolesbia griseiventris*	VU	048	2,750–3,170	Arid montane scrub, forest edge, thickets, agricultural land
Bearded Mountaineer *Oreonympha nobilis*	lc	—	2,500–3,700	Arid montane scrub, woodland, arid areas
Striated Earthcreeper *Upucerthia serrana*	lc	—	2,800–4,200	Arid montane scrub, *Polylepis* woodland, grassland, rocky slopes
Royal Cinclodes *Cinclodes aricomae*[1]	CR	056	3,600–4,550	Semi-humid/humid montane scrub, semi-humid woodlands mainly of *Polylepis*
Rusty-crowned Tit-spinetail *Leptasthenura pileata*	lc	—	2,500–3,500	Arid montane scrub, *Polylepis* woodland, thickets
White-browed Tit-spinetail *Leptasthenura xenothorax*	CR	—	3,700–4,550	Semi-humid *Polylepis* woodland
Apurímac Spinetail *Synallaxis courseni*	VU	—	2,450–3,500	Montane evergreen forest edge, secondary forest, scrub, semi-humid cloud forest
Russet-bellied Spinetail *Synallaxis zimmeri*	EN	—	1,800–2,900	Arid montane scrub, woodland
Creamy-crested Spinetail *Cranioleuca albicapilla*	lc	—	2,500–3,600	Semi-humid/humid montane scrub, *Polylepis* woodland
Canyon Canastero *Asthenes pudibunda*	lc	—	2,500–3,500	*Polylepis* woodland, rocky slopes, arid montane and thorn scrub, cactus, semi-arid forest
Rusty-fronted Canastero *Asthenes ottonis*	lc	—	2,750–4,000	Arid montane and semi-humid/humid montane scrub, *Polylepis* woodland and edge, rocky slopes, disturbed areas
Line-fronted Canastero *Asthenes urubambensis*	nt	056	3,200–4,300	Páramo grassland, *Polylepis* woodland, elfin forest, mossy slopes with scrub
Junín Canastero *Asthenes virgata*	lc	050	3,300–4,300	Páramo and puna grassland, scrub, forest edge, rocky areas
White-cheeked Cotinga *Zaratornis stresemanni*	VU	—	2,700–4,240	*Polylepis* woodland with mistletoes
Ash-breasted Tit-tyrant *Anairetes alpinus*	EN	056	3,700–4,500	Semi-humid *Polylepis* woodland
Rusty-bellied Brush-finch *Atlapetes nationi*	lc	—	1,800–4,000	Arid montane and semi-humid/humid montane scrub, *Polylepis* woodland
Rufous-eared Brush-finch *Atlapetes rufigenis*	nt	—	2,600–4,000	*Polylepis* woodland, montane evergreen forest edge, montane scrub, secondary growth
Great Inca-finch *Incaspiza pulchra*	lc	—	1,000–2,500	Arid montane scrub, cactus, terrestrial bromeliads
Rufous-backed Inca-finch *Incaspiza personata*	lc	048	2,200–3,400	Arid montane scrub, cactus
Grey-winged Inca-finch *Incaspiza ortizi*	nt	048	1,800–2,300	Arid montane scrub
Plain-tailed Warbling-finch *Poospiza alticola*	EN	—	3,200–4,300	*Polylepis* woodland, arid montane and semi-humid/humid montane scrub

cont.

Status and habitat of restricted-range species (cont.)

Species (ordered taxonomically)	Global status	Other EBAs (and SAs)	Altitude (m)	Habitat
Rufous-breasted Warbling-finch *Poospiza rubecula*	EN	—	2,500–3,700	Semi-humid/humid montane scrub, *Polylepis* woodland and edge
Chestnut-breasted Mountain-finch *Poospiza caesar*	lc	—	2,600–3,800	Semi-humid/humid montane and arid montane scrub, cactus, woodland
Brown-flanked Tanager *Thlypopsis pectoralis*	lc	—	2,500–3,100	Secondary forest, semi-humid/humid montane scrub, stream-sides, agricultural land, forest edge

| **Global status** (see p. 679 for definitions) | EX Extinct ⎫ with year EW Extinct in ⎬ of last the Wild ⎭ record CR Critical ⎫ EN Endangered ⎬ threatened VU Vulnerable ⎭ species | cd Conservation Dependent nt Near Threatened lc Least Concern DD Data Deficient NE Not Evaluated | **Other EBAs (and SAs)** (see p. 65 for locations)   **Notes** | Bracketed numbers are Secondary Areas. ˣ Extinct in that EBA or SA. ¹ Taxonomy follows Fjeldså and Krabbe (1990) and Collar *et al*. (1992, 1994). |

Line-fronted Canastero *Asthenes urubambensis* is restricted to the higher reaches of this EBA, in semi-humid, mossy vegetation.

G. Engblom

Andes (see 'Distribution patterns' table). Among the remaining species, those occurring within the Cordillera Occidental are found in the north-west cordilleras with all except one also in the Lago de Junín area (but none in the disjunct south-east Andes). The four species shared with the Marañón valley (EBA 048) are concentrated there in the higher altitudes of the southern part of that valley.

An unnamed form of *Taphrospilus* hummingbird has been recorded at 2,800–3,400 m in the *Podocarpus* forests of this region (Fjeldså and Krabbe 1990), but though the altitudinal range appears to be consistent with other species in this EBA, J. Fjeldså (*in litt*. 1993) suggests that it may belong with birds from the Peruvian East Andean foothills (EBA 053).

■ Threats and conservation

The vegetation of this large area is in a relatively good state, but locally it has been severely affected by domestic grazing animals, burning, cutting for fuel and clearance for cultivation (Fjeldså and Krabbe

1990, Collar *et al*. 1992). For example, the *Polylepis–Gynoxys* woodlands within Huascarán National Park are dwindling owing to the activities of man, although some large areas still exist (Wege and Long 1995).

Eleven of the restricted-range species are currently considered threatened, with *Nothoprocta tac-*

Distribution patterns of restricted-range species

Species (ordered geographically)	NW cordilleras	Lago de Junín area	Cordillera Occidental	SE Andes	Other EBAs, SAs
Synallaxis zimmeri	●	—	—	—	—
Poospiza alticola	●	—	—	—	—
Leucippus taczanowskii	●	—	—	—	●
Taphrolesbia griseiventris	●	—	—	—	●
Poospiza rubecula	●	●	—	—	—
Thlypopsis pectoralis	●	—	—	—	—
Incaspiza personata	●	—	—	—	●
Upucerthia serrana	●	●	●	—	—
Leptasthenura pileata	●	●	●	—	—
Asthenes pudibunda	●	●	●	—	—
Zaratornis stresemanni	●	●	●	—	—
Atlapetes nationi	●	●	●	—	—
Incaspiza pulchra	●	●	●	—	—
Chalcostigma olivaceum	●	●	—	●	—
Asthenes urubambensis	●	●	—	●	●
Nothoprocta kalinowskii	●	—	—	●	—
Atlapetes rufigenis	●	—	—	●	—
Anairetes alpinus	●	—	—	●	●
Nothoprocta taczanowskii	—	●	—	●	—
Aglaeactis castelnaudii	—	●	—	●	—
Cranioleuca albicapilla	—	●	—	●	—
Asthenes virgata	—	●	—	●	—
Oreonympha nobilis	—	●	—	●	—
Leptasthenura xenothorax	—	—	—	●	—
Asthenes ottonis	—	—	—	●	—
Synallaxis courseni	—	—	—	●	—
Poospiza caesar	—	—	—	●	—
Cinclodes aricomae	—	—	—	●	●
Incaspiza ortizi	—	—	—	●	●
Total	18	14	6	16	

● Present ? Present?
○ Extinct? R Reintroduced
X Extinct I Introduced

Threatened spp. shown in **bold**
Other EBAs, SAs

see 'Status and habitat' table

Polylepis woodland is characteristic of the more humid areas in this EBA, and is severely degraded in many parts due to cutting for fuel and clearance for cultivation.

C. Balchin

zanowskii, Cinclodes aricomae, Leptasthenura xenothorax and *Synallaxis courseni* (known from just one area in Abancay department) being primarily confined to the south-east Andes. The remaining threatened species tend to be poorly known and/or localized (e.g. *Nothoprocta kalinowskii*), or alternatively are more widely distributed but occur at very few localities, or in low densities and are presumed to be highly specialized (e.g. *Taphrolesbia griseiventris, Zaratornis stresemanni, Anairetes alpinus*). More-widespread threatened species that are known to occur in this EBA include Golden-plumed Parakeet *Leptosittaca branickii* (classified as Vulnerable), Pale-tailed Canastero *Asthenes huancavelicae* (Vulnerable) and White-tailed Shrike-tyrant *Agriornis*

andicola (Vulnerable) (Collar *et al.* 1992).

Thirty-three Key Areas were recently identified for the threatened birds in this EBA, though only three are currently protected: Huascarán National Park (in the Cordillera Blanca), Río Abiseo National Park and Ampay National Sanctuary (Wege and Long 1995). The only other significant protected area in this EBA is the Apurímac Reserve Zone. With such prominent geographic divisions in the endemic avifauna, a number of sites need to be conserved to ensure the survival of all species; particularly important areas are the Cordilleras Blanca and Negra, the mountains around Lago de Junín, the massif east of Lima and the Cuzco–Urubamba area in the south-east.

052 Peru–Chile Pacific slope

PRIORITY HIGH

Key habitats Desert, riparian scrub, lomas, *Polylepis* woodland, arid montane scrub

Main threats Moderate habitat loss (e.g. due to overgrazing)

Biological importance ● ●
Current threat level ● ● ●

Area 95,000 km² **Altitude** 0–4,000 m
Countries Chile, Peru

Restricted-range species	Threatened	Total
Confined to this EBA	3	6
Present also in other EBAs, SAs	0	3
Total	3	9

■ General characteristics

This long EBA embraces the Pacific slope and coastal lowlands from northernmost Lima department (c.11°S), south through Ica, Arequipa, Moquegua and Tacna departments of Peru, and Tarapaca department of Chile. Within this range are included all the arid zones on the Pacific slope (tropical to temperate), and some of the larger arid inter-montane valleys, from sea-level to c.4,000 m, the higher-altitude areas being mostly in the south of the EBA.

This EBA is desert, almost totally devoid of vegetation save strips of dense *Salix* and *Schinus* scrub along the few river valleys that bring water from the distant Andes. At slightly higher elevations (c.1,000 m), precipitation from winter coastal fogs (which form over the cool Pacific Ocean currents) support the 'lomas' formations of annuals, shrubs, cacti and *Tillandsia*-clad trees; elsewhere, the rocky mountain slopes are covered in arid cactus scrub, with higher areas supporting *Polylepis* woodland and scrub (Fjeldså and Krabbe 1990, Dinerstein *et al.* 1995).

■ Restricted-range species

The restricted-range species variously occupy all habitats, with populations or subspecies in the north tending to occur at lower altitudes than the equivalent populations further south (Fjeldså and Krabbe 1990).

Three species—*Cinclodes taczanowskii*, *Geositta peruviana* and *Sporophila simplex*—are shared with the adjacent Tumbesian region (EBA 045) to the north; they are primarily coastal birds with the

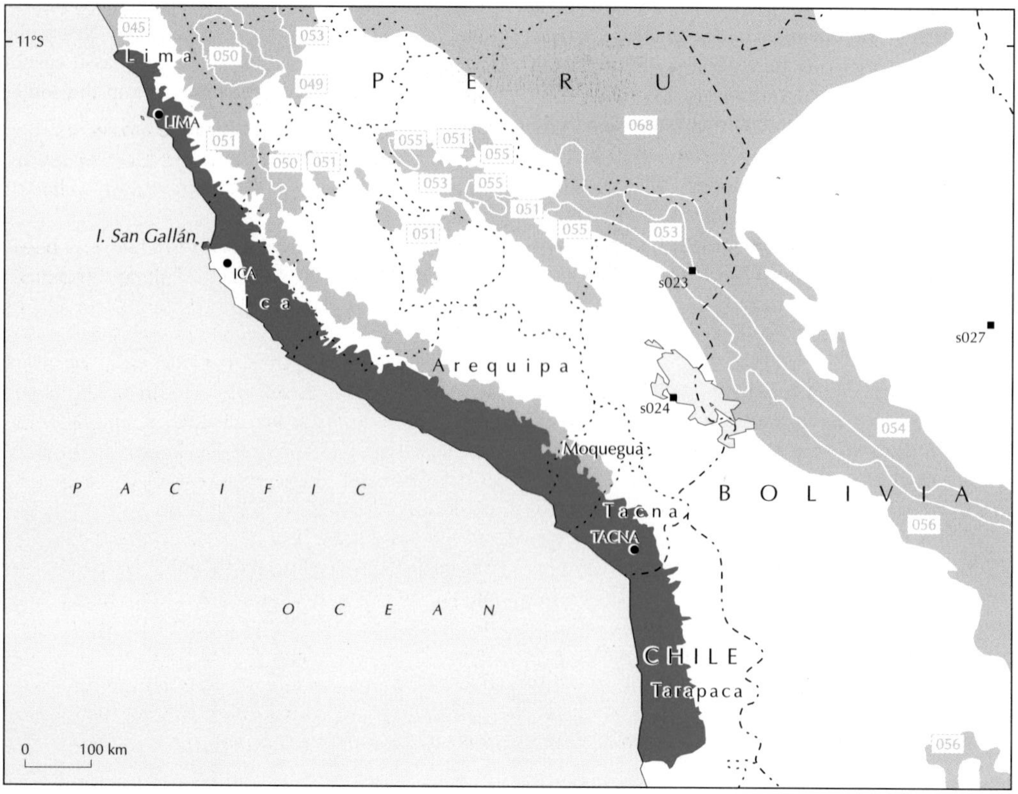

Status and habitat of restricted-range species

Species (ordered taxonomically)	Global status	Other EBAs (and SAs)	Altitude (m)	Habitat
Chilean Woodstar *Eulidia yarrellii*	VU	—	0–750 (–2,600)	Riparian thickets, secondary growth, desert river valleys, arid scrub, agricultural land, gardens
Coastal Miner *Geositta peruviana*	lc	045	0–400	Sandy/rocky deserts, arid lowland scrub
Thick-billed Miner *Geositta crassirostris*	lc	—	600–3,000	Dry valleys with cactus scrub and rocks, lomas, arid montane scrub
White-throated Earthcreeper *Upucerthia albigula*	lc	—	2,500–4,000	Desert river valleys, arid montane scrub, wet meadows
Surf Cinclodes *Cinclodes taczanowskii*	lc	045	0–100 (–370)	Rocky coasts and beaches
Cactus Canastero *Asthenes cactorum*	nt	—	50–2,500	Arid montane and rocky cactus scrub
Slender-billed Finch *Xenospingus concolor*	VU	—	0–300 (–3,500)	Arid lowland/desert scrub, riparian thickets
Drab Seedeater *Sporophila simplex*	lc	045	0–1,800	Arid lowland and arid montane scrub, *Acacia*, riparian thickets, agricultural land
Tamarugo Conebill *Conirostrum tamarugense*	VU	—	0–4,050	*Polylepis* woodland, arid montane, *Polylepis–Gynoxys* and riparian scrub, gardens

Global status (see p. 679 for definitions)
EX Extinct ⎫ with year
EW Extinct in ⎬ of last
　　the Wild ⎭ record
CR Critical ⎫
EN Endangered ⎬ threatened species
VU Vulnerable ⎭
cd Conservation Dependent
nt Near Threatened
lc Least Concern
DD Data Deficient
NE Not Evaluated

Other EBAs (and SAs) (see p. 65 for locations): bracketed numbers are Secondary Areas; [X] extinct in that EBA or SA.

greater part of their ranges in the northern coastal area, although both the genera *Cinclodes* and *Geositta* originated as radiations from southern Patagonia (J. Fjeldså *in litt.* 1993).

Streaked Tit-spinetail *Leptasthenura striata*, Pied-crested Tit-tyrant *Anairetes reguloides* and Raimondi's Yellow-finch *Sicalis raimondii* are all essentially confined to this EBA, but have breeding distributions that are too large to qualify them as restricted-range birds (and all three undertake movements beyond their breeding ranges, with *L. striata* and *A. reguloides* recorded up into the higher mountains of north-west Apurímac, Huancavelica and Ayacucho).

■ Threats and conservation

Overgrazing by domestic livestock, alteration of water flow patterns in the river valleys, and firewood collection all threaten the vegetation in this area (Dinerstein *et al.* 1995). Almost all available flat areas in the vegetated river valleys have been cultivated, as have many of the inter-montane valleys; however, the arid vegetation of the remaining areas is still essentially intact (Fjeldså and Krabbe 1990, Collar *et al.* 1992).

Three restricted-range species in this EBA are considered threatened, two of which (*Eulidia yarrellii* and *Conirostrum tamarugense*) are confined to the southernmost portion: *E. yarrellii* is confined to just

a few arid valleys where extensive cultivation has led to its almost total reliance on flowering plants in gardens; *C. tamarugense* is almost certainly an altitudinal migrant, and for at least part of the year relies wholly on the now much-depleted high-elevation *Polylepis* and *Gynoxys* woodlands; and *Xenospingus concolor*, despite its range (which embraces most of this EBA), is now restricted to the narrow strips of vegetation along rivers of the otherwise intensively irrigated and cultivated valleys (Collar *et al.* 1992).

Six Key Areas in Peru and six in Chile have been identified for the conservation of these threatened birds (Wege and Long 1995). These include, at the southernmost end of the EBA, two Key Areas for *Conirostrum tamarugense*, both of which are protected within the Pampa del Tamarugal National Reserve. In Peru, protected areas (important for threatened species) include the Salinas y Aguada Blanca National Reserve (from which there are records of the widespread but threatened White-tailed Shrike-tyrant *Agriornis andicola*, classified as Vulnerable) and the Laguna de Mejía National Sanctuary. The Paracas National Reserve embraces a number of arid islands, of which Isla San Gallán supports one of the largest remaining populations of the Peruvian Diving-petrel *Pelecanoides garnotii* (Endangered), and is potentially of importance for a couple of restricted-range species.

053 Peruvian East Andean foothills

PRIORITY
HIGH

Key habitats Tropical montane and lowland evergreen forest

Main threats Moderate habitat loss (e.g. due to agriculture, colonization, road-building)

Biological importance ● ● ○
Current threat level ● ○ ○

Area 32,000 km²   **Altitude** 600–2,200 m

Countries Peru

Restricted-range species	Threatened	Total
Confined to this EBA	0	6
Present also in other EBAs, SAs	1	8
Total	1	14

■ General characteristics

This EBA extends along the lower eastern slopes of the East Andes in southern Peru. It covers three apparently disjunct areas: the eastern slope of the mountains in Huánuco, Pasco (including the isolated Cerros del Sira) and northern Junín departments, from the southern end of the Huallaga river south into Junín (including the Cordillera Yanachaga); the eastern slopes of the Cordillera Vilcabamba into the Urubamba valley in Cuzco department (this area extends northwards due to records of restricted-range species in the Apurímac valley); and the slopes of the Cordillera Carabaya in Cuzco (and just into Madre de Dios), and along the length of the Inambari river in Puno to near the Bolivian border. South-east of the Inambari, this EBA abuts the Lower Bolivian yungas (EBA 054) with which a number of species are shared, and at higher altitudes it is adjacent to the Upper Bolivian yungas (EBA 055) in the south, and the Peruvian high Andes (EBA 051) in the north. The

altitude of this EBA is primarily centred at 600–2,200 m in the upper tropical and subtropical zones, the vegetation being humid evergreen forest.

■ Restricted-range species

All the restricted-range species are dependent on forest, some of the birds occurring in or restricted to secondary growth and forest edge. A wide range of altitudinal distributions is exhibited.

At least six species occur on the disjunct Cerros del Sira in the north of the EBA, with *Tangara phillipsi* endemic to the cerros, and *Pauxi unicornis* (the endemic subspecies *koepckeae*) present as a disjunct population from the Lower Bolivian yungas. *Zimmerius cinereicapillus* occurs (apparently) disjunctly with a population in north-east Ecuador in the Ecuador–Peru East Andes (EBA 044). *Tangara argyrofenges* is also known to have disjunct populations in the Ecuador–Peru East Andes (southern Amazonas and western San Martín in north-east

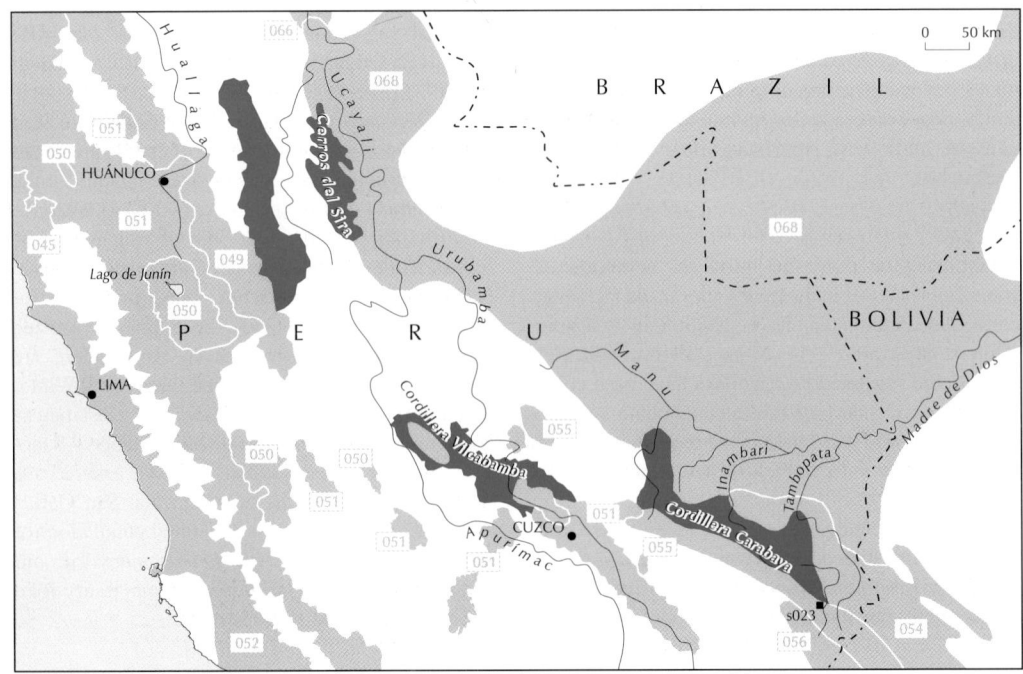

Status and habitat of restricted-range species

Species (ordered taxonomically)	Global status	Other EBAs (and SAs)	Altitude (m)	Habitat
Black Tinamou *Tinamus osgoodi*	DD	040,054	1,000	Montane evergreen forest
Southern Helmeted Curassow *Pauxi unicornis*	EN	054	450–1,200	Montane evergreen forest
Cloud-forest Screech-owl *Otus marshalli*[1]	lc	—	1,700–2,250	Montane evergreen forest
Green-and-white Hummingbird *Amazilia viridicauda*	lc	—	900–2,800	Montane evergreen forest edge, landslips, cleared slopes, secondary growth
Peruvian Piedtail *Phlogophilus harterti*	nt	054	750–1,200	Montane evergreen forest
Rufous-webbed Brilliant *Heliodoxa branickii*	lc	—	700–1,550	Montane evergreen and tropical lowland evergreen forest, forest edge
Creamy-bellied Antwren *Herpsilochmus motacilloides*	lc	—	1,000–2,200	Montane evergreen forest
Cerulean-capped Manakin *Pipra coeruleocapilla*	lc	—	500–2,100	Montane evergreen forest
Yungas Manakin *Chiroxiphia boliviana*	lc	054	650–2,150	Montane evergreen forest, forest edge, secondary growth
Bolivian Tyrannulet *Zimmerius bolivianus*	lc	054	1,000–2,600	Montane evergreen forest, esp. in clumps of mistletoes in forest canopy and edge
Red-billed Tyrannulet *Zimmerius cinereicapillus*	lc	044	750–1,200	Tropical lowland evergreen and montane evergreen forest
Slaty Tanager *Creurgops dentata*	lc	054	1,500–2,150	Montane evergreen forest, shrubby pre-montane forest, forest edge, secondary growth
Sira Tanager *Tangara phillipsi*	nt	—	1,300–1,600	Montane evergreen forest, forest edge
Straw-backed Tanager *T. argyrofenges*	lc	044,054	1,200–2,700	Montane evergreen forest, forest edge

Global status (see p. 679 for definitions)	EX Extinct EW Extinct in the Wild } with year of last record	CR Critical EN Endangered VU Vulnerable } threatened species	cd Conservation Dependent nt Near Threatened lc Least Concern DD Data Deficient NE Not Evaluated	**Other EBAs (and SAs)** (see p. 65 for locations) **Notes**	Bracketed numbers are Secondary Areas. X Extinct in that EBA or SA. [1] Taxonomy follows Fitzpatrick and O'Neill (1986).

Peru) and the Lower Bolivian yungas (EBA 054), but is known in the present EBA from an isolated population in eastern Junín department. Perhaps the most inexplicable distribution is that shown by the poorly known *Tinamus osgoodi*, represented by two distinct races confined to two areas 2,000 km apart: *hershkovitzi* at the head of the Magdalena valley in southern Colombia, and the nominate on the East Andean slopes in Cuzco and Madre de Dios departments of Peru (Collar *et al.* 1992). Recent records of *T. osgoodi* east of the Inambari in the Tambopata–Candamo Reserved Zone have extended the species' range to the Lower Bolivian yungas EBA. The more-widespread Rufous-lored Tyrannulet *Phylloscartes flaviventris* is known from two disjunct populations, in this EBA and in two EBAs in northern Venezuela (033 and 034); these almost certainly represent two distinct (restricted-range) species but are not considered as such in the present analysis. Red-and-white Antpitta *Grallaria* (*hypoleuca*) *erythroleuca*, confined to the higher elevations of this EBA, has recently been considered specifically distinct (Ridgely and Tudor 1994), but is not so treated here.

■ Threats and conservation

The forest in this area still remains relatively intact, especially above 900 m (Collar *et al.* 1992), although there are extensive areas undergoing land clearance, agricultural conversion and logging, the effects of which are being amplified by road-building and human colonization (Dinerstein *et al.* 1995).

The exceptionally poorly known *Pauxi unicornis* is genuinely localized and rare, and is considered threatened because of its vulnerability to hunting; there have been no records from this EBA since 1969. The widespread but threatened Golden-plumed Parakeet *Leptosittaca branickii* (Vulnerable) has been recorded towards the southern end of the EBA.

Reserves within the EBA which have habitat suitable for restricted-range species include Manu National Park (also a Biosphere Reserve and World Heritage Site, 15,300 km²), embracing the northern part of the Cordillera Carabay and supporting populations of a number of threatened species (Wege and Long 1995), and the Apurímac Reserve Zone (16,700 km²) centred on the Cordillera Vilcabamba between the Apurimac and Urubamba.

235

054 Bolivian and Peruvian lower yungas `PRIORITY URGENT`

Key habitats Lowland rain forest, lower montane forest

Area 58,000 km²   **Altitude** 400–2,000 m

Countries Bolivia, Peru

Main threats Major habitat loss (e.g. due to subsistence agriculture, cocoa and coffee cultivation)

Biological importance ● ● ○
Current threat level ● ● ○

Restricted-range species	Threatened	Total
Confined to this EBA	3	7
Present also in other EBAs, SAs	1	8
Total	4	15

■ General characteristics

This EBA runs from extreme south-east Peru north and east of the Inambari river and south-eastwards along the eastern Andean slope of west-central Bolivia in the departments of La Paz and Cochabamba and extreme western Santa Cruz. The southern part of the EBA ends on the northern slope of the Cordillera Central of Bolivia, which branches out westwards from the main Andean range. The EBA is primarily in the upper tropical and middle montane zone of the East Andean slope from 450 to 2,000 m (and occasionally as high as 2,600 m). The topography of the East Andes in this EBA is complex, there being numerous outlying ridges from the main Andean chain.

The EBA overlaps at its upper altitudinal limit with the Upper yungas of Bolivia and Peru (EBA 055). There is also overlap with the Peruvian East Andean foothills (EBA 053) in south-east Peru, and dry inter-montane Andean valleys (EBA 056 in part) lie close in west-central Bolivia. The South-east Peruvian lowlands (EBA 068) are found to the north.

The habitat of the lower yungas is mainly wet lowland evergreen forest and montane evergreen forest. Much of the terrain comprises rugged ridges and valleys which promote high plant diversity, especially along the wet ridges; at Cerros del Távara (Peru), for example, the forest is very mixed with considerable differences in species composition from hectare to hectare (Foster *et al.* 1994).

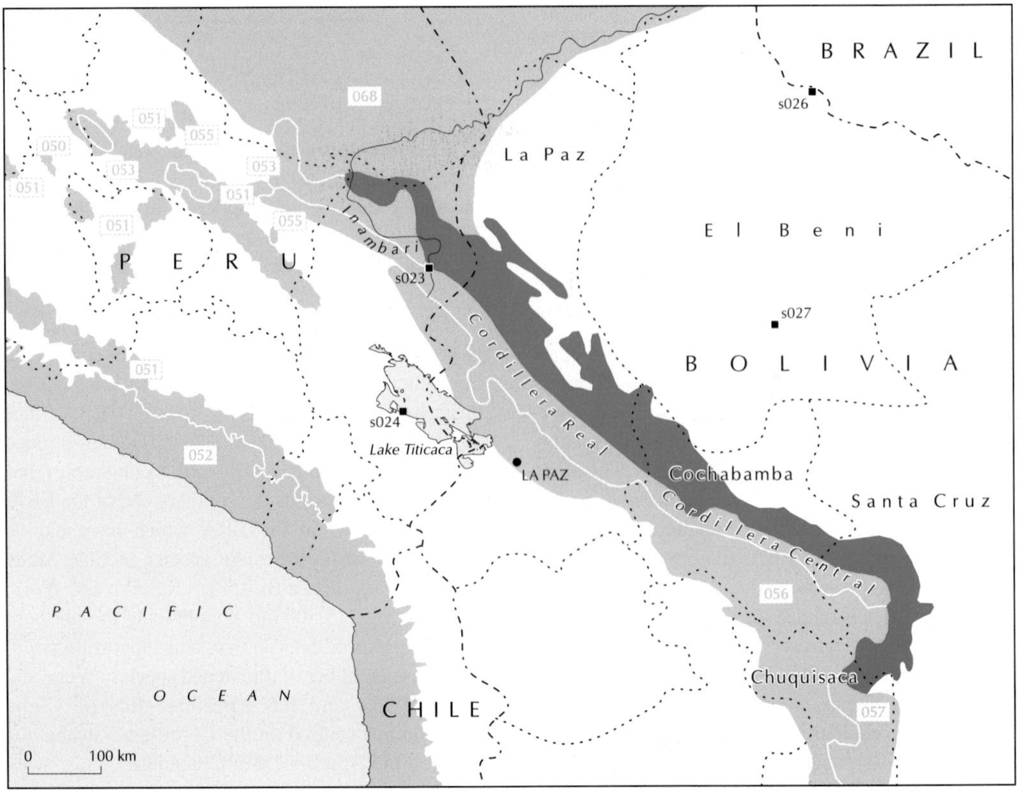

Status and habitat of restricted-range species

Species (ordered taxonomically)	Global status	Other EBAs (and SAs)	Altitude (m)	Habitat
Black Tinamou *Tinamus osgoodi*	DD	040,053	1,000	Montane evergreen forest
Southern Helmeted Curassow *Pauxi unicornis*	EN	053	450–1,200	Montane evergreen forest
Peruvian Piedtail *Phlogophilus harterti*	nt	053	750–1,200	Montane evergreen forest
Bolivian Recurvebill *Simoxenops striatus*	VU	—	670–900	Tropical lowland evergreen forest, dense undergrowth and vine tangles
Upland Antshrike *Thamnophilus aroyae*	lc	—	800–1,700	Montane evergreen forest edge, secondary growth
Ashy Antwren *Myrmotherula grisea*	VU	—	500–1,650	Tropical lowland evergreen and montane evergreen forest
Yellow-rumped Antwren *Terenura sharpei*	VU	—	1,100–1,680	Montane evergreen forest
White-throated Antpitta *Grallaria albigula*	lc	057	800–1,700	Montane evergreen forest, scrub
Yungas Manakin *Chiroxiphia boliviana*	lc	053	650–2,150	Montane evergreen forest, forest edge, secondary growth
Hazel-fronted Pygmy-tyrant *Pseudotriccus simplex*	lc	—	1,300–2,000	Montane evergreen forest, forest edge
Yungas Tody-tyrant *Hemitriccus spodiops*	lc	—	800–1,600	Montane evergreen forest edge, secondary growth
Bolivian Tyrannulet *Zimmerius bolivianus*	lc	053	1,000–2,600	Montane evergreen forest, esp. in clumps of mistletoe in forest canopy and edge
Unadorned Flycatcher *Myiophobus inornatus*	lc	—	1,000–2,000	Gallery forest edge, second-growth scrub
Slaty Tanager *Creurgops dentata*	lc	053	1,500–2,150	Montane evergreen forest, shrubby pre-montane forest, forest edge, secondary growth
Straw-backed Tanager *Tangara argyrofenges*	lc	044,053	1,300–1,700 (1,200–2,700)	Montane evergreen forest, forest edge

Global status (see p. 679 for definitions)	EX Extinct EW Extinct in the Wild	} with year of last record	CR Critical EN Endangered VU Vulnerable	} threatened species	cd Conservation Dependent nt Near Threatened lc Least Concern	DD Data Deficient NE Not Evaluated

Other EBAs (and SAs) (see p. 65 for locations): bracketed numbers are Secondary Areas; ˣ extinct in that EBA or SA.

■ Restricted-range species

All the restricted-range birds are found in lowland and/or montane evergreen forest. Many are present in montane forests which mark the lower limits of species confined to the upper montane zone of the eastern Andes yungas in Bolivia and south-east Peru (EBA 055).

Although the Inambari valley forms a geographical barrier between this EBA and the Peruvian East Andean foothills (EBA 053), seven species are shared between them, though, of these seven, most of the ranges of *Pauxi unicornis* (but see below), *Chiroxiphia boliviana* and *Tangara argyrofenges* fall within this EBA, whereas *Phlogophilus harterti* and *Tinamus osgoodi* are each known from only a single record within it.

Pauxi unicornis appears to have a particularly restricted range; it is believed to be confined to ridges which form outliers from the main Andean chain

(Foster *et al.* 1994). For a long time it was only known from the Bolivian part of the EBA but a disjunct population assigned to a new subspecies, *koepckeae*, was discovered at Cerros del Sira (in EBA 053) in 1969. A further sighting at Cerros del Távara (in the northern end of the present EBA) in 1992 suggests that the bird may be more continuously distributed between the known central Peruvian and Bolivian populations (Collar *et al.* 1992, Foster *et al.* 1994).

■ Threats and conservation

The forests which occur on moderate slopes with rich soils are well-suited to subsistence agriculture, as well as to the cultivation of cash crops such as coca and coffee and are both more accessible and easier to burn than true montane forest. For these reasons these forests are a favoured target for colonists from the altiplano, and large areas especially in La Paz and

Cochabamba (Bolivia) have already been deforested (Collar *et al.* 1992).

There are several enormous, and recently established, protected areas in both Peru and Bolivia that hold some of this EBA's habitat. The most important of these are, in Peru, the Tambopata–Candamo Reserved Zone (14,800 km²) and, in Bolivia, Madidi National Park and Integrated Management Area (19,000 km²), Amboró National Park (1,800 km²), Isiboro Sécure National Park (11,000 km²), Bellavista Protection Forest Reserve (900 km²) and Carrasco National Park (13,000 km²). The newly established Madidi reserve has created a continuous network of reserved land from Tambopata–Candamo in Peru to Ulla-Ulla and Pilon Lajas Biosphere Reserves in Bolivia.

Four of the restricted-range species are considered threatened, all known from just a handful of localities. There are single records of *Pauxi unicornis* and *Terenura sharpei* from the Tambopata–Candamo Reserved Zone, and *Pauxi unicornis*, *Simoxenops striatus* and *Myrmotherula grisea* are found in Amboró National Park. It is thought likely that most of the threatened species will eventually be found in Carrasco National Park, adjacent to Amboró, and within Madidi National Park (Collar *et al.* 1992, Remsen and Parker 1995).

055 Bolivian and Peruvian upper yungas

PRIORITY
URGENT

Key habitats Montane forest, elfin forest, cloud forest, montane scrub

Main threats Moderate habitat loss (e.g. due to subsistence agriculture)

Biological importance ● ● ●
Curent threat level ●

Area 35,000 km² **Altitude** 1,800–3,700 m

Countries Bolivia, Peru

Restricted-range species	Threatened	Total
Confined to this EBA	0	15
Present also in other EBAs, SAs	0	5
Total	0	20

◼ General characteristics

The humid forests of the eastern slope of the Andes of south-east Peru, Bolivia and Argentina are known collectively as the yungas. This EBA embraces the higher-altitude yungas (largely 1,800–3,700 m) on the northern slope of the Cordillera Central (a side branch of the main Andean range) from Cuzco and Puno departments of south-east Peru to La Paz, Cochabamba and extreme western Santa Cruz departments of central Bolivia. Also included are the parallel cordilleras of Vilcabamba, Vilcanota and Carabaya in south-east Peru which branch off northwards from the main Andean chain.

The climate's great humidity comes from the northerly trade winds which deposit water droplets as well as rain. The habitat is evergreen montane forest (including cloud forest), and is often on steep slopes, trees being laden with epiphytic bromeliads, orchids, ferns and mosses, and tree-ferns and bamboo (mainly *Chusquea*) are conspicuous (e.g. Remsen 1985, Whitney 1994). At or near crests and ridges the forest is lower in stature and even wetter (elfin forest), and at the EBA's upper elevational limits the vegetation changes to scrub, marking the transition between forest and the páramo grassland above.

◼ Restricted-range species

Most of the restricted-range species are typical of the montane evergreen forest. Some, however, such as the two hummingbirds (*Aglaeactis pamela* and *Metallura aeneocauda*) and the furnariids (*Cranioleuca albiceps*, *C. marcapatae*, *Schizoeaca harterti* and

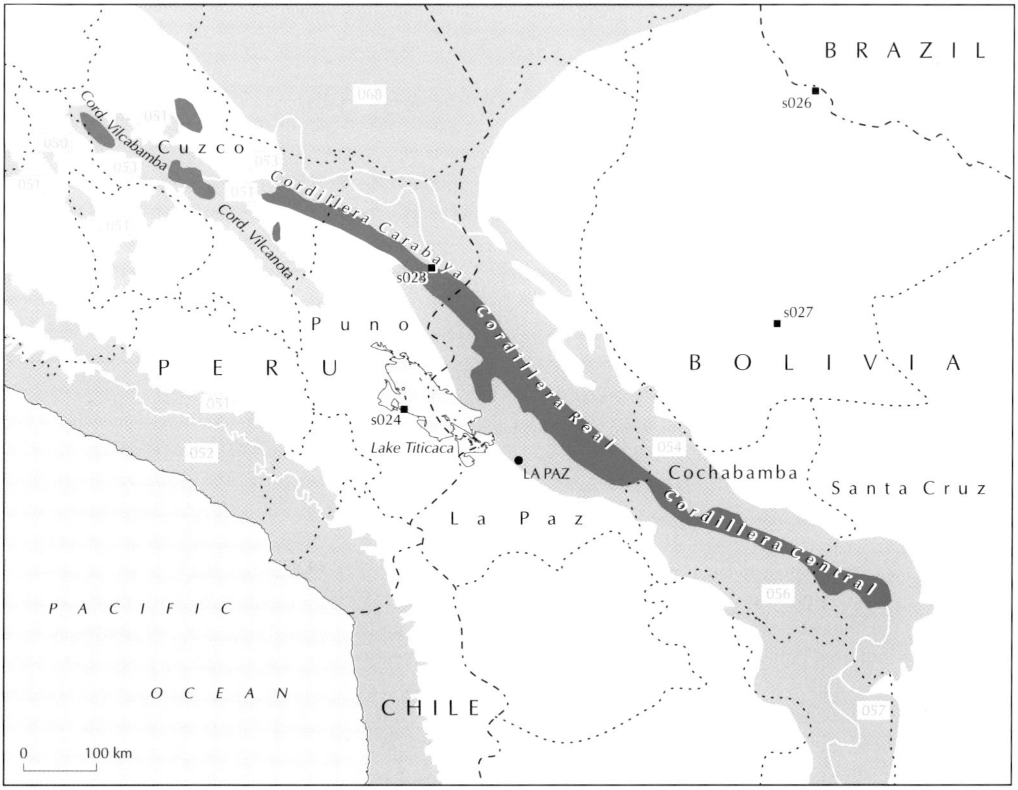

239

Status and habitat of restricted-range species

Species (ordered taxonomically)	Global status	Other EBAs (and SAs)	Altitude (m)	Habitat
Stripe-faced Wood-quail *Odontophorus balliviani*	lc	—	2,000–3,050	Montane evergreen forest
Black-winged Parrot *Hapalopsittaca melanotis*	lc	049	2,000–3,400	Montane evergreen forest
Black-hooded Sunbeam *Aglaeactis pamela*	lc	—	1,800–4,200	Semi-humid/humid montane scrub, elfin forest, rocky slopes
Scaled Metaltail *Metallura aeneocauda*	lc	—	2,800–3,600	Elfin forest, forest edge, scrub
Hooded Mountain-toucan *Andigena cucullata*	nt	—	2,500–3,300	Montane evergreen forest
Puna Thistletail *Schizoeaca helleri*	lc	—	2,800–3,600	Elfin forest near transition to páramo grassland, tangled undergrowth, bamboo thickets
Black-throated Thistletail *Schizoeaca harterti*	lc	—	2,900–3,400	Elfin forest near transition to páramo grassland, tangled undergrowth
Marcapata Spinetail *Cranioleuca marcapatae*	lc	—	2,700–3,400	Montane evergreen and elfin forest, bamboo thickets, humid forest edge, secondary growth
Light-crowned Spinetail *Cranioleuca albiceps*	lc	—	2,400–3,300	Montane evergreen forest, bamboo thickets, secondary growth
Red-and-white Antpitta *Grallaria erythroleuca*	lc	—	2,150–2,970	Montane evergreen and secondary forest, bamboo thickets
Rufous-faced Antpitta *Grallaria erythrotis*	lc	—	2,000–3,050	Montane evergreen forest, secondary growth
Diademed Tapaculo *Scytalopus schulenbergi* [1]	lc	—	2,975–3,400	Cloud forest, elfin forest, forest edge
Scimitar-winged Piha *Lipaugus uropygialis*	lc	—	1,800–2,575	Montane evergreen forest
Rufous-bellied Bush-tyrant *Myiotheretes fuscorufus*	nt	049	1,900–2,900	Montane evergreen forest, forest edge, adjacent secondary growth
Inca Wren *Thryothorus eisenmanni*	lc	—	1,800–3,400	Montane evergreen forest, forest edge, bamboo thickets
Orange-browed Hemispingus *Hemispingus calophrys*	lc	—	2,300–3,350	Montane evergreen and elfin forest, forest edge, secondary growth, bamboo thickets
Parodi's Hemispingus *Hemispingus parodii*	lc	—	2,750–3,500	Elfin forest near transition to páramo grassland, bamboo thickets
Golden-collared Tanager *Iridosornis jelskii*	lc	049	3,000–3,600	Elfin forest, forest edge, scrub, bamboo thickets
Yellow-scarfed Tanager *Iridosornis reinhardti*	lc	049	2,050–3,500	Montane evergreen and elfin forest, forest edge, scrub
Grey-bellied Flower-piercer *Diglossa carbonaria*	lc	056	2,100–4,300	Semi-humid/humid montane scrub, elfin forest, montane evergreen forest edge, secondary growth

Global status (see p. 679 for definitions)	EX Extinct EW Extinct in the Wild } with year of last record CR Critical EN Endangered VU Vulnerable } threatened species	cd Conservation Dependent nt Near Threatened lc Least Concern DD Data Deficient NE Not Evaluated	**Other EBAs (and SAs)** (see p. 65 for locations) **Notes**	Bracketed numbers are Secondary Areas. X Extinct in that EBA or SA. [1] New species (Whitney 1994).

S. helleri) are found mainly in the transition between elfin forest and páramo grassland and scrub that is prevalent at the highest elevations. The species differ in their distributional patterns: four are restricted to the Vilcabamba and Vilcanota, 11 occur in the Eastern Andes from Cuzco department (Peru) through to central Bolivia, and five are found throughout (see 'Distribution patterns' table, below).

■ Threats and conservation

Large tracts of forest are still present in this EBA but in some parts, most notably at lower altitudes, there is land clearance for subsistence agriculture and cash crops (coca, coffee, tea), and logging which is being intensified by colonization and roadbuilding (Dinerstein *et al.* 1995). None of the bird species, however, is currently considered threatened.

There are several protected areas in Peru and Bolivia that hold some of this EBA's habitat. Probably the most important are, in Peru, the Tambopata–Candamo Reserved Zone (14,800 km²), which includes Manu National Park and Manu Reserved Zone (a Biosphere Reserve and World Heritage Site), and, in Bolivia, Amboró National Park (1,800 km²), which holds most of the EBA's restricted-range species, and the newly created Madidi National Park and Integrated Management Area (19,000 km²), which includes land from peaks at 5,500 m down to lowland tropical rain forest and

Humid, often cloud-covered, montane forest characterizes the EBA. Fortunately, large tracts still remain untouched.

Distribution patterns of restricted-range species

Species (ordered geographically)	Vilcabamba	Vilconota	Cuzco to La Paz¹	Cochabamba to Santa Cruz	Other EBAs, SAs
Iridosornis reinhardti	●	–	–	–	◉
Grallaria erythroleuca	●	●	–	–	–
Thryothorus eisenmanni	●	●	–	–	–
Hemispingus parodii	●	●	–	–	–
Cranioleuca marcapatae	●	●	●	–	–
Odontophorus balliviani	●	–	●	●	–
Metallura aeneocauda	●	–	●	●	–
Myiotheretes fuscorufus	●	●	●	●	◉
Iridosornis jelskii	●	●	●	●	◉
Schizoeaca helleri	–	●	●	–	–
Lipaugus uropygialis	–	–	●	–	–
Hapalopsittaca melanotis	–	–	●	–	◉
Andigena cucullata	–	–	●	●	–
Scytalopus schulenbergi	–	–	●	●	–
Cranioleuca albiceps	–	–	●	●	–
Hemispingus calophrys	–	–	●	●	–
Aglaeactis pamela	–	–	–	●	–
Schizoeaca harterti	–	–	–	●	–
Grallaria erythrotis	–	–	–	●	–
Diglossa carbonaria	–	–	–	●	◉
Total	9	7	12	12	

● Present   ? Present?   Threatened spp. shown in **bold**   } see 'Status and habitat' table
○ Extinct?   R Reintroduced
X Extinct   I Introduced   Other EBAs, SAs

¹ From Cuzco department (Peru) to La Paz department (Bolvia); includes Carabaya mountains.

savanna (*World Birdwatch* 1995, 17 (4): 3), and so holds a significant tract of evergreen montane rain forest of the upper yungas (much of the park awaits survey but it is predicted to have the highest avian diversity of any protected area in the world; only three of the restricted-range birds of this EBA have been recorded so far, but a further 10 are expected to occur: Parker and Bailey 1991, Remsen and Parker 1995).

056 High Andes of Bolivia and Argentina

PRIORITY
CRITICAL

Key habitats *Polylepis* woodland, puna grassland, arid montane scrub, rock and boulder piles	Area 200,000 km²	Altitude 1,100–4,600 m

Countries Argentina, Bolivia, Peru

Main threats Major habitat loss (e.g. due to fuelwood collection, fire)

Biological importance ● ● ●
Current threat level ● ●

Restricted-range species	Threatened	Total
Confined to this EBA	7	16
Present also in other EBAs, SAs	2	5
Total	9	21

■ General characteristics

The area forming this EBA is the high Andes of south-east Peru through to northern Argentina, together with the region's arid intermontane valleys which lie mainly in Bolivia. North to south, the EBA runs from Aricoma in the Cordillera de Carabay in Puno department of extreme south-east Peru, through Bolivia along the eastern side of the Andes east of Lake Titicaca, and along the Cordilleras Real and

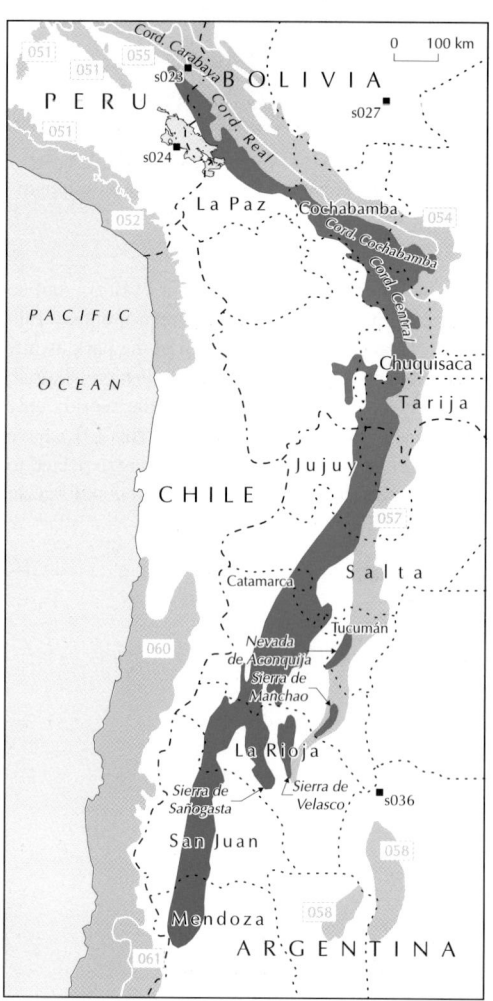

Cochabamba of the main Cordillera Oriental, then south along the Andes in northern Argentina through Jujuy, Tucumán, Salta, Catamarca, La Rioja, San Juan and Mendoza provinces. The EBA ranges in elevation from 1,100 m in the intermontane valleys to 4,600 m on the altiplano, and lies adjacent to the wet forests of the upper and lower yungas (EBAs 054, 055, 057). The Peruvian high Andes (EBA 051) to the north and west occupies similar altitude and climate zones.

The region tends to be dry at all altitudes and is cool and temperate in the high Andes (though there are occasional snowfalls and frosts) and warmer in the intermontane valleys. These differences result in a wide variety of vegetation types. Thus the high Andes part of the EBA conforms to the puna and pre-puna (transition) zones, the latter being between the puna and the humid temperate forest of the slopes. The puna zone is an open grassland without trees but with some low-lying scrub, and often including bare, rocky areas. The pre-puna zone is a complex mosaic of scrub dominated by tall columnar cacti with shrubs and small cacti forming the lower strata, areas of grassland with scattered trees, and open boggy grassland. Vegetation in the arid valleys consists mainly of arid scrub and columnar cacti. In semi-humid areas of the puna and pre-puna zones, and in the higher-altitude valleys, particularly along water-courses, there are patches of low-stature forest dominated by *Polylepis*.

■ Restricted-range species

Most of the restricted-range bird species are found in forested and scrub habitats within the puna and pre-puna zones, many of them occurring in *Polylepis*-dominated forest. A group of four restricted-range species (*Ara rubrogenys, Upucerthia harterti, Lophospingus griseocristatus* and *Oreopsar bolivianus*) is associated with the intermontane valleys: they occur mainly below 2,000 m, but—because their distributions vary and because other species from the higher Andes also range into these lower valleys, especially into the *Polylepis* forest—they are not considered to define a separate EBA; further information on the

Status and habitat of restricted-range species

Species (ordered taxonomically)	Global status	Other EBAs (and SAs)	Altitude (m)	Habitat
Bare-eyed Ground-dove *Metriopelia morenoi*	lc	—	2,000–4,000	Arid montane scrub with columnar cacti, montane grassland
Red-fronted Macaw *Ara rubrogenys*	EN	—	1,100–2,450	Arid deciduous open forest, scrub; feeds in agricultural land
Wedge-tailed Hillstar *Oreotrochilus adela*	nt	—	2,550–4,000	Arid montane scrub, *Polylepis* forest, disturbed habitats
Olivaceous Thornbill *Chalcostigma olivaceum*	lc	051	3,150–4,500	Grassland with composite scrub, *Polylepis–Ginoxys* forest edge
Bolivian Earthcreeper *Upucerthia harterti*	nt	—	1,450–2,960	Arid montane scrub
Royal Cinclodes *Cinclodes aricomae*[1]	CR	051	3,600–4,550	Semi-humid forest mainly of *Polylepis* with some *Gynoxys*, semi-humid/humid montane scrub
Maquis Canastero *Asthenes heterura*	VU	—	3,000–4,200	Arid montane scrub, open *Polylepis* forest
Berlepsch's Canastero *Asthenes berlepschi*	VU	—	2,700–3,700	Arid montane scrub, agricultural areas with scattered shrubs
Chestnut Canastero *Asthenes steinbachi*	VU	—	1,350–3,000	Arid montane scrub, dry slopes sparsely vegetated with shrubs and cacti
Line-fronted Canastero *Asthenes urubambensis*	nt	051	3,200–4,300	Montane grassland, *Polylepis* forest
Scribble-tailed Canastero *Asthenes maculicauda*	lc	—	3,000–4,300	Montane grassland, scrub, rocky slopes
Ash-breasted Tit-tyrant *Anairetes alpinus*	EN	051	3,700–4,500	*Polylepis* forest
Grey-crested Finch *Lophospingus griseocristatus*	lc	—	1,400–3,100	Arid montane and second-growth scrub, cultivated fields along watercourses
Short-tailed Finch *Idiopsar brachyurus*	lc	—	3,300–4,500	Boulder piles in montane grassland
Bolivian Warbling-finch *Poospiza boliviana*	lc	—	1,700–3,100	Montane scrub, open forest
Cochabamba Mountain-finch *Poospiza garleppi*	EN	—	3,000–3,800	*Polylepis* forest, semi-humid/humid montane scrub, agricultural land
Tucumán Mountain-finch *Poospiza baeri*	VU	—	2,000–3,000	Semi-humid/humid montane scrub, usually along stream gullies
Citron-headed Yellow-finch *Sicalis luteocephala*	nt	—	2,550–4,000	Arid montane scrub, grassland, agricultural land
Rufous-bellied Saltator *Saltator rufiventris*	VU	—	2,550–3,800	*Polylepis* forest, semi-humid/humid montane scrub, arid scrub, agricultural land
Grey-bellied Flower-piercer *Diglossa carbonaria*	lc	055	2,100–4,300	Semi-humid/humid montane scrub, elfin forest, montane evergreen forest edge, secondary growth
Bolivian Blackbird *Oreopsar bolivianus*	lc	—	1,800–3,200	Arid montane scrub, pasture/agricultural land, cacti, nests on cliffs

| **Global status** (see p. 679 for definitions) | EX Extinct EW Extinct in the Wild } with year of last record | CR Critical EN Endangered VU Vulnerable } threatened species | cd Conservation Dependent nt Near Threatened lc Least Concern DD Data Deficient NE Not Evaluated | **Other EBAs (and SAs)** (see p. 65 for locations) **Notes** | Bracketed numbers are Secondary Areas. × Extinct in that EBA or SA. [1] Taxonomy follows Fjeldså and Krabbe (1990) and Collar *et al.* (1992). |

habitats and distributions of these species could, however, change this assessment in due course.

Recent surveys have recorded new locations and extended the known distributions of several restricted-range species such as *Asthenes heterura*, *A. maculicauda*, *Idiopsar brachyurus* and *Saltator rufiventris* in Tarija department of Bolivia (Fjeldså and Mayer 1996) and *Oreotrochilus adela*, *A. heterura*, *Poospiza boliviana* and *Sicalis luteocephala* in Argentina (Pearman 1989, Moschione and San Cristóbal 1993, Alvarez and Blendinger 1995). The Bolivian and Argentine parts of this EBA were

Distribution patterns of restricted-range species

Species (ordered geographically)	Cordillera Carabaya	Cordillera Real	Valleys of Cord. Real, esp. La Paz prov.	Cord. Cochabamba	Cordillera Central	Valleys of N.Chuquisaca and Cochabamba	Andes in Chuquisaca	Andes in Tarija	Andes in Jujuy	Andes from Salta to La Rioja	Nevada de Aconquija	Andes in Mendoza	Other EBAs, SAs
Asthenes urubambensis	•	•	—	•	—	—	—	—	—	—	—	—	•
Asthenes maculicauda	•	•	?	•	—	—	—	•	—	—	•	—	—
Idiopsar brachyurus	•	•	—	•	•	?	?	•	•	•	•	—	—
Asthenes berlepschi	—	•	—	—	—	—	—	—	—	—	—	—	•
Chalcostigma olivaceum	—	•	—	—	—	—	—	—	—	—	—	—	•
Cinclodes aricomae	—	•	—	—	—	—	—	—	—	—	—	—	•
Anairetes alpinus	—	•	—	—	—	—	—	—	—	—	—	—	•
Diglossa carbonaria	—	•	•	•	•	•	—	—	•	—	—	—	•
Poospiza boliviana	—	?	•	•	?	•	•	•	•	—	—	—	—
Asthenes heterura	—	•	—	•	—	•	•	•	•	—	—	—	—
Saltator rufiventris	—	•	—	?	•	•	•	•	•	•	—	—	—
Lophospingus griseocristatus	—	•	•	•	•	•	•	•	•	•	—	—	•
Poospiza garleppi	—	—	•	•	•	—	—	—	—	—	—	—	—
Upucerthia harterti	—	—	•	—	•	—	—	—	—	—	—	—	—
Sicalis luteocephala	—	—	•	—	•	•	?	•	•	—	—	—	—
Ara rubrogenys	—	—	—	•	—	•	—	—	—	—	—	—	—
Oreopsar bolivianus	—	—	—	•	•	•	—	—	—	—	—	—	—
Oreotrochilus adela	—	—	—	•	•	•	•	—	•	—	—	—	—
Metriopelia morenoi	—	—	—	—	—	—	—	—	—	•	•	—	—
Poospiza baeri	—	—	—	—	—	—	—	—	—	•	•	—	—
Asthenes steinbachi	—	—	—	—	—	—	—	—	—	•	•	•	—
Total	3	11	6	11	6	10	5	7	8	6	6	1	

• Present	? Present?	Threatened spp. shown in **bold**	see 'Status and habitat' table
O Extinct?	R Reintroduced		
X Extinct	I Introduced	Other EBAs, SAs	

treated separately in the original EBA analysis (ICBP 1992), but these Argentine records, new for the country, have meant that several of the species formerly believed to be restricted to the high Andes and intermontane valleys of Bolivia actually overlap with species endemic to northern Argentina's puna and pre-puna zones; these EBAs have thus now been combined.

Four species (*Chalcostigma olivaceum*, *Cinclodes aricomae*, *Asthenes urubambensis* and *Anairetes alpinus*) have only small parts of their ranges in the present EBA and are more widely distributed in the High Peruvian Andes (EBA 051). Three species (*Metriopelia morenoi*, *Asthenes steinbachi* and *Poospiza baeri*) are found only within the Argentine part of the EBA. *Diglossa carbonaria* is shared with

Polylepis forest in the Cordillera Cochabamba is the critical habitat for several of the restricted-range species.

Polylepis forests have suffered extensively from clearance for firewood and agriculture. Here, potato fields have been established under *Polylepis racemosa*, thereby retaining some natural habitat.

T. Hjarsen

the Bolivian and Peruvian upper yungas (EBA 055) because, as well as being found in arid montane scrub, it occurs in humid habitats such as the elfin forest which is associated with the yungas EBA.

■ Threats and conservation

The puna zone of Peru, Bolivia, Argentina, and Chile has been extensively altered for agriculture and is degraded in many areas through the grazing of domestic livestock, burning and the collection of firewood (Dinerstein *et al.* 1995). Settlement and agricultural conversion have already had dramatic effects on the EBA, and further expansion seriously threatens remaining fragments of habitat. The destruction of *Polylepis* forest through clearance for cultivation, firewood-collection and burning for pasture is a particularly serious threat to many of the restricted-range birds. Nine of them are considered threatened, and in the case of four (*Cinclodes aricomae, Anairetes alpinus, Poospiza garleppi* and *Saltator rufiventris*) this is because of destruction of their *Polylepis* forest habitat. *A. berlepschi* is threatened because of its tiny range (near Nevado Illampu). *Ara rubrogenys*, which is found in the arid foothills, has declined in its tiny range in Bolivia owing to capture for the cage-bird trade, persecution as a pest in peanut and maize fields, and loss of trees. *Poospiza baeri* is threatened because the grassland which surrounds its tiny range is susceptible to fire, which could in turn reach the species' specialized habitat in the ravines. *Asthenes steinbachi* appears to have been largely extirpated by habitat loss, remaining common only in a few scattered localities mainly in the southern part of its range, especially in Mendoza.

Other more-widespread threatened species (all classified as Vulnerable) are found within the EBA, including Andean Flamingo *Phoenicopterus andinus*, Puna Flamingo *P. jamesi*, Horned Coot *Fulica cornuta* and White-tailed Shrike-tyrant *Agriornis andicola*.

Wege and Long (1995) list nine Key Areas in Bolivia for the threatened species found in this EBA, but only two of these have any protection: a small population of *Ara rubrogenys* occurred (at least formerly) on the edge of Amboró National Park (1,800 km²), and both *Poospiza garleppi* and *Saltator rufiventris* have been seen in Tunari National Park (60 km²). However, although none of the restricted-range species has yet been recorded from Bolivia's Madidi National Park and Integrated Management Area (19,000 km²), Remsen and Parker (1995) predict that eight will be found there when more biological surveys are carried out.

There are a number of key protected areas in Argentina overlapping with the EBA, several of which are known to hold the restricted-range species. These include El Leoncito Strict Nature Reserve (740 km²), Calilegua National Park (760 km²), Pozuelos Biosphere Reserve (3,640 km²) and Potrero de Yala Provincial Park (43 km²). Importantly, there is a proposal to gazette most of the Sierra de Aconquija within the Campo de los Alisos National Park (2,500 km²) (Halloy *et al.* 1994) which would secure protection for several of the restricted-range species found only in the Argentine part of this EBA (as well as most species in the adjacent Argentine and Bolivian yungas, EBA 057).

057 Argentine and south Bolivian yungas

PRIORITY URGENT

Key habitats Montane evergreen forest

Main threats Moderate habitat loss (e.g. due to logging, agricultural expansion)

Biological importance ● ● ●
Current threat level ● ● ●

Area 60,000 km²   **Altitude** 800–3,100 m

Countries Argentina, Bolivia

Restricted-range species	Threatened	Total
Confined to this EBA	1	8
Present also in other EBAs, SAs	0	1
Total	1	9

■ General characteristics

The yungas region essentially refers to the eastern slope of the Andes of extreme south-east Peru, Bolivia and Argentina. This particular EBA extends from Chuquisaca department of Bolivia, south through

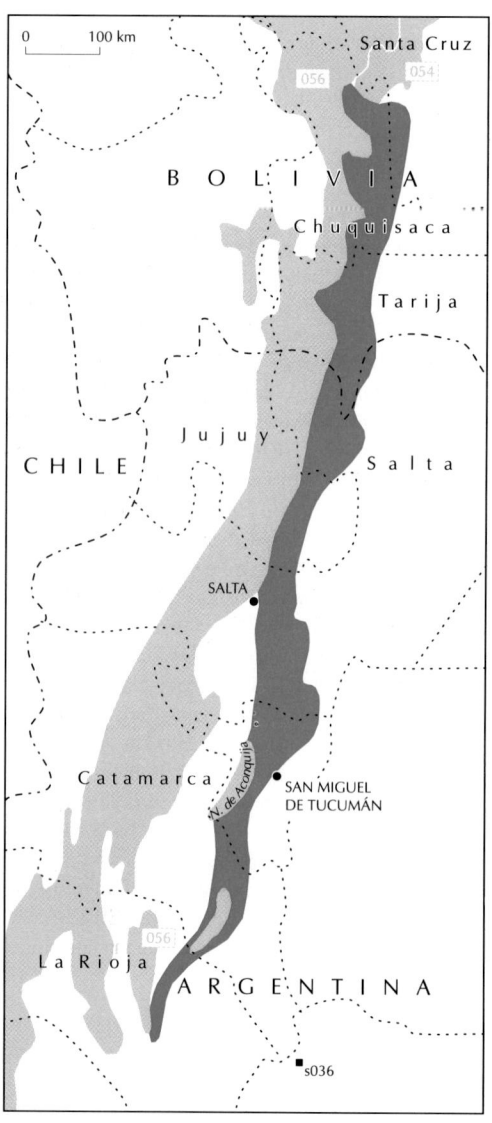

Tarija and the Argentine provinces of Jujuy, Salta, Tucumán, Catamarca and La Rioja. The altitude ranges from 800 m in the foothills up to 2,500 m, but sometimes reaches as high as 3,100 m. The northern end of the EBA is on the southern slope of the Cordillera Oriental of Bolivia, which branches out from the main Andean range running west to east. The northern slope of the Cordillera Oriental abuts the southern end of the Bolivian and Peruvian lower yungas (EBA 054). Adjacent to this EBA is the bottom end of the southern High Andes of Bolivia and Argentina (EBA 056 in part).

The climate is wet and humid with over 2,500 mm of rain annually brought along northerly trade winds. Correspondingly the vegetation consists of various evergreen forest formations, all of them with canopy heights not usually over 15 m. At higher altitudes, mainly between 1,200 m and 2,500 m, the forest is dominated by Andean alder *Alnus acuminata*, *Podocarpus* or pines. At lower altitudes these species are admixed with other trees, especially from the families Lauraceae and Myrtaceae.

■ Restricted-range species

The restricted-range bird species occur largely in the humid forests of the EBA, of which alder forest is especially important for *Amazona tucumana* and *Cinclus schulzi*, the latter being found always along fast-flowing streams in these forests. *Atlapetes citrinellus* shows the broadest habitat requirements, being found in hedgerows in agricultural areas, dense scrub and burnt forest as well as in coniferous and humid forests. *C. schulzi* winters at lower altitudes (to 800 m), and *A. tucumana* in other forests as low as 300 m. *Elaenia strepera* is an austral migrant, breeding only in this EBA and apparently wintering 3,000 km to the north in Venezuela (Marantz and Remsen 1991).

■ Threats and conservation

It has been estimated that as much as 60% of the forest in the yungas of Argentina has disappeared (Vervoorst 1979). There are no estimates for the Bolivian part of the EBA, but recent ornithological

Status and habitat of restricted-range species

Species (ordered taxonomically)	Global status	Other EBAs (and SAs)	Altitude (m)	Habitat
Red-faced Guan *Penelope dabbenei*	lc	—	800–2,700	Montane evergreen forest, esp. *Podocarpus*-dominated forests.
Tucumán Amazon *Amazona tucumana*	lc	—	1,750–3,000	Montane evergreen, esp. alder-dominated forest
Rothschild's Swift *Cypseloides rothschildi*	nt	—	800–2,000	Forest and open country
Blue-capped Puffleg *Eriocnemis glaucopoides*	lc	—	1,500–2,900	Secondary and montane evergreen forest, humid forest edge, scrub
White-throated Antpitta *Grallaria albigula*	lc	054	800–2,500	Montane evergreen forest, scrub
White-browed Tapaculo *Scytalopus superciliaris*	lc	—	1,800–2,800	Montane evergreen forest, alder scrub along streams
Slaty Elaenia *Elaenia strepera*	lc	—	500–2,000	Montane evergreen forest edge, esp. bushes or trees along streams in valleys
Rufous-throated Dipper *Cinclus schulzi*	VU	—	1,500–2,500	Fast-flowing mountain streams and rivers, bordered with alder
Yellow-striped Brush-finch *Atlapetes citrinellus*	lc	—	1,200–3,100	Montane evergreen forest edge, semi-humid/humid montane scrub, hedgerows in agricultural areas

Global status (see p. 679 for definitions)	EX EW	Extinct Extinct in the Wild	} with year of last record	CR EN VU	Critical Endangered Vulnerable	} threatened species	cd nt lc	Conservation Dependent Near Threatened Least Concern	DD NE	Data Deficient Not Evaluated

Other EBAs (and SAs) (see p. 65 for locations): bracketed numbers are Secondary Areas; [x] extinct in that EBA or SA.

surveys (e.g. Fjeldså and Mayer 1996, Tyler and Tyler 1996) have noted large areas of degraded land within the humid yungas—though there are also extensive forests remaining such as a 1,300 km² tract between the Pilcamayo and Pilaya rivers in Montes Chapeados. Natural forests in Argentina have disappeared mainly through logging of valuable woods, conversion for agriculture, and plantations of exotic pines *Pinus*; road-building, human colonization and uncontrolled tourism have further increased habitat destruction (WWF/IUCN 1997).

The alder forest zone is especially important for the threatened *Cinclus schulzi*; its riverine habitat is endangered by reservoir construction, hydroelectric and irrigation schemes, eutrophication, deforestation and stock-grazing (Tyler and Tyler 1996).

There are a number of protected areas overlapping with the EBA, several of which are known to hold the restricted-range birds. These include Tariquía National Reserve (2,469 km²) in Bolivia, and Calilegua National Park (760 km²), Baritú National Park (724 km²), El Rey National Park (442 km²) and Potrero de Yala Provincial Park (43 km²) in Argentina. Importantly, there is a proposal currently being considered by Tucumán provincial government in Argentina to create the Campo de los Alisos National Park (2,500 km²), which would cover much of the Sierra de Aconquija (Halloy *et al.* 1994). This national park would secure protection for populations of all the restricted-range species of this EBA (as well as several species from the High Andes of Bolivia and Argentina, EBA 056).

058 Sierras Centrales of Argentina

PRIORITY
HIGH

Key habitats Grassland, *Polylepis* woodland

Main threats Moderate habitat loss (e.g. due to overgrazing)

Biological importance ● ● ●
Current threat level ● ● ●

Area 22,000 km²   **Altitude** 1,500–2,800 m

Countries Argentina

Restricted-range species	Threatened	Total
Confined to this EBA	0	2
Present also in other EBAs, SAs	0	0
Total	0	2

■ General characteristics

The Sierras Centrales are a small group of mountain ranges located c.400 km east of the Andean chain in the provinces of Córdoba and San Luis of central Argentina, and are among a number of ranges, collectively named the Sierras Pampeanas, which are isolated from each other and from the Andes by dry lowlands. The Sierras Centrales are the easternmost of the Sierras Pampeanas and include the contiguous Sierra Grande, Pampa de Achala and Sierra de Comechingones, and, lying c.75 km west of them, the Sierra de San Luis. Most of the land is under 2,000 m but Cerro Champaqui in the Sierra de Comechingones rises to 2,880 m. There are plain-like areas, such as the Pampa de Achala, lying within the mountains. The landscape of this EBA is charac-terized by bunchgrass with scattered rocks, pockets

of *Polylepis australis* woodland and numerous streams.

■ Restricted-range species

The two endemic species are both found in the grassy and rocky areas with patches of *Polylepis australis* woodland, usually favouring sites near water. *Cinclodes olrogi* is at least in part an altitudinal migrant, being found above 1,500 m when breeding, but down to 1,000 m in winter. In winter *C. comechingones* also moves down from its breeding area (above 1,600 m) to 1,000 m, and is then found outside the Sierras Centrales in the lowlands of eastern Tucumán, northern Córdoba, Santiago del Estero and Formosa (Fjeldså and Krabbe 1990, M. Nores *in litt.* 1996).

This EBA is rich in endemic subspecies, at least

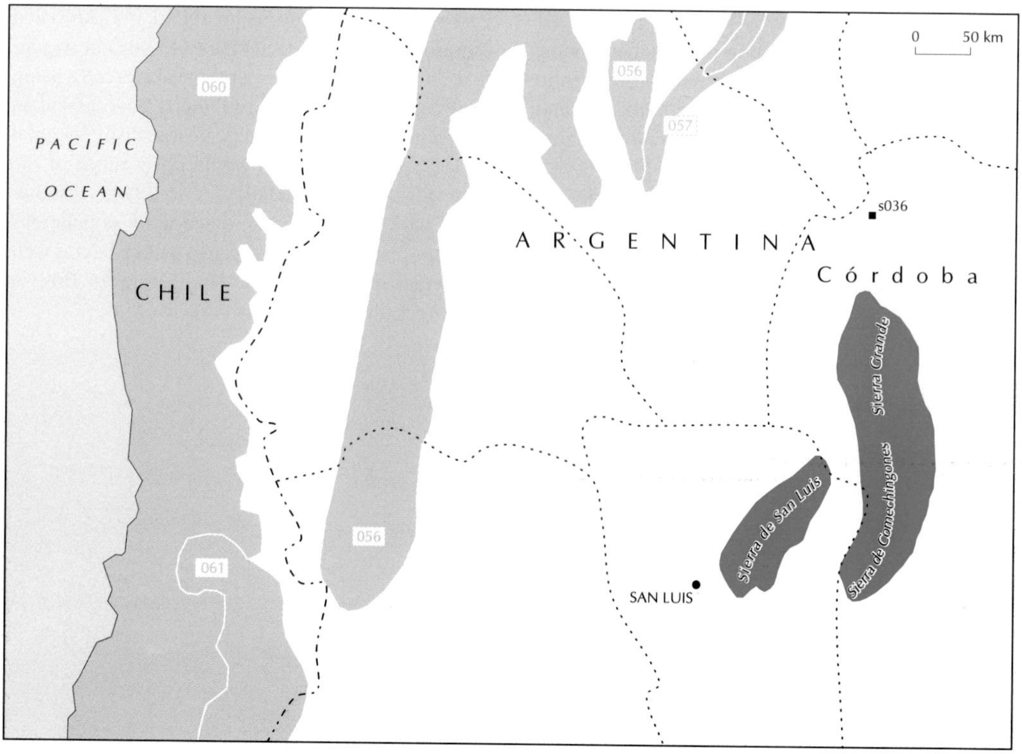

PACIFIC OCEAN

CHILE

ARGENTINA

Córdoba

s036

Sierra Grande

Sierra de Comechingones

Sierra de San Luis

SAN LUIS

0   50 km

060

056

057

056

061

Status and habitat of restricted-range species

Species (ordered taxonomically)	Global status	Other EBAs (and SAs)	Altitude (m)	Habitat
Córdoba Cinclodes *Cinclodes comechingonus*	lc	—	1,600–2,800	Grassland, small patches of *Polylepis*, usually near water, possibly arid montane scrub
Olrog's Cinclodes *Cinclodes olrogi*	lc	—	1,500–2,400	Open grassy and rocky areas near streams, sandy or stony edges of streams and lakes

Global status (see p. 679 for definitions)	EX Extinct EW Extinct in the Wild	with year of last record	CR Critical EN Endangered VU Vulnerable	threatened species	cd Conservation Dependent nt Near Threatened lc Least Concern	DD Data Deficient NE Not Evaluated

Other EBAs (and SAs) (see p. 65 for locations): bracketed numbers are Secondary Areas; ˣ extinct in that EBA or SA.

12 having been described (J. C. Chebez *in litt.* 1992; see also Nores and Yzurieta 1983). Several authors consider both of the endemic *Cinclodes* (treated here as full species) to be well marked subspecies: *comechingonus* would thus be considered a race of Bar-winged Cinclodes *C. fuscus* and *olrogi* a race of Grey-flanked Cinclodes *C. oustaleti* (Olrog 1979) or possibly of *C. fuscus* (Nores 1986). However, Sibley and Monroe (1990, 1993) follow Vuilleumier and Mayr (1987) who tentatively treat *olrogi* as an allospecies of *oustaleti* but do acknowledge that a thorough study of *Cinclodes* is needed in the Sierras Pampeanas and adjacent Andes.

■ Threats and conservation

The area is not greatly threatened and has not been subjected to much human disturbance (Nores 1995). The main problem is overgrazing but apparently this has not affected the endemic taxa up to now, and both are common within the EBA. There is a project to create the Quebrada del Condorito National Park in Sierra Grande (M. Nores *in litt.* 1996).

059 Juan Fernández Islands

PRIORITY
CRITICAL

Key habitats Evergreen forest, tree-fern forest, introduced scrub

Main threats Severe habitat loss (e.g. due to overgrazing), introduced species

Biological importance ● ● ●
Current threat level ● ● ●

Area 180 km² **Altitude** 0–1,300 m

Countries Chile

Restricted-range species	Threatened	Total
Confined to this EBA	2	3
Present also in other EBAs, SAs	0	0
Total	2	3

■ General characteristics

The Juan Fernández archipelago comprises three principal islands of volcanic origin, located some 680–800 km west of continental Chile, to which it belongs politically. Isla Robinson Crusoe (or Más á Tierra, 93 km²) and Isla Alejandro Selkirk (Más á Fuera, 85 km²) are the two islands with endemic birds (and therefore constitute this EBA), with none occurring on the third main island, Santa Clara. Land rises to 915 m at the dormant El Yunque on Robinson Crusoe and to 1,380 m at Los Inocentes on Alejandro Selkirk.

'Luna' woodland *Nothomyrica fernandeziana* on Isla Robinson Crusoe. This tree is one of the numerous endemic plant species within the EBA.

The climate is temperate and the islands were originally covered with forests of diverse origin. There are nearly 100 species of endemic flowering plant, including a monotypic family (the Lactor-idaceae), several gigantic forms (e.g. the rhubarb *Gunnera peltata*), and numerous species of 'cabbage trees' of the endemic genus *Dendroseris*. Nineteen of the 54 ferns, including another monotypic family (Thrysopteridaceae), are endemic to the archipelago (Bourne *et al.* 1992). The native forest of Robinson Crusoe consists of evergreen trees dominated by *Nothomyrica fernandeziana, Myrceugenia fernandeziana, Fagara mayu* and *Drimys confertifolia* with a luxuriant understorey of ferns and epiphytes. The main native vegetation on Alejandro Selkirk is a tree-fern forest of *Dicksonia externa* on the wetter south-western part and *Myrceugenia schulzei* woodland on the higher land around Los Inocentes.

■ Restricted-range species

Sephanoides fernandensis is a bird of forest on both Robinson Crusoe (nominate race) and Alejandro Selkirk (race *leyboldi*), but is believed extinct on the latter island where it has not been recorded since 1908 (Brooke 1987, Meza 1989). *Aphrastura masa-fuerae* is confined to the *Dicksonia externa* fern-forests of Alejandro Selkirk (Brooke 1988, Hahn and Römer 1996), and *Anairetes fernandezianus* is found in all the scrub and remaining forested habitats of Robinson Crusoe.

Two species of seabird, Juan Fernández Petrel *Pterodroma externa* and Stejneger's Petrel *P. longirostris*, are endemic breeders to Isla Alejandro Selkirk.

■ Threats and conservation

The flora and fauna of the Juan Fernández Islands have declined drastically owing to the effects of two waves of introduced animals: goats, rats, cats and

0   25 km

J u a n   F e r n á n d e z   I s l a n d s

CHILE

Robinson Crusoe

Alejandro Selkirk

Santa Clara

Status and habitat of restricted-range species

Species (ordered taxonomically)	Global status	Other EBAs (and SAs)	Altitude (m)	Habitat
Juan Fernández Firecrown *Sephanoides fernandensis*	CR	—	0–800	Native and introduced forest and scrub
Masafuera Rayadito *Aphrastura masafuerae*	VU	—	600–1,300	Dense, humid tree-fern forest and scrub dominated by *Dicksonia* ferns
Juan Fernández Tit-tyrant *Anairetes fernandezianus*	lc	—	0–900	Forest and scrub, inc. those with natural, disturbed and exotic vegetation

Global status (see p. 679 for definitions)	EX Extinct EW Extinct in the Wild	} with year of last record	CR Critical EN Endangered VU Vulnerable	} threatened species	cd Conservation Dependent nt Near Threatened lc Least Concern	DD Data Deficient NE Not Evaluated

Other EBAs (and SAs) (see p. 65 for locations): bracketed numbers are Secondary Areas; [x] extinct in that EBA or SA.

Cumberland Bay, on Isla Robinson Crusoe. Near-total clearance of native forest from the lower slopes, compounded by the effects of introduced herbivores and invasive plants, has resulted in only 10% of the island still supporting natural vegetation.

M. de L. Brooke

dogs introduced by the first colonists in the 1600s (though the dogs died out in the early 1800s), and then cattle, sheep, rabbits *Oryctolagus cuniculus* and coatis *Nasua nasua* introduced in the 1800s. The native flora has also been displaced by introduced plants, especially the shrub *Aristotelia chilensis*, bramble *Rubus ulmifolius* and the herb *Acaena argentea* (Bourne *et al.* 1992).

Much of the native forest has been cleared below an altitude of 500 m on both islands, and on Robinson Crusoe introduced species such as bramble provide the only vegetation cover. It is estimated that only 10% (5 km²) of the island is covered with natural vegetation and c.46% has suffered erosion (Hulm 1995).

Sephanoides fernandensis and *Aphrastura masafuerae* are both considered threatened. Summer numbers of *S. fernandensis* have been estimated at up to 800 birds, falling to 440 or so in winter, but there is also a long-term decline related to loss and degrada-

tion of natural vegetation, increased interspecific competition from Green-backed Firecrown *S. sephanoides* (as a result of that species' greater use of invasive exotic plants) and predation by introduced animals such as rats and coatis (Meza 1989, Collar *et al.* 1992). The population of *A. masafuerae* was estimated at c. 500 birds in 1986 (Brooke 1988).

The islands are very important for seabirds (see 'Restricted-range species', above), with six species breeding, including the threatened Defilippe's Petrel *Pterodroma defilippiana* and Pink-footed Shearwater *Puffinus creatopus* (both classified as Vulnerable).

The entire archipelago, except San Juan Bautista village on Isla Robinson Crusoe, was designated a national park in 1935, and then a Biosphere Reserve in 1977. The Chilean government proposed a US$2.5 million restoration programme in 1995, and the islands have been nominated for World Heritage listing (Hulm 1995).

060 Central Chile

PRIORITY
URGENT

| Key habitats | Scrub, sclerophyllous forest |
| Main threats | Major habitat loss (e.g. due to agricultural conversion, logging, fire) |

Area 160,000 km² **Altitude** 0–2,400 m

Countries Chile

Biological importance ● ● ●
Current threat level ● ● ●

Restricted-range species	Threatened	Total
Confined to this EBA	0	7
Present also in other EBAs, SAs	0	1
Total	0	8

■ General characteristics

This EBA is centred on one of the few areas of the world that has a Mediterranean climate, characterized by modest annual precipitation (totalling less than 800 mm, of which 90% falls in winter), warm

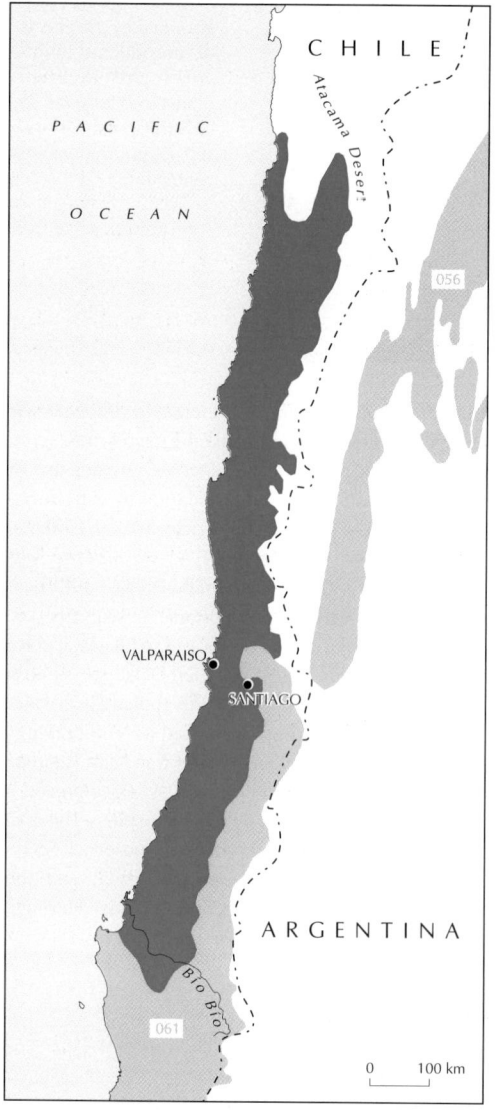

S. N. G. Howell and S. Webb

The matorral habitat in coastal central Chile is a well-known floristic hotspot with a high percentage of plants endemic to the region.

summers and cool winters when frosts are rare. The EBA follows the Pacific coast from Quebrada Paposa and Antofagasta provinces in Chile, south to around the Bío Bío river, and inland to the lower slopes of the Andes. The northern end of the EBA is formed by the southern boundary of the Atacama desert, where the climate is arid (annual rainfall less than 25 mm), and the southern end is the northern boundary of the Chilean temperate forests (EBA 061), where there is a marked increase in summer rainfall.

The vegetation is essentially scrub matorral and semi-arid grassland, but there are also hard-leaf (sclerophyllous) forests located in the more humid southern end of the EBA, mainly in the coastal hills south of Valparaiso in Maule, Ñuble, and Concepción provinces, and in the Andean foothills in Santiago province. There is high vegetational diversity, more than 56% of Chile's plant species being present in an

Status and habitat of restricted-range species

Species (ordered taxonomically)	Global status	Other EBAs (and SAs)	Altitude (m)	Habitat
Chilean Tinamou *Nothoprocta perdicaria*	lc	—	400–2,000	Arid scrub, semi-arid grasslands and wheat fields
Crag Chilia *Chilia melanura*	lc	—	1,400–2,400	Arid montane scrub, dry rocky areas
Dusky-tailed Canastero *Asthenes humicola*	lc	—	0–1,200	Arid montane and lowland scrub, semi-arid thorn scrub, thickets
Chestnut-throated Huet-huet *Pteroptochos castaneus*[1]	lc	—	0–1,500	Bamboo understorey within humid to semi-arid sclerophyllous forest and secondary growth
Moustached Turca *Pteroptochos megapodius*	lc	—	0–2,300	Arid montane, arid lowland and humid scrub, bamboo thickets
White-throated Tapaculo *Scelorchilus albicollis*	lc	—	0–1,600	Arid lowland and montane scrub, rocky slopes
Ochre-flanked Tapaculo *Eugralla paradoxa*	lc	061	0–1,000	Sclerophyllous forest, humid scrub, bamboo thickets
Chilean Mockingbird *Mimus thenca*	lc	—	0–700	Open arid lowland and second-growth scrub of slopes and hills

Global status (see p. 679 for definitions): EX Extinct, EW Extinct in the Wild } with year of last record; CR Critical, EN Endangered, VU Vulnerable } threatened species; cd Conservation Dependent, nt Near Threatened, lc Least Concern, DD Data Deficient, NE Not Evaluated

Other EBAs (and SAs) (see p. 65 for locations): Bracketed numbers are Secondary Areas. [X] Extinct in that EBA or SA.

Notes: [1] Taxonomy follows Howell and Webb (1995b).

area which comprises only 6% of the national territory; more than 2,900 species have been recorded, at least 50% being endemic (Myers 1990).

Restricted-range species

The majority of the restricted-range birds are found, through a wide range of altitudes, in arid scrub lying among rocky slopes. However, *Pteroptochos castaneus* is confined to the sclerophyllous forest in the southern part of the EBA, often favouring areas with a bamboo understorey. *P. castaneus* was listed as a subspecies of Black-throated Huet-huet *P. tarnii* by Sibley and Monroe (1990, 1993), but striking differences in plumage and consistent differences in song and call indicate that it should be considered a full species (Howell and Webb 1995b). *Eugralla paradoxa* is the only species shared with another EBA; it is principally a species of the Chilean

White-throated Tapaculo *Scelorchilus albicollis* is one restricted-range species which is common in remaining habitat.

temperate forests (EBA 061), but also occurs in the sclerophyllous forest of central Chile. Most of the species confined to the EBA are not found south of the Bío Bío river, but *Nothoprocta pedicaria* and *Mimus thenca* extend beyond it where there are grassy and shrubby habitats. Additionally, Chilean Pigeon *Columba araucana* and Slender-billed Parrot *Enicognathus leptorhynchus*, two restricted-range species of the Chilean temperate forests (EBA 061), are found in this EBA as wintering birds.

Threats and conservation

Scrub and grassland habitats, particularly in the lowlands, are threatened by conversion to agriculture and pasture, and by development, frequent anthropogenic fires, exotic species and grazing, while the forest is threatened by intensive logging, timber plantations and firewood collection. Only a third of the original 140,000 km² of Mediterranean-type habitat remains (Myers 1990, Dinerstein *et al.* 1995). The region is the most densely inhabited part of Chile, holding over half the country's human population, and continued habitat destruction is likely as the rate of population growth is 1.7% per year (Myers 1990).

Nevertheless, the restricted-range species are considered to be common in remaining habitat—except for *Nothoprocta perdicaria* which is scarce in the north of its range owing to hunting (Fjeldså and Krabbe 1990). This contrasts markedly with the plants, of which 580 species are already characterized as rare or threatened (Myers 1990). There are few protected areas in the EBA, especially in comparison to adjacent areas in the Andes.

061 Chilean temperate forests

PRIORITY HIGH

Key habitats Temperate forest

Main threats Major habitat loss (e.g. due to commercial logging)

Biological importance ● ● ○
Current threat level ● ○ ○

Area 230,000 km² **Altitude** 0–1,500 m

Countries Argentina, Chile

Restricted-range species	Threatened	Total
Confined to this EBA	0	4
Present also in other EBAs, SAs	0	1
Total	0	5

■ General characteristics

This EBA embraces the temperate forest zone of southern South America, mainly in southern Chile but also in extreme western Argentina. The northern limits of these forests are at the Bío Bío river on the Pacific coast and further inland north along the Andes, the boundary marking the beginning of an extensive region characterized by a Mediterranean

S. N. G. Howell and S. Webb

Temperate *Nothofagus* forest—the characteristic habitat of this EBA—in Nahuel Buta National Park.

climate of hot, dry summers and wetter, mild winters (see EBA 060). In this EBA there is c.2,000 mm of rainfall annually and 40 days of rain during the summer in the central part at Puerto Montt (Stone 1992).

Immediately south of the Bío Bío river, and south to Valdivia, *Nothofagus* forest (comprising deciduous species such as *N. obliqua* and *N. procera*) is dominant, and further inland on the Andean slopes at this latitude the forest is dominated by *Araucaria araucana*, with also some *Nothofagus* and *Podocarpus* species. South of Valdivia a wetter, more luxuriant and species-rich forest persists (often referred to as the Valdivian rain forest) supporting evergreen trees (principal genera being *Libocedrus*, *Fitzroya*,

Status and habitat of restricted-range species

Species (ordered taxonomically)	Global status	Other EBAs (and SAs)	Altitude (m)	Habitat
Chilean Pigeon *Columba araucana*[1]	nt	—	0–1,000	Southern temperate forest, bamboo thickets, particularly associated with *Araucaria araucana* trees
Slender-billed Parakeet *Enicognathus leptorhynchus*[1]	nt	—	0–540	Southern temperate forest, open pastureland, agricultural land
Black-throated Huet-huet *Pteroptochos tarnii*[2]	lc	—	0–1,500	Boulder- and log-strewn areas within *Nothofagus* forest, southern temperate forest
Chucao Tapaculo *Scelorchilus rubecula*	lc	—	0–1,500	Southern temperate (esp. *Nothofagus*) forest, bamboo thickets
Ochre-flanked Tapaculo *Eugralla paradoxa*	lc	060	0–1000	Southern temperate forest, humid scrub, bamboo thickets

Global status (see p. 679 for definitions)	EX Extinct EW Extinct in the Wild } with year of last record	cd Conservation Dependent	**Other EBAs (and SAs)** (see p. 65 for locations)	Bracketed numbers are Secondary Areas. X Extinct in that EBA or SA.
	CR Critical EN Endangered VU Vulnerable } threatened species	nt Near Threatened lc Least Concern DD Data Deficient NE Not Evaluated	**Notes**	[1] Winters partly outside the EBA in Central Chile (EBA 060). [2] Taxonomy follows Howell and Webb (1995b).

Aextoxicon, Laurelia, Nothofagus and *Drymys*), some as tall as 50 m and laden with epiphytes and lianas (Stone 1992), and some estimated to be 4,000 years old. Further south still, cold deciduous forests of *Nothofagus* and evergreen swamp forests are the dominant habitat (Dinerstein *et al.* 1995).

■ Restricted-range species

All the restricted-range species are forest-dwellers, many apparently occurring in secondary forest and forests fragmented among cultivation. *Columba araucana, Enicognathus leptorhynchus* and *Eugralla paradoxa* do not occur as far south as *Pteroptochos tarnii* and *Scelorchilus rubecula*; in fact *E. paradoxa* is shared with Central Chile (EBA 060), also occurring in the semi-humid sclerophyllous forests in the southern part of that EBA. Both *C. araucana* and *E. leptorhynchus* wander widely north into the Central Chilean region outside the breeding season and also occur in cultivated areas, where in certain parts they are considered to be agricultural pests.

■ Threats and conservation

Intensive logging and timber plantations are especially severe threats to the EBA, and other threats include firewood-gathering and, in the southern part of the EBA, overgrazing from domestic animals and introduced rabbits (Dinerstein *et al.* 1995). Large areas of old-growth forest have already been lost to logging concessions, and the industry is still active.

S. N. G. Howell and S. Webb

Deforestation is a severe threat to large areas of the EBA. These *Nothofagus* forests have been cleared for cattle-grazing.

However, none of the restricted-range species is currently considered threatened, although two are judged to be Near Threatened. *Columba araucana* populations were decimated in the 1950s by an epidemic of Newcastle disease (Johnson 1967), but the species has recovered well and is again fairly common.

There are a high number of protected areas throughout the EBA. Indeed, most of its southern end is covered by very large national reserves and national parks, especially part of Katalalixar (6,745 km²) and Laguna San Rafael (17,420 km²).

062 Southern Patagonia

Key habitats Grassland, rocky and sandy coasts, lakes and ponds

Main threats Moderate habitat loss (e.g. due to overgrazing), introduced species, hunting

Biological importance ● ● ●
Current threat level ● ○ ○

Area 170,000 km^2 **Altitude** 0–1,200 m
Countries Argentina, Chile, Falkland Islands (to UK)

Restricted-range species	Threatened	Total
Confined to this EBA	1	10
Present also in other EBAs, SAs	0	0
Total	1	10

■ General characteristics

This large EBA at the southernmost tip of South America embraces the southern half of Santa Cruz province (Argentina), Isla Grande de Tierra del Fuego (split between Chile and Argentina), Isla de los Estados (Argentina), mainland Chile in Magallanes province just west of the Straits of Magellan, and the islands south of the Beagle Channel (Chile); it also incorporates the Falkland Islands (which are a UK dependent territory). The boundaries of the EBA coincide with the distribution of the Patagonian grasslands (and include the southern portion of Patagonian steppe). The EBA does not include the subpolar *Nothofagus* woodlands to the south and west of this area. Apart from the obvious coastal habitats (rocky shores and sandy beaches), the characteristic vegetation of the EBA is sparse steppe-like vegetation, tussock grasslands (*Poa* spp.), open scrub and tundra.

J. P. Croxall

Falkland Steamerduck *Tachyeres brachypterus*, one of two species endemic to the Falkland Islands, is still numerous along parts of the coastlline.

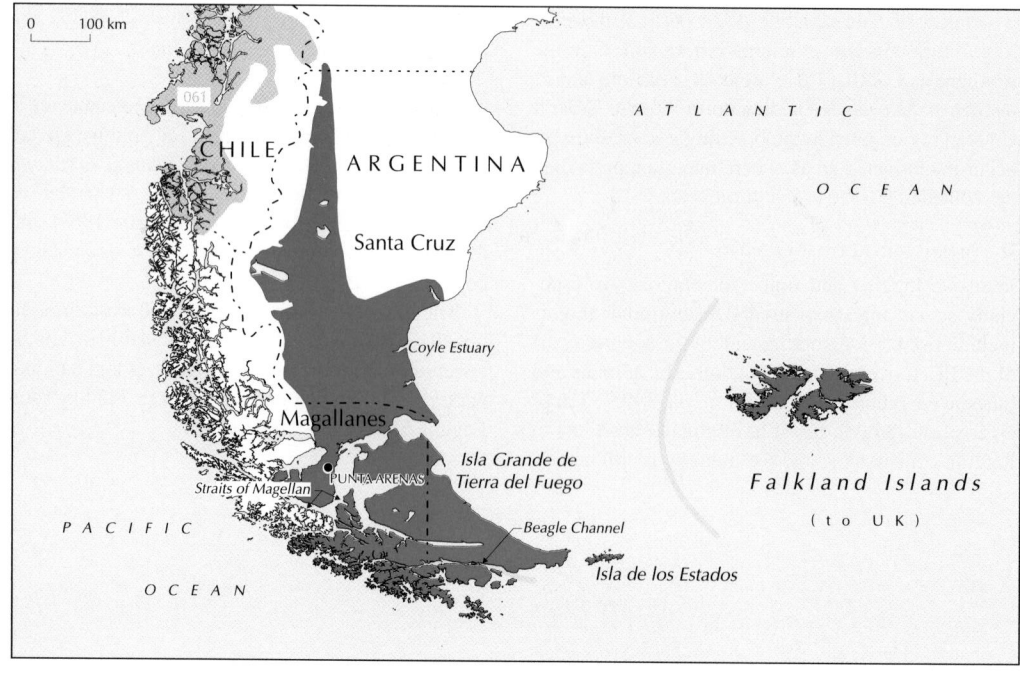

Status and habitat of restricted-range species

Species (ordered taxonomically)	Global status	Other EBAs (and SAs)	Altitude (m)	Habitat
Hooded Grebe *Podiceps gallardoi*	nt	—	500–1,200	Clear, slightly alkaline freshwater lakes and ponds
Ruddy-headed Goose *Chloephaga rubidiceps*	nt	—	Lowlands	Southern temperate grassland, pasture/agricultural land
Falkland Steamerduck *Tachyeres brachypterus*	lc	—	Coastal	Coastal waters and rocky shores
Striated Caracara *Phalcoboenus australis*	nt	—	Coastal	Southern temperate grassland, rocky sea coasts
Magellanic Plover *Pluvianellus socialis*	nt	—	Lowlands to 1,200	Alkaline, freshwater or brackish lakes, ponds and lagoons
Short-billed Miner *Geositta antarctica*	lc	—	500–1,000	Southern temperate grassland, sandy coastal areas
Blackish Cinclodes *Cinclodes antarcticus*	lc	—	0–100	Rocky coasts and beaches with sparse vegetation
Chocolate-vented Tyrant *Neoxolmis rufiventris*	lc	—	<500	Tussocky southern temperate grassland, open scrub
Cobb's Wren *Troglodytes cobbi*[1]	VU	—	Lowlands	Tussocky southern temperate grassland
Canary-winged Finch *Melanodera melanodera*	nt	—	c.0–580	Moist southern temperate grassland, pasture/agricultural land, areas around settlements

Global status (see p. 679 for definitions)	EX Extinct EW Extinct in the Wild	} with year of last record	cd Conservation Dependent nt Near Threatened	**Other EBAs (and SAs)** (see p. 65 for locations)	Bracketed numbers are Secondary Areas. X Extinct in that EBA or SA.
	CR Critical EN Endangered VU Vulnerable	} threatened species	lc Least Concern DD Data Deficient NE Not Evaluated	**Notes**	[1] Taxonomy follows Woods (1993) and Collar *et al.* (1994).

■ Restricted-range species

Although the EBA is a large region, the actual area occupied by the restricted-range species is substantially smaller as most are coastal and lowland birds, although some records come from as high as 1,200 m.

Ten species are entirely restricted to this EBA, at least during the breeding season (see below). As there are some widely differing habitat requirements among the nine species, a number of distributional patterns arise: *Podiceps gallardoi* is restricted during the breeding season to the lakes of interior Santa Cruz province (up to 1,200 m), wintering on the Atlantic coast of Santa Cruz in (at least) the Coyle estuary (*Cotinga* 1995, 3: 9). Similarly, *Pluvianellus socialis* breeds around the shores of ponds and lakes in the southern part of this province, but also in eastern Tierra del Fuego and along the southern side of the Straits of Magellan (Woods 1988); this wader has been recorded as a vagrant on the Falklands, for, although part of the population is resident, some

Distribution patterns of restricted-range species

Species (ordered geographically)	Santa Cruz province	N/cent. Tierra del Fuego, Magallanes	S Tierra del Fuego	Falkland Islands	Other EBAs, SAs
Podiceps gallardoi	●	–	–	–	–
Pluvianellus socialis	●	●	–	–	–
Neoxolmis rufiventris	●	●	–	–	–
Melanodera melanodera	●	●	–	●	–
Geositta antarctica	–	●	–	–	–
Chloephaga rubidiceps	–	●	–	●	–
Phalcoboenus australis	–	●	●	●	–
Cinclodes antarcticus	–	–	●	●	–
Tachyeres brachypterus	–	–	–	●	–
Troglodytes cobbi	–	–	–	●	–
Total	4	6	2	6	

● Present	? Present?	Threatened spp. shown in **bold**	} see 'Status and habitat' table
O Extinct?	R Reintroduced		
X Extinct	I Introduced	Other EBAs, SAs	

Tierra del Fuego National Park, Argentina, is one of the few protected areas in this EBA, but is probably important for just two of the restricted-range birds.

M. Davies

birds move northwards up the coast of Argentina in winter (Clark 1986, Woods 1988). These and *Melanodera melanodera* are the only restricted-range species to be found regularly in the interior of mainland Argentina, the remaining birds being primarily coastal, although *Neoxolmis rufiventris* migrates north to the interior during the winter months, and *Geositta antarctica* has also been recorded as a migrant in central and northern Argentina. *Tachyeres brachypterus* is endemic to the Falklands, where it is most numerous around large kelp beds in harbours and creeks, and the recently split *Troglodytes cobbi* (also a Falklands endemic) appears to be restricted to tiny offshore islands where it inhabits areas with mature tussock grass (Woods 1993). *Cinclodes antarcticus* and *Melanodera melanodera* are represented on the Falklands by endemic subspecies (Woods 1988).

■ Threats and conservation

Among the EBA's endemics there is a great reliance, direct or indirect, on natural grassland, especially

The Falkland Islands are vitally important for a number of breeding seabirds such as Gentoo Penguins *Pygoscelis papua*.

J. P. Croxall

tussock grass, much of which has now been destroyed by grazing livestock and introduced herbivores (Woods 1988, Dinerstein *et al*. 1995). *Troglodytes cobbi* has a minute range, its distribution being inversely related to the presence of introduced predators whose impact may have increased with the long-term destruction of the bird's grassland habitat (Woods 1993). A number of other restricted-range species are of conservation concern, with three birds especially standing out in this respect: *Podiceps gallardoi* due to its small breeding range and relatively small population (fewer than 5,000); *Chloephaga rubidiceps*, which has declined dramatically on the mainland and Tierra del Fuego, and presently finds its stronghold on the Falklands; and *Phalcoboenus australis*, which has been subject to hunting throughout its range and is much reduced in numbers (Woods 1988), with a Falkland Islands population estimated at 337 breeding pairs and an immature population probably capable of no more than replacing losses in the breeding population (Strange 1996).

The widespread threatened Austral Rail *Rallus antarcticus* (classified as Critical) and Austral Canastero *Asthenes anthoides* (Vulnerable) also occur in this EBA. It has been suggested that the Falklands are the most important known breeding site for Black-browed Albatross *Diomedea melanophrys*, Gentoo Penguin *Pygoscelis papua*, Rockhopper Penguin *Eudyptes chrysocome* and Thin-billed Prion *Pachyptila belcheri*, and support important populations of a number of other seabirds (Croxall *et al*. 1984).

Protected areas in the EBA are relatively few, but include Tierra del Fuego National Park in Argentina and Magallanes National Reserve in Chile (IUCN 1992a). A number of predator-free islands supporting populations of *Troglodytes cobbi* are currently managed as protected areas (*Warrah* 1995, 7: 8–9).

063 Rio Branco gallery forest

PRIORITY
URGENT

Key habitats Gallery forest

Main threats Moderate habitat loss (e.g. due to cattle-ranching, rice plantations)

Biological importance ●
Current threat level ● ●

Area 94,000 km² Altitude 0–100 m

Countries Brazil, Guyana

Restricted-range species	Threatened	Total
Confined to this EBA	2	2
Present also in other EBAs, SAs	0	0
Total	2	2

■ General characteristics

This EBA consists of the upper Branco and associated rivers of northern Roraima in northernmost Brazil and extreme western Guyana. Rivers found within this EBA include the Tacutu and Ireng (which form the Guyana–Brazil border), Surumu (a right-bank tributary of the lower Tacutu), Cotingo (a left-bank affluent of the Surumu) and Mucajaí and Pirara in Guyana. The area is flanked to the north, east and

west by higher land, most notably the Gran Sabana part of the Tepuis (EBA 064). The vegetation is a mosaic of open savanna and gallery forest which is seasonally flooded, especially along the larger rivers.

■ Restricted-range species

Cercomacra carbonaria and *Synallaxis kollari* are restricted to the gallery forest and both are known from no more than a handful of localities. They were thought to be endemic to Brazil until found in Guyana along the Pirara river in 1993 (Forrester 1993, 1995). The spinetail is particularly rare, being known from a total of just six specimens and two observations, along six different rivers. The antbird has been observed in recent years on riverine islands near to Boa Nova town, such as Ilha São José and Ilha Boa Água, where it was found to be relatively common in suitable forest.

■ Threats and conservation

Cattle-ranching, rice plantations, and other agricultural expansion pose substantial continuing threats, as do man-induced fires and major road-building schemes, e.g. the 'perimetal norte', which is going to open up formerly remote areas (Dinerstein *et al.* 1995, Forrester 1995). However, much of the forest along the rivers is relatively untouched but, with so little known about the requirements of the two restricted-range species, the potential exists for threats to take a toll on them before their ecologies become better known. In recognition of their small ranges rendering them vulnerable to habitat destruction, both species are considered threatened.

Status and habitat of restricted-range species

Species (ordered taxonomically)	Global status	Other EBAs (and SAs)	Habitat
Hoary-throated Spinetail *Synallaxis kollari*	VU	—	Seasonally flooded riverine forest with understorey of dense thickets and vines
Rio Branco Antbird *Cercomacra carbonaria*	VU	—	Gallery forest

Global status (see p. 679 for definitions)	EX Extinct EW Extinct in the Wild } with year of last record	CR Critical EN Endangered VU Vulnerable } threatened species	cd Conservation Dependent nt Near Threatened lc Least Concern	DD Data Deficient NE Not Evaluated

Other EBAs (and SAs) (see p. 65 for locations): bracketed numbers are Secondary Areas; ˣ extinct in that EBA or SA.

064 Tepuis

Key habitats Tropical montane evergreen forest, montane scrub, savanna

Main threats Limited habitat loss (e.g. due to burning, mining, agriculture)

Biological importance ● ● ●
Current threat level ● ● ●

Area 57,000 km² **Altitude** 600–2,800 m
Countries Brazil, Guyana, Venezuela

Restricted-range species	Threatened	Total
Confined to this EBA	2	36
Present also in other EBAs, SAs	0	2
Total	2	38

■ General characteristics

The tepuis (or table-mountains) are scattered throughout Bolívar and Amazonas states of southern Venezuela (south of the Orinoco river), penetrating as far as west-central Guyana and northern Brazil, although the main centre is the Gran Sabana in south-east Bolívar. They are the relics of a vast sandstone plateau, whose erosion (other than in the Gran Sabana area) cut right through to the ancient Guiana shield below. For the main part they are surrounded by lowland tropical forest which covers most of the states of Bolívar and Amazonas (this being one of the largest remaining tracts of tropical forest in the world), although in eastern Bolívar, on the Gran Sabana, they rise instead out of the surrounding savannas.

The tepuis rise to heights of 1,500–2,800 m above sea-level, often with vertical cliffs of up to 1,000 m. At the base of these cliffs are talus (scree) slopes consisting of rock debris from above, and these are covered in wet tropical and subtropical forest fed by moisture from clouds that form on a daily basis around the cliffs. The plateau summits are often strongly dissected by canyons and gorges due directly to differential weathering, and some of the larger tepuis have permanent streams or rivers which often result in dramatic waterfalls (e.g. Angel Falls on Auyán-tepui). The vegetation of the summits and higher-elevation slopes is a diverse mixture of elfin forest (rich in mosses, lichens, bromeliads and orchids), scrub, savanna and bogs—and is still essentially untouched (Mayr and Phelps 1967, Maguire 1970). With the extreme conditions of intense light, low temperatures, strong winds, etc., the endemic flora tends to have xeromorphic adaptations (in spite of the heavy rainfall) resulting in unusual growth forms giving the landscape a characteristic appearance (Steyermark 1979).

Status and habitat of restricted-range species

Species (ordered taxonomically)	Global status	Other EBAs (and SAs)	Altitude (m)	Habitat
Tepui Tinamou *Crypturellus ptaritepui*	VU	—	1,350–1,800	Montane evergreen forest
Fiery-shouldered Parakeet *Pyrrhura egregia*	lc	—	700–1,800	Montane evergreen forest
Tepui Parrotlet *Nannopsittaca panychlora*	lc	032	750–1,850	Montane evergreen forest
Roraiman Nightjar *Caprimulgus whitelyi*	nt	—	1,300–1,800	Elfin forest edge, semi-humid/humid montane scrub
Tepui Swift *Cypseloides phelpsi*	lc	033	400–1,400	Montane evergreen and tropical lowland evergreen forest, low, seasonally wet grassland, cliffs, rocky canyons, waterfalls
Rufous-breasted Sabrewing *Campylopterus hyperythrus*	lc	—	1,200–2,600	Montane evergreen forest, forest edge, scrub
Buff-breasted Sabrewing *Campylopterus duidae*	lc	—	1,200–2,400	Montane evergreen and elfin forest, semi-humid/humid montane scrub
Peacock Coquette *Lophornis pavoninus*	lc	—	500–2,000	Secondary and montane evergreen forest, forest edge, clearings
Tepui Goldenthroat *Polytmus milleri*	lc	—	1,200–2,200	Possibly humid forest edge and low, seasonally wet grassland, scrub
Velvet-browed Brilliant *Heliodoxa xanthogonys*	lc	—	950–2,000	Montane evergreen forest, forest edge, clearings, semi-humid/humid montane scrub
Tepui Spinetail *Cranioleuca demissa*	lc	—	1,100–2,450	Montane evergreen forest, forest edge
Roraiman Barbtail *Roraimia adusta*	lc	—	1,000–2,500	Montane evergreen and elfin forest, scrub
White-throated Foliage-gleaner *Automolus roraimae*	lc	—	1,100–2,400	Montane evergreen forest
Streak-backed Antshrike *Thamnophilus insignis*	lc	—	900–2,000	Montane evergreen and elfin forest
Roraiman Antwren *Herpsilochmus roraimae*	lc	—	900–2,000	Montane evergreen forest
Caura Antbird *Percnostola caurensis*	lc	—	<1,300	Tropical lowland evergreen forest
Brown-breasted Antpitta *Myrmothera simplex*	lc	—	600–2,400	Montane evergreen and elfin forest, scrub
Red-banded Fruiteater *Pipreola whitelyi*	lc	—	1,300–2,230	Montane evergreen forest
Rose-collared Piha *Lipaugus streptophorus*	lc	—	1,000–1,800	Montane evergreen forest, forest edge
Scarlet-horned Manakin *Pipra cornuta*	lc	—	900–1,600	Montane evergreen forest, secondary growth
Orange-bellied Manakin *Lepidothrix suavissima* [1]	lc	—	500–1,400	Montane evergreen forest, forest edge
Olive Manakin *Chloropipo uniformis*	lc	—	800–2,100	Montane evergreen forest
Ruddy Tody-flycatcher *Todirostrum russatum*	lc	—	1,200–2,500	Montane evergreen forest, often near streams
Great Elaenia *Elaenia dayi*	lc	—	1,500–2,600	Elfin forest, semi-humid/humid montane scrub, forest edge
Black-fronted Tyrannulet *Phylloscartes nigrifrons*	lc	—	900–1,800	Montane evergreen forest
Chapman's Tyrannulet *Phylloscartes chapmani*	lc	—	1,000–2,000	Montane evergreen forest
Tepui Wren *Troglodytes rufulus*	lc	—	1,000–2,800	Montane evergreen forest edge, elfin forest, scrub, savanna

cont.

Status and habitat of restricted-range species (cont.)

Species (ordered taxonomically)	Global status	Other EBAs (and SAs)	Altitude (m)	Habitat
Flutist Wren *Microcerculus ustulatus*	lc	—	1,200–2,100	Montane evergreen forest
Tepui Brush-finch *Atlapetes personatus*	lc	—	1,000–2,500	Montane evergreen forest, forest edge, clearings, scrub
Duida Grass-finch *Emberizoides duidae*	lc	—	1,300–2,100	Campo grasslands
Olive-backed Tanager *Mitrospingus oleagineus*	lc	—	900–1,800	Montane evergreen forest, forest edge
Scaled Flower-piercer *Diglossa duidae*	lc	—	1,400–2,500	Montane evergreen and elfin forest, forest edge, semi-humid/humid montane scrub
Greater Flower-piercer *Diglossa major*	lc	—	1,400–2,800	Montane evergreen and elfin forest, forest edge, semi-humid/humid montane scrub
Tepui Whitestart *Myioborus castaneocapillus*	lc	—	1,200–2,200	Montane evergreen forest, forest edge, semi-humid/humid montane scrub
White-faced Whitestart *Myioborus albifacies*	nt	—	900–2,250	Montane evergreen forest, forest edge
Guaiquinima Whitestart *Myioborus cardonai*	VU	—	1,200–1,600	Montane evergreen forest, forest edge
Tepui Greenlet *Hylophilus sclateri*	lc	—	900–2,000	Montane evergreen forest, forest edge, thickets
Golden-tufted Grackle *Macroagelaius imthurni*	lc	—	700–2,000	Montane evergreen forest

Global status (see p. 679 for definitions)	EX Extinct EW Extinct in the Wild } with year of last record	cd Conservation Dependent	**Other EBAs (and SAs)** (see p. 65 for locations)	Bracketed numbers are Secondary Areas. ^x Extinct in that EBA or SA.
	CR Critical EN Endangered VU Vulnerable } threatened species	nt Near Threatened lc Least Concern DD Data Deficient NE Not Evaluated	**Notes**	¹ Nomenclature follows Prum (1994).

The tepuis are famous for their high numbers of relict endemics, even within single plateaus. The Guiana floristic province comprises more than 8,000 species of which c.4,000 are endemic to the tepuis; there are 79 plant genera (17% of the province's total) endemic to the tepui summits, vertical bluffs and talus slopes, and 39 (8.5%) are endemic to the summits alone (Steyermark 1979). The fauna of the tepuis, despite being highly endemic, is quite limited in its diversity, with the avifauna being the most conspicuous component (and the most commonly observed plant pollinators) (Wege 1989).

■ Restricted-range species

The restricted-range species in this EBA are primarily montane birds occurring in the subtropical and temperate zones from c.600 m upwards (the boundary of the subtropical zone in the tepuis is anywhere from 600 to 1,000 m depending on the region), and principally inhabiting humid forest. Various other habitats are utilized to a lesser extent, although *Cypseloides phelpsi*, *Heliodoxa xanthogonys*, *Troglodytes rufulus* and *Emberizoides duidae* rely mostly on non-forest situations. *Percnostola caurensis* is restricted to the tropical zone (occasionally as low as

100 m), but is directly associated with the lower slopes of the tepuis, whereas Spot-backed Antwren *Herpsilochmus dorsimaculatus* is found in the lowlands around the tepuis, but is apparently not dependent on them, so is considered to be confined to the Orinoco–Negro white-sand forests (EBA 065).

At least seven restricted-range bird species are confined to the Gran Sabana, and this area of tepuis forms the EBA's centre in terms of the abundance of restricted-range species (Wege 1989). However, a number of species are endemic to single tepuis away from this region, e.g. *Emberizoides duidae* on Cerro Duida, and *Myioborus cardonai* on Cerro Guaiquinima. The two species present also in other EBAs are worthy of mention: *Nannopsittaca panychlora* is found north of the Orinoco only on Cerro Papelón and the Paria peninsula (in EBA 032); and *Cypseloides phelpsi* is known away from the tepuis by just one record (possibly of a vagrant) at Rancho Grande in Aragua state (in EBA 033) (Meyer de Schauensee and Phelps 1978).

■ Threats and conservation

Due to the largely inaccessible nature of this isolated region, the tepuis have not yet been seriously affected by human intervention, and at present remain relatively undisturbed (Huber and Alarcón 1988). However, the highland ecosystems are very fragile and highly vulnerable to disturbance. The effects of fire (which is frequently man-induced) can be dramatic, especially as the endemic plants of the tepuis often harbour flammable secondary compounds such as resins and oils, and the results of such destruction can be seen on many of the tepuis, as the vegetation is replaced by bracken *Pteridium* (Wege 1989).

Currently, other than burning, the primary threats to certain tepui mountain-tops are high-impact adventure tourism and pseudo-scientific exploration (A. Grajal *in litt.* 1993). The uncontrolled invasion of illegal gold-miners from Venezuela and Brazil has also caused grave problems, especially in La Neblina National Park (M. L. Goodwin *in litt.* 1993), but also in Jaua-Sarisariñama and (parts of) Canaima National Parks (C. J. Sharpe *in litt.* 1997). Changes in rainfall patterns from lowland deforestation have the potential to degrade sensitive tepui ecosystems in the future (Dinerstein *et al.* 1995).

Two of the tepui endemics, are due to their very small ranges, considered to be Vulnerable. *Crypturellus ptaritepui* is a species known only from Cerro Ptari-tepui and Cerro Sororopán-tepui in southeast Bolívar, where it inhabits cloud forest between 1,350 and 1,800 m. The combined area of the summit and talus at these two sites is only 28 km²; fire has been shown to be a threat to the slope vegetation in the past, and the forest is beginning to be cleared for subsistence agriculture. *Myioborus cardonai* occupies cloud forest between 1,200 and 1,600 m on Cerro Guaiquinima in west-central Bolívar; the mountain, which rises to 1,800 m, has a talus-slope area of only 110 km², and is being affected by mining activities (Mayr and Phelps 1967, Meyer de Schauensee and Phelps 1978, Ridgely and Tudor 1989, C. J. Sharpe *in litt.* 1997).

C. J. Sharpe

The vertical cliffs and flat, often cloud-covered summits of the tepuis make this one of the most spectacular and mysterious regions of South America.

A number of parks protect (though to varying degrees) large parts of the Tepuis EBA (e.g. Alto Orinoco–Casiquiare Biosphere Reserve, Canaima, Jaua-Sarisariñama and Duida National Parks), and recently all lands over 800 m and south of the Orinoco were declared national monuments, thus effectively putting all the tepuis within the protected-area system (A. Grajal *in litt.* 1993).

065 Orinoco–Negro white-sand forests

PRIORITY HIGH

Key habitats	Tropical lowland moist forest, riverine white-sand forest, scrub

Area 62,000 km² **Altitude** 0–500 m

Countries Brazil, Colombia, Venezuela

Main threats Limited habitat loss (e.g. due to mining, burning)

Biological importance ● ● ○
Current threat level ● ○ ○

Restricted-range species	Threatened	Total
Confined to this EBA	1	11
Present also in other EBAs, SAs	0	1
Total	1	12

■ General characteristics

This EBA follows the course of the upper Orinoco (south of Puerto Ayacucho) and its tributaries such as the Ventuari (Amazonas state, southern Venezuela) and Vichada (Vichada department, eastern Colombia), and also the upper Río Negro watershed including the Casiquiare (in Amazonas department, Venezuela), the Guainía, Tomo and Vaupés (in Guainía, Guaviare and Vaupés departments, southeast Colombia), and the Cauaburi, Xie, Içana, Uaupés and Curicuriari (mostly west of Uaupés, in northern Amazonas state, Brazil).

The EBA is cloaked in (mostly undisturbed) primary lowland humid forest up to c.500 m, although along many of the rivers (especially the upper Orinoco watershed) this is more specifically described as riverine white-sand forest. There are numerous small patches and pockets of rocky (partially deciduous) vegetation and savanna (Huber and Alarcón 1988) similar to 'campina' and 'caatinga';

partially inundated 'igapó' forest is also present along some of the rivers. The low sandstone serranías of south-east Colombia are also included.

■ Restricted-range species

Most of the birds appear confined to or associated with the relatively specialized humid lowland forest growing on the white-sand soils, but some species are also found in more open woodland, forest-edge and savanna situations. These vegetation types, and thus the birds, seem to be restricted to the lowlands and low serranías below 500 m.

The species in this EBA are all relatively poorly known (most being recorded from less than 10 localities), with (apparently) large gaps in their distributions. Recent surveys in east and south-east Colombia (Serranía de Naquen in southern Guainía and Serranía de Teraira in southern Vaupés) have extended the known ranges of many of the endemic birds (Anon. 1992a, A. Payne *in litt.* 1995), but further work is needed to determine precise ecological requirements in order to be able to predict more precisely what their distributions are likely to be.

Thripophaga cherriei is known from just seven specimens taken in 1899 and 1970 along a single affluent (the Capuana river) of the upper Orinoco in Venezuela (Collar *et al.* 1992), but, with further searching, it is likely to be found along other rivers and across the border in Colombia. In Colombia, outside the immediate area of the EBA as defined above, *Crypturellus duidae* has been found in the Serranía de la Macarena in Meta department (Secondary Area s019), and is predicted to occur on the table mountains in Vaupés department (Hilty and Brown 1986). In Venezuela, *Herpsilochmus dorsimaculatus* is found in the lowlands around the Tepuis (EBA 064), although it does not seem to be directly associated with them and so is considered confined to the present EBA.

■ Threats and conservation

This EBA is relatively unaffected by human activities, due primarily to the low human population density and the difficulty of access. However, the

Status and habitat of restricted-range species

Species (ordered taxonomically)	Global status	Other EBAs (and SAs)	Altitude (m)	Habitat
Grey-legged Tinamou *Crypturellus duidae*	lc	(s019)	100–500	White-sand forest, possibly tropical lowland evergreen forest
Barred Tinamou *Crypturellus casiquiare*	lc	—	100–300	White-sand forest, possibly tropical lowland evergreen forest
Orinoco Piculet *Picumnus pumilus*	lc	—	100–300	Humid forest, savanna, gallery forest borders, scrubby thickets
Orinoco Softtail *Thripophaga cherriei*	VU	—	c.150	Presumably river-edge forest, clearings, river banks
Yellow-throated Antwren *Myrmotherula ambigua*	lc	—	<200	Tropical lowland evergreen and white-sand forest
Spot-backed Antwren *Herpsilochmus dorsimaculatus*	lc	—	<c.300	Tropical lowland evergreen forest
Yapacana Antbird *Myrmeciza disjuncta*	lc	—	c.100	Tropical lowland evergreen and white-sand forest, undergrowth, scrub
Grey-bellied Antbird *Myrmeciza pelzelni*	lc	—	200–400	Tropical lowland evergreen and white-sand forest
Chestnut-crested Antbird *Rhegmatorhina cristata*	lc	—	200–250	Tropical lowland evergreen and white-sand forest, undergrowth
Pelzeln's Tody-tyrant *Hemitriccus inornatus*	lc	—	Lowlands	Presumably white-sand forest, savanna, thorn thickets
White-naped Seedeater *Dolospingus fringilloides*	lc	—	100–450	White-sand forest and forest edge, clearings, savanna
Azure-naped Jay *Cyanocorax heilprini*	lc	—	100–450	Tropical lowland evergreen forest edge, white-sand forest, possibly river-edge forest, savanna

Global status (see p. 679 for definitions)	EX Extinct EW Extinct in the Wild } with year of last record	CR Critical EN Endangered VU Vulnerable } threatened species	cd Conservation Dependent nt Near Threatened lc Least Concern	DD Data Deficient NE Not Evaluated

Other EBAs (and SAs) (see p. 65 for locations): bracketed numbers are Secondary Areas; ˣ extinct in that EBA or SA.

extraction of white-sand silica, the expansion of gold mining and frequent burning pose major threats to some portions of the EBA, with clearance for cattle-grazing also having an impact (Dinerstein *et al.* 1995, A. Grajal *in litt.* 1993).

Only *Thripophaga cherriei* is presently thought to be threatened, although this is due mainly to the paucity of records (see 'Restricted-range species', above) rather than any immediate or perceived threat from habitat destruction (Collar *et al.* 1992, 1994). The only known locality for this species was identified as a Key Area for threatened birds in Wege and Long (1995).

The vast Alto Orinoco–Casiquiare Biosphere Reserve (840,000 km²) presumably provides some formal protection to the EBA in southern Venezuela,

as do a number of indigenous reserves (e.g. Alto Río Guainía, Bajo Río Guainía y Río Negro, and Cuiari-Isana) in south-east Colombia, and the Rio Negro Forest Reserve and indigenous areas (e.g. Içana-Ajari and Içana-Xie) in north-west Brazil (IUCN 1992a). The extent to which any of these reserves provides adequate, on-the-ground protection is unknown. The whole of Amazonas state in Venezuela is legally protected from mining and forestry by governmental decree, although a proposal has recently been tabled to revoke the relevant decrees in order to legalize these activities within the state (C. J. Sharpe *in litt.* 1996). Irrespective of the decrees, all protected areas within Amazonas state are currently affected by gold- and diamond-mining (C. J. Sharpe *in litt.* 1997),

066 Upper Amazon–Napo lowlands

PRIORITY HIGH

Key habitats Tropical lowland evergreen and flooded forest

Main threats Moderate habitat loss (e.g. due to road-building, oil extraction, colonization)

Biological importance ● ● ●
Current threat level ● ○ ○

Area 130,000 km² **Altitude** 0–600 m

Countries Brazil, Colombia, Ecuador, Peru

Restricted-range species	Threatened	Total
Confined to this EBA	1	10
Present also in other EBAs, SAs	0	0
Total	1	10

■ General characteristics

The upper Amazon–Napo lowlands cover a vast area of eastern Ecuador (Napo and Pastaza states), northern Peru (Amazonas, Loreto and San Martín departments), westernmost Amazonas state of Brazil and the southern border area of Colombia. The area is centred on the lowland and foothill forests of the upper Putumayo river, the middle and upper Napo, the Marañón (including the Pastaza and Huallaga rivers), the Ucayali (and possibly the Javarí), and the Amazonas drainages, generally west of the confluence of the Putumayo and Amazonas, and primarily from the lowlands up to 600 m. The area is characterized by high rainfall (which is relatively constant year-round), complex topography and soils, and vast meandering river systems that create habitat mosaics. This ecosystem is extraordinarily diverse and comprises primary humid forest, some of which is seasonally inundated (várzea) forest, with other areas more characteristic of nutrient-poor white-sand forest.

■ Restricted-range species

All the EBA's restricted-range species occur in the humid lowland forest (either terra firme or várzea), or within more open areas of secondary vegetation and woodland. Within the EBA there are a number of interesting distributional patterns. Only two species are found on the Amazonas and Ucayali rivers: *Myrmoborus melanurus* occurs only on these two rivers, and *Leucippus chlorocercus* is present also on the Napo and Marañón, but both are found exclusively along the river systems or on river islands, either in riverine or várzea forest. *Thamnophilus praecox* is apparently confined to seasonally flooded (blackwater) várzea forest (R. S. Ridgely *in litt.* 1991), and it has been suggested that *Heterocercus aurantiivertex* is restricted to areas of riverine white-sand forest (T. A. Parker *in litt.* 1991).

The species in this area are the most restricted of a larger suite of birds that are variously distributed throughout the river islands and riverine forest of the Amazon basin rivers. Many of the endemics appear to be confined to riverine situations (Meyer de

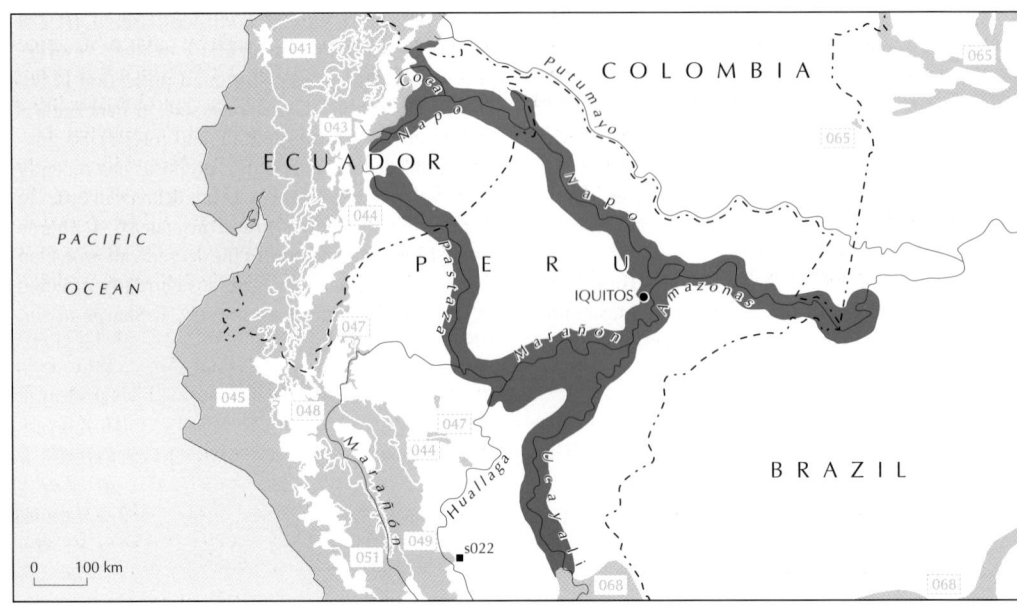

Status and habitat of restricted-range species

Species (ordered taxonomically)	Global status	Other EBAs (and SAs)	Altitude (m)	Habitat
Olive-spotted Hummingbird *Leucippus chlorocercus*	lc	—	Lowlands to 430	River island scrub, riverine forest, secondary growth, scrub at forest edge
Brown Nunlet *Nonnula brunnea*	lc	—	0–600	Tropical lowland evergreen forest, secondary forest
Cocha Antshrike *Thamnophilus praecox*	nt	—	200–250	Flooded tropical evergreen forest, forest edge
Black-tailed Antbird *Myrmoborus melanurus*	VU	—	<125	Flooded tropical evergreen forest
White-masked Antbird *Pithys castanea*	DD	—	c.250	Presumably tropical lowland evergreen forest
Ochre-striped Antpitta *Grallaria dignissima*	lc	—	Lowlands to 500	Tropical lowland evergreen forest
Orange-crested Manakin *Heterocercus aurantiivertex*	lc	—	Lowlands to 300	Flooded tropical evergreen forest, white-sand forest
Golden-winged Tody-flycatcher *Todirostrum calopterum*	lc	—	Lowlands to 1,100	Tropical lowland evergreen forest edge, dense bushy pasture, low shrubby clearings
Olive-chested Flycatcher *Myiophobus cryptoxanthus*	lc	—	Lowlands to 1,100	Tropical lowland evergreen forest edge
Ecuadorian Cacique *Cacicus sclateri*	lc	—	0–600	River-edge forest, forest borders

Global status (see p. 679 for definitions)	EX Extinct EW Extinct in the Wild	}with year of last record	CR Critical EN Endangered VU Vulnerable	}threatened species	cd Conservation Dependent nt Near Threatened lc Least Concern	DD Data Deficient NE Not Evaluated

Other EBAs (and SAs) (see p. 65 for locations): bracketed numbers are Secondary Areas; ˣ extinct in that EBA or SA.

Schauensee 1982, Hilty and Brown 1986, Ridgely and Tudor 1989), although bird distributions in this part of the Amazon basin are very poorly known. This is perhaps best demonstrated by *Pithys castanea*, which is still known only from the type-specimen collected in 1937 along the upper Pastaza (Collar *et al.* 1992); by *Thamnophilus praecox*, which until 1991 (when it was found to be quite common) was only known from the type-specimen taken in 1926 on the Napo in Ecuador (R. S. Ridgely *in litt.* 1991); and by *Myrmoborus melanurus*, which is known from just a few localities south of the Amazonas and east of the Ucayali (Ridgely and Tudor 1994). To help better define the EBA, further work is needed to determine the true distributions and ecology of the endemics in this area.

White-lored Antpitta *Hylopezus fulviventris* has recently been considered as distinct from *H. dives* by Ridgely and Tudor (1994), and is endemic to the northern portion of the EBA.

■ Threats and conservation

The forest in this region is reasonably intact (Forero 1989, Gentry 1989), although deforestation has been quite extensive in western Ecuador and parts of south-east Colombia, and the region is also under threat from oil exploration and extraction (L. M. Renjifo *in litt.* 1993), while associated road-building has caused degradation and fragmentation, and has

accelerated these processes by facilitating further human colonization; virtually all of the Ecuadorian portion of the Napo is open for oil leasing. Border controversies between Ecuador and Peru have spurred further colonization in attempts to claim disputed territory (Dinerstein *et al.* 1995).

Due to the relatively good state of the forest in this region, none of the endemics is presently considered threatened solely from habitat destruction. *Myrmoborus melanurus* is threatened by virtue of its apparent rarity and small range within which it is poorly known, and it is particularly susceptible to any future habitat loss. *Pithys castanea* is considered Data Deficient due to an almost total lack of information (see above). Widespread threatened species in this region include the Wattled Curassow *Crax globulosa* (Vulnerable), which is suffering from the loss of its riverine habitat and from hunting pressure (Collar *et al.* 1992, 1994).

In Ecuador, typical lowland forest habitat is protected by the Yasuní National Park, Limoncocha Biological Reserve and Cuyabeno Faunal Production Reserve (IUCN 1992a), with the private Zancudo Multiple-use Reserve also providing protection (R. S. Ridgely *in litt.* 1992). In Colombia, the only sizeable protected areas are Amacayacu and La Paya National Parks, with the Pacaya–Samiria National Reserve protecting a large area of forest between the Marañón and Ucayali rivers in Peru (IUCN 1992a).

067 Amazon flooded forests

PRIORITY HIGH

Key habitats Várzea and igapó flooded forest

Main threats Moderate habitat loss (e.g. due to logging, cattle-ranching, oil-palm plantations

Biological importance ● ● ●
Current threat level ● ● ●

Area 140,000 km² **Altitude** 0–200 m

Countries Brazil

Restricted-range species	Threatened	Total
Confined to this EBA	0	4
Present also in other EBAs, SAs	0	0
Total	0	4

■ General characteristics

This EBA comprises the Amazon's seasonally inundated tropical evergreen forests in Brazil, a major part of this huge river basin. The area covered follows the course and floodplains of the lower Solimões, lower Madeira and lower Negro eastward along the Amazon at least as far as its confluence with the Xingu—and it may extend to the islands in the Amazon's mouth as there are records for one of the restricted-range species from Ilha Mexiana (see 'Restricted-range species', below). The forests are divided into two main types: várzea forest occurs on the floodplains of the major white-water (sediment and mineral-rich) rivers of the Amazon basin, so in this EBA it is the predominant vegetation, being found on the Solimões-Amazon and on the lower Madeira; igapó forest occurs primarily on sandy soils bordering mineral-poor black-water or clear-water rivers, and in this EBA is found only on the Negro and its tributaries.

■ Restricted-range species

The restricted-range species are all poorly known, each being found at just a handful of localities. For

Nonnula amaurocephala there are three historical records along the lower Solimões and more recent observations on the lower Unini and Jaú, both black-water tributaries of the Negro (Whittaker *et al.* 1995). Both of the recent records were made in igapó forest, although the historical records on the white-water Solimões presumably came from várzea. *Picumnus varzeae* is a várzea species, which is found from the very lower reaches of the Madeira along the Amazon to westernmost Pará state and including the lower Jamundá river (Short 1982). *Myrmotherula klagesi* has been found at sites on the Anavilhanas archipelago in the Negro north of Manaus, and 600 km east of there along both banks of the Amazon and the mouth of the Tapajós near Santarém; this canopy species inhabits the borders of flooded forest especially on river islands (Ridgely and Tudor 1994). The range of *Cranioleuca muelleri* overlaps with the other species only in its western part from near the mouth of the Tapajós to Jamundá. Museum specimens show that it is distributed further east in Amapá state and Ilha Mexiana (Vaurie 1980) where vegetation maps show the predominant habitats to be savanna and flooded grassland, but, as it is unknown

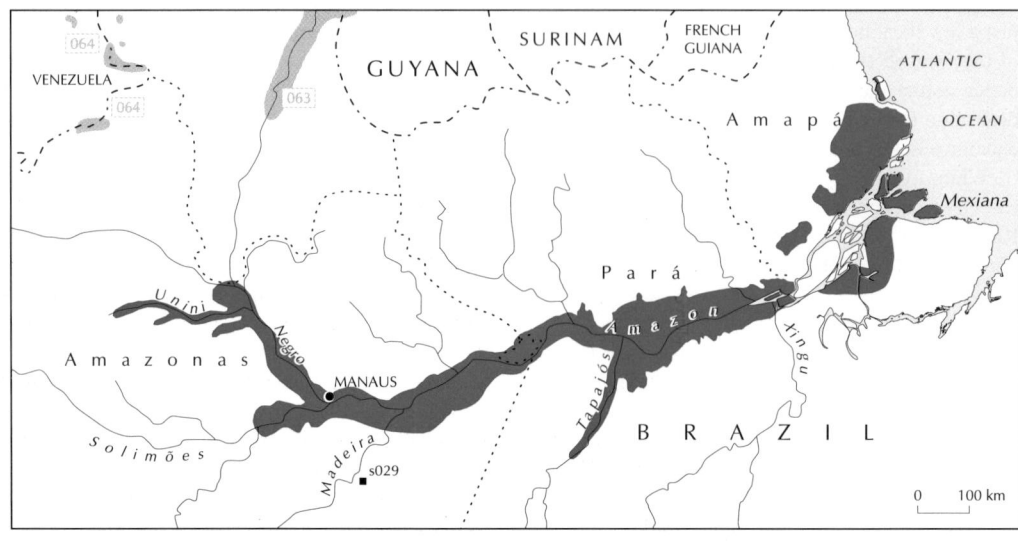

Status and habitat of restricted-range species

Species (ordered taxonomically)	Global status	Other EBA (and SAs)	Habitat
Chestnut-headed Nunlet *Nonnula amaurocephala*	nt	—	Igapó and várzea flooded forest
Várzea Piculet *Picumnus varzeae*	lc	—	Várzea flooded forest
Scaled Spinetail *Cranioleuca muelleri*	lc	—	Not known (presumably flooded forest in savanna and grassland)
Klages's Antwren *Myrmotherula klagesi*	nt	—	Várzea flooded forest, forest on river islands

Global status (see p. 679 for definitions): EX Extinct, EW Extinct in the Wild } with year of last record; CR Critical, EN Endangered, VU Vulnerable } threatened species; cd Conservation Dependent, nt Near Threatened, lc Least Concern; DD Data Deficient, NE Not Evaluated

Other EBAs (and SAs) (see p. 65 for locations): bracketed numbers are Secondary Areas; ˣ extinct in that EBA or SA.

in life, its habitat requirements are unclear (Ridgely and Tudor 1994).

■ Threats and conservation

Intensive logging and selective exploitation of the tree *Ceiba pentandra* are accelerating deforestation in the várzea forest of the Amazon basin and there appears already to be an extensive industrial timber infrastructure to maintain the logging. Some of the floodplains are being converted for cattle-ranching and oil-palm plantations, especially north of Manaus (Dinerstein *et al.* 1995, WWF/IUCN 1997).

The records of *Nonnula amaurocephala* from the lower Unini and Jaú rivers are both within the extensive Jaú National Park (22,720 km²). The Anavilhanas archipelago, site of the only recent sightings of *Myrmotherula klagesi*, lies inside the Anavilhanas Ecological Station (3,350 km²), which is itself now within the Rio Negro State Park (4,360 km²), established in 1995. Jaú National Park and Rio Negro State Park are adjacent to one another, and the huge area they form is further extended by a 12,300-km² buffer zone (*Conservation Biology* 1995, 9: 1,353). However, there is apparently no protected area further east on the lower Amazon which could protect the other restricted-range species of this EBA. *Cranioleuca muelleri* which is currently listed as being of low concern should, in view of the lack of recent records, be classified as Data Deficient.

068 South-east Peruvian lowlands

PRIORITY
URGENT

Key habitats Tropical lowland evergreen and riverine forest

Main threats Moderate habitat loss (e.g. due to logging, mining, oil and gas extraction, road-building)

Biological importance ● ● ●
Current threat level ● ○ ○

Area 260,000 km²   **Altitude** 0–800 m

Countries Bolivia, Brazil, Peru

Restricted-range species	Threatened	Total
Confined to this EBA	2	12
Present also in other EBAs, SAs	0	0
Total	2	12

■ General characteristics

This large lowland EBA is centred on south-east Peru, primarily in Madre de Dios department, but extending into northernmost Puno, and across the Bolivian border into Pando and northern La Paz departments. Records of a number of the endemics extend the EBA into Acre and south-east Amazonas states of Brazil. As the birds that identify this EBA are primarily riverine or floodplain forest-dwellers, the boundaries are more precisely defined by the river drainages involved. Most of the birds occur within the Madre de Dios drainage, including the Manu, Inambari, Tambopata and Heath rivers; other records are from the Madidi, Tahuamanu and Ortho rivers in Bolivia, the Ucayali in Peru, the Madeira in Brazil, and the Purús in both Peru and Brazil.

The forest in this region is humid lowland (rarely up to humid upper tropical) forest, comprising (the floristically diverse) tall, irregularly inundated floodplain and riverine forest and (the less diverse) interpluvial terra firme forest (T. A. Parker *in litt.* 1991).

■ Restricted-range species

The restricted-range birds of the EBA primarily occupy the tall floodplain and riverine forest, rather than the terra firme forest (Collar *et al.* 1992, T. A. Parker *in litt.* 1991), with a number apparently being undergrowth, thicket, scrub and/or bamboo specialists. Most of the species thus occur below 400 m, although records of some are from as high as c.800 m in the foothills of the East Andes, where this EBA

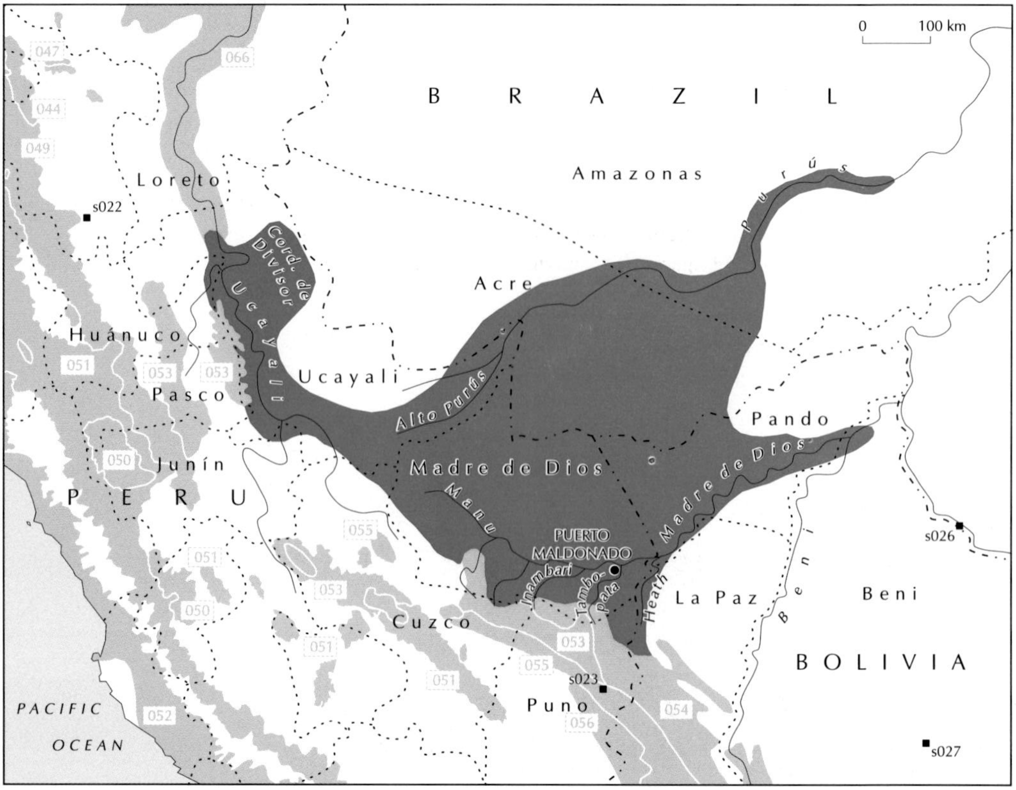

270

Status and habitat of restricted-range species

Species (ordered taxonomically)	Global status	Other EBAs (and SAs)	Altitude (m)	Habitat
Semicollared Puffbird *Malacoptila semicincta*	lc	—	0–1,050	Tropical lowland evergreen forest
Scarlet-hooded Barbet *Eubucco tucinkae*	nt	—	0–800	River-edge and secondary forest, forest edge, scrub
Fine-barred Piculet *Picumnus subtilis*	nt	—	0–1,100	River-edge and secondary forest
White-lined Antbird *Percnostola lophotes*	lc	—	Lowlands to 1,050	River-edge and secondary forest, tropical lowland evergreen forest edge, bamboo thickets, cane
Goeldi's Antbird *Myrmeciza goeldii*	lc	—	<550	River-edge and tropical lowland evergreen forest, forest undergrowth, bamboo thickets, swamp forest
Rufous-fronted Antthrush *Formicarius rufifrons*	VU	—	350–400	River-edge forest
Elusive Antpitta *Grallaria eludens*	nt	—	c.300	Tropical lowland evergreen forest
Black-faced Cotinga *Conioptilon mcilhennyi*	nt	—	Lowlands to 300	River-edge forest
White-cheeked Tody-tyrant *Poecilotriccus albifacies*	nt	—	<1,050	Tropical lowland evergreen forest, bamboo
Black-backed Tody-flycatcher *Todirostrum pulchellum*	lc	—	300–1,100	Tropical lowland evergreen forest and edge, scrub
Long-crested Pygmy-tyrant *Lophotriccus eulophotes*	lc	—	c.300–400	Tropical lowland evergreen forest, clearings, bamboo thickets
Selva Cacique *Cacicus koepckeae*	VU	—	c.300	River-edge forest, *Heliconia* thickets, possibly forest edge

Global status (see p. 679 for definitions)
EX Extinct
EW Extinct in the Wild } with year of last record
CR Critical
EN Endangered } threatened species
VU Vulnerable
cd Conservation Dependent
nt Near Threatened
lc Least Concern
DD Data Deficient
NE Not Evaluated

Other EBAs (and SAs) (see p. 65 for locations): bracketed numbers are Secondary Areas; ˣ extinct in that EBA or SA.

abuts the Peruvian East Andean foothills (EBA 053).

Most of the restricted-range species are found in the core area of Madre de Dios, northern Puno (Peru), western Pando and north-west La Paz, with *Grallaria eludens* presently known from the Curanja river (and probably the Alto Purús) in extreme south-east Ucayali. However, a number of species are known from records that extend the boundaries of the EBA to the north-west and north-east: *Picumnus subtilis* and *Percnostola lophotes* have been noted (albeit from few records) along the Ucayali drainage in Loreto department; and *Malacoptila semicincta* has been recorded to the north and north-east into the lower areas of the Amazon basin (in Brazil and

S. Butchart

An oxbow lake in the Tambopata–Candamo Reserve Zone. Most of the birds that define this EBA are riverine or floodplain forest-dwellers.

J. P. C'Neill

Elusive Antpitta *Grallaria eludens* is perhaps not so much elusive as poorly known and under-recorded, a description that can be used for many of the species in this EBA.

northernmost Bolivia). With additional information and records, some of the species in this EBA may yet prove to overlap with the Upper Amazon–Napo lowlands (EBA 066), including the Ucayali, and the Peruvian East Andean foothills (EBA 053).

■ Threats and conservation

The forest in this region has been subject to selective logging, and is being opened up for development schemes, oil/gas extraction and mining, each of which brings with it the associated road-building and human colonization, resulting in yet further degradation (Collar *et al.* 1992, Dinerstein *et al.* 1995). However, the EBA as a whole remains relatively intact due primarily to the inaccessibility of major portions of it.

Two of the restricted-range species in this EBA are currently considered threatened, both being restricted to the core area and inhabiting floodplain forest. *Cacicus koepckeae* is known with certainty only from the type-locality (Balta, on a tributary of the Alto Purús), and *Formicarius rufifrons* is apparently confined to river-edge habitat along tributaries of the Madre de Dios (Collar *et al.* 1992, Kratter 1995). While too little is known about *C. koepckeae* to identify specific threats, it seems probable that it may be vulnerable to the proposed development of this area. *F. rufifrons* is certainly at risk due to its preference for the very river-edge vegetation that is first to be destroyed and fragmented by human colonization (Kratter 1995). The widespread and threatened Wattled Curassow *Crax globulosa* (classified as Vulnerable) also occurs in this EBA.

Four Key Areas—Balta, Manu, the Colorado river mouth and Tambopata–Candamo—were identified for the conservation of the threatened species mentioned above (Wege and Long 1995). Of these, Manu National Park (and Biosphere Reserve) and the Tambopata–Candamo Reserve Zone are both formally protected and cover a total of c.30,000 km^2, although their integrity is by no means assured (Collar *et al.* 1992). The Madidi National Park in Bolivia also harbours populations of species from this and other EBAs (A. H. Perry *in litt.* 1994).

069 Fernando de Noronha

Key habitats Tropical deciduous forest and scrub

Main threats Major habitat loss (e.g. due to settlement), introduced species

Biological importance ●
Current threat level ●

Area 18 km²   **Altitude** 0–60 m

Countries Brazil

Restricted-range species	Threatened	Total
Confined to this EBA	1	2
Present also in other EBAs, SAs	0	0
Total	1	2

■ General characteristics

This volcanic archipelago is the easternmost extension of land in the Neotropical region. The main island and its 12 smaller associated islets (which lie to the north-east of it) are situated in the South Atlantic, some 345 km east of the most easterly point of mainland Brazil (to which it belongs politically). The main island is primarily low-lying (maximum altitude c.60 m), with cliffs forming much of the western coastline and extensive areas of dunes in the east. The land is well vegetated, with secondary forest in the east and extensive areas of scrub elsewhere.

■ Restricted-range species

Two species are endemic to the archipelago, both being present on the main island, but only *Elaenia ridleyana* occurs on Ilha Rata, the second largest island. Both species are most abundant in the forested areas, but are still common in scrub, trees along roadsides and around dwellings. The greatest numbers of *Vireo gracilirostris* have been found in the forest around Morro do Pico, and in the forest that covers the western quarter of the island (Olson 1981, 1994).

Although a total of 54 species of bird have now been recorded on the islands (Nacinovic and Teixeira 1989), the two endemics and the endemic subspecies of Eared Dove *Zenaida auriculata noronha* are the only resident landbirds, with an extinct, but undescribed fossil rail (Rallidae) presumably having constituted a forth resident (Olson 1981). The archipelago is also extremely important for colonies of many breeding seabirds (Olson 1981, Antas 1991).

■ Threats and conservation

Fernando de Noronha was originally forested throughout, but, with the islands having been inhabited since their discovery in 1503 (c.1,200 people are present today), all the large trees have been cut, and all the vegetation which now remains is secondary (Olson 1981). There are proposals to further develop tourism, and this would cause yet greater damage to the remaining vegetation. Already *Vireo gracilirostris* is absent from large areas in the centre of the island that have been cleared for airport runways, fields, etc. Fortunately, the two endemics appear to survive in secondary habitats, although introduced pigs, rats, mice, cats and caviomorph rodents (Ridley 1890, Olson 1981) are likely to threaten all native wildlife. *V. gracilirostris* (and presumably the other landbirds) is a favourite target of children who kill them to eat or purely for fun, although this is probably a minor cause of mortality, and the species should not be in any danger as long as existing forested areas of the island are preserved (Olson 1994). Due to the minute land area it occupies, *V. gracilirostris* was recently considered threatened (Collar *et al.* 1994), and, on the basis of this range criterion, *Elaenia ridleyana*, with a population of c.100 individuals (Ridgely and Tudor 1994), should likewise be listed. Fernando de Noronha is a Federal Environment Protection Area of 1,692 ha (IUCN 1992a), although the protection that this status affords it on the ground is unknown.

Status and habitat of restricted-range species

Species (ordered taxonomically)	Global status	Other EBAs (and SAs)	Altitude (m)	Habitat
Noronha Elaenia *Elaenia ridleyana*	lc	—	0–60	Tropical deciduous forest, secondary growth, scrub, thickets
Noronha Vireo *Vireo gracilirostris*	VU	—	0–60	Tropical deciduous forest, secondary growth, scrub, trees near roads

Global status (see p. 679 for definitions)	EX Extinct EW Extinct in the Wild	} with year of last record	CR Critical EN Endangered VU Vulnerable	} threatened species	cd Conservation Dependent nt Near Threatened lc Least Concern	DD Data Deficient NE Not Evaluated

Other EBAs (and SAs) (see p. 65 for locations): bracketed numbers are Secondary Areas; ˣ extinct in that EBA or SA.

070 North-east Brazilian caatinga

PRIORITY
CRITICAL

Key habitats Deciduous forest, gallery forest, arid scrub

Main threats Major habitat loss (e.g. due to agricultural expansion, grazing, burning)

Biological importance ● ●
Current threat level ● ● ●

Area 200,000 km²   **Altitude** 0–1,000 m

Countries Brazil

Restricted-range species	Threatened	Total
Confined to this EBA	3	5
Present also in other EBAs, SAs	1	1
Total	4	6

■ General characteristics

The caatinga region covers more than 750,000 km² of north-east Brazil, from the north Atlantic coast of Ceará and Rio Grande do Norte states south to southern Bahia. This EBA is centred on the middle reaches of the São Francisco river and includes southern Ceará, eastern Piauí, western Paraíba and Pernambuco, and northern Bahia states. The climate is very dry with little cloud, sunlight exceeding 3,200 hours per year (Hueck 1978). The caatinga vegetation consists of a wide variety of semi-desert and dry deciduous forest formations, ranging from savanna dominated by cacti to thorn scrub and gallery forest with trees up to 15 m tall.

In the dry plains of western Pernambuco, most of the woody vegetation comprises tangled, brushy trees less than 4 m tall, with some emergent trees reaching 8–10 m (common species are *Cnidoscolus phyllacanthus*, *Spondius tuberosa*, *Bursera leptophloeos* and *Ziziphus joazeiro*: Rizzini 1979); a large terrestrial bromeliad *Bromelia laciniosa* is abundant and dominates the ground cover (Whitney and Pacheco 1994). In northern Bahia, trees and shrubs of the subfamilies Cesalpinioideae and Mimosoideae (both Leguminosae) are important components of the caatinga vegetation. Along rivers, including seasonally inundated watercourses and small rivers ('riachos'), and especially by the São Francisco, a more humid gallery woodland persists, sometimes with caraiba *Tabebuia caraiba* trees. Also in Bahia are areas of caatinga vegetation dominated by licuri *Syagrus coronata* palm trees.

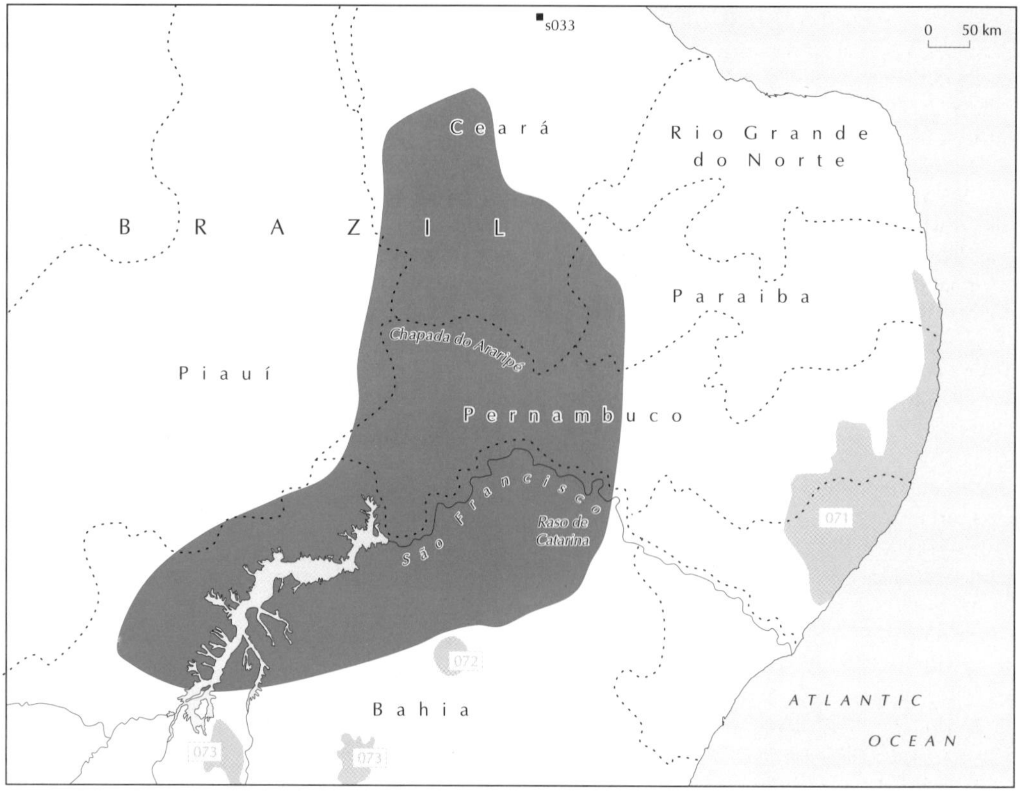

s033

0   50 km

Ceará

Rio Grande do Norte

B R A Z I L

Paraiba

Chapada do Araripe

Piauí

Pernambuco

São Francisco

Raso de Catarina

071

072

073

073

Bahia

ATLANTIC

OCEAN

Status and habitat of restricted-range species

Species (ordered taxonomically)	Global status		Other EBAs (and SAs)	Habitat
Lear's Macaw *Anodorhynchus leari*	CR	—	400–800	Deciduous and ilicuri palm forest, thorn scrub, arid canyons
Spix's Macaw *Cyanopsitta spixii*	CR	—	Lowlands	Gallery forest, deciduous forest, thorn scrub
Caatinga Nighthawk[1] *Chordeiles vielliardi*	NE	—	Lowlands	Thorn and cactus scrub?
Pygmy Nightjar *Caprimulgus hirundinaceus*	nt	—	Lowlands	Deciduous forest, esp. with open sandy areas
Tawny Piculet *Picumnus fulvescens*	VU	071	0–950	Deciduous forest, secondary forest
Red-shouldered Spinetail *Gyalophylax hellmayri*	VU	—	<c.500	Usually around terrestrial bromeliads in deciduous forest

Global status (see p. 679 for definitions)

EX Extinct ⎤ with year
EW Extinct in ⎬ of last
   the Wild ⎦ record
CR Critical ⎤ threatened
EN Endangered ⎬ species
VU Vulnerable ⎦

cd Conservation
   Dependent
nt Near Threatened
lc Least Concern
DD Data Deficient
NE Not Evaluated

Other EBAs (and SAs) (see p. 65 for locations)
Bracketed numbers are Secondary Areas. ˣ Extinct in that EBA or SA.

Notes
[1] New species (Lencioni-Neto 1994). No English name was proposed in the type description; we suggest this name as reflecting the species' habitat preference.

■ Restricted-range species

As well as the five restricted-range species which are endemic to this EBA, a further five species whose ranges are considered to be greater than 50,000 km² (thus excluding them from the EBA analysis) are also endemic. These are Great Xenops *Megaxenops parnaguae*, Moustached Woodcreeper *Xiphocolaptes falcirostris*, Broad-tipped Hermit *Phaethornis gounellei*, Pectoral Antwren *Herpsilochmus pectoralis* and Yellow-faced Siskin *Carduelis yarrellii* (an estimation of their range size has been particularly difficult because they appear to show patchy distributions within a considerable area). *Caprimulgus hirundinaceus* and *Gyalophylax hellmayri* also have ranges which were difficult to judge owing to large gaps between records, and with better distributional information their ranges may also be shown to be greater than 50,000 km². Most of the 14 localities where *G. hellmayri* has been recorded are from a small part of northern Bahia and western Pernambuco, but there is a single sighting from north-east Piauí (Whitney and Pacheco 1994).

The two species of macaw found in this EBA do not overlap in range: *Anodorhynchus leari* is confined principally to the middle course of the Vaza-Barris south of the Raso da Catarina plateau in north-east Bahia, and *Cyanopsitta spixii* occurs only in the middle reaches of the São Francisco. The distribution of *A. leari* seems to fit well with that of licuri palms, whereas that of *C. spixii* matches that of the gallery woodland dominated by caraiba trees.

Picumnus fulvescens is distributed further east than the EBA's other restricted-range species, being found also in more humid woodlands associated with

the Atlantic forests of Alagoas (EBA 071). *Chordeiles vielliardi* was described only in 1994 and is currently known from just one locality on the banks of the São

P. Hayman

The desperate conservation situation of Spix's Macaw *Cyanopsitta spixii* reflects the long history of human pressure on the region.

Francisco in the centre of this EBA (Lencioni-Neto 1994), though it will undoubtedly be found in other localities when its voice is better known.

■ Threats and conservation

The general disturbance (agricultural expansion, grazing, hunting and burning) of this EBA is testimony to the prevalence of human pressure on the region. Much of the area has been populated since the late eighteenth century, and the general level of human disturbance increased 30 years ago when the Brazilian oil company, Petrobrás, became established: new roads into the region were immediately used by settlers and hunters. Relocation of many families to the region by government agencies is an additional problem (Hart 1991).

All the restricted-range species except for the two nightjars are considered threatened, and the widespread threatened species *Megaxenops parnaguae*, *Xiphocolaptes falcirostris*, *Herpsilochmus pectoralis* and *Carduelis yarrellii* (see 'Restricted-range species', above; all classified as Vulnerable) also have significant parts of their ranges in this EBA.

The two species of macaw are both on the brink of extinction in the wild. Currently there is only one wild individual (a male) of *Cyanopsitta spixii*, and

attempts to reintroduce a wild-caught female alongside it failed in 1995; only three patches of its caraiba woodland habitat are known to remain in Bahia, totalling just c.30 km² (Juniper and Yamashita 1990). There is one main population of *Anodorhynchus leari*, which has been estimated at 117 individuals, but over the past 2–3 years trappers are thought to have taken c.20 birds; encouragingly, a new population of c.20 individuals was discovered several hundred kilometres from the main group in June 1995 (Munn 1995).

There are few protected areas within this EBA or, indeed, within the whole of the caatinga region: Capivara National Park (980 km²) holds *Gyalophylax hellmayri* and *Picumnus fulvescens* (as well as *Megaxenops parnaguae* and *Carduelis yarrellii*); Serra Negra Federal Biological Reserve (10 km²) holds *Gyalophylax hellmayri* (as well as *Megaxenops parnaguae* and *Carduelis yarrellii*); Aiuaba Federal Ecological Station (115 km²) lies within the EBA but lacks ornithological data. The main breeding site for *Anodorhynchus leari* (Toca cliffs) was bought by Fundação Biodiversitas, and lies adjacent to the Raso da Catarina Ecological Station (998 km²), but is heavily used for animal grazing by local people.

071 Atlantic slope of Alagoas and Pernambuco

PRIORITY
CRITICAL

Key habitats Lowland evergreen forest

Main threats Severe habitat loss (e.g. due to sugar-cane plantations)

Biological importance ● ●
Current threat level ● ● ●

Area 23,000 km² **Altitude** 0–1,000 m

Countries Brazil

Restricted-range species	Threatened	Total
Confined to this EBA	7	7
Present also in other EBAs, SAs	5	5
Total	12	12

■ General characteristics

This EBA comprises the Atlantic coastal forest in north-east Brazil, mainly in the states of Pernambuco and Alagoas, but also in Paraíba, and embraces the narrow coastal slope and low-lying mountain ridges (up to 1,000 m) such as the Chapada de Borborena in Alagoas. The main habitat is tropical evergreen forest, which is similar to the Atlantic forest lowlands of south-east Brazil (see EBA 075). These forests are characterized by species-rich biotas and high levels of endemism (Dinerstein *et al.* 1995).

■ Restricted-range species

All the restricted-range species inhabit forest or forest edge, but *Curaeus forbesi* is the only one whose preferred habitat is forest edge and freshwater marsh. *Mitu mitu* is the only species found exclusively in flat lowland forest. A distinct group of species—*Philydor novaesi*, *Myrmotherula snowi*, *Terenura sicki* and *Phylloscartes ceciliae*—is confined entirely to the tropical evergreen forest on the slopes of Alagoas and Pernambuco, mostly above 500 m. Remarkably, all these species were first discovered in the last 15 years at the same locality, Fazenda Pedra Branca, which is located on the Chapada da Borborena.

Four of the restricted-range species (*Myrmeciza ruficauda*, *Iodopleura pipra*, *Xipholena atropurpurea* and *Curaeus forbesi*) are shared with the Atlantic forests lowlands (EBA 075), and one (*Picumnus fulvescens*) also occurs in the North-east Brazilian caatinga (EBA 070). Additionally, there are isolated populations of *Hemitriccus mirandae* in the Serras da Baturite and Ibiapaba (Secondary Area s033) in northern Ceará state. White-collared Kite *Leptodon forbesi*, treated as a species by Sibley and Monroe (1990), is confined entirely to this EBA. However, much evidence indicates that this is not a valid taxon (N. J. Collar verbally 1997).

■ Threats and conservation

It is estimated that only 2% of the original forest cover remains in Alagoas and Pernambuco states and just 6% in Paraíba (Brown and Brown 1992), and other recent figures show that these last forests are severely fragmented: estimates of the remaining area of Atlantic forest and associated habitats are 878 km² in blocks averaging 1.5 km² for Alagoas and 1,524 km² in 1.3-km² blocks for Pernambuco (Conservation International *et al.* 1995).

Sugar-cane plantations have replaced virtually all the lower-altitude forest in Alagoas and Pernambuco. The remaining forest in the higher parts of the EBA, although not under threat from this industry, is affected by other pressures such as selective logging,

Status and habitat of restricted-range species

Species (ordered taxonomically)	Global status	Other EBAs (and SAs)	Altitude (m)	Habitat
Alagoas Curassow *Mitu mitu*	EW	—	0	Tropical lowland evergreen forest, only on flat terrain
Tawny Piculet *Picumnus fulvescens*	VU	070	0–950	Semi-deciduous forest, secondary forest
Plain Spinetail *Synallaxis infuscata*	EN	—	0–500	Tropical evergreen forest, secondary growth, forest edge
Alagoas Foliage-gleaner *Philydor novaesi*	CR	—	400–550	Tropical evergreen forest, logged forest, old secondary growth
Alagoas Antwren *Myrmotherula snowi*[1]	CR	—	400–550	Tropical evergreen forest
Orange-bellied Antwren *Terenura sicki*	VU	—	300–700	Tropical evergreen forest
Scalloped Antbird *Myrmeciza ruficauda*	VU	075	0–500	Tropical evergreen forest, secondary growth, forest edge
Buff-throated Purpletuft *Iodopleura pipra*	VU	075	0–1,000	Tropical evergreen forest, secondary growth, forest edge
White-winged Cotinga *Xipholena atropurpurea*	VU	075	0–700	Tropical evergreen forest, secondary growth, forest edge
Buff-breasted Tody-tyrant *Hemitriccus mirandae*	VU	(s033)	700–1,000	Tropical evergreen forest on slopes, often near dense vine tangles; forest clearings
Alagoas Tyrannulet *Phylloscartes ceciliae*	EN	—	400–550	Tropical evergreen forest, forest edge, forest clearings
Seven-coloured Tanager *Tangara fastuosa*	EN	—	0–850	Tropical evergreen forest, secondary growth, forest edge
Forbes's Blackbird *Curaeus forbesi*	CR	—	0–600	Tropical evergreen forest edge, freshwater marshes

Global status (see p. 679 for definitions)				
EX Extinct	with year of last record	cd Conservation Dependent		
EW Extinct in the Wild		nt Near Threatened		
CR Critical	threatened species	lc Least Concern		
EN Endangered		DD Data Deficient		
VU Vulnerable		NE Not Evaluated		

Other EBAs (and SAs) (see p. 65 for locations) — Bracketed numbers are Secondary Areas. [X] Extinct in that EBA or SA.

Notes [1] Taxonomy follows Collar *et al.* (1992).

firewood removal and small-scale cultivation (e.g. of bananas), which are steadily eradicating forest remaining on steep mountain slopes (Teixeira and Gonzaga 1983, Teixeira 1986).

The massive deforestation which has taken place throughout this EBA has certainly had a major impact on its restricted-range species, their current distributions being now heavily fragmented, with most lowland forest localities cleared or under pressure, and even reserves (see below) being insecure. Alarmingly, all of the restricted-range species are considered threatened, and a further five widespread threatened species occur in the EBA: White-necked Hawk *Leucopternis lacernulata* (classified as Vulnerable), Red-browed Amazon *Amazona rhodocorytha* (Endangered), Golden-tailed Parrolet *Touit surda* (Endangered), Black-headed Berryeater *Carpornis melanocephalus* (Vulnerable) and Yellow-faced Siskin *Carduelis yarrellii* (Vulnerable).

The extensive habitat destruction has already produced one casualty, *Mitu mitu*, which is now considered Extinct in the Wild. This curassow was rediscovered in 1951 and, although it was apparently fairly easily found then, its extinction was forecast by its finder (Pinto 1952). Destruction of its habitat for sugar-cane duly proceeded, it was ceaselessly hunted, and no conservation measures were taken at the local level despite continued concerns that it would soon become extinct (e.g. Coimbra-Filho 1970, Sick 1972, King 1978–1979). It was still found in Alagoas in the late 1970s and the last sighting of a wild bird was probably in early 1987. A captive population has been kept privately since 1977.

The forest at Pedra Branca is an extremely important site in this EBA (and probably one of the most important forests in the world), being the type-locality for four of the restricted-range species (and still the only known place for two of them, *Philydor novaesi* and *Myrmotherula snowi*), and holding another 11 threatened species (including eight of the restricted-range birds). It covered c.70 km² in the late 1970s, but has largely disappeared, such that in 1990 just 15 km² remained in an area called Bananeira. Although this remnant forest is included within the

Seven-coloured Tanager *Tangara fastuosa* has been affected by trapping for the cage-bird trade as well as the extensive deforestation in the region.

P. Hayman

Murici Biological Reserve (30 km²), indiscriminate small-scale logging was evidently still occurring in 1992 (Collar *et al*. 1992), and the area is further threatened by fires spreading from adjacent sugar-cane plantations (Wege and Long 1995).

Another very important area in this EBA is Pedra Talhada Federal Biological Reserve (45 km²), which holds 12 threatened species and is one of the last remaining upland Atlantic forests in Alagoas. Five other Key Areas for threatened birds have been identified in the EBA (Wege and Long 1995), and a workshop in 1993 recognized a further 30 priority areas for biodiversitry conservation (Conservation International *et al*. 1995), most being unprotected.

072 Deciduous forests of Bahia

PRIORITY URGENT

Key habitats Deciduous forest

Main threats Severe habitat loss (e.g. due to agriculture, cattle-ranching, coffee plantations)

Biological importance ● ○ ○
Current threat level ● ● ●

Area 10,000 km² **Altitude** 600–1,000 m

Countries Brazil

Restricted-range species	Threatened	Total
Confined to this EBA	2	2
Present also in other EBAs, SAs	0	0
Total	2	2

■ General characteristics

This EBA is located on the eastern edge of the interior of eastern Brazil in south-central Bahia and north-east Minas Gerais states. It is principally a gently rolling elevated region, which marks the

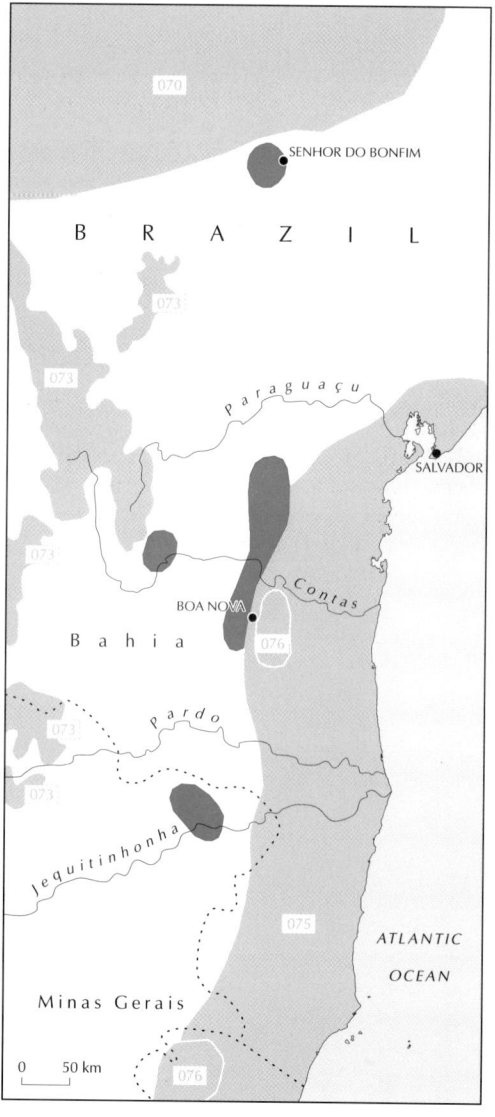

J. Tobias

Characteristic dry deciduous forest at Boa Nova, a site that is vitally important for the conservation of both restricted-range (and threatened) species in this EBA.

continental divide between the wet forests of the Atlantic slope and the arid scrub of Brazil's interior caatinga region (Willis and Oniki 1981). The northern end of the Atlantic forest lowlands (EBA 075) is adjacent to this EBA. Within the rolling topography there are four major rivers: from north to south, Paraguaçu, das Contas, Pardo and Jequitinhonha.

The main habitat is dry deciduous forest, often referred to as 'mata-de-cipó'. The forest is normally less than 10 m in stature, and characteristically has a mid-storey of small trees and bushes covered in bromeliads and vine tangles, and a dense understorey of large terrestrial bromeliads *Aechmea*, some reaching nearly 2 m tall. In drier areas there are caatinga-

Status and habitat of restricted-range species

Species (ordered taxonomically)	Global status	Other EBAs (and SAs)	Altitude (m)	Habitat
Narrow-billed Antwren *Formicivora iheringi*	VU	—	600–900	Tropical deciduous and semi-deciduous forest with vines and dense understorey of terrestrial bromeliads
Slender Antbird *Rhopornis ardesiaca*	EN	—	700–1,000	Tropical deciduous forest with vines and dense understorey of terrestrial bromeliads

Global status (see p. 679 for definitions) — EX Extinct, EW Extinct in the Wild (with year of last record); CR Critical, EN Endangered, VU Vulnerable (threatened species); cd Conservation Dependent, nt Near Threatened, lc Least Concern; DD Data Deficient, NE Not Evaluated

Other EBAs (and SAs) (see p. 65 for locations): bracketed numbers are Secondary Areas; ˣ extinct in that EBA or SA.

like scrub habitats comprising a main tree- and scrub-layer up to 3 m tall, often with terrestrial bromeliads.

Restricted-range species

Both of the restricted-range species are confined to the dry deciduous forest. *Formicivora iheringi* forages by gleaning in foliage, along branches and in vine tangles mixed with dead leaves (Tobias *et al.* 1993, Ridgely and Tudor 1994), while the ground-dwelling *Rhopornis ardesiaca* prefers areas with a dense layer of terrestrial bromeliads (Willis and Oniki 1981).

Rhopornis ardesiaca has a smaller range than *Formicivora iheringi*, being restricted to south-east Bahia between the Paraguaçu and Pardo rivers. The majority of the records of *F. iheringi* are also from areas between these two rivers but its northernmost records are from near Senhor do Bonfim, and it occurs further south in the Jequitinhonha valley in Minas Gerais.

Threats and conservation

Primary dry forest has been rapidly cleared for cattle pasture in central-southern Bahia, and much of the forest in north-east Minas Gerais and adjacent southern Bahia has been cleared for coffee plantations (Collar *et al.* 1992). Cleared slopes can be seen all around the vicinity of Boa Nova where both species occur, with natural habitats reduced to scattered fragments mostly on the hilltops (Whitney 1996). The remaining forest patches are highly disturbed by livestock and are also subject to continuous local exploitation of trees for firewood and fenceposts (Collar *et al.* 1992, Tobias *et al.* 1993).

With such high levels of forest clearance, both the restricted-range bird species are considered threatened. However, none of the EBA is currently under any official protection, in spite of various calls for the creation of a forest reserve of mata-de-cipó (e.g. Willis and Oniki 1981, Teixeira 1987). It has been suggested that this could be carried out in conjunction with an experimental agricultural station which is needed on the south Bahian plateau because of its distinctive climate and soils (Willis and Oniki 1981), or as a community-level conservation initiative (Whitney 1996). Three Key Areas for the two threatened restricted-range birds have been identified (Wege and Long 1995): Jequié and Boa Nova, both in Bahia, where both species occur, and Almenara in the Jequitinonha valley of Minas Gerais, where only *Formicivora iheringi* is found.

073 | Central Brazilian hills and tablelands | PRIORITY URGENT

Key habitats Shrubby savanna		**Area** 67,000 km²	**Altitude** 700–2,000 m
Main threats Moderate habitat loss (e.g. due to cattle-ranching, gold-mining)		**Countries** Brazil	

Restricted-range species	Threatened	Total
Confined to this EBA	1	4
Present also in other EBAs, SAs	1	3
Total	2	7

Biological importance ● ● ●
Current threat level ● ●

■ General characteristics

This EBA comprises the Cadeia do Espinhaço mountains of interior Brazil in Minas Gerais and Bahia states. The mountains vary from 50 to 100 km wide, and lie mainly at 1,000–1,500 m altitude, with some peaks of over 2,000 m (to 2,107 m in Serra de Barbado). The Cadeia do Espinhaço consists of a

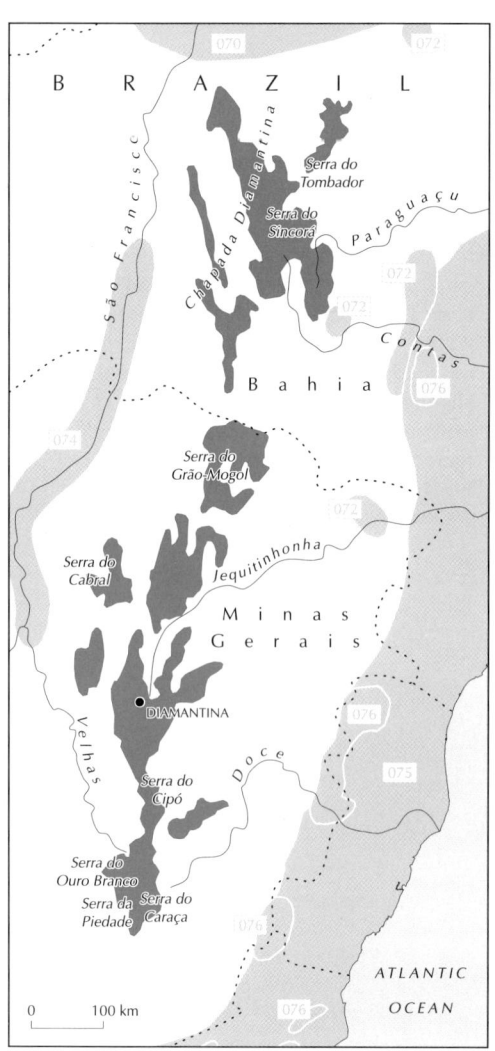

number of different mountain ranges separated from each other by river valleys. These ranges divide into two main groups, separated by a 300-km plateau area lying 500 m above sea-level in northern Minas Gerais and southern Bahia. The southern group of mountains in the Cadeia do Espinhaço includes the following important mountain ranges: from south to north, Serra do Ouro Branco, Serra da Piedade, Serra do Caraça, Serra do Cipó, Serra do Cabral, Diamantina plateau and Serra do Grão-Mogol. The Serra do Ouro Branco, which marks the southern end of the EBA, lies close to the northern extension of the Serra da Mantiqueira (whose peaks and seaward slope form part of the Atlantic forest mountains, EBA 076) and to the Atlantic forest lowlands (EBA 075). The northern group of mountains is collectively named the Chapada Diamantina and includes the main ranges of the Serra do Sincorá and Serra do Rio das Contas. Further north, the Chapada and the EBA ends in a number of isolated massifs, the main ones being Morro do Chapéu (in the Serra do Tombador) and the Serra da Jacobina.

Overall, the climate is strongly seasonal, with mild summers (in which much of the rain falls) and a dry winter. The northern part of the EBA experiences hotter, drier weather, but clouds provide humidity even in the dry season there. The mountains are noted for their very high floral diversity, with probably more than 4,000 species of vascular plants found in a mosaic of communities from gallery forest and semi-humid forest ('capões') to shrubby savanna and arid montane scrub with variable numbers of small trees and palms ('campos cerrados'), to open and rocky grasslands ('campos rupestres'). The dominant vegetation between 700 and 2,000 m is campos rupestres, noted for a high degree of endemism at both genus and species level (WWF/IUCN 1997).

■ Restricted-range species

All the restricted-range birds are found in the campos habitats of the EBA, principally above 700 m. There are some distributional differences, with *Polystictus superciliaris* and *Embernagra longicauda* being found throughout the EBA, whereas the two *Augustes*

Status and habitat of restricted-range species

Species (ordered taxonomically)	Global status	Other EBAs (and SAs)	Altitude (m)	Habitat
Hooded Visorbearer *Augastes lumachellus*	nt	—	950–1,600	Arid montane and semi-arid scrub
Hyacinth Visorbearer *Augastes scutatus*	nt	—	900–2,000	Arid montane scrub, rocky outcrops in grassland
Cipó Canastero *Asthenes luizae*	EN	—	1,000–1,200	Isolated rocky crags in undulating grassland
Brasília Tapaculo *Scytalopus novacapitalis*	VU	(s032)	800–1,000	Swampy gallery forest, secondary growth
Serra do Mar Tyrant-manakin *Neopelma chrysolophum*[1]	NE	076	1,150–1,750	Dense regrowth, forest edge and stunted woody vegetation
Grey-backed Tachuri *Polystictus superciliaris*	nt	076	1,100–1,600	Arid montane scrub, rocky outcrops in savanna and grassland
Pale-throated Pampa-finch *Embernagra longicauda*	nt	—	700–1,300	Arid montane scrub and dry savanna, agricultural land

Global status (see p. 679 for definitions)	EX Extinct EW Extinct in the Wild	} with year of last record	cd Conservation Dependent	**Other EBAs (and SAs)** (see p. 65 for locations)	Bracketed numbers are Secondary Areas. ˣ Extinct in that EBA or SA.
	CR Critical EN Endangered VU Vulnerable	} threatened species	nt Near Threatened lc Least Concern DD Data Deficient NE Not Evaluated	**Notes**	[1] Taxonomy follows Whitney *et al.* (1995).

hummingbirds form a superspecies with *A. lumachellus* confined to the northern half of the EBA and *A. scutatus* to the southern. *Neopelma chrysolophum* is found at only the southern end of the EBA in the Serra do Caraça with most of it range lying in the Serra do Mar (EBA 076). *Asthenes luizae* was discovered only in 1985 and was not described formally until 1990. To date, it is known only from a small part of the Serra do Cipó in the south, where it inhabits rock crevices and bushes on isolated outcrops in grassland. It is separated geographically from its closest relative, Short-billed Canestero *A. baeri*, by at least 1,450 km to the south-west (Pearman 1990). *Scytalopus novacapitalis* is found in this EBA mainly at Caraça (although this population may represent an as-yet-undescribed taxon), with a single sighting from Serra do Cipó; it occurs mainly west of the EBA in Goiás, Federal District and western Minas Gerais (s032). Populations of other tapaculos further north may also represent other undescribed taxa (R. Williams verbally 1997).

■ Threats and conservation

Much of this EBA has been colonized since diamonds and gold were found in the mountains in the 1800s, and up to 1890 it was estimated that one million people lived in the Minas Gerais part of the region. Gold-mining on a large scale died out at the turn of the century but small operations still continue, and quartz crystals and manganese are also mined (WWF/IUCN 1997). The major land use today is cattle-ranching, with cultivation being less of a threat owing to the generally low soil fertility compared to

the surrounding central Brazilian plateau. Cattle are grazed in natural grasslands, but fire is a threat in areas where new pastures are being created. The forests are used for timber extraction, charcoal and building materials, and all these developments are rapidly destroying large areas of pristine habitat.

Currently *Asthenes luizae* and *Scytalopus novacapitalis* are the only restricted-range species which are considered threatened, although a further four are Near Threatened. This treatment reflects the tiny range of *A. luizae* compared to the other species, and there is some evidence that it suffers from brood-parasitism by cowbirds (Vielliard 1990). *S. novacapitalis* is listed because it is vulnerable to habitat loss through fire (Collar *et al.* 1992).

As many as seven other threatened species have been recorded in the EBA (albeit mostly sporadically) within four Key Areas (Wege and Long 1995): Morro do Chapéu (unprotected) and Chapada Diamantina National Park (1,520 km²) in Bahia where arid-scrub species such as Great Xenops *Megaxenops parnaguae* and Pectoral Antwren *Herpsilochmus pectoralis* (both classified as Vulnerable) occur, and Serra do Cipó National Park (338 km²) and Caraça Natural Park, both in Minas Gerais, which have a few records of threatened species associated more with the Atlantic forests of south-east Brazil. Unfortunately, *Asthenes luizae* is not found in any of these reserves, although its small range falls close to the Serra do Cipó National Park boundary, and so only a small extension of the protected area would be needed to include it (Collar *et al.* 1992).

074 Deciduous forests of Minas Gerais and Goiás

PRIORITY
CRITICAL

Key habitats Deciduous forest	Area 33,000 km²	Altitude 0–500 m

Main threats Severe habitat loss (e.g. due to timber extraction, agriculture especially for soya beans)

Countries Brazil

Biological importance ● ● ●
Current threat level ● ● ●

Restricted-range species	Threatened	Total
Confined to this EBA	1	2
Present also in other EBAs, SAs	0	0
Total	1	2

■ General characteristics

This central Brazilian EBA is located along the upper drainage of the São Francisco river at the southern end of the caatinga region in north-west Minas Gerais and south-west Bahia and on the upper Rio Paraná in eastern Goiás. The area is characterized by gently rolling land with prominent limestone outcrops. The Paraná and São Francisco parts of the EBA are separated from each other by the Serras de Santa Maria and do Paraná, located on the Minas Gerais–Goiás state border.

The vegetation is tropical deciduous and semi-deciduous forest with some trees up to 30 m tall, and more arid scrub and cacti (characteristic of the caatinga region). Lower-stature forest and scrub tends to persist on the limestone outcrops whereas taller forest is found in the more humid areas between the ridges ('serras') and outcrops. Typical trees of semi-deciduous forests in Minas Gerais where the restricted-range species occur are *Bursera lepto-*

phloeos, *Astronium urundeuva*, *Chorisia venticosa*, *Cavanillesia arborea*, *Spondias tuberosa*, *Hymenaea martiana* and *Schinopsis* spp. (de Andrade *et al.* 1986).

■ Restricted-range species

Phylloscartes roquettei is known from Brejo-Januária (now Brejo do Amparo) in the São Francisco valley: a single specimen was collected in 1926 and field observations were made in 1977 (Willis and Oniki 1991). In 1997 it was recorded 40 km north-north-east of here (R. Williams verbally 1997). Brejo-Januária is also the type locality for Snethlage's Woodcreeper *Xiphocolaptes falcirostris franciscanus*, a taxon which is restricted to this EBA and which was treated as a species by Sibley and Monroe (1990, 1993), but is considered by most authorities (and here) to be a subspecies of Moustached Woodcreeper *X. falcirostris* (see Collar *et al.* 1992; also C. G. Sibley *in litt.* 1996).

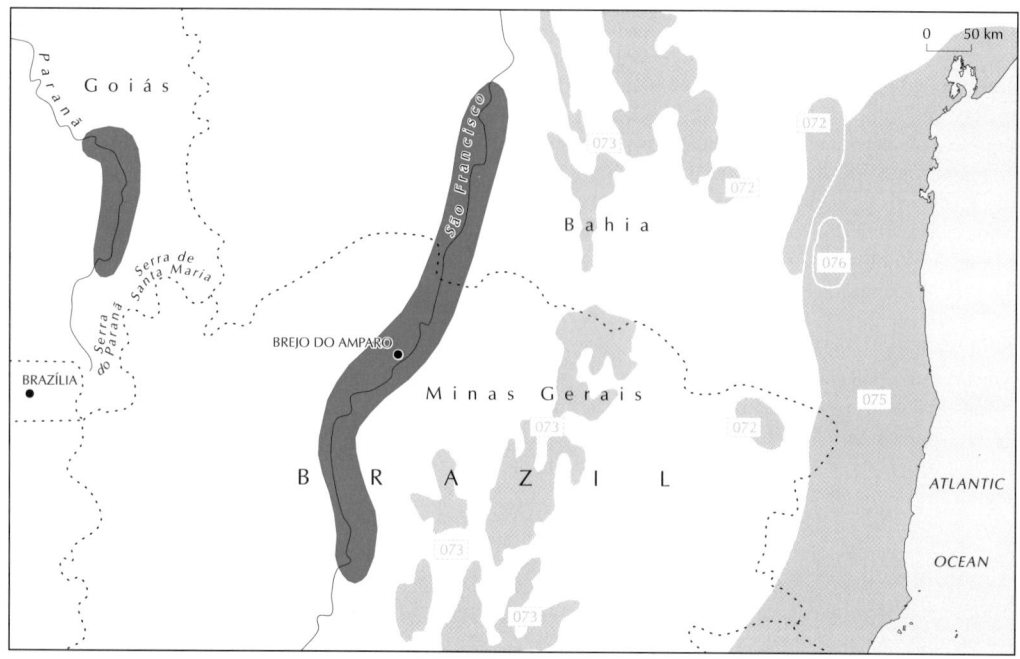

Status and habitat of restricted-range species

Species (ordered taxonomically)	Global status	Other EBAs (and SAs)	Altitude (m)	Habitat
Minas Gerais Tyrannulet *Phylloscartes roquettei*	EN	—	c.450	Probably dry tropical deciduous forest
Brazilian Black-tyrant *Knipolegus franciscanus* [1]	NE	—	c.500	Dry tropical deciduous forest on rich soils

Global status (see p. 679 for definitions)	EX Extinct EW Extinct in the Wild	with year of last record	cd Conservation Dependent	Other EBAs (and SAs) (see p. 65 for locations)	Bracketed numbers are Secondary Areas. X Extinct in that EBA or SA.
	CR Critical EN Endangered VU Vulnerable	threatened species	nt Near Threatened lc Least Concern DD Data Deficient NE Not Evaluated	Notes	[1] Taxonomy follows Silva and Oren (1992).

The other restricted-range species, *Knipolegus franciscanus*, occurs in both the upper São Francisco and Paraná valleys (da Silva and Oren 1992). It is often considered to be a subspecies of White-winged Black-tyrant *K. aterrimus*, but da Silva and Oren (1992) presented a number of morphological, ecological and distributional characters that indicate it should be considered a full species. The range of White-eared Parakeet *Pyrrhura leucotis pfrimeri* matches *franciscanus* and that taxon might also be given full specific status (da Silva 1989, Stotz *et al.* 1996).

■ Threats and conservation

Semi-deciduous forest is possibly the most threatened habitat in central Brazil. This is due to the presence of aroeira *Astronium urundeuva* (a valuable timber tree) as well as the fact that the region has relatively fertile soils (Collar *et al.* 1992). There has been extensive destruction of the forests in this EBA for timber, cultivation (especially soya beans), cattle-farming, charcoal production (to fuel the iron and steel industries of Minas Gerais) and limestone quarrying (da Silva and Oren 1992).

Given its presumed tiny range and the threats to remaining forest, *Phylloscartes roquettei* is considered threatened. In 1985–1986 charcoal-burners were in full activity around its type-locality, where forest cutting for pasture, and other agricultural development, were also rife (Collar *et al.* 1992). Searches for the species in the area since the last observations in 1977 have failed to find it there (Wege and Long 1995). There are four other more-widespread threatened birds that also occur in this EBA, namely Vinaceous Amazon *Amazona vinacea* (classified as Endangered), Golden-capped Parakeet *Aratinga auricapilla* (Vulnerable), *Xiphocolaptes falcirostris* (Vunerable; see 'Restricted-range species', above) and Great Xenops *Megaxenops parnaguae* (Vulnerable). *Knipolegus franciscanus* is listed in Collar *et al.* 1994 (p. 11) as a threatened subspecies which may be a valid species but has yet to be formally evaluated.

No reserve has been established so far to protect the natural habitat in this EBA although the creation of one by governmental and non-governmental organizations has been under consideration for some time (Collar *et al.* 1992).

075 Atlantic forest lowlands

Key habitats Restinga woodland, evergreen forest, bamboo forest

Main threats Severe habitat loss (e.g. due to logging, agriculture, urbanization)

Biological importance ● ● ●
Current threat level ● ● ●

Area 290,000 km²   **Altitude** 0–1,700 m

Countries Argentina, Brazil, Paraguay

Restricted-range species	Threatened	Total
Confined to this EBA	28	52
Present also in other EBAs, SAs	3	3
Total	31	55

■ General characteristics

This EBA covers an extensive stretch of coastal eastern Brazil and also parts of north-east Argentina and eastern Paraguay. It spans more than 2,500 km of the Atlantic slope coastline from central Bahia state south through the states of Espírito Santo, Rio de Janeiro, São Paulo, Paraná and Santa Catarina to Rio Grande do Sul. The southern end of the EBA extends inland into Minas Gerais, São Paulo, Paraná and Santa Catarina, and into north-east Argentina and eastern Paraguay in Caaguazú, Alto Paraná, Caazapá, Itapúa and easternmost Canindeyú. The continental divide between the Atlantic forest and the more arid region of interior Brazil is higher in altitude in the Serra do Mantaquiera and Serra do Mar in the south-eastern part of the EBA. In the higher-altitude areas

of these mountains and embraced within this EBA lie the Atlantic forest mountains (EBA 076).

The Atlantic forest is estimated originally to have covered 1.09 million km² (Brown and Brown 1992, Fearnside 1996), but a large proportion of this is the forest of the interior slopes of the continental divide. Indeed, Dinerstein *et al.* (1995) defined the Atlantic forest as comprising two ecoregions: coastal Atlantic forest (233,266 km²) and interior Atlantic forest (803,908 km²). This EBA relates best to the coastal Atlantic forest ecoregion as most of the restricted-range species are confined to the coastal slope, with fewer found in the interior Atlantic forest.

The natural vegetation of this region is mainly humid forest, often referred to as the 'Mata Atlântica'. These forests continue north of the EBA along the

Status and habitat of restricted-range species

Species (ordered taxonomically)	Global status	Other EBAs (and SAs)	Altitude (m)	Habitat
Red-billed Curassow *Crax blumenbachii*	CR	—	100–600	Tropical lowland evergreen forest, forest edge
Brown-backed Parrotlet *Touit melanonota*	EN	—	500–1,000	Tropical lowland evergreen and montane evergreen forest
Red-tailed Amazon *Amazona brasiliensis*	EN	—	Littoral lowlands	Tropical lowland evergreen and coastal forests, inc. restinga; roosts in mangroves
Blue-bellied Parrot *Triclaria malachitacea*	EN	—	300–1,000	Tropical lowland evergreen and montane evergreen forest
Tawny-browed Owl *Pulsatrix koeniswaldiana*	lc	—	0–1,500	Montane evergreen and tropical lowland evergreen forest
Minute Hermit *Phaethornis idaliae*	lc	—	0–300	Tropical lowland evergreen forest, forest edge, scrub
Saw-billed Hermit *Ramphodon naevius*	nt	—	0–900	Tropical lowland evergreen and secondary forest
Hook-billed Hermit *Glaucis dohrnii*	CR	—	Lowlands	Tropical lowland evergreen forest
Three-toed Jacamar *Jacamaralcyon tridactyla*	EN	—	0–1,000	Tropical lowland evergreen forest edge, gallery forest, secondary forest
Yellow-eared Woodpecker *Veniliornis maculifrons*	lc	—	0–1,300	Tropical lowland evergreen and secondary forest
Pink-legged Graveteiro *Acrobatornis fonsecai*[1]	NE	—	0–550	Canopy and subcanopy in lowland forest, canopy trees in cocoa plantations
Striated Softtail *Thripophaga macroura*	VU	—	<1,000	Tropical lowland evergreen forest
Red-eyed Thornbird *Phacellodomus erythrophthalmus*	lc	—	0–750	Tropical lowland evergreen, montane evergreen, and secondary forest, forest edge, thickets
Canebrake Groundcreeper *Clibanornis dendrocolaptoides*	nt	—	<800	Bamboo in tropical lowland evergreen forest
Pale-browed Treehunter *Cichlocolaptes leucophrus*	lc	—	0–1,400	Tropical lowland evergreen and montane evergreen forest
White-browed Foliage-gleaner *Philydor amaurotis*	nt	—	100–1,600	Montane and lowland evergreen forest
White-bearded Antshrike *Biatas nigropectus*	VU	—	<1,300	Tropical lowland evergreen and montane evergreen forest; associated with bamboo
Spot-breasted Antvireo *Dysithamnus stictothorax*	nt	—	<1,100	Tropical lowland evergreen and montane evergreen forest with vines
Plumbeous Antvireo *Dysithamnus plumbeus*	VU	—	<100	Tropical lowland evergreen forest
Star-throated Antwren *Myrmotherula gularis*	lc	—	300–1,200	Tropical lowland evergreen and montane evergreen forest
Rio de Janeiro Antwren *Myrmotherula fluminensis*	VU	—	c.20	Tropical lowland evergreen forest
Salvadori's Antwren *Myrmotherula minor*	VU	—	<500	Tropical lowland evergreen and mature secondary forest
Unicoloured Antwren *Myrmotherula unicolor*	VU	—	0–800	Tropical lowland evergreen forest, and secondary forest
Band-tailed Antwren *Myrmotherula urosticta*	VU	—	<100	Tropical lowland evergreen forest
Serra Antwren *Formicivora serrana*	nt	—	c.1,000	Tropical lowland evergreen forest edge, second-growth scrub
Black-hooded Antwren *Formicivora erythronotos*	CR	—	0–1,000	Swampy secondary forest near mangroves
Restinga Antwren *Formicivora littoralis*[2]	EN	—	Littoral lowlands	Bromeliad and cactus-rich restinga woodland and secondary scrub

cont.

Status and habitat of restricted-range species (cont.)

Species (ordered taxonomically)	Global status	Other EBAs (and SAs)	Altitude (m)	Habitat
Bertoni's Antbird *Drymophila rubricollis*	lc	—	100–2,000	Montane evergreen and tropical lowland evergreen forest, bamboo
Rio de Janeiro Antbird *Cercomacra brasiliana*	nt	—	c.1,000	Tropical lowland evergreen forest with vines
Fringe-backed Fire-eye *Pyriglena atra*	EN	—	<100	Tropical lowland evergreen forest edge, tall secondary growth
Scalloped Antbird *Myrmeciza ruficauda*	VU	071	0–500	Tropical evergreen forest, secondary growth, forest edge
White-bibbed Antbird *Myrmeciza loricata*	lc	—	700–1,300	Tropical lowland evergreen and montane evergreen forest
Squamate Antbird *Myrmeciza squamosa*	lc	—	c.100–1,000	Tropical lowland evergreen and montane evergreen forest
Such's Antthrush *Chamaeza meruloides*	lc	—	200–1,500	Tropical lowland evergreen and montane evergreen forest
Spotted Bamboowren *Psilorhamphus guttatus*	nt	—	<800	Bamboo thickets in tropical lowland evergreen forest
Slaty Bristlefront *Merulaxis ater*	nt	—	<1,300	Tropical lowland and montane evergreen forest, thickets
Stresemann's Bristlefront *Merulaxis stresemanni*	CR	—	Lowlands	Tropical lowland evergreen forest
Bahia Tapaculo *Scytalopus psychopompus*	EN	—	c.45	Flooded areas of thick vegetation in tropical lowland evergreen forest
Hooded Berryeater *Carpornis cucullatus*	nt	—	500–1,500	Tropical lowland evergreen and montane evergreen forest
Buff-throated Purpletuft *Iodopleura pipra*	VU	071	0–1,000	Tropical evergreen forest, secondary growth, forest edge
Kinglet Calyptura *Calyptura cristata*	CR	—	<c.900	Tropical lowland evergreen forest
Banded Cotinga *Cotinga maculata*	EN	—	<200	Tropical lowland evergreen forest
White-winged Cotinga *Xipholena atropurpurea*	VU	071	0–700	Tropical evergreen forest, secondary growth, forest edge
Kaempfer's Tody-tyrant *Hemitriccus kaempferi*	EN	—	c.150	Tropical lowland evergreen forest
Fork-tailed Pygmy-tyrant *Hemitriccus furcatus*	VU	—	<1,200	Bamboo in tropical lowland evergreen forest
Oustalet's Tyrannulet *Phylloscartes oustaleti*	nt	—	0–800	Tropical lowland evergreen forest
Restinga Tyrannulet *Phylloscartes kronei*[3]	VU	—	Littoral lowlands	Restinga woodland, secondary forest, scrub
Buffy-fronted Seedeater *Sporophila frontalis*	EN	—	0–1,500	Bamboo in tropical lowland evergreen and montane evergreen forest
Temminck's Seedeater *Sporophila falcirostris*	EN	—	0–1,500	Bamboo in tropical lowland evergreen and secondary forest, forest edge
Dubois's Seedeater *Sporophila ardesiaca*	lc	—	0–900	Riparian thickets, freshwater marshes, second-growth scrub, grassland
Cherry-throated Tanager *Nemosia rourei*	CR	—	0–900	Unknown, but possibly tropical lowland evergreen forest
Azure-shouldered Tanager *Thraupis cyanoptera*	nt	—	200–1,200	Tropical lowland evergreen and montane evergreen forest, forest edge, secondary growth
Gilt-edged Tanager *Tangara cyanoventris*	lc	—	0–1,200	Tropical lowland evergreen, montane evergreen and secondary forest, forest edge, clearings
Black-backed Tanager *Tangara peruviana*	EN	—	0–600	Restinga woodland, secondary forest, tropical lowland evergreen forest edge, scrub and thickets

cont.

Status and habitat of restricted-range species (cont.)

Species (ordered taxonomically)	Global status	Other EBAs (and SAs)	Altitude (m)	Habitat
Black-legged Dacnis *Dacnis nigripes*	VU	—	0–1,700	Tropical lowland evergreen forest, forest edge, secondary growth

Global status (see p. 679 for definitions)

EX Extinct ⎱ with year
EW Extinct in ⎰ of last
  the Wild ⎰ record
CR Critical ⎱
EN Endangered ⎰ threatened
VU Vulnerable ⎰ species

cd Conservation Dependent
nt Near Threatened
lc Least Concern
DD Data Deficient
NE Not Evaluated

Other EBAs (and SAs) (see p. 65 for locations)
Bracketed numbers are Secondary Areas.   ˣ Extinct in that EBA or SA.

Notes
[1] New species (Pacheco *et al.* 1996).
[2] Treated as a species by Collar *et al.* (1992); see also Ridgely and Tudor (1944).
[3] New species (Willis and Oniki 1992).

Atlantic slope as far as Ceará and Rio Grande do Norte states. The forest includes a number of distinct types ranging from coastal low-lying woodland scrub ('restinga') to tall evergreen formations (which are related both structurally and in species composition to Amazonian rain forest, characterized by over 1,000 mm of rainfall annually with no distinct dry period), semi-deciduous forest (normally found inland of the coastal slope and described as having c.1,000 mm annual rainfall with a clear dry season) and 'liana forest' (which marks the transition zone between the humid forest and the dry deciduous forest of interior Brazil). There is no defined dry season in the southern part of the EBA in Paraguay; any month can have the most rainfall. The climate at this latitude is much more a summer/winter one. Floral diversity is very high, with several thousand species occurring, and the forests are probably among the richest areas in the world for tree diversity (some 53% are thought to be endemic), some studies in southern Bahia having found 425–450 species per ha (WWF/IUCN 1997).

■ Restricted-range species

This EBA has a particularly distinct avifauna including ten endemic genera—*Triclaria, Ramphodon, Jacamaralcyon, Acrobatornis, Clibanornis, Cichlocolaptes, Biatas, Psilorhamphus, Merulaxis* and *Calyptura.*

All the EBA's restricted-range bird species are forest-dwelling, but show distinct forest-type or altitudinal preferences (see 'Habitat associations' table): some, such as the recently described *Phylloscartes kronei* and *Formicivora littoralis*, are found only in the restinga woodland, which makes up a small fraction of the habitat in the EBA; others, such as several *Sporophila* spp., are found mainly in the bamboo stands which are present patchily within the forest.

In the original analysis (ICBP 1992; see also Brandão 1990), two EBAs were defined within this current EBA. Species confined to the Bahia and Espírito Santo lowlands were treated separately, but a further examination of their ranges showed that there is considerable overlap with the ranges of foothill species, and both groups have thus been combined into one EBA in the present study. A

Restinga (coastal low-lying woodland scrub) is a key, diminishing habitat for at least four of the restricted-range (and threatened) birds in this EBA.

Rio de Janeiro Antbird *Cercomacra brasiliana* is one of 18 antbirds found in this EBA.

C. Byers

number of the birds in this newly defined EBA do not overlap with each other in distribution with, for instance, those formerly in the Bahia and Espírito lowlands EBA (*Crax blumenbachii, Phaethornis idaliae, Glaucis dohrnii* and *Dysithamnus plumbeus*) not co-occurring with species confined to the southern part of the EBA (such as *Amazona brasiliensis, Phylloscartes kronei, Clibanornis dendrocolaptoides* and *Hemitriccus kaempferi*). Overall, however, many species do overlap in São Paulo, Rio de Janeiro and southern Espírito Santo states (see 'Distribution patterns' table).

Many other bird species are largely confined to the Atlantic forest of Brazil (some entirely), but their ranges are judged to be greater than 50,000 km² and they have therefore not been considered to have restricted ranges. Stotz *et al.* (1996) list 199 bird species as endemic to the Atlantic forest. Within their

N. Arlott

Remaining populations of Red-tailed Amazon *Amazona brasiliensis* are declining precipitously as a result of trapping and habitat loss.

Habitat associations of restricted-range species

Restinga woodland and/ or mangrove in littoral lowlands
Amazona brasiliensis
Formicivora erythronotos
Formicivora littoralis
Phylloscartes kronei

Tropical forest in lowlands (mainly below 500 m)
Crax blumenbachii
Phaethornis idaliae
Glaucis dohrnii
Jacamaralcyon tridactyla
Acrobatornis fonsecai
Thripophaga macroura
Dysithamnus plumbeus
Myrmotherula fluminensis
Myrmotherula minor
Myrmotherula unicolor
Myrmotherula urosticta
Pyriglena atra
Myrmeciza ruficauda
Merulaxis stresemanni
Scytalopus psychopompus
Iodopleura pipra
Calyptura cristata
Cotinga maculata
Xipholena atropurpurea
Hemitriccus kaempferi
Tangara peruviana

Tropical forest (inc. viny transitional forest) mainly 500-1,250 m, also lower
Ramphodon naevius
Veniliornis maculifrons
Phacellodomus erythrophthalmus

Dysithamnus stictothorax
Formicivora serrana
Cercomacra brasiliana
Nemosia rourei
Dacnis nigripes

Lowland and montane tropical forest mainly in foothills and lower mountains
Touit melanonota
Triclaria malachitacea
Pulsatrix koeniswaldiana
Cichlocolaptes leucophrus
Philydor amaurotis
Myrmotherula gularis
Drymophila rubricollis
Myrmeciza loricata
Myrmeciza squamosa
Chamaeza meruloides
Merulaxis ater
Carpornis cucullatus
Phylloscartes oustaleti
Thraupis cyanoptera
Tangara cyanoventris

Bamboo associations in lowland and/or montane forest
Clibanornis dendrocolaptoides
Biatas nigropectus
Psilorhamphus guttatus
Hemitriccus furcatus
Sporophila frontalis
Sporophila falcirostris

Riparian scrub, freshwater marshes, grassland
Sporophila ardesiaca

Threatened species (Critical, Endangered, Vulnerable) are shown in **bold**; see 'Status and habitat' table.

Distribution patterns of restricted-range species

Species (ordered geographically)	Coastal Bahia N of 14°S	Coastal Bahia 14–17°30'S	Coastal Bahia S of 17°30'S	N Espírito Santo	S Espírito Santo	E Minas Gerais	Rio de Janeiro	N São Paulo	S São Paulo	Paraná	Santa Catarina	R. Grande do Sul	Misiones, Argentina	E Paraná, Paraguay	Other EBAs, SAs
Acrobatornis fonsecai	●	–	–	–	–	–	–	–	–	–	–	–	–	–	–
Pyriglena atra	●	●	–	–	–	–	–	–	–	–	–	–	–	–	–
Merulaxis stresemanni	●	–	–	–	–	–	–	–	–	–	–	–	–	–	–
Scytalopus psychopompus	●	●	–	–	–	–	–	–	–	–	–	–	–	–	–
Myrmotherula urosticta	●	●	●	●	●	●	–	–	–	–	–	–	–	–	–
Xipholena atropurpurea	●	●	–	–	●	●	●	–	–	–	–	–	–	–	○
Myrmeciza loricata	●	●	●	●	●	●	●	●	–	–	–	–	–	–	–
Crax blumenbachii	–	●	●	●	●	●	–	–	–	–	–	–	–	–	–
Myrmeciza ruficauda	–	●	●	●	●	●	●	–	–	–	–	–	–	–	○
Glaucis dohrnii	–	●	●	●	–	●	?	–	–	–	–	–	–	–	–
Thripophaga macroura	–	●	●	●	●	●	●	–	–	–	–	–	–	–	–
Cotinga maculata	–	●	●	●	●	●	●	–	–	–	–	–	–	–	–
Cercomacra brasiliana	–	●	?	?	●	●	●	?	–	–	–	–	–	–	–
Hemitriccus furcatus	–	●	?	?	●	?	●	●	–	–	–	–	–	–	–
Sporophila falcirostris	–	●	?	●	●	●	●	●	●	●	–	●	–	●	–
Dysithamnus plumbeus	–	–	●	●	●	●	●	–	–	–	–	–	–	–	–
Sporophila ardesiaca	–	–	●	●	●	●	●	–	–	–	–	–	–	–	–
Tangara cyanoventris	–	–	●	●	●	●	●	●	–	–	–	–	–	–	–
Merulaxis ater	–	–	●	●	–	●	●	●	●	●	–	–	–	–	–
Phylloscartes oustaleti	–	–	●	●	?	●	●	●	●	●	–	–	–	–	–
Phacellodomus erythrophthalmus	–	–	●	●	●	●	●	●	●	●	●	–	–	–	–
Triclaria malachitacea	–	–	●	●	●	●	●	●	●	●	●	●	–	–	–
Dysithamnus stictothorax	–	–	●	●	●	●	●	●	●	●	●	●	–	–	–
Cichlocolaptes leucophrus	–	–	–	●	●	●	●	●	●	●	●	●	–	–	–
Myrmotherula gularis	–	–	–	●	●	●	●	●	●	●	●	●	–	–	–
Thraupis cyanoptera	–	–	–	●	●	●	●	●	●	●	●	●	–	–	–
Ramphodon naevius	–	–	–	●	●	●	●	●	●	●	●	●	–	–	–
Sporophila frontalis	–	–	–	●	●	●	●	●	●	?	?	●	–	●	–
Formicivora serrana	–	–	–	–	●	●	●	–	–	–	–	–	–	–	–
Jacamaralcyon tridactyla	–	–	–	–	●	●	●	●	●	●	–	–	–	–	–
Myrmotherula minor	–	–	–	–	●	●	●	●	●	●	●	–	–	–	–
Chamaeza meruloides	–	–	–	–	●	●	●	●	●	●	●	–	–	–	–
Carpornis cucullatus	–	–	–	–	●	●	●	●	●	●	●	–	–	–	–
Psilorhamphus guttatus	–	–	–	–	●	●	●	●	●	●	●	–	●	–	–
Biatas nigropectus	–	–	–	–	●	●	–	●	●	●	●	●	●	–	–
Philydor amaurotis	–	–	–	–	●	●	?	●	●	●	●	●	●	–	–
Pulsatrix koeniswaldiana	–	–	–	–	●	●	–	●	●	●	–	●	●	–	–
Phaethornis idaliae	–	–	–	–	–	●	●	–	–	–	–	–	–	–	–
Nemosia rourei	–	–	–	–	–	●	–	●	–	–	–	–	–	–	–
Veniliornis maculifrons	–	–	–	–	–	●	●	●	●	–	–	–	–	–	–
Iodopleura pipra	–	–	–	–	–	●	●	●	●	–	–	–	–	–	○
Dacnis nigripes	–	–	–	–	–	●	●	●	●	–	–	–	–	–	–
Myrmotherula unicolor	–	–	–	–	–	●	●	●	●	●	●	●	–	–	–
Drymophila rubricollis	–	–	–	–	–	?	●	●	●	●	●	●	●	–	–
Myrmotherula fluminensis	–	–	–	–	–	–	●	–	–	–	–	–	–	–	–
Formicivora erythronotos	–	–	–	–	–	–	●	–	–	–	–	–	–	–	–
Formicivora littoralis	–	–	–	–	–	–	●	–	–	–	–	–	–	–	–
Calyptura cristata	–	–	–	–	–	–	●	–	–	–	–	–	–	–	–
Touit melanonota	–	–	–	–	–	–	●	●	●	–	–	–	–	–	–
Tangara peruviana	–	–	–	–	–	–	●	●	●	●	●	–	–	–	–
Myrmeciza squamosa	–	–	–	–	–	–	●	●	●	●	●	–	–	–	–
Amazona brasiliensis	–	–	–	–	–	–	–	–	●	●	●	?	–	–	–
Phylloscartes kronei	–	–	–	–	–	–	–	–	●	●	●	–	–	–	–
Clibanornis dendrocolaptoides	–	–	–	–	–	–	–	–	●	●	●	●	●	●	–
Hemitriccus kaempferi	–	–	–	–	–	–	–	–	–	–	●	–	–	–	–
Total	7	14	16	22	26	35	42	31	31	24	21	12	10	6	

● Present	? Present?	Threatened spp.	see 'Status
○ Extinct?	R Reintroduced	shown in **bold**	and habitat' table
X Extinct	I Introduced	Other EBAs, SAs	

defined area they recognize four subregions of which two are largely embraced within this EBA: the Rio de Janeiro–Bahia lowlands (22 endemics), which corresponds to the central and northern half of this EBA, and the southern Atlantic coast (101 endemics), which is equivalent partly to the southern half of this EBA plus the Atlantic forest mountains (EBA 076).

Knowledge of south-east Brazil's avifauna is constantly improving through fieldwork and museum-based research, which is demonstrated by the discoveries in the last 10 years of *Myrmotherula fluminensis*, *Formicivora littoralis*, *Scytalopus psychopompus*, *Phylloscartes kronei* and *Acrobatornis fonsecai* as species new to science and all endemic to this EBA (with another three new species in adjacent EBA 076). *A. fonsecai* is a particularly interesting and remarkable find, being in its own genus and, although not a particularly cryptic bird, discovered only in 1995 in southern Bahia (Pacheco *et al.* 1996). Several new populations of restricted-range birds have been found in this region in recent years, providing further indication of the need for continuing surveys: *Calyptura cristata*, which had been unrecorded for more than a century and was thus thought possibly to be extinct, was rediscovered in

Flat lowland forest now covers just a tiny fraction of its original extent in this EBA. Larger forest blocks survive on the foothills above the coastal plain.

N. J. Collar/BirdLife International

1996 (L. P. Gonzaga *in litt.* 1996), and *Hemitriccus kaempferi*, known from just two specimens, both collected before 1950, has now been seen regularly at its type-locality.

■ Threats and conservation

This EBA lies within the most densely populated region of Brazil, being one of the first places in South America to be colonized by Europeans, 400 years ago. Destruction of the forest (e.g. for timber such as brazilwood *Caesalpina echinata*) began soon after their arrival. The fertile lands of the coastal plain were converted to agriculture, and then deforestation for mining, coffee, banana and rubber plantations occurred as the settlers moved inland (Fearnside 1996). The main threats to the remaining forest over the next 10 years will be urbanization, industrialization, agricultural expansion, colonization and associated road-building (Dinerstein *et al.* 1995). All this destruction has reduced the Atlantic forest in this EBA to less than 20% of its original extent, and in some parts, such as Bahia and Espírito Santo states, less than 10% remains (based on 1990 figures given in Brown and Brown 1992).

The poor state of the forest in the EBA is reflected by the fact that 31 of the restricted-range species are threatened; these include six classified as Critical and 12 as Endangered. An additional 10 more-widespread threatened species are almost wholly confined to the EBA: Black-fronted Piping-guan *Pipile jacutinga* (Vulnerable), Helmeted Woodpecker *Dryocopus galeatus* (Endangered), Golden-tailed Parrotlet *Touit surda* (Endangered), Red-browed Amazon *Amazona rhodocorytha* (Endangered), Blue-chested Parakeet *Pyrrhura cruentata* (Vulnerable), Purple-winged Ground-dove *Claravis godefrida* (Critical), White-necked Hawk *Leucopternis lacernulata* (Vulnerable), Black-headed Berryeater *Carpornis melanocephalus* (Vulnerable), Cinnamon-vented Piha *Lipaugus lanioides* (Vulnerable), Shrike-like Cotinga *Laniisoma elegans* (Vulnerable), São Paulo Tyrannulet *Phylloscartes paulistus* (Vulnerable) and Russet-winged Spadebill *Platyrinchus leucoryphus* (Vulnerable). Thus, c.13% of all the threatened birds in the Americas occur in this EBA, highlighting the exceptional importance of this area and the great need for conservation action to prevent future extinctions (Brooks and Balmford 1996, Collar *et al.* 1997).

A total of 73 Key Areas for threatened birds have been identified within the EBA, including 51 in Brazil, 13 in Paraguay and 8 in Argentina (Wege and Long 1995). Many of these areas hold more than five threatened species and 18 threatened species have been recorded from Desengano State Park in Rio de Janeiro, probably the highest total for any locality in

This EBA has suffered
severe habitat loss.

N. J. Collar/BirdLife International

the world. The level of protection in this EBA is quite good, 56 of the Key Areas having some form of protected status. It is clear, however, that on-the-ground protection, with adequate infrastructure to maintain and manage these areas, is often lacking.

Particularly important Key Areas in Brazil are Serra do Ouricana/Boa Nova (unprotected), Monte Pascoal National Park (225 km^2), Porto Seguro/Florestas Rio Doce SA Forest (60 km^2), Rio Doce State Forest Park (359 km^2), Sooretama Federal Biological (240 km^2), CVRD Forestry Reserve of Linhares (220 km^2), Augusto Ruschi (Nova Lombardia) Federal Biological Reserve (45 km^2), Desengano State Park (225 km^2), Itatiaia National Park (300 km^2), Serra dos Órgãos National Park (110 km^2), Angra dos Reis (unprotected), Bairro do Corcovado in Serra do Mar State Park (3,148 km^2), Fazenda Intervales State Reserve (380 km^2), Ilhas Comprida and Cananéia Environmental Protection Area (2,028 km^2) and Ilha do Cardoso State Park (225 km^2). In Paraguay four Key Areas are of special importance for threatened and restricted-range birds: San Rafael National Park (600 km^2), Mbaracayú Forest Nature Reserve (644 km^2), Caaguazú National Park (160 km^2) and Itabó Private Nature Reserve (27 km^2) (Lowen *et al.* 1996). Notable areas in Argentina are Iguazú National Park (536 km^2) and Arroyo Urugua-í Natural Reserve (840 km^2) (Wege and Long 1995).

076 Atlantic forest mountains

PRIORITY URGENT

| Key habitats | Pine forest |
| Main threats | Moderate habitat loss (e.g. due to commercial logging) |

| Area | 260,000 km² | Altitude | 500–2,800 m |
| Countries | Argentina, Brazil |

Biological importance ● ● ●
Current threat level ● ○ ○

Restricted-range species	Threatened	Total
Confined to this EBA	3	21
Present also in other EBAs, SAs	0	2
Total	3	23

■ General characteristics

This EBA encompasses the upper subtropical and montane areas of eastern Brazil, and extreme north-east Argentina. The EBA is centred on the upland areas of Serra da Mantiqueira (with its highest point at Pico Agulhas Negras, 2,787 m) and Serra do Mar of Minas Gerais, Rio de Janeiro and São Paulo states—but it also extends further to the north, south and west. In the north there are small and often isolated pockets of montane forest in Espírito Santo, eastern Minas Gerais (e.g. Serra do Caparaó) and in Serra do Ouricana in south-central Bahia. To the south the EBA extends into Paraná along the Serra

Paranapiacaba and into Santa Catarina and Rio Grande do Sul along the Serra do Mar, Serra Geral and into the Serra do Sudeste of south-east Rio Grande do Sul. To the west the EBA reaches extreme north-east Argentina in Misiones state. Lying adjacent to this EBA are the south-east Brazilian Atlantic forest lowlands (EBA 075).

The natural vegetation is a variety of humid forest with increasing proportions of conifer forest (*Araucaria angustifolia* and *Podocarpus lambertii*) in the south and west. At upper elevations of the Serras da Mantiqueira, do Mar, and Paranapiacaba there are extremely humid cloud-forests (elfin for-

Status and habitat of restricted-range species

Species (ordered taxonomically)	Global status	Other EBAs (and SAs)	Altitude (m)	Habitat
Red-spectacled Amazon *Amazona pretrei*	EN	—	500–1,000	Southern temperate forest, primarily *Araucaria*
Long-tailed Cinclodes *Cinclodes pabsti*	lc	—	750–1,700	Southern temperate grassland, pasture/agricultural land, rocky savanna
Striolated Tit-spinetail *Leptasthenura striolata*	lc	—	500–1,900	Southern temperate forest, *Podocarpus* woodland, low trees, riparian thickets
Araucaria Tit-spinetail *Leptasthenura setaria*	nt	—	750–1,100	Southern temperate and secondary forest, *Araucaria* woodland
Itatiaia Thistletail *Schizoeaca moreirae*	lc	—	2,000–2,800	Semihumid/humid montane scrub, bamboo, woodland, grassland
Bahia Spinetail *Synallaxis whitneyi* [1]	NE	—	750–1,000	Humid forest, esp. dense tangles of vines, ferns and bamboo near forest edge
Rufous-backed Antvireo *Dysithamnus xanthopterus*	lc	—	900–2,000	Montane evergreen forest
Rufous-tailed Antbird *Drymophila genei*	nt	—	1,200–2,200	Montane evergreen forest, bamboo *Chusquea*
Ochre-rumped Antbird *Drymophila ochropyga*	nt	—	600–1,300	Tropical lowland evergreen and montane evergreen forest, thickets
Rufous-tailed Antthrush *Chamaeza ruficauda*	lc	—	1,000–2,000	Montane evergreen forest
Black-and-gold Cotinga *Tijuca atra*	nt	—	1,200–2,100	Montane evergreen forest
Grey-winged Cotinga *Tijuca condita*	VU	—	1,400–1200	Elfin forest, bamboo, tussock-grass
Serra do Mar Tyrant-manakin *Neopelma chrysolophum* [2]	NE	073	1,150–1,750	Montane evergreen forest, esp. in dense regrowth, forest edge and stunted woody vegetation
Black-capped Manakin *Piprites pileatus*	VU	—	900–2,000	Southern temperate, montane evergreen and *Araucaria* forest, forest edge
Brown-breasted Bamboo-tyrant *Hemitriccus obsoletus*	lc	—	1,300–2,300	Montane evergreen forest, bamboo
Grey-capped Tyrannulet *Phyllomyias griseocapilla*	nt	—	750–1,850	Montane evergreen and tropical lowland evergreen forest
Grey-backed Tachuri *Polystictus superciliaris*	nt	073	1,100–1,600	Arid montane scrub ('campos cerrados'), rocky outcrops in savanna and grassland ('campos rupestres')
Serra do Mar Tyrannulet *Phylloscartes difficilis*	nt	—	900–2,100	Montane evergreen forest, forest edge
Bahia Tyrannulet *Phylloscartes beckeri* [3]	NE	—	900–1,100	Montane evergreen forest and edge
Bay-chested Warbling-finch *Poospiza thoracica*	lc	—	900–2,100	Montane evergreen and southern temperate forest, forest edge, clearings, scrub
Black-bellied Seedeater *Sporophila melanogaster*	nt	—	700–1,100	Freshwater marshes, southern temperate grassland, scrub
Olive-green Tanager *Orthogonys chloricterus*	lc	—	700–1,800	Montane evergreen and secondary forest, forest edge
Brassy-breasted Tanager *Tangara desmaresti*	lc	—	600–2,200	Montane evergreen forest, forest edge, secondary growth

Global status (see p. 679 for definitions)

EX	Extinct	cd	Conservation Dependent
EW	Extinct in the Wild		
		nt	Near Threatened
CR	Critical	lc	Least Concern
EN	Endangered	DD	Data Deficient
VU	Vulnerable	NE	Not Evaluated

EX Extinct, EW Extinct in the Wild — with year of last record. CR Critical, EN Endangered, VU Vulnerable — threatened species.

Other EBAs (and SAs) (see p. 65 for locations)

Bracketed numbers are Secondary Areas. ˣ Extinct in that EBA or SA.

Notes

[1] New species (Gonzaga and Pacheco 1995).
[2] Taxonomy follows Whitney *et al.* (1995)
[3] New species (Pacheco and Gonzaga 1995).

est), which are open and low in stature (up to 15 m tall), dominated by *Weinmannia*, *Drymys brasiliensis*, *Lamanonia speciosa*, *Rapanea* and *Miconia*. The mountain slopes (mainly above 800 m) are dominated by humid montane forest which holds many trees taller than 30 m covered in epiphytes and lianas, with a rich understorey including tree ferns. The montane forest, like that in the lowlands, is very rich in plant species, with high levels of endemism (WWF/IUCN 1997).

■ Restricted-range species

Most of the restricted-range bird species are forest-dwelling, the exceptions being *Cinclodes pabsti*, which is found in the rocky savanna, and *Sporophila melanogaster*, which occurs in scrub and marsh (both breed in north-east Rio Grande Sul and adjacent Santa Catarina). Three species—*Drymophila genei*, *D. rubricollis* and *Hemitriccus obsoletus*—favour bamboo stands. Only a few are restricted to upper altitudes, notably *Schizoeaca moreirae* and *Tijuca condita*, but also *Drymophila genei*, *Tijuca atra* and *Phylloscartes difficilis*. Thus many of the birds in this EBA can overlap at their lower altitudinal limits with a few of the species found in the adjacent south-east Brazilian Atlantic forest lowlands (EBA 075).

In the previous analysis (ICBP 1992) four species (*Amazona pretrei*, *Leptasthenura striolata*, *L. setaria* and *Piprites pileatus*) were treated as forming their own EBA, being associated mainly with *Araucaria* forest. However, *L. setaria* is the only one found exclusively in such forest; *A. pretrei* also breeds in forest dominated by *Podocarpus lambertii*, especially in the Serra do Sudeste (Varty *et al.* 1994), and possibly wanders in the austral winter as far north as Paraguay (Lowen *et al.* 1996); *L. striolata* is also associated with *Podocarpus*-dominated forest mixed in with *Araucaria* forest; and *Piprites pileatus* is found in humid montane forest in the north of its range in Rio de Janeiro state.

Knowledge of the avifauna of south-east Brazil is constantly improving through fieldwork and museum-based research, as demonstrated by the discoveries over the last 20 years of *Synallaxis whitneyi* and *Phylloscartes beckeri* (from southern Bahia, described as new to science in 1995: Gonzaga and Pacheco 1995, Pacheco and Gonzaga 1995), and *Tijuca condita* (from the Serra do Mar in Rio de Janeiro state: Snow 1980). *S. whitneyi* and *P. beckeri* are both confined to the northernmost part of the EBA in the Serra do Ouricana; recent surveys in this small range of isolated hills not only discovered these

Distribution patterns of restricted-range species Species (ordered geographically)	Coastal Bahia 14–17°30′S	N Espírito Santo	S Espírito Santo	SE Minas Gerais	Rio de Janeiro	N São Paulo	S São Paulo	Paraná	Santa Catarina	R. Grande do Sul	Misiones, Argentina	Alto Paraná, Paraguay	Other EBAs, SAs
Synallaxis whitneyi	•	–	–	–	–	–	–	–	–	–	–	–	–
Phylloscartes beckeri	•	–	–	–	–	–	–	–	–	–	–	–	–
Drymophila ochropyga	•	–	–	•	•	•	•	•	–	–	–	–	–
Phyllomyias griseocapilla	•	•	•	•	•	•	•	•	•	–	–	–	–
Tangara desmaresti	–	•	•	•	•	•	•	•	•	–	–	–	–
Drymophila genei	–	–	•	•	•	•	–	–	–	–	–	–	–
Schizoeaca moreirae	–	–	•	–	•	•	–	–	–	–	–	–	–
Tangara desmaresti	–	–	•	–	•	•	•	–	–	–	–	–	–
Dysithamnus xanthopterus	–	–	?	–	•	•	•	•	–	–	–	–	–
Chamaeza ruficauda	–	–	•	•	•	•	•	•	•	•	–	–	–
Phylloscartes difficilis	–	–	•	•	•	•	•	•	•	•	–	–	–
Neopelma chrysolophum	–	–	–	•	•	•	•	–	–	–	–	–	•
Orthogonys chloricterus	–	–	–	•	•	•	•	•	•	–	–	–	–
Poospiza thoracica	–	–	–	•	•	•	•	•	•	–	–	–	–
Leptasthenura setaria	–	–	–	?	•	•	•	•	•	•	•	–	–
Piprites pileatus	–	–	–	•	•	•	•	•	•	•	•	–	–
Tijuca condita	–	–	–	–	•	–	–	–	–	–	–	–	–
Tijuca atra	–	–	–	–	•	•	–	–	–	–	–	–	–
Hemitriccus obsoletus	–	–	–	–	•	•	•	•	•	•	–	–	–
Polystictus superciliaris	–	–	–	–	–	•	–	–	–	–	–	–	•
Leptasthenura striolata	–	–	–	–	–	–	–	–	•	•	–	–	–
Sporophila melanogaster	–	–	–	–	–	M	M	•	•	–	–	–	–
Cinclodes pabsti	–	–	–	–	–	–	–	–	–	•	–	–	–
Amazona pretrei	–	–	–	–	–	–	–	–	?	•	•	M?	–
Total	4	2	7	11	17	17	13	13	11	10	3	?	

● Present	? Present?	Threatened spp. shown in **bold**	see 'Status and habitat' table
○ Extinct?	R Reintroduced	Other EBAs, SAs	
M Migrant	I Introduced		

High-altitude forest at Itatiaia National Park, an important site for many restricted-range and threatened species.

J. Tobias

new taxa but made significant northward range extensions for more than 20 species, including some of this EBA's restricted-range species (Gonzaga *et al.* 1995); see 'Distribution patterns' table.

■ Threats and conservation

The historical size of this EBA is difficult to assess as the extent of *Araucaria* forest has been much reduced by man. In the state of Paraná alone, for example, it has been estimated that the original forest covered 73,780 km², but in 1965 only 15,932 km² remained (Hueck 1978). However, the humid montane forest in the centre of the EBA in Rio de Janeiro and São Paulo has suffered less destruction than forest in the neighbouring lowlands, and large areas remain, notably in São Paulo. Nevertheless, the isolated montane forests in the north of the EBA, especially in the Serra do Ouricana, have virtually disappeared owing to the expansion of pastureland and cultivation. It is likely that the remaining forest patches will be under pressure from clearance or from fires spreading out of cultivated areas (Gonzaga *et al.* 1995). This part of the EBA is of critical priority for conservation action (Whitney 1996).

Only three restricted-range species in the EBA are presently considered threatened; the threat status of the two new species from the Serra do Ouricana is yet to be formally evaluated, but both will certainly be considered threatened because of their small ranges and diminishing habitat. A further nine more-widespread threatened birds occur in this region, including a large part of the range of the threatened Vinaceous Amazon *Amazona vinacea* (classified as Endangered) in upland forest in the southern part of this EBA. The greatly reduced extent of the *Araucaria* forest is the principal reason for *Amazona pretrei* and *Piprites pileatus* being classified as threatened, and *Tijuca condita* is listed because of its highly restricted range which could be susceptible to disturbance such as fires started by hikers (Collar *et al.* 1992).

There are a large number of national and state parks that hold suitable habitat for, and populations of, the restricted-range species. These include Caparaó (Minas Gerais–Espírito Santo), Itatiaia (Rio de Janeiro–Minas Gerais, 300 km²), Serra dos Órgãos (Rio de Janeiro, 110 km²), Serra do Tinguá (Rio de Janeiro, 260 km²), Campos do Jordão (São Paulo, 83 km²), Serra da Bocaina (São Paulo, 1,000 km²), Serra do Mar State Park (São Paulo, 3,148 km²), Fazenda Intervales (São Paulo, 380 km²), Alto Ribeira (São Paulo, 377 km²) and Aparados da Serra (Rio Grande do Sul, 123 km²).

077 Argentine Mesopotamian grasslands

Key habitats Seasonally wet grassland, marshes, woodland

Main threats Severe habitat loss and degradation (e.g. due to cattle-ranching, drainage)

Biological importance ● ● ○
Current threat level ● ● ●

Area 160,000 km²   **Altitude** 0–1,100 m

Countries Argentina, Brazil, Uruguay

Restricted-range species	Threatened	Total
Confined to this EBA	2	3
Present also in other EBAs, SAs	0	0
Total	2	3

■ General characteristics

Mesopotamia is a low-lying region covering Misiones, Corrientes and Entre Ríos provinces of north-west Argentina. The EBA is restricted to the two southernmost provinces of Mesopotamia, covering much of Corrientes and eastern Entre Ríos, along the floodplains of the lower Uruguay river to where it enters the Río de la Plata in the Paraná delta. Also included in the EBA is western and south-east Uruguay and southern Rio Grande do Sul state in Brazil. The EBA probably also extends into extreme southern Paraguay as two of the restricted-range birds have been found recently during the breeding season (R. P. Clay *in litt.* 1997). The principal habitat is marshes and periodically inundated wet grassland,

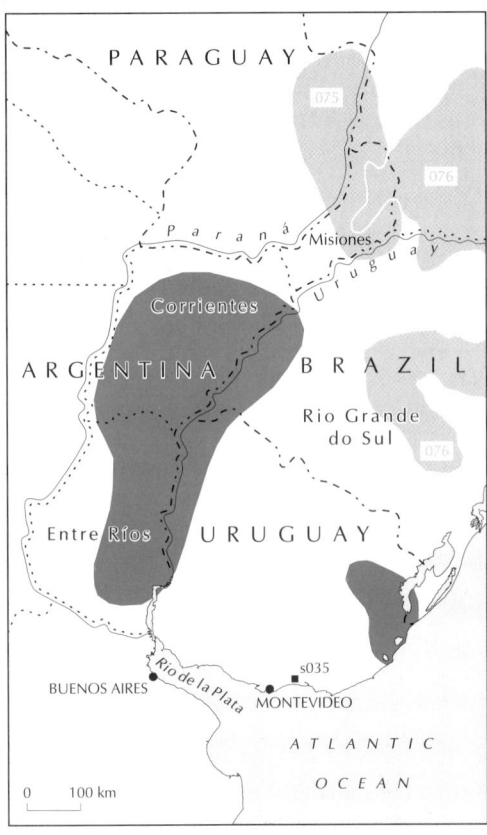

which are interspersed in a mosaic of other habitats, especially spiny woodland ('espinal'), gallery forest and large bodies of standing water ('esteros').

■ Restricted-range species

The three restricted-range species are in the genus *Sporophila*, all breeding in periodically inundated grassland and marsh, especially those supporting tall, dense grasses (especially *Paspalum*), often with isolated bushes (including *Acacia caven* and *Solanum glaucophyllum*) and herbaceous plants such as *Eryngium* (Pearman and Abadie in press). They are all austral migrants, wintering north of the EBA mainly in the pantanal of central Brazil, birds on migration having been recorded in Paraguay and other parts of Brazil.

The three species are patchily distributed within their breeding ranges. They all overlap only in eastern Entre Ríos province, where *Sporophila zelichi* is known from only two adjacent breeding localities (Collar *et al.* 1992, Pearman and Abadie in press). *S. cinnamomea* is found mainly in central and south-east Corrientes and scattered locally in eastern Entre Ríos, with single records over the border in Rio Grande do Sul in Brazil (Belton 1984–1985) and now recent records from Artigas, Salto Paysandú, Río Negro and Soriano departments in western Uruguay and Trenta y Tres and Rocha departments in eastern Uruguay (A. Aspiroz *in litt.* 1997). *S. palustris* is spread more widely through the EBA, but eastern Entre Ríos is its main breeding area; also Rocha department in eastern Uruguay is now thought to be important for the species (A. Aspiroz *in litt.* 1997). There are also a handful of historical records from Rio Grande do Sul in Brazil. It has also probably bred further south in the Paraná delta but these records could possibly refer to escaped cage-birds (M. Pearman *in litt.* 1996).

The taxonomic status of *S. zelichi* (described as recently as 1977) is controversial owing to its clear morphological affinities with other species in the genus. A recent study conducted in 1991–1993 found it always to breed in close association with *S. palustris*, and concluded through preliminary DNA work that

Status and habitat of restricted-range species

Species (ordered taxonomically)	Global status	Other EBAs (and SAs)	Altitude (m)	Habitat
Marsh Seedeater *Sporophila palustris*	EN	—	Lowlands to 1,100	Low, seasonally wet grassland, freshwater marshes, riparian thickets, scrub
Chestnut Seedeater *Sporophila cinnamomea*	nt	—	Lowlands to 1,100	Low, seasonally wet grassland, freshwater marshes
Entre Ríos Seedeater *Sporophila zelichi*	CR	—	Lowlands	Low, seasonally wet grassland, freshwater marshes, riparian thickets

Global status (see p. 679 for definitions)
EX Extinct
EW Extinct in the Wild } with year of last record
CR Critical
EN Endangered
VU Vulnerable } threatened species
cd Conservation Dependent
nt Near Threatened
lc Least Concern
DD Data Deficient
NE Not Evaluated

Other EBAs (and SAs) (see p. 65 for locations): bracketed numbers are Secondary Areas; ˣ extinct in that EBA or SA.

the bird represents a distinct colour morph of *palustris*. The situation is still more complicated than this, however, for the affinities of *palustris* are unclear, Pearman and Abadie (in press) having suggested that it is probably conspecific with southern populations of Rufous-rumped Seedeater *S. hypochroma*, a widespread species which occurs in western Corrientes, Bolivia, Brazil and probably Paraguay. For the moment, all three taxa are recognized as separate species (e.g. Ridgely and Tudor 1989, Sibley and Monroe 1991, Collar *et al.* 1992, Stotz *et al.* 1996), but there is a clear need for a taxonomic review that incorporates not only morphology but song, breeding ecology and genetics.

■ Threats and conservation

Much of the land within this EBA is under agricultural production, especially for cattle-ranching in Corrientes. Degradation of grassland through overgrazing and trampling is a common problem, while drainage of marshes and the burning of stands of tall natural grasses pose additional threats to the area. A recent development is afforestation projects mainly of *Eucalyptus* and pine, with greatest interest focused on eastern Entre Ríos and north-east Corrientes (Collar *et al.* 1992, Pearman and Abadie in press).

Two of the species, *Sporophila zelichi* and *S. palustris*, are considered threatened, not only owing to destruction of their breeding habitat, but also because the males are popular cage-birds; heavy trapping pressure has led to serious declines in their populations. Several widespread threatened birds also occur in the EBA, including Crowned Eagle *Harpyhaliaetus coronatus* (classified as Vulnerable), Speckled Crake *Coturnicops notatus* (Data Deficient), Sickle-winged Nightjar *Eleothreptus anomalus* (Near Threatened), Strange-tailed Tyrant *Yetapa risora* (Vulnerable), Ochre-breasted Pipit *Anthus nattereri* (Endangered), Black-and-white Monjita *Heteroxolmis dominicana* (Vulnerable), Yellow Cardinal *Gubernatrix cristata* (Endangered), Saffron-cowled Blackbird *Xanthopsar flavus* (Endangered) and Pampas Meadowlark *Sturnella militaris* (Endangered). Moreover, the EBA is undoubtedly the most important region for several of these species, especially *Y. risora*, *A. nattereri*, and *X. flavus* (Wege and Long 1995, Pearman and Abadie in press), and so the conservation of the grassland there is crucial.

Strange-tailed Tyrant *Yetapa risora* is a more widespread threatened species that occurs in this EBA, and an indicator of natural grassland in the Pampas region.

Eight Key Areas for threatened birds have been identified within this EBA (Wege and Long 1995): five in Argentina (Caza Pava and Colonia Carlos Pellegrini in Corrientes, and Selva de Montiel, El Palmar National Park and Gualeguaychú in Entre Ríos) and three in Uruguay (El Rosario in Río Negro, and Bañados de India Muerta, Bañados de Santa Teresa and Los Indios in Rocha). Of these, Colonia Carlos Pellegrini (holding eight threatened species) and Gualeguaychú (with seven threatened species and all the restricted-range species) are the two most important sites, and both are in need of better protection (Pearman and Abadie in press).

078 | Cape Verde Islands

PRIORITY
URGENT

Key habitats Arid scrub, rocky ravines, cliffs

Main threats Severe habitat loss (e.g. due to agriculture, grazing), introduced species

Biological importance ● ● ●
Current threat level ● ●

Area 4,000 km² **Altitude** 0–2,800 m

Countries Cape Verde

Restricted-range species	Threatened	Total
Confined to this EBA	2	4
Present also in other EBAs, SAs	0	0
Total	2	4

■ General characteristics

The Cape Verdes, an independent republic, are situated c.500 km off the west coast of Africa. They consist of two groups of volcanic islands of which the largest is Santiago (991 km²). The islands are either mountainous with peaks reaching over 1,000 m (and up to 2,800 m on Fogo, the only active volcano), or have low relief and consequently receive little and irregular rain.

The original vegetation, before human colonization started during the fifteenth century, included savanna or steppe vegetation, perhaps with scattered *Acacia* and figs, with the flatter islands supporting semi-desert plants.

■ Restricted-range species

Alauda razae is confined to uninhabited Raso (7 km²) where suitable breeding habitat represents less than half of the islet's total area, and *Acrocephalus brevipennis* is now confined to Santiago where it is locally distributed mainly in the interior. The other two species are more widely dispersed.

An additional seven landbirds are recognized by Hazevoet (1995) as being endemic phylogenetic species, and these forms contribute significantly to the uniqueness of the islands: Cape Verde Purple Heron *Ardea (purpurea) bournei* (see also Hazevoet

Raso Lark *Alauda razae* is considered threatened on account of its very small population and range, and is also at risk from the accidental introduction of alien predators such as rats, cats and dogs.

1992), Cape Verde Kite *Milvus (milvus) fasciicauda*, Cape Verde Buzzard *Buteo (buteo) bannermani*, Alexander's Kestrel *Falco (tinnunculus) alexandri*, Neglected Kestrel *Falco (tinnunculus) neglectus*, Cape Verde Peregrine *Falco (peregrinus) madens* and Cape Verde Barn Owl *Tyto (alba) detorta* (see Hazevoet 1996 for a discussion of the phylogenetic species concept in relation to the Cape Verde avifauna, also Collar 1996).

Fea's Petrel *Pterodroma feae* is a seabird which is largely endemic (when breeding) to this EBA (a second smaller population breeds in the Desertas, see EBA 120). The population of *P. feae* on the Cape Verdes is also recognized as a phylogenetic species by Hazevoet (1995), as are two other seabirds: Cape Verde Shearwater *Calonectris (diomedea) edwardsii* and Cape Verde Little Shearwater *Puffinus (assimilis) boydi*.

■ Threats and conservation

Over the past five centuries, the combined effects of drought, poor agricultural techniques, the introduction of large numbers of alien herbaceous plant and tree species, the devastating effects of an abundance of goats, and high human population pressure have led to an almost complete destruction of the original

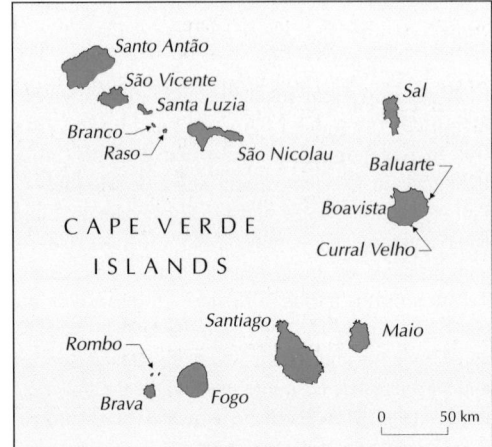

Santo Antão
São Vicente
Santa Luzia
Branco
Raso
São Nicolau
Sal
Baluarte
Boavista
Curral Velho

CAPE VERDE
ISLANDS

Santiago
Maio
Rombo
Brava
Fogo

0   50 km

Status and habitat of restricted-range species

Species (ordered taxonomically)	Global status	Other EBAs (and SAs)	Habitat
Cape Verde Swift *Apus alexandri*	lc	—	All altitudes in valleys, ravines, around cliffs, rock-faces, in towns and villages
Raso Lark *Alauda razae*	EN	—	Vegetated parts of plains and valleys (breeding), dry plains (non-breeding)
Cape Verde Warbler *Acrocephalus brevipennis*	VU	—	Well-vegetated valleys (esp. with patches of reeds), also irrigated plantations, gardens
Iago Sparrow *Passer iagoensis*	lc	—	Stony plains, rocky ravines with sparse vegetation, cliffs, cultivated areas

Global status (see p. 679 for definitions)	EX Extinct	with year of last record	CR Critical	threatened species	cd Conservation Dependent	DD Data Deficient
	EW Extinct in the Wild		EN Endangered		nt Near Threatened	NE Not Evaluated
			VU Vulnerable		lc Least Concern	

Other EBAs (and SAs) (see p. 72 for locations): bracketed numbers are Secondary Areas; [x] extinct in that EBA or SA.

Distribution patterns of restricted-range species

Species (ordered geographically)	Santo Antão	São Vicente	Santa Luzia	Raso	São Nicolau	Boavista	Sal	Brava	Fogo	Santiago	Maio	Other EBAs, SAs
Passer iagoensis	●	●	●	●	●	●	●	●	–	●	●	–
Apus alexandri	●	N	–	N	●	N	N	●	●	●	N	–
Alauda razae	–	–	–	●	–	–	–	–	–	–	–	–
Acrocephalus brevipennis	–	–	–	–	X	–	–	X	–	●	–	–
Total	2	1	1	2	2	1	1	2	1	3	1	

● Present	N Non-breeding	Threatened spp. shown in **bold**	see 'Status and habitat' table
O Extinct?	R Reintroduced		
X Extinct	I Introduced	Other EBAs, SAs	

vegetation on many of the islands of the Cape Verdes, most arable land now being cleared and planted with maize and beans. Dry woodland and scrub occupy large areas of the arid plains, which have been afforested in the last few decades, but the avifauna of these areas is generally poor.

Two of the endemic bird species are considered threatened: *Alauda razae* on account of its very small population (c.250 birds in 1992) and range, and *Acrocephalus brevipennis* because of its small and declining population (500 pairs) and range (extinct on two islands probably through drought and associated habitat loss). As a ground-nester, *A. razae* is extremely vulnerable to the accidental introduction of rats, cats and dogs by fisherman visiting the islet to collect seabirds' eggs and young; a lone dog was seen on Raso in 1994 (C. J. Hazevoet *in litt.* 1995).

Several of the subspecies (see 'Restricted-range species', above) are uncommon, including *Ardea (purpurea) bournei* (c.25 pairs on Santiago), *Milvus (milvus) fasciicauda* and *Buteo (buteo) bannermani* (both rare on Santiago and Santo Antão), and *Falco (peregrinus) madens* (small numbers on all islands, perhaps fewer than 20 pairs).

Pterodroma feae (see 'Restricted-range species') has a population estimated at 500–1,000 pairs and is classified as Vulnerable. It is likely that this species once bred in burrows, but has retreated to mountain ledges after the destruction of the indigenous shrubland. All seabirds have been exploited for centuries on the Cape Verdes and have also suffered from predation by introduced mammals (e.g. cats, rats, green monkeys *Cercopithecus aethiops*), and as a result there has been a dramatic decline in their populations over the last 100 years. *Calonectris (diomedea) edwardsii* has suffered in particular, with at least 5,000–6,000 fledglings being collected each year and the likelihood of a disastrous decline within the next few decades (C. J. Hazevoet *in litt.* 1995).

In 1988 a 'National Parks and Protected Areas Programme' (NPPAP) was initiated, including strategies for the conservation of all flora and fauna, and, as a consequence of this, several important seabird islets were declared as nature reserves in 1990, including Raso, Branco, Ilhéus do Rombo, Ilhéu de Curral Velho and Ilhéu de Baluarte (Hazevoet 1994, C. J. Hazevoet *in litt.* 1995).

079 Tristan Islands

Key habitats Tussock grassland, fern-bush, tree thickets, heath, beaches

Main threats Moderate habitat loss (e.g. due to grazing), introduced species

Biological importance ● ●
Current threat level ● ●

Area 110 km² **Altitude** 0–2,000 m

Countries St Helena (to UK)

Restricted-range species	Threatened	Total
Confined to this EBA	3	4
Present also in other EBAs, SAs	0	0
Total	3	4

■ General characteristics

The islands of the Tristan group—Tristan da Cunha (96 km²), Inaccessible (13 km²) and Nightingale (4 km²)—are of volcanic origin and lie within 40 km of each other in the mid South Atlantic Ocean, c.2,800 km from South Africa and 3,200 km from South America. The group is a dependency of St Helena (some 2,000 km to the north, Secondary Area s038), which is itself a UK dependent territory. The island of Gough, about 350 km to the south-east, is also politically part of the same group, but is treated separately here (as EBA 080). Tristan is the largest and highest of the islands in the EBA, and is the only one to be inhabited.

On Tristan, the vegetation consists of tussock grassland on the coast, fern-bush and island tree *Phylica arborea* thickets at low elevations, wet heath above 750 m, moor and 'feldmark' vegetation (an assemblage of dwarf, cushion-forming and crevice plants) on higher slopes, and alpine tundra above 1,500 m. On Inaccesible, the vegetation includes

tussock grassland, fern-bush and freshwater bogs, while on Nightingale the predominant vegetation is dense tussock grassland (see Wace and Holdgate 1976, Clark and Dingwall 1985).

■ Restricted-range species

This tiny EBA is exceptional in having three endemic genera—*Atlantisia*, *Nesocichla* and *Nesospiza*. The *Nesospiza* buntings are of particular interest because, like the famous Darwin's finches from the Galápagos Islands (see EBA 031), they have undergone remarkable speciation, with the two species (*N. acunhae* and *N. wilkinsi*) differing markedly in size and co-occurring without interbreeding on Nightingale. On Inaccessible, where they also co-occur, there are two altitudinally segregated colour morphs of *N. acunhae*, as well as a hybrid complex involving *acunhae* and *wilkinsi* (Ryan *et al.* 1994). Distinct subspecies are recognized of the thrush *N. eremita* from each of the three main islands.

All of the EBA's restricted-range species are found in a wide variety of habitats, but are more abundant in some than in others (e.g. *Atlantisia rogersi* is most common in coastal tussock grassland away from the cliffs). All the extant species occur on Inaccessible, and *A. rogersi* is confined to it. On Tristan there is a small population of Gough Moorhen *Gallinula comeri* introduced from Gough (see EBA 080).

Tristan da Cunha
EDINBURGH
Inaccessible I.
Stoltenhoff I.
Middle I.
Nightingale I.
Tristan Group

to St Helena
(to UK)

ATLANTIC

OCEAN

Gough Island

0   50 km

080

Distribution patterns of restricted-range species

Species (ordered geographically)	Tristan da Cunha	Inaccessible	Nightingale	Other EBAs, SAs
Gallinula nesiotis	X	–	–	–
Nesocichla eremita	●	●^M,S	●	–
Nesospiza acunhae	X	●^M,S	●	–
Atlantisia rogersi	–	●	–	–
Nesospiza wilkinsi	–	●	●	–
Total	1	4	3	

● Present   R Reintroduced   Threatened spp. shown in **bold**
○ Extinct?   I Introduced, not   Other EBAs, SAs
X Extinct   yet established

see 'Status and habitat' table

^M,S Also on tiny Middle and Stoltenhoff islands off Nightingale.

Status and habitat of restricted-range species

Species (ordered taxonomically)	Global status	Other EBAs (and SAs)	Habitat
Inaccessible Rail *Atlantisia rogersi*	VU	—	Most habitats inc. boulder beaches, tussock grassland, fern-bush, tree thickets, heath
Tristan Moorhen *Gallinula nesiotis*[1]	EX (1872)	—	Tussock grassland?
Tristan Thrush *Nesocichla eremita*	nt	—	Boulder beaches, tussock grassland, fern-bush, tree thickets
Tristan Bunting *Nesospiza acunhae*	VU	—	Tussock grassland, fern-bush, wet heath
Grosbeak Bunting *Nesospiza wilkinsi*	VU	—	Tussock grassland, tree thickets

| Global status (see p. 679 for definitions) | EX Extinct
 EW Extinct in the Wild } with year of last record
 CR Critical
 EN Endangered } threatened species
 VU Vulnerable | cd Conservation Dependent <br> nt Near Threatened <br> lc Least Concern
 DD Data Deficient
 NE Not Evaluated | **Other EBAs (and SAs)** (see p. 72 for locations)
 Notes | Bracketed numbers are Secondary Areas.
 ˣ Extinct in that EBA or SA.
 [1] Taxonomy follows Cooper and Ryan (1994). |

As well as its restricted-range landbirds, there are several seabird subspecies and species which are largely confined to these islands and to Gough when breeding, including Tristan (Wandering) Albatross *Diomedea exulans dabbenena* (Inaccessible and Gough; treated as a good species by Robertson and Nunn in press), White-chinned Petrel *Procellaria aequinoctialis conspicillata* (Inaccessible only; probably a good and hence endemic species: P. Ryan *in litt.* 1993), Great Shearwater *Puffinus gravis* (mainly Tristan–Gough group), and Atlantic Petrel *Pterodroma incerta* (Tristan–Gough group only).

■ Threats and conservation

On Tristan, most of the vegetation has been considerably modified as a result of grazing by livestock, and the coastal tussock grassland has been largely destroyed. This loss of habitat is likely to have contributed to the extinction of *Gallinula nesiotis* and *Nesospiza acunhae*, although introduced predators (cats and rats) must also have played an important part (Fraser and Briggs 1992, P. Ryan *in litt.* 1993). *Nesocichla eremita* is the only native landbird surviving on Tristan, although the population has decreased markedly since the island has been colonized by man and his commensals (Fraser *et al.* 1994).

On Inaccessible and Nightingale, habitat destruction (through the deliberate introduction of livestock) is a potential problem, but by far the greatest

threat would come from the accidental introduction of alien species, especially predatory mammals (P. Ryan *in litt.* 1993). Thus, despite being numerically strong, all the restricted-range birds are considered threatened or Near Threatened. *Atlantisia rogersi* is arguably the most vulnerable of the threatened species, being flightless (indeed the world's smallest flightless bird), although it lives at high density (probably at carrying capacity) and numbers an estimated 8,400 birds (Fraser *et al.* 1992, M. W. Fraser *in litt.* 1993). *Gallinula comeri* (see 'Restricted-range species', above), also considered threatened (Vulnerable), numbers c.250 pairs on Tristan.

In addition to their importance for endemic landbirds, the Tristan islands are internationally important for their colonies of some 20 species of seabirds (Richardson 1984, Williams 1984, Fraser *et al.* 1988). Threatened and Near Threatened species include *Diomedea exulans* (Vulnerable, at its northernmost breeding locality on Inaccessible, but only a few pairs; see 'Restricted-range species'), *Pterodroma incerta* (Vulnerable, some hundreds of pairs; see 'Restricted-range species') and Sooty Albatross *Phoebetria fusca* (Near Threatened).

Inaccessible was declared a nature reserve in 1994, and although Tristan islanders still retain the right to collect driftwood and guano from this uninhabited island, other access is restricted and all living resources are protected.

080 Gough Island

PRIORITY
URGENT

| Key habitats | Tussock grassland, fern-bush, heath |
| Main threats | Possible habitat loss, possible introduction of alien species |

Area 65 km²   **Altitude** 0–900 m

Countries St Helena (to UK)

Restricted-range species	Threatened	Total
Confined to this EBA	2	2
Present also in other EBAs, SAs	0	0
Total	2	2

Biological importance ● ● ●
Current threat level ● ●

■ General characteristics

Gough is a volcanic island lying in the middle of the South Atlantic Ocean, c.2,800 km from South Africa and 3,200 km from South America. Politically it is part of the Tristan da Cunha group (EBA 079, some 350 km to the north-west), which is a dependency of St Helena (Secondary Area s038), itself a UK Dependent Territory (see p. 302 for map).

Gough is uninhabited apart from a small meteorological station manned by South Africans. The vegetation consists of tussock grassland on the coast and up to 300 m above sea-level, fern-bush occasionally interrupted by island trees *Phylica arborea* to c.500 m, and wet heath to 800 m; above 600 m occur bog and swamp communities and 'feldmark' (an assemblage of dwarf, cushion-forming and crevice plants on exposed areas such as ridges) (see Wace and Holdgate 1976, Clark and Dingwall 1985, also Oldfield 1987).

■ Restricted-range species

Gallinula comeri and Tristan Moorhen *G. nesiotis* (see EBA 079) are treated here as separate species following Collar and Stuart (1985) and Cooper and Ryan (1994), contra Sibley and Monroe (1990, 1993) who considered them to be conspecific.

As well as its two endemic landbirds, there are several seabird species and subspecies which are largely confined to these islands and to Tristan when breeding, including Tristan (Wandering) Albatross *Diomedea exulans dabbenena* (this population is treated as a full species by Robertson and Nunn in press), Great Shearwater *Puffinus gravis* (mainly Tristan–Gough group) and Atlantic Petrel *Pterodroma incerta* (Tristan–Gough group only).

■ Threats and conservation

Gough is the largest scarcely modified cool temperate island ecosystem in the South Atlantic. House mice *Mus musculus* are the only introduced mammals, although goats and sheep have been introduced in the past, but are no longer present. Nevertheless, both the restricted-range bird species are considered threatened due to the risk of other alien species (especially rats) being introduced into their tiny ranges. This threat status is despite the fact of the species' numerical strength: there are up to 3,000 pairs of *Gallinula comeri* (Watkins and Furness 1986), though only 200 pairs of *Rowettia goughensis* (Collar and Stuart 1985).

Gough is internationally important for its seabird colonies comprising some 20 species (Richardson 1984, Williams 1984), including *Diomedea exulans* (Vulnerable, c.3,300 breeding individuals on Gough; see 'Restricted-range species', above), *Pterodroma incerta* (Vulnerable, some thousands of pairs; see above) and Sooty Albatross *Phoebetria fusca* (Near Threatened). Gough was granted World Heritage status in December 1995, only the third British site to be so recognized for its biological value.

Status and habitat of restricted-range species

Species (ordered taxonomically)	Global status	Other EBAs (and SAs)	Habitat
Gough Moorhen *Gallinula comeri*[1]	VU	—	Tussock grassland, fern-bush
Gough Bunting *Rowettia goughensis*	VU	—	Wet heath, mires, feldmark

Global status (see p. 679 for definitions)						**Other EBAs (and SAs)** (see p. 72 for locations)	Bracketed numbers are Secondary Areas.
	EX	Extinct	with year of last record	cd	Conservation Dependent		ˣ Extinct in that EBA or SA.
	EW	Extinct in the Wild		nt	Near Threatened		
	CR	Critical		lc	Least Concern	**Notes**	[1] Taxonomy follows Cooper and Ryan
	EN	Endangered	threatened species	DD	Data Deficient		(1994). Introduced to Tristan da Cunha
	VU	Vulnerable		NE	Not Evaluated		(EBA 079).

081 Annobón

Key habitats Lowland rain forest, upland mossy forest

Main threats Limited habitat loss (e.g. due to oil-palm, fruit and sugar-cane plantations)

Biological importance ●
Current threat level ● ●

Area 17 km²   **Altitude** 0–600 m

Countries Equatorial Guinea

Restricted-range species	Threatened	Total
Confined to this EBA	2	2
Present also in other EBAs, SAs	0	1
Total	2	3

■ General characteristics

This tiny volcanic island (formerly known as Pagalu) off the west coast of Africa forms part of Equatorial Guinea. It is the most remote of the Gulf of Guinea islands, which include São Tomé (EBA 082), Príncipe (EBA 083) and Bioko (part of EBA 086) (see p. 306 for map). Unlike Bioko, which lies on the continental shelf and has probably been linked with continental Africa in the relatively recent past, Príncipe, São Tomé and Annobón are true oceanic islands, and have a depauperate avifauna typical of such places, with low diversity but a high degree of endemism.

The native vegetation on Annobón includes lowland rain forest with mossy forest above 500 m, and, in the drier north, a savanna-like formation of grassland and scattered bushes.

■ Restricted-range species

Information on the birds comes from a brief visit in 1989, the first one by an ornithologist in 30 years (Harrison 1990a), when the two endemic species (the only two passerines on the island) appeared common and widespread, occurring wherever bush- and tree-cover existed. On the other hand, comparison of records of *Columba malherbii* from the turn of the century (when it was very common) with those from the 1950s indicated that this species had become rarer: in 1989 it was only seen twice, although it may remain common in the less-disturbed southern forests, which were not visited.

■ Threats and conservation

Although the vegetation on the island has, to some extent, been modified (e.g. plantations of fruit, oil-palm and sugar-cane in the north), the changes are not as extensive as on São Tomé and Príncipe.

Both the endemic bird species are classified as Vulnerable on account of their tiny ranges, which makes them especially susceptible to chance events—even though it is possible that the population of *Zosterops griseovirescens* may be growing as a result of disturbance to the vegetation which creates habitat favourable to it.

There are currently no protected areas on Annobón.

Status and habitat of restricted-range species

Species (ordered taxonomically)	Global status	Other EBAs (and SAs)	Habitat
São Tomé Bronze-naped Pigeon *Columba malherbii*	lc	082,083	Forest, secondary forest, plantations with shade trees, savanna
Annobón Paradise-flycatcher *Terpsiphone smithii*[1]	VU	—	Moist forest at higher altitudes, secondary forest, cultivated areas
Annobón White-eye *Zosterops griseovirescens*	VU	—	Everywhere with cover, inc. moist forest, dry forest, secondary forest, oil-palm swamp, cultivated areas

Global status (see p. 679 for definitions)	EX Extinct	with year of last record	cd Conservation Dependent	**Other EBAs (and SAs)** (see p. 72 for locations)	Bracketed numbers are Secondary Areas. ˣ Extinct in that EBA or SA.
	EW Extinct in the Wild		nt Near Threatened		
	CR Critical	threatened species	lc Least Concern	**Notes**	[1] Taxonomy follows Harrison (1990a);
	EN Endangered		DD Data Deficient		see also Collar *et al.* (1994).
	VU Vulnerable		NE Not Evaluated		

082 São Tomé

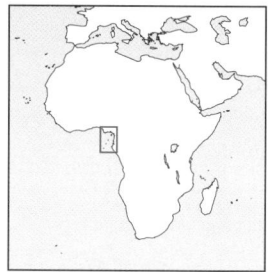

PRIORITY
CRITICAL

Key habitats Lowland and montane rain forest, 'shade' forest

Main threats Limited habitat loss (e.g. due to cocoa plantations, firewood-gathering), introduced species

Biological importance ● ● ●
Current threat level ● ●

Area 860 km² **Altitude** 0–2,000 m

Countries São Tomé e Príncipe

Restricted-range species	Threatened	Total
Confined to this EBA	7	16
Present also in other EBAs, SAs	1	5
Total	8	21

■ General characteristics

São Tomé is a volcanic island situated in the Gulf of Guinea, off the west coast of Africa, in the middle of a chain of islands which includes Bioko (part of EBA 086), Príncipe (EBA 083, with which it forms the twin-island nation of São Tomé e Príncipe) and Annobón (EBA 081).

The original vegetation included lowland rain forest to c.800 m, with montane forest extending from 800 to 1,400 m, and mossy forest above. Dry forest occurs in the north of the island, but has largely been replaced by savanna and open cultivation.

■ Restricted-range species

All the restricted-range species occur in forest and—although a number have adapted to plantations where

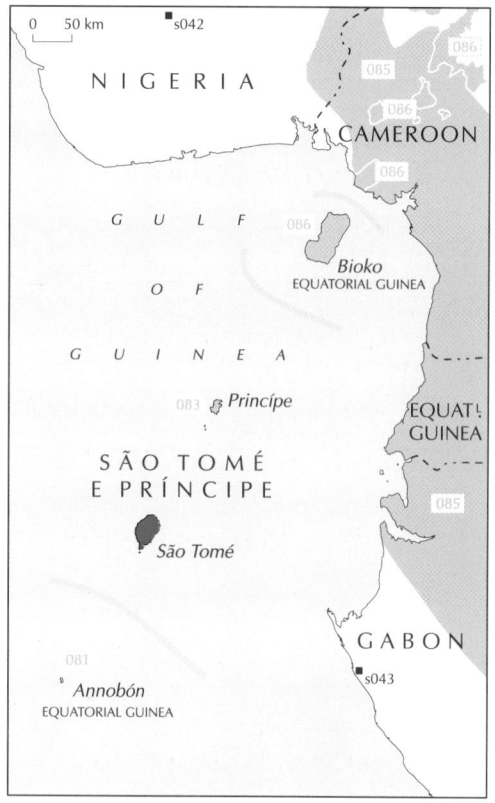

large shade-trees are retained—several species are primary-forest specialists and four apparently occur only in the lowlands (*Bostrychia bocagei*, *Lanius newtoni*, *Amaurocichla bocagii*, *Neospiza concolor*, all rediscovered in 1990 and 1991). Further detailed accounts on individual species can be found in Jones and Tye (1988) and Atkinson *et al.* (1991, 1994a).

São Tomé's distinctive avifauna includes two endemic monospecific genera, *Amaurocichla* and *Neospiza*, as well as two remarkable 'giants', *Nectarinia thomensis* (formerly placed in the monospecific genus *Dreptes*) and *Ploceus grandis*, and a remarkable 'dwarf', *Bostrychia bocagei*. Sibley and Monroe's (1990, 1993) taxonomic review elevated several São Tomé taxa to specific status, including *Alcedo thomensis*, although the status of this species remains uncertain (Peet and Atkinson 1994).

■ Threats and conservation

The lowlands of São Tomé are almost entirely cultivated and primary forest remains only in the southwest and centre of the island, largely at higher altitudes. However, since independence in 1975 many plantations have reverted to secondary growth, and habitat conditions for birds are thus probably as favourable as they have been for a long time.

A forest survey in 1989 found total forest cover to be c.90%; of this, 28% was primary forest, 30% secondary forest and 32% shade forest. All endemic species remain threatened to some degree by forest loss from the likely expansion of agriculture, possible revitalization of plantations, and the increasing consumption of timber for domestic cooking and construction, but also for drying cocoa, for which the demand is likely to rise sharply if the cocoa market expands (N. B. Peet and P. W. Atkinson *in litt.* 1993).

If the four lowland forest species are indeed restricted to altitudes below 500 m, then only the forest in the Xufexufe and Ana Chaves valleys will be of sufficient area to support viable populations, though even these would be precariously small and thus highly vulnerable to development. However, there are considerable areas of primary forest between 500 and 1,000 m in the centre of the island

Status and habitat of restricted-range species

Species (ordered taxonomically)	Global status	Other EBAs (and SAs)	Altitude (m)	Habitat
Dwarf Olive Ibis *Bostrychia bocagei*[1]	CR	—	Lowlands	Forest
Maroon Pigeon *Columba thomensis*	VU	—	Usually >1,400	Forest, sometimes secondary forest
São Tomé Bronze-naped Pigeon *Columba malherbii*	lc	081,083	Lowlands to 1,600+	Forest, secondary forest, plantations with shade trees, savanna
São Tomé Green-pigeon *Treron sanctithomae*	lc	—	Lowlands (occ. higher)	Forest, secondary forest, sometimes plantations
São Tomé Scops-owl *Otus hartlaubi*	nt	—	Lowlands (occ. 1,600+)	Forest, secondary forest
São Tomé Spinetail *Zoonavena thomensis*	lc	083	Most	Forest clearings, secondary forest, plantations, savanna
São Tomé Kingfisher *Alcedo thomensis*	lc	—	Most	Streams, lakes, ponds, marshes in forest, secondary forest, savanna
São Tomé Fiscal *Lanius newtonii*	CR	—	Lowlands	Forest, may prefer ridge areas
São Tomé Thrush *Turdus olivaceofuscus*	nt	083	Lowlands to 1,600+	Forest, secondary forest, plantations, dry forest pockets in savanna
São Tomé Prinia *Prinia molleri*	lc	—	Most	Forest, secondary forest, plantations, savanna
São Tomé Short-tail *Amaurocichla bocagii*	VU	—	Lowlands	Riparian areas in forest, forested ridges if rocks and boulders present
São Tomé Paradise-flycatcher *Terpsiphone atrochalybeia*	lc	—	Lowlands to 1,600+	Forest, secondary forest, plantations with shade trees, savanna
Newton's Sunbird *Nectarinia newtoni*	lc	—	Lowlands to 1,600+	Forest, secondary forest, plantations, savanna
Giant Sunbird *Nectarinia thomensis*	VU	—	Lowlands (occ. 1,600+)	Forest, sometimes secondary forest
Black-capped Speirops *Speirops lugubris*	lc	—	Lowlands to 1,600+	Forest, secondary forest, plantations
São Tomé White-eye *Zosterops ficedulinus*	VU	083	Lowlands (occ. 1,600+)	Forest, mature secondary forest, sometimes plantations, savanna
Príncipe Seedeater *Serinus rufobrunneus*	lc	083	Most	Forest, secondary forest, plantations
São Tomé Grosbeak *Neospiza concolor*	CR	—	Lowlands	Forest
Giant Weaver *Ploceus grandis*	lc	—	Most	Secondary forest, plantations, savanna, sometimes forest
São Tomé Weaver *Ploceus sanctithomae*	lc	—	Lowlands to 1,600+	Forest, secondary forest, plantations, dry forest in savanna
São Tomé Oriole *Oriolus crassirostris*	VU	—	Lowlands (occ. 1,600+)	Forest, mature secondary forest, sometimes savanna

Global status (see p. 679 for definitions)
EX Extinct
EW Extinct in the Wild } with year of last record
CR Critical
EN Endangered } threatened species
VU Vulnerable
cd Conservation Dependent
nt Near Threatened
lc Least Concern
DD Data Deficient
NE Not Evaluated

Other EBAs (and SAs) (see p. 72 for locations)
Bracketed numbers are Secondary Areas.
[X] Extinct in that EBA or SA.

Notes [1] Taxonomy follows de Naurois (1973); see also Collar and Stuart (1985).

which have not been visited by ornithologists and which may harbour these species (Peet and Atkinson 1994). These birds may, however, also be under pressure from alien mammals (e.g. black rat *Rattus rattus*, mona monkey *Cercopithecus mona*, African civet *Civettictis civetta* and weasel *Mustela nivalis*), which, coupled with possible further forest clear-

ance, could lead to species extinctions (Dutton 1994).

Collar and Stuart (1988) ranked the forests in south-west and central São Tomé second in a list of 75 of the most important forests for conservation of threatened birds in tropical Africa. These forests were proposed for protection by Jones *et al.* (1991) and were gazetted in 1993 (Jones 1994a).

083 Príncipe

PRIORITY HIGH

Key habitats Lowland rain forest, 'shade' forest

Main threats Moderate habitat loss (e.g. due to cocoa, sugar-cane and coffee plantations)

Biological importance ● ●

Current threat level ●

Area 140 km² **Altitude** 0–900 m

Countries São Tomé e Príncipe

Restricted-range species	Threatened	Total
Confined to this EBA	1	6
Present also in other EBAs, SAs	1	5
Total	2	11

■ General characteristics

Príncipe lies in the middle of a chain of islands—which includes Bioko (part of EBA 086), São Tomé (EBA 082, with which it forms the twin-island nation of São Tomé e Príncipe) and Annobón (EBA 081)—situated off the west coast of Africa in the Gulf of Guinea (see p. 306 for map).

The island is volcanic and was once covered in tropical rain forest, but this was largely destroyed in the 1800s to make way for cash-crop plantations such as cocoa, sugar-cane and coffee. Since then, forest has regenerated extensively and, more recently, many plantations have reverted to secondary growth. Today primary forest is only found on the steepest slopes of the south-west of the island and has not been successfully visited by ornithologists during the twentieth century.

■ Restricted-range species

All the restricted-range species are forest birds and most appear to have adapted well to secondary growth and to plantations (where, traditionally, shade trees are retained). Detailed accounts of individual species can be found in Jones and Tye (1988) and Atkinson *et al.* (1991, 1994a).

Príncipe's distinctive avifauna includes the very interesting *Horizorhinus dohrni*, a bird in its own genus and of puzzling affinities, having been considered by different authorities to be a babbler, a flycatcher, a thrush and a warbler. Sibley and Monroe's

P. J. Jones

View from the west coast of Príncipe towards the volcanic plugs of João Dias Pai e Filho (João Dias father and son). Although most lowland forest was destroyed in the 1800s for plantations, many of these have now reverted to secondary growth, and most of the restricted-range species are common.

Status and habitat of restricted-range species

Species (ordered taxonomically)	Global status	Other EBAs (and SAs)	Habitat
São Tomé Bronze-naped Pigeon *Columba malherbii*	lc	081,082	Forest, secondary forest, plantations
São Tomé Spinetail *Zoonavena thomensis*	lc	082	Forest clearings, secondary forest, plantations
Príncipe Kingfisher *Alcedo nais*	lc	—	Streams, lakes, ponds, marshes in forest, secondary forest, plantations
São Tomé Thrush *Turdus olivaceofuscus*	nt	082	Forest
Dohrn's Thrush-babbler *Horizorhinus dohrni*	lc	—	Forest, secondary forest, plantations
Príncipe Sunbird *Nectarinia hartlaubii*	lc	—	Forest, secondary forest, plantations
Príncipe Speirops *Speirops leucophaeus*	VU	—	Forest, secondary forest, plantations
São Tomé White-eye *Zosterops ficedulinus*	VU	082	Forest
Príncipe Seedeater *Serinus rufobrunneus*	lc	082	Forest, secondary forest, plantations
Príncipe Golden-weaver *Ploceus princeps*	lc	—	Forest, secondary forest, plantations
Príncipe Glossy-starling *Lamprotornis ornatus*	lc	—	Forest, secondary forest, plantations

Global status (see p. 679 for definitions): EX Extinct, EW Extinct in the Wild (with year of last record); CR Critical, EN Endangered, VU Vulnerable (threatened species); cd Conservation Dependent, nt Near Threatened, lc Least Concern; DD Data Deficient, NE Not Evaluated

Other EBAs (and SAs) (see p. 72 for locations): bracketed numbers are Secondary Areas; ˣ extinct in that EBA or SA.

(1990, 1993) taxonomic review elevated several Príncipe taxa to specific status, including *Alcedo nais*, although the status of this species remains uncertain; conversely, Príncipe Drongo *Dicrurus (adsimilis) modestus*, not elevated in the review, is regarded as a full species by some experts (Peet and Atkinson 1994).

■ Threats and conservation

Approximately 90% of Príncipe is covered with primary and secondary forest, and many of the restricted-range species are consequently common. Nevertheless, habitat destruction remains the most important threat facing the endemic species as, owing to the small size of the island, any reduction in areas of suitable habitat could jeopardize the ability of some species to maintain a viable population (Peet and Atkinson 1994).

Two of the restricted-range species are considered threatened: the endemic *Speirops leucophaeus*, which is possibly declining, perhaps due to plantation development and pesticide use, and *Zosterops ficedulinus*, of which the Príncipe (nominate) race has not been seen since the 1970s, although the reasons for its scarcity are unclear. Additionally, the Príncipe (nominate) race of *Serinus rufobrunneus* is

very scarce in accessible areas, while the race *xanthorhynchus* of *Turdus olivaceofuscus* has been considered extinct, although the recent discovery of three thrush anvils provides the strongest evidence yet of its continuing existence (Christy 1996). *Dicrurus (adsimilis) modestus* (see 'Restricted-range species', above) may be threatened if increased pesticide use reduces its invertebrate prey (Atkinson *et al.* 1991).

Príncipe's remaining primary forest was proposed for protection as a national park by Jones and Tye (1988) and Jones *et al.* (1991), and was gazetted as such in 1993 (Jones 1994a). It is believed that the establishment of a 'Free Zone' on Príncipe to provide services to the oil-rich countries around the Gulf of Guinea is not currently a cause for concern (the multinational consortium concerned has agreed to the need for independent environmental impact assessments and is committed to the protection of the area's unique ecosystems). However, because a significant part of the proposed concession area is within the core zone of the proposed protected-area system, potential conflicts between the developer's land-use proposals and conservation issues need to be resolved as soon as possible (*Gulf of Guinea Conservation Newsl.* 1996, 5: 1–3).

084 Upper Guinea forests

PRIORITY
CRITICAL

Key habitats Lowland rain forest, gallery forest

Main threats Major habitat loss (e.g. due to logging, agriculture, mining), hunting

Biological importance ● ● ●
Current threat level ● ● ●

Area 340,000 km² **Altitude** 0–1,000 m
Countries Ghana, Guinea, Ivory Coast, Liberia, Sierra Leone

Restricted-range species	Threatened	Total
Confined to this EBA	11	15
Present also in other EBAs, SAs	0	0
Total	11	15

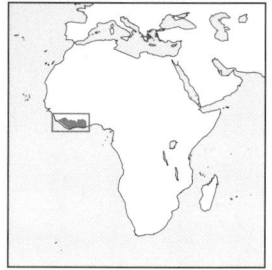

■ General characteristics

One of Africa's two major lowland rain forest regions (see White 1983), the Upper Guinea forest originally covered most of Sierra Leone, south-east Guinea, Liberia, southern Ivory Coast and south-west Ghana, but much of this area is now deforested. The restricted-range species are mainly confined to the lowland rain forests of Upper Guinea, although one ranges up to 1,550 m in the Guinea highlands.

■ Restricted-range species

The distribution and status of the birds of the Upper Guinea forests are generally rather poorly known, although recent survey work has generated much new information (Allport 1991, Demey and Fishpool 1991, Francis *et al.* 1992, Thompson 1993, Wood 1993, Atkinson *et al.* 1994b, Fishpool *et al.* 1994, Gartshore *et al.* 1995). *Phyllastrephus leucolepis*, *Melaenornis annamarulae* and *Malimbus ballmanni* were all described as new to science in the past 25 years, and at least two undescribed bird species are suspected to occur in the EBA (Allport 1991).

All the species endemic to the Upper Guinea forest are here considered to have restricted ranges, because, although the forest originally covered several hundred thousand square kilometres, this area

was already much reduced when ornithological exploration began, and few (if any) of the species appear to occur throughout the region (see Hall and Moreau 1970, Snow 1978). Many of these species are known from scattered records in most countries of the EBA, but *Phyllastrephus leucolepis*, *Melaenornis annamarulae* and *Malimbus ballmanni* (see Gatter and Gardner 1993) appear to be limited to the wet/dry mosaic forests in the west, in western Ivory Coast, Liberia, Sierra Leone and Guinea; *Phyllastrephus leucolepis* is only known from a single locality in Liberia, where it has been found in the transitional zone between evergreen and semi-deciduous tropical rain forest (Allport 1991).

Prinia leontica has rather different habitat requirements from the other species, being associated with gallery forest in the Guinea highlands in the EBA's north-west, at 500–1,550 m. Two of the restricted-range species appear not to be entirely confined to the EBA: *Criniger olivaceus* is known by one nineteenth-century record from Senegal and anomalous records from south-west Mali (Lamarche 1980–1981) and *Illadopsis rufescens* has been recorded from Senegal and Togo (Dowsett and Forbes-Watson 1993). Note that the species limits and distribution of *Bleda eximia* follow those of Chappuis and Erard (1993).

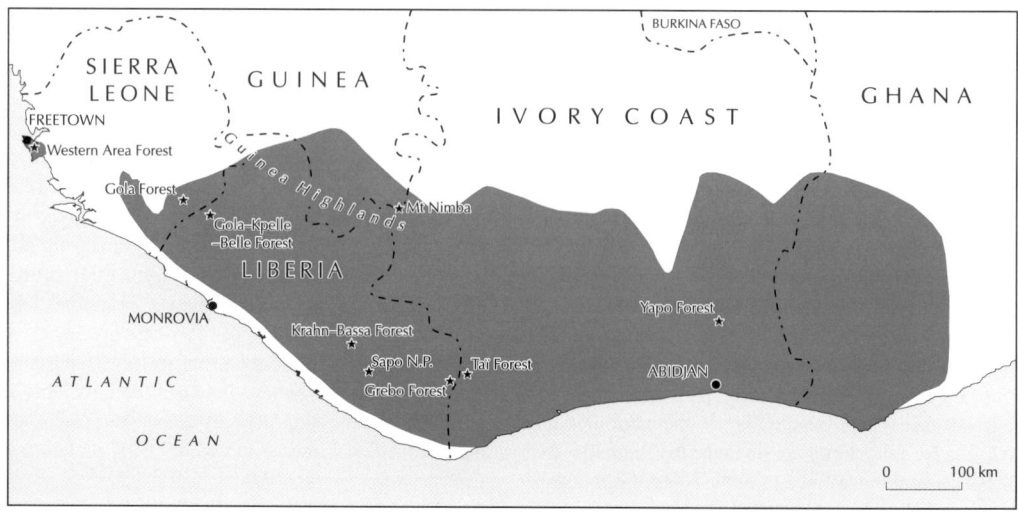

Status and habitat of restricted-range species

Species (ordered taxonomically)	Global status	Other EBAs (and SAs)	Habitat
White-breasted Guineafowl *Agelastes meleagrides*	VU	—	Lowland rain forest
Rufous Fishing-owl *Scotopelia ussheri*	EN	—	Along rivers in lowland rain forest, mangroves
Brown-cheeked Hornbill *Ceratogymna cylindricus*	nt	—	Lowland rain forest, and adjacent cocoa plantations and agricultural land
Western Wattled Cuckoo-shrike *Campephaga lobata*	VU	—	Lowland rain forest, occasionally cocoa plantations
Liberian Greenbul *Phyllastrephus leucolepis*	CR	—	Transition zone between evergreen and semi-deciduous rain forest
Green-tailed Bristlebill *Bleda eximia*	VU	—	Lowland rain forest
Yellow-throated Olive Greenbul *Criniger olivaceus*	VU	—	Lowland rain forest
Rufous-winged Illadopsis *Illadopsis rufescens*	nt	—	Lowland rain forest
White-necked Rockfowl *Picathartes gymnocephalus*	VU	—	Lowland rain forest with caves or large rocks
White-eyed Prinia *Prinia leontica*	VU	—	Gallery forest, thickets near streams, ravines at 500–1,550 m
Sharpe's Apalis *Apalis sharpei*	lc	—	Lowland rain forest
Black-capped Rufous Warbler *Bathmocercus cerviniventris*	VU	—	Lowland rain forest, gallery forest and streamside vegetation
Nimba Flycatcher *Melaenornis annamarulae*	VU	—	Lowland rain forest, plantations
Gola Malimbe *Malimbus ballmanni*	EN	—	Lowland rain forest
Copper-tailed Glossy-starling *Lamprotornis cupreocauda*	nt	—	Lowland rain forest

Global status (see p. 679 for definitions) — EX Extinct / EW Extinct in the Wild } with year of last record — CR Critical / EN Endangered / VU Vulnerable } threatened species — cd Conservation Dependent / nt Near Threatened / lc Least Concern — DD Data Deficient / NE Not Evaluated

Other EBAs (and SAs) (see p. 72 for locations): bracketed numbers are Secondary Areas; [x] extinct in that EBA or SA.

■ Threats and conservation

Allport (1991) estimated that c.77% of the EBA's original forest has been lost, mainly as a result of logging, agricultural encroachment and mining; the less than 80,000 km^2 of forest which remains is being rapidly degraded and fragmented. Current threats are logging and agricultural encroachment, and rates of forest loss are probably still increasing, with most forest outside protected areas (including forest reserves) likely to disappear within the next 25 years (N. D. Burgess *in litt.* 1993). In Liberia, the civil war continues to devastate the remaining forests and threatens Sapo National Park, as uncontrolled logging for export has been carried out to pay for troops and arms, and food shortages have led to large-scale hunting for food (M. E. J. Gore *in litt.* 1993). Eleven restricted-range birds are threatened, principally because of the continuing loss of their habitat. A more-widespread threatened species which occurs in the EBA is Yellow-footed Honeyguide *Melignomon eisentrauti* (classified as Vulnerable).

The protected areas within the EBA are concen-

trated in the two most important areas of surviving forest (see IUCN 1992b). Those in south-east Liberia and south-west Ivory Coast include Taï National Park (the largest and best-preserved area of Upper Guinea forest: Francis *et al.* 1992, Gartshore *et al.* 1995), Marahoué National Park, Yapo forest and N'zo Fauna Reserve in Ivory Coast (R. Demey *in litt.* 1993), and Grebo, Gio and Krahn–Bassa National Forests and Sapo National Park in Liberia. Some forests of south-east Sierra Leone and north-west Liberia are protected in Gola Forest Reserves in Sierra Leone and the Gola–Kpelle–Belle National Forest in Liberia (Allport 1991). The forests on Mount Nimba are protected in strict nature reserves in Guinea and Ivory Coast, but the Liberian section of this mountain is unprotected. In Sierra Leone, Western Area, Loma Mountain, Tingi Hills and Kangari Hills Forest Reserves and Tiwai Island Game Sanctuary are important for several restricted-range species, including *Prinia leontica* which occurs in the Loma Mountain and Tingi Hills reserves (P. Wood *in litt.* 1993; see Davies and Palmer 1989).

085 Cameroon and Gabon lowlands

PRIORITY HIGH

Key habitats Lowland rain forest	**Area** 280,000 km²	**Altitude** 0–1,000 m
Main threats Moderate habitat loss (e.g. due to logging), hunting	**Countries** Cameroon, Equatorial Guinea, Gabon, Nigeria	

Restricted-range species	Threatened	Total
Confined to this EBA	1	5
Present also in other EBAs, SAs	1	1
Total	2	6

Biological importance ● ● ●
Current threat level ● ● ●

■ General characteristics

The Lower Guinea forest is one of the world's great lowland rain forests, and together with the Upper Guinea forest (EBA 084) constitutes the Guineo-Congolian Region of White (1983). The restricted-range birds of this EBA are confined to the north-west part of the Lower Guinea forest, in south-east Nigeria, southern Cameroon, northern and central Gabon and continental Equatorial Guinea. The Cameroon mountains (EBA 086) lie adjacent, but the restricted-range birds of that EBA generally occur at higher altitudes in montane forest, although a few of them occur locally in lowland forest, e.g. on the southern slopes of Mt Cameroon.

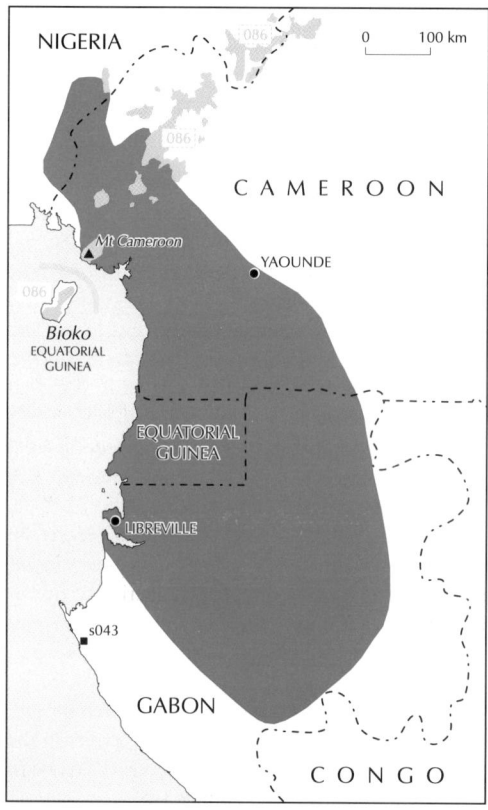

■ Restricted-range species

Bradypterus grandis is found in contact zones between forest and more open areas such as savannas and river borders, but otherwise the restricted-range species of this EBA are all found in lowland rain forest. Their distributions are generally poorly understood (see Brosset and Erard 1986, Erard and Colston 1988, Ash 1990, Rodewald *et al.* 1994). *Bradypterus grandis* and *Batis minima* are known only from a few localities in southern Cameroon and Gabon, and *Ploceus batesi* is only recorded from southern Cameroon. The other three species are relatively widespread within the EBA, but appear to be localized; the distribution of *Picathartes oreas*, for example, is closely related to the availability of rock faces in forests suitable for nesting (Ash 1991).

■ Threats and conservation

The major pressures in this EBA are forest loss and hunting. Large areas of forest have already been cleared or degraded, logging is reported to be continuing at an alarming rate in southern Cameroon, and there are plans for further exploitation (see, e.g., Webb 1995). However, extensive tracts of virgin forest still exist, particularly in sparsely populated Gabon and the Lake Lobeke region of south-east Cameroon (Thiollay 1985, P. Rodewald *in litt.* 1993). Two of the restricted-range birds are threatened, including *Picathartes oreas* which is under pressure from hunting as well as from habitat loss. *Bradypterus grandis* and *Batis minima* are classified as Data Deficient because of the paucity of records and the uncertainty about their susceptibility to habitat loss and degradation.

There are nine protected areas within the EBA (IUCN 1992b), but many of them have seen little or no ornithological investigation. Large reserves which are known (or believed) to be important for the restricted-range species are Dja and Campo Faunal Reserves and Korup National Park (Rodewald *et al.* 1994) in Cameroon, Cross River National Park in Nigeria and Lope Faunal Reserve and Wonga-Wongué Presidential Reserve in Gabon (P. D. Alexander-Marrack *in litt.* 1993, P. Rodewald *in litt.*

Status and habitat of restricted-range species

Species (ordered taxonomically)	Global status	Other EBAs (and SAs)	Altitude (m)	Habitat
Forest Swallow *Hirundo fuliginosa*	lc	—	Lowlands	Clearings in lowland rain forest
Grey-necked Rockfowl *Picathartes oreas*	VU	086	0–2,000	Forest with caves and rock faces
Dja River Warbler *Bradypterus grandis*	DD	—	c.600–800	Forest edge, tall grassland, marshland
Gabon Batis *Batis minima*	DD	—	Lowlands	Lowland rain forest
Bates's Weaver *Ploceus batesi*	VU	—	Lowlands	Lowland rain forest
Rachel's Malimbe *Malimbus racheliae*	lc	—	Lowlands	Lowland rain forest

| **Global status** (see p. 679 for definitions) | EX Extinct
 EW Extinct in the Wild | } with year of last record | CR Critical
 EN Endangered
 VU Vulnerable | } threatened species | cd Conservation Dependent <br> nt Near Threatened <br> lc Least Concern | DD Data Deficient
 NE Not Evaluated |

Other EBAs (and SAs) (see p. 72 for locations): bracketed numbers are Secondary Areas; ˣ extinct in that EBA or SA.

Grey-necked Picathartes *Picathartes oreas* breeds (usually colonially) in caves and on rock faces in both lowland and (in EBA 086) montane rain forests.

BirdLife

1993). *Bradypterus grandis* was recently recorded in the La Lopé–Okanda Reserve in central Gabon, and several of the restricted-range species are recorded from Park of Monte Alen in Equatorial Guinea (J. Pérez del Val *in litt.* 1993). Several of these species, including *Ploceus batesi*, have been recorded in the lowland forests on the lower slopes of Mt Kupe in Cameroon where BirdLife International initiated a forest conservation project (Bowden and Bowden 1993, Bowden and Andrews 1994) which is now managed by WWF. Important new protected areas have been proposed to the north-east of Makokou in Gabon (P. D. Alexander-Marrack *in litt.* 1993) and in the south-east corner of Cameroon (P. Rodewald *in litt.* 1993), while in south-east Nigeria the proposed Obudu and Boshi–Okwangwo National Parks are contiguous with Cross River National Park (J. S. Ash *in litt.* 1993).

086 Cameroon mountains

PRIORITY
CRITICAL

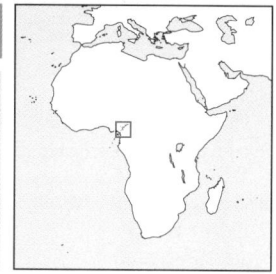

Key habitats Montane forest, montane scrub

Main threats Major habitat loss (e.g. due to logging, firewood collection, fire, overgrazing)

Biological importance ● ● ●
Current threat level ● ● ○

Area 14,000 km² **Altitude** 800–3,000 m
Countries Cameroon, Equatorial Guinea, Nigeria

Restricted-range species	Threatened	Total
Confined to this EBA	10	27
Present also in other EBAs, SAs	2	2
Total	12	29

■ General characteristics

This EBA comprises the mountains which run south-west to north-east through western Cameroon and adjacent south-eastern Nigeria, and the mountains on the island of Bioko (or Fernando Po; politically part of Equatorial Guinea but lying c.30 km off the coast of Cameroon). These mountains are volcanic in origin, and both Mt Cameroon (at 4,095 m the highest mountain in West Africa) and Pico Basilé (Pico de Santa Isabel) on Bioko are still active.

There are considerable local variations in rainfall within the EBA, with a continuous wet rainy season on the coastal (southern) slopes of Mt Cameroon and the South Massif on Bioko, but progressively drier conditions further inland, which results in major differences in the altitude at which montane forest is

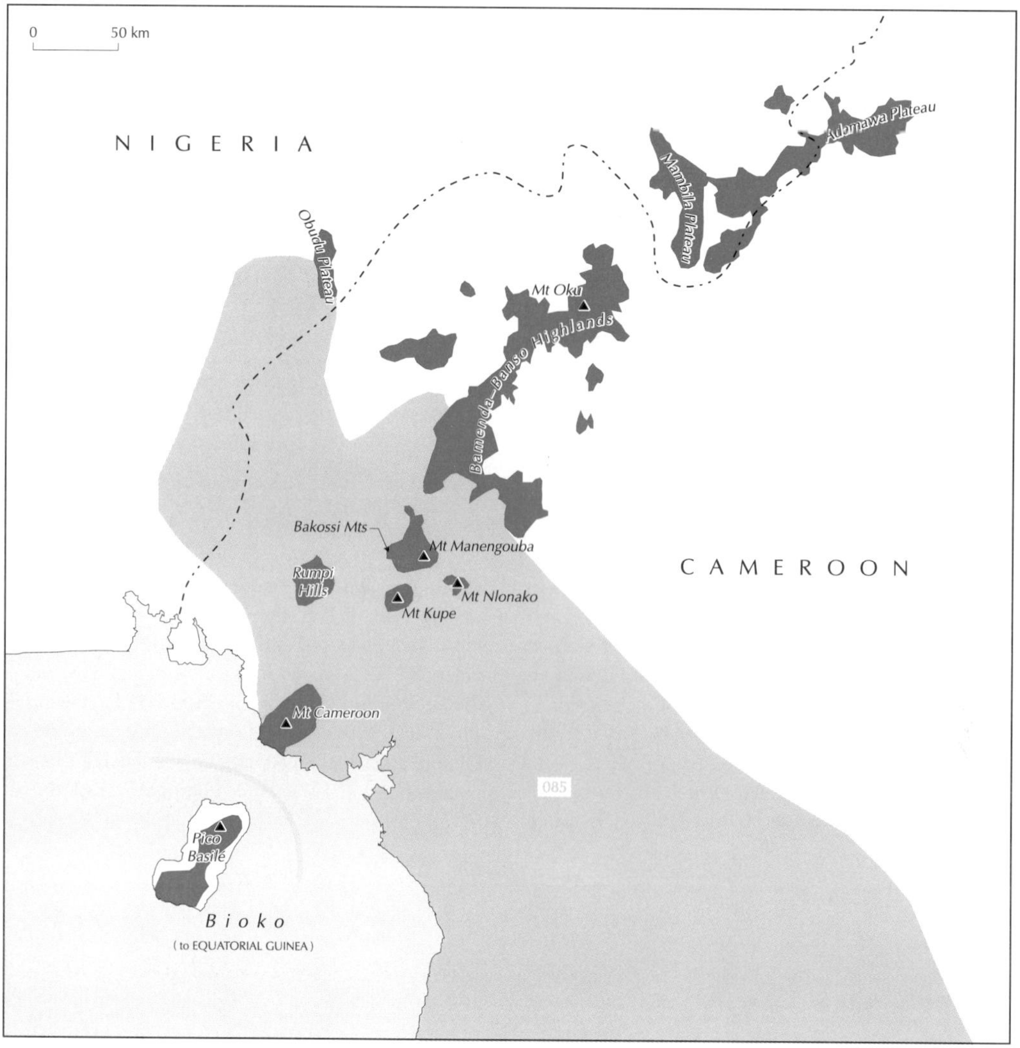

0   50 km

NIGERIA

Obudu Plateau

Adamawa Plateau

Mambila Plateau

Mt Oku

Bamenda–Banso Highlands

Bakossi Mts

Mt Manengouba

Rumpi Hills

Mt Nlonako

Mt Kupe

CAMEROON

Mt Cameroon

085

Pico Basilé

Bioko
(to EQUATORIAL GUINEA)

Status and habitat of restricted-range species

Species (ordered taxonomically)	Global status	Other EBAs (and SAs)	Altitude (m)	Habitat
Mount Cameroon Francolin *Francolinus camerunensis*	VU	—	850–2,100	Dense undergrowth in montane forest
Cameroon Olive-pigeon *Columba sjostedti*	lc	—	1,000–2,500	Montane forest, forested gullies
Bannerman's Turaco *Tauraco bannermani*	VU	—	1,700–2,800	Montane forest, bamboo
Mountain Sawwing *Psalidoprocne fuliginosa*	nt	—	0–3,000	Forest interior and clearings, montane grassland, agricultural land
Cameroon Greenbul *Andropadus montanus*	nt	—	550–2,500	Montane forest
Grey-throated Greenbul *Andropadus tephrolaemus*	lc	—	400–2,850	Montane forest
Cameroon Olive Greenbul *Phyllastrephus poensis*	lc	—	750–2,200	Montane forest
Grey-headed Greenbul *Phyllastrephus poliocephalus*	nt	—	500–1,600 (–2,000)	Montane forest
Yellow-breasted Boubou *Laniarius atroflavus*	lc	—	700–2,900	Montane forest, scrub, bamboo
Mount Kupe Bush-shrike *Telophorus kupeensis*	CR	—	950–1,450	Montane forest
Green-breasted Bush-shrike *Malaconotus gladiator*	VU	—	950–2,300	Montane forest
Monteiro's Bush-shrike *Malaconotus monteiri*	EN	087	c.1,000–1,600	Montane forest
Mountain Robin-chat *Cossypha isabellae*	lc	—	800–2,700	Montane forest
White-throated Mountain-babbler *Kupeornis gilberti*	VU	—	950–2,050	Montane forest
Grey-necked Rockfowl *Picathartes oreas*	VU	085	0–2,000	Forest with caves and rock faces
Brown-backed Cisticola *Cisticola discolor*	lc	—	850–3,000	Scrub at forest edge and in clearings, less commonly bracken and grass
Green Longtail *Urolais epichlora*	lc	—	520–2,500	Montane forest, plantations, isolated trees in grassland
Bamenda Apalis *Apalis bamendae*	VU	—	c.1,100–1,600	Gallery forest
Bangwa Forest Warbler *Bradypterus bangwaensis*[1]	nt	—	1,700–2,950	Undergrowth in open montane forest and plantations; tall grass, scrub, bracken, brambles
White-tailed Warbler *Poliolais lopezi*	lc	—	800–2,700	Montane forest, scrub
Black-capped Woodland-warbler *Phylloscopus herberti*	lc	—	700–2,200	Montane forest
Fernando Po Batis *Batis poensis*	lc	—	0–1,100	Forest, well-wooded cocoa plantations
Banded Wattle-eye *Platysteira laticincta*	VU	—	1,700–2,900	Montane forest, bamboo
Cameroon Sunbird *Nectarinia oritis*	lc	—	600–2,900	Montane forest, esp. along streams
Ursula's Sunbird *Nectarinia ursulae*	nt	—	650–2,050	Montane forest
Mount Cameroon Speirops *Speirops melanocephalus*	VU	—	1,800–3,000	Montane forest, grassland with trees, scrub above treeline
Fernando Po Speirops *Speirops brunneus*	VU	—	>1,900	Open montane forest, scrub above the treeline

cont.

Status and habitat of restricted-range species (cont.)

Species (ordered taxonomically)	Global status	Other EBAs (and SAs)	Altitude (m)	Habitat
Fernando Po Oliveback *Nesocharis shelleyi*	lc	—	(0–) 1,200–2,400	Open montane forest
Bannerman's Weaver *Ploceus bannermani*	VU	—	1,100–2,850	Trees and shrubs at edge of montane forest, gallery forest, scrub

Global status (see p. 679 for definitions)

EX Extinct ⎫ with year
EW Extinct in ⎬ of last
the Wild ⎭ record

CR Critical ⎫
EN Endangered ⎬ threatened
VU Vulnerable ⎭ species

cd Conservation Dependent
nt Near Threatened
lc Least Concern
DD Data Deficient
NE Not Evaluated

Other EBAs (and SAs) (see p. 72 for locations)
Bracketed numbers are Secondary Areas.   ˣ Extinct in that EBA or SA.

Notes
¹ Treated as a full species, following Dowsett and Forbes-Watson (1993), contra Sibley and Monroe (1990, 1993), who considered it a form of the more-widespread Cinnamon Bracken-warbler *Bradypterus cinnamomeus*.

found and in the forest type. On Mt Cameroon and the South Massif on Bioko, montane forest is found at relatively low elevations, generally above 800 m, but on the seaward (southern) slopes montane species of tree appear as low as 500 m; this is possibly because the extensive cloud cover and frequent mists caused by the proximity of the sea result in a severe reduction in the temperature (Tye 1986), or because of the exceptionally high rainfall (J. Pérez del Val *in litt.* 1993). Further inland, on Mt Kupe, montane forest is only found above 1,200 m. On nearby Mt Manenguba, the montane forest has rather a poor development of epiphytes, suggesting that this mountain is drier than Mt Kupe or Mt Cameroon. Further inland still, in the Bamenda–Banso highlands, montane forest is found from 2,000 to 2,950 m, and there is a transition to savanna (or now more usually farmland) at the base, rather than to the lowland rain forest found nearer the coast; the forest resembles the drier type found on Mt Manenguba, and a zone of mixed *Podocarpus* and bamboo appears above c.2,600 m (Thomas 1986). The Cameroon and Gabon lowlands (EBA 085) overlap geographically with the southern part of the present EBA, but the birds of the lowland EBA are generally found at lower altitudes, although there is some altitudinal overlap.

■ Restricted-range species

The monotypic genera *Poliolais* and *Urolais* are endemic to this EBA, and the genus *Speirops* is only found here and on the islands in the Gulf of Guinea (EBAs 082, 083). The restricted-range species present are all found within Afromontane habitats, principally montane forest, although several of them also range into more open areas. Many of the species appear to have wide altitudinal ranges, but this is largely because montane forest is found at different altitudes in different parts of the EBA. A few species range down into lowland forest in parts of their ranges, and several occur at or near sea-level on the seaward slopes of Mt Cameroon and on Bioko's South Massif.

The distributions of the restricted-range species of this EBA are relatively well known (see Stuart 1986), although recent fieldwork has extended the known ranges of several species in the northern part of the EBA (Smith and McNiven 1993) and Nigeria (Ash *et al.* 1989). Several species are highly localized in range: *Batis poensis* and *Speirops brunneus* are endemic to Bioko, and *Francolinus camerunensis* and *Speirops melanocephalus* to Mt Cameroon; *Telophorus kupeensis* is only known from Mt Kupe, where it is found around the transition from lowland to montane forest; *Tauraco bannermani* and

N. Arlott

BirdLife's Kilum–Ijim Mountain Forest Project is vital for the survival of the threatened Bannerman's Turaco *Tauraco bannermani*.

Mount Kupe Bush-shrike *Telophorus kupeensis* is known from a single mountain, where only 21 km² of its forest habitat remains.

Platysteira laticincta are restricted to montane forests in the Bamenda–Banso highlands; and *Apalis bamendae* to riverine vegetation at lower altitudes on the Adamawa plateau and the Bamenda–Banso highlands. *Kupeornis gilberti* has an unusual distribution in the central part of the EBA, being absent from Mt Cameroon and only recorded from the extreme south of the Bamenda–Banso highlands.

Another taxon confined to this EBA, considered by Sibley and Monroe (1990, 1993) to be a full species, is Cameroon Scrub-warbler *Bradypterus lopezi*, but it is here treated as a form of a more widespread species, Evergreen Forest-warbler *B. lopezi*, following Dowsett and Forbes-Watson (1993) and is therefore excluded from this analysis.

N. Arlott

Distribution patterns of restricted-range species

Species (ordered geographically)	Mambila & Adamawa plateaux	Obudu plateau	Bamenda–Banso highlands	Mts Manengouba, Kupe & Nlonako, Bakossi mts	Rumpi hills	Mt Cameroon	Bioko	Other EBAs, SAs
Apalis bamendae	●	–	●	–	–	–	–	–
Bradypterus bangwaensis	●	●	●	●	–	–	–	–
Ploceus bannermani	●	●	●	●	–	–	–	–
Laniarius atroflavus	●	●	●	●	–	●	–	–
Cisticola discolor	●	●	●	●	–	●	–	–
Andropadus montanus	●	●	●	●	●	●	–	–
Phyllastrephus poliocephalus	●	●	●	●	●	●	–	–
Cossypha isabellae	●	●	●	●	●	●	–	–
Nesocharis shelleyi	●	●	●	●	–	●	●	–
Phylloscopus herberti	●	●	–	●	●	●	●	–
Columba sjostedti	●	●	●	●	●	●	●	–
Andropadus tephrolaemus	●	●	●	●	●	●	●	–
Phyllastrephus poensis	●	●	●	●	●	●	●	–
Urolais epichlora	●	●	●	●	●	●	●	–
Nectarinia oritis	●	●	●	●	●	●	●	–
Kupeornis gilberti	–	●	●F	●	●	–	–	–
Malaconotus gladiator	–	●	●	–	●	●	–	–
Psalidoprocne fuliginosa	–	●	–	–	–	●	●	–
Picathartes oreas	–	●	–	●	●	●	●	◐
Poliolais lopezi	–	●	●	●	●	●	●	–
Tauraco bannermani	–	–	●	–	–	–	–	–
Platysteira laticincta	–	–	●	–	–	–	–	–
Nectarinia ursulae	–	–	●	●	●	●	●	–
Telophorus kupeensis	–	–	–	●K	–	–	–	–
Malaconotus monteiri	–	–	–	●K	–	●	–	◐
Francolinus camerunensis	–	–	–	–	–	●	–	–
Speirops melanocephalus	–	–	–	–	–	●	–	–
Batis poensis	–	–	–	–	–	–	●	–
Speirops brunneus	–	–	–	–	–	–	●	–
Total	15	19	20	21	14	20	13	

● Present   ? Present?
○ Extinct?   R Reintroduced
X Extinct   I Introduced

Threatened spp. shown in **bold**   ⎫ see 'Status and habitat' table
Other EBAs, SAs   ⎭

F Recorded only near Foto in south of Bamenda–Banso highlands
K Mt Kupe only

317

■ Threats and conservation

Forest loss is the main threat to the EBA. This is caused by unsustainable exploitation for timber and firewood, overgrazing, fire damage and agricultural encroachment, and is particularly serious in the Bamenda–Banso highlands (where it is estimated that half of the forest cover was lost between 1965 and 1985), the Obudu plateau and the eastern side of Mt Cameroon (Collar and Stuart 1988). Twelve of the restricted-range species are considered threatened, mainly those with particularly small ranges, or those which occur at low population densities and appear to be restricted to undisturbed forest.

Protected areas which may support some of the restricted-range birds include Cross River and Gashaka/Gumti National Parks in Nigeria (see IUCN 1992b), and several of these species occur in Nta Ali Forest Reserve between the Bakossi range and the Bamenda–Banso highlands (P. Rodewald *in litt.* 1993). However, most of the important sites in the EBA are not officially protected, including the areas which have their own endemic species: the Bamenda–Banso highlands, Mt Kupe, Mt Cameroon and Bioko. Mt Oku is the largest area of forest remaining in the Bamenda–Banso highlands, and represents the only hope for survival for *Tauraco bannermani* and *Platysteira laticincta* (Collar and Stuart 1988). BirdLife International has been running the Kilum–Ijim Mountain Forest Project to conserve the montane forests there for several years (Macleod 1987, Macleod and Parrott 1992, Alpert 1993, Edwards 1993a), and initiated a similar project on Mt Kupe (Bowden and Bowden 1993, Bowden and Andrews 1994) which is now managed by WWF. Mt Cameroon is particularly important because its southern slopes, between Batoke and Isongo, are mainland West Africa's best remaining example of an altitudinal gradient from lowland rain forest to montane forest and grassland (Thomas 1986), and a joint ODA/Cameroon Government project to protect a large section of the mountain has recently been started (L. D. C. Fishpool *in litt.* 1996). Pico Basilé and the South Massif on Bioko are also important because of their two endemic species, and because the forests on the southern slope of the latter are completely undisturbed from sea-level up to 2,200 m (J. Pérez del Val *in litt.* 1993). The montane habitats on Bioko remain largely intact, although fire may be a threat (Pérez del Val *et al.* 1994, Koster and Butynski undated). Other important forests in the EBA are on the Obudu plateau, Rumpi hills, Mt Manenguba, the Bakossi mountains and Mt Nlonako (Collar and Stuart 1988).

Large areas of montane forest in the Bamenda–Banso highlands have been cleared for cultivation.

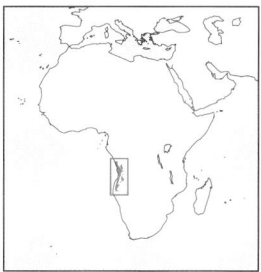

087 | **Western Angola**

PRIORITY
CRITICAL

Key habitats Semi-evergreen forest, gallery forest, montane forest, montane grassland, scrub

Main threats Unquantified habitat loss (e.g. due to fire, cultivation)

Biological importance ●
Current threat level ● ● ●

Area 150,000 km²   **Altitude** 0–2,000 m

Countries Angola, Namibia

Restricted-range species	Threatened	Total
Confined to this EBA	7	13
Present also in other EBAs, SAs	1	1
Total	8	14

■ General characteristics

Several vegetation zones meet in western Angola: it is bounded to the north by the lowland rain forests of the Zaïre basin, to the south by the Namib desert and to the east by a vast area of Zambesian miombo woodland. At the western edge of Angola's high plateau is a steep escarpment (at 400–1,000 m) where the cold Benguela current creates almost continuous cloud cover. A band of semi-evergreen forest which

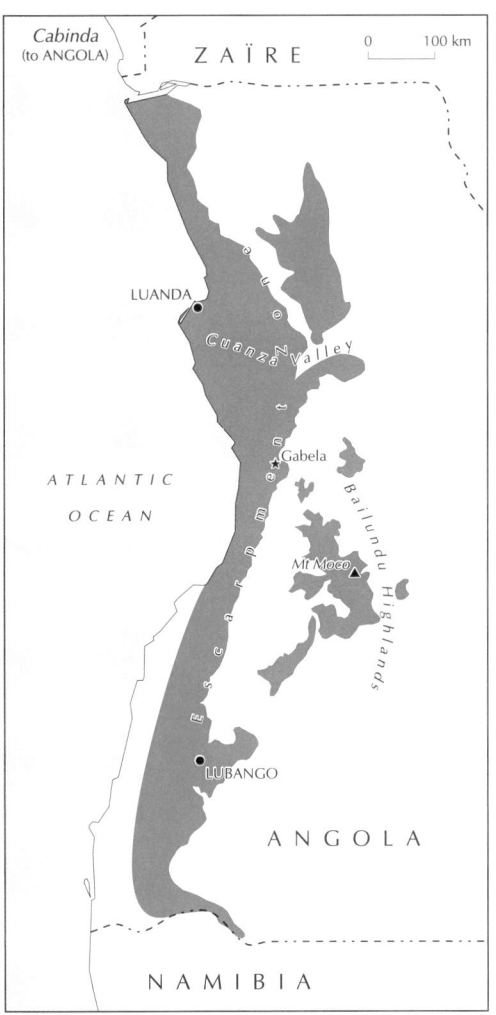

is between 1 km and 15 km wide extends here for c.300 km almost as far south as Lubango—but becomes very narrow and dry at the southern end; the estimate of its area (1,300–2,000 km²) requires confirmation by satellite imagery. This habitat—one of the most important for the EBA's restricted-range species—is bordered to the west by an arid coastal belt and inland by miombo woodland. Another important habitat is Afromontane forest, of which there are now only a few isolated patches in Huambo, Benguela, Cuanza Sul and Huila provinces, mainly in deep mountain ravines (Barbosa 1970, White 1983, Huntley 1992, Hawkins 1993).

■ Restricted-range species

Angola is among Africa's ornithologically least-known countries (Dowsett 1985, Dean *et al.* 1987). In the arid lowlands (see 'Habitat associations' table), *Euplectes aureus* is found in northern and central Angola below the escarpment zone, but most records of *Estrilda thomensis* are from south-west Angola and along the Angola–Namibia border, further south than any of the other restricted-range species. Seven species appear confined to the semi-evergreen forests of the escarpment zone, and *Platysteira albifrons* is only in the escarpment forest and coastal lowland gallery forest; note that, according to Lippens and Wille (1976), this species occurs in extreme south-west Zaïre, but we have been unable to trace the source of this record. *Laniarius*

Habitat associations of restricted-range species

Arid lowlands	
Estrilda thomensis	**Laniarius amboimensis**
Euplectes aureus	**Malaconotus monteiri**
	Prionops gabela
Escarpment zone and	**Sheppardia gabela**
lowland gallery forest	**Macrosphenus pulitzeri**
Platysteira albifrons	
	Montane
Escarpment zone	**Francolinus swierstrai**
Francolinus griseostriatus	*Xenocopsychus ansorgei*
Laniarius brauni	*Dioptrornis brunneus*
	Nectarinia ludovicensis

Threatened species (Critical, Endangered, Vulnerable) are shown in **bold**; see 'Status and habitat' table.

Status and habitat of restricted-range species

Species (ordered taxonomically)	Global status	Other EBAs (and SAs)	Altitude (m)	Habitat
Grey-striped Francolin *Francolinus griseostriatus*	VU	—	c.800–1,200	Undergrowth of gallery and secondary forest
Swierstra's Francolin *Francolinus swierstrai*	VU	—	c.1,500	Montane forest, tall grassland, rocky/grassy slopes
Orange-breasted Bush-shrike *Laniarius brauni*	EN	—	c.500	Gallery and secondary forest
Gabela Bush-shrike *Laniarius amboimensis*	EN	—	Escarpment zone	Evergreen forest
Monteiro's Bush-shrike *Malaconotus monteiri*	EN	086	Escarpment zone	Evergreen and gallery forest
Gabela Helmet-shrike *Prionops gabela*	EN	—	c.100–900	Forest underplanted with coffee, thicket in agricultural land
Gabela Akalat *Sheppardia gabela*	EN	—	Escarpment zone	Forest
Angola Cave-chat *Xenocopsychus ansorgei*	nt	—	Escarpment zone, mts	Rocky hills and gorges, esp. with weathered sandstone boulders adjacent to forest patches
Pulitzer's Longbill plantations *Macrosphenus pulitzeri*	EN	—	c.300–1,030	Dry evergreen forest, possibly coffee
Angola Slaty-flycatcher *Dioptrornis brunneus*	lc	—	Mountains	Forest
White-fronted Wattle-eye *Platysteira albifrons*	nt	—	Lowlands, escarpment zone	Gallery forest, plantations
Montane Double-collared Sunbird *Nectarinia ludovicensis*	lc	—	>1,400	Forest
Cinderella Waxbill *Estrilda thomensis*	nt	—	c.200–500	Riverine scrub, mopane woodland
Golden-backed Bishop *Euplectes aureus*[1]	nt	—	Coastal	Dry scrub

Global status (see p. 679 for definitions)	EX Extinct EW Extinct in the Wild } with year of last record	cd Conservation Dependent nt Near Threatened lc Least Concern DD Data Deficient NE Not Evaluated	**Other EBAs (and SAs)** (see p. 72 for locations)	Bracketed numbers are Secondary Areas. ˣ Extinct in that EBA or SA.	
	CR Critical EN Endangered VU Vulnerable } threatened species		**Notes**	[1] Also breeds in São Tomé (EBA 082) but is most likely to have been introduced (P. J. Jones *in litt.* 1997).	

amboimensis, *Prionops gabela* and *Sheppardia gabela* are known only from the escarpment in the vicinity of Gabela, south of the Cuanza valley, and *Macrosphenus pulitzeri* is known just from here and one other locality further south on the escarpment. *Laniarius brauni* has been recorded only from the escarpment in Cuanza Norte, north of the Cuanza valley, and *Malaconotus monteiri* (in this EBA) from here and the vicinity of Gabela. Four of the restricted-range species are associated with Afromontane vegetation (both forest and non-forest) in the higher parts of western Angola, including the monotypic endemic genus *Xenocopsychus*. Three of these species are locally common and occur on vegetated quartzite outcrops which are probably not threatened (W. R. J. Dean *in litt.* 1993), but *Francolinus swierstrai* is present in just a few small forest patches.

■ Threats and conservation

The density of Angola's human population is relatively low, but some of the EBA's most important forests are believed threatened. For example, the montane forests on Mt Moco in the Bailundu highlands (which are the EBA's best remaining examples of this forest type: Huntley 1992) are small and are vulnerable to fire and felling (Dowsett 1985). The escarpment zone was developed for coffee-growing from the 1930s, and by the 1970s there was little undisturbed forest remaining; it was estimated then that 95% of forest was under coffee production (which leaves the canopy largely intact), although much of this has now been abandoned for 30 years or more, with (possibly much) less than 25% now producing coffee. Clearance for subsistence agriculture is now a threat, and an estimated 30% of the forest has been so used; some forms of agriculture leave some canopy trees, but others remove virtually

Clearance for subsistence agriculture is the main threat to the semi-evergreen forests in the escarpment zone, the key habitat for seven of the restricted-range species.

F. Hawkins/BirdLife International

all of them. Hunting for food is probably widespread (Hawkins 1993).

All seven restricted-range birds confined to escarpment forest, and the montane *Francolinus swierstrai*, are threatened by habitat pressures, and the two

F. Hawkins/BirdLife International

A coffee-drying station near Gabela. Many coffee plantations have been abandoned in the past 30 years because of coffee-berry disease and a drop in prices in the mid-1970s.

francolins are also probably widely hunted. A more-widespread threatened species in montane habitats in the Bailundu highlands is Black-chinned Weaver *Ploceus nigrimentum* (classified as Vulnerable).

There are several protected areas in the EBA, but a number of new ones have been proposed to improve coverage of key habitats (Huntley 1992; see also Collar and Stuart 1988, IUCN 1992b). Kisama National Park includes an area of escarpment forest, but probably supports only a few of the restricted-range species, so Gabela and Chongoroi Strict Nature Reserves and Tala Mungongo National Monument have been proposed as new conservation areas. It may also prove possible to designate most of the southern part of the escarpment as a Biosphere Reserve (Hawkins 1993). The Afromontane habitats of western Angola are currently unprotected, so Namba and Monte Moco Strict Nature Reserves and Tundavala Regional Nature Park have been proposed. *Estrilda thomensis* occurs in Iona National Parks, and Chimalavera Regional Nature Park may support all three of the lowland species. The proposed Serra de Neve Strict Nature Reserve could also support some restricted-range species.

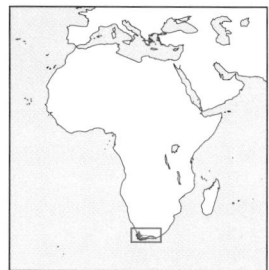

088 Cape fynbos

PRIORITY
HIGH

Key habitats Fynbos, rocky slopes

Main threats Moderate habitat loss (e.g. due to agriculture, urbanization, commercial afforestation)

Biological importance ● ● ●
Current threat level ● ● ●

Area 110,000 km²   **Altitude** 0–1,500 m

Countries South Africa

Restricted-range species	Threatened	Total
Confined to this EBA	0	6
Present also in other EBAs, SAs	0	0
Total	0	6

■ General characteristics

The winter rainfall district of south-western and southern Cape Province in South Africa comprises an EBA, which extends from the Cedarberg mountains near Clanwilliam, south to the Cape of Good Hope, and then eastwards to just west of Algoa Bay. This is the Cape shrubland (fynbos) zone of White (1983). The landscape is dominated by mountain ranges with an average altitude of 1,000–1,500 m. The prevalent vegetation is fynbos, which most characteristically occurs in the form of sclerophyllous shrubland 1–3 m tall. There is some overlap between this EBA and the South African forests (EBA 089), but the restricted-range species of the latter are birds of evergreen forest which seldom enter fynbos vegetation.

■ Restricted-range species

The restricted-range species are all widespread within the EBA (see Hockey *et al.* 1989). They are found in

Fynbos on the slopes of Table Mountain. This vegetation zone is probably the richest plant area on earth with some 8,600 species and 68% endemism.

M. Davies

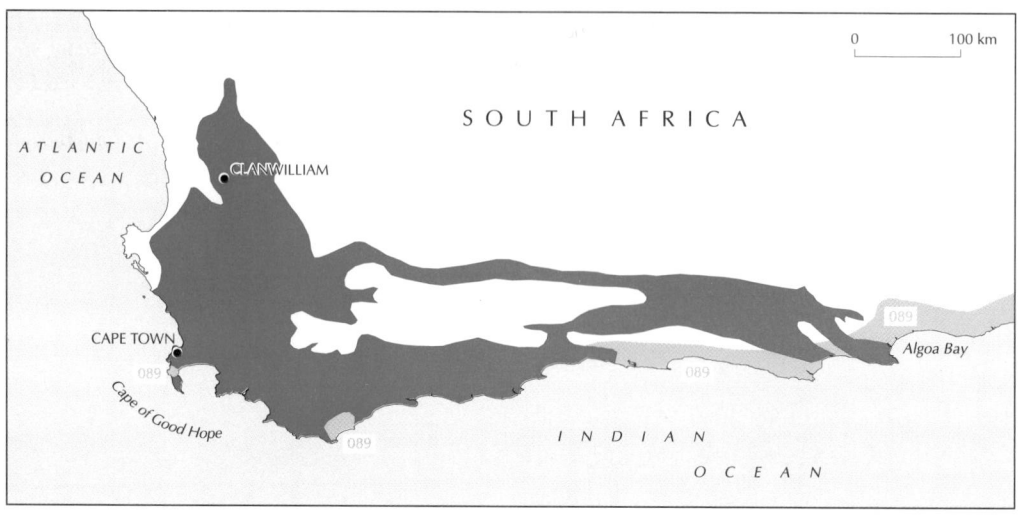

Status and habitat of restricted-range species

Species (ordered taxonomically)	Global status	Other EBAs (and SAs)	Altitude (m)	Habitat
Rufous Rockjumper *Chaetops frenatus*	nt	—	Sea-level to mountains	Rocky, boulder-strewn areas
Victorin's Scrub-warbler *Bradypterus victorini*	lc	—	0–1,000	Scrub, riverine vegetation, moist thick grass, rocky mountain slopes
Orange-breasted Sunbird *Nectarinia violacea*	lc	—	Sea-level to mountains	Fynbos with *Protea* and *Erica*, open mountain slopes
Cape Sugarbird *Promerops cafer*	lc	—	Sea-level to mountains	Fynbos, esp. where dominated by *Protea* bushes
Protea Canary *Serinus leucopterus*	nt	—	Sea-level to mountains	*Protea* fynbos
Cape Siskin *Serinus totta*	nt	—	Sea-level to mountains	Rocky slopes and fynbos

Global status (see p. 679 for definitions)

EX	Extinct	with year of last record	CR	Critical	threatened species	cd	Conservation Dependent	DD	Data Deficient
EW	Extinct in the Wild		EN	Endangered		nt	Near Threatened	NE	Not Evaluated
			VU	Vulnerable		lc	Least Concern		

Other EBAs (and SAs) (see p. 72 for locations): bracketed numbers are Secondary Areas; ˣ extinct in that EBA or SA.

Cape fynbos and open, rocky areas from near sea-level to the higher mountain slopes. Two species are particularly associated with *Protea* bushes.

■ Threats and conservation

The Cape fynbos, often referred to as the Cape Floristic Region or Kingdom, is remarkable for the high levels of plant diversity and endemism; a total of approximately 8,579 vascular plant species have been recorded in this biome, of which about 68% are endemic (WWF/IUCN 1994). Lowland fynbos is highly threatened by crop farming and urbanization, and both lowland and mountain fynbos are affected by commercial afforestation, dam-building and uncontrolled burning (D. G. Allan *in litt.* 1993). Large parts of the Cape lowlands, where not cultivated, are today occupied by secondary shrubland. However, the restricted-range birds all appear to be adaptable to man-modified habitats, and none is classified as threatened. A more widespread threatened species which occurs in the EBA is Cape Griffon *Gyps coprotheres* (classified as Vulnerable).

About 35 protected areas have been established to conserve the Cape fynbos, principally because of its botanical importance (see IUCN 1992b), and it is estimated that 26% of the EBA is included within protected areas (Allan and Nuttall 1995).

C. Spottiswoode

Orange-breasted Sunbird *Nectarinia violacea* is particularly associated with fynbos dominated by *Protea* and *Erica* bushes.

089 South African forests

PRIORITY HIGH

Key habitats Evergreen forest, scrub	**Area** 91,000 km²	**Altitude** 0–1,900 m
Main threats Possible habitat loss	**Countries** Mozambique, South Africa, Swaziland	

Restricted-range species	Threatened	Total
Confined to this EBA	0	7
Present also in other EBAs, SAs	0	0
Total	0	7

Biological importance ● ● ●
Current threat level ● ● ●

■ General characteristics

In South Africa, evergreen forest is confined to a band of Afromontane 'mist-belt' forest on the eastern escarpment which extends southwards from the Soutpansberg in northern Transvaal through eastern Transvaal, Natal, Transkei and adjacent parts of Swaziland to the eastern Cape, and along the southern and eastern coasts in southern Mozambique, eastern Natal, Transkei and the Cape.

A group of restricted-range species is endemic to these forests, several of which occur in both coastal and montane forests, so they are treated together as a single EBA (see Allan and Nuttall 1995). In the southern Cape, there is some overlap between this EBA and the Cape fynbos (EBA 088), as a few of the restricted-range birds of this EBA range into the forest mosaic within the fynbos biome, but seldom enter fynbos vegetation (K. Barnes *in litt.* 1996). This EBA is also adjacent to the South African grasslands (EBA 091), but there is no overlap, as the birds of that EBA occur in open grasslands. One species of the South African forests ranges close to the South-east African coast (EBA 092), but there is no true overlap as the birds of that EBA do not occur in evergreen forest.

■ Restricted-range species

The restricted-range bird species are all found in evergreen forest, and some also range into adjacent scrub and thickets. Most are found in both montane and coastal forest, but *Lioptilus nigricapillus* is confined to montane mist-belt forest and adjacent scrubby hillsides, and *Campethera notata* and *Bradypterus sylvaticus* are confined to the coastal lowlands. *Cercotrichas signata* is the only species which extends up the northern Natal coast into Mozambique, where it ranges northwards to Ponta Zavora (near Lagoa Poelela).

■ Threats and conservation

None of the restricted-range birds is threatened because the forests of the EBA are relatively well

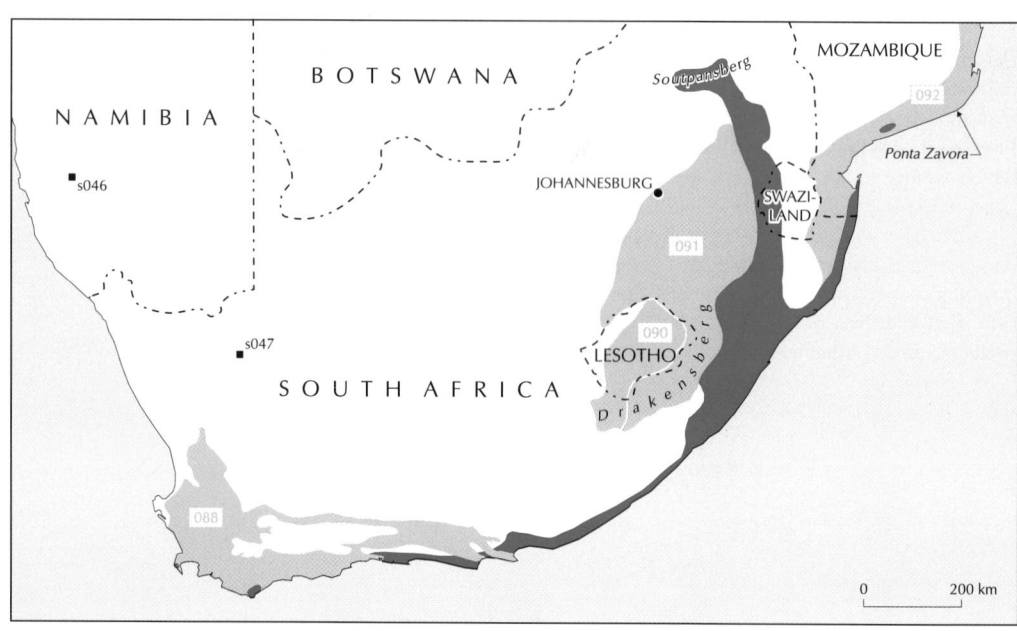

Status and habitat of restricted-range species

Species (ordered taxonomically)	Global status	Other EBAs (and SAs)	Altitude (m)	Habitat
Knysna Turaco *Tauraco corythaix*	lc	—	Coastal and montane	Evergreen and gallery forest, coastal scrub, dense thickets
Knysna Woodpecker *Campethera notata*	nt	—	Coastal lowlands	Coastal and riverine scrub, evergreen forest
Chorister Robin-chat *Cossypha dichroa*	lc	—	Coastal and montane	Evergreen forest
Brown Scrub-robin *Cercotrichas signata*	lc	—	Coastal and montane	Evergreen forest
Bush Blackcap *Lioptilus nigricapillus*	nt	—	750–1,850	Evergreen montane forest and adjacent scrubby hillsides
Knysna Scrub-warbler *Bradypterus sylvaticus*	lc	—	Coastal lowlands	Evergreen forest and dense undergrowth, often near streams
Forest Canary *Serinus scotops*	lc	—	Coastal and montane	Evergreen forest and adjacent plantations, fynbos, scrub and well-wooded gardens

Global status (see p. 679 for definitions)

EX Extinct	} with year of last record	
EW Extinct in the Wild		
CR Critical	} threatened species	
EN Endangered		
VU Vulnerable		
cd Conservation Dependent	DD Data Deficient
nt Near Threatened	NE Not Evaluated
lc Least Concern	

Other EBAs (and SAs) (see p. 72 for locations): bracketed numbers are Secondary Areas; ˣ extinct in that EBA or SA.

Coastal evergreen forest in Tsitsikama National Park, Cape province. Most of the remaining forest in this EBA lies within protected areas.

J. P. Croxall

protected (about 77% of the EBA's remaining area of natural forest is included within protected areas: Allan and Nuttall 1995) and because several of the species appear able to adapt to man-modified habitats. A more widespread threatened species which occurs in this EBA (and is migratory within it) is Spotted Ground-thrush *Zoothera guttata* (classified as Endangered).

090 Lesotho highlands

PRIORITY
HIGH

Key habitats Alpine grassland, montane scrub, rocky slopes

Main threats Moderate habitat loss (e.g. due to overgrazing, uncontrolled burning, road-building)

Biological importance ● ● ●
Current threat level ● ● ●

Area 30,000 km² **Altitude** 1,000–3,000 m

Countries Lesotho, South Africa

Restricted-range species	Threatened	Total
Confined to this EBA	0	3
Present also in other EBAs, SAs	0	0
Total	0	3

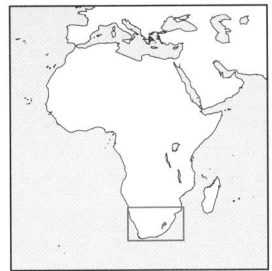

■ General characteristics

The highlands as defined here include the higher mountains of the Drakensberg and Maluti ranges in Lesotho and the adjacent parts of the South African provinces of the eastern Cape, Natal and Orange Free State (see p. 324 for map). The area lies adjacent to the South African grasslands (EBA 091), but the birds of that EBA mainly occur in grasslands at lower altitudes—although there is some overlap, as one species from that EBA (Yellow-breasted Pipit *Anthus chloris*) occurs locally in the alpine zone.

■ Restricted-range species

The restricted-range species are all widespread and locally common within the EBA (Osborne and Tigar 1992). They breed in open alpine grassland, rocky slopes and Afromontane scrub above c.2,000 m. *Chaetops aurantius* and *Serinus symonsi* descend to slightly lower altitudes outside the breeding season, and *Anthus hoeschi* is migratory, apparently wintering in Angola or central Africa.

■ Threats and conservation

Parts of the EBA are densely populated and subject to overgrazing and uncontrolled burning. The various developments associated with the Lesotho Highlands Water Scheme, including its dams, roads and new settlements will also lead to increased disturbance (D. G. Allan *in litt.* 1993; see Osborne and Tigar 1992). However, extensive areas of suitable habitat remain for the restricted-range species, and none is classified as threatened. More-widespread threatened birds which occur in the EBA are Southern Bald Ibis *Geronticus calvus* and Cape Griffon *Gyps coprotheres* (both classified as Vulnerable).

The EBA has several protected areas which contain suitable habitat for the restricted-range birds (see IUCN 1992b). All of the species are known from Sehlabathebe National Park in Lesotho (K. Barnes *in litt.* 1996); in South Africa, *Chaetops aurantius* and *Serinus symonsi* are present in Giant's Castle Game Reserve, and *C. aurantius* occurs additionally in Royal Natal National Park and Golden Gate Highlands National Park (D. G. Allan *in litt.* 1993).

Status and habitat of restricted-range species

Species (ordered taxonomically)	Global status	Other EBAs (and SAs)	Altitude (m)	Habitat
Mountain Pipit *Anthus hoeschi*	nt	—	>2,000	Short montane grassland
Orange-breasted Rockjumper *Chaetops aurantius*	nt	—	1,000–3,000	Rocky slopes and scree, either bare or with grass or low scrub
Drakensberg Siskin *Serinus symonsi*	nt	—	High altitudes, down to 1,500 in winter	Montane scrub, alpine grassland, rocky hillsides

Global status (see p. 679 for definitions)
EX Extinct
EW Extinct in the Wild } with year of last record
CR Critical
EN Endangered } threatened species
VU Vulnerable
cd Conservation Dependent
nt Near Threatened
lc Least Concern
DD Data Deficient
NE Not Evaluated

Other EBAs (and SAs) (see p. 72 for locations): bracketed numbers are Secondary Areas; ˣ extinct in that EBA or SA.

091 South African grasslands

PRIORITY
CRITICAL

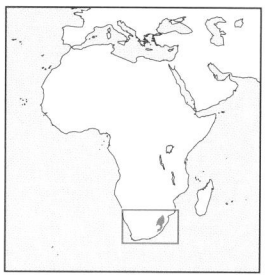

Key habitats Montane grassland

Main threats Major habitat loss (e.g. due to agriculture, commercial afforestation, overgrazing)

Biological importance ●
Current threat level ● ● ●

Area 110,000 km² **Altitude** 1,700–2,400 m

Countries Lesotho, South Africa

Restricted-range species	Threatened	Total
Confined to this EBA	3	3
Present also in other EBAs, SAs	0	0
Total	3	3

General characteristics

The northern part of the South African highveld grassland zone constitutes an EBA, in south-east Transvaal, north-east Orange Free State, western Natal and the eastern Cape, and a few adjacent areas of Lesotho (see p. 324 for map). The restricted-range birds occur in a variety of grassland types (see the botanical analysis of Acocks 1988). The birds of the adjacent Lesotho highlands (EBA 090) occur at higher altitudes in the alpine zone, although there is a partial overlap because *Anthus chloris* occurs locally in the alpine zone.

Restricted-range species

The restricted-range species are all highly localized within the EBA. *Heteromirafra ruddi* occurs in eastern Transvaal, eastern Orange Free State, southern Natal and East Griqualand in the north-east Cape (Hockey *et al.* 1988), *Spizocorys fringillaris* occurs in northern Orange Free State and south-east Transvaal (Allan *et al.* 1983), and *Anthus chloris* breeds in the north-east Cape, western Natal, eastern Orange Free State, south-east Transvaal and Lesotho, moving lower down in winter. North-Eastern Sandy Highveld (see Acocks 1988) is the most important grassland type in the EBA, as it supports all three species.

Threats and conservation

This part of South Africa is densely populated, either in sprawling urban centres such as Johannesburg, or in rural settings such as parts of Eastern Cape Province. Much of South Africa's crop farming occurs in these relatively high-rainfall areas and much grassland has been transformed by agriculture, principally maize-farming. Many of the remaining grasslands are subject to overgrazing and uncontrolled burning, or are being destroyed by open-cast coal mining and urbanization. However, commercial afforestation is probably the most critical threat, and is likely to alter vast areas drastically in the next 20 years. This could lead to the extinction of *Heteromirafra ruddi*, and could affect *Anthus chloris* significantly, but the range of *Spizocorys fringillaris* lies slightly to the west of the areas to be afforested so it will not be affected as severely (D. G. Allan *in litt.* 1993); all three species are considered threatened.

More-widespread threatened birds which occur in the EBA are Southern Bald Ibis *Geronticus calvus*, Cape Griffon *Gyps coprotheres*, Blue Crane *Grus paradiseus*, Wattled Crane *Grus carunculatus*, Blue Swallow *Hirundo atrocaerulea* (all classified as Vulnerable), and non-breeding Lesser Kestrel *Falco naumanni* (Vulnerable) and White-winged Flufftail *Sarothrura ayresi* (Endangered).

Spizocorys fringillaris does not occur within any protected area, and the only protected area with reasonable numbers of *Heteromirafra ruddi* is Verloren Valei Nature Reserve in the Transvaal, although it also occurs in Nooitgedacht Dam Nature Reserve. *Anthus chloris* occurs at Verloren Valei and at least three other reserves in South Africa, and in Sehlabathebe National Park in Lesotho (D. G. Allan *in litt.* 1993; see IUCN 1992b), but such populations are mostly small (K. Barnes *in litt.* 1996).

Status and habitat of restricted-range species

Species (ordered taxonomically)	Global status	Other EBAs (and SAs)	Altitude (m)	Habitat
Rudd's Lark *Heteromirafra ruddi*	CR	—	1,700–2,200	Short grassland in broken, sloping terrain
Botha's Lark *Spizocorys fringillaris*	VU	—	c.1,700–1,800	Open grassland
Yellow-breasted Pipit *Anthus chloris*	VU	—	1,800–2,400	Tracts of dense wiry grassland

Global status (see p. 679 for definitions)
EX Extinct
EW Extinct in the Wild } with year of last record
CR Critical
EN Endangered
VU Vulnerable } threatened species
cd Conservation Dependent
nt Near Threatened
lc Least Concern
DD Data Deficient
NE Not Evaluated

Other EBAs (and SAs) (see p. 72 for locations): bracketed numbers are Secondary Areas; ˣ extinct in that EBA or SA.

092 South-east African coast

PRIORITY
HIGH

Key habitats Dry woodland, dune forest, scrub

Main threats Unquantified habitat loss (e.g. due to logging, commercial afforestation, agriculture)

Biological importance ● ● ○
Current threat level ● ● ○

Area 87,000 km²   **Altitude** 0–200 m
Countries Malawi, Mozambique, South Africa, Swaziland, Zimbabwe

Restricted-range species	Threatened	Total
Confined to this EBA	0	4
Present also in other EBAs, SAs	0	0
Total	0	4

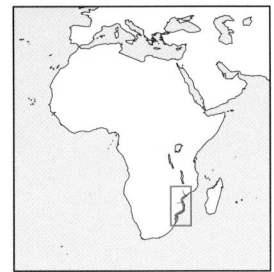

■ General characteristics

This EBA includes the broad coastal plain of southern Mozambique, northern Natal and the southeastern extreme of Transvaal in South Africa, and eastern Swaziland. It corresponds to the southern part of the Zanzibar–Inhambane East African coastal mosaic (White 1983). On this sandy plain there is dune forest along the coast, together with a mixture of palm savanna, bush-clump savanna, secondary scrub, riparian forest, wetland vegetation types and sand forest, and *Acacia* thornveld as another compo-

nent further inland (Acocks 1988). Some of the restricted-range species occur inland along the valleys of some of the larger rivers, including the Shire river in extreme southern Malawi and several tributaries of the upper Save river in south-east Zimbabwe. This EBA overlaps with the northern coastal section of the South African forests (EBA 089), but the restricted-range species of that EBA are confined to evergreen forest.

■ Restricted-range species

The restricted-range birds occur in a variety of wooded and open habitats, but not in evergreen forest. Their distribution and status remain poorly known in Mozambique (Clancey 1971)—which is one of the least-known countries ornithologically in south-central and southern Africa (Dowsett 1985)—but are relatively well documented in the South African part of the EBA (Cyrus and Robson 1980, Tarboton *et al.* 1987). *Apalis ruddi* and *Serinus citrinipectus* are recorded from southern Malawi, and *S. citrinipectus* from south-east Zimbabwe.

■ Threats and conservation

Coastal forest is probably the most immediately threatened forest type in Mozambique (Dowsett 1985). The whole of Maputo province is under pressure from requests for logging concessions, and a 300–km² proposed eucalyptus plantation adjacent to the South African frontier could have significant hydrological and other impacts (J. Oglethorpe *in litt.* to J. Fanshawe 1995). In South Africa, the main pressures are a result of the increasing human population, including the loss of natural habitats resulting from commercial forestry and slash-and-burn agriculture. However, plans for strip mining of coastal dunes for mineral sands at Lake St Lucia have been abandoned in the face of public protest (Barnes 1996). Despite these pressures, extensive areas of suitable habitats remain, and none of the restricted-range birds is classified as threatened.

There are approximately 15 protected areas in the EBA which contain habitats suitable for the restricted-range birds; all of these are in the southern

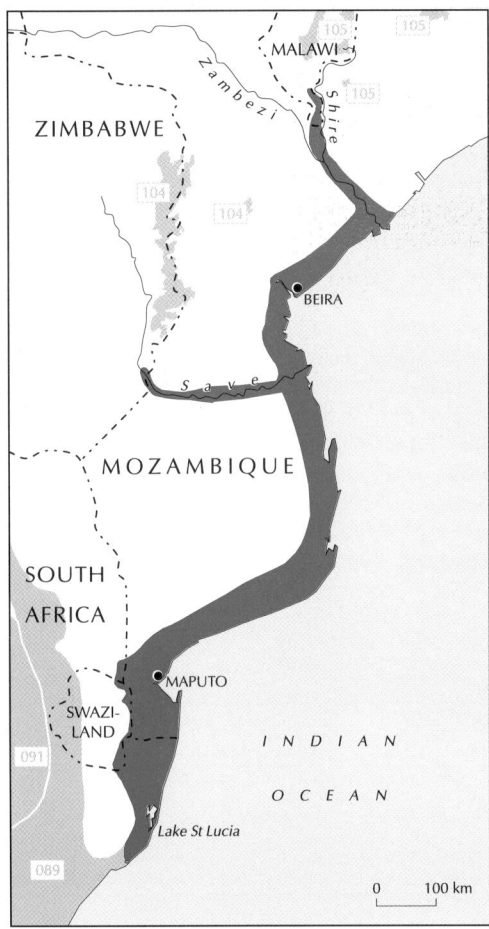

Status and habitat of restricted-range species

Species (ordered taxonomically)	Global status	Other EBAs (and SAs)	Altitude (m)	Habitat
Rudd's Apalis *Apalis ruddi*	lc	—	<200	Dry woodland, edges of gallery and dune forest
Neergaard's Sunbird *Nectarinia neergaardi*	nt	—	Coastal lowlands	Dry woodland, coastal scrub, dune forest
Lemon-breasted Seedeater *Serinus citrinipectus*	lc	—	Lowlands	Open country with bush-clump grasslands and palm savanna
Pink-throated Twinspot *Hypargos margaritatus*	lc	—	Coastal lowlands	Scrub, dry forest edge

Global status (see p. 679 for definitions)	EX Extinct EW Extinct in the Wild	} with year of last record	CR Critical EN Endangered VU Vulnerable	} threatened species	cd Conservation Dependent nt Near Threatened lc Least Concern	DD Data Deficient NE Not Evaluated

Other EBAs (and SAs) (see p. 72 for locations): bracketed numbers are Secondary Areas; ˣ extinct in that EBA or SA.

Rudd's Apalis *Apalis ruddi* is found in dry forest and forest edge in Mkusi National Park. These characteristic habitats of the EBA are well protected in South Africa, but there are few protected areas elsewhere.

J. P. Croxall

part of the EBA and there is only one in Mozambique (IUCN 1992b, D. G. Allan *in litt.* 1993, A. Berruti and R. Taylor *in litt.* 1993). In this part of South Africa there has recently been a considerable increase in the amount of land managed for conservation and/or sustainable utilization, as practised in the reserves protected by the Natal Parks Board, the KwaZulu Bureau of Natural Resources and some private concerns (A. Berruti *in litt.* 1993).

093 West Malagasy dry forests

PRIORITY
HIGH

Key habitats Dry deciduous forest

Main threats Major habitat loss (e.g. due to subsistence cultivation, commercial logging)

Biological importance ● ● ●
Current threat level ● ● ●

Area 150,000 km²   **Altitude** 0–800 m

Countries Madagascar

Restricted-range species	Threatened	Total
Confined to this EBA	3	3
Present also in other EBAs, SAs	1	5
Total	4	8

■ General characteristics

This EBA corresponds to the Western Domain of the Western Malagasy Region (a biogeographic region recognized by White 1983) in Madagascar, where the characteristic vegetation is seasonally dry deciduous forest.

The boundary of the EBA includes all remaining patches of deciduous forest, which occur on various distinctive rock types, largely below 800 m, from Antsiranana in the north to Morombe in the south-west; forest cover is based on satellite imagery of the vegetation taken between 1972 and 1979, these data being simplified and interpreted by Du Puy and Moat (1996) from Faramalala (1988, 1995).

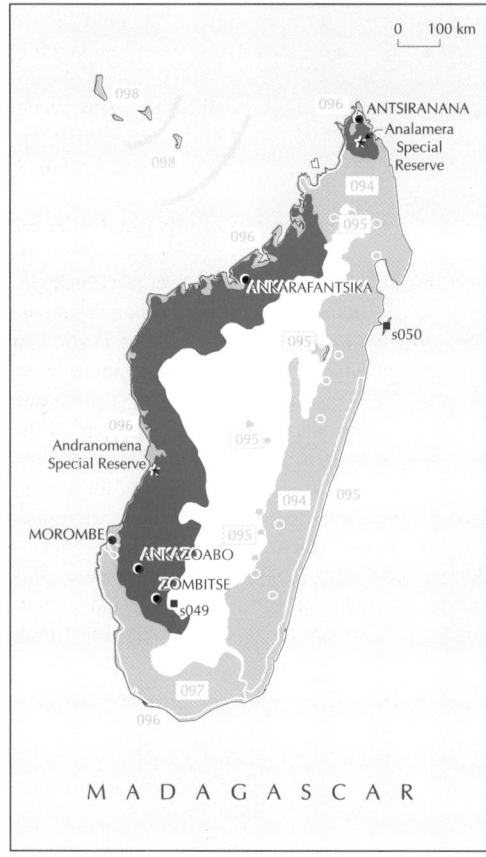

■ Restricted-range species

All the restricted-range species are forest birds and most are very local in distribution, e.g. *Xenopirostris damii* which is known from only two sites (Ankarafantsika and Analamera), and *Phyllastrephus apperti* which is recorded from just one forest complex (including the Zombitse and Vohibasia forests).

Mesitornis variegata is treated as endemic to this EBA but has one anomalous record in the East Malagasy wet forests (EBA 094). *Coua coquereli* and *Philepitta schlegeli* also occur in the Sambirano Domain (EBA 094), but their core ranges lie in the western dry forests. *Thamnornis chloropetoides* and *Newtonia archboldi* occur only in the extreme south of this EBA, the majority of their ranges falling within the South Malagasy spiny forest (EBA 097).

Benson's Rock-thrush *Monticola bensoni* was thought to breed on the Isalo Massif (Secondary Area s049) and in a few sites in the East Malagasy wet forests (EBA 094), dispersing to the western lowlands of the present EBA in winter—but breeding populations have recently been found west to Ankazoabo (S. M. Goodman *in litt.* 1996).

In the north-west, the EBA is bisected by the so-called Sambirano Domain which is treated here as part of the East Malagasy wet forests (EBA 094; see that text), as is the Montagne d'Ambre Massif in the far north. On its western boundary, the EBA is skirted by the West Malagasy wetlands (EBA 096), which also intersects it along rivers and around inland lakes, overlapping in some places.

■ Threats and conservation

Estimates of the surface area of the remaining western dry forests vary from less than 12,000 km² to less than 20,000 km² (Smith *et al.* 1991a, Du Puy and Moat 1996; see also Nelson and Horning 1993), although misclassification of forest and inaccurate boundaries can result in wide margins of error (Hawkins 1994). Whatever the exact figures, it is certain that much of the dry deciduous forest within the boundaries of this EBA has been replaced by bush, wooded savanna and sterile grassland.

Status and habitat of restricted-range species

Species (ordered taxonomically)	Global status	Other EBAs (and SAs)	Altitude (m)	Habitat
White-breasted Mesite *Mesitornis variegata*[1]	VU	—	0–300	Dry deciduous forest
Coquerel's Coua *Coua coquereli*	lc	094	0–800	Dry deciduous forest (rain forest edge in Sambirano, EBA 094)
Schlegel's Asity *Philepitta schlegeli*	nt	094	0–800	Dry deciduous forest (rain forest in Sambirano, EBA 094)
Appert's Greenbul *Phyllastrephus apperti*	VU	—	600–800	Dry deciduous forest
Van Dam's Vanga *Xenopirostris damii*	VU	—	0–300	Dry deciduous forest
Benson's Rock-thrush *Monticola bensoni*	VU	094 (s049)	<1,000	Rocky canyons with dry deciduous forest?
Thamnornis Warbler *Thamnornis chloropetoides*	lc	097	0–500	Sub-arid scrub, adjacent secondary growth, dry forest
Archbold's Newtonia *Newtonia archboldi*	lc	097	0–100	Sub-arid scrub, dry forest edge

Global status (see p. 679 for definitions)
EX Extinct ⎫ with year
EW Extinct in ⎬ of last
       the Wild ⎭ record
CR Critical ⎫
EN Endangered ⎬ threatened species
VU Vulnerable ⎭

cd Conservation Dependent
nt Near Threatened
lc Least Concern
DD Data Deficient
NE Not Evaluated

Other EBAs (and SAs) (see p. 72 for locations)
Bracketed numbers are Secondary Areas.
ˣ Extinct in that EBA or SA.

Notes
[1] Also known from one anomalous record in the East Malagasy wet forests (EBA 094).

The extent to which man is responsible for these habitat changes is uncertain, as climatic changes resulting in desiccation over the last 2,000 years (since settlement) may also have contributed to modifications of the native vegetation (Burney 1995; see also Langrand and Goodman 1995). Nevertheless, forest has unquestionably been destroyed by man over the last 50 years and the main threats today come from subsistence cultivation involving the felling and burning of forest for maize-growing, commercial logging followed by fire and/or cultivation, and exploitation for charcoal and firewood (Jenkins 1987, A. F. A. Hawkins *in litt.* 1995).

Three of the EBA's endemic species are classified as threatened on account of their small and declining ranges. Although protected areas appear to provide fairly good protection of the forest environment (Nicoll and Langrand 1989), and there are several strict nature reserves and special reserves in this EBA representing c.15% of extant forest, this protection is often nominal (Hawkins 1994). Du Puy and Moat (1996) calculate that only 9% of western forests are well protected, and note that many of the reserves are in areas of Mesozoic limestone where highly eroded limestone karst and pinnacles (known as 'tsingy')

make access extremely limited and are an effective natural protection against overexploitation, burning and cattle-grazing; they suggest that protection of vegetation on other rock types should be carefully examined. In addition, the pressures on the dry forests are increasing very rapidly, and conservation action in this EBA should thus be viewed as a major priority for Madagascar (A. F. A. Hawkins verbally 1997).

Two key forests were identified by Collar and Stuart 1988 (see also Collar *et al.* 1987): the Ankarafantsika Strict Nature Reserve (which provides some protection for *Mesitornis variegata* and *Xenopirostris damii*) and the Zombitse Forest (important for *Phyllastrephus apperti*), the latter the subject of a NORAD-funded WWF project to establish it and Vohibasia Forest as a national park. Other important sites include Analamera Special Reserve (which protects the second known site for *Xenopirostris damii* and also holds *Mesitornis variegata*), Menabe Forest (including Andranomena Special Reserve and Kirindy Forest, a logging concession which is being exploited sustainably) and Analabe Private Reserve (A. F. A. Hawkins verbally 1996).

094 East Malagasy wet forests

Key habitats Lowland evergreen rain forest, montane forest

Main threats Major habitat loss (e.g. due to subsistence cultivation, commercial logging)

Biological importance ● ● ●
Current threat level ● ●

Area 160,000 km² **Altitude** 0–2,000 m

Countries Madagascar

Restricted-range species	Threatened	Total
Confined to this EBA	13	20
Present also in other EBAs, SAs	1	3
Total	14	23

■ General characteristics

This EBA corresponds to the so-called Eastern and Sambirano Domains, and also includes part of the Central Mountain Domain of the Eastern Malagasy Region of Madagascar (biogeographic regions identified by White 1983). The Sambirano Domain, at the northern end of the central mountain ranges, embraces the Tsaratanana Massif and Mt Maromokotra, at 2,876 m the highest point in the EBA. Rainfall is high in this region and, there being little seasonal variation in climate, the characteristic vegetation is evergreen rain forest. The Montagne d'Ambre Massif in the far north also has rain forest and is included within this EBA.

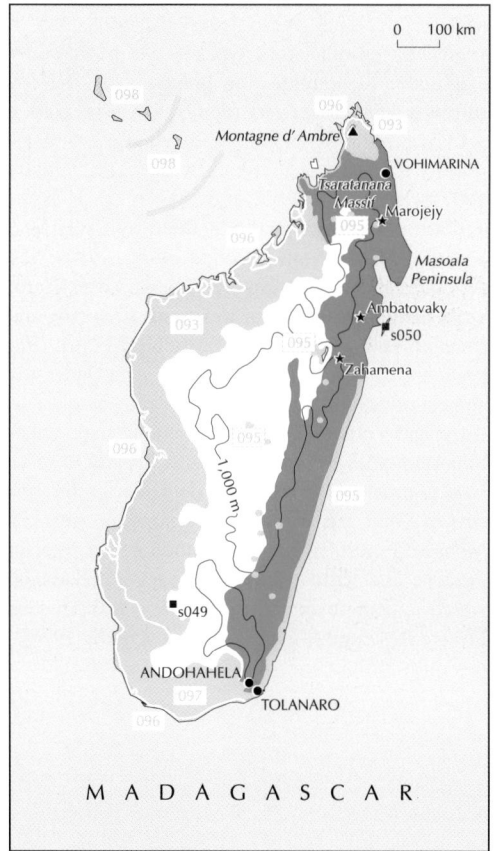

Indri *Indri indri* is the largest of the living lemurs. It is now confined to the north and central eastern rain forest, in a much smaller area than it inhabited even a few decades ago. Population figures are not known, but it is not thought to occur at high densities anywhere.

The western boundary of the EBA has been drawn to include all the main areas of remaining rain forest, largely lying between Vohimarina in the north and Tolanaro in the south, based on satellite imagery of the vegetation taken between 1972 and 1979, these data being simplified and interpreted by Du Puy and Moat (1996) from Faramalala (1988, 1995).

The forest can be divided into three main categories: low-altitude evergreen rain forest (c.0–800 m, with some reduction in the upper limit probable towards the south of the island); mid-altitude evergreen rain forest (c.800–1,800 m), where the canopy

Status and habitat of restricted-range species

Species (ordered taxonomically)	Global status	Other EBAs (and SAs)	Altitude (m)	Habitat
Madagascar Serpent-eagle *Eutriorchis astur*	CR	—	0–1,000	Rain forest
Brown Mesite *Mesitornis unicolor*	VU	—	0–1,200	Rain forest
Coquerel's Coua *Coua coquereli*	lc	093	0–800	Rain forest edge (dry deciduous forest in West Malagasy dry forests, EBA 093)
Red-breasted Coua *Coua serriana*	lc	—	0–1,000	Rain forest
Madagascar Red Owl *Tyto soumagnei*	EN	—	0–1,200	Rain forest
Short-legged Ground-roller *Brachypteracias leptosomus*	VU	—	0–1,200, prefers lower altitudes	Rain forest
Scaly Ground-roller *Brachypteracias squamigera*	VU	—	0–950, prefers lower altitudes	Rain forest
Rufous-headed Ground-roller *Atelornis crossleyi*	VU	—	0–2,000, mainly higher part	Rain forest
Schlegel's Asity *Philepitta schlegeli*	nt	093	0–800	Rain forest (dry deciduous forest in West Malagasy dry forests, EBA 093)
Yellow-bellied Asity *Neodrepanis hypoxanthus*	EN	—	900–2,000	Rain forest
Dusky Greenbul *Phyllastrephus tenebrosus*	EN	—	0–950	Rain forest
Grey-crowned Greenbul *Phyllastrephus cinereiceps*	VU	—	600–2,000	Rain forest
Pollen's Vanga *Xenopirostris polleni*	VU	—	0–2,000	Rain forest
Bernier's Vanga *Oriolia bernieri*	VU	—	0–900	Rain forest
Helmet Vanga *Euryceros prevostii*	nt	—	0–1,300	Rain forest
Nuthatch Vanga *Hypositta corallirostris*	lc	—	0–1,000	Rain forest
Forest Rock-thrush *Monticola sharpei*	nt	—	Usually >800	Rain forest
Benson's Rock-thrush *Monticola bensoni*	VU	093 (s049)	c.2,600 and lower?	Montane scrubland, rocky canyons with rain forest?
Wedge-tailed Jery *Hartertula flavoviridis*	nt	—	(0–) 800–2,300	Rain forest
Madagascar Yellowbrow *Crossleyia xanthophrys*	VU	—	600–2,300	Rain forest
Brown Emu-tail *Dromaeocercus brunneus*	nt	—	500–2,000	Rain forest
Red-tailed Newtonia *Newtonia fanovanae*	VU	—	0–800 (–1,300)	Rain forest
Cryptic Warbler *Cryptosylvicola randrianasoloi*[1]	NE	—	900–2,100	Rain forest

Global status (see p. 679 for definitions)	EX Extinct EW Extinct in the Wild	} with year of last record	cd Conservation Dependent	**Other EBAs (and SAs)** (see p. 72 for locations)	Bracketed numbers are Secondary Areas. X Extinct in that EBA or SA.	
	CR Critical EN Endangered VU Vulnerable	} threatened species	nt Near Threatened lc Least Concern DD Data Deficient NE Not Evaluated	**Notes**	[1] New species (Goodman *et al.* 1996).	

is lower and epiphytes are common (called 'moist montane' by White 1983); and montane evergreen forest (c.1,800–2,000 m). Montane scrubland occurs at the highest altitudes (Du Puy and Moat 1996).

■ Restricted-range species

Madagascar is well known for its very distinct avifauna, and this EBA is particularly unusual in having nine monospecific endemic genera with re-stricted-range species only: *Brachypteracias*, *Eutriorchis*, *Oriolia*, *Euryceros*, *Hypositta*, *Hartertula*, *Crossleyia*, *Dromaeocercus* and *Cryptosylvicola*, .

The restricted-range species all occur in forest and can be divided into two main groups: 12 species which are largely confined to low-altitude forest (rare or absent above 1,000 m), and eight species which are largely confined to mid-altitude and montane forest (rare or absent below 800 m); of the three remaining species, one occurs in montane scrubland (but is expected to occur in rain forest too), one apparently shows no altitudinal preference and the other has uncertain preferences (see 'Habitat associations' table).

Three species appear to be restricted entirely to the northern half of this EBA (*Coua serriana*, *Oriolia bernieri* and *Euryceros prevostii*); on the other hand, *Xenopirostris polleni* is rarer in this region than in other parts of the EBA. Ornithological exploration is, however, still incomplete and some species are proving to be more widespread than once thought: for example, *Newtonia fanovanae* was known only from the type-specimen collected in 1931 in Fanovana Forest (now cleared) in east-central Madagascar

until its rediscovery in the reserves of Andohahela in 1989 and Ambatovaky in 1990, with sites on the Masoala peninsula and elsewhere being subsequently added. Still more dramatically, the discovery in 1992 of a new genus of passerine, *Cryptosylvicola randrianasoloi*, subsequently revealed to have a rela-tively broad distribution in the eastern rain forests, indicates that much still remains to be learned about the avifauna of Madagascar (Goodman *et al.* 1996). Breeding populations of *Monticola bensoni* (previ-ously though to be endemic to the Isalo massif, Secondary Area s049) have recently been located in the high mountain zone of the Andringitra Strict Nature Reserve west to Ankazoabo in the West Malagasy dry forests (EBA 093) (S. M. Goodman *in litt.* 1996). A new species of vanga, *Hypositta perdita*, collected in 1931 from near Tolanaro, has recently been described (Peters 1996) and may represent another (possibly extinct) restricted-range species from this EBA.

Two other restricted-range species are shared with the West Malagasy dry forests (EBA 093), *Coua coquereli* and *Philepitta schlegeli*; both occur in the present EBA only in the Sambirano Domain. An-other restricted-range species, White-breasted Mesite *Mesitornis variegata*, is known from one anomalous record in this EBA but is treated as being endemic to the West Malagasy dry forests (EBA 093).

An additional 16 species which occur widely in the EBA and at most altitudes, and are largely endemic to it, are not considered to have restricted ranges. These include species in a further four en-demic genera—*Mystacornis*, *Randia*, *Pseudobias* and *Oxylabes*.

Habitat associations of restricted-range species

Low-altitude forest	Mid-altitude and montane forest
These species are rare or absent above 1,000 m:	These species are rare or absent below 800 m:
Eutriorchis astur	**Atelornis crossleyi**
Mesitornis unicolor	**Neodrepanis hypoxanthus**
Coua coquereli	**Phyllastrephus cinereiceps**
Coua serriana	Monticola sharpei
Brachypteracias leptosomus	Hartertula flavoviridis
Brachypteracias squamigera	**Crossleyia xanthophrys**
Philepitta schlegeli	Dromaeocercus brunneus
Phyllastrephus tenebrosus	Cryptosylvicola randrianasoloi
Oriolia bernieri	
Euryceros prevostii	**Montane scrubland**
Hypositta corallirostris	**Monticola bensoni**
Newtonia fanovanae	
	Uncertain altitudinal affinities
Low-altitude to montane forest	**Tyto soumagnei**
Xenopirostris polleni	

Threatened species (Critical, Endangered, Vulnerable) are shown in **bold**; see 'Status and habitat' table.

■ Threats and conservation

Figures for the extent of surviving tree cover in the east of Madagascar vary. There is an estimate that only 38,000 km² of forest remained in 1985, while reports from Sambirano indicated that the forests of that region did not exceed 400 km², and that they were fragmented and rapidly decreasing in size (Sayer *et al.* 1992; see also Nelson and Horning 1993). Du Puy and Moat (1996), however, calculate that there still remains 30,000–35,000 km² of low-altitude forest and the same amount of mid-altitude forest. Whatever the exact figures, secondary vegeta-tion, largely grassland and savanna, is now widely distributed, and the eastern forests have been much reduced in historical times.

The principal threat is slash-and-burn ('tavy') cultivation by subsistence farmers, which results in progressively more degraded regrowth, turning land ultimately into grassland or bracken-covered areas. By far the biggest part of the coastal plain has either been cleared of forest or has now only highly de-

The principal threat to the birds of this EBA is loss of forest owing to slash-and-burn or 'tavy' cultivation by subsistence farmers, as here at Andohahela.

graded forest, and any remaining habitat is highly threatened owing to increasing pressure from the human population (Jenkins 1987). Commercial timber exploitation is an additional threat in some areas

(A. F. A. Hawkins *in litt*. 1995) and, if current trends continue, it is likely that virtually all remaining native forest, particularly in the lowlands, will be destroyed within decades.

The majority of the restricted-range species are classified as threatened on account of their small ranges and populations, which are presumed to continue to decline with loss of habitat. However, the protected areas here do provide fairly good protection of the forest environment overall (Nicoll and Langrand 1989), and the present EBA has within it three national parks, one biosphere reserve and several strict nature and special reserves, areas which amount to some 5% of remaining low-altitude forest, 10% of mid-altitude forest and 9% of montane forest, although the amount of low-altitude forest below 600 m which is well protected is very much less (Du Puy and Moat 1996).

It is difficult to select key sites for conservation in this EBA because the known distribution of threatened species appears largely to reflect fieldwork (when new areas within the EBA are surveyed, the majority of the region's restricted-range species tend to be found). It is nevertheless likely that the EBA's central forests will eventually turn out to be the most important. Zahamena Strict Nature Reserve, Ambatovaky Special Reserve (see Thompson and Evans 1992), Masoala Natural Park and Marojejy Strict Nature Reserve (see Evans *et al.* 1992a) all have significant areas of lowland forest (the most threatened habitat in this EBA) and are thus very important (A. F. A. Hawkins *in litt*. 1995, verbally 1997; see also Collar *et al.* 1987, Collar and Stuart 1988, Thorstrom and Watson 1997).

095 East Malagasy wetlands

PRIORITY
CRITICAL

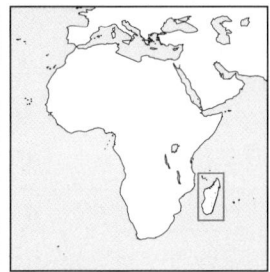

Key habitats Lakes, pools, marshes, rocky shorelines

Main threats Major habitat loss (e.g due to rice growing, siltation, pollution)

Biological importance ● ● ●
Current threat level ● ● ●

Area 17,000 km² **Altitude** 0–2,700 m

Countries Madagascar

Restricted-range species	Threatened	Total
Confined to this EBA	3	6
Present also in other EBAs, SAs	0	2
Total	3	8

■ General characteristics

This EBA includes lakes, pools and marshes in eastern Madagascar, including those at sea-level (notably in the region of the Pangalanes Canal) and in the uplands. The boundary of the EBA has been difficult to define as these wetland areas are patchy and often small, being, in many cases, small areas of aquatic habitat within the East Malagasy wet forests (EBA 094), and therefore not always featuring on generalized vegetation maps. The extent of the EBA is thus similar to that of the eastern rain forests, although the EBA has been represented by a coastal strip and a handful of key inland localities, including the wetlands around Lake Alaotra (220 km², the

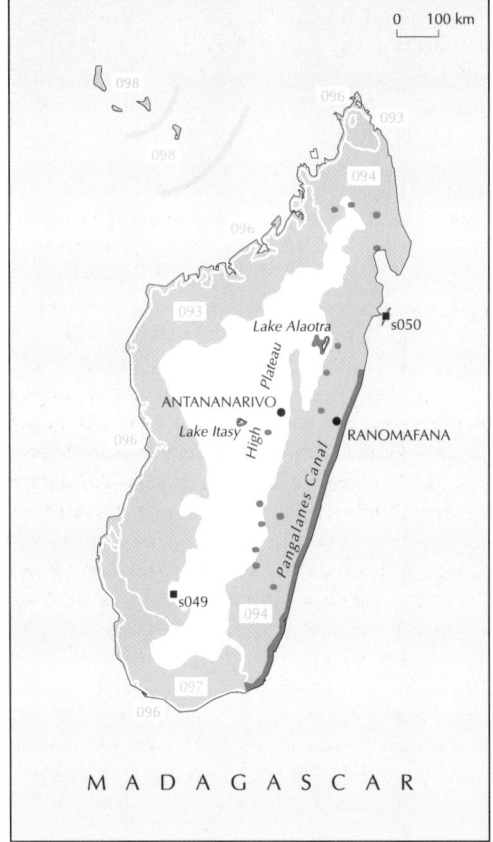

R. J. Safford

More surveys are needed to identify key sites for wetland species, especially those that are far from habitation and thus unlikely to be under threat from conversion to rice paddies such as these.

largest lake in Madagascar) and those around Lake Itasy, which are (or have been) very important sites for restricted-range species.

■ Restricted-range species

Two species have very small distributions: *Tachybaptus rufolavatus* is known chiefly from Lake Alaotra, and *Aythya innotata* is also restricted largely to this same region although there are isolated data on its presence elsewhere, including at Lake Itasy. The remaining extant species are more widespread, with *Anas melleri* being also known from a few sightings in the West Malagasy wetlands (EBA 096) and *Actophilornis albinucha* largely occurring there, being extremely rare and possibly extinct in this EBA.

Status and habitat of restricted-range species

Species (ordered taxonomically)	Global status	Other EBAs (and SAs)	Altitude (m)	Habitat
Alaotra Grebe _Tachybaptus rufolavatus_	CR	—	750	Lakes, ponds
Meller's Duck _Anas melleri_	nt	096	0–1,500	Lakes, rivers, streams, ponds, channels in marshes
Madagascar Pochard _Aythya innotata_	CR	—	750–1,500	Shallow lakes/pools with many islets of vegetation
Madagascar Fish-eagle _Haliaeetus vociferoides_[1]	CR	096	0–1,200	Rocky shorelines and mangroves (inc. offshore islands), lakes, rivers
Slender-billed Flufftail _Sarothrura watersi_	EN	—	950–1,800	Wetlands with adjacent dense grassy terrain near rain forest
Madagascar Rail _Rallus madagascariensis_	lc	—	0–1,800, mainly higher part	Marshy meadows, flooded fields, dense wet grass, sometimes rice paddies
Madagascar Jacana _Actophilornis albinucha_	lc	096	0–750	Small lily-covered ponds, lake margins, more rarely banks of sluggish rivers
Madagascar Snipe _Gallinago macrodactyla_	lc	—	0–2,700	Marshy meadows, flooded fields, dense wet grass, muddy areas, sometimes rice paddies
Grey Emu-tail _Amphilais seebohmi_	lc	—	700–2,600	Marshy meadows, dense grass or bush on rain forest edge near stagnant water, abandoned rice paddies; also montane scrub

Global status (see p. 679 for definitions)
EX Extinct
EW Extinct in the Wild } with year of last record
CR Critical
EN Endangered } threatened species
VU Vulnerable
cd Conservation Dependent
nt Near Threatened
lc Least Concern
DD Data Deficient
NE Not Evaluated

Other EBAs (and SAs) (see p. 72 for locations) — Bracketed numbers are Secondary Areas. [x] Extinct in that EBA or SA.

Notes [1] Extinct in this EBA.

Another species of the West Malagasy wetlands, Madagascar Heron _Ardea humbloti_, has also been recorded in this EBA but has not been included as one of its restricted-range species because the records are presumed to be of wandering juveniles.

■ Threats and conservation

Lake Alaotra is a rice-producing centre of national importance; since 1923 it has been undergoing a transformation for agricultural purposes and its water has become heavily laden with sediments because of the intense erosion affecting neighbouring hills (Langrand 1990, Pidgeon 1996). It is also heavily polluted with insecticides (including DDT), and, as a result, there is very little aquatic vegetation. In addition, areas under rice cultivation quickly become unusable, resulting in new areas constantly being required and the continuing erosion of reedbed and shallow water (A. F. A. Hawkins _in litt._ 1995).

Three of the four species endemic to this EBA are considered highly threatened: there have been no reliable records in the last 10 years of _Tachybaptus rufolavatus_, which is in the irreversible process of disappearing through hybridization with Little Grebe _T. ruficollis_ (a recent colonizer of Madagascar), hunting and trapping, the various impacts of introduced fish (which considerably limit the development of aquatic vegetation), probably poisoning through pesticides and loss of habitat; _Aythya innotata_

has also become increasingly rare during the twentieth century, with one record at Lake Alaotra in 1960, a sighting near Antananarivo in 1970, and the capture of a single bird in 1991 which later died in captivity (Wilmé 1994); _Sarothrura watersi_ is known only from a few well-separated areas in this EBA, including most recently from Ranomafana, now a national park; its distribution appears coincident with that of the much-pressurised East Malagasy wet forests (EBA 094), and habitat loss and degradation there will also affect this wetland species.

There is currently no protection specifically for wetlands in this EBA, although some sites (e.g. Vohiparara marsh in Ranomafana) fall incidently within protected areas. Conservation action in Madagascar has traditionally been oriented towards forests as they harbour the highest proportion of endemic species (Langrand and Goodman 1995). More surveys are therefore required to identify sites holding wetland species, especially those that are far from habitation and thus unlikely to be under immediate threat from conversion to ricefields (A. F. A. Hawkins _in litt._ 1996; see also Langrand and Wilmé 1993). To assess and prioritize suitable wetlands for protection, a monitoring procedure has been proposed using birds as indicators, e.g. Madagascar Grebe _Tachybaptus pelzelnii_, a widespread threatened species (classified as Vulnerable), and _Anas melleri_ (Langrand and Goodman 1995; see also Pidgeon 1996).

096 | West Malagasy wetlands

PRIORITY
CRITICAL

Key habitats Lakes, rivers, marshes, deltas, rocky shorelines, mangroves

Main threats Moderate habitat loss (e.g. due to rice growing, siltation, alien fish)

Biological importance ● ● ●
Current threat level ● ● ●

Area 26,000 km²   **Altitude** 0–1,500 m
Countries Madagascar

Restricted-range species	Threatened	Total
Confined to this EBA	5	5
Present also in other EBAs, SAs	0	2
Total	5	7

■ General characteristics

This EBA in Madagascar skirts and penetrates the West Malagasy dry forests (EBA 093), extends south into the South Malagasy spiny forest (EBA 097), and includes wetlands adjacent to the Sambirano rain forest (included in EBA 094).

A variety of habitats is present within the EBA, ranging from sandy coasts and islets, rocky coasts, mangroves, salt pans, mudflats and river mouths, to inland lakes and lake shores. The limits of the EBA are based on a vegetation map by Du Puy and Moat (1996), and include all of the western and southern coastline, all significant patches of mangrove and marsh, and the mouths and deltas of major rivers.

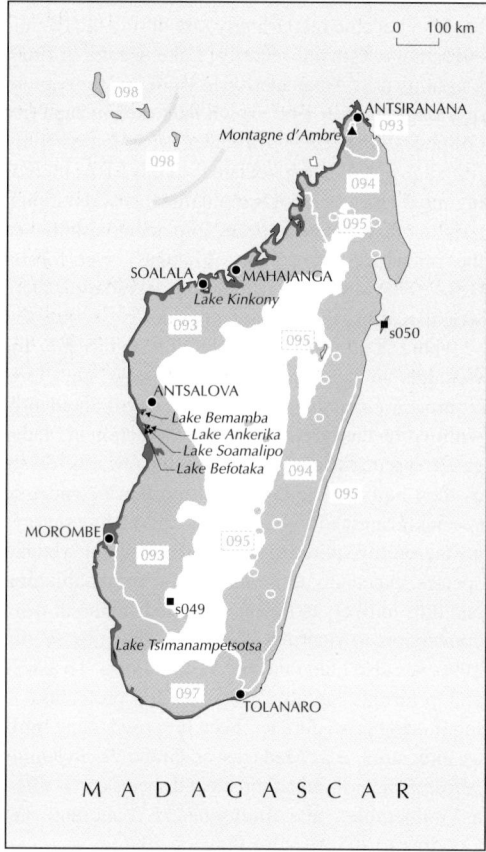

■ Restricted-range species

There is no particular pattern in the distributions of the EBA's restricted-range species. *Ardea humbloti* is the most widespread in the EBA, from Antsiranana in the north to Tolanaro in the south, and has also been recorded in areas beyond the limits of the EBA, including Madagascar's high plateau and east coast (EBA 095, although these records usually involve immature individuals), and in the Comoro Islands (EBA 098, where it possibly breeds).

Haliaeetus vociferoides, *Anas bernieri* and *Actophilornis albinucha* share similar coastal distributions between Antsiranana and Morombe, although *H. vociferoides* also occurs at Lake Maudit in the Montagne d'Ambre National Park and immatures may wander beyond these limits. *Amaurornis olivieri* is known only from a few sites between Mahajanga and Morombe, while *Charadrius thoracicus* occurs mainly in the west and south, between Soalala and Tolanaro, although it is also infrequently reported from the east coast. *Anas melleri* is largely a species of the East Malagasy wetlands (EBA 095), and in the present EBA is known only from a few sightings including ones at Bemamba and Kinkony lakes.

Madagascar Sacred Ibis *Threskiornis aethiopicus bernieri* is a bird of shallow lakes, estuaries and exposed sand bars, also confined to this EBA. It was considered a full species by Sibley and Monroe (1990) but given subspecific rank by Sibley and Monroe (1993) and has not been included in this study.

■ Threats and conservation

Madagascar has experienced natural desiccation over the past few thousand years and wetland habitats have thus long been in decline (Langrand and Goodman 1995). The problem is compounded by the conversion of surviving relicts to rice paddy (which

Because the wetland habitats are patchy (and many may be too small to feature on the map used), it has been difficult to define the boundary of the EBA, and some of the restricted-range birds may occur outside the area shown.

Status and habitat of restricted-range species

Species (ordered taxonomically)	Global status	Other EBAs (and SAs)	Altitude (m)	Habitat
Madagascar Heron *Ardea humbloti*[1]	VU	—	0–1,500	Lakes (freshwater, saline, brackish), rivers, coral islets, mangroves, estuaries, seashores, rarely rice paddies
Meller's Duck *Anas melleri*[2]	nt	095	0–1,500	Lakes, rivers, streams, ponds, channels in marshes
Madagascar Teal *Anas bernieri*	EN	—	0–200	Marshes, shallow alluvium-rich lakes (freshwater, saline, brackish), mudflats
Madagascar Fish-eagle *Haliaeetus vociferoides*	CR	095[x]	0–1,200	Rocky shorelines and mangroves (inc. offshore islands), lakes, rivers
Sakalava Rail *Amaurornis olivieri*	CR	—	Sea-level	Marshes inc. patches of floating vegetation and reedbeds
Madagascar Jacana *Actophilornis albinucha*	lc	095	0–750	Small lily-covered ponds, lake margins, more rarely banks of sluggish rivers
Madagascar Plover *Charadrius thoracicus*	VU	—	Sea-level	Sandy beaches, mudflats, saltflats and coastal grassy areas

Global status (see p. 679 for definitions)	EX Extinct ⎫ EW Extinct in ⎬ with year of last record the Wild ⎭	cd Conservation Dependent nt Near Threatened	**Other EBAs (and SAs)** (see p. 72 for locations)	Bracketed numbers are Secondary Areas. [x] Extinct in that EBA or SA.
	CR Critical ⎫ EN Endangered ⎬ threatened VU Vulnerable ⎭ species	lc Least Concern DD Data Deficient NE Not Evaluated	**Notes**	[1] Also recorded in EBAs 094 and 098 (see text). [2] Introduced to Mauritius (EBA 102).

is taking place extremely rapidly with the arrival of rice-growing immigrants from the east), and siltation due to watershed deforestation. Additional threats to some species are the introduction of alien fish (which considerably limit the development of aquatic vegetation), hunting, and the cutting of mangroves for fuel.

Wetland degradation is a cause of major concern for *Anas bernieri*, a species which does not use ricefields but only areas of shallow water over mud, the habitat type preferred for agricultural conversion (Young *et al.* 1993; see also Safford 1993a); also for *Amaurornis olivieri*, which had not been seen since the mid-1970s until reported from Lake Bemamba in 1995 (Ramanampamonjy 1995). *Haliaeetus vociferoides* survives in extremely low numbers, estimated at 100 breeding pairs; habitat alteration (loss of both nesting and foraging habitat) and direct persecution have been identified as the major threats to the species (Watson *et al.* 1993). The single most important concentration of 10 pairs breeds on three adjacent lakes—Befotaka, Soamalipo and Ankerika—near

the southern end of the species' range; fishing is the main livelihood of local Sakalava tribespeople who have harmoniously shared these wetlands with fish-eagles for centuries, but recently there has been a massive influx of migrant fishermen who do not share the same traditional resource extraction rules (Watson and Rabarisoa in press).

In general, mangroves, wetlands and coasts have little legal protection; the strict nature reserve which includes Lake Tsimanampetsotsa (60 km²) is one exception (Langrand 1990; see also Langrand and Wilmé 1993), although this soda lake has little importance for restricted-range species apart from *Charadrius thoracicus* (A. F. A. Hawkins *in litt.* 1996). In order to assess and prioritize suitable wetlands for protection, a monitoring procedure has been proposed using birds as indicators, e.g. Madagascar Grebe *Tachybaptus pelzelnii*, a widespread threatened species (classified as Vulnerable), and *Haliaeetus vociferoides* (Langrand and Goodman 1995).

097 South Malagasy spiny forests

PRIORITY
URGENT

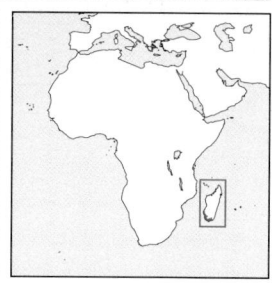

Key habitats	Dry spiny forest, sub-arid thorn scrub
Area	46,000 km²	Altitude	0–500 m
Countries	Madagascar

Main threats Moderate habitat loss (e.g. due to charcoal production, cultivation, grazing)

Biological importance ● ● ●
Current threat level ● ○ ○

Restricted-range species	Threatened	Total
Confined to this EBA	2	8
Present also in other EBAs, SAs	0	2
Total	2	10

■ General characteristics

This EBA corresponds to the Southern Domain of the Western Malagasy Region in Madagascar (a biogeographic region recognized by White 1983), where the vegetation is deciduous dry (spiny) forest and thorny scrubland, and the most characteristic plants are the Didiereaceae (an endemic family) and arborescent euphorbias.

The northern (inland) boundary of the EBA has been drawn to include all remaining habitat, largely below 500 m, running southward from Morombe, along the coastal strip to just west of Tolanaro; forest cover is based on satellite imagery of the vegetation taken between 1971 and 1979, these data being

simplified and interpreted by Du Puy and Moat (1996) from Faramalala (1988, 1995). The southern (coastal) boundary skirts coastal wetlands that are included in the West Malagasy wetlands (EBA 096), which also intersects the present EBA along rivers.

■ Restricted-range species

Several species have very small ranges. For example, *Monias benschi* and *Uratelornis chimaera* (both in monospecific genera) are very local, being distributed only in the northernmost part of the EBA, along a narrow coastal strip 70 km wide by 200 km long. The recently described *Calicalicus rufocarpalis* is currently known only from the Toliara region, while *Coua verreauxi* is only known from the south-west.

Thamnornis chloropetoides and *Newtonia archboldi* are now both known to occur c.100 km north of the northern limits of this EBA in the West Malagasy dry forests (EBA 093), but the cores of their ranges remain in the present EBA.

■ Threats and conservation

The spiny forest is the most nearly intact of Madagascar's climax vegetation types because it is largely found on poor substrates and/or where the climate is least suited to cultivation. Recent estimates from satellite imagery suggest between 14,000 and 17,000 km² remaining (Nelson and Horning 1993, Du Puy and Moat 1996).

The principal threat to the region comes from the collection of wood for conversion to charcoal for fuel, particularly near major urban areas (Jenkins 1987, Langrand 1990), but there are also significant problems with clearance for cultivation (mainly maize), degradation through grazing by cattle and goats (of unknown long-term effect), and timber exploitation for commercial construction (A. F. A. Hawkins *in litt.* 1995). *Monias benschi* and *Uratelornis chimaera* are classified as threatened on account of their very restricted ranges, and are also threatened by hunting.

There are four strict nature or special reserves in this EBA, including the Beza-Mahafaly Special Reserve, which gives protection to some restricted-

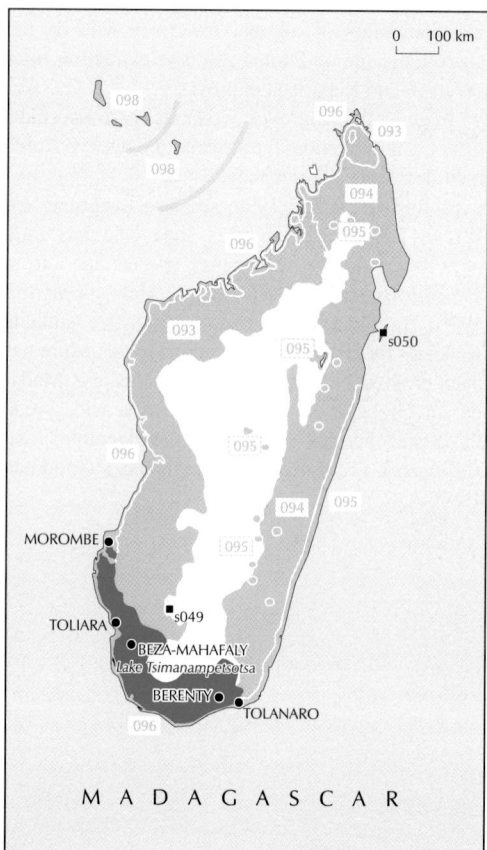

MOROMBE
TOLIARA
s049
BEZA-MAHAFALY
Lake Tsimanampetsotsa
BERENTY
TOLANARO
s050

M A D A G A S C A R

0   100 km

Status and habitat of restricted-range species

Species (ordered taxonomically)	Global status	Other EBAs (and SAs)	Altitude (m)	Habitat
Subdesert Mesite *Monias benschi*	VU	—	0–100	Undisturbed or slightly degraded sub-arid thickets on sandy soil
Running Coua *Coua cursor*	lc	—	0–200	Sub-arid thorn scrub, dry woodlands free of grassy vegetation
Verreaux's Coua *Coua verreauxi*	nt	—	0–100	Sub-arid thorn scrub, adjacent degraded areas
Long-tailed Ground-roller *Uratelornis chimaera*	VU	—	0–80	Undisturbed or slightly degraded sub-arid thickets on sandy soil
Red-shouldered Vanga *Calicalicus rufocarpalis*[1]	NE	—	Coastal plain, plateau?	Sub-arid thorn scrub
Lafresnaye's Vanga *Xenopirostris xenopirostris*	lc	—	0–100	Sub-arid thorn scrub
Littoral Rock-thrush *Monticola imerinus*	lc	—	0–190	Sub-arid scrub on sandy soil along coast or on coastal dunes
Lantz's Brush-warbler *Nesillas lantzii*[2]	NE	—	0–500	Sub-arid thorn scrub
Thamnornis Warbler *Thamnornis chloropetoides*	lc	093	0–500	Sub-arid scrub, adjacent secondary growth, dry forest
Archbold's Newtonia *Newtonia archboldi*	lc	093	0–100	Sub-arid scrub, dry forest edge

Global status (see p. 679 for definitions)
EX Extinct ⎫ with year of last record
EW Extinct in the Wild ⎬
CR Critical ⎫ threatened species
EN Endangered ⎬
VU Vulnerable ⎭
cd Conservation Dependent
nt Near Threatened
lc Least Concern
DD Data Deficient
NE Not Evaluated

Other EBAs (and SAs) (see p. 72 for locations) Bracketed numbers are Secondary Areas.
X Extinct in that EBA or SA.

Notes [1] New species (Goodman *et al.* 1997).
[2] Taxonomy follows Schulenberg *et al.* (1993).

Much of the southern spiny forest has been burnt for conversion to charcoal, here sold at the side of the road.

C. Harcourt

range species, and Lake Tsimanampetsotsa Strict Nature Reserve, which includes an important area of euphorbia forest. Berenty Private Reserve and the forest north of Toliara have also been identified as important sites by Langrand (1990), the latter because of the occurrence of *Monias benschi* and *Uratelornis*

chimaera. Du Puy and Moat (1996) calculate that only 2% of the remaining deciduous, dry, southern forest and scrubland is well protected, and identify this vegetation type as having the most outstanding need for additional reserves in Madagascar.

098 Comoro Islands

PRIORITY
CRITICAL

Key habitats Lowland and montane evergreen rain forest, 'pioneer' forest, upland heath	Area 2,200 km² Altitude 0–2,600 m

Countries Comoros, Mayotte (to France)

Main threats Major habitat loss (e.g. due to cultivation, grazing)

Biological importance ● ● ●
Current threat level ● ● ●

Restricted-range species	Threatened	Total
Confined to this EBA	6	16
Present also in other EBAs, SAs	0	2
Total	6	18

■ General characteristics

The Comoro Islands are situated in the western Indian Ocean in the northern part of the Mozambique Channel, equidistant from continental Africa and Madagascar. Three islands—Grand Comoro (or Ngazidja, 1,148 km²), Moheli (Mwali, 290 km²) and Anjouan (Ndzuani, 424 km²)—constitute the independent republic of the Comoros, and one island—Mayotte (Maore, 370 km²)—is a French collectivité territoriale. The highest point is Mt Karthala, an active volcano in the south of Grand Comoro.

The native vegetation on the islands is evergreen forest, with the forest on Mt Karthala naturally occurring up to c.1,800 m, above which giant-heath vegetation, with stands of *Philippia*, predominates.

■ Restricted-range species

All the restricted-range species occur in forest, largely in the uplands (where there is forest remaining), apart from *Zosterops mouroniensis* which is now confined to the higher-altitude heath zone of Mt Karthala on Grand Comoro. Colonizing ('pioneer') forest on recent lava-flows on this mountain may be an important habitat for some species, e.g. *Otus pauliani*, and, on Mayotte, mangroves may be an alternative habitat for some forest birds (Louette 1988a,b, Louette *et al.* 1988, 1993, Herremans *et al.* 1991, Louette and Stevens 1992).

The distribution of species across the islands is not uniform, with each island having its own endemic species (five on Grand Comoro, one on Moheli, three on Anjouan, and three on Mayotte). Mt Karthala is the most important area ornithologically, four species being restricted to this one mountain alone; all the other multi-island, restricted-range species as well as *Nesillas brevicaudata* (which occurs more widely on Grand Comoro) also have significant populations there, further emphasizing its importance.

Another restricted-range species which occurs on the Comoros (and possibly breeds) is Madagascar Heron *Ardea humbloti* (see EBA 096).

■ Threats and conservation

Today, forest has been largely cleared from the lowlands and grazing by cattle prevents regeneration; on Mt Karthala cultivation now extends as high

Distribution patterns of restricted-range species

Species (ordered geographically)	Grand Comoro	Moheli	Anjouan	Mayotte	Other EBAs, SAs
Otus pauliani	●ᵏ	–	–	–	–
Nesillas brevicauda	●	–	–	–	–
Humblotia flavirostris	●ᵏ	–	–	–	–
Zosterops mouroniensis	●ᵏ	–	–	–	–
Dicrurus fuscipennis	●ᵏ	–	–	–	–
Hypsipetes parvirostris	●	●	–	–	–
Nectarinia humbloti	●	●	–	–	–
Turdus bewsheri	●	●	●	–	–
Columba polleni	●	●	●	●	–
Alectroenas sganzini	●	●	●	●	●
Foudia eminentissima	●	●	●	●	●
Nesillas mariae	–	●	–	–	–
Otus capnodes	–	–	●	–	–
Nesillas longicaudata	–	–	●	–	–
Nectarinia comorensis	–	–	●	–	–
Nectarinia coquerellii	–	–	–	●	–
Dicrurus waldenii	–	–	–	●	–
Zosterops mayottensis	–	–	–	●	X
Total	11	7	7	6	

● Present R Reintroduced
O Extinct? I Introduced, not
X Extinct   yet established
ᵏ Mt Karthala only

Threatened spp. shown in **bold**
Other EBAs, SAs
} see 'Status and habitat' table

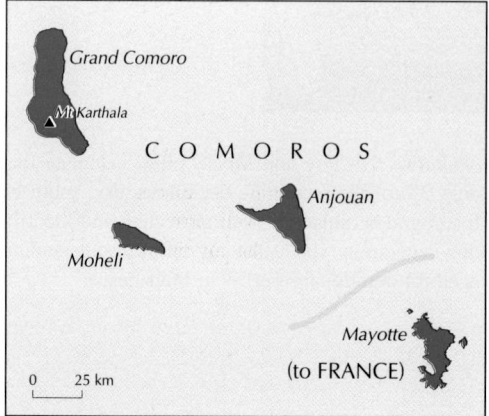

Grand Comoro
Mt Karthala
COMOROS
Anjouan
Moheli
Mayotte
(to FRANCE)
0   25 km

Status and habitat of restricted-range species

Species (ordered taxonomically)	Global status	Other EBAs (and SAs)	Altitude (m)	Habitat
Comoro Olive-pigeon *Columba pollenii*	nt	—	400–1,750	Forest
Comoro Blue-pigeon *Alectroenas sganzini*	lc	099	Usually 400–1,850	Forest, logged forest, secondary forest
Anjouan Scops-owl *Otus capnodes*[1]	CR	—	>800	Forest
Grand Comoro Scops-owl *Otus pauliani*	CR	—	1,000–1,900	Forest, degraded forest, 'pioneer' forest
Comoro Bulbul *Hypsipetes parvirostris*	lc	—	400–1,850	Forest
Comoro Thrush *Turdus bewsheri*	lc	—	400–1,250	Forest, secondary forest, plantations
Anjouan Brush-warbler *Nesillas longicaudata*	lc	—	All	Forest, secondary forest, agricultural land, urban areas
Grand Comoro Brush-warbler *Nesillas brevicaudata*	lc	—	Usually 500–2,000	Forest, heath
Moheli Brush-warbler *Nesillas mariae*	nt	—	150–800	Forest, sometimes lower than forest edge
Grand Comoro Flycatcher *Humblotia flavirostris*	VU	—	800–2,000	Forest, heath
Humblot's Sunbird *Nectarinia humbloti*	lc	—	All	Forest, secondary forest, gardens
Anjouan Sunbird *Nectarinia comorensis*	lc	—	All	Forest, secondary forest, gardens
Mayotte Sunbird *Nectarinia coquerellii*	lc	—	All	Thickets, plantations, gardens
Chestnut-sided White-eye *Zosterops mayottensis*	lc	100[x]	All	Forest, secondary forest, gardens
Mount Karthala White-eye *Zosterops mouroniensis*	CR	—	1,700–2,600	Heath, formerly forest
Red-headed Fody *Foudia eminentissima*	lc	099	All	Forest, secondary forest, heath, plantations
Grand Comoro Drongo *Dicrurus fuscipennis*	CR	—	Usually 500–900	Forest clearings, forest edge; has been observed in coconut plantations
Mayotte Drongo *Dicrurus waldenii*	CR	—	All	Forest, secondary forest, plantations

Global status (see p. 679 for definitions)	EX Extinct EW Extinct in the Wild } with year of last record	cd Conservation Dependent nt Near Threatened	**Other EBAs (and SAs)** (see p. 72 for locations)	Bracketed numbers are Secondary Areas. [x] Extinct in that EBA or SA.
	CR Critical EN Endangered VU Vulnerable } threatened species	lc Least Concern DD Data Deficient NE Not Evaluated	**Notes**	[1] Taxonomy follows Safford (1993b).

as 1,400 m in places. Very little intact, upland forest remains on Anjouan, while most that exists on Moheli and Grand Comoro is badly degraded. On the other hand, the pioneer forest on Mt Karthala is not (yet) exploited (being marginal for agriculture) and could therefore play an important role for bird conservation on Grand Comoro (Stevens *et al.* 1995).

The four species restricted to Mt Karthala are considered threatened, and, consequently, the forests here rank highly amongst the key forests for threatened birds in Africa (Collar and Stuart 1988). Further habitat degradation and fragmentation (from fires, logging and as a result of a proposed road to the crater rim) in this region are particularly threatening to *Zosterops mouroniensis* (confined to the heath zone) and *Otus pauliani* (wetter north, west and south

flanks). Although *Dicrurus fuscipennis* was judged to number c.100 birds in 1985, it appears to prefer forest edge and is probably at no immediate risk.

On Anjouan, the recently rediscovered *Otus capnodes* (found in 1992 after an absence of records dating back to 1886), confined to c.10 km² of native forest (i.e. all that remains), is estimated to number just 48 birds; accelerating habitat clearance and capture for food render it highly threatened (Moorcroft 1996, Safford 1993b). On Mayotte, *Dicrurus waldenii* lives at low density (the entire population may not exceed a few dozen pairs); protection of the forests on Mts Sapéré, Bénara and Choungi has been proposed (Louette 1988b). Reserves have also been proposed on Mt Karthala, on Moheli (Louette and Stevens 1992), and on Anjouan (Moorcroft 1996).

099 Aldabra

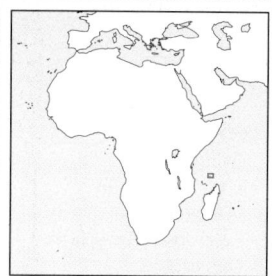

PRIORITY HIGH

Key habitats Mixed scrub, mangroves	**Area** 160 km²	**Altitude** 0–20 m
Main threats Limited habitat loss (e.g. due to coconut and *Casuarina* groves), introduced species	**Countries** Seychelles	

Restricted-range species	Threatened	Total
Confined to this EBA	0	1
Present also in other EBAs, SAs	0	2
Total	0	3

Biological importance ● ● ●
Current threat level ● ● ●

■ General characteristics

Aldabra, the world's largest atoll, is one of the coralline islands of the Seychelles, lying some 1,000 km to the south-west of the granitic Seychelles (EBA 100). Within the same remote archipelago, but not included in the EBA, are three other islands: Astove, Cosmoledo and Assumption. Aldabra comprises four main islands—Malabar (or Middle Island), Grand Terre (South Island), Picard (West Island) and Polymnie—enclosing a large central lagoon bordered by mangroves. Mixed scrub (a particularly complex association) grows on the higher and more consolidated rock which runs round the north, west and south ocean coast edges, as well as covering much of a large area of flat rock at the east end of the atoll; between the mangroves and mixed scrub, there is a band (of varying width) of scrub which is heavily dominated by the salt-tolerant shrub *Pemphis acidula* (Prys-Jones and Diamond 1984).

■ Restricted-range species

This EBA has been identified on the basis of its one endemic extant and one endemic extinct species; two additional (extant) restricted-range species also occur there. *Nesillas aldabrana* was only known from a 10-ha strip of dense mixed scrub on the north-west

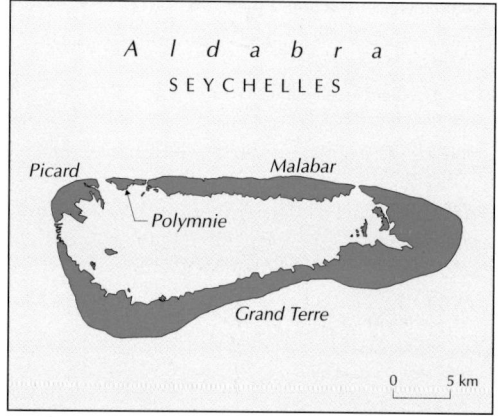

Aldabra
SEYCHELLES

Picard
Malabar
Polymnie
Grand Terre

0   5 km

coast of Malabar (an area free from goats), where no more than seven birds have ever been seen, and since 1977 there have been only two records, both of males; in 1986 the species could not be found, despite intensive searches, and it is now feared extinct (Roberts 1987). *Dicrurus aldabranus* is widespread and is considered (based on territory sizes and habitat distribution) to number roughly 1,500 birds (Collar and Stuart 1985).

In addition to the restricted-range species, there are ten endemic subspecies including: Aldabra Sacred

Giant tortoises were once widespread on many of the Indian Ocean islands, but today survive in the wild only on Aldabra, where the species is *Geochelone gigantea*.

G. Rocamora

Status and habitat of restricted-range species

Species (ordered taxonomically)	Global status	Other EBAs (and SAs)	Habitat
Comoro Blue-pigeon *Alectroenas sganzini*	lc	098	Mangroves, mixed scrub
Aldabra Warbler *Nesillas aldabrana*	EX (1986)	—	Dense mixed scrub
Red-headed Fody *Foudia eminentissima*	lc	098	Scrub, coconut groves, *Casuarina* trees
Aldabra Drongo *Dicrurus aldabranus*	nt	—	Mangroves, dense mixed scrub, *Casuarina* trees

Global status (see p. 679 for definitions)	EX Extinct EW Extinct in the Wild } with year of last record	CR Critical EN Endangered VU Vulnerable } threatened species	cd Conservation Dependent nt Near Threatened lc Least Concern	DD Data Deficient NE Not Evaluated

Other EBAs (and SAs) (see p. 72 for locations): bracketed numbers are Secondary Areas; ˣ extinct in that EBA or SA.

Ibis *Threskiornis aethiopica abbotti*, once very scarce due to human exploitation and disturbance but now widespread; and Aldabra White-throated Rail *Dryolimnas cuvieri aldabranus*, now only on two of the main islands (Malabar and Polymnie) and one of the few small islets (this race differs from the nominate form in Madagascar by being flightless, and is thus the only remaining flightless bird on western Indian Ocean islands) (Collar 1982, Collar 1993, Hambler *et al.* 1993). The ecology of all landbirds on Aldabra is discussed in Prys-Jones and Diamond (1984).

Aldabra Sacred Ibis *Threskiornis aethiopica abbottii* (above) and Aldabra White-throated Rail *Dryolimnas cuvieri aldabranus* (below) are two of several sub-species which are endemic to Aldabra.

■ Threats and conservation

Unlike neighbouring islands, Aldabra has escaped extensive interference by man and is now one of the few elevated limestone atolls in the world to remain relatively undisturbed (see also Henderson Island in the south-east Pacific Ocean, EBA 215). Nevertheless, coconut palms and *Casuarina* trees, probably introductions, have become established groves in a few places, and substantial amounts of mangrove wood were once exported to Mahé, and its marine resources (in particular fish, oysters and shells, but also seabirds) were harvested for sale on Mahé and overseas.

The past introduction of cats, goats and rats poses a significant threat to the bird populations, and it is likely that rats were the main cause of the (presumed) extinction of *Nesillas aldabrana*. There is also a very real risk that an array of exotic bird species (including Red-whiskered Bulbul *Pycnonotus jocosus*, a nest predator of small passerines) introduced to neighbouring Assumption Island in the 1970s, will reach Aldabra, just 27 km away (Roberts 1988).

In 1982 Aldabra was decreed a World Heritage Site in recognition of its unique unspoilt environment. The island is managed by the Seychelles Island Foundation which has recently been the beneficiary of a Global Environment Facility grant to fund conservation/research officers and to refurbish the infrastructure on the island including the research station, as well as funding a goat-eradication program which is now virtually complete (although, given the size of Aldabra, there is some doubt about whether complete elimination is possible: A. Skerrett *in litt.* 1996). Tourists may visit Aldabra for the day, arriving by boat, and will be able to stay overnight in small numbers in the near future. If this tourism is not managed adequately, Aldabra's fragile ecosystems and wildlife could be locally threatened (G. Rocamora *in litt.* 1996, N. Jivan Shah *in litt.* 1996).

100 Granitic Seychelles

Key habitats Dry forest, upland rain forest

Main threats Major habitat loss (e.g. due to plantations, cultivation), introduced species

Biological importance ● ● ○
Current threat level ● ● ●

Area 240 km²   **Altitude** 0–900 m

Countries Seychelles

Restricted-range species	Threatened	Total
Confined to this EBA	8	11
Present also in other EBAs, SAs	0	0
Total	8	11

■ General characteristics

The Granitic Seychelles are in the north-east of a larger archipelago which includes a chain of low-lying coralline islands (see Aldabra, EBA 099). The inner islands were once part of the ancient landmass of Gondwanaland, and are the world's only isolated granite islands, all other oceanic islands being lime-stone or volcanic. The largest island is Mahé (154 km²), which rises to 914 m on Morne Sechellois, the highest point in the group.

The native vegetation of the Granitic Seychelles before settlement was probably closed broadleaved forest, which can be divided into lowland rain forest (long since disappeared), dry forest (including the palm forests of Praslin and Curieuse where the famous coco de mer palm *Lodoicea maldivica* survives), and moist forest at high altitudes (e.g. on Mahé and Silhouette). Vegetation on the lower gra-nitic islands (e.g. Frégate, Aride and Cousin) is scrubby (but includes important stands of native trees) and has more in common with the coralline islands (Procter 1984).

■ Restricted-range species

The endemic birds are all forest species, and several are able to use secondary forest and plantations. Distribution between islands appears patchy (see 'Distribution patterns table', below) as several of the multi-island species have become extinct on at least one island (although some have been reintroduced).

N. Arlott

As a result of specific conservation efforts, Seychelles Magpie Robin *Copsychus sechellarum* has been saved from almost certain extinction. However, the acci-dental introduction of rats on the island of Frégate, its main stronghold, is cause for concern.

Today only two species are confined to single is-lands: *Otus insularis* on Mahé and *Terpsiphone corvina* on La Digue.

The EBA also holds two endemic subspecies of particular note: Black Parrot *Coracopsis nigra barklyi*, the national bird of the Seychelles, which is confined to palm forest on Praslin, with a few birds also on Curieuse; and Seychelles Turtle-dove *Streptopelia picturata rostrata*, which has interbred with the introduced nominate race from Madagascar such that only a very few individuals showing characteristics of true *rostrata* survive, with examples on Cousin, Cousine, Frégate and Bird Island (to the north of the EBA).

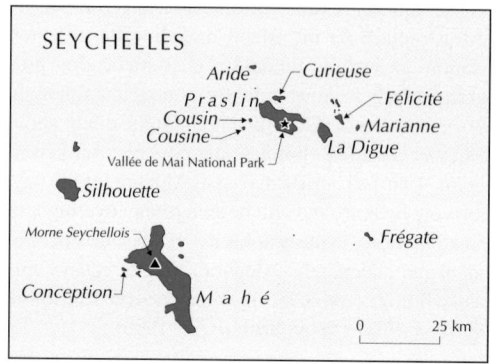

SEYCHELLES

Aride Curieuse
Praslin Félicité
Cousin Marianne
Cousine La Digue
Vallée de Mai National Park

Silhouette

Morne Seychellois

Conception Mahé

Fregate

0   25 km

Status and habitat of restricted-range species

Species (ordered taxonomically)	Global status	Other EBAs (and SAs)	Habitat
Seychelles Kestrel *Falco araea*	VU	—	Upland forest, lowland plantations
Seychelles Blue-pigeon *Alectroenas pulcherrima*	lc	—	Forest
Seychelles Parakeet *Psittacula wardi*	EX (1906)	—	Forest
Seychelles Scops-owl *Otus insularis* [1]	CR	—	Moist forest, boulder valleys
Seychelles Swiftlet *Collocalia elaphra*	VU	—	Variety of habitats inc. forest and wetlands for feeding; caves, rocky slopes, boulder valleys for nesting
Seychelles Bulbul *Hypsipetes crassirostris*	lc	—	Forest, gardens
Seychelles Magpie-robin *Copsychus sechellarum*	CR	—	Open areas under tree cover (originally in mature coastal forest), plantation, gardens
Seychelles Warbler *Acrocephalus sechellensis*	VU	—	*Pisonia* woodland, scrub, low vegetation
Seychelles Paradise-flycatcher *Terpsiphone corvina*	CR	—	Mature stands of *Calophyllum* and *Terminalia* trees, esp. near marshy areas
Seychelles Sunbird *Nectarinia dussumieri*	lc	—	Forest, secondary growth, gardens
Chestnut-sided White-eye *Zosterops mayottensis* [2]	lc	098	Forest
Seychelles White-eye *Zosterops modestus*	CR	—	Mixed secondary forest, forest edge, plantations, gardens
Seychelles Fody *Foudia sechellarum* [3]	VU	—	Forest, secondary growth, plantations, gardens

Global status (see p. 679 for definitions)

EX	Extinct	cd	Conservation Dependent
EW	Extinct in the Wild	with year of last record	
CR	Critical	nt	Near Threatened
EN	Endangered	threatened species	lc	Least Concern
VU	Vulnerable		DD	Data Deficient
		NE	Not Evaluated

Other EBAs (and SAs) (see p. 72 for locations)
Bracketed numbers are Secondary Areas.   X Extinct in that EBA or SA.

Notes
[1] Taxonomy follows Collar and Stuart (1985).
[2] Extinct in this EBA (1940).
[3] Introduced to D'Arros in 1965 (Amirantes Islands, coralline Seychelles) and found to be thriving in 1995 (Skerrett 1995).

Distribution patterns of restricted-range species

Species (ordered geographically)	Aride	Praslin	Curieuse	Cousin	Cousine	Félicité	Marianne	La Digue	Silhouette	Mahé	Frégate	Other EBAs, SAs
Acrocephalus sechellensis	I	–	–	•	I	X	X	–	–	–	–	–
Terpsiphone corvina	X	X	–	–	–	X	X	•	–	–	–	–
Foudia sechellarum	•¹	X	–	•	•	–	X	X	–	–	•	–
Copsychus sechellarum	I	X	–	I	I	–	X	X	–	X	•	–
Alectroenas pulcherrima	•	•	•	•	•	•	•	•	•	•	•	–
Nectarinia dussumieri	•	•	•	•	•	•	•	•	•	•	•	–
Collocalia elephra	–	•	–	–	–	X	–	•	–	•	–	–
Falco araea	–	R	–	–	–	X	X	X	•	•	–	–
Hypsipetes crassirostris	–	•	–	–	–	•	X	•	•	•	–	–
Zosterops mayottensis	–	–	–	–	–	–	X	–	–	–	–	●
Psittacula wardi	–	–	–	–	–	–	–	X	X	–	–	–
Otus insularis	–	–	–	–	–	–	–	–	–	•²	–	–
Zosterops modestus	–	–	–	–	–	–	–	–	–	•	–	–
Total	5	5	2	5	5	3	2	5	4	7	4	

• Present	? Present?	Threatened spp. shown in **bold**	[1] One individual only (see text).
O Extinct?	R Reintroduced	Other EBAs, SAs — see 'Status and habitat' table	[2] Also on Conception (see text).
X Extinct	I Introduced		

Seychelles Paradise-flycatcher *Terpsiphone corvina* survives only on the island of La Digue where any further loss of mature trees from the tiny area it occurs in (less than 50 km²) could lead to its extinction. A large decline in the numbers of invertebrates which the bird feeds on has been recently noted and may be related to an enormous increase in the introduced water lettuce *Pistia stratiotes*, which now covers most of the marsh area. Although it seems unlikely that the adults themselves will starve, the number of young raised each year could be reduced.

■ Threats and conservation

The lowland forests of this EBA were cleared by early settlers for timber, for spice and later coconut plantations, and for firewood to fuel the cinnamon distilleries. Today pockets of near-natural forest remain only at higher altitudes in the more inaccessible central areas but these often contain exotic species. Not surprisingly the islands have suffered many extinctions including the loss of two bird taxa, *Psittacula wardi* and *Zosterops mayottensis semiflava*, and at least 41% of their island populations of birds (Diamond 1984). Habitat alteration and predation by introduced cats and rats (especially black rat *Rattus rattus*) are the likely causes of most such extinctions, and these factors continue to be major threats. Frégate, Aride, Cousin and Cousine are the only islands to have remained rat-free (but see below) and have therefore been vitally important refuges. In 1995 it was discovered that Frégate had been invaded by brown rats *R. norvegicus* via boat cargo and, although a poisoning and trapping programme is under way, total eradication is unlikely unless substantial additional funding is obtained (McCulloch 1996).

Introduced predators (e.g. rats and Common Mynah *Acridotheres tristis*) and habitat destruction continue to pose a serious threat to the species with tiny ranges. Thus, on Mahé, *Zosterops modestus* is confined to three tiny rural and residential areas (totalling less than 5 km²) and may number just 5–6 pairs (25–30 individuals) (Rocamora *et al.* in press), although these white-eyes have recently been discovered on Conception (L. Chong-Seng per G. Rocamora *in litt.* 1997), a small island c.2 km from Mahé; this population is being censused and hosts at least eight more pairs, though the total world population of this species is still probably under 100 birds (G. Rocamora *in litt.* 1997). Also on Mahé, *Otus insularis* is recorded only from forest (virtually all secondary) at

Wright's Skink *Mabuya wrightii* belongs to an endemic genus and feeds on birds' eggs and young fledglings. It has declined or been exterminated on islands with introduced rats, but continues to flourish on Cousin Island which has a breeding population of some 200,000 pairs of seabirds.

The transfer of Seychelles Warbler *Acrocephalus sechellensis* from the tiny island of Cousin (29 ha), where it had reached carrying capacity, to the islands of Aride and Cousine will help to safeguard its future.

250–600 m with a population of perhaps 80 pairs. On La Digue, *Terpsiphone corvina* inhabits mature stands of trees (estimated to cover 41 km² in 1992) and numbers c.70 territorial pairs, habitat destruction for housing development being the main problem (Rocamora *et al.* 1997).

On Aride, where a single female *Foudia sechellarum* has become established within a population of introduced Madagascar Red Fody *F. madagascariensis*, there is concern that hybridization between the two species could endanger any future of *F. sechellarum* on Aride and, in the longer term, on neighbouring islands (Lucking 1997).

Specific conservation efforts, including several years of research and species/habitat management by BirdLife International, have been directed in particular towards two of the highly threatened species, *Copsychus seychellarum* and *Acrocephalus sechellensis*. As a result the population of *C. seychellarum* on Frégate has risen from 12 individuals in 1965 to 42 in 1996, with additional translocated birds on Cousine (six birds), Aride (one surviving out of six) and Cousin (six, which have produced 11 additional young) (Watson *et al.* 1992, R. Lucking per G. Rocamora verbally 1996; see also McCulloch

1996). The population of *A. sechellensis* on Cousin has risen from c.30 birds in 1965 to c.350 in the 1990s, when subsequent monitoring showed that this represented the carrying capacity for the island, and thus permitted a translocation programme to Aride (1,000+ birds in 1996) and Cousine (80 birds in March 1994) (Komdeur *et al.* 1991, Komdeur 1994, Cuthbert and Denny 1995, A. Skerrett *in litt.* 1996). A specific project to save *Zosterops modestus* from extinction has recently been proposed by BirdLife International in collaboration with the Division of the Environment.

There are several protected areas in this EBA, namely the Morne Seychellois National Park (30 km²) on Mahé, the Praslin National Park (3.4 km²) which includes the Vallée de Mai National Park (a World Heritage Site, 0.2 km²) on Praslin, Aride Special Reserve (0.6 km²), Cousin Special Reserve (0.3 km²), La Veuve Special Reserve (0.1 km²) on La Digue which protects some habitat for *Terpsiphone corvina*, Curieuse National Park (15 km²) which covers both the island and surrounding sea, and three islets, Ile Seche, Vache Marine and Les Mamelles, originally established to protect seabird nesting sites.

101 Réunion

PRIORITY URGENT

Key habitats Lowland and montane rain forest, tamarin forest, heath	Area 2,500 km²	Altitude 0–3,000 m

Main threats Moderate habitat loss (e.g. due to cultivation), hunting, introduced species

Countries Réunion (to France)

Biological importance ● ● ●
Current threat level ● ●

Restricted-range species	Threatened	Total
Confined to this EBA	1	4
Present also in other EBAs, SAs	0	3
Total	1	7

■ General characteristics

Réunion, an overseas département of France in the Indian Ocean, is the largest of the Mascarene Islands (see also EBAs 102, 103), rising steeply to over 3,000 m on the Piton des Neiges (see p. 354 for map). Over 60% of its land area is above 1,000 m and the island has a remarkable relief of volcanic massifs (one still active), dissected by deep erosion ravines and cliffs.

The island was covered with forest, including dry forest on the leeward side of the island, mixed evergreen forest (the climax vegetation) and tamarin *Acacia heterophylla* forest (an endemic tree which may be a fire-climax vegetation related to vulcanism). Heath vegetation is extensive at higher altitudes.

■ Restricted-range species

All the extant restricted-range species inhabit the remaining evergreen forest; the two species of *Zosterops* are the only native birds which have adapted to gardens. Most species are found throughout the island (but not at the lowest elevations), apart from *Coracina newtoni*, which has a particularly small range in the north-west on the forested plains of Chicots and d'Affouches (total area less than 16 km²); it is not clear why this species is only found in this region, although a recent study on the closely related Mauritius Cuckoo-shrike *C. typica* suggests that specialized diet and foraging methods may be significant in determining specific habitat requirements (Safford and Beaumont 1996).

The endemic Réunion Marsh-harrier *Circus maillardi maillardi* is usually considered conspecific with the Madagascar form *macrosceles* but is very different in its habitat requirements, calls and coloration (V. Bretagnolle and C. Attié *in litt.* 1993), and may justify recognition as a full species. A sighting of a small owl-like bird has recently been speculated to be a possible new species of scops-owl *Otus* (Renman 1995).

A further four endemic species are known from subfossils (including a night-heron, stork, sheldgoose and kestrel) with two more (a rail and an owl) shared with Mauritius (Cowles 1987). The Réunion Soli-

taire or White Dodo *Raphus solitarius* was also endemic to Réunion, but is only known from descriptions and pictures, and probably died out c.1710–1715. However, there is some evidence which suggests that the 'solitaire' described by the early travellers was not related to either Mauritius Dodo *R. cucullatus* or to Rodrigues Solitaire *Pezophaps solitaria*, but was probably an extinct endemic ibis *Borbonibis latipes*, also known only from subfossils (Mourer-Chauviré and Moutou 1987, Mourer-Chauviré *et al.* 1995).

Two seabirds are believed to be endemic breeders to Réunion: Mascarene Petrel *Pterodroma aterrima* is only known from four specimens collected in the nineteenth century, by three birds found dead (two in the 1970s and one in 1995) and by (at best) one sighting per year in the waters south of Réunion; Barau's Petrel *P. baraui* nests in burrows at high altitudes on Piton des Neiges.

■ Threats and conservation

Réunion is the least ecologically disturbed of the Mascarene Islands, having escaped the introductions of monkeys and mongooses, which have caused extensive damage on the other islands. However, other introduced predators such as rats and cats, and extensive hunting during the seventeenth century have resulted in the extinction of many (at least 16) bird taxa. Competitors are also well established although it is difficult to say how much these introduced birds affect native forms; the recent (1972) introduction of Red-whiskered Bulbul *Pycnonotus jocosus*, a nest-robber, may be serious as it has been blamed for causing heavy losses to white-eyes *Zosterops*, especially in Mauritius.

Key factors which threaten and determine the distribution of the restricted-range species today are deforestation (less than 40% of the island remains under native vegetation), habitat degradation through the introduction of alien plants and herbivores (resulting in the restriction of native forest to the steep sides of rivers at lower elevations), and hunting/poaching (e.g. of *Hypsipetes borbonicus* for the cage-bird trade); the retreat of some species from the

Status and habitat of restricted-range species

Species (ordered taxonomically)	Global status	Other EBAs (and SAs)	Altitude (m)	Habitat
Mascarene Parrot *Mascarinus mascarinus*	EX (1834)	—	No data	Unknown
Mascarene Swiftlet *Collocalia francica*	nt	102	All	Forest and open country for feeding; caves for breeding
Réunion Cuckoo-shrike *Coracina newtoni*	EN	—	1,300–1,800	Forest, heath
Olivaceous Bulbul *Hypsipetes borbonicus* [1]	lc	—	400–2,250	Forest inc. tamarin forest, slightly degraded forest
Réunion Stonechat *Saxicola tectes*	lc	—	100–3,000	Forest inc. tamarin forest with clearings
Mascarene Paradise-flycatcher *Terpsiphone bourbonnensis*	lc	102	100–2,000	Forest, slightly degraded forest
Mascarene Grey White-eye *Zosterops borbonicus*	lc	102	0–2,750	Forest, heath, gardens
Réunion Olive White-eye *Zosterops olivaceus*	lc	—	400–2,250	Forest, secondary forest, gardens (recently)
Réunion Starling *Fregilupus varius*	EX (1854)	—	No data	Unknown

Global status (see p. 679 for definitions)
EX Extinct ⎫ with year
EW Extinct in ⎬ of last
    the Wild ⎭ record
CR Critical ⎫
EN Endangered ⎬ threatened species
VU Vulnerable ⎭
cd Conservation Dependent
nt Near Threatened
lc Least Concern
DD Data Deficient
NE Not Evaluated

Other EBAs (and SAs) (see p. 72 for locations)
Bracketed numbers are Secondary Areas.
[x] Extinct in that EBA or SA.

Notes [1] Taxonomy follows Cheke (1987a).

lowlands may be also (partly) explained by the introduction of pathogens. Cyclones also cause extensive damage to habitats and their birds: one in 1980, for example, resulted in the deaths of up to 50% of the endemic birds and destroyed all nests (Cheke 1987a,b).

Coracina newtoni is the EBA's only species currently to be classified as threatened—due to its tiny range and population (120 pairs); it is at some risk from inappropriate forestry, poaching and impaired forest regeneration as a result of introduced deer, which are maintained at artificially high densities for the purposes of hunting (Cheke 1987a, N. Barré *in litt.* 1993). Part of its range—the Plaine des Chicots—was recognized as a being key forest for the conservation of threatened birds in tropical Africa by Collar and Stuart (1988). Tourism is a potential new threat, as St Denis, the largest city on the island, is close by and there are plans to build roads, hotels and parks, etc. (V. Bretagnolle and C. Attié *in litt.* 1993).

Both endemic petrels (see 'Restricted-range species', above) are classified as Critical: the breeding population of *Pterodroma aterrima* is estimated to be probably fewer than 20 pairs, while that of *P. baraui* is believed to have halved in recent years from an estimated 3,000 pairs owing to illegal, but persistently unpoliced, shooting by local people. The tiny breeding range of *P. baraui* makes it particularly vulnerable to any changes within the area, such as proposed road and cable-car projects. *Circus maillardi maillardi* (see 'Restricted-range species') numbers fewer than 50 pairs (although there may be several hundred individuals) and is also illegally shot (Bretagnolle and Attié 1991, V. Bretagnolle and C. Attié *in litt.* 1993, 1994, 1995, Attié and Bretagnolle in prep.).

There are two protected areas on the island but these are not large enough to protect the flora and fauna contained within them (Barré 1988), and their status is uncertain (C. Attié *in litt.* 1993; see also Doumenge and Renard 1989).

102 Mauritius

Key habitats Upland evergreen rain forest, dwarf forest, exotic forest

Main threats Severe habitat loss (e.g. due to plantations), introduced species

Biological importance ● ● ●
Current threat level ● ● ●

Area 1,900 km²   **Altitude** 0–800 m

Countries Mauritius

Restricted-range species	Threatened	Total
Confined to this EBA	7	7
Present also in other EBAs, SAs	0	3
Total	7	10

■ General characteristics

Together with Rodrigues (EBA 103), the volcanic Indian Ocean island of Mauritius is an independent nation, and both are part of the so-called Mascarene Islands (see also EBA 101) (see p. 354 for map). On Mauritius, the land rises from low plains in the north and east to a plateau in the south-west which descends steeply to the sea and includes a deeply dissected riverbed, the Black River Gorge. The island was once covered in forest, including palm forest in the northern lowlands (now virtually gone), dry forest elsewhere in the lowlands, and, at higher altitudes, wet evergreen and dwarf forest.

■ Restricted-range species

All the extant restricted-range species occur in remaining native evergreen forest, with only *Zosterops borbonicus* and, to a lesser extent, *Terpsiphone bourbonnensis* currently living also in entirely exotic vegetation. None of the restricted-range species shows true altitudinal specialization, and although some appear limited to a particular altitudinal range, this is due to factors such as the distribution of predators (R. J. Safford *in litt.* 1993; detailed information about all the restricted-range birds is given in Cheke 1987c, Jones 1987; see also Jones and Hartley 1995). Three species are shared with neighbouring Réunion (EBA 101), and another restricted-range species which occurs on Mauritius is Meller's Duck *Anas melleri*, introduced from Madagascar (EBA 096).

The best-known of Mauritius's endemic birds was the (now extinct) Dodo *Raphus cucullatus*, which became very scarce on the mainland in the 1640s, persisting until c.1662 on offshore islets (Cheke 1987b). A further nine endemic species are known from subfossils (including a night-heron, goose, duck, harrier, two rails, two parrots and an owl), and two more are shared with Réunion (a rail and an owl) (Cowles 1987).

■ Threats and conservation

Most of the native vegetation on Mauritius has been cleared and replaced by sugar-cane, tea and conifer plantations. Only remnants of original forest remain (c.5% of the island), mainly in the south-west around the Black River Gorge, but even here it is severely degraded by introduced animals and plants (Safford 1997a). Introduced deer *Cervus timorensis*, pigs and monkeys *Macaca fascicularis* cause the most damage, but other exotics affecting forest regeneration are rats (principally black rat *Rattus rattus*, although brown rat *R. norvegicus* is also present) and introduced invertebrates (especially the giant African snails *Achatina fulica* and *A. panthera*, and many insects) (WWF/IUCN 1994). Cyclones occur regularly and can cause extensive damage, especially to already-degraded habitat (e.g. Jones 1994b).

Not surprisingly, all the endemic birds are threatened as a result of habitat loss and continuing degradation, and also because of nest-predation by

N. Arlott

Mauritius Kestrel *Falco punctatus* is one of Mauritius's endemic bird species which has made a spectacular recovery following a captive breeding and release programme.

Status and habitat of restricted-range species

Species (ordered taxonomically)	Global status	Other EBAs (and SAs)	Habitat
Mauritius Kestrel *Falco punctatus*	EN	—	Forest, secondary forest, exotic forest, adjacent scrubby areas
Pink Pigeon *Columba mayeri*	CR	—	Forest, dwarf forest in uplands; now breeds in (exotic) Japanese cedar *Cryptomeria*
Mauritius Blue-pigeon *Alectroenas nitidissima*	EX (1830s)	—	Riparian forest?
Mauritius Parakeet *Psittacula eques*	CR	—	Forest, riparian forest
Mascarene Swiftlet *Collocalia francica*	nt	101	Caves (breeding), forest and open country (feeding)
Mauritius Cuckoo-shrike *Coracina typica*	VU	—	Forest, adjacent secondary and degraded forest usually >450 m
Mauritius Bulbul *Hypsipetes olivaceus*[1]	VU	—	Forest inc. degraded remnants
Mascarene Paradise-flycatcher *Terpsiphone bourbonnensis*	lc	101	Forest, secondary forest, exotic vegetation
Mascarene Grey White-eye *Zosterops borbonicus*	lc	101	All habitats with trees or shrubs, exotic vegetation
Mauritius Olive White-eye *Zosterops chloronothos*	CR	—	Forest, dwarf forest
Mauritius Fody *Foudia rubra*	CR	—	Forest, dwarf forest in uplands; now breeds in (exotic) Japanese cedar *Cryptomeria*

Global status (see p. 679 for definitions)
EX Extinct
EW Extinct in the Wild } with year of last record
CR Critical
EN Endangered } threatened species
VU Vulnerable

cd Conservation Dependent
nt Near Threatened
lc Least Concern
DD Data Deficient
NE Not Evaluated

Other EBAs (and SAs) (see p. 72 for locations)
Bracketed numbers are Secondary Areas.
x Extinct in that EBA or SA.

Notes [1] Taxonomy follows Cheke (1987c).

introduced rats, monkeys and birds (e.g. Red-whiskered Bulbul *Pycnonotus jocosus* which affects white-eyes *Zosterops* in particular). *Falco punctatus* suffered from organochlorine pesticides in the 1960s, but, following a captive breeding and release programme, made a spectacular recovery from a known population of only six birds to a wild population of 56–68 pairs, with a post-breeding estimate of 229–286 birds in 1994. The population is expected to continue to rise to 500–600 birds (C. G. Jones *in litt.* 1994).

The status of four species is considered Critical. *Columba mayeri* was reduced to very low numbers (c.20) with breeding restricted to a single tiny grove of exotic *Cryptomeria* trees, but a second population from captive-bred birds has been established (aided by supplementary feeding and rat-control and numbering 52 in 1994), and there are plans to extend the release programme, for example to predator-free Ile aux Aigrettes and to a lowland site at Bel Ombre (C. G. Jones *in litt.* 1994). *Psittacula eques*, having long since become extinct in the nominate form on Réunion (probably before 1800) but surviving as the race *echo* on Mauritius, was reduced to 10 or so birds in the 1970s and appeared to suffer almost total breeding failure, but bred successfully subsequently resulting in 16–22 birds in 1993–1994. *Zosterops chloronothos* was estimated to number some 275 pairs in the mid-1980s, but this figure may have been over-optimistic: intensive fieldwork in the early 1990s indicated only

150 pairs (R. J. Safford *in litt.* 1994). *Foudia rubra* has declined from c.250 pairs in 1975 to c.90 pairs in 1990 owing to almost total breeding failure over most of its range, currently being remedied by birds nesting in dense exotic *Cryptomeria* trees and by a rat-control programme. Fodies unexpectedly disappeared from relatively intact habitat probably because these were 'sink' areas which depended upon adjacent 'source' areas, now destroyed (Safford 1997b; see also Safford 1997c).

The Macchabé/Bel Ombre Nature Reserve (36 km²) has been recognized as the most important key forest (out of 75) for the conservation of threatened birds in tropical Africa (Collar and Stuart 1988), and is now included in the newly created Black River National Park (70 km²). The reserve partly covers the distributions of all the endemic birds, and, although the habitat around Bassin Blanc (especially important for *Columba mayeri*, *Zosterops chloronothos* and *Foudia rubra*: Safford 1991) was not originally included within the boundary of the national park, this area is being bought by compulsory purchase (Jones and Hartley 1995).

Certain offshore island reserves, such as Ile aux Aigrettes (25 ha), show excellent potential for ecological restoration and, where necessary, eradication of introduced predators. These could become key sites for endemic birds (R. J. Safford *in litt.* 1993; see also Safford and Jones in press).

103 Rodrigues

Key habitats Native and introduced evergreen trees

Main threats Severe habitat loss (e.g. due to cultivation, wood-cutting and grazing), introduced species

Biological importance ● ● ●

Current threat level ● ● ●

Area 110 km² **Altitude** 0–300 m

Countries Mauritius

Restricted-range species	Threatened	Total
Confined to this EBA	2	2
Present also in other EBAs, SAs	0	0
Total	2	2

■ General characteristics

Rodrigues, the smallest and most ecologically devastated of the Mascarene Islands, is politically part of Mauritius (EBA 102, see also EBA 101). The terrain is hilly, mostly gently so, with a central ridge rising to 390 m. Originally the island was covered with rather open evergreen forest but this has been almost totally destroyed. Some parts are planted with *Casuarina* or gums *Eucalyptus*, but these woodlands are devoid of native birds.

■ Restricted-range species

Both extant restricted-range birds have shown some adaptation to the habitat changes, and survive in some non-native vegetation, especially introduced evergreen trees. The population of *Acrocephalus rodericanus* is concentrated mainly in Cascade Pigeon valley. *Foudia flavicans* shares a similar distribution with records largely from the adjacent Cascade Pigeon, Solitude and Sygangue valleys (Cheke 1987d).

Status and habitat of restricted-range species

Species (ordered taxonomically)	Global status	Other EBAs (and SAs)	Habitat
Rodrigues Parakeet *Psittacula exsul*	EX (1875)	—	Forest
Rodrigues Warbler *Acrocephalus rodericanus*	CR	—	Dense thickets, inc. those of introduced vegetation
Rodrigues Fody *Foudia flavicans*	VU	—	Forest, mixed woodland with exotics
Rodrigues Starling *Necropsar rodericanus*	EX (1879)	—	Forest?

Global status								
(see p. 679 for definitions)	EX	Extinct	with year of last record	CR	Critical	threatened species	cd	Conservation Dependent	DD	Data Deficient
	EW	Extinct in the Wild		EN	Endangered		nt	Near Threatened	NE	Not Evaluated
				VU	Vulnerable		lc	Least Concern		

Other EBAs (and SAs) (see p. 72 for locations): bracketed numbers are Secondary Areas; ˣ extinct in that EBA or SA.

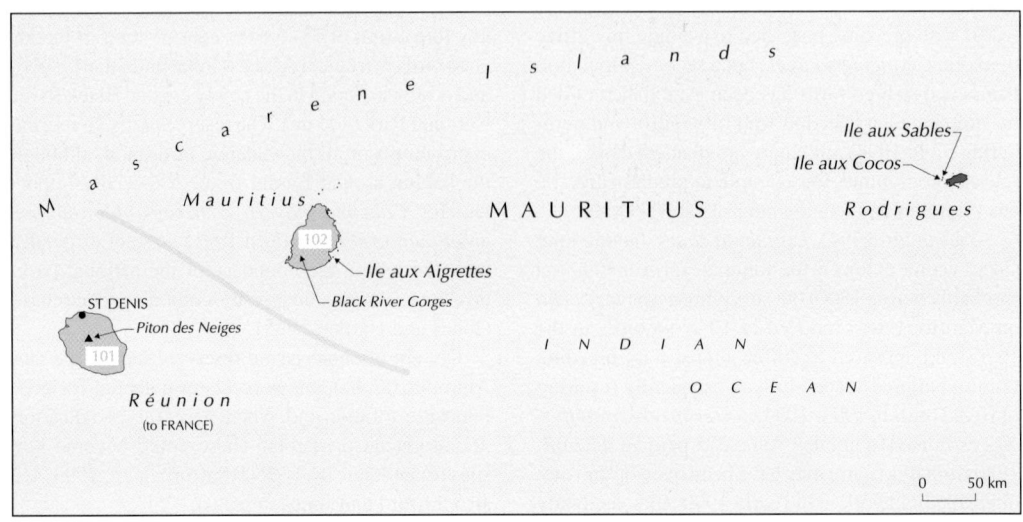

Rodrigues is the most devastated of the Mascarene Islands. Grazing by feral livestock and shifting cultivation have resulted in the replacement of most of the native forest with barren savanna.

The Rodrigues Solitaire *Pezophaps solitaria*, a close relative of the Dodo *Raphus cucullatus* from Mauritius, died out in the 1760s, and another native parrot *Necropsittacus rodericanus* (known only from contemporary accounts and from subfossil bones) is believed to have existed until that time too. A further six endemic species are known from subfossils (including a night-heron, rail, pigeon, owl, babbler and bulbul) (Cowles 1987). These species have not been included in this study, which deals only with restricted-range species extant post-1800.

■ Threats and conservation

The cumulative effects of feral livestock and shifting cultivation have, since the beginning of permanent settlement in the early 1790s, reduced the vegetation on much of Rodrigues to a savanna with scattered trees. It is likely that both *Psittacula exsul* and *Necropsar rodericanus* became extinct because they were unable to withstand predation pressure and the effects of cyclones, having already been reduced in numbers through the loss of native habitat and hunting (Cheke 1987b). Today, remnants of native vegetation only exist on the tops of hills and in a few ravines, altogether accounting for less than 1% of the land area; however, even some of these patches are

declining due to grazing and illegal woodcutting (WWF/IUCN 1994).

Both endemic species are considered threatened because of their tiny ranges and populations. *Foudia flavicans* was reduced to fewer than 10 pairs in 1968 through habitat loss, competition from an introduced congener (Madagascar Fody *F. madagascariensis*) and cyclone impact, but had recovered to 350–400 birds in 1991. *Acrocephalus rodericanus* has also declined steadily with the clearance and disturbance of its dense thicket habitat, and was judged to be reduced to eight pairs and one unpaired bird after a cyclone in 1979, recovering to 45–65 birds in 1991 (MWAF 1992). Habitat conservation and habitat creation have helped to mitigate some of the impact of recent cyclones, but predation by introduced black rats *Rattus rattus* is probably detrimental to both the endemics (Collar and Stuart 1985, Cheke 1987d).

There are three small nature reserves (covering just 58 ha) which include the only surviving remnants of native vegetation, and larger areas have been protected by fencing (WWF/IUCN 1994). Offshore island reserves of Ile aux Cocos (15 ha) and Ile aux Sables (84 ha) may be restored so as to support populations of the endemic birds (R. J. Safford *in litt.* 1993).

355

104 Eastern Zimbabwe mountains

PRIORITY HIGH

Key habitats Montane forest, dense undergrowth at forest edge

Main threats Moderate habitat loss (e.g. due to agriculture)

Biological importance ● ● ●
Current threat level ● ● ●

Area 12,000 km² **Altitude** 800–2,400 m

Countries Mozambique, Zimbabwe

Restricted-range species	Threatened	Total
Confined to this EBA	0	2
Present also in other EBAs, SAs	1	1
Total	1	3

■ General characteristics

This EBA includes the isolated Mt Gorongosa in Mozambique and the mountains which follow the border between Zimbabwe and Mozambique. The latter mountains extend from the Inyangani high-lands in the north, which reach 2,592 m above sea-level, to the Chipinge uplands in the south, and include the Vumba and Chimanimani highlands, which rise to 2,436 m. These ranges mainly lie within Zimbabwe, other than the Chimanimani highlands, which are mostly on the Mozambique side of the border. The most important habitat for the restricted-range species is montane forest. Mt Gorongosa sup ports the largest block of this type of forest south of the Zambezi river (Oatley and Tinley 1987).

■ Restricted-range species

The distribution and habitat requirements of the restricted-range bird species are well known in Zimbabwe (see, e.g., Irwin 1979, 1981), but relatively poorly documented in Mozambique where there has been little recent ornithological survey work. All of the species occur in montane forest, although *Prinia robertsi* is often found in more open habitats. *P. robertsi* is endemic to the eastern highlands of Zimbabwe and adjacent Mozambique, and *Apalis chirindensis* to these mountains and Mt Gorongosa.

■ Threats and conservation

The montane forests of eastern Zimbabwe are currently well protected (Dowsett 1985, Muller and

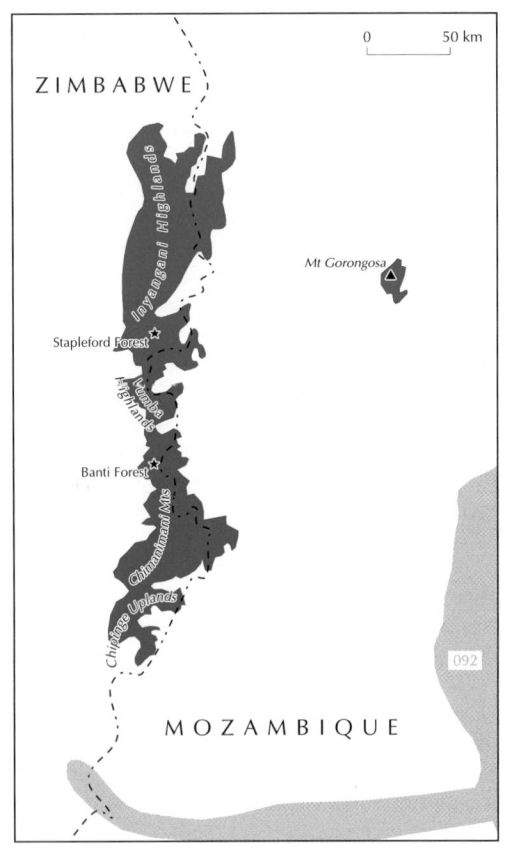

Distribution patterns of restricted-range species	Mt Gorongosa	Inyangani highlands	Stapleford forest	Vumba highlands	Banti forest	Chimanimani mts	Chipinge uplands	Other EBAs, SAs
Species (ordered geographically)								
Swynnertonia swynnertoni	●	–	●	●	–	–	●	●
Apalis chirindensis	●	●	●	●	●	●	●	–
Prinia robertsi	–	●	–	●	●	●	–	–
Total	2	2	2	3	2	2	2	

● Present	? Present?	Threatened spp. shown in **bold**	see 'Status and habitat' table
○ Extinct?	R Reintroduced		
X Extinct	I Introduced	Other EBAs, SAs	

Status and habitat of restricted-range species

Species (ordered taxonomically)	Global status	Other EBAs (and SAs)	Altitude (m)	Habitat
Swynnerton's Robin *Swynnertonia swynnertoni*	VU	105	850–1,800	Montane forest
Briar Warbler *Prinia robertsi*	lc	—	1,200–2,200	Thickets, heath, bracken and other dense vegetation, often at edge of forest
Chirinda Apalis *Apalis chirindensis*	lc	—	850–2,400	Montane forest

Global status (see p. 679 for definitions)	EX Extinct EW Extinct in the Wild	with year of last record	CR Critical EN Endangered VU Vulnerable	threatened species	cd Conservation Dependent nt Near Threatened lc Least Concern	DD Data Deficient NE Not Evaluated

Other EBAs (and SAs) (see p. 72 for locations): bracketed numbers are Secondary Areas; ˣ extinct in that EBA or SA.

Timberlake 1992, M. P. S. Irwin *in litt.* 1993). In Mozambique, although extensive forests remain on Mt Gorongosa (Dowsett 1985), encroachment upwards by shifting cultivators into the montane forests is a chronic problem (Collar and Stuart 1988). *Swynnertonia swynnertoni* is threatened, because it is highly localized in distribution and its habitat is being lost on Mt Gorongosa and in some of the localities where it occurs in the Tanzania–Malawi mountains (EBA 105).

There are two large protected areas in the eastern mountains of Zimbabwe: Nyanga National Park in the Inyangani highlands, and Chimanimani National Park (IUCN 1992b). Mt Gorongosa is said by Dowsett

(1985) to be within a national park, but this park is not listed by IUCN (1992b). There are also several important forest reserves in the EBA, including Chirinda forest (in the Chipinge uplands), at 6 km² the largest example of moist evergreen forest in Zimbabwe (Banks 1976), and two reserves which total 120 km² in the Chimanimani highlands of Mozambique (Muller and Timberlake 1992). The Vumba highlands in Zimbabwe contain numerous discontinuous relic patches of closed evergreen forest which are protected on private land, or where the ground is too steep or rocky for cultivation (Collar and Stuart 1988, M. P. S. Irwin *in litt.* 1993).

105 Tanzania–Malawi mountains

Key habitats Montane and lowland forest, scrub and grassland

Main threats Moderate habitat loss (e.g. due to agriculture, afforestation, timber extraction)

Biological importance ● ● ●
Current threat level ● ● ○

Area 72,000 km²   **Altitude** 200–3,000 m
Countries Kenya, Malawi, Mozambique, Tanzania, Zambia

Restricted-range species	Threatened	Total
Confined to this EBA	16	31
Present also in other EBAs, SAs	4	6
Total	20	37

■ General characteristics

The Tanzania–Malawi mountains EBA includes the chain of isolated mountain ranges which extends for c.1,900 km from the Taita hills and Mt Kasigau in south-east Kenya southwards to the southern highlands of Tanzania and the mountains of Malawi, the extreme north-east of Zambia and the northern half of Mozambique (to the north of the Zambezi river). The region covered by the EBA corresponds closely to the Tanganyika–Nyasa Mountain Group of Moreau's (1966) classification, although the Ufipa plateau in south-west Tanzania is included in the EBA because two of the restricted-range species occur there. Most of the mountain ranges in the EBA

An illegal cardamom plantation inside a forest reserve in the East Usambaras has destroyed the forest understorey which is important for many of the birds in this EBA.

rise to over 2,000 m, and the southern highlands of Tanzania reach 3,000 m.

The restricted-range species occur in a variety of Afromontane habitats, principally montane forest, which is currently estimated to cover c.5 km² in Kenya, 7,200 km² in Tanzania and 300 km² in Malawi, with no recent data available for Mozambique (L. A. Hansen and J. O. Svendsen *in litt.* 1993). The altitude at which montane vegetation occurs varies widely in different parts of the EBA; it is typically found above 1,500 m, but montane conditions occur as low as 900 m on the eastern and southern slopes of several of the mountain ranges in Tanzania.

Status and habitat of restricted-range species

Species (ordered taxonomically)	Global status	Other EBAs (and SAs)	Altitude (m)	Habitat
Udzungwa Forest-partridge *Xenoperdix udzungwensis*[1]	EN	—	1,350–1,900	Montane forest
Fischer's Turaco *Tauraco fischeri*	nt	111	Lowlands to 1,500	Lowland and montane forest
Sokoke Scops-owl *Otus ireneae*	VU	111	200–400	Lowland forest
Usambara Eagle-owl *Bubo vosseleri*	VU	—	Lowlands to 1,500	Lowland and montane forest
Green-throated Greenbul *Andropadus chlorigula*	lc	—	>1,400	Montane forest, bamboo
Sharpe's Greenbul *Phyllastrephus alfredi*	lc	—	1,400–2,300	Montane forest
Uhehe Fiscal *Lanius marwitzi*	lc	—	>1,500	Open country with bushes and trees, agricultural land
Fuelleborn's Boubou *Laniarius fuelleborni*	lc	—	900–2,800	Montane forest, bamboo, agricultural land adjacent to forest
Uluguru Bush-shrike *Malaconotus alius*	CR	—	1,300–2,100	Montane forest
Taita Thrush *Turdus helleri*[2]	CR	—	(1,200–) 1,500–1,725	Montane forest
Thyolo Alethe *Alethe choloensis*	VU	—	700–1,900	Montane forest
Swynnerton's Robin *Swynnertonia swynnertoni*	VU	104	200–1,800	Montane and lowland forest
Sharpe's Akalat *Sheppardia sharpei*	lc	—	600–2,600	Montane forest, bamboo
Usambara Akalat *Sheppardia montana*	VU	—	1,600–2,300	Montane forest
Iringa Akalat *Sheppardia lowei*	VU	—	1,350–2,450	Montane forest
Spot-throat *Modulatrix stictigula*	lc	—	900–2,700	Montane forest
Dappled Mountain-robin *Modulatrix orostruthus*	VU	—	900–1,700	Montane forest
Black-lored Cisticola *Cisticola nigriloris*	lc	—	1,100–2,750	Scrub and bracken at forest edge and along wooded streams
Churring Cisticola *Cisticola njombe*	nt	—	1,850–3,000	Grassland and bracken at forest edge
Taita Apalis *Apalis fuscigularis*[2]	CR	—	1,200–1,725	Montane forest
Namuli Apalis *Apalis lynesi*[2]	VU	—	1,400–2,000	Montane forest
White-winged Apalis *Apalis chariessa*	VU	111	500–2,000	Montane forest
Chapin's Apalis *Apalis chapini*	lc	—	600–2,250	Montane forest
Mrs Moreau's Warbler *Bathmocercus winifredae*	VU	—	1,300–2,350	Montane forest
African Tailorbird *Orthotomus metopias*	lc	—	1,000–2,500	Montane forest, dense vegetation at forest edge
Long-billed Tailorbird *Orthotomus moreaui*	CR	—	900–1,650	Montane forest, scrub
Amani Sunbird *Anthreptes pallidigaster*	VU	111	Lowlands to 1,550	Lowland and montane forest

cont.

Status and habitat of restricted-range species (cont.)

Species (ordered taxonomically)	Global status	Other EBAs (and SAs)	Altitude (m)	Habitat
Banded Sunbird *Anthreptes rubritorques*	VU	—	200–1,600	Montane and lowland forest
Loveridge's Sunbird *Nectarinia loveridgei*	nt	—	(800–) 1,500–2,350	Montane forest
Moreau's Sunbird *Nectarinia moreaui*	nt	—	1,200–1,850	Montane forest
Rufous-winged Sunbird *Nectarinia rufipennis*	VU	—	600–1,700	Montane forest
Taita White-eye *Zosterops silvanus*[2]	CR	—	1,200–1,725	Montane forest
Yellow-browed Seedeater *Serinus whytii*	lc	—	>1,500	Montane forest edge, scrub, heath, agricultural land
Kipengere Seedeater *Serinus melanochrous*	nt	—	>1,700	Montane forest
Tanzanian Mountain Weaver *Ploceus nicolli*	VU	—	900–2,200	Montane forest
Buff-shouldered Widowbird *Euplectes psammocromius*	lc	—	1,800–3,000	Moist montane grassland, often near streams
Kenrick's Starling *Poeoptera kenricki*	lc	109	300–2,500	Montane forest

Global status (see p. 679 for definitions)

EX	Extinct	} with year	cd	Conservation
EW	Extinct in	of last		Dependent
	the Wild	} record	nt	Near Threatened
CR	Critical	} threatened	lc	Least Concern
EN	Endangered	} species	DD	Data Deficient
VU	Vulnerable		NE	Not Evaluated

Other EBAs (and SAs) (see p. 72 for locations)
Bracketed numbers are Secondary Areas.   [x] Extinct in that EBA or SA.

Notes
[1] Newly described by Dinesen *et al.* (1994).
[2] Treated here as full species following Collar *et al.* (1994), but contra Sibley and Monroe (1990, 1993) and Dowsett and Dowsett-Lemaire (1993).

Several of the restricted-range species occur in lowland forests in the foothills of the Usambara mountains; these forests are therefore included in this EBA. Three of the restricted-range species characteristic of the East African coastal forests (EBA 111) also occur in the Usambara mountains, and are therefore considered to be shared between the two EBAs. Other EBAs with close affinities to the Tanzania–Malawi mountains are the Eastern Zimbabwe mountains (EBA 104) and the Pare mountains in the Kenyan mountains (EBA 109) (see the biogeographical analysis in Stuart *et al.* 1993, who considered their avifauna to be closer to that of the Kenyan mountains EBA 109). The Taita hills and Mt Kasigau are included in this EBA (following Moreau 1966 but contra Stuart *et al.* 1993), rather than being treated as a separate EBA, because the taxonomic status of all those 'species' endemic to that area is unclear (see 'Status and habitat' and 'Distribution patterns' tables).

■ Restricted-range species

The genera *Xenoperdix* and *Modulatrix* are endemic to this EBA, and the monotypic endemic genus *Swynnertonia* is shared with the Eastern Zimbabwe mountains (EBA 104). Most of the restricted-range birds occur in montane forest, but six of these species

have been recorded in lowland forest in the foothills of the Usambara mountains (Evans and Anderson 1992, 1993, Evans *et al.* 1994, Hipkiss *et al.* 1994,

Habitat associations of restricted-range species

Lowland and/or montane forest	
Tauraco fischeri	*Modulatrix orostruthus*
Otus ireneae	**Apalis fuscigularis**
Bubo vosseleri	**Apalis lynesi**
Swynnertonia	**Apalis chariessa**
swynnertoni	*Apalis chapini*
Anthreptes pallidigaster	**Bathmocercus winifredae**
Anthreptes rubritorques	*Orthotomus metopias*
	Orthotomus moreaui
	Nectarinia loveridgei
Montane forest	*Nectarinia moreaui*
Xenoperdix	**Nectarinia rufipennis**
udzungwensis	**Zosterops silvanus**
Andropadus chlorigula	*Serinus melanochrous*
Phyllastrephus alfredi	**Ploceus nicolli**
Laniarius fuelleborni	*Poeoptera kenricki*
Malaconotus alius	
Turdus helleri	**Open habitats**
Alethe choloensis	*Lanius marwitzi*
Sheppardia sharpei	*Cisticola nigriloris*
Sheppardia montana	*Cisticola njombe*
Sheppardia lowei	*Serinus whytii*
Modulatrix stictigula	*Euplectes*
	psammocromius

Threatened species (Critical, Endangered, Vulnerable) are shown in **bold**; see 'Status and habitat' table.

Watson and Perkin undated). Five species are associated with forest edge and non-forest habitats, including four with ranges centred on the higher parts of the Udzungwa mountains, southern highlands and Nyika plateau.

Many parts of the EBA are unexplored or only partially explored ornithologically, so the documented distributions of many of the restricted-range species are undoubtedly incomplete. For example, almost nothing is known of the Rubeho mountains, the Uvidunda mountains and most parts of the Udzungwa mountains and southern highlands (Stuart et al. 1993); civil war in Mozambique has prevented ornithological work there for decades, and the lowland forests in the foothills of many of the Tanzanian

J. M. M. Ekstrom/Project Mount Nilo

Spot-throat *Modulatrix stictigula* is one of two species in a genus which is unique to this EBA.

Distribution patterns of restricted-range species

Species (ordered geographically)	Taita hills, Mt Kasigau	Usambara mts	Nguru and Nguu mts	Ukaguru mts	Uluguru mts	Udzungwa mts	Southern highlands	Ufipa plateau	NW Malawi mts [1]	Matengo highlands, Songea mts	Njesi plateau	S Malawi mts, Mt Chiperone	Mt Namuli	Other EBAs, SAs
Turdus helleri	●	–	–	–	–	–	–	–	–	–	–	–	–	–
Apalis fuscigularis	●	–	–	–	–	–	–	–	–	–	–	–	–	–
Zosterops silvanus	●	–	–	–	–	–	–	–	–	–	–	–	–	–
Sheppardia montana	–	●	–	–	–	–	–	–	–	–	–	–	–	–
Tauraco fischeri	–	●	–	–	–	–	–	–	–	–	–	–	–	●
Otus ireneae	–	●	–	–	–	–	–	–	–	–	–	–	–	●
Bubo vosseleri	–	●	–	–	●	–	–	–	–	–	–	–	–	–
Swynnertonia swynnertoni	–	●	–	–	–	●	–	–	–	–	–	–	–	●
Anthreptes pallidigaster	–	●	–	–	–	●	–	–	–	–	–	–	–	●
Ploceus nicolli	–	●	–	–	●	●	–	–	–	–	–	–	–	–
Anthreptes rubritorques	–	●	●	–	●	●	–	–	–	–	–	–	–	–
Poeoptera kenricki	–	●	●	●	●	●	●	–	–	–	–	–	–	●
Sheppardia sharpei	–	●	●	?	●	●	●	–	–	●	–	–	–	–
Laniarius fuelleborni	–	●	●	●	●	●	●	–	–	●	–	–	–	–
Modulatrix stictigula	–	●	●	●	●	●	●	–	●[2]	–	–	–	–	–
Orthotomus moreaui	–	●	–	–	–	–	–	–	–	–	●	–	–	–
Orthotomus metopias	–	●	●	●	●	●	●	–	–	●	–	–	–	–
Modulatrix orostruthus	–	●	–	–	–	–	–	–	–	–	–	–	●	–
Nectarinia moreaui	–	–	●	●	–	●	●	–	–	–	–	–	–	–
Andropadus chlorigula	–	–	●	●	–	●	●	–	–	–	–	–	–	–
Apalis chapini	–	–	●	●	●	●	–	–	●	–	●	–	–	–
Bathmocercus winifredae	–	–	–	●	●	●	–	–	–	–	–	–	–	–
Sheppardia lowei	–	–	–	●	–	●	●	–	–	–	–	–	–	–
Lanius marwitzi	–	–	–	●	●	●	●	–	–	–	–	–	–	–
Malaconotus alius	–	–	–	–	●	–	–	–	–	–	–	–	–	–
Nectarinia loveridgei	–	–	–	–	●	–	–	–	–	–	–	–	–	–
Apalis chariessa	–	–	–	–	●	●	–	–	–	–	–	●	–	●
Xenoperdix udzungwensis	–	–	–	–	–	●	–	–	–	–	–	–	–	–
Nectarinia rufipennis	–	–	–	–	–	●	–	–	–	–	–	–	–	–
Serinus melanochrous	–	–	–	–	–	●	●	–	●	–	–	–	–	–
Cisticola njombe	–	–	–	–	–	●	●	–	●	–	–	–	–	–
Serinus whytii	–	–	–	–	–	●	●	–	●	–	–	–	–	–
Euplectes psammocromius	–	–	–	–	–	●	●	–	●	–	–	–	–	–
Cisticola nigriloris	–	–	–	–	–	●	●	●	●	–	–	–	–	–
Phyllastrephus alfredi	–	–	–	–	–	–	–	●	●	–	–	–	–	–
Alethe choloensis	–	–	–	–	–	–	–	–	–	–	●[3]	●	●	–
Apalis lynesi	–	–	–	–	–	–	–	–	–	–	–	–	●	–
Total	3	15	9	10	14	23	14	2	8	3	3	2	3	

● Present ? Present? Threatened spp. shown in **bold** } see 'Status and habitat' table
○ Extinct? R Reintroduced
X Extinct I Introduced Other EBAs, SAs

1 Including Nyika plateau, north and south Viphya mountains and Kirk range (see Dowsett-Lemaire 1989).
2 Also recorded in Misuku, in extreme north-west Malawi.
3 Only recorded from southern edge of Njesi plateau, Malawi (Dowsett-Lemaire 1989).

N. Arlott

ranges remain unstudied (L. A. Hansen and J. O. Svendsen *in litt.* 1993). Recent fieldwork has led to new discoveries and major range extensions in the Usambara mountains (see above), Udzungwa mountains (Jensen and Brøgger-Jensen 1992, Dinesen *et al.* 1993), Nguu mountains (Seddon *et al.* 1996) and elsewhere.

Species which are known only from a single mountain range include *Turdus helleri*, *Apalis fuscigularis* and *Zosterops silvanus* in the Taita hills, *Sheppardia montana* in the Usambara mountains, *Malaconotus alius* and *Nectarinia loveridgei* in the Uluguru mountains, the recently described *Nectarinia rufipennis* (Jensen 1983) and *Xenoperdix udzungwensis* (Dinesen *et al.* 1994) in the Udzungwa mountains, and *Apalis lynesi* on Mt Namuli. *Bubo vosseleri* was previously believed to be confined to the Usambaras but has recently been found in the Ulugurus (Hunter *et al.* 1996). Several of the restricted-range species appear to have remarkably disjunct distributions, for example *Orthotomus moreaui*, which is known only from the Usambara mountains and the Njesi plateau, and *Modulatrix orostruthus*, known from the Usambara and the Udzungwa mountains, although in some cases this may reflect gaps in knowledge.

■ Threats and conservation

The main threat to the EBA is forest loss and degradation as a result of clearance for agriculture, the replacement of natural forest with plantations, and the collection of timber and firewood (Rodgers 1993). Twenty of the restricted-range species are threatened, principally the forest birds with particularly small ranges which are likely to be most vulnerable to habitat loss. More widespread threatened species which occur in the EBA are East Coast

Akalat *Sheppardia gunningi* (classified as Vulnerable) and Spotted Ground-thrush *Zoothera guttata* (Endangered).

In the Taita hills, most forest has been cleared for cultivation or forested with exotic timbers, and the

N. Seddon/Project Mount Nilo

A crop being burnt after harvesting inside a water catchment reserve in the Nguu mountains. The boundaries of these reserves are often not clearly known by local people or even village foresters, and such activities are therefore difficult to control.

remaining 3 km² is under serious threat (McGuigan 1987, Beentje 1988, Collar and Stuart 1988, B. W. Finch *in litt.* 1993). The forest on Mt Kasigau is certain to be similarly restricted (L. A. Bennun *in litt.* 1994).

In the Usambara mountains, the large human population is putting increasing pressure on the land, and the forests are now highly fragmented (Collar and Stuart 1988, Newmark 1991). A current project run by the Finnish International Development Agency and the Tanzanian Forest Division aims to reconcile conservation and development in the East Usambara mountains by increasing the amount of forest in protected areas, including all lowland remnants (Hamilton and Benstead-Smith 1989, Tye 1993).

The Udzungwa mountains support 23 (62%) of the EBA's restricted-range species, more than any other section of it. Some of the most important sites are included in the Udzungwa Mountains National Park, including Mwanihana forest. However, many important areas lie outside this national park, including Ndundulu and Nyumbanitu mountains, although these are inside the West Kilombero Scarp Forest Reserve (Dinesen *et al.* 1993).

In the Ulugurus, the main mountain block has been partially protected by its extremely inhospitable terrain, but forest only covers c.120 km² and the lower slopes are being steadily cleared as a result of increasing human population pressures. The forests here are included in catchment forest reserves, and the best-quality forests are in the Uluguru North Forest Reserve (Stuart and Jensen 1985, N. D. Burgess *in litt.* 1993). Important forests are also found on the Nguru and Ukaguru mountains, which are not currently considered to be threatened because of their precipitous terrain and low human population, and the southern highlands, where the threats to the forest patches are unknown (see Collar and Stuart 1988).

Much of Nyika plateau is included within a national park, with sections in both Malawi and Zambia, which contains some of the area's finest Afromontane forest remnants; however, fire is a problem in the eastern foothills (Dowsett-Lemaire 1989). Most of the surviving forests in south-east Malawi lie within forest reserves, but increasing human population has posed a serious threat to the survival of mid-altitude forest; for example, over 15 km² has been lost to agricultural encroachment on the slopes of Mt Mulanje and 5 km² around Mt Thyolo, and felling for firewood is damaging montane forests near Blantyre (Dowsett-Lemaire 1989). There is no information on the status of the forest on Mt Chiperone and Mt Namuli in Mozambique (Collar and Stuart 1988).

106 | Albertine Rift mountains

PRIORITY URGENT

Key habitats Montane and transitional forest, bamboo, alpine heath

Main threats Moderate habitat loss (e.g. due to agriculture, timber extraction, gold-mining)

Biological importance ●●●
Current threat level ●○○

Area 56,000 km² **Altitude** 1,000–4,300 m
Countries Burundi, Rwanda, Tanzania, Uganda, Zaïre

Restricted-range species	Threatened	Total
Confined to this EBA	10	36
Present also in other EBAs, SAs	1	1
Total	11	37

■ General characteristics

This EBA includes the mountains which flank the Albertine Rift Valley in the Haut-Zaïre, Kivu and Shaba regions of eastern Zaïre, and in south-west Uganda, Rwanda, Burundi and extreme western Tanzania. It consists of a number of mountain ranges which vary considerably in extent and altitude. The

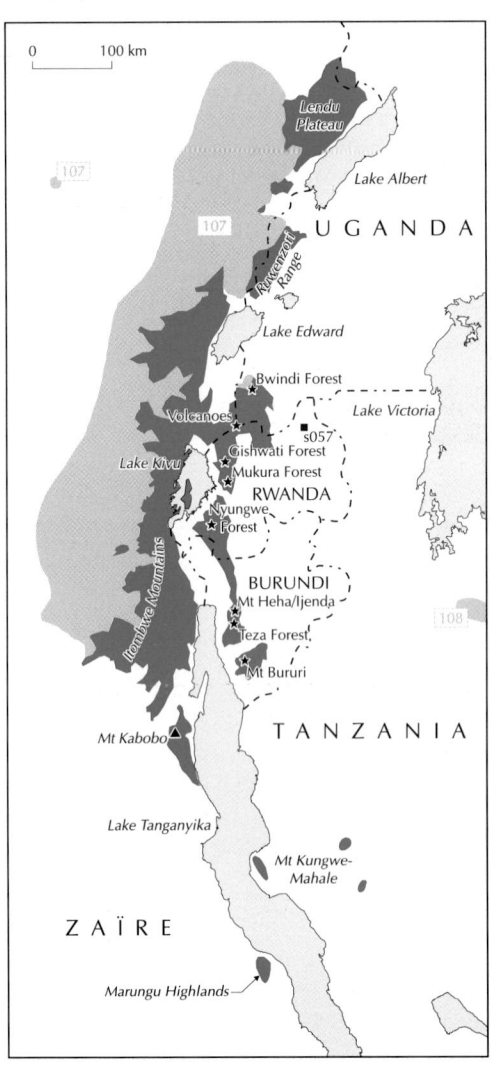

highest peak is at 5,110 m in the Ruwenzori range, but most of the mountain blocks reach maximum altitudes of between 2,000 and 3,500 m.

There are several forest types: transitional forest, intermediate between lowland and true montane forest, is found at about 1,000–1,750 m, mainly on the western flanks of the mountains in Zaïre; montane forest is found from about 1,600 m to 3,500 m, with bamboo and elfin forest above 2,400 m (although bamboo is found as low as 1,600 m on the Kungwe-Mahale mountains in Tanzania). Afroalpine moorlands are found above 3,500 m, with a variety of ericaceous shrubs and grassland species (Britton 1980, White 1983, Dowsett 1985, Prigogine 1985, Sayer et al. 1992).

The Eastern Zaïre lowlands (EBA 107) lies immediately to the west of the western flanks of the Albertine Rift mountains. The birds of that EBA tend to occur at lower altitudes, but some range into the transitional forest zone and there is thus some altitudinal overlap between the two EBAs.

■ Restricted-range species

The restricted-range species of this EBA include the monotypic endemic genera *Pseudocalyptomena*, *Graueria* and *Hemitesia*. They occur in a variety of Afromontane vegetation types, principally forest, although *Bradypterus graueri* is confined to highland swamps. Most of them occur in montane forest and range upwards into the bamboo zone, and a few also occur in Afroalpine moorland; *Nectarinia stuhlmanni* is mainly confined to the bamboo and moorland zones. Six species appear to have been recorded only in transitional forest, which is mainly confined to the western part of the EBA in Zaïre, although one of them, *Glaucidium albertinum*, also occurs in Rwanda. These include some poorly known birds which appear to be highly restricted in range: *Sylvietta chapini* is only known from the Lendu plateau and *Chlorocichla prigoginei* from the Lendu plateau (see Webb 1994) and the mountains to the west of Lake Edward; the recently described *Caprimulgus prigoginei* (Louette 1990) is only known from the Itombwe mountains. The montane *Phodilus*

Status and habitat of restricted-range species

Species (ordered taxonomically)	Global status	Other EBAs (and SAs)	Altitude (m)	Habitat
Handsome Francolin *Francolinus nobilis*	lc	—	2,100–3,700	Dense undergrowth in montane forest, bamboo, alpine heath
Ruwenzori Turaco *Musophaga johnstoni*	lc	—	2,000–3,500	Montane forest
Congo Bay-owl *Phodilus prigoginei*	VU	—	c.2,430	Grass clearing in montane forest
Albertine Owlet *Glaucidium albertinum*	VU	—	c.1,100–1,700	Montane and transitional forest
Itombwe Nightjar *Caprimulgus prigoginei*	VU	—	c.1,280	Probably transitional forest
Ruwenzori Nightjar *Caprimulgus ruwenzorii*	lc		>1,600	Montane forest and adjacent clearings and tea estates
Dwarf Honeyguide *Indicator pumilio*	nt	—	1,500–2,400	Montane forest
African Green Broadbill *Pseudocalyptomena graueri*	VU	—	1,700–2,500	Montane forest
Grauer's Cuckoo-shrike *Coracina graueri*	nt	—	1,150–1,900	Montane and transitional forest
Prigogine's Greenbul *Chlorocichla prigoginei*	VU	—	1,300–1,800	Undergrowth in montane and transitional forest
Yellow-crested Helmet-shrike *Prionops alberti*	VU	—	>1,400	Montane forest
Kivu Ground-thrush *Zoothera tanganjicae*	nt	—	1,500–2,900	Montane forest
Red-throated Alethe *Alethe poliophrys*	lc	—	1,300–3,000	Montane forest, bamboo
Archer's Robin-chat *Cossypha archeri*	lc	—	1,600–4,300	Montane forest, bamboo, giant heath
Red-collared Mountain-babbler *Kupeornis rufocinctus*	nt	—	1,500–3,200	Montane forest, bamboo
Chapin's Mountain-babbler *Kupeornis chapini*	nt	—	1,000–1,650	Transitional forest
Collared Apalis *Apalis ruwenzorii*	lc	—	Montane	Montane forest
Black-faced Apalis *Apalis personata*	lc	—	>1,500	Montane forest
Kungwe Apalis *Apalis argentea*	VU	—	1,300–2,350	Montane forest, bamboo
Kabobo Apalis *Apalis kaboboensis*	DD	—	1,600–2,480	Montane forest
Grauer's Swamp-warbler *Bradypterus graueri*	VU	—	1,950–2,600	Highland swamps
Grauer's Warbler *Graueria vittata*	lc	—	1,600–2,300	Montane forest
Chapin's Crombec *Sylvietta chapini*	lc	—	c.1,500	Montane forest
Neumann's Warbler *Hemitesia neumanni*	lc	—	1,200–2,300	Montane forest
Red-faced Woodland-warbler *Phylloscopus laetus*	lc	—	>1,500	Montane forest, bamboo, plantations
Yellow-eyed Black-flycatcher *Melaenornis ardesiacus*	lc	—	1,300–2,300	Montane forest
Chapin's Flycatcher *Muscicapa lendu*	VU	(s058)	1,470–2,150	Montane forest
Ruwenzori Batis *Batis diops*	lc	—	>1,600	Montane forest, bamboo, scrub
Stripe-breasted Tit *Parus fasciiventer*	lc	—	1,800–3,400	Montane forest, bamboo, tree heath
Blue-headed Sunbird *Nectarinia alinae*	lc	—	>1,400	Montane forest
Stuhlmann's Double-collared Sunbird *Nectarinia stuhlmanni*	lc	—	2,600–3,500	Bamboo, tree heath, montane forest
Regal Sunbird *Nectarinia regia*	lc	—	1,550–3,000	Montane forest, bamboo, scrub
Rockefeller's Sunbird *Nectarinia rockefelleri*	VU	—	2,050–3,300	Thickets along streams in bamboo forest, montane forest, heath

cont.

Status and habitat of restricted-range species (cont.)

Species (ordered taxonomically)	Global status	Other EBAs (and SAs)	Altitude (m)	Habitat
Purple-breasted Sunbird *Nectarinia purpureiventris*	lc	—	1,500–2,600	Montane forest
Dusky Crimson-wing *Cryptospiza jacksoni*	lc	—	>1,550	Montane forest
Shelley's Crimson-wing *Cryptospiza shelleyi*	VU	—	1,550–3,500	Montane forest
Strange Weaver *Ploceus alienus*	lc	—	>1,500	Montane forest, bamboo, more open country

Global status (see p. 679 for definitions)
EX Extinct
EW Extinct in the Wild } with year of last record
CR Critical
EN Endangered } threatened species
VU Vulnerable
cd Conservation Dependent
nt Near Threatened
lc Least Concern
DD Data Deficient
NE Not Evaluated

Other EBAs (and SAs) (see p. 72 for locations): bracketed numbers are Secondary Areas; ˣ extinct in that EBA or SA.

prigoginei has also been recorded definitely only from the Itombwe mountains (Butynski *et al.* 1997), although it probably occurs in Nyungwe and Kibira (Mt Heha/Ijenda and Teza forests) (J.-P. Vande weghe *in litt.* 1991). Other montane forest species with particularly restricted distributions are *Nectarinia stuhlmanni*, which is only known from the Ruwenzori range (but see Dowsett and Dowsett-Lemaire 1993 for a discussion of the unresolved taxonomy and distributions of this and other closely related forms), and *Apalis kaboboensis*, which is confined to Mt Kabobo. *Apalis argentea* has an unusual distribution, being found only in the south-eastern part of the EBA.

The form of Prigogine's Double-collared Sunbird *Nectarinia prigoginei* which is confined to the Marungu highlands in the south of the EBA was considered to be a full species by Collar and Stuart (1985), but is here treated as part of a more widespread species of the same name following Sibley and Monroe (1990, 1993).

■ Threats and conservation

The main threat to this EBA is deforestation, mainly as a result of encroachment for agriculture and unregulated timber felling (Howard 1991) which has recently been exacerbated by the effects of warfare (Kanyamibwa 1995), and there is some localized forest loss in Itombwe due to gold-mining (R. Beyers *in litt.* 1993). Rwanda and Burundi are small, very densely populated countries, and have already lost most of their forest (Dowsett 1985), as has south-west Uganda. Eastern Zaïre is more sparsely populated, and large areas of undisturbed montane forest still survive, but the transitional forest associated with the lower levels of the montane blocks is threatened because it is relatively accessible to local farmers. For example, the Maboya to Beni region, where *Chlorocichla prigoginei* is found, is densely populated and the area of transitional forest is shrinking rapidly (Prigogine 1985). Eleven of the re-

stricted-range birds are threatened; these include those which are particularly restricted in distribution or habitat, or are known from just a few records, and are therefore judged to be most vulnerable to forest loss; one further species is classified as Data Deficient.

There are seven protected areas in this EBA (IUCN 1992b), and several forest reserves, but they do not cover all of the most important areas. The mountain ranges with their own endemic species of bird are of particular conservation concern: parts of the Ruwenzori range are included in the Virunga National Park in Zaïre and in the Mount Ruwenzori National Park in Uganda, but the Itombwe mountains, Lendu plateau and Mt Kabobo currently have no official protection. The Itombwe mountains are particularly important, as they contain the largest block of montane forest in the EBA (estimated to

Habitat associations of restricted-range species

Transitional forest
Glaucidium albertinum
Caprimulgus prigoginei
Coracina graueri
Chlorocichla prigoginei
Kupeornis chapini
Sylvietta chapini

Montane forest
Francolinus nobilis
Musophaga johnstoni
Phodilus prigoginei
Caprimulgus ruwenzorii
Indicator pumilio
Pseudocalyptomena graueri
Prionops alberti
Zoothera tanganjicae
Alethe poliophrys
Cossypha archeri
Kupeornis rufocinctus
Apalis ruwenzorii

Apalis personata
Apalis argentea
Apalis kaboboensis
Graueria vittata
Hemitesia neumanni
Phylloscopus laetus
Melaenornis ardesiacus
Muscicapa lendu
Batis diops
Parus fasciiventer
Nectarinia alinae
Nectarinia stuhlmanni
Nectarinia regia
Nectarinia rockefelleri
Nectarinia purpureiventris
Cryptospiza jacksoni
Cryptospiza shelleyi
Ploceus alienus

Montane swamps
Bradypterus graueri

Threatened species (Critical, Endangered, Vulnerable) are shown in **bold**; see 'Status and habitat' table.

Distribution patterns of restricted-range species

Species (ordered geographically)	Lendu plateau	Ruwenzori range	Mts W of Lake Edward	Bwindi forest	Volcanoes	Gishwati/ Mukura/Busaga	Mts W of Lake Kivu	Itombwe mts	Mt Kabobo	Nyungwe forest	Mt Heha/Ijenda & Teza forests	Mt Bururi	Mt Kungwe-Mahale	Marungu highlands	Other EBAs, SAs
Sylvietta chapini	●	–	–	–	–	–	–	–	–	–	–	–	–	–	–
Chlorocichla prigoginei	●	–	●	–	–	–	–	–	–	–	–	–	–	–	–
Kupeornis chapini	●	–	●	–	–	–	●	–	–	–	–	–	–	–	–
Muscicapa lendu	●	–	–	●	–	–	●	●	–	–	–	–	–	–	○
Coracina graueri	●	●	●	–	–	–	●	●	–	–	–	–	–	–	–
Francolinus nobilis	●	●	●	●	●	●	●	●	●	●	●	–	–	–	–
Phylloscopus laetus	●	●	●	●	●	●	●	●	●	●	●	●	–	–	–
Nectarinia alinae	●	●	●	●	●	●	●	●	●	●	●	●	–	–	–
Cryptospiza jacksoni	●	●	●	●	●	●	●	●	●	●	●	–	–	–	–
Apalis personata	●	●	●	●	●	–	●	●	●	●	●	–	–	●	–
Nectarinia stuhlmanni	–	●	–	–	–	–	–	–	–	–	–	–	–	–	–
Indicator pumilio	–	●	●	●	●	●	●	●	●	●	●	–	–	–	–
Cryptospiza shelleyi	–	●	●	●	●	●	●	●	●	●	●	–	–	–	–
Musophaga johnstoni	–	●	●	●	●	●	●	●	●	●	●	–	–	–	–
Cossypha archeri	–	●	●	●	●	●	●	●	●	●	●	–	–	–	–
Parus fasciiventer	–	●	●	●	●	●	●	●	●	●	●	–	–	–	–
Caprimulgus ruwenzorii	–	●	●	●	●	–	●	●	●	●	●	–	–	–	–
Alethe poliophrys	–	●	●	●	●	●	●	●	●	●	●	–	–	–	–
Nectarinia purpureiventris	–	●	●	●	–	●	●	●	–	●	●	–	–	–	–
Apalis ruwenzorii	–	●	●	●	●	●	●	●	●	●	●	–	–	–	–
Batis diops	–	●	●	●	●	●	●	●	●	●	●	–	–	–	–
Ploceus alienus	–	●	●	●	●	●	●	●	●	●	●	–	–	–	–
Nectarinia regia	–	●	●	●	●	●	●	●	●	●	●	–	–	●	–
Prionops alberti	–	–	●	●	–	●	–	●	●	●	–	–	–	–	–
Glaucidium albertinum	–	●	●	–	–	–	●	●	–	●	–	–	–	–	–
Hemitesia neumanni	–	●	●	–	–	–	●	●	–	●	–	–	–	–	–
Bradypterus graueri	–	●	●	●	–	●	●	–	–	●	●	–	–	–	–
Graueria vittata	–	●	●	–	–	–	●	●	–	●	–	–	–	–	–
Melaenornis ardesiaca	–	●	●	–	–	●	●	●	–	●	●	–	–	–	–
Zoothera tanganjicae	–	●	●	●	●	●	●	●	–	●	●	●	–	–	–
Pseudocalyptomena graueri	–	–	–	●	–	–	●	●	–	–	–	–	–	–	–
Nectarinia rockefelleri	–	–	–	–	●	–	●	●	–	?	?	–	–	–	–
Phodilus prigoginei	–	–	–	–	–	–	–	●	–	–	–	–	–	–	–
Caprimulgus prigoginei	–	–	–	–	–	–	–	●	–	–	–	–	–	–	–
Kupeornis rufocinctus	–	–	?	–	–	–	–	●	●	●	●	–	–	–	–
Apalis kaboboensis	–	–	–	–	–	–	–	–	●	–	–	–	–	–	–
Apalis argentea	–	–	–	–	–	–	–	–	–	●	●	●	●	–	–
Total	10	19	27	24	20	19	29	31	19	25	23	12	2	1	

● Present ? Present?
○ Extinct? R Reintroduced
X Extinct I Introduced

Threatened spp. shown in **bold**
Other EBAs, SAs } see 'Status and habitat' table

cover c.10,000 km²) and support 31 of the restricted-range species; the available evidence suggests that habitat there remains reasonably intact (Collar and Stuart 1988, Wilson and Catsis 1990). The Lendu plateau is now largely deforested, and Djuga forest is perhaps the most important remaining site (see Webb 1994). At Mt Kabobo, montane forest covers no more than 2,000 km², but its current status is unknown (Collar and Stuart 1988). The Itombwe mountains, and some other important parts of this EBA such as the Bwindi Impenetrable National Park, Kahuzi-Biega National Park (west of Lake Kivu) and the Virunga National Park, are exceptional in Africa in having an unbroken progression from lowland to montane evergreen forest; they are therefore impor-

tant for the birds of both this EBA and the Eastern Zaïre lowlands (EBA 107). The threatened Nyungwe forest in Rwanda (see Dowsett-Lemaire 1990, Dowsett-Lemaire and Dowsett 1990, Gibson 1992), which has been proposed as a protected area but is not yet gazetted, and the adjacent Kibira National Park, are important for the conservation of *Apalis argentea* and many of the other restricted-range species. Another important area for *A. argentea* in the Kungwe-Mahale mountains in western Tanzania is included in Mahali National Park. Bwindi Impenetrable, Virunga and the Mgahinga Gorilla National Parks support most of the world population of mountain gorilla *Gorilla gorilla berengei* (Lee *et al.* 1988, I. S. Francis *in litt.* 1993).

107 Eastern Zaïre lowlands

PRIORITY HIGH

Key habitats Lowland rain forest, transitional forest

Main threats Moderate habitat loss (e.g. due to agriculture, gold-mining)

Biological importance ● ○ ○
Current threat level ● ● ○

Area 75,000 km²   **Altitude** 700–1,800 m

Countries Uganda, Zaïre

Restricted-range species	Threatened	Total
Confined to this EBA	3	6
Present also in other EBAs, SAs	0	0
Total	3	6

■ General characteristics

The Lower Guinea forest is one of the world's great lowland rain forests, and together with the Upper Guinea forest (EBA 084) constitutes the Guineo-Congolian Region of White (1983). The Eastern Zaïre lowlands EBA lies at the eastern edge of the Lower Guinea forest, in the Haut-Zaïre and Kivu regions of eastern Zaïre and the extreme west of Uganda, and is adjacent to the western edge of the Albertine Rift mountains (EBA 106). The restricted-range birds of this EBA occur in lowland rain forest, but also range up into transitional forest, the forest type found between lowland and montane forest on the lower slopes of the mountains between approximately 1,000 and 1,750 m (White 1983). Several of the restricted-range species from the Albertine Rift mountains EBA also occur in transitional forest, so there is some altitudinal overlap between the two EBAs. These two EBAs together constitute the Central Refugium, one of Africa's major centres of endemism and species richness for forest animals and plants, as it is one of the places where forest is believed to have survived during the driest periods of the Pleistocene (Hamilton 1981, Prigogine 1985, Stuart 1985).

Distribution patterns of restricted-range species

Species (ordered geographically)	Bambesa	Semliki/Ituri	E. of Lake Kivu	Itombwe	Other EBAs, SAs
Phyllastrephus lorenzi	●	●	–	●	–
Ploceus flavipes	–	●	–	–	–
Ploceus aureonucha	–	●	●	–	–
Zoothera oberlaenderi	–	●	–	●	–
Terpsiphone bedfordi	–	●	●	●	–
Schoutedenapus schoutedeni	–	–	–	●	–
Total	1	5	2	4	

● Present   ? Present?   Threatened spp.   ⎱ see 'Status
○ Extinct?   R Reintroduced   shown in **bold**   ⎰ and habitat'
X Extinct   I Introduced   Other EBAs, SAs   ⎰ table

■ Restricted-range species

The distributions of the restricted-range species are incompletely known. Most records of these birds come from the Semliki and Ituri forests and the foothills of the Itombwe mountains, but it is likely that most of them also occur in the intervening region. There is also an apparently disjunct record of *Phyllastrephus lorenzi* from Bambesa, well to the north-west of the rest of the EBA. *Ploceus flavipes* is only known from the Ituri forest in Zaïre, and *Ploceus aureonucha* from here and by a recent sighting from Irangi Forest Reserve (B. W. Finch *in litt.* 1993). *Schoutedenapus schoutedeni* is only known from

[Map shows: ZAÏRE, Ituri Forest, 106, Bambesa, Semliki Forest, Lake Edward, UGANDA, Bwindi Forest, 106, s057, Lake Kivu, RWANDA, Itombwe Mountains, BURUNDI, TANZANIA, 0 50 km]

Status and habitat of restricted-range species

Species (ordered taxonomically)	Global status	Other EBAs (and SAs)	Altitude (m)	Habitat
Schouteden's Swift *Schoutedenapus schoutedeni*	VU	—	c.1,000–1,470	Clearings in transitional and lowland forest, probably breeds on cliffs
Sassi's Greenbul *Phyllastrephus lorenzi*	nt	—	700–1,800	Lowland and transitional forest
Forest Ground-thrush *Zoothera oberlaenderi*	nt	—	700–1,620	Transitional forest
Bedford's Paradise-flycatcher *Terpsiphone bedfordi*	nt	—	980–1,500 (-1,800)	Transitional forest
Golden-naped Weaver *Ploceus aureonucha*	VU	—	Lowlands	Lowland rain forest, forest edge and adjacent agricultural land
Yellow-legged Weaver *Ploceus flavipes*	VU	—	Lowlands	Lowland rain forest

Global status (see p. 679 for definitions)	EX Extinct EW Extinct in the Wild	with year of last record	CR Critical EN Endangered VU Vulnerable	threatened species	cd Conservation Dependent nt Near Threatened lc Least Concern	DD Data Deficient NE Not Evaluated

Other EBAs (and SAs) (see p. 72 for locations): bracketed numbers are Secondary Areas; ˣ extinct in that EBA or SA.

five records from the foothills of the Itombwe mountains. Two of the restricted-range species have been recorded in Uganda, *Zoothera oberlaenderi* in Semliki and Bwindi (Impenetrable) forests, and *Phyllastrephus lorenzi* from Ntandi in Semliki forest (Friedmann and Williams 1968, Butynski and Kalina 1993, M. Carswell *in litt.* 1993).

Hall's Greenbul *Andropadus hallae*, described from a single specimen collected in lowland forest in this EBA (Prigogine 1972), was treated as a full species by Sibley and Monroe (1990, 1993), but is here considered to be a form of the widespread Little Greenbul *A. virens*, following Dowsett and Dowsett-Lemaire (1993).

■ Threats and conservation

The main threat to the EBA is deforestation (Hamilton 1984, Sayer *et al.* 1992), mainly for cultivation, and there is some localized forest loss as a result of gold-mining in Itombwe, around Maiko and possibly in other places (R. Beyers *in litt.* 1993). It is likely that the rate of deforestation has been increased recently by the effects of warfare (Kanyamibwa 1995). The three restricted-range birds with particularly small ranges are threatened because of their vulnerability to habitat loss. More widespread threatened forest birds which occur in this EBA are Congo Peacock

Afropavo congensis and Turner's Eremomela *Eremomela turneri* (both classified as Vulnerable); Nahan's Francolin *Francolinus nahani* (Data Deficient) also occurs.

There are several protected areas within this EBA (Howard 1991, IUCN 1992b). Part of the lowland Semliki forest is included in the Virunga National Park, but, although some forest remains, this part of the park has been devastated by human settlement (Stuart 1985), and the illegal growing of cocoa as an understorey species is leading to the replacement of forest by species-poor plantation (Howard 1991). This protected area is contiguous with the large Ituri forest, and could be extended to include its eastern part (Prigogine 1985). Another part of Ituri forest is now included in Okapi Faunal Reserve (Blom 1990). Other existing reserves which are likely to be important for the birds of the EBA are the western section of Kahuzi-Biega National Park, the eastern section of Maiko National Park, the lower forests on the western side of Mount Ruwenzori National Park, Bwindi Impenetrable Forest National Park (I. S. Francis *in litt.* 1993) and Irangi Forest Reserve (R. Beyers *in litt.* 1993). The Itombwe mountains are currently unprotected, but the forests there apparently remain reasonably intact (Collar and Stuart 1988, Wilson and Catsis 1990).

108 Serengeti plains

Key habitats *Acacia* scrub, grassland with open *Acacia* woodland

Main threats Moderate habitat loss (e.g. due to overgrazing, agriculture), trapping for cage-bird trade

Biological importance ● ● ○
Current threat level ● ○ ○

Area 160,000 km² **Altitude** 1,000–2,200 m

Countries Kenya, Tanzania

Restricted-range species	Threatened	Total
Confined to this EBA	1	5
Present also in other EBAs, SAs	1	1
Total	2	6

■ General characteristics

This EBA includes the semi-arid plains to the south and east of Lake Victoria in north-central Tanzania and south-west Kenya. Its boundaries, defined by the combined distributions of the restricted-range species, correspond to an isolated region of Somalia–Masai *Acacia–Commiphora* deciduous bushland and thicket (White 1983). In Tanzania, the EBA extends southwards from Serengeti National Park to the Lake Eyasi basin, which includes the Wembere steppe. In Kenya, it extends northwards from the border with Tanzania through the plateau to the west of the Rift Valley to the high valley bottom regions surrounding Lakes Naivasha and Nakuru. The northern part of this EBA lies adjacent to the Kenyan mountains (EBA 109), but the birds of the latter area occur mainly in montane habitats at higher altitudes.

■ Restricted-range species

The restricted-range species include the monotypic endemic genus *Histurgops*. They all occur in *Acacia* or *Acacia–Commiphora* woodland and bushed or wooded grassland, habitats which are patchily distributed within the EBA. Only two of the restricted-range species, *Trachyphonus usambiro* and *Prionops*

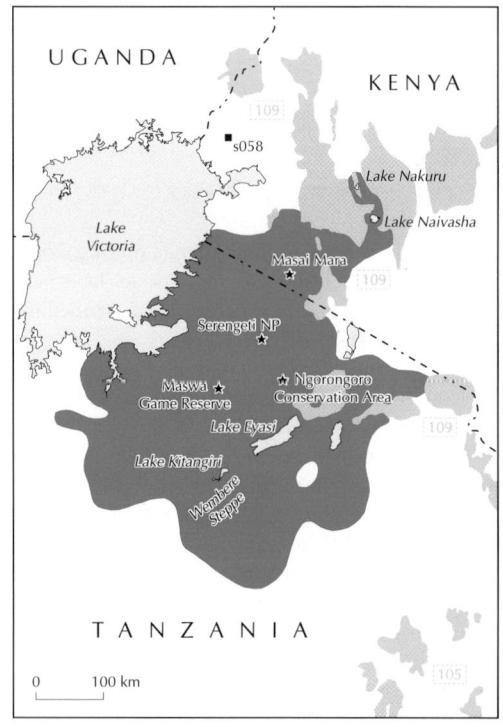

The Serengeti plains are famous for the huge concentrations of large mammals which they support, but are also an area of endemism for birds.

Status and habitat of restricted-range species

Species (ordered taxonomically)	Global status	Other EBAs (and SAs)	Altitude (m)	Habitat
Grey-breasted Spurfowl *Francolinus rufopictus*	lc	—	c.1,000	Grassland with scattered *Acacias*, *Acacia* woodland, thickets and small trees along drainage lines
Fischer's Lovebird *Agapornis fischeri*[1]	nt	—	1,100–2,000	*Acacia* woodland, wooded grassland, agricultural land
Usambiro Barbet *Trachyphonus usambiro*	lc	—	1,100–2,100	Wooded grassland, open woodland, thorn scrub, grassland with scattered *Acacias*
Grey-crested Helmet-shrike *Prionops poliolophus*	VU	—	1,200–2,200	Open woodland, wooded grassland, *Acacia* scrub
Karamoja Apalis *Apalis karamojae*	VU	(s060)	c.1,150	*Acacia* scrub
Rufous-tailed Weaver *Histurgops ruficauda*	lc	—	960–2,000	*Acacia* woodland, wooded grassland, woodland along drainage lines, agricultural land around long-established villages

Global status (see p. 679 for definitions)

EX	Extinct ⎱ with year	cd	Conservation
EW	Extinct in ⎰ of last		Dependent
	the Wild ⎰ record	nt	Near Threatened
CR	Critical ⎱ threatened	lc	Least Concern
EN	Endangered ⎰ species	DD	Data Deficient
VU	Vulnerable ⎰	NE	Not Evaluated

Other EBAs (and SAs) (see p. 72 for locations)
Bracketed numbers are Secondary Areas.   ˣ Extinct in that EBA or SA.

Notes
[1] There are feral populations in southern Kenya (Lewis and Pomeroy 1989), and around Dar es Salaam, Tanga and Dodoma in Tanzania (N. E. Baker *in litt.* 1993).

poliolophus, are recorded from Kenya, where they both range northwards up the Rift Valley to the area around Lake Naivasha, *P. poliolophus* also as far as Lake Nakuru (Lewis and Pomeroy 1989). *P. poliolophus* is rare and localized in Tanzania (N. E. Baker *in litt.* 1993), but *T. usambiro* is widespread in the Tanzanian section of the EBA, as are *Francolinus rufopictus*, *Agapornis fischeri* and *Histurgops ruficauda* (see Schmidl 1982, Stronach 1990, Moyer 1995). *Apalis karamojae* is restricted (in this EBA) to stands of whistling thorn *Acacia drepanolobium* in the southern Serengeti National Park, Maswa Game Reserve and the Wembere steppe (D. C. Moyer *in litt.* 1994).

■ Threats and conservation

A large part of the EBA is included in protected areas, but outside the reserves the habitats of the restricted-range species are coming under increasing pressure from pastoralists and agriculturalists. In the past, some habitat was lost through the tsetse fly control programme, but now human population pressure is leading to general degradation because of overstocking and the cultivation of marginal areas. The band of woodland and wooded grassland which extends south from Maswa Game Reserve to the Wembere steppe is of particular concern, as it probably supports populations of all of the restricted-range species but is under considerable pressure. There is currently no protection for the whole of Lake Eyasi basin, includ-

ing the Wembere steppe and Lake Kitangiri (N. E. Baker *in litt.* 1993). The main threat to the EBA in Kenya is the spread of agriculture in and around the Rift Valley, where areas of grassland and woodland outside protected areas are vanishing, such that the populations of the restricted-range species are likely to become confined to the area protected in the Serengeti and Masai Mara reserves (L. A. Bennun *in litt.* 1993). *Prionops poliolophus* and *Apalis karamojae* are threatened because their particularly restricted ranges largely lie outside protected areas. *Agapornis fischeri* populations have been reduced locally by capture for the wild-bird trade, but it remains a numerous species within protected areas (Moyer 1995, N. Stronach *in litt.* 1993).

A large part of this EBA is protected within the contiguous Serengeti National Park, Maswa Game Reserve, Ngorongoro Conservation Area and Masai Mara Game Reserve. However, much of this area (such as the extensive grasslands in the north of the Serengeti National Park) contains no suitable habitat for the restricted-range species. The Masai Mara Game Reserve itself will not effectively conserve the restricted-range species in Kenya, but its buffer zones, which are presently managed in a similar way to the main reserve, should contain both *Trachyphonus usambiro* and *Prionops poliolophus* (L. A. Bennun *in litt.* 1996). At least three other protected areas contain suitable habitat for the restricted-range birds (see IUCN 1992b).

109 Kenyan mountains

Key habitats	Montane forest, bamboo, montane grassland, alpine scrub

Area 48,000 km²   **Altitude** 900–4,400 m

Countries Kenya, Tanzania, Uganda

Main threats Moderate habitat loss (e.g. due to agriculture)

Biological importance ● ●
Current threat level ● ●

Restricted-range species	Threatened	Total
Confined to this EBA	3	8
Present also in other EBAs, SAs	0	1
Total	3	9

■ General characteristics

This EBA includes the mountains around the Rift Valley in the interior of Kenya and northern Tanzania, and on the eastern border of Uganda. These mountains include extensive areas lying above 2,500 m, and most of the main ranges rise to well over 3,000 m; they include the great isolated volcanoes of Mt Kilimanjaro (at 5,895 m the highest mountain in Africa), Mt Kenya (5,200 m) and Mt Elgon (4,321 m). The main habitats are Afromontane forest (from c.900 m up to 2,600 m), bamboo (mainly at 2,400–3,500 m), montane grassland (up to 3,500 m) and moorland (lying above 3,500 m). The southern part of this EBA overlaps geographically with the Serengeti plains (EBA 108), but the birds in the latter

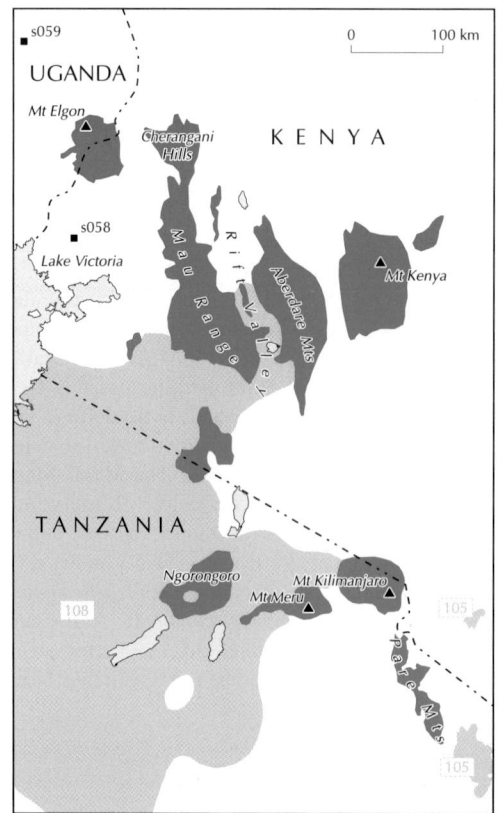

The Afromontane grasslands in this EBA support some spectacular endemic plants, such as this thistle *Carduus keniensis*, which is known from Mt Kenya and Mt Elgon.

area occur mainly at lower altitudes and in non-forest habitats.

■ Restricted-range species

The restricted-range species vary in distribution and occur in a wide variety of Afromontane habitats (see Lewis and Pomeroy 1989, Stronach 1990). *Cinnyricinclus femoralis* and *Poeoptera kenricki* are confined to montane forests below the bamboo zone in the eastern part of the EBA. Both of them occur in the Pare mountains in northern Tanzania, which is therefore included within this EBA, although the forest avifauna there has affinities with both this EBA and the Tanzania–Malawi mountains (EBA 105) (Stuart

Status and habitat of restricted-range species

Species (ordered taxonomically)	Global status	Other EBAs (and SAs)	Altitude (m)	Habitat
Jackson's Francolin *Francolinus jacksoni*	lc	—	2,200–3,700	Dense undergrowth in montane forest, bamboo, dense scrub in moorland
Sharpe's Longclaw *Macronyx sharpei*	nt	—	1,850–3,400	Open grassland
Hinde's Pied-babbler *Turdoides hindei*	EN	—	1,070–1,700	*Lantana* scrub, open woodland in steep-sided valleys and gullies
Hunter's Cisticola *Cisticola hunteri*	lc	—	1,550–4,400	Scrub and other vegetation on the forest edge, bamboo, giant heath
Aberdare Cisticola *Cisticola aberdare*	lc	—	2,300–3,700	Moist montane grassland
South Pare White-eye[1] *Zosterops winifredae*	VU	—	2,000–2,465	Heath at the forest edge, montane forest clearings
Jackson's Widowbird *Euplectes jacksoni*	nt	—	1,500–3,000	Open montane grassland, feeds in agricultural land
Kenrick's Starling *Poeoptera kenricki*	lc	105	900–2,500	Montane forest
Abbott's Starling *Cinnyricinclus femoralis*	VU	—	1,800–2,600	Montane forest

Global status (see p. 679 for definitions)

EX	Extinct ⎫ with year	cd	Conservation
EW	Extinct in ⎬ of last		Dependent
	the Wild ⎭ record	nt	Near Threatened
CR	Critical ⎫	lc	Least Concern
EN	Endangered ⎬ threatened species	DD	Data Deficient
VU	Vulnerable ⎭	NE	Not Evaluated

Other EBAs (and SAs) (see p. 72 for locations)
Bracketed numbers are Secondary Areas. ˣ Extinct in that EBA or SA.

Notes
[1] Treated here as a full species following Collar *et al.* (1994), but contra Sibley and Monroe (1990, 1993) and Dowsett and Dowsett-Lemaire (1993).

Distribution patterns of restricted-range species

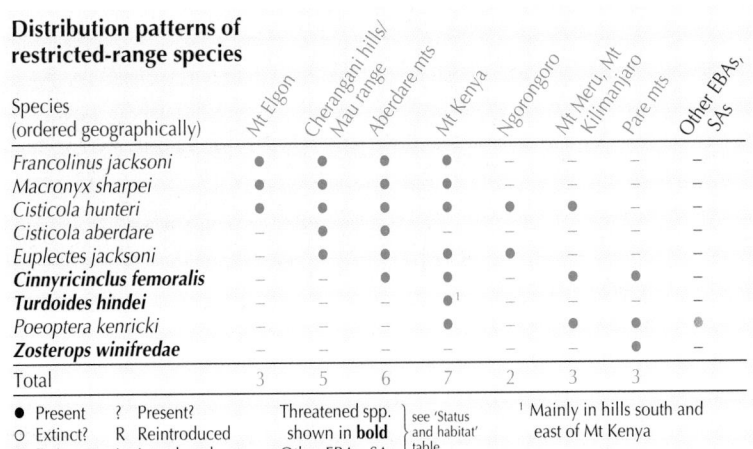

Species (ordered geographically)	Mt Elgon	Cherangani hills/ Mau range	Aberdare mts	Mt Kenya	Ngorongoro	Mt Meru, Mt Kilimanjaro	Pare mts	Other EBAs, SAs
Francolinus jacksoni	●	●	●	●	—	—	—	—
Macronyx sharpei	●	●	●	●	—	—	—	—
Cisticola hunteri	●	●	●	●	●	●	—	—
Cisticola aberdare	—	●	●	—	—	—	—	—
Euplectes jacksoni	—	●	●	●	●	—	—	—
Cinnyricinclus femoralis	—	—	●	●	—	●	●	—
Turdoides hindei	—	—	—	●[1]	—	—	—	—
Poeoptera kenricki	—	—	—	●	—	●	●	●
Zosterops winifredae	—	—	—	—	—	—	●	—
Total	3	5	6	7	2	3	3	

● Present ? Present?   Threatened spp. ⎫ see 'Status [1] Mainly in hills south and
○ Extinct? R Reintroduced   shown in **bold** ⎬ and habitat' east of Mt Kenya
X Extinct I Introduced   Other EBAs, SAs ⎭ table

et al. 1993, Cordeiro and Kiure 1995). *Zosterops winifredae* is only known from the South Pare mountains. *Macronyx sharpei* and *Euplectes jacksoni* are birds of open montane grasslands, although *E. jacksoni* also ranges into grasslands at intermediate altitudes and occurs, for example, in the long grass habitats in the Masai Mara Game Reserve and Nairobi National Park (L. A. Bennun *in litt.* 1996). *Turdoides hindei* is particularly associated with scrub and open woodland in the foothills of the eastern part of the EBA, to the south and east of Mt Kenya.

■ Threats and conservation

Three of the restricted-range species are threatened, *Turdoides hindei* because its range has contracted considerably during the twentieth century and its habitat continues to be cleared rapidly for intensive agriculture (Njoroge and Bennun 1996), *Zosterops winifredae* because the forests are under pressure within its small range, and *Cinnyricinclus femoralis* because it is an extremely localized forest species which is believed to be declining in parts of its range because of forest loss. Montane grassland is also

Mt Kenya, one of the great isolated mountains of East Africa. The restricted-range bird species occur in a variety of montane forest and non-forest habitats on its slopes.

J.P. Croxall

being rapidly lost because of agricultural development, which is probably affecting the two grassland specialist species (Lens *et al.* 1996, L. A. Bennun *in litt.* 1993), and consequently these are classified as Near Threatened.

IUCN (1992b) lists nine protected areas within this EBA which contain suitable habitat for the restricted-range birds, including Aberdare, Mount Elgon, Mount Kenya and Chyulu National Parks in Kenya, and Kilimanjaro National Park and Mount Meru Game Reserve in Tanzania. There are also a number of forest reserves which are very important for the conservation of the habitats of these birds (L. A. Bennun *in litt.* 1993, N. Stronach *in litt.* 1993).

110 Pemba

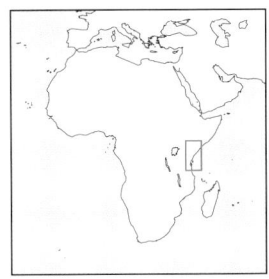

Key habitats Coastal forest, wooded habitats

Main threats Major habitat loss (e.g. due to clove and coconut plantations)

Biological importance ●
Current threat level ●

Area 1,000 km² **Altitude** 0–100 m
Countries Tanzania

Restricted-range species	Threatened	Total
Confined to this EBA	0	4
Present also in other EBAs, SAs	0	0
Total	0	4

■ General characteristics

Pemba (lying c.40 km north-east of Zanzibar, both politically part of Tanzania) became separated from the African mainland some four to five million years ago and is today isolated by a trough c.800 m deep. Thus, despite being a mere 50 km offshore, it is regarded as an oceanic island (Archer and Turner 1993; see p. 376 for map). Much of the island is broken up into little valleys and hills thickly covered with plantations (mostly cloves) and coconuts, interspersed with food crops. In addition, it supports a number of other exotic plants and spices, an endemic palm *Chrysalidocarpus pembanus* and a small area of indigenous coastal forest.

■ Restricted-range species

Pemba qualifies as an EBA following the elevation of *Treron* (*australis*) *pembaensis* to full species status (Sibley and Monroe 1993), and of *Otus* (*rutilus*) *pembaensis* and *Nectarinia* (*notata*) *pembae* (Archer and Turner 1993).

Over much of Pemba the endemic species are widespread and common or locally common; both *Zosterops vaughani* and *Nectarinia pembae* have been recorded from the smaller offshore islands.

■ Threats and conservation

Most of the original evergreen forest on Pemba has been destroyed, and the endemic species are judged to be Near Threatened, given this loss of habitat and their small ranges—despite the fact that all are common. Given the current human population density (estimated at c.280 per km²) and projected population increase over the next 20 years, the threat of deforestation on Pemba can only increase. The status of the endemic birds on the island should therefore be carefully monitored.

The largest area of forest now surviving is Ngezi Forest Reserve (14 km²) which is located at the base of the Kingomasha peninsula in north-west Pemba. However, this forest has been selectively logged, and the shrub layer has been damaged to favour timber production. Smaller areas of forest are located at Mwitu Mkuu, Ras Kiuyu and on certain islands off the coast, but the largest of these occupies only 2–3 km² (Burgess *et al.* 1992). Traditional graveyards, where logging is prohibited, may provide pockets of suitable, undisturbed habitat in otherwise impoverished agricultural areas for the endemic Pemba flying fox *Pteropus voeltzkowi* (Entwistle and Corp 1997) as well as for the endemic birds.

Status and habitat of restricted-range species

Species (ordered taxonomically)	Global status	Other EBAs (and SAs)	Habitat
Pemba Green-pigeon *Treron pembaensis*	nt	—	Forest, wooded habitats
Pemba Scops-owl *Otus pembaensis*[1]	nt	—	Forest, wooded habitats, clove plantations, trees around villages
Pemba Sunbird *Nectarinia pembae*[1]	nt	—	Forest, wooded habitats, towns and villages
Pemba White-eye *Zosterops vaughani*	nt	—	Forest, wooded habitats

| **Global status** (see p. 679 for definitions) | EX Extinct EW Extinct in the Wild | } with year of last record | CR Critical EN Endangered VU Vulnerable | } threatened species | cd Conservation Dependent nt Near Threatened lc Least Concern DD Data Deficient NE Not Evaluated | **Other EBAs (and SAs)** (see p. 72 for locations) **Notes** | Bracketed numbers are Secondary Areas. ˣ Extinct in that EBA or SA. [1] Taxonomy follows Archer and Turner (1993). |

111 East African coastal forests

PRIORITY URGENT

Key habitats Lowland forest, *Brachystegia* woodland, *Acacia* scrub

Main threats Major habitat loss (e.g. due to agriculture, wood collection)

Biological importance ● ● ●
Current threat level ● ● ●

Area 25,000 km²   **Altitude** 0–500 m

Countries Kenya, Somalia, Tanzania

Restricted-range species	Threatened	Total
Confined to this EBA	2	3
Present also in other EBAs, SAs	3	4
Total	5	7

■ General characteristics

This EBA includes the coastal and riverine lowlands of southern Somalia, Kenya and central Tanzania and the island of Zanzibar, and corresponds to the northern part of the Zanzibar–Inhambane regional mosaic of White (1983). A variety of vegetation types is found, including semi-evergreen and deciduous forest, woodland and scrub, much of which has been modified by people harvesting wood products over centuries and by clearance for shifting agriculture (White 1983, S. A. Robertson *in litt.* 1993).

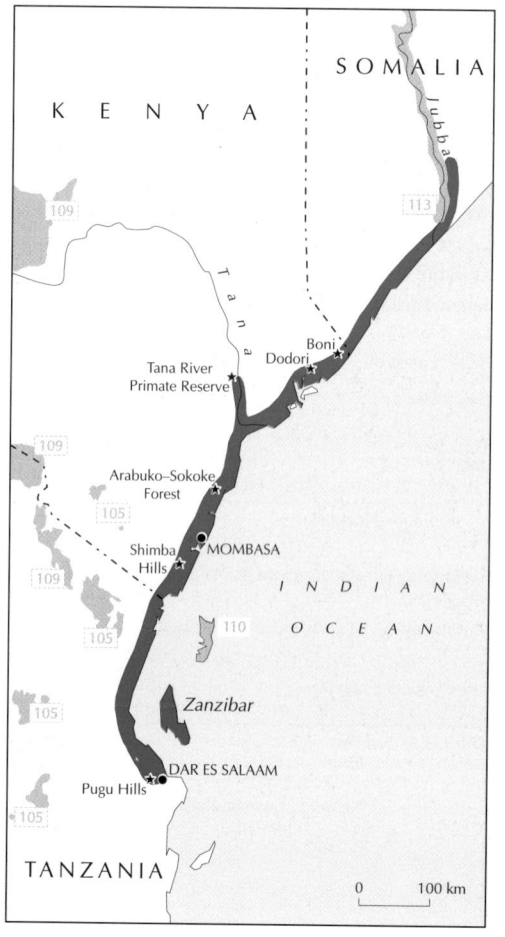

J. H. Fanshawe

Arabuko–Sokoke is by far the largest remaining area of closed-canopy forest in this EBA, and is becoming a popular destination for birdwatchers and other ecotourists.

There is minor overlap between this EBA and the Jubba and Shabeelle valleys (EBA 113) in the lower Jubba valley, but the birds of that area occur in more open, non-forest habitats. The lowland forests at the base of the Usambara mountains are included in the Tanzania–Malawi mountains (EBA 105) because several of the species characteristic of that EBA (which elsewhere occur mainly in montane forest) are found there. However, three of the restricted-range species of the present EBA also occur there, so these forests have affinities with both EBAs.

■ Restricted-range species

Most of the restricted-range species are found in coastal forest and woodland, but their distributions are incompletely known because many forests are

Status and habitat of restricted-range species

Species (ordered taxonomically)	Global status	Other EBAs (and SAs)	Altitude (m)	Habitat
Fischer's Turaco *Tauraco fischeri*	nt	105	Lowlands	Lowland forest, well-wooded country
Sokoke Scops-owl *Otus ireneae*	VU	105	Lowlands	Lowland forest
Sokoke Pipit *Anthus sokokensis*	VU	—	Lowlands	Lowland forest, thickets within degraded forest
Tana River Cisticola *Cisticola restrictus*	DD	—	Lowlands to 500	Semi-arid *Acacia* scrub
White-winged Apalis *Apalis chariessa*	VU	105	Lowlands	Gallery forest
Amani Sunbird *Anthreptes pallidigaster*	VU	105	Lowlands	*Brachystegia* woodland, lowland forest
Clarke's Weaver *Ploceus golandi*	VU	—	Lowlands	Lowland forest, *Brachystegia* woodland

Global status (see p. 679 for definitions)	EX	Extinct	with year of last record	CR	Critical	threatened species	cd	Conservation Dependent	DD	Data Deficient
	EW	Extinct in the Wild		EN	Endangered		nt	Near Threatened	NE	Not Evaluated
				VU	Vulnerable		lc	Least Concern		

Other EBAs (and SAs) (see p. 72 for locations): bracketed numbers are Secondary Areas; ˣ extinct in that EBA or SA.

Distribution patterns of restricted-range species

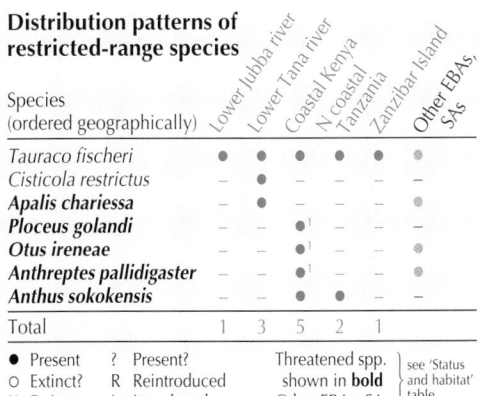

Species (ordered geographically)	Lower Jubba river	Lower Tana river	Coastal Kenya	N coastal Tanzania	Zanzibar Island	Other EBAs, SAs
Tauraco fischeri	●	●	●	●	●	○
Cisticola restrictus	–	●	–	–	–	–
Apalis chariessa	–	●	–	–	–	○
Ploceus golandi	–	–	●¹	–	–	–
Otus ireneae	–	–	●¹	–	–	○
Anthreptes pallidigaster	–	–	●¹	–	–	○
Anthus sokokensis	–	–	●	●	–	○
Total	1	3	5	2	1	

●	Present	?	Present?	Threatened spp. shown in **bold**	see 'Status and habitat' table
○	Extinct?	R	Reintroduced		
X	Extinct	I	Introduced	Other EBAs, SAs	

¹ In coastal Kenya, only recorded from the Arabuko–Sokoke forest area.

difficult of access and have not been ornithologically surveyed (Waiyaki and Bennun 1996, S. A. Robertson *in litt.* 1993). *Ploceus golandi* has only been recorded in the Arabuko–Sokoke forest and immediately to the north in the Dakacha area north of the Sabaki river (L. A. Bennun *in litt.* 1996), and *Otus ireneae* and *Anthreptes pallidigaster* are only known (in this EBA) from Arabuko–Sokoke. *Anthus sokokensis* has been found in seven coastal forest sites, including Arabuko–Sokoke, and can persist in thickets within degraded forest. *Tauraco fischeri* is relatively widespread, and is the only species recorded from southern Somalia and Zanzibar. *Cisticola restrictus* and *Apalis chariessa* are only recorded (in this EBA) from the lower Tana valley; *C. restrictus* is known from a small number of specimens collected in semi-arid *Acacia* scrub and has not been found during recent field surveys (and is perhaps not a valid

species: e.g. Lewis and Pomeroy 1989), while *A. chariessa* has been recorded in gallery forest but is now possibly extinct in this EBA.

■ Threats and conservation

The main threat to the EBA is forest loss and degradation. The coastal forests were probably natu-

Clarke's Weaver *Ploceus golandi* is known only from Arabuko–Sokoke and adjacent forests in coastal Kenya.

N. Arlott

rally patchily distributed in places with suitable soils and climatic conditions, but exploitation has reduced them to scattered remnants. Many of these are under pressure from agricultural encroachment by an increasing human population, and the extraction of firewood and house-building materials. The expanding tourist industry is taking land for hotel and recreational development, and provides a lucrative market for wood for construction, furniture and carvings (which are exported in bulk); timber is harvested both legally and illegally from protected and unprotected forests (Douthwaite 1987, Varty and Hill 1988, Burgess *et al.* 1992, Sheil 1992, Waiyaki and Bennun 1996, S. A. Robertson *in litt.* 1993). Five of the restricted-range birds are threatened because of these pressures on their habitats, and *Cisticola restrictus* is classified as Data Deficient. Two more-widespread threatened species which occur in this EBA are East Coast Akalat *Sheppardia gunningi* (classified as Vulnerable) and Spotted Ground-thrush *Zoothera guttata* (present here as a non-breeder and classified as Endangered).

The 372-km² Arabuko–Sokoke forest supports five of the restricted-range birds, and has the largest known populations of four threatened species, including *Ploceus golandi* which is only known from this area. Since 1989 it has been the subject of an integrated forest conservation programme run jointly by the National Museums of Kenya and BirdLife International (Fanshawe 1991, 1993). Although *Cisticola restrictus* has not been recorded in the Tana valley since 1972, and *Apalis chariessa* not since 1961, suitable habitat for them may be contained in

Arabuko–Sokoke forest, both provides a place where tree-rearing techniques can be demonstrated, and supplies seedlings to the forest-adjacent households, to school wildlife clubs and others.

the Tana River Primate Reserve. The Shimba Hills Nature Reserve and 10 forest reserves in Kenya (in addition to Arabuko–Sokoke) provide some protection to areas of indigenous forest, and several Kayas (small traditionally protected forests) are in the process of gazettement as forest reserves (S. A. Robertson *in litt.* 1993). The poorly known Boni (joined to Bushbuck National Park in Somalia) and Dodori National Reserves in northern Kenya both contain patches of coastal forest, and the area between them has been designated for gazettement as Lunghi and Boni Forest Reserves; the insecurity of this area has probably helped to protect its wildlife (S. A. Robertson *in litt.* 1993). The surviving coastal forest sites in Tanzania are currently not well protected (Collar and Stuart 1988, Burgess *et al.* 1992, Sheil 1992, Burgess and Mlingwa 1993).

112 Central Somali coast

Key habitats Fixed-dune grassland

Main threats Possibly habitat loss

Area 15,000 km² **Altitude** 0–60 m

Countries Somalia

Biological importance ●
Current threat level ● ● ●

Restricted-range species	Threatened	Total
Confined to this EBA	1	2
Present also in other EBAs, SAs	0	0
Total	1	2

■ General characteristics

This EBA extends along the coast of south-east Somalia (from near Mogadishu at about 1°30′N to 7°N), and consists of a narrow strip of large, fixed, vegetated dunes, which are mostly 10–15 km wide and vary between 20 and 60 m in height (WWF/IUCN 1994). The main vegetation type is fixed-dune grassland dominated by perennial grasses and sedges (Barker *et al.* 1989).

■ Restricted-range species

The extent of the EBA is defined by the range of *Spizocorys obbiensis* (see Ash 1981), as the other restricted-range species, *Mirafra ashi*, is only known from a single locality on the coastal plain to the north of Uarsciek, although it is speculated that it may occur along the coast to the north-east, which is ornithologically very poorly known (Collar and Stuart 1985). Both of these larks appear to be restricted to coastal fixed-dune grassland.

■ Threats and conservation

Mirafra ashi is threatened because of its highly restricted range, where the chronic and continuing political crisis in Somalia may result in an as-yet-undocumented loss of habitat. WWF/IUCN (1994) identify the Hobyo (or Obbia) area as a Centre of Plant Diversity, based upon the high level of plant species endemism, and list overgrazing and fuelwood cutting as the main threats to this part of the EBA. Grazing by ungulates and campsite occupation by

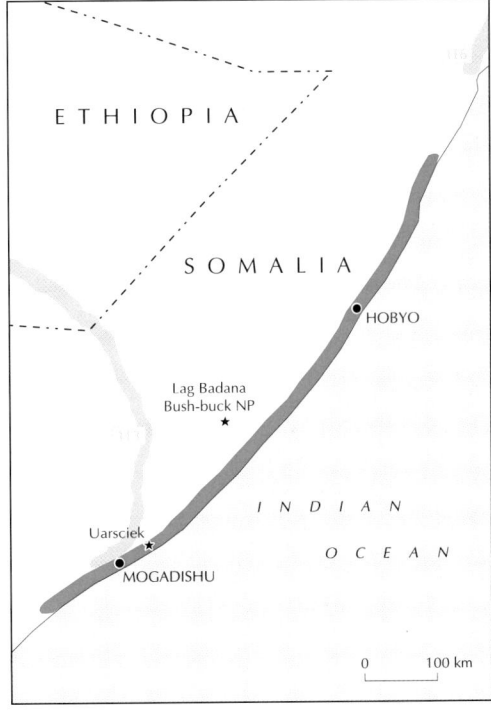

nomads affect the vegetation of the coastal grassland (Barker *et al.* 1989).

Some of this EBA is inside the Lag Badana Bush-bush National Park, but this is apparently not functional (I. Friis pers. comm. in WWF/IUCN 1994).

Status and habitat of restricted-range species

Species (ordered taxonomically)	Global status	Other EBAs (and SAs)	Habitat	
Ash's Lark *Mirafra ashi*	EN	—	Coastal plain	Coastal fixed-dune grassland
Obbia Lark *Spizocorys obbiensis*	nt	—	Coastal plain	Coastal fixed-dune grassland

Global status (see p. 679 for definitions)							
EX	Extinct	with year of last record	CR	Critical	threatened species	cd	Conservation Dependent	DD	Data Deficient
EW	Extinct in the Wild		EN	Endangered		nt	Near Threatened	NE	Not Evaluated
			VU	Vulnerable		lc	Least Concern	

Other EBAs (and SAs) (see p. 72 for locations): bracketed numbers are Secondary Areas; ˣ extinct in that EBA or SA.

113 Jubba and Shabeelle valleys

PRIORITY
CRITICAL

Key habitats Riverine woodland, *Acacia* scrub, marshland

Main threats Unquantified habitat loss (e.g. due to agriculture, refugees displaced by warfare)

Biological importance ● ● ○
Current threat level ● ● ●

Area 35,000 km²   **Altitude** 0–800 m

Countries Ethiopia, Kenya, Somalia

Restricted-range species	Threatened	Total
Confined to this EBA	2	4
Present also in other EBAs, SAs	0	0
Total	2	4

■ General characteristics

The middle reaches of the Shabeelle (or Shebele) river, the entire length of the Jubba and its tributaries and the area around lakes Chamo and Abaya in southern Somalia, south-east Ethiopia and extreme north-east Kenya constitute an EBA. The restricted-range birds are found in a variety of lowland habitats, mainly riverine. There is some geographical overlap between this EBA and the Kenyan and Tanzanian coastal forests (EBA 111) in the lower Jubba valley, but the birds of that EBA occur mainly in forest. There is also some geographical overlap between this EBA and the South Ethiopian highlands (EBA 114), but the birds of the latter occur at relatively high altitudes and are not riverine in distribution.

■ Restricted-range species

Two of the restricted-range species are widespread within the EBA: *Streptopelia reichenowi* is usually found in riparian woodland dominated by doum

N. Arlott

Bulo Burti Bush-shrike *Laniarius liberatus* is known by a single bird trapped in *Acacia* scrub in the Shabeelle valley in Somalia.

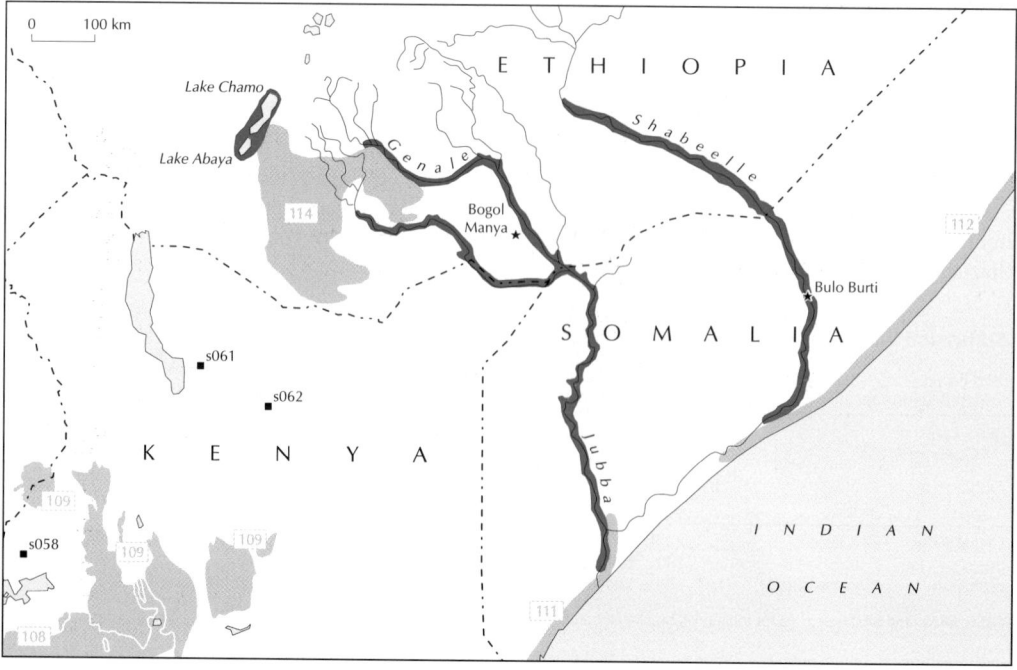

Status and habitat of restricted-range species

Species (ordered taxonomically)	Global status	Other EBAs (and SAs)	Altitude (m)	Habitat
White-winged Collared-dove *Streptopelia reichenowi*	nt	—	Lowlands to c.750	Riverine woodland
Degodi Lark *Mirafra degodiensis*	VU	—	c.350	Sparse low *Acacia* scrub on bare soil
Bulo Burti Bush-shrike *Laniarius liberatus*	CR	—	c.140	*Acacia* thicket, riverine woodland
Salvadori's Weaver *Ploceus dicrocephalus*	lc	—	Lowlands	Riverine vegetation, reedbeds, grassland, areas around villages

Global status (see p. 679 for definitions)	EX	Extinct	with year of last record	CR	Critical	threatened species	cd	Conservation Dependent	DD	Data Deficient
	EW	Extinct in the Wild		EN	Endangered		nt	Near Threatened	NE	Not Evaluated
				VU	Vulnerable		lc	Least Concern		

Other EBAs (and SAs) (see p. 72 for locations): bracketed numbers are Secondary Areas; ˣ extinct in that EBA or SA.

Riverine vegetation in Somalia's lower Jubba valley, habitat of White-winged Collared-dove *Streptopelia reichenowi* and Salvadori's Weaver *Ploceus dicrocephalus*.

palms *Hyphaene thebaica* and fan palms on the banks and floodplains of large rivers, tending to avoid the adjacent dry *Acacia* woodland, but in Ethiopia it also ranges into drier vegetation a few kilometres from rivers (Urban *et al.* 1986, P. O. Syvertsen *in litt.* 1993); *Ploceus dichrocephalus* is found in riverine marshland and grassland, and is the only restricted-range species which occurs around lakes Chamo and Abaya in the west of the EBA. The other two species are known from single localities— *Mirafra degodiensis* from open scrub near Bogol Manya in south-east Ethiopia (Erard 1975, Ash and Gullick 1990, Webb and Smith 1996), which is a few kilometres from the Genale river (a tributary of the Jubba), and *Laniarius liberatus* by a single bird

trapped in *Acacia* scrub at Bulo Berti (Buulobarde) in the Shabeelle valley in Somalia (Smith *et al.* 1991b).

■ Threats and conservation

Mirafra degodiensis and *Laniarius liberatus* are threatened because of their highly restricted distributions. Increased grazing pressure is a possible future threat to the habitat of *M. degodiensis* (Ash and Gullick 1990), and the vegetation in the area where *L. liberatus* was discovered is rapidly being destroyed by refugees displaced by warfare, while clearance of vegetation for agriculture is also taking place elsewhere in the Shabeelle valley (Smith *et al.* 1991b). There are no protected areas in this EBA (IUCN 1992b).

114 South Ethiopian highlands

Key habitats Thorn-bush savanna, grassland, juniper forest, scrub

Main threats Unquantified habitat loss (e.g. due to agriculture, overgrazing, burning)

Biological importance ● ● ●
Current threat level ● ● ●

Area 37,000 km²   **Altitude** 1,000–2,000 m

Countries Ethiopia

Restricted-range species	Threatened	Total
Confined to this EBA	4	5
Present also in other EBAs, SAs	0	0
Total	4	5

■ General characteristics

This EBA lies at the southern extreme of the Ethiopian highlands, in Oromo (formerly Sidamo, or Borana) region of southern Ethiopia. The five restricted-range species which occur close together here are found in a wide variety of habitat types. An approximate boundary for the EBA has been drawn based on the documented records and altitudinal limits of these birds. The Jubba and Shabeelle valleys (EBA 113) lie immediately to the east of this EBA, and one of the restricted-range species of that EBA also occurs around Lakes Abaya and Chamo—but

the birds of that EBA are found at low altitudes (below 750 m), and there is no altitudinal overlap.

■ Restricted-range species

The habitat requirements and distributions of the restricted-range species of this EBA are generally poorly known. *Hirundo megaensis* and *Zavattariornis stresemanni* are both found in thorn-bush savanna around the towns of Yabello and Mega, in an area of about 10,000 km² (Collar and Stuart 1985); the latter is a monotypic genus which is endemic to the EBA. *Heteromirafra sidamoensis* is only known

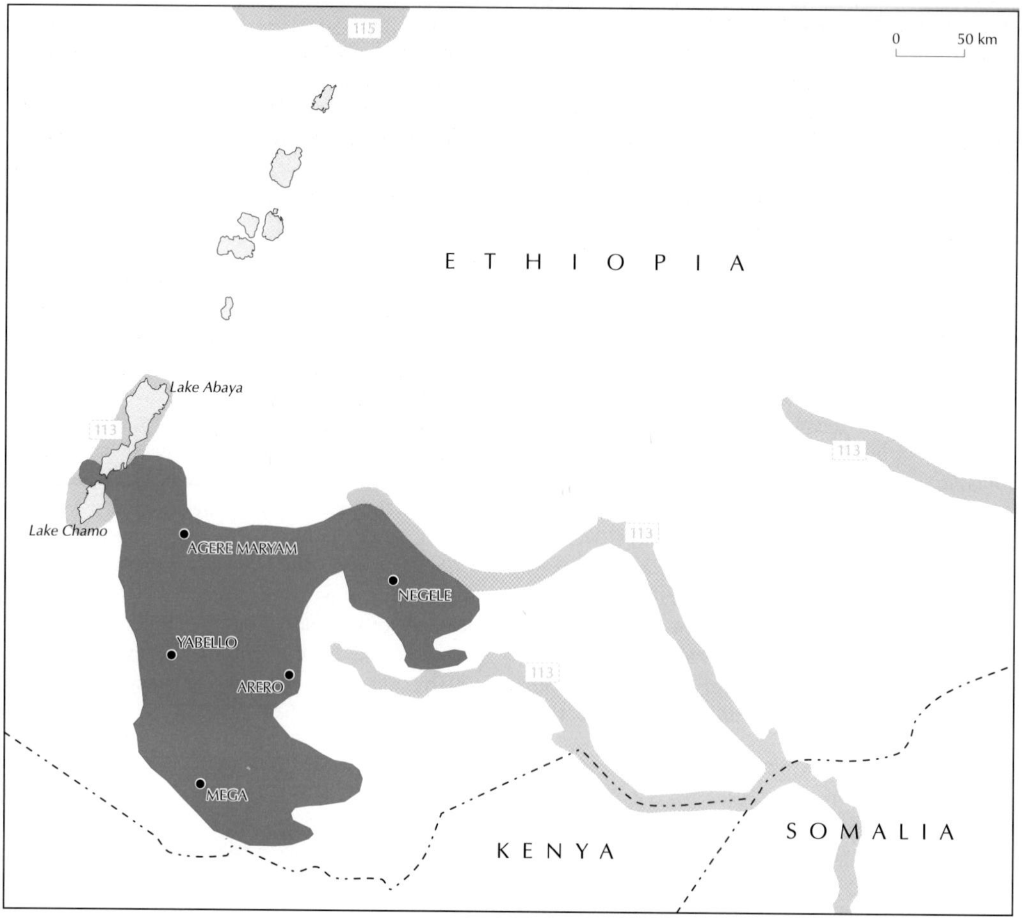

Status and habitat of restricted-range species

Species (ordered taxonomically)	Global status	Other EBAs (and SAs)	Altitude (m)	Habitat
Prince Ruspoli's Turaco *Tauraco ruspolii*	EN	—	1,100–1,860	*Podocarpus* and juniper forest, and *Acacia* woodland with figs
Nechisar Nightjar *Caprimulgus solala*[1]	NE	—	c.1,200	Short grassland
Sidamo Lark *Heteromirafra sidamoensis*	EN	—	c.1,450	Open grassland surrounded by dense scrub
White-tailed Swallow *Hirundo megaensis*	VU	—	1,000–1,700	Arid grassland with scattered low thorn bushes
Ethiopian Bush-crow *Zavattariornis stresemanni*	VU	—	1,500–2,000	Thorn scrub, short-grass savanna

Global status (see p. 679 for definitions)	EX Extinct EW Extinct in the Wild	} with year of last record	cd Conservation Dependent nt Near Threatened	**Other EBAs (and SAs)** (see p. 72 for locations)	Bracketed numbers are Secondary Areas. [X] Extinct in that EBA or SA.	
	CR Critical EN Endangered VU Vulnerable	} threatened species	lc Least Concern DD Data Deficient NE Not Evaluated	**Notes**	[1] Newly described by Safford *et al.* (1995).	

from grasslands in the vicinity of the town of Negele (Neghelli) (Robertson 1995a,b, P. O. Syvertsen *in litt.* 1993). *Tauraco ruspolii* occurs in *Podocarpus* and juniper *Juniperus* forests, and *Acacia* woodlands where figs *Ficus* are available, in the vicinity of the towns of Arero and Negele (Sørensen *et al.* 1997, Borghesio in prep.), although it may prove to have a much greater range, for example in Harenna forest in the Bale mountains well to the east (J. C. Hillman *in litt.* 1993). The recently described *Caprimulgus solala* (Safford *et al.* 1995) is included in this EBA, as the type-specimen (the only record) was found in grassland on the Nechisar plains between lakes Abaya and Chamo, a short distance to the north-west of the known ranges of the other restricted-range species. An undescribed unstreaked *Serinus* has been reported from near Agere Mariam (or Agere Maryam), c.100 km east of Lake Chamo (Ash 1979).

■ Threats and conservation

All the restricted-range species are subject to human activities modifying their habitat (J. C. Hillman *in litt.* 1993), and all are treated as threatened apart from *Caprimulgus solala*, which was described too late for consideration by Collar *et al.* (1994). A more-widespread threatened species which has been recorded in the EBA is Salvadori's Serin *Serinus xantholaema* (classified as Vulnerable). Threats to the habitats of the EBA include the conversion of grassland for dry-land agriculture, cattle-ranching leading to increased grazing pressure, the burning of forest and woodland, and commercial fuelwood cutting (J. S. Ash *in litt.* 1993, J. C. Hillman *in litt.* 1993, P. O. Syvertsen *in litt.* 1993). A military training establishment at one of the known sites for *Heteromirafra sidamoensis* has now been removed, and there is little sign of human activity there (Robertson 1995a).

The only protected area within the EBA is the large (2,540-km²) Yabello Sanctuary (IUCN 1992b), which supports populations of *Hirundo megaensis* and *Zavattariornis stresemanni*. However, it has never been gazetted and has no active management (P. O. Syvertsen *in litt.* 1994), and it coincides almost exactly with the area of a cattle-breed-improvement ranch (J. C. Hillman *in litt.* 1993).

115 Central Ethiopian highlands

PRIORITY
CRITICAL

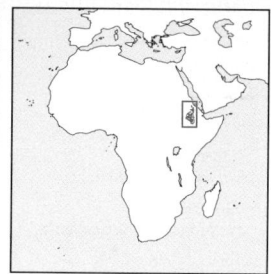

Key habitats Scrub, rocky cliffs and
ravines

Main threats Unquantified habitat
loss (e.g. due to agriculture,
fuelwood collection), hunting

Biological importance ● ● ●
Current threat level ● ● ●

Area 120,000 km²   Altitude 1,300–3,300 m

Countries Eritrea, Ethiopia

Restricted-range species	Threatened	Total
Confined to this EBA	3	4
Present also in other EBAs, SAs	0	0
Total	3	4

■ General characteristics

A total of 29 species of birds are endemic to Ethiopia
and Eritrea, including the endemic genera *Cyanochen*,
Rougetius, *Parophasma* and *Zavattariornis*. Most of
them are associated with the extensive areas of
Afromontane habitats in the Ethiopian highlands
(see White 1983), and many are too widespread to be
treated as restricted-range species. The eleven species whose ranges are estimated to be less than
50,000 km² are grouped in this EBA and the South
Ethiopian highlands (EBA 114), with single species
in the Jubba and Shabeelle valleys (EBA 113) and
Northern Ethiopia (Secondary Area s063).

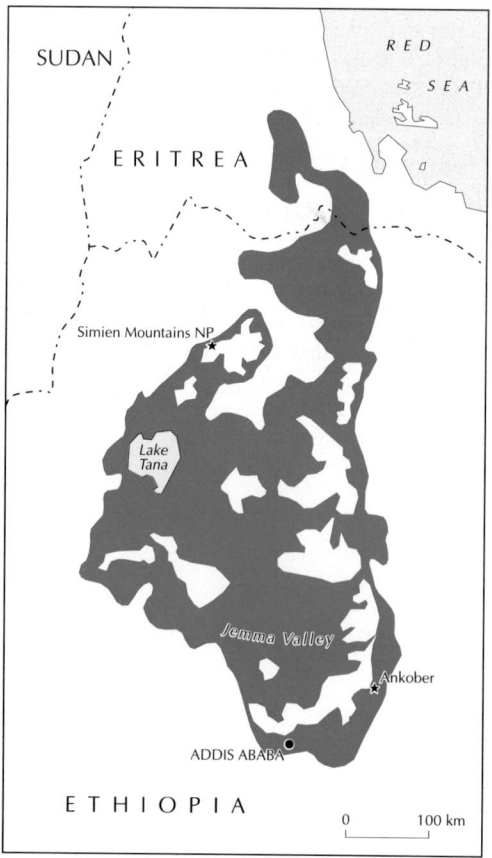

The species included in this EBA are found in a
variety of montane grassland–scrub mosaic habitats
in the central and northern parts of the highlands,
from near Addis Ababa northwards to central Eritrea.
The boundary of the EBA has been based on the
documented records and altitudinal limits of the
restricted-range bird species present.

■ Restricted-range species

The distributions and habitat requirements of the
restricted-range species are, in general, known only
poorly. Three of them are associated with sparse
vegetation in rocky areas: *Serinus ankoberensis* has
been recorded only from escarpment tops and faces
near Ankober, where it is known from just two sites
15 km apart, although there is other suitable adjoining habitat where it may occur (Atkins 1992, J.
Atkins *in litt.* 1993); *Serinus flavigula* is recorded
from an area of c.30 km² in the highlands of north-
west Shoa region, c.20 km to the east of Ankober
(Ash and Gullick 1990); *Myrmecocichla melaena* is
relatively widespread in the central and northern
highlands, and extends northwards to central Eritrea.
A survey in 1996 to assess the current status of
Francolinus harwoodi recorded it at several localities in the Jemma valley and adjacent river systems in
North Shoa administrative region, where it was
locally common, and there were local reports that its
range extends northwards into Southern Wello administrative region; it was mainly recorded in, or
close to, thorn scrub, and was rarely observed near
Typha beds which had previously been thought to be
its main habitat (Robertson *et al.* in prep.).

■ Threats and conservation

All the endemic species of the Ethiopian highlands
are under some degree of threat from habitat modification (J. C. Hillman *in litt.* 1993). Three of the
restricted-range birds are threatened, the two *Serinus*
species because of their vulnerability to habitat loss
in their tiny known ranges, and *Francolinus harwoodi*
because its thorn scrub habitat continues to be cleared
for cultivation, fuelwood and construction and to
control crop pests, and it is hunted for food (Robertson

Status and habitat of restricted-range species

Species (ordered taxonomically)	Global status	Other EBAs (and SAs)	Altitude (m)	Habitat
Harwood's Francolin *Francolinus harwoodi*	VU	—	c.1,300–1,800	Thorn scrub, fallow fields with adjacent cover
Rüppell's Chat *Myrmecocichla melaena*	lc	—	c.1,800–2,700	Waterfalls and precipitous ravines
Yellow-throated Serin *Serinus flavigula*	EN	—	c.1,350–1,500	Scattered trees interspersed with dense scrub on arid, rocky hillsides; cultivated patches
Ankober Serin *Serinus ankoberensis*	EN	—	c.2,900–3,250	Broken cliff-tops, with sheer rock-faces interspersed with steep vegetated slopes and earth banks

Global status (see p. 679 for definitions)	EX Extinct EW Extinct in the Wild	} with year of last record	CR Critical EN Endangered VU Vulnerable	} threatened species	cd Conservation Dependent nt Near Threatened lc Least Concern	DD Data Deficient NE Not Evaluated

Other EBAs (and SAs) (see p. 72 for locations): bracketed numbers are Secondary Areas; [x] extinct in that EBA or SA.

The restricted-range birds of this EBA are mainly associated with rocky cliffs and ravines.

et al. in prep.). More widespread threatened species which have been recorded in this region include White-winged Flufftail *Sarothrura ayresi* (classified as Endangered) in marshes near Addis Ababa (Atkinson *et al.* 1996), and Wattled Crane *Grus carunculatus* (Vulnerable).

The only restricted-range species recorded from a protected area in this EBA is *Myrmecocichla melaena* in Simien Mountains National Park (P. O.

Syvertsen *in litt.* 1993; see IUCN 1992b). A proposed new highland conservation area in the Termaber–Wufwasha–Ankober area would be far more relevant to the conservation of the restricted-range species, and the small-scale and dispersed relict forest conservation carried out by FARM-Africa will also benefit these birds (J. C. Hillman *in litt.* 1993).

116 North Somali mountains

Key habitats Juniper forest and scrub, rocky hillsides with sparse vegetation

Main threats Unquantified habitat loss

Biological importance ● ● ○
Current threat level ● ● ●

Area 32,000 km² **Altitude** 300–2,100 m

Countries Somalia

Restricted-range species	Threatened	Total
Confined to this EBA	3	3
Present also in other EBAs, SAs	0	0
Total	3	3

■ General characteristics

This EBA includes several isolated areas of Afromontane vegetation in the higher mountains of northern Somalia (see White 1983), and the rocky coastal escarpment of northern and north-east Somalia. Most of this region has been inacessible to ornithologists for years, and the status of the birds and their habitats are exceptionally poorly known.

■ Restricted-range species

Two of the EBA's restricted-range bird species are particularly associated with Afromontane habitats in the northern mountains of Somalia: *Turdus ludoviciae* is locally very common in mountain-top juniper *Juniperus* forest, and *Carduelis johannis* is found within juniper forest as well as in the open, rocky areas which lie adjacent to it (Ash and Miskell 1981).

Status and habitat of restricted-range species

Species (ordered taxonomically)	Global status	Other EBAs (and SAs)	Altitude (m)	Habitat
Somali Pigeon *Columba oliviae*	VU	—	Mainly 300–800	Arid, rocky maritime hills with sparse vegetation
Somali Thrush *Turdus ludoviciae*[1]	EN	—	Mountains	Juniper forest
Warsangli Linnet *Carduelis johannis*	EN	—	c.1,800–2,100	Juniper forest and scrub, open rocky grassland

Global status (see p. 679 for definitions)

EX Extinct } with year
EW Extinct in } of last
    the Wild } record
CR Critical }
EN Endangered } threatened species
VU Vulnerable }

cd Conservation Dependent
nt Near Threatened
lc Least Concern
DD Data Deficient
NE Not Evaluated

Notes

[1] Treated as a full species following Collar *et al.* (1994), but considered a subspecies of the widespread Olive Trush *Turdus olivaceus* by Ash and Miskell (1983), Sibley and Monroe (1990, 1993), Dowsett and Forbes-Watson (1993) and J. S. Ash *in litt.* (1995).

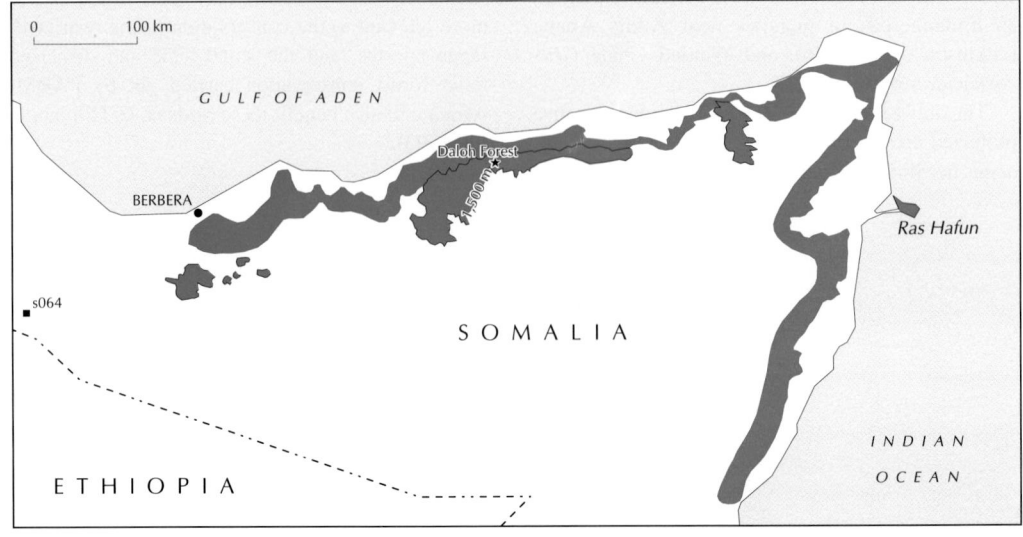

The extent of land within their altitudinal ranges is shown on the map by the 1,500-m contour, but within this area juniper forest is highly restricted and localized, and both of these species are known from no more than a handful of sites. *Columba oliviae* has a more coastal distribution, and usually occurs at relatively low altitudes along both the north and east coasts of Somalia (Ash and Miskell 1983, Collar and Stuart 1985).

Another taxon confined to Afromontane habitats in this EBA which was considered to be a full species by Sibley and Monroe (1990, 1993), Archer's Buzzard *Buteo archeri*, is here treated as a form of the widespread Augur Buzzard *B. augur*, following Dowsett and Dowsett-Lemaire (1993).

■ Threats and conservation

All three of the restricted-range species are threatened, *Columba oliviae* because its limited habitat may be under pressure and *Turdus ludoviciae* and *Carduelis johannis* because they are known only from a handful of localities where the remaining juniper forests have been degraded. It is feared that the chronic and continuing political crisis in Somalia may be causing further, but as-yet-undocumented, loss of habitat.

According to IUCN (1992b) there are no protected areas within this EBA. Daloh Forest Reserve, just north of Erigavo, is a key site for the conservation of the EBA, but there have been reports of plans to exploit and replant it (Collar and Stuart 1988).

117 Socotra

Key habitats Arid, deciduous and evergreen scrub, rocky areas

Main threats Major habitat loss (e.g. due to grazing, wood-cutting)

Biological importance ● ● ●
Current threat level ● ● ●

Area 3,500 km² **Altitude** 0–1,500 m

Countries Yemen

Restricted-range species	Threatened	Total
Confined to this EBA	3	6
Present also in other EBAs, SAs	0	0
Total	3	6

■ General characteristics

Socotra is the largest and most easterly island of an archipelago—including the Brothers (Abd al Kuri, al Ikhwan and Darsa)—administered by Yemen and located in the Indian Ocean c.190 km east of the horn of Africa and 480 km off the Arabian coast. An undulating limestone plateau (at 300–700 m) extends across much of the island, being interrupted in the north-east by the Hajhir (or Hagghier) massif which reaches 1,519 m.

Since the pioneering expeditions of the 1880s, Socotra has been renowned for botanical curiosities (e.g. the endemic tree *Dracaena cinnabari* whose resin, 'dragon's blood', has been used for dyeing since ancient times), with 28–32% of plant species being endemic (WWF/IUCN 1994). Socotra's location subjects it to a wet–dry climatic regime, and the mountains attract sufficient precipitation for the growth of evergreen bushes and scrub. The coastal plains are vegetated with semi-desert dwarf shrubs and grasses, developing into a more diverse, decidu-ous shrubland on the lower mountain slopes, on the limestone plateau and on escarpments. Some places are dominated by succulent trees (such as cucumber tree *Dendrosicyos socotranus*, the only arborescent species in the family Cucurbitaceae). Western areas are very arid.

There have been few ornithological studies on Socotra (Porter and Martins 1996), and some areas, especially those in the west, remain unexplored (Porter and Stone 1996).

■ Restricted-range species

There is some evidence that different vegetation types influence the distribution of restricted-range species on the island. *Cisticola haesitatus*, for example, favours scrub at lower altitudes, while *Onychognathus frater* prefers areas with wild fruit, and *Emberiza socotrana*, the rarest of the endemic bird species, is apparently confined to high plateaus (Al Sagheir and Porter 1996). A further 11 subspecies are endemic to the island (Martins 1996).

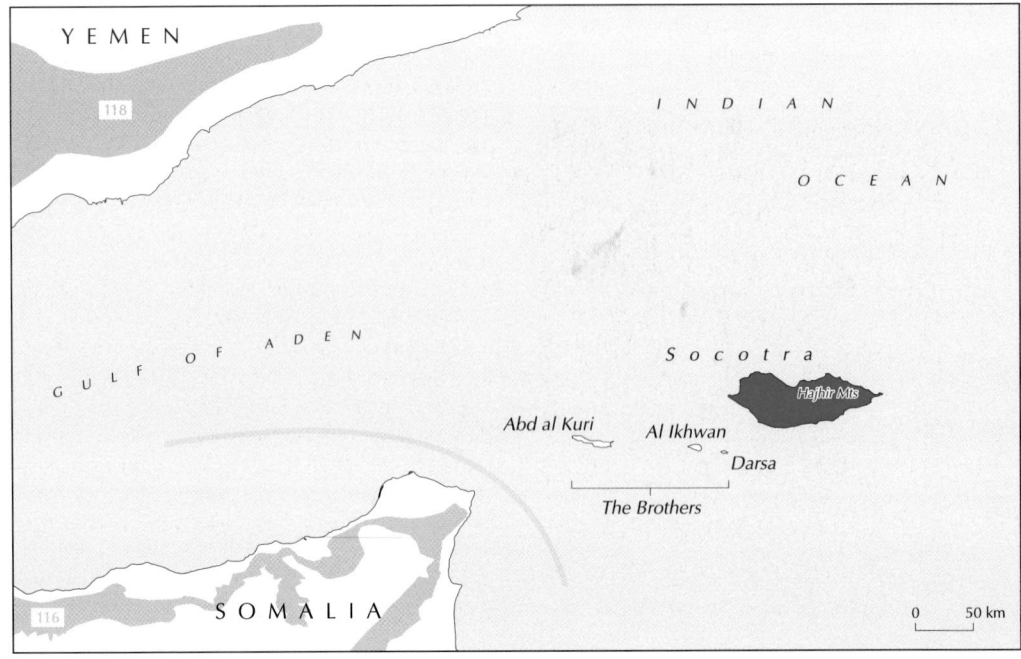

Status and habitat of restricted-range species

Species (ordered taxonomically)	Global status	Other EBAs (and SAs)	Altitude (m)	Habitat
Socotra Cisticola *Cisticola incanus*	lc	—	0–850	Coastal sand-dunes, patchy climax wood-land interspersed with dense low shrubs
Island Cisticola *Cisticola haesitatus*	VU	—	0–5	Lowland scrub, scattered bushes, grassland
Socotra Sunbird *Nectarinia balfouri*	lc	—	0–1,500	Woodland, scrub
Socotra Bunting *Emberiza socotrana*	VU	—	1,200–1,500? lower in winter?	Thickets, scrub, rock-face ledges, open slopes
Socotra Sparrow *Passer insularis*	lc	—	0–1,200+	Most habitat inc. urban and rural settlements
Socotra Starling *Onychognathus frater*	VU	—	0–1,500	Most habitats inc. lagoons, pools, plains, thickets, grassy uplands and high peaks

Global status (see p. 679 for definitions)
EX Extinct ⎫ with year
EW Extinct in ⎬ of last
      the Wild ⎭ record

CR Critical ⎫ threatened
EN Endangered ⎬ species
VU Vulnerable ⎭

cd Conservation Dependent
nt Near Threatened
lc Least Concern

DD Data Deficient
NE Not Evaluated

Other EBAs (and SAs) (see p. 72 for locations): bracketed numbers are Secondary Areas; ˣ extinct in that EBA or SA.

■ Threats and conservation

Much of the climax vegetation on Socotra has been destroyed through overgrazing (mainly by goats and, to a lesser extent, cattle) and by the cutting of wood for timber and fuel. Because wood-cutting is largely controlled sustainably by local people, the most important factor in the survival of the remaining native habitat is the density of livestock. The sinking of new wells and the construction of cisterns to hold rainwater is extending grazing areas and seasons, but drought, disease and the lack of supplementary fodder currently constrain flock sizes. There are, however, various development plans, including the building of roads and provision of port facilities, which, if implemented, could have serious environmental consequences (Evans 1994, WWF/IUCN 1994). Oil and gas exploration may also be a threat in the future (O. Al-Saghier verbally 1996).

Three restricted-range species are judged to be threatened based upon their small populations, believed to number under 1,000 individuals. Habitat loss and degradation are the most likely causes for their rarity, although *Emberiza socotrana* may also be confined to slightly moister areas through competition with Cinnamon-breasted Bunting *E. tahapisi* which is widespread in the Afrotropical region.

Egyptian Vulture *Neophron percnopterus* is a common and widespread resident with a locally significant breeding population possibly exceeding 1,000 pairs, thus making Socotra the most important breeding area for the species in the Middle East (Evans 1994). Socotra Cormorant *Phalacrocorax nigrogularis* (a Near Threatened seabird endemic within the Arabian Gulf, Arabian Sea and Gulf of Aden) occurs in small numbers as a non-breeding visitor on all islands in the Socotran archipelago.

There are currently no protected areas on Socotra although some areas are believed to be managed for their traditional resources (e.g. for bee-keeping and grazing) and there is a proposal to declare the island a Biosphere Reserve. Evans (1994) lists 19 sites as Important Bird Areas, based upon standard criteria including the presence of threatened species, regionally threatened or declining species and concentrations in significant numbers of endemic or regional populations. A biodiversity survey of the Socotran archipelago started in 1997—a joint 3-year project run by the Environment Protection Council of Yemen, BirdLife International, the Royal Botanic Gardens of Edinburgh and the University of Aden—and will result in a detailed inventory of the birds and plants of the islands. This Darwin Initiative project will work collaboratively with a larger multidisciplinary GEF-funded conservation programme which is awaiting final approval.

Socotra Sunbird *Nectarinia balfouri* is one of six bird species endemic to Socotra.

118 South-west Arabian mountains [PRIORITY HIGH]

Key habitats	Deciduous woodland and scrub, juniper forest, rocky hillsides

Area 150,000 km²   **Altitude** 1,200–3,600 m

Countries Saudi Arabia, Yemen

Main threats Moderate habitat loss (e.g. due to cultivation, grazing)

Biological importance ● ● ●
Current threat level ● ● ●

Restricted-range species	Threatened	Total
Confined to this EBA	2	7
Present also in other EBAs, SAs	0	0
Total	2	7

■ General characteristics

This EBA comprises the Asir mountains of south-west Saudi Arabia and the highlands of southern and western Yemen. In the west, just inland and east of the Red Sea and Gulf of Aden, an escarpment rises to a high plateau, which drops to the sandy Rub' al Khali (or Empty Quarter) in the interior of southern Arabia.

Formerly, large areas of the EBA were forested, but agricultural activities over millenia, including exploitation for timber, charcoal and firewood, have diminished this habitat. Patches of forest still survive in deep valleys (wadis) and on some steep slopes, and well-developed juniper *Juniperus* forest remains intact in the Asir mountains above c.1,900 m. The most widespread vegetation today is deciduous woodland, often characterized by *Acacia*, with many endemic plants (WWF/IUCN 1994).

Arabia lies at the junction of three distinct biogeographical realms: the Afrotropical to the west, the western Palearctic to the north and the Oriental to the east. The avifaunal interest of the south-western part of the peninsula has long been recognized, though there have been relatively few studies because of (until fairly recently) problems of access.

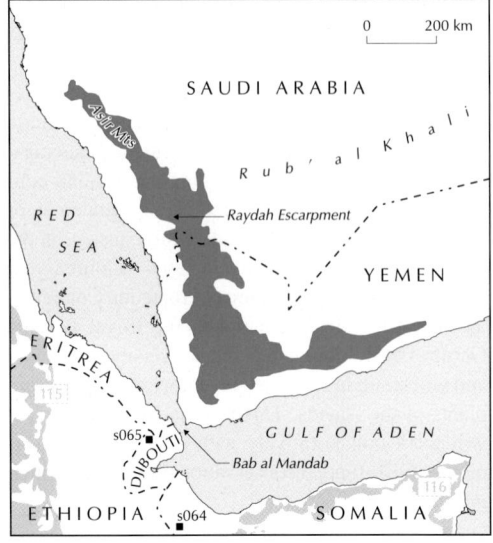

■ Restricted-range species

The restricted-ranges species occur throughout the EBA apart from *Prunella fagani*, which is confined to the Yemen highlands, and *Estrilda rufibarba*, which has not been recorded in the Asir mountains. Most are found in deciduous woodland and scrub, and can be widespread in secondary vegetation (see *Sandgrouse* 1987, 9).

Several other birds are also largely confined to this region but were judged to have ranges which exceed 50,000 km² and therefore do not qualify as restricted-range species: they include Arabian Partridge *Alectoris melanocephala*, Arabian Woodpecker *Dendrocopos dorae*, South Arabian Wheatear *Oenanthe (lugens) lugentoides*, Arabian Golden Sparrow *Passer euchlorus* (adjacent lowlands only), Arabian Warbler *Sylvia leucomelaena*, Arabian Serin *Serinus rothschildi* and Golden-winged Grosbeak *Rhynchostruthus socotranus* (see Jennings 1991).

■ Threats and conservation

During recent decades roads have improved access to the mountains and, in some areas, economic activity has shifted from agriculture to local tourism. Consequently, traditional cultivated terracing (and associated uncultivated scrub), which can provide important habitats for some birds, are deteriorating and are subject to severe soil erosion on steeper slopes; habitat is further degraded as a result of uncontrolled cutting of fuelwood and timber and overgrazing (Jennings *et al.* 1988, WWF/IUCN 1994). More insidiously, however, in many areas mature trees are currently known to suffer from die-back; this may have resulted from climate change (reduced precipitation or drought) exacerbated by a range of other biological stresses (Gardner and Fisher 1994). Both *Turdus menachensis* and *Sylvia (Parisoma) buryi* are considered threatened because they occur at low densities and are thus most at risk from continuing loss of habitat.

As well as being important for restricted-range species, the Arabian peninsula is a major flyway for migrating birds: it has been estimated that some two to three billion migrants of up to 200 species pass

Status and habitat of restricted-range species

Species (ordered taxonomically)	Global status	Other EBAs (and SAs)	Altitude (m)	Habitat
Philby's Partridge *Alectoris philbyi*	lc	—	(1,500–) 2,400+	Rocky hillsides and scrub; sometimes near cultivation
Yemen Accentor *Prunella fagani*	nt	—	Mountains, often 2,500+	Scrub in rocky mountains
Yemen Thrush *Turdus menachensis*	VU	—	1,800–2,000 (1,200–2,900)	Rocky hillsides and scrub (esp. *Acacia* and juniper); tree-lined terraces, cultivated wadis
Yemen Warbler *Sylvia buryi*	VU	—	1,700–2,800	Rocky hillsides and scrub (inc. *Acacia* and juniper); lightly wooded cultivated valleys
Yemen Serin *Serinus menachensis*	lc	—	2,000–3,200	Rocky hillsides with patches of cultivation or scrub; around villages
Yemen Linnet *Carduelis yemenensis*	lc	—	1,700–3,000	Cultivation and scattered trees, inc. *Acacia* and juniper scrub, lightly wooded slopes and wadis
Arabian Waxbill *Estrilda rufibarba*	lc	—	250–2,400	Rocky hillsides with trees, wadis, *Typha* beds, thick bushes, patches of agriculture

Global status (see p. 679 for definitions)	EX Extinct EW Extinct in the Wild	} with year of last record	CR Critical EN Endangered VU Vulnerable	} threatened species	cd Conservation Dependent nt Near Threatened lc Least Concern	DD Data Deficient NE Not Evaluated

Other EBAs (and SAs) (see p. 72 for locations): bracketed numbers are Secondary Areas; [x] extinct in that EBA or SA.

through Saudi Arabia during both spring and autumn *en route* between sub-Saharan Africa and the Palearctic; the mountains no doubt provide vital habitat for feeding and resting. The region is also an important flyway for birds of prey that cross the Red Sea at and around the Bab al Mandab, the narrowest crossing point between the peninsula and Africa (Welch and Welch 1992). Threatened passage or wintering birds include Greater Spotted Eagle *Aquila clanga*, Imperial Eagle *A. heliaca* and Lesser Kestrel *Falco naumanni*, all classified as Vulnerable. The main problem facing these raptors on migration is persecution, although definitive published evidence for this (in this EBA) appears to be lacking (Rands 1989).

The Critical—but historically widespread—Northern Bald Ibis *Geronticus eremita* has been recorded as a rare spring passage migrant and non-breeding visitor at a few sites in the EBA (in both Saudi Arabia and Yemen). The species is known to survive only at a few breeding colonies in Morocco, and the wintering of birds in this EBA suggests either that some of the birds from the extinct breeding colony in Turkey have remained in the winter quarters over several years, or that an undiscovered breeding area exists in Turkey, Oman, Ethiopia, Syria or Iraq, or even in south-west Arabia.

Within the Saudi Arabian part of the EBA there are several protected areas. One of these, Asir National Park (4,150 km², established in 1981), is actually more of an umbrella organization promoting tourism and recreation in a generally unprotected area of outstanding natural beauty. However, the special nature reserve which protects the Raydah

Most of the forest in this EBA has been replaced by terraces for cultivation, such as these near the Sumarah pass. These can provide habitat for some of the endemic birds but, once abandoned, are subject to severe erosion on the steeper slopes.

escarpment (c.12 km²) encompasses one of the best-preserved tracts of juniper forest (Newton and Newton 1996) and is possibly the most important compact site in Saudi Arabia for the endemic birds (Evans 1994). There are no protected areas in Yemen but a network of reserves has been recommended by UNEP/IUCN, and some areas—scattered throughout the western highlands and believed to be managed for their traditional resources (e.g. for bee-keeping and grazing)—offer improved habitat quality for some of the endemics. Evans (1994) identified some 25 Important Bird Areas (including the Raydah escarpment) in this EBA, and an assessment of the biological diversity of Yemen has been made by Varisco *et al.* (1992).

119 Mesopotamian marshes

PRIORITY HIGH

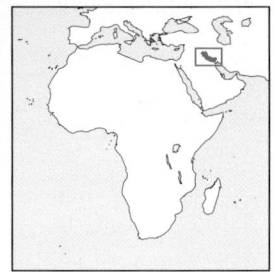

Key habitats Marshes, lakes, floodplains

Main threats Major habitat loss (e.g. due to flood control, drainage, irrigation)

Biological importance ● ● ●
Current threat level ● ● ●

Area 130,000 km²   **Altitude** 0–100 m

Countries Iran, Iraq

Restricted-range species	Threatened	Total
Confined to this EBA	2	2
Present also in other EBAs, SAs	0	0
Total	2	2

■ General characteristics

The Mesopotamian marshlands are one of the most extensive wetland ecosystems in western Eurasia. They comprise a complex of interconnected, shallow, freshwater lakes, marshes and seasonally inundated floodplains following the lower courses of the Tigris and Euphrates rivers, extending from Baghdad in the north to the Basrah region in the south. The boundaries of the EBA fall largely within Iraq but also extend into extreme south-west Iran (Khuzestan province). Throughout these wetlands, the emergent vegetation is dominated by reeds *Phragmites*, reedmace *Typha* and papyrus *Cyperus*, and there is a rich submerged flora of aquatic plants.

■ Restricted-range species

Two restricted-range species are endemic to this EBA. *Turdoides altirostris* is confined to the lower Tigris and Euphrates valleys of central and southern Iraq and extreme south-west Iran. Its distribution is centred on the reedbeds of the marshes although it also occurs in rural habitats along rivers and irrigation canals. *Acrocephalus griseldis* is a summer visitor, breeding in reedbeds between Baghdad and Basrah, and wintering in central East Africa.

A further two widespread waterbirds have subspecies which are endemic to this EBA: Little Grebe *Tachybaptus ruficollis iraquensis* and African Darter *Anhinga rufa chantrei*. Mesopotamian Crow *Corvus (corone) capellanus*, also endemic to this EBA, is a very distinct taxon within the Carrion/Hooded Crow complex, which could possibly be a good species (Madge and Burn 1993).

■ Threats and conservation

There has been considerable loss of wetland habitat in this EBA owing to large-scale projects for flood control, drainage and irrigation (Maltby 1994). Many large dams and barrages have been installed on the upper and lower Tigris and Euphrates (in Iraq and in

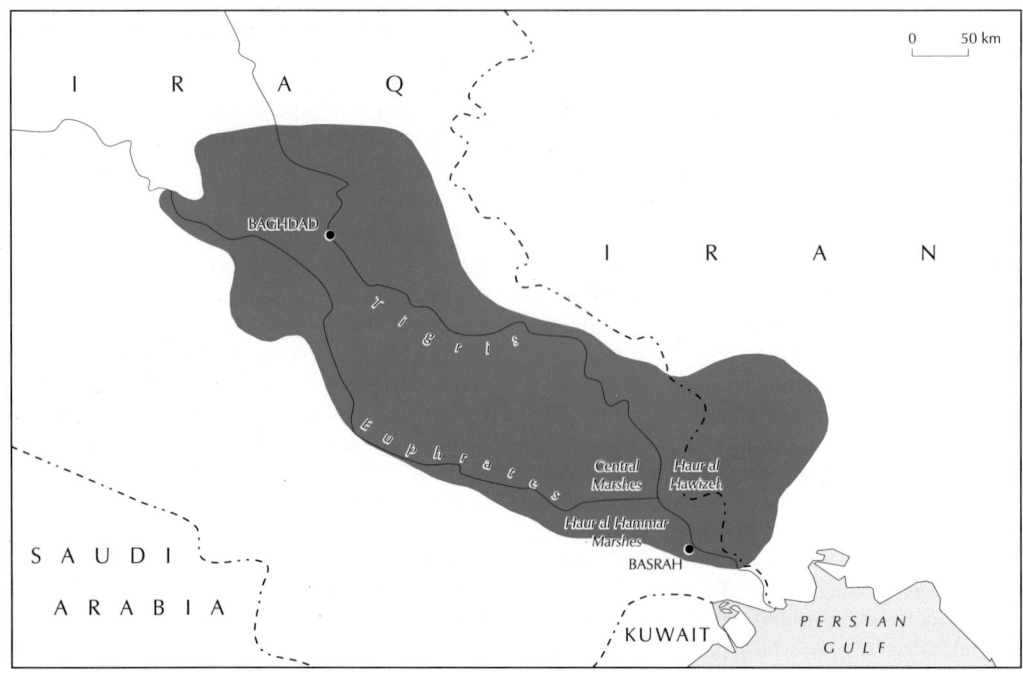

Status and habitat of restricted-range species

Species (ordered taxonomically)	Global status	Other EBAs (and SAs)	Habitat
Iraq Babbler *Turdoides altirostris*	nt	—	Reedbeds, riverine thickets, palm groves, cultivated fields, vegetation along irrigation channels
Basra Reed-warbler *Acrocephalus griseldis*	nt	—	Reedbeds

Global status (see p. 679 for definitions)	EX Extinct EW Extinct in the Wild	} with year of last record	CR Critical EN Endangered VU Vulnerable	} threatened species	cd Conservation Dependent nt Near Threatened lc Least Concern	DD Data Deficient NE Not Evaluated

Other EBAs (and SAs) (see p. 72 for locations): bracketed numbers are Secondary Areas; [X] extinct in that EBA or SA.

neighbouring Turkey and Syria), and an elaborate network of canals has been constructed for irrigation of the fertile alluvial plains between the two rivers. In addition, water from the Euphrates has been diverted away from the marshes into a huge man-made canal, the 'Third River', which discharges irrigation waste-water directly into the Gulf. These measures—together with the recent building of high embankments along both rivers and compartmentalization of the marshes with dykes—are said to have prevented water from entering up to two-thirds of the marshes during 1992–1993, and satellite images show huge areas drying up (Evans 1993, Pearce 1993).

Increasing salinity is another serious threat, owing to the continuous flushing of salts from irrigated land via the drainage canals. Wetlands have also been degraded owing to regional conflicts, such as the Iran–Iraq War (1980–1988), when much of the fighting took place in and around the Mesopotamian wetlands, resulting in extensive burning, heavy bombing and the widespread use of chemical weapons. Levels of pollution have also increased substantially through the use of insecticides (as a quick method of poisoning and catching large quantities of fish) and the introduction of motorboats. In addition, the increased settlement throughout the region, coupled with improved access, will undoubtedly have resulted in wildlife being subjected to more disturbance and higher levels of hunting and persecution.

Despite these changes, both of the endemic species are still common in the suitable habitat that remains, but they are judged to be Near Threatened because of continuing habitat loss and degradation. The region is probably extremely important also for one threatened widespread species, Marbled Teal *Marmaronetta angustirostris* (classified as Vulnerable), which has a major breeding population (perhaps thousands of pairs) within the EBA—although this population may currently be highly threatened by habitat degradation and is totally unprotected; this number is possibly more than breeds in any other single state, and the EBA may also be important for the species in winter (Green 1993).

The EBA is also one of the most important areas in western Eurasia for the wintering and staging of waterbirds (especially from western Siberia), for wintering raptors, and as a refuge for waterfowl during periods of exceptionally severe weather further north. Threatened and Near Threatened species with important populations which winter in the marshes include Dalmatian Pelican *Pelecanus crispus* (classified as Vulnerable; c.10% of the world population), Pygmy Cormorant *Phalacrocorax pygmeus* (Near Threatened; c.10% of the flyway population, current breeding status in this EBA obscure) and Imperial Eagle *Aquila heliaca* (Vulnerable; c.5–10% of the world population). In addition, Ferruginous Duck *Aythya nyroca* (Vulnerable) is a scarce winter visitor, White-tailed Eagle *Haliaeetus albicilla* (Near Threatened) is likely to winter in small numbers, Greater Spotted Eagle *Aquila clanga* (Vulnerable) is a fairly common winter visitor and Slender-billed Curlew *Numenius tenuirostris* (Critical) may also winter (only three records, but coverage by ornithologists has been poor). The marshes are also home to small and very isolated populations of two Afrotropical species (Goliath Heron *Ardea goliath* and Sacred Ibis *Threskiornis aethiopicus*) and hold a significant proportion of the world breeding populations of Grey Hypocolius *Hypocolius ampelinus* and Dead Sea Sparrow *Passer moabiticus*.

Evans (1994) has identified 12 Important Bird Areas in lower Mesopotamia as being of global and/or regional importance for bird populations. The largest and most important wetland systems within the EBA include: Haur al Hammar and its associated marshes south of the Euphrates (3,500 km²); the central marshes, a vast complex of permanent lakes and marshes north of the Euphrates and west of the Tigris (3,000 km²); and Haur al Hawizeh and its associated marshes, east of the Tigris extending into Iran (2,200 km²). These areas are currently unprotected although it has been recommended that some form of conservation area or special wetland management zone be established urgently.

120 Madeira and the Canary Islands

PRIORITY HIGH

Key habitats Laurel forest, pine forest, arid scrub, rocky areas

Main threats Major habitat loss (e.g. due to cultivation, grazing), introduced species

Biological importance ● ● ●
Current threat level ● ● ●

Area 8,000 km²   **Altitude** 0–3,700 m

Countries Portugal, Spain

Restricted-range species	Threatened	Total
Confined to this EBA	2	8
Present also in other EBAs, SAs	0	1
Total	2	9

■ General characteristics

Madeira (politically part of Portugal) and the Canary Islands (Spain) are two volcanic archipelagos in the North Atlantic, c.90 km off north-west Africa. Madeira (including the Desertas) is c.800 km² in area and reaches 1,860 m, while the Canary Islands total c.7,500 km² and rise (on Tenerife) to 3,700 m. The Selvagens (Portugal), situated between the two, are also part of the EBA.

On Madeira the characteristic vegetation is laurel forest. On the western and central Canaries laurel forest occurs at 400–1,300 m and montane *Pinus canariensis* forest at 800–1,900 m. The lower-lying and arid eastern Canaries (Fuerteventura, Lanzarote, Graciosa) are vegetated with semi-desert scrub.

■ Restricted-range species

Several of the restricted-range species are forest birds including the three endemic pigeons, which are laurel forest specialists (of the two which co-occur in the Canaries, *Columba junoniae* prefers scrubbier areas above and below major stands of laurel). *Fringilla teydea* is restricted to pine forest.

Tenerife has the greatest number of restricted-range species. Madeira and Fuerteventura each have their own endemic birds and the forested western and

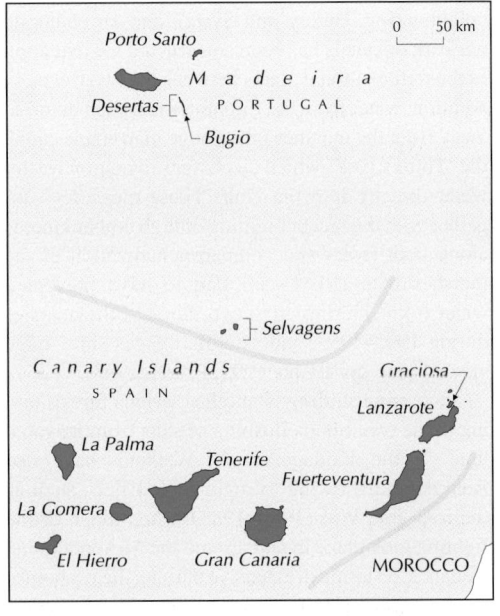

central Canary Islands support four endemics.

The islands also hold many endemic subspecies of widespread birds, notably the distinctive race *fuertaventurae* of Houbara Bustard *Chlamydotis undulata*, which is confined to the eastern Canaries.

Distribution patterns of restricted-range species

Species (ordered geographically)	Porto Santo	Madeira	Desertas	Selvagens	La Palma	El Hierro	La Gomera	Tenerife	Gran Canaria	Fuerteventura	Lanzarote	Other EBAs, SAs
Anthus berthelotii	●	●	●	●	●	●	●	●	●	●	●	–
Apus unicolor	●	●	●	–	–	●	●	●	–	●	–	–
Serinus canaria	●	●	●	–	●	●	●	●	●	–	–	●
Columba trocaz	X	●	–	–	–	–	–	–	–	–	–	–
Columba bollii	–	–	–	–	●	●	●	●	–	–	–	–
Regulus teneriffae	–	–	–	–	●	●	●	●	–	–	–	–
Columba junoniae	–	–	–	–	●	–	●	●	–	–	–	–
Fringilla teydea	–	–	–	–	–	–	–	●	●	–	–	–
Saxicola dacotiae	–	–	–	–	–	–	–	–	–	●	–	–
Haematopus meadewaldoi	–	–	–	–	–	–	–	–	–	X	X	–
Total	3	4	3	1	5	5	6	7	3	3	1	

● Present   ? Present?
O Extinct?   R Reintroduced
X Extinct   I Introduced

Threatened spp. shown in **bold**   } see 'Status and habitat' table
Other EBAs, SAs }

Status and habitat of restricted-range species

Species (ordered taxonomically)	Global status	Other EBAs (and SAs)	Habitat
Canary Islands Oystercatcher *Haematopus meadewaldoi*	EX (c.1940)	—	Rocky and sandy shorelines
Madeira Laurel Pigeon *Columba trocaz*	cd	—	Laurel forest
Dark-tailed Laurel Pigeon *Columba bollii*	VU	—	Laurel forest, sometimes heath vegetation; occasionally open degraded habitats and cultivated areas
White-tailed Laurel Pigeon *Columba junoniae*	VU	—	Laurel forest, mixed pine–laurel forest; also mixed vegetation in steep-sloped areas and deep ravines
Plain Swift *Apus unicolor*[1]	lc	—	Cliffs and caves for breeding; all habitats for feeding
Berthelot's Pipit *Anthus berthelotii*	lc	—	Sandy plains, rocky and stony areas, cultivated areas
Fuerteventura Chat *Saxicola dacotiae*	nt	—	Rocky hillsides with sparse vegetation, edges of lava flows, watercourses, cultivated areas; locally seashores
Canary Islands Kinglet *Regulus teneriffae*	lc	—	Pine forest, also tree-heath and laurel forest
Blue Chaffinch *Fringilla teydea*	cd	—	Pine forest, both natural and replanted on Tenerife
Island Canary *Serinus canaria*[2]	lc	(s069)	Forest, cultivated fields, open areas with trees or shrubs

Global status (see p. 679 for definitions)
EX Extinct ⎱ with year
EW Extinct in ⎰ of last
 the Wild ⎰ record
CR Critical ⎱ threatened
EN Endangered ⎰ species
VU Vulnerable ⎰
cd Conservation Dependent
nt Near Threatened
lc Least Concern
DD Data Deficient
NE Not Evaluated

Other EBAs (and SAs) (see p. 72 for locations)
Bracketed numbers are Secondary Areas.   ˣ Extinct in that EBA or SA.

Notes
[1] Presumed to winter in north-west Africa inc. Morocco and Mauritania.
[2] Introduced to Midway Island (north-west Hawaiian Islands) and Bermuda.

Madeira is particularly important for breeding seabirds, including Zino's Petrel *Pterodroma madeira*, an endemic breeder on Madeira itself, and Fea's Petrel *P. feae*, which nests on Bugio in the Desertas (one of a few breeding populations; see also EBA 078) (Zino and Biscoito 1994).

■ Threats and conservation

Today native forest is greatly reduced: 14% of the original area is left on Madeira (where the largest and best examples of laurel habitat remain), 10% on Tenerife and less than 1% on Gran Canaria.

On Madeira the creation of the Parque Natural da Madeira (covering almost two-thirds of the island and virtually all the remaining laurel forest) has contributed to the recovery of *Columba trocaz* (3,500–5,000 birds and increasing), along with the prohibition of hunting under the European Union Wild Birds Directive. These actions keep this species classified as Conservation Dependent rather than qualifying as threatened. Forests on Madeira nevertheless remain threatened by fire and by grazing and browsing by goats and pigs. The Parque Natural da Madeira also protects the sheer grassy cliffs where *Pterodroma madeira* breeds (Critical, probably fewer than 30 pairs; see 'Restricted-range species', above), although predation by black rats *Rattus rattus* and feral cats, and habitat degradation remain threats. The Desertas Special Protected Area protects *P. feae* (Vulnerable, 150–200 pairs nesting; see above).

In the western and central Canaries, the protection of pine forest has resulted in *Fringilla teydea* (2,000–3,000 birds) being judged as Conservation Dependent. However, inappropriate management of laurel forest, small-scale clearance (inside and outside existing protected areas), illegal hunting and introduced predators (rats and cats) continue to threaten *Columba bollii* (c.1,700) and *C. junoniae* (1,200–1,500) (Tucker and Heath 1994).

In the eastern Canaries, the continuing natural desertification of Fuerteventura, together with water extraction and grazing by goats, may damage the future prospects of *Saxicola dacotiae* (1,500–1,700 birds) (Bibby and Hill 1987). Fuerteventura and Lanzarote are important for *Chlamydotis undulata fuertaventurae* (see 'Restricted-range species' above; the most threatened of the species' three races); the entire population of this subspecies was thought to number 200–400 birds, chiefly on Fuerteventura, until a recent survey of Lanzarote and Graciosa estimated 400 birds for these islands alone (Martín *et al*. 1996). No cause is known for the disappearance of *Haematopus meadewaldoi* from the eastern Canaries, although competition from man for the intertidal invertebrates on which both once depended seems the most likely factor (Hockey 1987).

Grimmett and Jones (1989) identified over 60 Important Bird Areas in the EBA, and detailed action plans for the threatened and Conservation Dependent taxa are given in Heredia *et al*. (1996).

121 Cyprus

PRIORITY HIGH

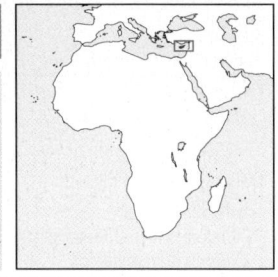

Key habitats Pine and oak forest, mediterranean scrub (maquis)

Main threats Major habitat loss (e.g. due to cultivation, grazing, tourism, fire), hunting

Biological importance ● ● ●
Current threat level ● ● ●

Area 9,300 km²   **Altitude** 0–1,800 m

Countries Cyprus

Restricted-range species	Threatened	Total
Confined to this EBA	0	2
Present also in other EBAs, SAs	0	0
Total	0	2

■ General characteristics

This EBA covers the island of Cyprus (today divided politically between Greece and Turkey) which lies in the north-east of the Mediterranean basin, c.100 km south of Turkey and c.170 km west of Syria. The island is occupied by two mountain ranges—the Troodos in the south and west, and the Kyrenia along the north coast—which were once largely forested, mainly with pine *Pinus* and oak *Quercus*. Lowlands and hills were covered with xerophytic shrubs form-ing a low maquis (a plant assemblage typical of the Mediterranean region), while high maquis occurred mainly in the east or on coastal promontories.

■ Restricted-range species

The two restricted-range species occur in a wide variety of habitats, with *Sylvia melanothorax* being absent when breeding from the drier central plain, favouring *Cistus* scrub mainly in the Troodos mountains. Both species are migrants: *Oenanthe cypriaca*

Status and habitat of restricted-range species

Species (ordered taxonomically)	Global status	Other EBAs (and SAs)	Altitude (m)	Habitat
Cyprus Wheatear *Oenanthe cypriaca*	lc	—	All (prefers hills to c.1,800	Rough open ground with scattered trees, pine forest, plantations, cultivation, areas around houses and gardens
Cyprus Warbler *Sylvia melanothorax*	lc	—	Lowland to c.1,400	Low maquis, open areas within pine forest, oak forest, forest edges, citrus and other orchards

Global status (see p. 679 for definitions) EX Extinct / EW Extinct in the Wild } with year of last record   CR Critical / EN Endangered / VU Vulnerable } threatened species   cd Conservation Dependent / nt Near Threatened / lc Least Concern   DD Data Deficient / NE Not Evaluated

Other EBAs (and SAs) (see p. 72 for locations): bracketed numbers are Secondary Areas; ˣ extinct in that EBA or SA.

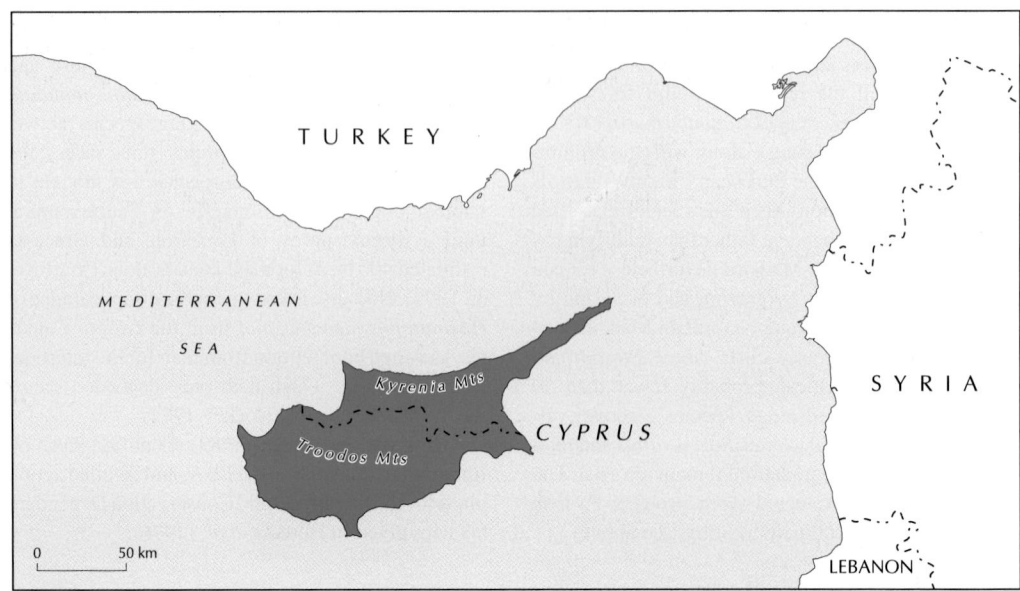

Shooting, liming and netting remain serious threats to the birds of Cyprus, particularly those on migration. Here local people watch and photograph instead.

T. Salathé/BirdLife International

(only recently recognized as a distinct species) to southern Sudan and Ethiopia, and *S. melanothorax* partially to Lebanon, Israel, Egypt and northern Sudan. A further five endemic subspecies have been recognized (more by some authorities), emphasizing the distinct nature of this island's avifauna (see Flint 1995).

■ Threats and conservation

Clearance over many centuries (c.50% of the island is classed as farmland) and unrestricted grazing by goats have destroyed much of Cyprus's original vegetation. There is no evidence that any woodland species have been lost as a result of deforestation, but in view of the greatly reduced habitat, the loss of species does seem very probable. It also seems likely that the distribution of some woodland species which are now confined to the forests of the Troodos range (the Paphos forest in particular) was more general in the past (Flint and Stewart 1983). Today the greatest threat to the habitat comes from increased tourism, with the construction of associated facilities, and the risk of fire during the dry summer months (WWF/IUCN 1994). The two restricted-range species, however, remain common (3,000–7,000 pairs for *Oenanthe cypriaca*, more than 4,000 pairs for *Sylvia melanothorax*) and widespread throughout the island, and are not considered to be globally threatened, although both are treated by Tucker and Heath (1994) as Species of European Conservation Concern with an unfavourable conservation status.

Hunting is a particularly serious conservation problem on Cyprus, and it is likely that shooting has contributed to the extinction of at least two species of breeding bird: Dipper *Cinclus cinclus* (the endemic race *olympicus*) and the threatened Lesser Kestrel *Falco naumanni*, as well as causing a decline in numbers of many other resident species, especially raptors such as the threatened Imperial Eagle *Aquila heliaca* (Vulnerable; only 2–4 pairs now remaining).

Cyprus's geographical location relative to the western Palearctic and Africa results in some 200 species occurring as regular passage migrants, and many of these are subject to shooting, liming and netting. Although the island's hunting regulations are fairly comprehensive, the enforcement of the laws is inadequate and thousands of birds of many species are illegally killed each year. Threatened species which occur on migration include Ferruginous Duck *Aythya nyroca*, White-headed Duck *Oxyura leucocephala* and *F. naumanni* (all classified as Vulnerable).

Audouin's Gull *Larus audouinii*, classified as Conservation Dependent, is a seabird which has a small breeding population of 10–20 pairs.

Grimmett and Jones (1989) recognized a total of 17 Important Bird Areas on Cyprus. These include several sites which harbour the two restricted-range species, as well as sites for breeding birds of prey, and wetlands which are important for passage and wintering birds.

122 Caucasus

Key habitats Subalpine and alpine meadows, montane steppe, coniferous and broadleaf forest

Main threats Major habitat loss (e.g. due to logging, pasture, grazing)

Biological importance ● ● ●
Current threat level ● ● ●

Area 170,000 km²   **Altitude** 1,200–4,000 m
Countries Armenia, Azerbaijan, Georgia, Iran, Turkey, Russia

Restricted-range species	Threatened	Total
Confined to this EBA	0	3
Present also in other EBAs, SAs	0	0
Total	0	3

■ General characteristics

This mountainous EBA lies between the Black and Caspian Seas, extending from the southern Russian Federation, through Georgia and Armenia into north-west Iran, and including north-east Turkey and northern and western Azerbaijan. Several mountain ranges are included but the EBA is largely defined by the Greater Caucasus (reaching 5,600 m) and, to the south, the Lesser Caucasus (4,095 m). These mountains support a diverse variety of vegetation types including broadleaved and coniferous forests, montane steppe and woodlands, subalpine and alpine meadows and semi-desert vegetation.

■ Restricted-range species

The subalpine and alpine zones are used by all the restricted-range species. Forested habitats close to the treeline are important for *Phylloscopus lorenzii*, a species which is sometimes considered to be conspecific with the widespread Mountain Chiffchaff *P. sindianus* of south-west Asia; this view was followed (e.g.) by Sibley and Monroe (1990), but the taxon was subsequently given full species status in Sibley and Monroe (1993) and this treatment is followed here. *P. lorenzii* breeds in the western Greater Caucasus, most of the Lesser Caucasus and

adjacent parts of north-east Turkey, and, in winter, disperses south as far as Iraq.

■ Threats and conservation

Habitat loss and deterioration is a major threat in this EBA, with some 50% of forests in the Greater Caucasus being subject to logging, 40% of the subalpine meadows suffering from overgrazing, and semi-desert areas being used as winter pastures for sheep-grazing (WWF/IUCN 1994). Nevertheless none of the restricted-range birds is considered globally threatened as the remoteness of much of the habitat gives natural protection to many areas. *Tetrao mlokosiewiczi* is, however, judged to be Near Threatened and is treated by Tucker and Heath (1994) as a Species of European Conservation Concern with an unfavourable conservation status. Although the population of *T. mlokosiewiczi* is numerically strong (c.70,000 birds in the Greater Caucasus and c.500 in the Lesser Caucasus), since the 1930s a slow decline in numbers and some local reductions in range have been detected (chiefly in the southern parts of its range), owing to the deterioration in the suitability of the alpine meadows through overgrazing. Unfortunately there appear to be no data for the last decade because of political unrest in the region.

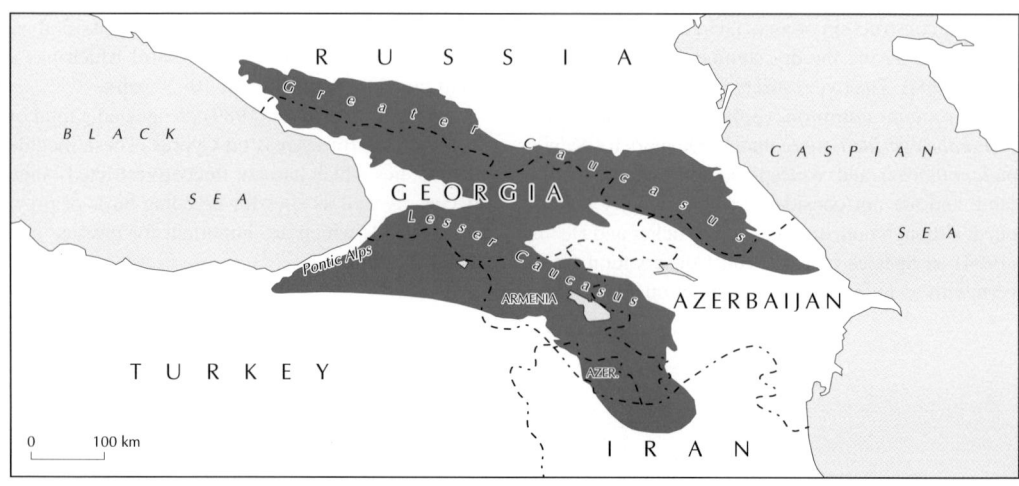

Status and habitat of restricted-range species

Species (ordered taxonomically)	Global status	Other EBAs (and SAs)	Altitude (m)	Habitat
Caucasian Grouse *Tetrao mlokosiewiczi*	nt	—	1,700–3,300, lower in winter	Subalpine and alpine meadows, slopes with *Rhododendron* and juniper *Juniperus*; birch forest edge in spring and winter
Caucasian Snowcock *Tetraogallus caucasicus*	lc	—	2,200–4,000, lower in winter	Subalpine and alpine meadows, stony slopes with sparse vegetation
Caucasian Chiffchaff *Phylloscopus lorenzii*	lc	—	1,800–2,400 (1,200–2,600)	Coniferous and mixed forest (mainly close to treeline), subalpine bush (mainly *Rhododendron*)

Global status (see p. 679 for definitions)
EX	Extinct	with year of last record	CR	Critical	threatened species	cd	Conservation Dependent	DD Data Deficient
EW	Extinct in the Wild		EN	Endangered		nt	Near Threatened	NE Not Evaluated
			VU	Vulnerable		lc	Least Concern	

Other EBAs (and SAs) (see p. 72 for locations): bracketed numbers are Secondary Areas; ˣ extinct in that EBA or SA.

As well as being important for its restricted-range species, this EBA holds significant breeding populations of raptors (including Lammergeier *Gypaetus barbatus*, Griffon Vulture *Gyps fulvus* and Cinereous Vulture *Aegypius monachus*), and vast numbers also migrate through the area. The Caucasus is also important for supporting the most northerly populations of Caspian Snowcock *Tetraogallus caspius* and Radde's Accentor *Prunella ocularis*, the most easterly ones of Krüper's Nuthatch *Sitta krueperi*, Firecrest *Regulus ignicapillus* and Short-toed Treecreeper *Certhia brachydactyla*, and most westerly ones of Güldenstädt's Redstart *Phoenicurus erythrogaster* and Great Rosefinch *Carpodacus rubicilla* (R. Potapov *in litt.* 1996). All these species are treated as Species of European Conservation Concern by Tucker and Heath (1994).

Several Important Bird Areas (IBAs) have been identified for the region (Grimmett and Jones 1989, Magnin and Yarar 1997), and key reserves for *Tetrao mlokosiewiczi* are listed in Tucker and Heath (1994).

The Pontic Alps IBA (12,300 km²) in the Little Caucasus of north-east Turkey covers the Turkish distribution of *T. mlokosiewiczi*. Overall, some 2% of the Caucasus is protected in c.40 nature reserves, but this network of protected areas needs to be substantially expanded, and existing nature reserves require improved management including the control of grazing levels, disturbance to breeding birds and illegal hunting; it is also necessary to implement wide-scale measures to reduce overgrazing and disturbance throughout the region (Tucker and Heath 1994). In the Turkish part of the EBA there are plans for large dams and virtually every stream in the area has been subject to development plans; large-scale water manipulation schemes could have far-reaching consequences for the natural habitats through flooding, climate change, access roads and construction. In addition, there is already much mining activity (e.g. for copper), and pollution in the vicinity of some of these mines is a major problem (Magnin and Yarar 1997).

123 Western Ghats

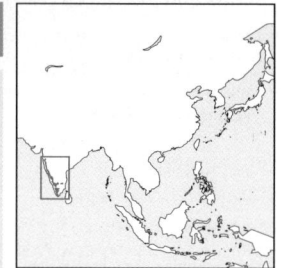

Key habitats Lowland evergreen rain forest, montane evergreen forest, montane grassland

Main threats Major habitat loss (e.g. due to agriculture, overgrazing)

Biological importance ● ● ●
Current threat level ● ● ●

Area 61,000 km²   **Altitude** 0–2,600 m

Countries India

Restricted-range species	Threatened	Total
Confined to this EBA	0	16
Present also in other EBAs, SAs	0	0
Total	0	16

■ General characteristics

The Western Ghats are ranges of hills along the western edge of the Deccan plateau in peninsular India. The EBA extends along the Ghats from just north of Bombay south to the tip of the peninsula, in the states of Maharashtra, Goa, Karnataka, Kerala and Tamil Nadu, although a few of the restricted-range species present are also recorded from disjunct localities in the hills to the east, in northern Tamil Nadu and southern Andhra Pradesh.

The Western Ghats receive heavy monsoon rainfall, and tropical lowland evergreen rain forest formerly occurred in areas of highest rainfall along virtually their entire length—but most forests of this type have been cleared in the north of the EBA (Champion 1936). The evergreen rain forests are bordered by narrow strips of tropical semi-evergreen rain forest. Tropical moist deciduous forest is found where rainfall is lower and more seasonal, mainly in a narrow belt on the eastern side of the Ghats. In the higher hills in the south of the EBA, wet temperate forest is found above c.1,500 m, an evergreen forest type which is usually found in patches ('sholas') in the more sheltered sites on rolling montane grassland, and subtropical broadleaf hill forest is found at c.1,000–1,700 m (Champion and Seth 1968, Whit-

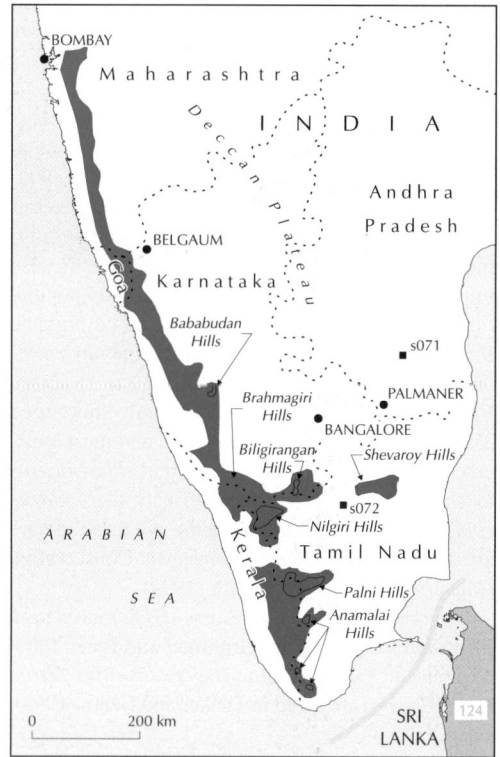

S. Butchart

Upland grassland and montane Shola forest at Muthukhuzhi in the Western Ghats—the key habitats for seven of the restricted-range species in this EBA.

Status and habitat of restricted-range species

Species (ordered taxonomically)	Global status	Other EBAs (and SAs)	Altitude (m)	Habitat
Nilgiri Wood-pigeon *Columba elphinstonii*	nt	—	Foothills to 2,100	Evergreen forest, montane shola, occasionally moist deciduous forest
Malabar Parakeet *Psittacula columboides*	lc	—	Foothills to 1,500	Evergreen forest, abandoned plantations, moist deciduous forest
Malabar Grey-hornbill *Ocyceros griseus*	nt	—	Foothills to 1,600	Open evergreen forest, moist deciduous forest
Nilgiri Pipit *Anthus nilghiriensis*	lc	—	1,000–2,600	Open grassland
Grey-headed Bulbul *Pycnonotus priocephalus*	nt	—	Lowlands to 1,200	Evergreen forest; swampy areas with cane brakes, thickets or reeds and bamboo
White-bellied Shortwing *Brachypteryx major*	nt	—	900–2,500	Evergreen forest, montane shola
Wynaad Laughingthrush *Garrulax delesserti*	nt	—	Foothills to 1,500	Evergreen forest, cane brakes, *Strobilanthes* undergrowth
Rufous-breasted Laughingthrush *Garrulax cachinnans*	nt	—	1,200–2,600	Evergreen forest, montane shola, scrub, gardens
Grey-breasted Laughingthrush *Garrulax jerdoni*	nt	—	1,100–2,150	Evergreen forest edge, montane shola, *Rubus* thickets, scrub, occasionally gardens
Rufous Babbler *Turdoides subrufus*	lc	—	Foothills to 1,200	Dense scrub, tall grass and bamboo brakes, evergreen and moist deciduous forest edge
Broad-tailed Grassbird *Schoenicola platyura*	nt	—	900–2,000	Tall grassland and bracken on hillsides, reeds and grass in marshy depressions, near streams
Black-and-rufous Flycatcher *Ficedula nigrorufa*	nt	—	(700–) 1,500–2,600	Undergrowth in evergreen forest, montane shola, plantations; occasionally moist deciduous forest
Nilgiri Flycatcher *Eumyias albicaudata*	nt	—	(600–) 1,200–2,600	Evergreen forest, montane shola, cardamom plantations, occasionally gardens
White-bellied Blue-flycatcher *Cyornis pallipes*	nt	—	Foothills to 1,500+	Undergrowth in evergreen forest, moist deciduous forest
Crimson-backed Sunbird *Nectarinia minima*	lc	—	Foothills to 2,100	Evergreen forest, moist deciduous forest, shade trees in plantations, gardens
White-bellied Treepie *Dendrocitta leucogastra*	nt	—	Lowlands to 1,500	Evergreen forest, moist deciduous forest, abandoned plantations

Global status (see p. 679 for definitions)	EX Extinct EW Extinct in the Wild	with year of last record	CR Critical EN Endangered VU Vulnerable	threatened species	cd Conservation Dependent nt Near Threatened lc Least Concern	DD Data Deficient NE Not Evaluated

Other EBAs (and SAs) (see p. 77 for locations): bracketed numbers are Secondary Areas; ˣ extinct in that EBA or SA.

more 1984, Pascal 1988). The approximate lower limit of these montane forest types is represented on the map by the 1,000 m contour.

■ Restricted-range species

Seven of the restricted-range bird species are found between sea-level and c.1,500 m, and they are particularly associated with evergreen and semi-evergreen rain forest, although most also occur in moist deciduous forest and subtropical hill forest (see 'Habitat associations' table). Of these seven species, five are found along the entire length of the Ghats, but two—*Garrulax delesserti* and *Dendrocitta leucogastra*—have not been recorded from north of Goa. *D. leucogastra* is known also from two disjunct localities to the east of the Ghats outside the EBA—Bangalore and Palmaner (Ali and Ripley 1987).

Habitat associations of restricted-range species

Lowland and mid-elevation forest	Montane forest
Psittacula columboides	*Brachypteryx major*
Ocyceros griseus	*Garrulax cachinnans*
Pycnonotus priocephalus	*Garrulax jerdoni*
Garrulax delesserti	*Ficedula nigrorufa*
Turdoides subrufus	*Eumyias albicaudata*
Cyornis pallipes	
Dendrocitta leucogastra	**Montane grassland**
	Anthus nilghiriensis
Lowland and montane forest	*Schoenicola platyura*
Columba elphinstonii	
Nectarinia minima	

Threatened species (Critical, Endangered, Vulnerable) are shown in **bold**; see 'Status and habitat' table.

Turdoides subrufus also occurs east of the Ghats, in the Shevaroy hills.

Five of the restricted-range species are particularly associated with wet temperate sholas and subtropical broadleaf hill forest, in the Bababudan, Brahmagiri, Biligirangan, Nilgiri, Palni and Anamalai hills, and *Garrulax jerdoni* is also recorded further north in Goa (Rane 1984). One of these species, *G. cachinnans*, is restricted to just the Nilgiri hills, where it replaces the more widespread *G. jerdoni*. *Anthus nilghiriensis* and *Schoenicola platyura* are found in the montane grassland on the higher southern ranges (*S. platyura* is also known from a nineteenth-century record further north near Belgaum: MacGregor 1887). In the southern part of the EBA, the lowland and montane forest groups of birds overlap at c.1,000–1,500 m. *Columba elphinstonii* and *Nectarinia minima* range along the entire length of the Ghats and are found from the lowlands to high altitudes.

■ Threats and conservation

The main threat is habitat loss and degradation. The lowland evergreen and semi-evergreen rain forests probably once extended onto the coastal plain to the west of the Ghats, but almost all forest below 500 m has long been cleared. The remaining forests face a number of pressures, as increasing human population has led to increased illegal encroachment into forest lands, livestock-grazing, and the harvesting of fuelwood and huge quantities of minor forest products such as bamboo and canes. The steep western slopes of the Ghats are ideal for generating hydroelectric power, and dams are flooding large areas of valley forest and leading to developments such as new access roads which are increasing encroachment into the forest. The high-altitude shola grasslands have traditionally been burnt annually by nomadic graziers, which has probably much reduced the extent of wet temperate forest sholas, but these grasslands continue to be converted to plantations of tea, eucalyptus and wattle *Acacia dealbata* (Champion 1936, Collins *et al.* 1991, V. J. Zacharias *in litt.* 1993, L. Vijayan *in litt.* 1996).

There is a network of c.40 protected areas in the Western Ghats, many of which include extensive areas of the EBA's characteristic habitats (MacKinnon and MacKinnon 1986, IUCN 1992c). They are located along the entire length of the Ghats, and support populations of all of the restricted-range birds. The protection which they afford to the remaining forest and grassland is the main reason that none of the restricted-range species is currently considered threatened. The threatened Kashmir Flycatcher *Ficedula subrubra* breeds in the Western Himalayas (EBA 128) and winters in montane forest in this EBA and Sri Lanka (EBA 124).

124 Sri Lanka

PRIORITY
URGENT

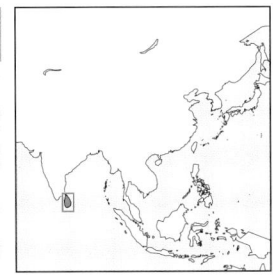

Key habitats Lowland and dry evergreen rain forest, montane forest

Main threats Major habitat loss (e.g. due to agriculture, fuelwood collection, afforestation)

Biological importance ●
Current threat level ● ●

Area 66,000 km² **Altitude** 0–2,400 m

Countries Sri Lanka

Restricted-range species	Threatened	Total
Confined to this EBA	6	23
Present also in other EBAs, SAs	0	0
Total	6	23

■ General characteristics

The climate and vegetation of Sri Lanka are greatly influenced by the ranges of mountains which rise to 2,518 m in the south of the island. The south-western quarter of the island receives very heavy rainfall, and the natural vegetation below c.900 m is tropical lowland evergreen rain forest, although much of this has now been cleared. Tropical montane rain forest occurs above this altitude, with areas of wet temperate forest and montane grassland at the greatest heights. This part of the island is often referred to as the wet zone (including the montane habitats, which are sometimes described separately as the hill zone) and most of the remainder of the island as the dry zone. There is also an intermediate zone between the wet and dry zones, formed by a band of tropical semi-evergreen rain forest which bounds the tropical evergreen rain forest block in the south-west. The dry zone receives lower, more seasonal rainfall, and the vegetation here includes monsoon forest (principally tropical dry evergreen forest) and the savannas and grasslands which are derived from them by clearance and repeated burning (Champion and Seth 1968, Crusz 1984, Ratnapala 1984, Whitmore 1984).

■ Restricted-range species

Twenty-three restricted-range species are confined to this EBA, more than any other EBA in this region. All are forest birds, but they can be subdivided into several groups with distinct habitat requirements. Two species are confined to the lowland evergreen rain forests of the wet zone below c.900 m, and six to the montane habitats of the hill zone above this altitude. A further six species are confined to the rain forests of the wet zone (including the hill zone) in the

INDIA

SRI LANKA

D r y Z o n e

Intermediate Zone

Intermediate Zone

W e t Z o n e · Hill Zone

COLOMBO ● Horton Plains ★ ★ Hakgala
Peak Wilderness ★ 900 m

★ Uda Walawe

Sinharaja ★

0   50 km

Habitat associations of restricted-range species

Lowland evergreen rain forest (wet zone)
Centropus chlororhynchus
Dicaeum vincens

Montane forest (hill zone)
Columba torringtoni
Pycnonotus penicillatus
Myiophonus blighi
Bradypterus palliseri
Eumyias sordida
Zosterops ceylonensis

Lowland evergreen forest and montane forest (wet and hill zones)
Glaucidium castanonotum
Garrulax cinereifrons

Turdoides rufescens
Sturnus albofrontatus
Gracula ptilogenys
Urocissa ornata

All forest types (all zones[1])
Galloperdix bicalcarata[1]
Gallus lafayetii
Loriculus beryllinus[1]
Psittacula calthropae[1]
Phaenicophaeus pyrrhocephalus[1]
Ocyceros gingalensis
Megalaima flavifrons[1]
Zoothera spiloptera[1]
Pellorneum fuscocapillum

Threatened species (Critical, Endangered, Vulnerable) are shown in **bold**; see 'Status and habitat' table.

[1] Localized in distribution outside the wet and hill zones, being largely confined to semi-evergreen rain forests of the intermediate zone and riverine forest in the dry zone (S. Kotagama, p. xxxi in Legge 1983).

Status and habitat of restricted-range species

Species (ordered taxonomically)	Global status	Other EBAs (and SAs)	Altitude (m)	Habitat
Sri Lanka Spurfowl *Galloperdix bicalcarata*	lc	—	Lowlands to 2,100	Tall rain forest, copses, plantation edge
Sri Lanka Junglefowl *Gallus lafayetii*	lc	—	Lowlands to 2,400	All forest types, scrub, tea plantations gardens
Sri Lanka Wood-pigeon *Columba torringtoni*	VU	—	(300–) 1,000–2,100	Evergreen forest, copses, plantations, village
Sri Lanka Hanging-parrot *Loriculus beryllinus*	lc	—	0–1,300	Open evergreen forest, plantations, agricultural areas, village gardens
Layard's Parakeet *Psittacula calthropae*	lc	—	0–1,800	Forest, forest edge and clearings, fruiting trees
Red-faced Malkoha [1] *Phaenicophaeus pyrrhocephalus*	VU	—	0–1,700	Tall evergreen forest, in the dry zone largely confined to riverine forest
Green-billed Coucal *Centropus chlororhynchus*	EN	—	0–800	Rain forest with dense undergrowth, particularly of bamboo and rattan in disturbed areas
Chestnut-backed Owlet *Glaucidium castanonotum*	nt	—	Foothills to 1,950	Evergreen forest
Sri Lanka Grey-hornbill *Ocyceros gingalensis*	lc	—	Lowlands to 1,200(–2,000)	All lowland forest types
Yellow-fronted Barbet *Megalaima flavifrons*	lc	—	Lowlands to 2,000	Forest, fruiting trees, agricultural land
Yellow-eared Bulbul *Pycnonotus penicillatus*	nt	—	900–2,300	Forest, scrub, fruiting trees, well-wooded gardens
Sri Lanka Whistling-thrush *Myiophonus blighi*	EN	—	1,300–2,300	Fast-flowing mountain streams in fern-clad ravines and gorges running through dense, damp forest
Spot-winged Thrush *Zoothera spiloptera*	nt	—	Lowlands to 1,500	Forest undergrowth, copses, plantations; scarce in dry zone
Ashy-headed Laughingthrush *Garrulax cinereifrons*	VU	—	Lowlands to 1,200	Tall evergreen forest
Brown-capped Babbler *Pellorneum fuscocapillum*	lc	—	Lowlands to 1,650	Forest, scrub, tea plantations
Orange-billed Babbler *Turdoides rufescens*	lc	—	Lowlands to 2,100	Rain forest, thickets, scrub, bamboo
Sri Lanka Bush-warbler *Bradypterus palliseri*	nt	—	900–2,400	Undergrowth in damp forest, scrub
Dull-blue Flycatcher *Eumyias sordida*	nt	—	(450–) 900–2,100	Forest, well-wooded ravines, plantations, gardens
White-throated Flowerpecker *Dicaeum vincens*	nt	—	Lowlands to 900	Tall rain forest, flowering trees, plantations, gardens
Sri Lanka White-eye *Zosterops ceylonensis*	lc	—	(450–) 900–2,100	Forest, scrub, plantations, gardens
White-faced Starling *Sturnus albofrontatus* [2]	nt	—	Foothills to 1,300	Tall forest, fruiting trees, clearings
Sri Lanka Myna *Gracula ptilogenys*	lc	—	Lowlands to 2,100	Tall rain forest, fruiting trees, village gardens
Sri Lanka Magpie *Urocissa ornata*	VU	—	Lowlands to 2,100	Evergreen forest

Global status (see p. 679 for definitions)

EX Extinct } with year of last record
EW Extinct in the Wild

CR Critical
EN Endangered } threatened species
VU Vulnerable

cd Conservation Dependent
nt Near Threatened
lc Least Concern
DD Data Deficient
NE Not Evaluated

Other EBAs (and SAs) (see p. 77 for locations)
Bracketed numbers are Secondary Areas.   ˣ Extinct in that EBA or SA.

Notes
[1] Unconfirmed sight records from southern Kerala and Tamil Nadu in peninsular India (Ali and Ripley 1987).

[2] Generally known as *Sturnus senex*, but correct nomenclature recently clarified by Mees (1997).

C. Rose

Red-faced Malkoha *Phaenicophaeus pyrrhocephalus* requires tall evergreen forest, and has declined because of the loss and degradation of its habitat.

lowlands and the mountains, although *Garrulax cinereifrons* is mainly found in the lowlands and *Sturnus albofrontatus* at intermediate altitudes in the foothills. The remaining nine species are more widespread, although only three of them occur widely in the dry zone. Outside the wet zone, the other six appear to range only into the semi-evergreen forests of the intermediate zone and riverine forests in the dry zone (S. Kotagama, p. xxxi in Legge 1983). The lowland rain forests and montane forests in the southwest of Sri Lanka are therefore by far the most important habitats of the EBA.

■ Threats and conservation

Sri Lanka has suffered rapid forest loss and degradation in the past 40 years, largely to meet the demands of an expanding population. The major causes of

deforestation include the gathering of fuelwood, clearance of forest for permanent agriculture, shifting cultivation, replacement of natural forest by tree plantations, fire, urbanization and timber felling. Natural closed-canopy forest is estimated to have declined in extent from 29,000 km^2 (44% of the island's land area) in 1956 to 12,260 km^2 in 1983, of which only 1,440 km^2 was rain forest (Collins *et al.* 1991). It is feared that the forest loss will continue, as the existing forest conservation laws have proved to be ineffective, and emergency regulations have had to be declared to halt illegal logging (Anon. 1992b).

Many of the island's restricted-range birds are adaptable to man-modified habitats and remain common. Six species, however, are listed as threatened because they appear to be confined to closed-canopy forests and are therefore vulnerable to forest loss within their small ranges. Another threatened restricted-range species, Kashmir Flycatcher *Ficedula subrubra*, breeds in the Western Himalayas (EBA 128) and winters in montane forest in Sri Lanka and the Western Ghats (EBA 123). More widespread threatened species which occur on Sri Lanka are Spot-billed Pelican *Pelecanus philippensis* and Lesser Adjutant *Leptoptilos javanicus* (both classified as Vulnerable), wetland birds which do not occur in the same habitats as the restricted-range species.

IUCN (1990, 1992c) lists 67 protected areas for Sri Lanka, but most of these are in the dry zone and only contain suitable habitat for a few of the restricted-range species. The most important reserves for the majority of them are Sinharaja National Heritage Wilderness Area, Peak Wilderness Sanctuary, Horton Plains National Park and Hakgala Strict Nature Reserve. Together, these areas include the largest remaining areas of lowland and montane rain forest in Sri Lanka's wet zone, although many remnant patches of forest are unprotected. Uda Walawe National Park in the intermediate zone also supports several of the restricted-range species (IUCN 1990). Green and Gunawardena (1993) describe a current project to evaluate the conservation importance of remaining natural forests, with the aim of identifying an optimum network of conservation areas to protect forest biodiversity and important watersheds.

125 Andaman Islands

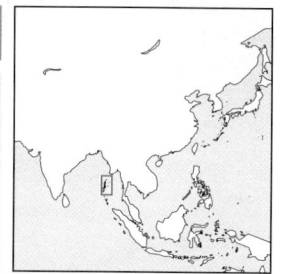

Key habitats Lowland rain forest, mangroves

Main threats Moderate habitat loss (e.g. due to cultivation, grazing, logging), introduced species

Biological importance ● ● ●
Current threat level ● ● ●

Area 8,200 km² **Altitude** 0–700 m

Countries India, Myanmar

Restricted-range species	Threatened	Total
Confined to this EBA	2	8
Present also in other EBAs, SAs	0	4
Total	2	12

■ General characteristics

The Andaman Islands comprise c.325 islands and islets in the Bay of Bengal. They are the summits of a submarine mountain range which stretches still further to the south and east to form the Nicobar Islands (EBA 126) and then Sumatra (EBA 158). The Andamans' major islands—North, Middle and South Andaman—are nearly contiguous and together make up more than two-thirds of the archipelago's land area. The few small northernmost islands, including Table, Great Coco and Little Coco, are politically part of Myanmar, while those further south belong to India.

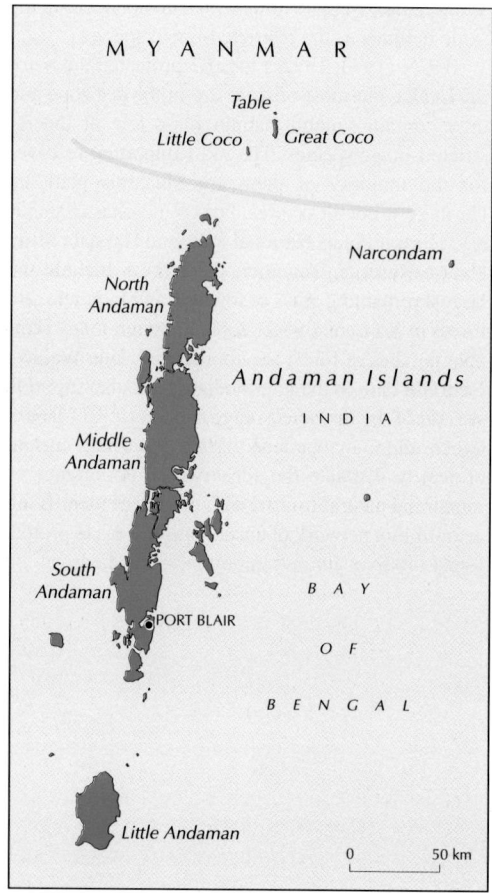

Native vegetation includes tropical evergreen and semi-evergreen rain forest, moist deciduous forest, and mangroves around the coasts and on some islands.

■ Restricted-range species

All the restricted-range birds are forest-dwelling species; some appear quite common in disturbed forest and have been recorded near the capital, Port Blair, in South Andaman (Curson 1989).

Access to some of the islands is extremely limited—most records and collections are from Middle and South Andaman—and many species have thus appeared to be restricted to these two islands. A recent survey has shown, however, that they occur more widely (L. Vijayan *in litt.* 1996) (see 'Distribution patterns' table). One species with an extraordinarily small range is *Aceros narcondami*, being confined to the small, isolated island of Narcondam (6.82 km²).

Reports from the early twentieth century mention that *Megapodius nicobariensis* occurred on Little Andaman and the Coco Islands (R. W. R. J. Dekker

Distribution patterns of restricted-range species	Narcondam	Table and Coco Is	North Andaman	Middle Andaman	South Andaman	Little Andaman	Other EBAs, SAs
Species (ordered geographically)							
Aceros narcondami	●	–	–	–	–	–	–
Otus balli	●	–	?	–	●	–	–
Dicrurus andamanensis	–	●	●	●	●	●	–
Centropus andamanensis	–	●	–	●	●	●	–
Megapodius nicobariensis	–	X	–	–	–	X	●
Rallina canningi	–	–	●	●	●	●	–
Dryocopus hodgei	–	–	●	●	●	●	–
Columba palumboides	–	–	●	●	●	●	●
Dendrocitta bayleyi	–	–	●	●	●	●	–
Macropygia rufipennis	–	–	●	●	●	●	●
Sturnus erythropygius	–	–	●	●	●	●	●
Spilornis elgini	–	–	●	●	●	●	–
Ninox affinis	–	–	●	–	●	–	●
Total	2	2	9	9	11	8	

● Present   ? Present?   Threatened spp. shown in **bold**   see 'Status and habitat' table
○ Extinct?   R Reintroduced
X Extinct   I Introduced   Other EBAs, SAs

Status and habitat of restricted-range species

Species (ordered taxonomically)	Global status	Other EBAs (and SAs)	Habitat
Andaman Serpent-eagle *Spilornis elgini*	nt	—	Inland forest, hillsides covered with scattered trees
Nicobar Scrubfowl *Megapodius nicobariensis*[1]	VU	126	Forest, secondary growth
Andaman Crake *Rallina canningi*	VU	—	Marshland in forest, streams, mangrove creeks
Andaman Wood-pigeon *Columba palumboides*	nt	126	Forest
Andaman Cuckoo-dove *Macropygia rufipennis*	nt	126	Forest, clearings, gardens
Brown Coucal *Centropus andamanensis*	nt	—	Forest edge, gardens, cultivation, mangroves
Andaman Scops-owl *Otus balli*	nt	—	Forest, around settlements and cultivation
Andaman Hawk-owl *Ninox affinis*	nt	126	Forest
Narcondam Hornbill *Aceros narcondami*	VU	—	Forest
Andaman Woodpecker *Dryocopus hodgei*	nt	—	Tall forest; also observed in lightly logged hill forest
White-headed Starling *Sturnus erythropygius*	nt	126	Forest, forest clearings, secondary growth, open grassland, cultivation
Andaman Drongo *Dicrurus andamanensis*	nt	—	Forest
Andaman Treepie *Dendrocitta bayleyi*	nt	—	Forest

Global status (see p. 679 for definitions)

EX	Extinct	} with year of last record	cd	Conservation Dependent
EW	Extinct in the Wild		nt	Near Threatened
CR	Critical	} threatened species	lc	Least Concern
EN	Endangered		DD	Data Deficient
VU	Vulnerable		NE	Not Evaluated

Other EBAs (and SAs) (see p. 77 for locations) Bracketed numbers are Secondary Areas. [X] Extinct in that EBA or SA.

Notes [1] Extinct in this EBA (see 'Restricted-range species').

in litt. 1993), but the species is presumed extinct there now. A further four species are shared with the Nicobar Islands (EBA 126) indicating the affinity between the two EBAs (see Ripley and Beehler 1989).

■ Threats and conservation

In recent years the human population on some of the larger islands has grown rapidly due to the settlement of people from mainland India. Remaining forest is consequently under severe pressure from agriculture and grazing, with habitat loss and degradation from logging being another major threat to wildlife (Whitaker 1985, Curson 1989, Sinha 1992).

Introduced species also threaten native ones either directly through predation or indirectly by degradation of their habitat; for example, spotted deer *Axis axis*, introduced in the early twentieth century and now widely distributed, is a particularly disruptive alien, adversely affecting forest regeneration as well as causing serious crop losses (Pande *et al.* 1991). Hunting is another major threat, with a lack of

awareness among local people regarding the status of their avifauna (L. Vijayan *in litt.* 1996).

Not surprisingly all the restricted-range bird species of this EBA are classified as threatened or Near Threatened. Of the two threatened extant species, *Aceros narcondami* (numbering only c.400 individuals in 1993) is especially vulnerable because of its exceptionally tiny range, and *Rallina canningi*, a terrestrial wetland species, may be threatened additionally by introduced predators (J. C. Eames *in litt.* 1993) such as dogs, cats and rats. Nicobar Pigeon *Caloenas nicobarica*, a widespread species classified as Near Threatened, also occurs on the islands.

A few small national parks have been established in the Andamans and many more sanctuaries, largely on offshore islands (including Narcondam Island), have been notified recently (see Pande *et al.* 1991). However, there are concerns that these protective regulations are not sufficient to conserve wildlife, and the recent rapid increase of tourism in particular urgently requires some scientific management (Sinha 1992).

126 Nicobar Islands

| Key habitats | Lowland rain forest | Area 1,800 km² | Altitude 0–600 m |

Key habitats Lowland rain forest

Main threats Moderate habitat loss (e.g. due to grazing, plantations), hunting

Biological importance ● ● ●
Current threat level ● ● ●

Area 1,800 km² **Altitude** 0–600 m

Countries India

Restricted-range species	Threatened	Total
Confined to this EBA	2	5
Present also in other EBAs, SAs	0	4
Total	2	9

■ General characteristics

Politically part of India, the Nicobar Islands are the peaks of a submerged mountain range, and comprise some 24 islands (12 inhabited) lying in the Bay of Bengal between the Andaman Islands (EBA 125) and Sumatra (EBA 158). The islands can be divided into three distinct groups: Car Nicobar and Batti Malv in the north, the Nancowry group in the centre (including the main islands of Teressa, Camorta, Trinkat, Nancowry and Katchall), and the Great

Nicobar group in the south (including the main islands of Little and Great Nicobar).

The native vegetation can be broadly classified as tropical lowland evergreen rain forest, with mangroves in some coastal areas.

■ Restricted-range species

All the EBA's restricted-range species inhabit forest and a few have also been recorded in secondary and man-made habitats.

The avifaunas of the islands are largely similar but there are a few significant differences in the species' distribution patterns (see table): for example, *Psittacula caniceps* occurs only in the Great Nicobar group, while *Hypsipetes nicobariensis* is present only in the Nancowry group, and several other species have distinct subspecies on the three different island groups. There are records of restricted-range species from many of the offshore islands but it is doubtful whether some of the tiny ones harbour viable populations (R. W. R. J. Dekker *in litt.* 1993).

There is some evidence that *Megapodius nicobariensis* occurred earlier in the twentieth century on some of the Andaman Islands to the north (Little Andaman and Coco Islands, EBA 125) (R. W. R. J. Dekker *in litt.* 1993), and a further four species are still shared with the Andamans, indicating affinity between these EBAs (see Ripley and Beehler 1989).

■ Threats and conservation

Most of the islands in the Nicobar archipelago have been designated as tribal areas where local people have a subsistence lifestyle, but there has been an influx of people from mainland India, resulting in increased pressure on natural resources. Large areas of forest have consequently been felled and some islands now have extensive grasslands (e.g. the Nancowry islands) or coconut plantations (e.g. Car Nicobar, where there is some uncertainty about whether forest species continue to survive). The most immediate threat in the Nicobars is, however, the proposal to make Great Nicobar a free port and to create a dry dock and refuelling base there for international shipping (Sankaran 1995).

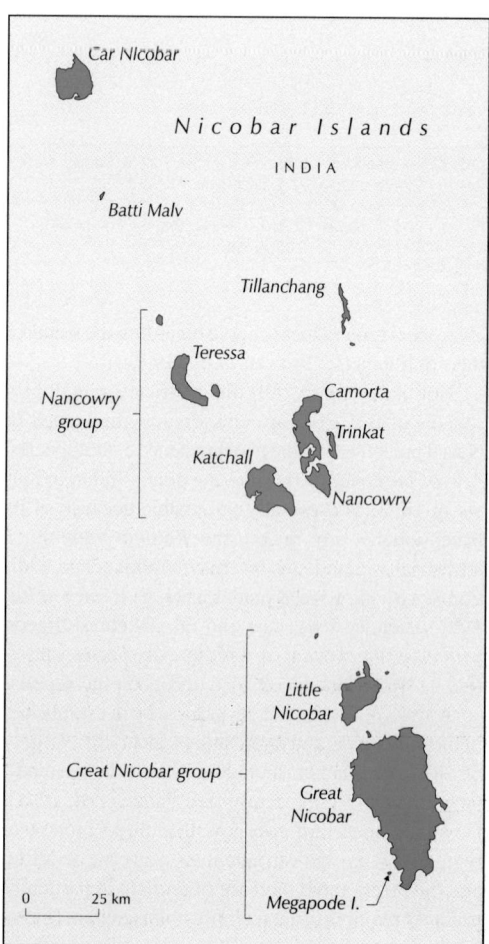

Car Nicobar

Nicobar Islands

INDIA

Batti Malv

Tillanchang

Teressa

Nancowry group

Camorta

Trinkat

Katchall

Nancowry

Little Nicobar

Great Nicobar group

Great Nicobar

0   25 km

Megapode I.

Status and habitat of restricted-range species

Species (ordered taxonomically)	Global status	Other EBAs (and SAs)	Habitat
Nicobar Serpent-eagle *Spilornis minimus*	nt	—	Forest, cultivated areas
Nicobar Sparrowhawk *Accipiter butleri*	nt	—	Forest
Nicobar Scrubfowl *Megapodius nicobariensis*	VU	125[X]	Forest, secondary growth
Andaman Wood-pigeon *Columba palumboides*	nt	125	Forest
Andaman Cuckoo-dove *Macropygia rufipennis*	nt	125	Forest, clearings, gardens
Nicobar Parakeet *Psittacula caniceps*	nt	—	Forest
Andaman Hawk-owl *Ninox affinis*	nt	125	Forest
Nicobar Bulbul *Hypsipetes nicobariensis*	VU	—	Forest, gardens
White-headed Starling *Sturnus erythropygius*	nt	125	Forest, forest clearings, secondary growth, open grassland, cultivation

Global status (see p. 679 for definitions)	EX Extinct	with year of last record	CR Critical	threatened species	cd Conservation Dependent	DD Data Deficient
	EW Extinct in the Wild		EN Endangered		nt Near Threatened	NE Not Evaluated
			VU Vulnerable		lc Least Concern	

Other EBAs (and SAs) (see p. 77 for locations): bracketed numbers are Secondary Areas; [X] extinct in that EBA or SA.

Distribution patterns of restricted-range species

Species (ordered geographically)	Car Nicobar	Tillanchang	Teressa	Camorta	Trinkat	Nancowry	Katchall	Little Nicobar	Great Nicobar	Megapode I.	Other EBAs, SAs
Sturnus erythropygius	●	–	–	–	–	–	●	–	–	–	●
Accipiter butleri	●	–	●	●	–	–	●	●	●	–	–
Ninox affinis	●	–	–	●	●	–	●	–	●	–	●
Columba palumboides	●	–	●	●	●	●	–	?	●	–	●
Hypsipetes nicobariensis	–	●	●	●	●	●	●	–	–	–	–
Megapodius nicobariensis	–	●	●	●	●	●	●	●	●	●	X
Macropygia rufipennis	–	●	●	●	●	●	●	●	●	●	●
Spilornis minimus	–	–	●	●	●	●	●	●	●	–	–
Psittacula caniceps	–	–	–	–	–	–	–	●	●	–	–
Total	4	3	5	7	6	5	6	5	7	2	

● Present	? Present?	Threatened spp. shown in **bold**	see 'Status and habitat' table
○ Extinct?	R Reintroduced	Other EBAs, SAs	
X Extinct	I Introduced		

All the restricted-range bird species are classified as threatened or Near Threatened, owing to their small ranges and populations, and the continuing threat of habitat destruction. A recent study of *Megapodius nicobariensis* has shown this species to be more common than once thought (between 4,500 and 8,000 birds: Sankaran 1995), although it has declined in the Nancowry group as a result of forest loss and localized hunting for food and egg collection. *Hypsipetes nicobariensis* appears to have declined on the Nancowry group, possibly through displacement by the introduced Red-whiskered Bulbul *Pycnonotus jocosus* (Sankaran 1993a,b). Despite its name, Nicobar Pigeon *Caloenas nicobarica* is a widespread (Near Threatened) species, also occurring on these islands.

There are a few protected areas in this EBA (covering c.30% of the land area) including Batti Malv, Tillanchang and Megapode islands which are all uninhabited wildlife sanctuaries. Great Nicobar is a Biosphere Reserve, and the designation in 1992 of two large national parks (covering 536 km² of primary forest) will help to secure the future of some of the restricted-range species there. Nevertheless the existing network of protected areas is still considered inadequate to conserve all endemic subspecies and a proposal has been made to redefine the boundaries of the Great Nicobar Biosphere Reserve and to establish a Nancowry Biosphere Reserve to cover four important core areas on Tillanchang, Camorta, Nancowry and Katchall (Sankaran 1995; see also Sankaran 1997).

127 Taklimakan desert

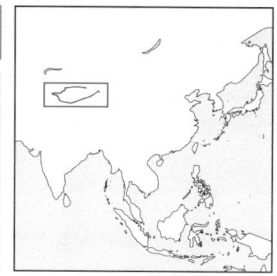

Key habitats Sandy desert, scrub

Main threats Unquantified habitat loss (e.g. due to overgrazing, fuelwood collection, irrigation)

Biological importance ● ● ●
Current threat level ● ● ●

Area 60,000 km² **Altitude** 900–1,300 m

Countries China

Restricted-range species	Threatened	Total
Confined to this EBA	2	2
Present also in other EBAs, SAs	0	0
Total	2	2

■ General characteristics

The area covered by this EBA forms a narrow band around the edge of the Taklimakan desert in Xinjiang autonomous region of western China. This large desert basin is bordered by high mountains: the Kunlun Shan and Altun Shan ranges to the south, the Kok Shaal Tau range to the north-west and the Tien Shan to the north.

At the foot of the mountain slopes around the edge of the basin is a mixture of stone and sand, inside of which lies a band of stone desert with scattered oases. The interior of the basin is made up of mobile sand dunes, largely devoid of vegetation, which cover 85% of the total desert area. The remaining 15% or so of the desert comprises dunes stabilized or semi-stabilized by bushes of tamarisk *Tamarix* and poplar *Populus* which are scattered mainly at the edge of the sandy desert and along the banks of the few rivers which flow into it from the mountains (Zhao Ji *et al.* 1990).

■ Restricted-range species

The records of *Podoces biddulphi* have been used to define the extent of this EBA, as *Caprimulgus centralasicus* is known only from the type-specimen collected in 1929 in sandy desert scrub at Guma (Ludlow and Kinnear 1933–1934), a locality where *P. biddulphi* has also been recorded. *P. biddulphi* is a

bird of sandy desert with poplar and tamarisk bushes (Grimmett 1991), and the only records of it are from scattered sites close to the edge of the Taklimakan basin; it is assumed here to be restricted to the areas

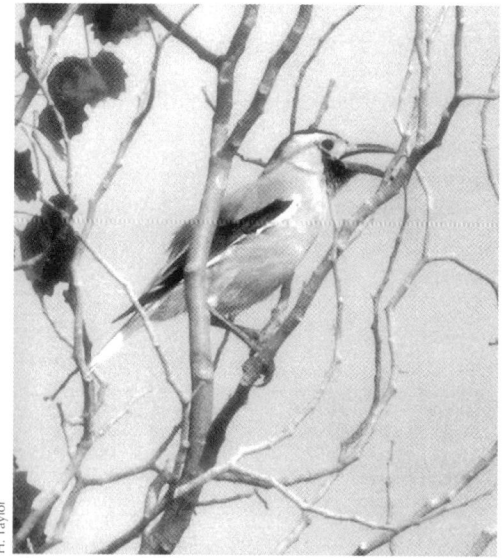

H. Taylor

Xinjiang Ground-jay *Podoces biddulphi* appears to be confined to a band of poplar and tamarisk scrub around the margins of the Taklimakan desert.

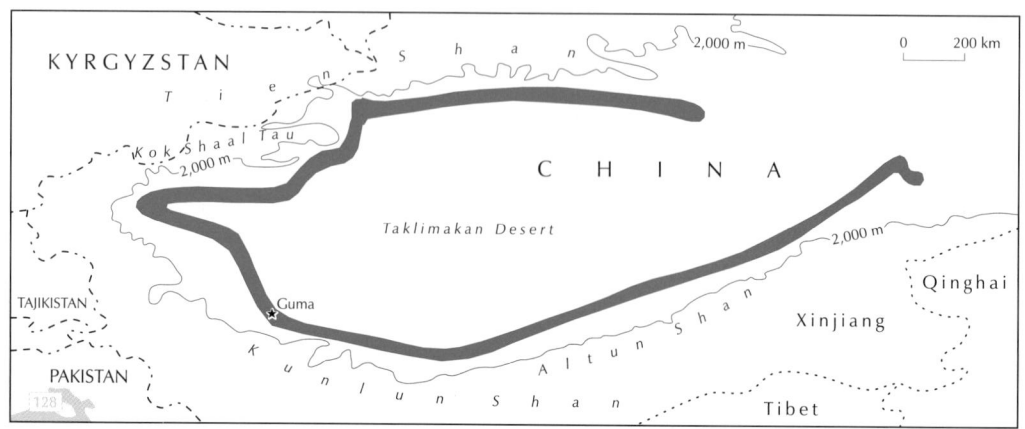

Status and habitat of restricted-range species

Species (ordered taxonomically)	Global status	Other EBAs (and SAs)	Altitude (m)	Habitat
Vaurie's Nightjar *Caprimulgus centralasicus*[1]	VU	—	No data	Probably scrub in sandy desert
Xinjiang Ground-jay *Podoces biddulphi*	VU	—	c.900–1,300	Sandy desert, scrub, desert poplar

Global status (see p. 679 for definitions)	EX Extinct ⎱ with year EW Extinct in ⎰ of last 　　the Wild ⎰ record CR Critical ⎱ threatened EN Endangered ⎰ species VU Vulnerable ⎰	cd Conservation Dependent nt Near Threatened lc Least Concern DD Data Deficient NE Not Evaluated	**Other EBAs (and SAs)** (see p. 77 for locations) **Notes**	Bracketed numbers are Secondary Areas. ˣ Extinct in that EBA or SA. [1] Known from a single female specimen collected in 1929 (Ludlow and Kinnear 1933–1934, Vaurie 1960).

of stabilized dunes which lie around the edge of the sandy desert, but this is a region poorly explored ornithologically and it is possible that the species also occurs along rivers within the basin's interior.

■ Threats and conservation

Both the restricted-range species are threatened, principally because evidence exists for the widespread degradation of the region's desert habitats through the intensive grazing of goats and camels, extraction of fuelwood, and the conversion of huge areas to irrigated farmland (Grimmett 1991, Grimmett

and Taylor 1992). A survey at Guma in 1990 failed to locate *Caprimulgus centralasicus*, and found that the desert habitats there have been converted to cultivation since the time when the single specimen was collected (Dissing *et al.* 1990).

There are three large protected areas in the northeastern part of the EBA—Bayanbulak, Huocheng and Tarim Nature Reserves (IUCN 1993)—but it is not known whether they include significant areas of habitat suitable for the area's restricted-range bird species.

128 Western Himalayas

PRIORITY
CRITICAL

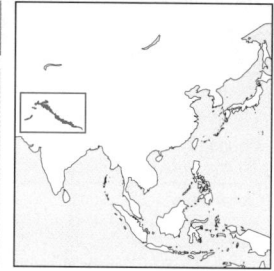

Key habitats Temperate coniferous/ broadleaf forest, subalpine forest, montane grassland

Main threats Moderate habitat loss (e.g. due to timber extraction)

Biological importance ● ● ●
Current threat level ● ● ○

Area 130,000 km² **Altitude** 1,500–3,600 m

Countries Afghanistan, India, Nepal, Pakistan

Restricted-range species	Threatened	Total
Confined to this EBA	4	11
Present also in other EBAs, SAs	0	0
Total	4	11

■ General characteristics

The Western Himalayas EBA extends along the mountain chain from western Nepal (west of the Kali Gandaki valley) through Uttar Pradesh, Himachal Pradesh, Jammu and Kashmir in north-west India and northern Pakistan, and then south-west along the mountains in the border region between Pakistan and Afghanistan.

The restricted-range birds breed in west Himalayan temperate forest (see Champion and Seth 1968 for definition), including coniferous, broadleaf and mixed broadleaf–coniferous, and some of them range into adjacent montane grassland and subalpine forest. There is a small geographical overlap in Nepal between this EBA and the Central Himalayas (EBA 129).

■ Restricted-range species

The EBA's restricted-range birds include two endemic genera, *Ophrysia* and *Callacanthis*. The breeding-habitat requirements and distributions of most species are relatively well known (Paludan 1959, Ali

G. Duke/BirdLife International

BirdLife International's Himalayan Jungle Project is working with local communities to conserve the remaining areas of pristine forest in the Palas valley, northern Pakistan.

and Ripley 1987, Roberts 1991, 1992): six of them— *Tragopan melanocephalus, Phylloscopus tytleri, Ficedula subrubra, Aegithalos niveogularis, Callacanthis burtoni* and *Pyrrhula aurantiaca*—are found in temperate zone forest between eastern Afghanistan and western Nepal, although *A. niveogularis* is

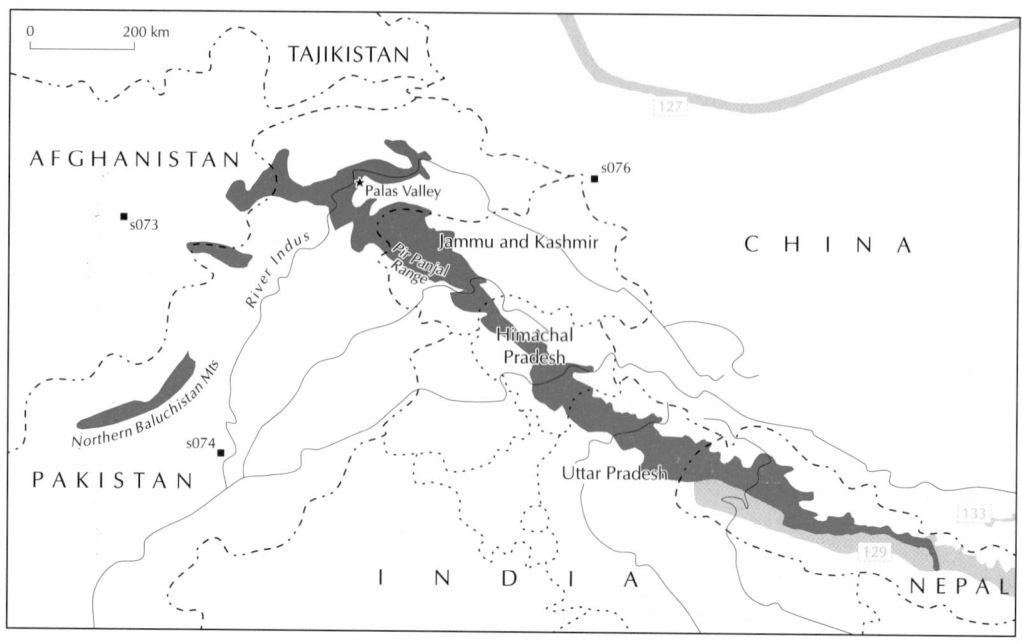

Status and habitat of restricted-range species

Species (ordered taxonomically)	Global status	Other EBAs (and SAs)	Altitude (m)	Habitat
Himalayan Quail [1] *Ophrysia superciliosa*	CR	—	1,650–2,100	Long grass and brushwood on steep hillsides
Western Tragopan *Tragopan melanocephalus*	VU	—	2,400–3,600, to 1,350 in winter	Dense undergrowth in coniferous, mixed and oak forest
Cheer Pheasant *Catreus wallichi*	VU	—	1,400–3,500	Steep grassy slopes, open coniferous or deciduous forest; appears to like early successional habitats
Brooks's Leaf-warbler [2] *Phylloscopus subviridis*	lc	—	2,100–3,600	Coniferous and mixed forests in drier, cooler
Tytler's Leaf-warbler [3] *Phylloscopus tytleri*	nt	—	2,400–3,600	Coniferous forest, dwarf willows and birches near treeline
Kashmir Flycatcher [4] *Ficedula subrubra*	VU	—	1,800–2,700	Temperate mixed broadleaf forest, esp. where there is dense growth of *Parrotia*
White-cheeked Tit *Aegithalos leucogenys*	lc	—	1,500–3,600, to 450 in winter	Pine forest, oak forest and scrub, juniper forest, riverine tamarisk scrub
White-throated Tit *Aegithalos niveogularis*	nt	—	2,400–3,600, to 1,800 in winter	Coniferous, mixed and deciduous forest; rhododendrons and willow scrub near treeline
Kashmir Nuthatch *Sitta cashmirensis*	lc	—	1,800–3,500	Coniferous, mixed and deciduous forest
Spectacled Finch *Callacanthis burtoni*	lc	—	2,400–3,350, to 1,800 in winter	Open coniferous forest, occasionally birch
Orange Bullfinch *Pyrrhula aurantiaca*	nt	—	2,700–3,300, to 1,600 in winter	Open coniferous and mixed forest

Global status (see p. 679 for definitions)

EX	Extinct	with year of last record	cd	Conservation Dependent
EW	Extinct in the Wild		nt	Near Threatened
CR	Critical	threatened species	lc	Least Concern
EN	Endangered		DD	Data Deficient
VU	Vulnerable		NE	Not Evaluated

Other EBAs (and SAs) (see p. 77 for locations)
Bracketed numbers are Secondary Areas.
[x] Extinct in that EBA or SA.

Notes

[1] Possibly extinct, last recorded 1889 (specimen in British Museum of Natural History).

[2] Migratory, wintering in Himalayan foothills and plains south of breeding range.

[3] Migratory, wintering in Western Ghats (EBA 123) and elsewhere in peninsular India.

[4] Migratory, wintering in the Western Ghats (EBA 123) and mountains of Sri Lanka (EBA 124).

the only one known definitely to breed in Nepal (Inskipp and Inskipp 1991). *F. subrubra* has a particularly restricted distribution in Kashmir and the Pir Panjal range.

Phylloscopus subviridis and *Aegithalos leucogenys* appear particularly associated with relatively dry temperate forests in the western part of the EBA, in northern Pakistan and eastern Afghanistan. *Aegi-*

G. Duke/BirdLife International

West Himalayan temperate forests in the rugged mountains of northern Pakistan. Many of the valleys have lost their forests in recent years as a result of logging.

Distribution patterns of restricted-range species — Species (ordered geographically)	N Baluchistan mts	N Pakistan (W of Indus), adjacent E Afghanistan	N Pakistan (E of Indus)	Jammu, Kashmir	Himachal Pradesh	Uttar Pradesh	W Nepal	Other EBAs, SAs
Aegithalos leucogenys	●	●	●	●	–	?	–	–
Sitta cashmirensis	●	●	●	●	●	●	●	–
Phylloscopus subviridis	–	●[1]	●	–	–	–	–	–
Pyrrhula aurantiaca	–	●	●	●	–	–	–	–
Tragopan melanocephalus	–	●	●	●	●	●	–	–
Phylloscopus tytleri	–	●	●	●	●	●	●[2]	–
Callacanthis burtoni	–	●	●	●	●	●	●[2]	–
Ficedula subrubra	–	–	●	●	–	–	●	–
Catreus wallichi	–	–	●	●	●	●	●	–
Aegithalos niveogularis	–	–	●	●	●	●	●	–
Ophrysia superciliosa	–	–	–	–	–	●	–	–
Total	2	7	10	9	7	7	5	

● Present   ? Present?   Threatened spp. shown in **bold**   } see 'Status and habitat' table

○ Extinct?   R Reintroduced   Other EBAs, SAs }

X Extinct   I Introduced

[1] Birds probably of this species also recorded in adjacent eastern Tajikistan (Dement'ev and Gladkov 1968).

[2] Perhaps only a non-breeding visitor (Inskipp and Inskipp 1991).

thalos leucogenys and *Sitta cashmirensis* are the only species which range into the mountains of northern Baluchistan, where they occur in juniper *Juniperus* forest. Two species are associated with open habitats

Like most EBAs, the Western Himalayas is important for a wide range of endemic plants and animals. This species of *Delphinium*, new to science, was discovered recently in the Palas valley.

adjacent to forest: *Catreus wallichi*, which ranges from northern Pakistan to western Nepal, and *Ophrysia superciliosa*, which is only known from northern Uttar Pradesh in north-west India where it was last recorded about 1889.

■ Threats and conservation

The principal threat is loss, degradation and fragmentation of habitat. In the Himalayan region of Afghanistan, most forest has been destroyed for fuelwood and timber, and little now remains (IUCN 1993, Evans 1994). In northern Pakistan, there has been extensive forest loss in the past, and, although reafforestation schemes have increased overall forest cover considerably (IUCN 1993), many Himalayan forests are under constant threat from timber extraction (T. J. Roberts *in litt.* 1993). In north-west India, forest cover remains extensive and relatively stable in most states, although destruction of the understorey through overgrazing by livestock is a major problem (IUCN 1993), and habitat is being lost at important sites because of development projects such as roads and dams (V. Sharma *in litt.* 1993). In Nepal, the area of forest in the temperate zone seems to have been stable in recent years, but there has been rapid degradation by uncontrolled cutting for fuelwood and animal fodder, livestock grazing and burning (Inskipp 1989).

Four of the restricted-range species are classified as threatened through their particular vulnerability to habitat loss: *Tragopan melanocephalus* and *Catreus wallichi* have specialized habitat requirements and are both historically recorded from isolated pockets of suitable habitat (V. Sharma *in litt.* 1993), and their populations are now much reduced and fragmented;

G. Duke/BirdLife International

In Palas, most agriculture is restricted to the valley bottom, and the mountain slopes remain forested.

R. F. A. Grimmett/BirdLife International

G. Duke/BirdLife International

Feathers of Western Tragopan *Tragopan melanocephalus* adorn the cap of a young Palasi villager.

Ophrysia superciliosa and *Ficedula subrubra* have particularly restricted distributions in areas where extensive habitat loss has taken place, and *O.*

superciliosa may already be extinct (King 1978–1979); *C. wallichi* is additionally subject to excessive hunting. Long-billed Bush-warbler *Bradypterus major* is a more widespread threatened species (classified as Vulnerable) which occurs in this EBA, where it is found at 2,400–3,600 m in low scrub and rank grass and bracken on open slopes, often near forest edge.

There are about 50 protected areas in the Western Himalayas which contain suitable habitats for the restricted-range species (IUCN 1993). These are spread through most parts of the EBA, although there are none in Afghanistan and few in Pakistan, and many of them are relatively small as well as being isolated. They are known to support numbers of all the restricted-range species except *Ophrysia superciliosa*, but only a few are likely to be large enough to hold viable populations of *Tragopan melanocephalus* or *Catreus wallichi*. The largest population now known of *Tragopan melanocephalus* is in the Palas valley in northern Pakistan, which also supports many other restricted-range bird species, and populations of many rare and endemic plants (Royal Botanic Gardens Kew 1995); the BirdLife Himalayan Jungle Project is working with the local communities there to conserve the remaining areas of pristine forest (Duke 1994). Dachigam National Park and Overa-Aru Sanctuary in Jammu and Kashmir are probably important for the conservation of *Ficedula subrubra*.

129 Central Himalayas

Key habitats Moist temperate mixed forest, dense secondary forest, scrub

Main threats Moderate habitat loss (e.g. due to fuelwood collection, overgrazing, burning)

Biological importance ● ○ ○
Current threat level ● ○ ○

Area 56,000 km²   **Altitude** 1,500–3,300 m

Countries Nepal

Restricted-range species	Threatened	Total
Confined to this EBA	0	2
Present also in other EBAs, SAs	0	1
Total	0	3

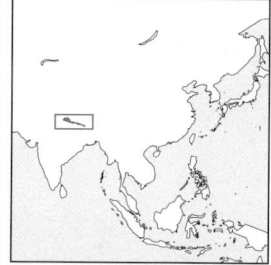

■ General characteristics

Nepal is one of the most mountainous countries in the world, ranging in altitude almost from sea-level to over 8,000 m. The Himalayan range runs east to west through the country, so the topography changes dramatically from north to south, and the country has an exceptional variety of climatic conditions and vegetation types. This EBA extends through the Himalayas from the extreme east of Nepal to the extreme west, and possibly into adjacent regions of India.

The restricted-range species of the EBA breed in a variety of habitats in the temperate zone. There is geographical overlap in western Nepal between this EBA and the Western Himalayas (EBA 128), but the birds of that EBA tend to occur in relatively dry habitat types and only two of them are known definitely to breed in Nepal. A minor overlap also exists in the extreme east of Nepal with the Eastern Himalayas (EBA 130).

■ Restricted-range species

Two of the three restricted-range birds, *Pnoepyga immaculata* and *Actinodura nipalensis*, breed in Himalayan moist temperate forest between about 1,800 and 3,300 m, and *Turdoides nipalensis* occupies dense scrub and secondary growth at slightly lower altitudes. The newly described *P. immaculata* (Martens and Eck 1991) is apparently an altitudinal

M. J. Crosby

Moist temperate forests in Annapurna Conservation Area in central Nepal.

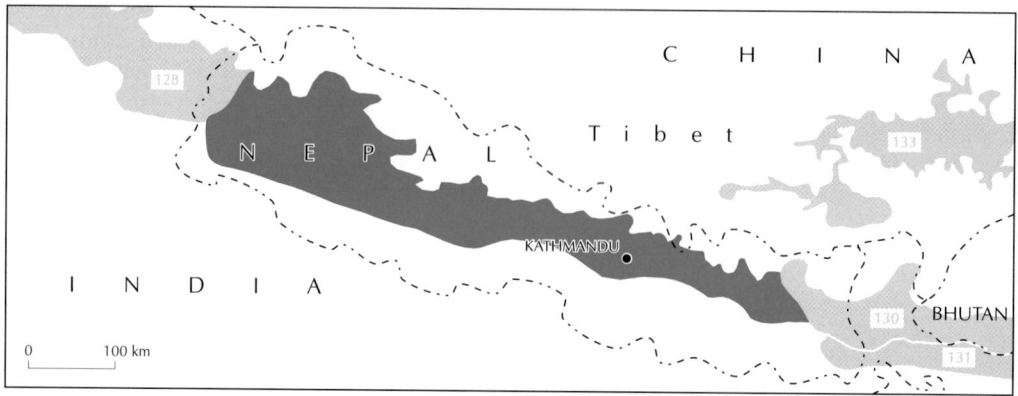

Status and habitat of restricted-range species

Species (ordered taxonomically)	Global status	Other EBAs (and SAs)	Altitude (m)	Habitat
Nepal Wren-babbler *Pnoepyga immaculata*	nt	—	2,100–3,100, to 250 in winter	Forest
Spiny Babbler *Turdoides nipalensis*	lc	—	1,500–2,100, to 900 in winter	Dense secondary scrub
Hoary-throated Barwing *Actinodura nipalensis*	lc	130	1,800–3,300	Mixed oak, rhododendron and coniferous forest with plenty of undergrowth

| **Global status** (see p. 679 for definitions) | EX Extinct
EW Extinct in the Wild | } with year of last record | CR Critical
EN Endangered
VU Vulnerable | } threatened species | cd Conservation Dependent
nt Near Threatened
lc Least Concern | DD Data Deficient
NE Not Evaluated |

Other EBAs (and SAs) (see p. 77 for locations): bracketed numbers are Secondary Areas; ˣ extinct in that EBA or SA.

migrant, as it has been recorded in the lowlands of southern Nepal outside the breeding season; it has only been recorded in Nepal so far, but may prove to be present elsewhere in the Himalayas, although no specimens were found to be present among dozens of Scaly-breasted Wren-babbler *P. albiventer* skins collected to the east of Nepal in Sikkim, Darjeeling and Bhutan (Martens and Eck 1995). It has also been suggested that *Turdoides nipalensis* may range further west than is currently known, into north-west India (Inskipp and Inskipp 1991).

■ Threats and conservation

None of the restricted-range bird species is considered to be threatened, as they all occur widely within Nepal and are locally common. However, the populations of the two forest species, *Pnoepyga immaculata* and *Actinodura nipalensis*, may have

declined because, although the area of forest in the temperate zone appears to have remained stable in recent years, its condition has rapidly been made worse by uncontrolled cutting (for fuelwood and animal fodder), livestock grazing and burning (Inskipp 1989).

Langtang, Royal Bardia and Khaptad National Parks and Shivapuri Wildlife and Watershed Reserve support populations of one or more of the restricted-range species (Inskipp 1989), and there are several other protected areas lying within the EBA (IUCN 1990, 1993). These areas are fairly well spread through the EBA, and include substantial tracts of habitat suitable for the restricted-range birds. Proposed protected areas which support some of the species are Phulchowki mountain, Annapurna Conservation Area and the Barun valley extension to Sagarmatha National Park (Inskipp 1989).

130 Eastern Himalayas

PRIORITY
URGENT

Key habitats Subtropical hill forest, temperate forest, subalpine forest

Main threats Moderate habitat loss (e.g. due to logging, agriculture, overgrazing), hunting

Biological importance ● ● ●
Current threat level ● ○ ○

Area 220,000 km² **Altitude** 300–4,000 m
Countries Bangladesh, Bhutan, China, India, Myanmar, Nepal

Restricted-range species	Threatened	Total
Confined to this EBA	10	19
Present also in other EBAs, SAs	1	3
Total	11	22

■ General characteristics

This EBA follows the Himalayan range east from the Arun–Kosi valley of eastern Nepal, through Bhutan, north-east India (Sikkim, northern West Bengal and Arunachal Pradesh), south-east Tibet autonomous region and north-east Myanmar to south-west China (north-west Yunnan province). It also includes the mountain ranges to the south of the Brahmaputra river, which extend through north-east India (Nagaland, Manipur, southern Assam, Meghalaya and Mizoram) to the Chin hills in western Myanmar, and the Chittagong hills in south-east Bangladesh.

As they lie further to the south, the mountains of this region have a distinctly different climate (and hence vegetation) from the rest of the Himalayas: they experience warmer mean temperatures and

fewer days with frost, and generally have a much higher rainfall (Ramdas 1974). Two evergreen forest types appear to be particularly important breeding habitats for the EBA's restricted-range birds, both of which reach their western limit in eastern Nepal: subtropical wet hill forest is found at altitudes between approximately 1,000 and 2,000 m, and wet temperate forest at altitudes of about 1,800–3,000 m. Some species also breed in moist temperate or subalpine forests, and many are altitudinal migrants, moving outside the breeding season into tropical lowland evergreen and semi-evergreen rain forest below 1,000 m (see Champion and Seth 1968, Mani 1974, Whitmore 1984).

Knowledge of the distribution of the restricted-range species is incomplete in many parts of the

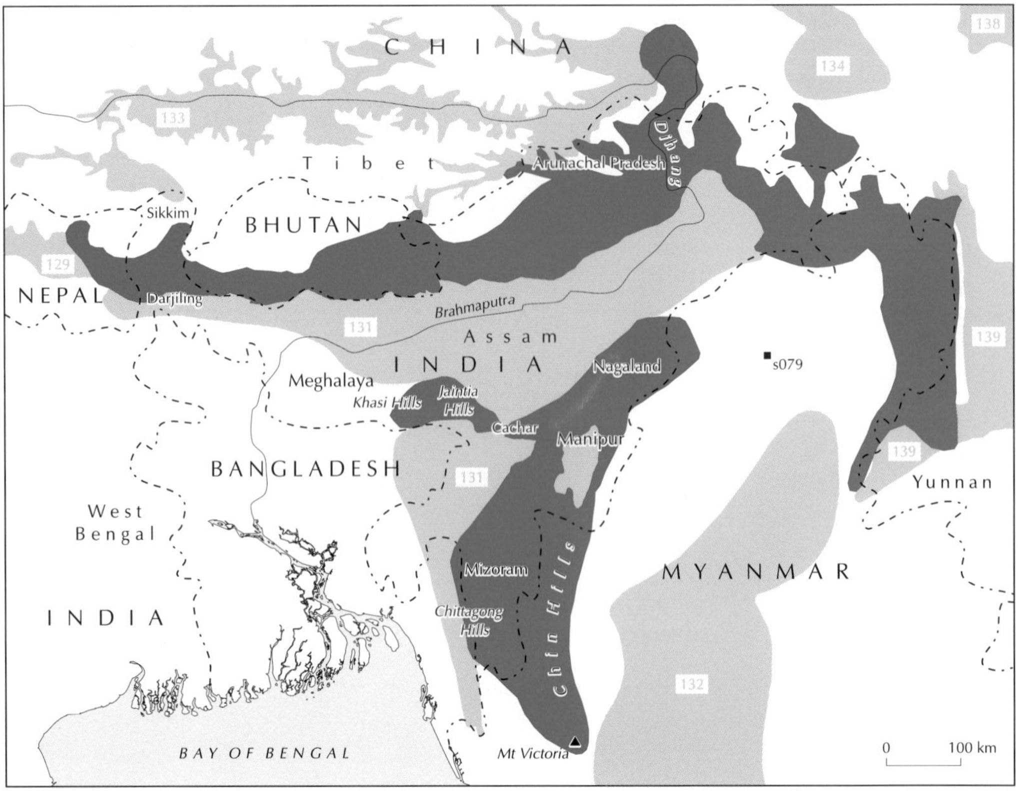

Status and habitat of restricted-range species

Species (ordered taxonomically)	Global status	Other EBAs (and SAs)	Altitude (m)	Habitat
Chestnut-breasted Partridge *Arborophila mandellii*	VU	—	350–2,450	Undergrowth in evergreen forest
Blyth's Tragopan *Tragopan blythii*	VU	—	1,800–3,300	Undergrowth (esp. bamboo) in evergreen forest, rhododendron forest
Sclater's Monal *Lophophorus sclateri*	VU	—	3,000–4,000, to 2,500 in winter	Silver fir forest with rhododendron undergrowth, subalpine rhododendron scrub, rocky slopes, grassland
Dark-rumped Swift *Apus acuticauda*[1]	VU	—	c.1,600	Rocky cliffs and deep gorges
Ward's Trogon *Harpactes wardi*	VU	(s082)	1,500–3,200	Broadleaf evergreen forest, bamboo
Rusty-bellied Shortwing *Brachypteryx hyperythra*	VU	—	c.1,800–3,000, lower in winter	Broadleaf evergreen forest, bamboo
Striped Laughingthrush *Garrulax virgatus*	nt	—	900–2,400	Evergreen forest with dense undergrowth, dense scrub
Brown-capped Laughingthrush *Garrulax austeni*	DD	—	(1,500–) 1,800–2,700	Oak and rhododendron forest, bamboo thickets
Rufous-throated Wren-babbler *Spelaeornis caudatus*	VU	—	1,600–3,100	Dense undergrowth and moss-covered boulders in broadleaf evergreen forest
Rusty-throated Wren-babbler *Spelaeornis badeigularis*[2]	VU	—	c.1,600	Breeding habitat unknown; in winter recorded in subtropical wet forest
Tawny-breasted Wren-babbler *Spelaeornis longicaudatus*	VU	—	1,000–2,000	Damp evergreen forest (mainly oak and rhododendron), ravines or steep rocky hillsides with moss, ferns and orchids
Wedge-billed Wren-babbler *Sphenocichla humei*	nt	—	900–2,300	Evergreen forest, bamboo
Snowy-throated Babbler *Stachyris oglei*	VU	—	c.1,800, to 450 in winter	Dense evergreen scrub in rocky ravines, winters in tropical evergreen and semi-evergreen rain forest
Hoary-throated Barwing *Actinodura nipalensis*	lc	129	1,800–3,300	Oak and rhododendron forest, mixed broadleaf and coniferous forest
Streak-throated Barwing *Actinodura waldeni*	lc	—	2,400–3,300, to 1,500 in winter	Broadleaf evergreen and mixed forest, rhododendron and bamboo forest
Ludlow's Fulvetta *Alcippe ludlowi*	lc	—	2,100–3,500	Rhododendron and bamboo forest, broadleaf and mixed pine and oak forest
Grey Sibia *Heterophasia gracilis*	nt	—	1,400–2,800, to 900 in winter	Evergreen and deciduous forest, pine forest
Beautiful Sibia *Heterophasia pulchella*	lc	—	2,100–3,000, to 400 in winter	Mossy evergreen forest
White-naped Yuhina *Yuhina bakeri*	lc	—	600–2,000	Broadleaf evergreen forest
Yellow-vented Warbler *Phylloscopus cantator*[3]	nt	—	c.300–2,000	Broadleaf evergreen forest
Broad-billed Warbler *Tickellia hodgsoni*	nt	(s082)	1,100–2,700, to 400 in winter	Broadleaf evergreen forest, dense scrub, bamboo
White-browed Nuthatch *Sitta victoriae*	VU	—	2,300–2,800	Stunted lichen-covered oak forest, avoiding pure stands of pines

Global status (see p. 679 for definitions)

EX Extinct ⎱ with year
EW Extinct in ⎰ of last
    the Wild ⎰ record

CR Critical
EN Endangered ⎱ threatened
VU Vulnerable ⎰ species

cd Conservation Dependent
nt Near Threatened
lc Least Concern
DD Data Deficient
NE Not Evaluated

Other EBAs (and SAs) (see p. 77 for locations)
Bracketed numbers are Secondary Areas.
[x] Extinct in that EBA or SA.

Notes

[1] Presumed migrants recorded northern Thailand and possibly Nepal (Boonsong and Round 1991, Inskipp and Inskipp 1991).

[2] Only known from the type-specimen, collected 1947 (Ali and Ripley 1948).

[3] Migrants recorded Myanmar, northern Thailand and northern Laos (King *et al.* 1975); precise limits of breeding and non-breeding ranges not known (C. R. Robson verbally 1990).

EBA, so the tentative boundary adopted has been based on the documented records of these birds and their known altitudinal ranges. There are minor geographical overlaps between this EBA and the Central Himalayas (EBA 129) in eastern Nepal, and the Yunnan mountains (EBA 139) in western Yunnan and northern Myanmar. The Assam plains (EBA 131) is in the adjacent lowlands and foothills, and there is some altitudinal overlap with this EBA, but the restricted-range species of the Assam plains are confined to non-forest habitats.

■ Restricted-range species

This part of the Himalayas is particularly rich in restricted-range birds, and the genus *Sphenocichla* is endemic to the EBA. For logistical and political reasons, these mountains have always been difficult of access for ornithologists, and there are many gaps in the knowledge of habitat requirements and distributions of these birds. Many of them are altitudinal migrants, and much of the ornithological work in the EBA has taken place outside the breeding season, so it is difficult from the available information to determine the exact breeding habitat requirements and altitudinal ranges of the species. It is clear, however, that subtropical wet hill forest and wet temperate forest are particularly important breeding habitats, and that tropical lowland evergreen and semi-ever-green rain forest is used by many of the species outside the breeding season. Important recent information on the EBA's restricted-range species is included in Peng Yan-zhang *et al.* (1980), Inskipp and Inskipp (1991, 1993a,b), Ripley *et al.* (1991), Clements (1992), Katti *et al.* (1992), Singh (1995) and Ali *et al.* (1996).

The Himalayan mountains in the northern part of the EBA (first four columns in the 'Distribution patterns' table) have an avifauna distinctly different from the mountain ranges in the south (next four columns); eight or nine of the restricted-range species are only known (in this EBA) from the north and four only from the south. These two regions are combined into a single EBA because of the 9–10 species common to both. Several species have particularly small ranges: *Spelaeornis badeigularis* and *Stachyris oglei* are known only from the Lohit and Tirap Frontier Divisions of eastern Arunachal Pradesh, *S. badeigularis* from just a single specimen; *Spelaeornis longicaudatus* is restricted to the hills of Meghalaya, southern Assam and western Manipur; *Apus acuticauda* is only known to breed in the Khasi hills in Meghalaya and the Blue mountains in Mizoram, but up to eight individuals were seen around cliffs in south-east Bhutan in May 1996 (B. King *in litt.* 1996); *Sitta victoriae* is only known from the southern Chin hills, where it was recorded in the

Distribution patterns of restricted-range species

Species (ordered geographically)	E. Nepal to cent. Bhutan	E. Bhutan to Dihang valley	E. Arunachal Pradesh, SE Tibet	N Myanmar, SE Tibet, NW Yunnan	Nagaland, Manipur & Cachar hills	Khasi & Jaintia hills	Mizoram, Chittagong hills	Chin hills	Other EBAs, SAs
Spelaeornis caudatus	●	●	–	–	–	–	–	–	–
Actinodura nipalensis	●	●	–	–	–	–	–	–	●
Arborophila mandellii	●	●	●	–	–	–	–	–	–
Harpactes wardi	●	●	●	●	–	–	–	–	●
Brachypteryx hyperythra	●	●	●	●	?	–	–	–	–
Sphenocichla humei	●	●	●	●	●	–	–	–	–
Yuhina bakeri	●	●	●	●	●	–	–	–	–
Phylloscopus cantator	●	●	–	–	●	●	–	–	–
Tickellia hodgsoni	●	●	●	–	●	–	–	●¹	●
Alcippe ludlowi	–	●	●	–	–	–	–	–	–
Lophophorus sclateri	–	●	●	●	–	–	–	–	–
Heterophasia pulchella	–	●	●	●	●	–	–	–	–
Tragopan blythii	–	●	●	●	●	–	–	●	–
Actinodura waldeni	–	●	●	●	●	–	–	●	–
Apus acuticauda	–	●	–	–	–	●	●	–	–
Spelaeornis badeigularis	–	–	●	–	–	–	–	–	–
Stachyris oglei	–	–	●	–	–	–	–	–	–
Heterophasia gracilis	–	–	●	●	●	●	●	●	–
Spelaeornis longicaudatus	–	–	–	–	●	●	–	–	–
Garrulax virgatus	–	–	–	–	●	–	–	●	–
Garrulax austeni	–	–	–	–	●	–	–	●¹	–
Sitta victoriae	–	–	–	–	–	–	–	●¹	–
Total	9	15	14	9	11	4	2	7	

● Present ? Present? Threatened spp. shown in **bold** } see 'Status and habitat' table
O Extinct? R Reintroduced
X Extinct I Introduced
Other EBAs, SAs

¹ In Chin hills, known only from vicinity of Mt Victoria.

summit area of Mt Victoria and near Mindat (22 km to the north-west of Mt Victoria) in 1995 (Robson 1995; see Harrap and Quinn 1996).

■ Threats and conservation

The principal threat facing the EBA is deforestation and forest degradation. Logging, both legal and illegal, is leading rapidly to the clearance of large areas of forest in north-east India, particularly affecting the tropical lowland forests, and is even taking place within some protected areas. In the subtropical and temperate forests in the mountains, shifting agriculture and livestock-grazing have cleared and degraded the forests in many areas. Shifting agriculture can be sustainable if practised on a small scale using clearing cycles of 15–20 years, but in many areas increased population pressure has led to a rapid reduction in this cycle—for example in Meghalaya, where this has resulted in the loss of large areas of forest and severe soil erosion (Champion 1936, Collins *et al.* 1991, Katti *et al.* 1992, Ma Shi-lai *et al.* 1995). In eastern Nepal, the proposed Arun III hydroelectric project threatens to flood one of the best remaining areas of forest in this part of the EBA (Poole 1994, T. P. and C. Inskipp *in litt.* 1993).

Eleven of the restricted-range species are considered to be threatened, a greater number than in any other EBA of this region. They include the species with very small ranges described above, which are particularly vulnerable to habitat loss, and several species which appear to occur at low densities, some of which (e.g. *Tragopan blythii*, *Lophophorus sclateri*) are subject to hunting pressure (McGowan and Garson 1995). The threatened Grey-sided Thrush *Turdus feae*, a restricted-range species which breeds in the Shanxi mountains (EBA 136), is a non-breeding visitor to the southern part of the Eastern Himalayas (Nagaland, Manipur, Khasi and Chin hills). More widespread threatened species which occur within the EBA include Hume's Pheasant *Syrmaticus humiae*, Wood Snipe *Gallinago nemoricola*, Blyth's Kingfisher *Alcedo hercules*, Rufous-necked Hornbill *Aceros nipalensis* and Beautiful Nuthatch *Sitta formosa* (all classified as Vulnerable).

The EBA contains about 30 protected areas which include areas of suitable habitat for the restricted-range birds (Li Wenhua and Zhao Xian-jing 1989, IUCN 1990, 1993). They are spread through most parts of the EBA, although there are none in the Chin hills in Myanmar and there are only a few relatively small reserves in Nagaland, Manipur, Cachar and the

K. D. Bishop

Natural habitats are under pressure in many parts of this EBA, but extensive tracts of pristine forest remain in Bhutan.

Khasi hills. Namdapha National Park is particularly important because it contains large areas of the EBA's key habitats and supports populations of many of the restricted-range species, including at least one of the two species which are known only from eastern Arunachal Pradesh (Ripley *et al.* 1991). Other large protected areas include Mehao and Pakhui Sanctuaries and Blue Mountain National Park in India, Black Mountain and Royal Manas National Parks in Bhutan, and the Makalu-Barun National Park (which now includes the Apsuwa river area: J. Bland *in litt.* 1997; see Tymstra 1993) in Nepal.

A proposed protected area which fills an important gap in coverage of the EBA is Natma Taung (Mt Victoria) in the Chin hills, a locality for *Sitta victoriae*. There is also a need for increased protected-area coverage in the Nagaland, Manipur, Cachar and Khasi hills, and a proposed reserve in the Barail range is likely to be important for the restricted-range species.

131 Assam plains

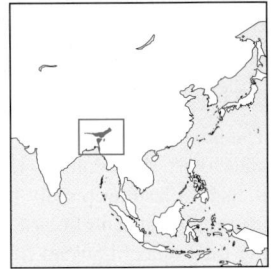

Key habitats Wet grassland, reedbeds, scrub on marshy ground

Main threats Major habitat loss (e.g. due to agriculture, urbanization, industrialization)

Biological importance ● ● ●
Current threat level ● ● ●

Area 126,000 km²   **Altitude** 0–1,000 m

Countries Bangladesh, India, Nepal

Restricted-range species	Threatened	Total
Confined to this EBA	3	3
Present also in other EBAs, SAs	0	0
Total	3	3

■ General characteristics

This EBA includes the plains and foothills of the Brahmaputra watershed in the north-east of the Indian subcontinent. It is centred around the Indian state of Assam, and includes the lowlands of extreme eastern Nepal (at least formerly), the Indian states of Sikkim, northern West Bengal, Arunachal Pradesh, Nagaland, Manipur and Meghalaya, the Bangladeshi divisions of Rajshahi and Chittagong, presumably southern Bhutan, and possibly the extreme west of Myanmar.

The original vegetation of the plains was seasonally inundated floodplain forest and grassland, with an adjacent strip of undulating land ('terai') at the base of the foothills; this land was often marshy and

supported tall elephant grass and forest. Most of the plains and foothills are now, however, converted to agricultural land (Gaston 1984, Ali and Ripley 1987), and the restricted-range birds are associated with the remaining grassland and wetland habitats, mainly at altitudes below 1,000 m.

This EBA is virtually enclosed by the mountains of the Eastern Himalayas EBA (130), and there is a slight overlap in the altitudinal ranges of the birds from the two. However, the species of that EBA breed in forest rather than in open habitats, and generally at higher altitudes, although many are altitudinal migrants which move down to forest in the foothills outside the breeding season.

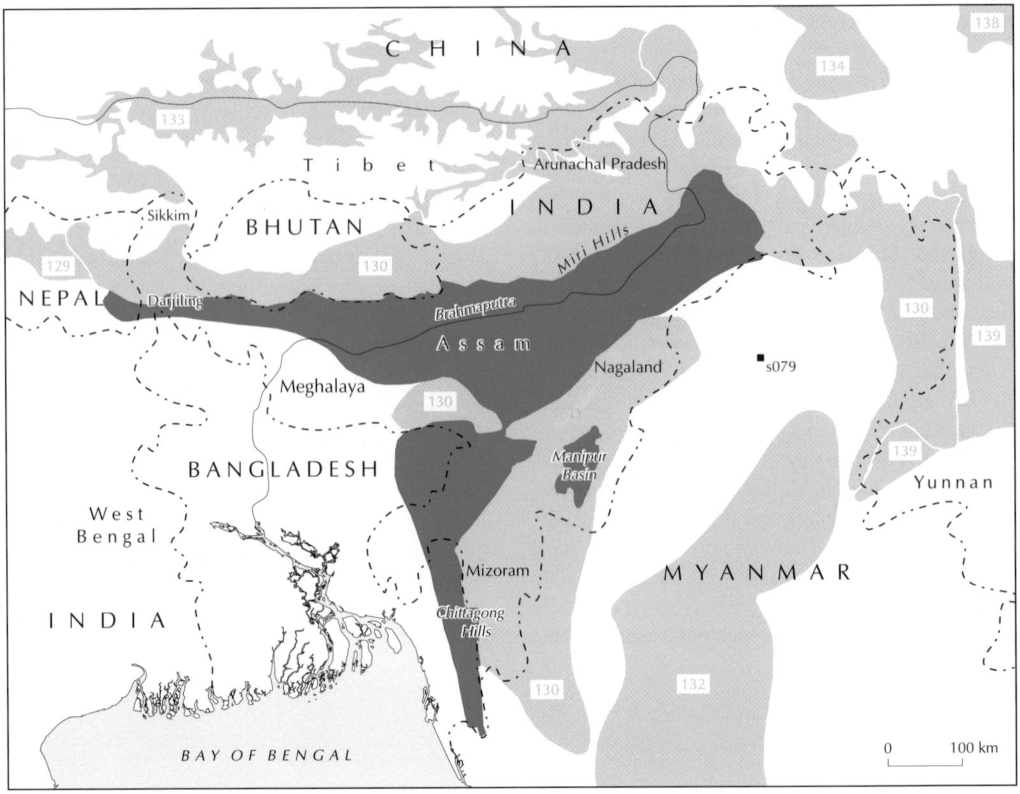

Status and habitat of restricted-range species

Species (ordered taxonomically)	Global status	Other EBAs (and SAs)	Altitude (m)	Habitat
Manipur Bush-quail *Perdicula manipurensis*	VU	—	Foothills to 1,000	Damp grassland (inc. tall elephant grass) and scrub, esp. along watercouses or ravines in foothills
Marsh Babbler *Pellorneum palustre*	VU	—	Lowlands to 800	Reedbeds, tall grassland and scrub alongside swamps and rivers
Black-breasted Parrotbill *Paradoxornis flavirostris*[1]	VU	—	Lowlands and foothills, locally to 2,400	Reedbeds, elephant grass, scrub and grassland along rivers; in the hills, grassland, bamboo and elephant grass

Global status (see p. 679 for definitions)

EX	Extinct	} with year	cd Conservation Dependent
EW	Extinct in the Wild	} of last record	
			nt Near Threatened
CR	Critical	} threatened species	lc Least Concern
EN	Endangered		DD Data Deficient
VU	Vulnerable		NE Not Evaluated

Other EBAs (and SAs) (see p. 77 for locations)
Bracketed numbers are Secondary Areas.   [x] Extinct in that EBA or SA.

Notes
[1] The record of this species on Mt Victoria (EBA 130) in western Myanmar in Smythies (1986) is in error for Spot-breasted Parrotbill *P. guttaticollis* (T. P. Inskipp verbally 1995).

■ Restricted-range species

The restricted-range birds are found in a variety of grassland, scrub and wetland habitats on the plains, often along rivers, and in the foothills. However, *Perdicula manipurensis* is confined to the foothills, and has a stronghold in the Manipur basin, where neither of the other species has been recorded. *Paradoxornis flavirostris* sometimes ranges to well above 1,000 m, but is much scarcer in the hills than the plains (Ali and Ripley 1987). *Pellorneum palustre* has not been recorded in the north-western section of the EBA, to the east of the Miri hills. There has been relatively little recent ornithological activity in this region, and there are few recent records of any of the three species.

■ Threats and conservation

The principal threat to this EBA is the continuing conversion of natural grassland and wetland to agricultural and urban land-uses, together with agricultural intensification and industrialization. These habitats are now much reduced in area and fragmented (see Majumdar and Brahmachari 1988, Rahmani 1988, Scott 1989).

All three restricted-range species are listed as threatened because of this loss of habitat and the paucity of recent records. A considerable number of more widespread threatened species occur, or formerly occurred, in the grasslands and wetlands of this EBA. Some of these are confined to the northern Indian subcontinent and Myanmar: White-bellied Heron *Ardea insignis* (classified as Endangered), Pink-headed Duck *Rhodonessa caryophyllacea* (Criti-cal, but probably already extinct), Swamp Francolin *Francolinus gularis* (Vulnerable), Jerdon's Babbler *Chrysomma altirostre* (Vulnerable), Rufous-vented Prinia *Prinia burnesii* (Vulnerable) and Yellow Weaver *Ploceus megarhynchus* (Vulnerable). Others range elsewhere: Spot-billed Pelican *Pelecanus philippensis* (Vulnerable), Lesser Adjutant *Leptoptilos javanicus* (Vulnerable), Greater Adjutant *L. dubius* (Endangered), White-winged Duck *Cairina scutulata* (Endangered), Pallas's Sea-eagle *Haliaeetus leucoryphus* (Vulnerable), Masked Finfoot *Heliopais personata* (Vulnerable), Bengal Florican *Houbaropsis bengalensis* (Endangered) and Bristled Grass-warbler *Chaetornis striatus* (Vulnerable).

There are over 30 protected areas in or near this EBA, including such large and important ones as Kaziranga National Park. They are spread throughout the area, but there is little published information to indicate which of them supports populations of the restricted-range (and other threatened) species or includes areas of habitat suitable for them. There has been extensive encroachment into protected areas in this part of India by people displaced by floods, erosion or inter-ethnic conflict; this is affecting grassland habitats, and wetland quality is deteriorating rapidly due to siltation and eutrophication; and in the protected areas management practices are oriented solely towards large mammals (Bhattacharjee 1995). There is therefore a need to investigate which of the established protected areas support the restricted-range birds, and to determine whether the current protected-area system is adequate and whether management practices are appropriate.

132 Irrawaddy plains

PRIORITY
HIGH

Key habitats Thorn forest and scrub, monsoon forest, agricultural land

Main threats Major habitat loss (e.g. due to agriculture)

Biological importance ● ● ●
Current threat level ● ● ●

Area 160,000 km²   **Altitude** 0–1,000 m

Countries Myanmar

Restricted-range species	Threatened	Total
Confined to this EBA	1	2
Present also in other EBAs, SAs	0	0
Total	1	2

■ General characteristics

The plains of the Irrawaddy and upper Sittang rivers in central Myanmar have a dry and seasonal climate, as they lie in the rain-shadow of mountain ranges which run from north to south through the western part of the country. The natural habitats of this region are known as 'indaing': tropical dry deciduous monsoon forest dominated by species of *Dipterocarpus*; there is also a small area of tropical thorn forest in the driest central part (Champion and Seth 1968, Collins *et al.* 1991). The restricted-range birds of the EBA are confined to this dry zone, at altitudes below 1,000 m, and this contour, together with the records of these birds, have been used to define an approximate boundary for the EBA.

■ Restricted-range species

The EBA's two restricted-range bird species are found in dry forest and scrub. *Turdoides gularis* has adapted to man-modified habitats, and is common and widespread within the EBA (Smythies 1986). *Crypsirina cucullata* was also common in the past, but it appears to require more extensive areas of forest or scrub and there had been few records in recent years until it was found in 1995 to be locally common (K. D. Bishop *in litt.* 1993, C. R. Robson verbally 1995). Two other taxa which are confined to this EBA, *Mirafra* (*assamica*) *microptera* and *Pericrocotus* (*erythropygius*) *albifrons*, may warrant full species status (Alström in prep., P. Alström *in litt.* 1996).

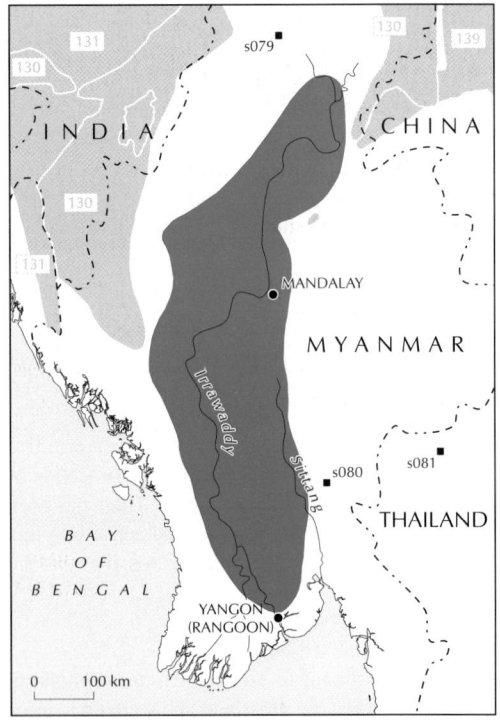

■ Threats and conservation

The Irrawaddy plains are now almost entirely cleared for agriculture (Collins *et al.* 1991). *Crypsirina cucullata* is classified as threatened because it appeared that it had been seriously affected by this loss

Status and habitat of restricted-range species

Species (ordered taxonomically)	Global status	Other EBAs (and SAs)	Altitude (m)	Habitat
White-throated Babbler *Turdoides gularis*	lc	—	Plains to 600	Thorn scrub, thickets, agricultural land
Hooded Treepie *Crypsirina cucullata*	VU	—	Lowlands to 1,000	Dry forest, scrub, agricultural land, gardens

Global status (see p. 679 for definitions)	EX Extinct EW Extinct in the Wild ⎱ with year of last record	CR Critical EN Endangered VU Vulnerable ⎱ threatened species	cd Conservation Dependent nt Near Threatened lc Least Concern	DD Data Deficient NE Not Evaluated

Other EBAs (and SAs) (see p. 77 for locations): bracketed numbers are Secondary Areas; ˣ extinct in that EBA or SA.

The plains of Myanmar have a long history of human habitation and cultivation, and natural habitats have been greatly modified.

P. Alström

of natural habitat, although more recent information suggests that its position is unlikely to be serious (C. R. Robson verbally 1995). More widespread threatened species which occur in this EBA (or formerly occurred here) include Spot-billed Pelican *Pelecanus philippensis* (classified as Vulnerable), White-bellied Heron *Ardea insignis* (Endangered), Lesser Adjutant *Leptoptilos javanicus* (Vulnerable), Greater Adjutant *L. dubius* (Endangered), Pallas's Sea-eagle *Haliaeetus leucoryphus* (Vulnerable) and Jerdon's Babbler *Chrysomma altirostre* (Vulner-

able); these are all wetland birds, with different habitat requirements from the restricted-range species.

There are several gazetted and proposed protected areas in central Myanmar, such as Shwesettaw, Minwun Taung and Maymyo Game Sanctuaries (Collins *et al.* 1991, MacKinnon in press), but it is not known whether they contain areas of habitat representative of the EBA. There is therefore a need for ornithological surveys and possibly a review of the boundaries of these protected areas.

133 Southern Tibet

Key habitats Mixed broadleaf–coniferous forest edge, scrub, grassland	**Area** 63,000 km²	**Altitude** 2,700–5,000 m	

Countries China, India

Restricted-range species	Threatened	Total
Confined to this EBA	1	2
Present also in other EBAs, SAs	0	0
Total	1	2

Main threats Unquantified habitat loss

Biological importance ● ● ○

Current threat level ● ○ ○

■ General characteristics

The area covered by this EBA lies at the southern edge of the Qinghai–Tibetan plateau, immediately to the north of the Himalayas. It includes the valleys of the Tsangpo (or Yarlung Zangbo) river and its tributaries, and several smaller, neighbouring valleys in southern Tibet autonomous region of China, and north-east Sikkim and possibly northern Arunachal Pradesh in India.

The boundary for the EBA has been drawn based on the documented records and altitudinal limits of the restricted-range bird species present. There are, however, some large gaps in their known distributions in the remoter parts of this ornithologically poorly known region (see Vaurie 1972), so a tentative definition of the area is the best that can be attempted thus far. There is minor geographical overlap between this EBA and the Eastern Himalayas (EBA 130).

■ Restricted-range species

The two species endemic to Southern Tibet are found in the subalpine zone, on the edge of coniferous and mixed broadleaf–coniferous forest and in adjacent rhododendron and juniper scrub and open habitats. They are both locally common (Ali and Ripley 1987, P. Alström *in litt.* 1993). *Crossoptilon harmani* is often considered to be a subspecies of White Eared-

Status and habitat of restricted-range species

Species (ordered taxonomically)	Global status	Other EBAs (and SAs)	Altitude (m)	Habitat
Tibetan Eared-pheasant *Crossoptilon harmani*	VU	—	(2,400–) 3,000–5,000	Edge of mixed broadleaf-coniferous forest; rhododendron, juniper and deciduous scrub; grassland
Giant Babax *Babax waddelli*	nt	—	2,700–4,400	Dense deciduous scrub above treeline, coniferous forest edge

Global status (see p. 679 for definitions)
EX Extinct — with year of last record
EW Extinct in the Wild
CR Critical — threatened species
EN Endangered
VU Vulnerable
cd Conservation Dependent
nt Near Threatened
lc Least Concern
DD Data Deficient
NE Not Evaluated

Other EBAs (and SAs) (see p. 77 for locations): bracketed numbers are Secondary Areas; ˣ extinct in that EBA or SA.

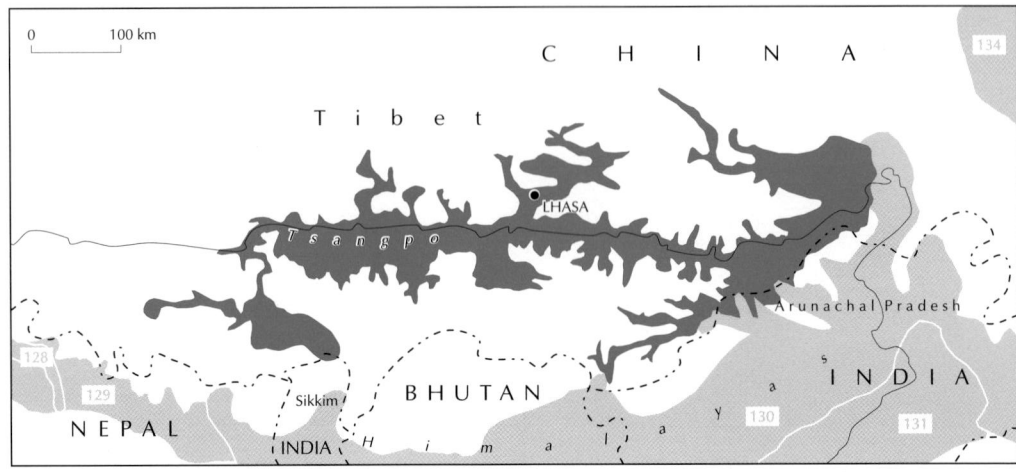

0 _____ 100 km

C H I N A
134

T i b e t

●LHASA

Tsangpo

Arunachal Pradesh

128

129

Sikkim

B H U T A N

130

131

N E P A L

INDIA

I N D I A

H i m a l a y a s

pheasant *C. crossoptilon* (e.g. Vaurie 1972), but is here treated as a full species following Ludlow (1951) and Sibley and Monroe (1990).

■ Threats and conservation

Crossoptilon harmani is considered threatened because deforestation and hunting may be having a significant impact on it (McGowan and Garson 1995), although the tameness of the flocks observed near Samye monastery suggests that hunting does not occur there (P. Alström *in litt.* 1993). The threat posed to the EBA by deforestation is unclear (see Smil 1984, 1993), and extensive pine and mixed coniferous forests with prickly oak and rhododendron remain to the east of Lhasa (Robson 1986). A more widespread threatened species which occurs (at least as a non-breeding visitor) in the EBA is Black-necked Crane *Grus nigricollis* (classified as Vulnerable), but this is a wetland bird with different habitat requirements to the restricted-range species.

Part of Medog Nature Reserve appears to lie within the EBA, and there are three other large protected areas close to the EBA which may contain areas of habitat suitable for the restricted-range birds (IUCN 1992d, 1993) although they have not yet been recorded there.

134 Eastern Tibet

PRIORITY
HIGH

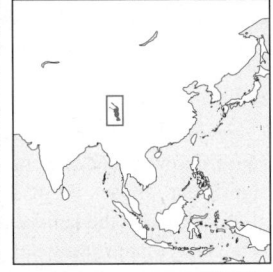

Key habitats Juniper/rhododendron scrub, mixed coniferous forest, barren areas above treeline

Main threats Unquantified habitat loss (e.g. due to logging)

Biological importance ● ● ○
Current threat level ● ○ ○

Area 65,000 km²   **Altitude** 3,600–4,600 m

Countries China

Restricted-range species	Threatened	Total
Confined to this EBA	0	2
Present also in other EBAs, SAs	0	0
Total	0	2

■ General characteristics

This EBA is located in the eastern part of the Qinghai–Tibetan plateau, in eastern Tibet autonomous region and southern Qinghai province of China, and possibly extends into adjacent parts of north-west Sichuan province. Several large valleys cut into the plateau in this region, including those of the Tongtian river (the upper reaches of the Chang Jiang or Yangtze), the Lancang Jiang (the upper Mekong) and the Nu Jiang (the upper Salween). This area is inaccessible and is poorly known ornithologically; the two restricted-range species present there are known from scattered records in the vicinity of these rivers and their tributaries, where they have been recorded in scrub, forest and open areas in the subalpine zone. The boundary of the EBA has therefore been drawn only tentatively, and is based on the documented records and altitudinal ranges of the two species.

■ Restricted-range species

Both of the species confined to this EBA appear to be rather scarce and localized (P. Alström *in litt.* 1993). Their habitat requirements differ somewhat, as *Emberiza koslowi* occurs in scrub and adjacent open areas on the valley slopes, while *Babax koslowi* is found in the valley bottoms (C. R. Robson *in litt.* 1993). However, they appear to have generally similar distributions, although *E. koslowi* has not been recorded in the southern third of the EBA (south of 31°N) (see Vaurie 1972, Robson 1986, Olsson 1995).

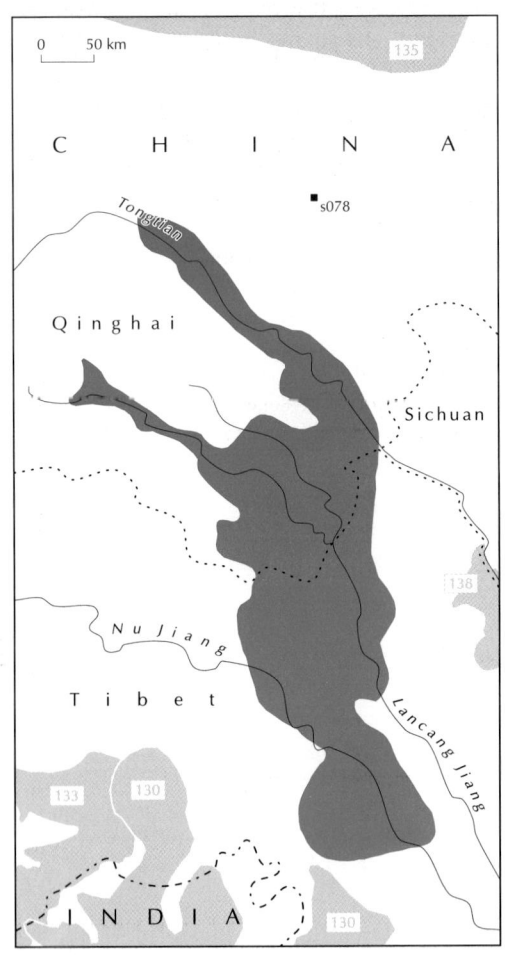

Status and habitat of restricted-range species

Species (ordered taxonomically)	Global status	Other EBAs (and SAs)	Altitude (m)	Habitat
Tibetan Babax *Babax koslowi*	nt	—	c.3,650 –4,500	Juniper forest and scrub, mixed fir and juniper forest, scrub bordering agricultural land
Tibetan Bunting *Emberiza koslowi*	nt	—	c.3,600 –4,600	Barren areas, juniper and rhododendron scrub above treeline

Global status (see p. 679 for definitions)	EX Extinct EW Extinct in the Wild } with year of last record	CR Critical EN Endangered VU Vulnerable } threatened species	cd Conservation Dependent nt Near Threatened lc Least Concern	DD Data Deficient NE Not Evaluated

Other EBAs (and SAs) (see p. 77 for locations): bracketed numbers are Secondary Areas; ˣ extinct in that EBA or SA.

The typical habitat of Tibetan Bunting *Emberiza koslowi* is scrub and adjacent open areas on valley slopes, while Tibetan Babax *Babax koslowi* is found in forest and scrub on the lower slopes and valley bottoms.

R. P. Martins

■ Threats and conservation

There is some logging of forest within the EBA, which may be reducing the habitat of *Babax koslowi* (M. Beaman *in litt.* 1993), but neither this species nor *Emberiza koslowi* appears to be immediately threatened by loss of habitat (P. Alström *in litt.* 1993). A more widespread threatened species which occurs in subalpine forest and adjacent open habitats in the EBA is White Eared-pheasant *Crossoptilon crossoptilon* (classified as Vulnerable).

The only large protected area within the Eastern Tibet EBA appears to be Longbao (IUCN 1992d, 1993), a wetland site which is unlikely to be important for the area's restricted-range species. However, both species were recorded in Beizha Forest Reserve, Nangqian, in 1992 (Robson 1993a).

135 Qinghai mountains

Key habitats Scrub, rocky areas, grassy slopes, possibly coniferous forest	**Area** 230,000 km²	**Altitude** 1,800–3,500 m
	Countries China	

Main threats Unquantified habitat loss

Biological importance ● ○ ○
Current threat level ● ○ ○

Restricted-range species	Threatened	Total
Confined to this EBA	0	2
Present also in other EBAs, SAs	0	0
Total	0	2

■ General characteristics

This EBA is defined by the distributions of two restricted-range species, which are recorded (in the breeding season) from northern Qinghai and central Gansu provinces, and along the border between Ningxia and Inner Mongolia autonomous regions of China. They are known by scattered records in the Qaidam basin and adjacent mountains, the mountains around Qinghai Lake, the mountains around the upper Huang He (or Yellow River) and its tributaries (in the vicinity of the cities of Xining and Lanzhou), and the Helan Shan. These species are so poorly known that it has only been possible to define an approximate boundary to the EBA, based on the

documented records and the little that is known of their altitudinal ranges; much of the area enclosed by this boundary is unlikely to have suitable habitats for these birds.

The south-eastern extreme of the EBA lies close to the Central Sichuan mountains (EBA 137) and the West Sichuan mountains (EBA 138), but it is unclear whether there is any geographical overlap with them. The Northern Qinghai–Tibetan plateau (Secondary Area s078) is immediately to the south-west of this EBA, but it is defined by the range of Tibetan Rosefinch *Carpodacus roborowskii*, which occurs at very high altitudes, and there is no overlap in range with the birds of the Qinghai mountains.

Status and habitat of restricted-range species

Species (ordered taxonomically)	Global status	Other EBAs (and SAs)	Altitude (m)	Habitat
Rusty-necklaced Partridge *Alectoris magna*	nt	—	c.1,800–3,500	Barren rocky areas, grassy slopes
Ala Shan Redstart[1] *Phoenicurus alaschanicus*	nt	—	c.2,800–3,500	Scrub-covered hillsides, rocky ravines, possibly coniferous forest

Global status (see p. 679 for definitions)

EX	Extinct	with year of last record	cd	Conservation Dependent
EW	Extinct in the Wild		nt	Near Threatened
CR	Critical	threatened species	lc	Least Concern
EN	Endangered		DD	Data Deficient
VU	Vulnerable		NE	Not Evaluated

Other EBAs (and SAs) (see p. 77 for locations)
Bracketed numbers are Secondary Areas.   ˣ Extinct in that EBA or SA.

Notes
[1] Migratory: recorded outside the breeding season east of the breeding range in Henan and Shanxi provinces and near Beijing (Meyer de Schauensee 1984, Cheng Tso-hsin 1987).

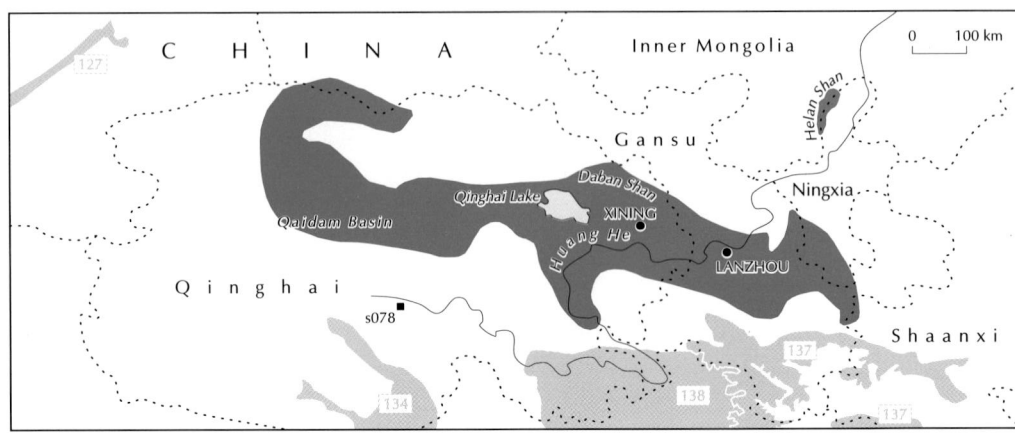

Ala Shan Redstart *Phoenicurus alaschanicus* has recently been found breeding on scrub-covered hillsides near the treeline.

G. Ekström

■ Restricted-range species

Alectoris magna is locally common on open slopes with low grasses and herbaceous vegetation (Liu Nai-fa *et al.* 1996), but appears to be patchily distributed. *Phoenicurus alaschanicus* is migratory, with non-breeding records from several Chinese provinces to the east of the EBA (Cheng Tso-hsin 1987). Its breeding range and habitat requirements remain poorly understood because of the sparse ornithological coverage of much of this region and because it is not clear whether many of the documented records relate to birds which are passage migrants rather than breeders. A pair with recently fledged young were seen on a scrub-covered hillside at c.3,300 m near Qinghai Lake in 1995 (P. Alström *in litt.* 1996), and the species has also been seen recently during the breeding season in the Helan Shan, in scrub near the treeline (He Fen-qi verbally 1993). *Alectoris magna* is not recorded from the Helan mountains (Cheng Tso-hsin 1987). Gansu Leaf-warbler *Phylloscopus (proregulus) kansuensis*, which is treated by Alström *et al.* (1997) as a full species, is known only from the eastern part of this EBA (P. Alström *in litt.* 1996).

■ Threats and conservation

Neither of the restricted-range species is listed as threatened. There are several large protected areas in the vicinity of the EBA (IUCN 1992d, 1993), but there is little information on whether they support populations of these two species. *Phoenicurus alaschanicus* has been recorded in the Helan Mountains Nature Reserve, and in or near to Yanchiwan Nature Reserve.

136 Shanxi mountains

PRIORITY
URGENT

Key habitats Broadleaf and mixed broadleaf–coniferous forest

Main threats Severe habitat loss (e.g. due to agriculture, logging)

Biological importance ● ● ○
Current threat level ● ● ○

Area 180,000 km²   **Altitude** 1,300–2,800 m

Countries China

Restricted-range species	Threatened	Total
Confined to this EBA	2	2
Present also in other EBAs, SAs	0	0
Total	2	2

■ General characteristics

This EBA includes the mountains of Shanxi and Hebei provinces and Beijing municipality in north-east China, and possibly also adjacent parts of Inner Mongolia autonomous region. The restricted-range species present are associated with a band of temperate-zone deciduous oak forest and pine forest which extends through the Luliang Shan and Taihang Shan in Shanxi to the mountains north of Beijing and the Yan Shan in north-east Hebei (see Hou 1979).

Status and habitat of restricted-range species

Species (ordered taxonomically)	Global status	Other EBAs (and SAs)	Altitude (m)	Habitat
Brown Eared-pheasant *Crossoptilon mantchuricum*	VU	—	>1,300	Broadleaf and mixed broadleaf–coniferous forest, and adjacent scrub and grassland
Grey-sided Thrush *Turdus feae*[1]	VU	—	Mountains	Broadleaf forest

Global status (see p. 679 for definitions)

EX	Extinct	} with year of last record	
EW	Extinct in the Wild		
CR	Critical	} threatened species	
EN	Endangered		
VU	Vulnerable		
cd	Conservation Dependent		
nt	Near Threatened		
lc	Least Concern		
DD	Data Deficient		
NE	Not Evaluated		

Other EBAs (and SAs) (see p. 77 for locations)
Bracketed numbers are Secondary Areas. ˣ Extinct in that EBA or SA.

Notes
[1] Migratory; winters in evergreen forest in mountains of north-east India, northern Myanmar and northern Thailand (inc. part of EBA 130).

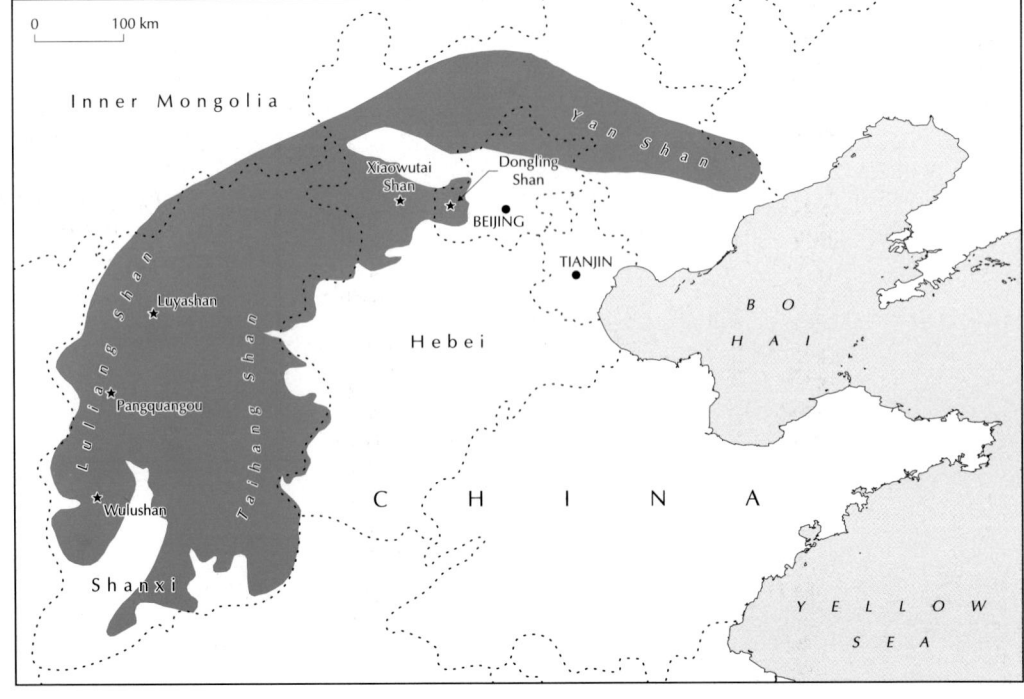

Only isolated areas of forest remain in this densely populated region of China, such as here in Pangquangou Nature Reserve.

Restricted-range species

This region of China is densely populated and extensively deforested, and the EBA's two restricted-range species are known from a small number of scattered, isolated forest remnants. Four of these forests have been established as protected areas for the conservation of *Crossoptilon mantchuricum*, which also occurs in at least two unprotected localities. Its distribution and ecology are relatively well studied (AOSNR 1990, Liu Huan-jin and Liu 1991), but the discovery of a new site in the western part of Beijing municipality in 1990 (Li Xiang-tao 1993, 1995) suggests that there may be undiscovered populations elsewhere in the EBA. *Turdus feae* is known relatively poorly, but there are recent records during the breeding season from at least four localities (Cai Gikan 1987, King 1987, Robson 1993b, P. Alström *in litt.* 1993). Another bird which is only known to breed in the forests of this EBA, *Ficedula (narcissina) elisae*, is probably best treated as a full species (Alström *et al.* in prep.).

Threats and conservation

Most of the natural forest in this part of China was lost and fragmented in the past, and the numbers of the restricted-range birds must have been much reduced. They are both listed as threatened because of continuing pressures on the remaining forests (see Smil 1984), and the eggs of *Crossoptilon mantchuricum* are collected for food (McGowan and Garson 1995). A more-widespread threatened forest species which is supposed to have been recorded from this EBA (see e.g. Cheng Tso-hsin 1987) is Reeves's Pheasant *Syrmaticus reevesii* (classified as Vulnerable), but the historical evidence for its occurrence here is questionable (Ding Chang-qing verbally 1996), and there have been no records of it from here in the last 10–20 years (McGowan and Garson 1995).

The most important sites for the conservation of the restricted-range birds are the protected areas established for *Crossoptilon mantchuricum*: Pangquangou, Wulushan and Luyashan Nature Reserves in Shanxi, and Xiaowutai Shan Nature Reserve in Hebei. Dongling Shan, the newly discovered site for this species near Beijing, has a population of 200–500 birds, but is threatened by plans to build a mine (Poole 1994).

137 Central Sichuan mountains

PRIORITY
HIGH

Key habitats Coniferous, broadleaf and mixed forest with bamboo

Main threats Major habitat loss (e.g. due to commercial logging, agriculture)

Biological importance ● ●
Current threat level ●

Area 140,000 km²   **Altitude** 1,500–3,700 m

Countries China

Restricted-range species	Threatened	Total
Confined to this EBA	5	10
Present also in other EBAs, SAs	0	1
Total	5	11

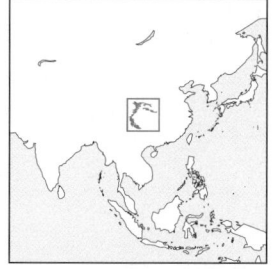

■ General characteristics

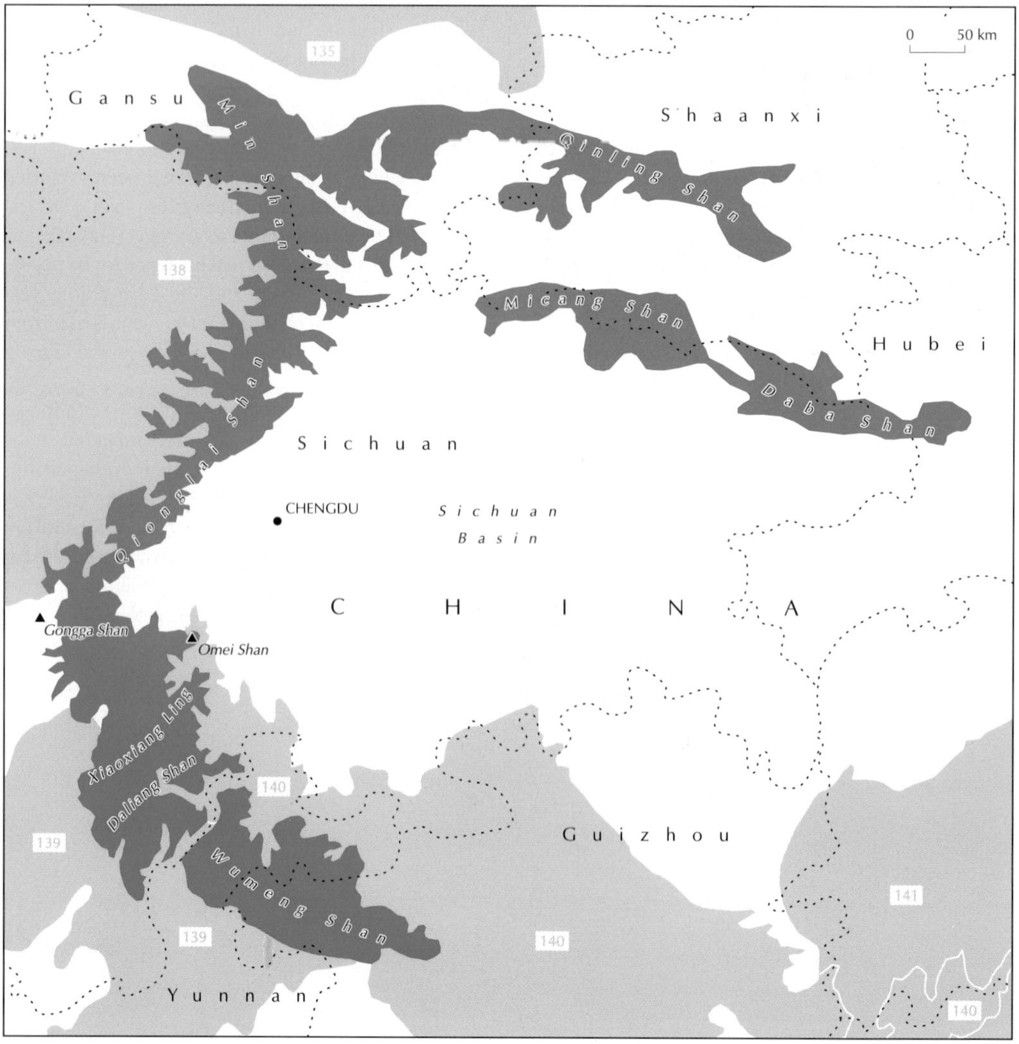

The Sichuan basin of central China is a fertile, densely populated region c.500 m above sea-level, and high mountains rise abruptly to several thousand metres (maximum 7,556 m at Gongga Shan) to the west of the basin and to over 3,000 m to the north of it. The mountains adjacent to the basin receive high rainfall and support rich forests. There are distinct subtropical, temperate, subalpine and alpine zones, similar to those on the south-facing Himalayas. This EBA comprises the forest areas of the temperate zone, and is represented on the map by all land between 1,500 and 3,650 m within the known distributions of the restricted-range birds. It spans several provinces: central and northern Sichuan, north-west Guizhou, extreme north-east Yunnan, southern Gansu, southern Shaanxi and extreme western Hubei (and possibly extreme western Henan).

In the high mountains to the west of the basin there is geographical overlap between this EBA and the West Sichuan mountains (EBA 138), but the birds of that EBA occur at higher altitudes in the subalpine zone. South-west of the basin, in the southern part of the Central Sichuan mountains, there is geographical overlap with the Chinese subtropical forests (EBA 140), but the birds of that EBA mainly occur at lower altitudes in the subtropical zone. The present EBA is also adjacent to the Qinghai mountains (EBA 135) and Yunnan mountains (EBA 139), but probably does not overlap geographically with either.

■ Restricted-range species

The restricted-range species—which include the monotypic endemic genus *Latoucheornis*—breed in coniferous, broadleaf and mixed broadleaf–coniferous forest in the temperate zone, mainly at c.1,800–3,650 m, and tend to be associated with areas having an understorey of bamboo or deciduous scrub. *Garrulax lunulatus* ranges down to 1,500 m, and *Aegithalos fuliginosus* down to 1,000 m, although there is some evidence that *A. fuliginosus* moves to these lower alti-

Temperate zone forest in Jiuzhaigou Nature Reserve.

M. J. Crosby

N. Arlott

During the breeding season, Rufous-headed Robin *Luscinia ruficeps* is known from just a handful of localities in the Qinling Shan and Min Shan ranges.

Status and habitat of restricted-range species

Species (ordered taxonomically)	Global status	Other EBAs (and SAs)	Altitude (m)	Habitat
Rufous-headed Robin *Luscinia ruficeps*[1]	VU	—	c.2,400–3,500	Bamboo and dense undergrowth in coniferous and mixed broadleaf–coniferous forest
Black-throated Blue Robin *Luscinia obscura*[2]	VU	—	c.3,050–3,400	Bamboo thickets in coniferous forest, scrub
Snowy-cheeked Laughingthrush *Garrulax sukatschewi*	VU	—	c.2,000–3,500	Undergrowth in coniferous and mixed broadleaf–coniferous forest
Barred Laughingthrush *Garrulax lunulatus*	nt	—	c.1,500–3,600	Bamboo thickets and undergrowth in mixed broadleaf–coniferous forest
Red-winged Laughingthrush *Garrulax formosus*[3]	nt	(s082)	c.1,200–2,600	Dense undergrowth and bamboo in broadleaf and mixed broadleaf–coniferous forest
Three-toed Parrotbill *Paradoxornis paradoxus*	lc	—	c.1,800–3,650	Bamboo and dense undergrowth in mixed broadleaf–coniferous forest
Grey-hooded Parrotbill *Paradoxornis zappeyi*	VU	—	c.2,500–3,200	Bamboo and other undergrowth in open coniferous and rhododendron forest
Rusty-throated Parrotbill *Paradoxornis przewalskii*	VU	—	c.2,440–3,050	Bamboo thickets and tussocks of grass in open coniferous forest
White-necklaced Tit *Aegithalos fuliginosus*	nt	—	c.1,000–2,600	Mixed broadleaf–deciduous forest, with well-developed understorey of deciduous scrub, rhododendrons or bamboo
Rusty-breasted Tit *Parus davidi*	lc	—	c.2,000–3,350	Coniferous and mixed broadleaf–coniferous forest with bamboo undergrowth
Slaty Bunting *Latoucheornis siemsseni*[4]	nt	—	c.1,800–2,000	Bamboo and other undergrowth in broadleaf and mixed broadleaf–coniferous forest, forest edge and clearings

Global status (see p. 679 for definitions)

EX Extinct } with year of last record
EW Extinct in the Wild
CR Critical } threatened species
EN Endangered
VU Vulnerable

cd Conservation Dependent
nt Near Threatened
lc Least Concern
DD Data Deficient
NE Not Evaluated

Other EBAs (and SAs) (see p. 77 for locations)
Bracketed numbers are Secondary Areas.
X Extinct in that EBA or SA.

Notes

[1] Migratory, recorded outside breeding season in Peninsular Malaysia (Meyer de Schauensee 1984).

[2] Migratory, recorded outside breeding season in Yunnan, southern China and northern Thailand (Meyer de Schauensee 1984).

[3] Possibly recorded in Guangxi autonomous region (Cheng Tso-hsin 1987).

[4] Migratory, with non-breeding records to the east of breeding range in Hubei, Anhui, Fujian and Guangdong provinces (Meyer de Schauensee 1984); one specimen collected Fujian in June, so possibly breeds there (Byers *et al.* 1995).

Distribution patterns of restricted-range species

Species (ordered geographically)	Micang Shan, Daba Shan	Qinling Shan	Min Shan	Qionglai Shan[1]	Omei Shan	Xiaoxiang Ling, Daliang Shan	Wumeng Shan	Other EBAs, SAs
Garrulax lunulatus	●	●	●	●	–	●	–	–
Aegithalos fuliginosus	●	●	●	●	–	●	–	–
Paradoxornis paradoxus	●	●	●	●	●	●	–	–
Latoucheornis siemsseni	●	●	●	●	●	●	–	–
Luscinia ruficeps	–	●	●	–	–	–	–	–
Luscinia obscura	–	●	●	●	–	–	–	–
Parus davidi	?	●	●	●	●	●	–	–
Garrulax sukatschewi	–	–	●	–	–	–	–	–
Paradoxornis przewalskii	–	–	●	–	–	–	–	–
Garrulax formosus	–	–	●	●	●	●	●	●
Paradoxornis zappeyi	–	–	–	●	●	●	●	–
Total	4	7	10	7	5	7	2	

● Present ? Present?
○ Extinct? R Reintroduced
X Extinct I Introduced

Threatened spp. shown in **bold**
Other EBAs, SAs
} see 'Status and habitat' table

[1] Includes adjacent slopes of Daxue Shan

Logs floating down a mountain river illustrate the scale of some of the logging operations outside the panda reserves.

M. J. Crosby

tudes only outside the breeding season (Harrap and Quinn 1996). *Garrulax formosus* appears to breed mainly in the temperate zone and descend to subtropical forests only outside the breeding season, when it overlaps in range and habitat requirements with the birds of EBA 140.

Several restricted-range species occur widely within the EBA, but some others seem far more localized, although much undoubtedly remains to be learned about their distributions in this poorly known region. *Paradoxornis przewalskii* and *Garrulax sukatschewi* are only known from the Min Shan, and *Luscinia obscura* and *L. ruficeps* are both recorded from just a handful of breeding localities in the northern half of the EBA. *Paradoxornis zappeyi* is confined to the southern part of the EBA.

■ Threats and conservation

The main threat to this EBA is forest loss. Forest cover has declined rapidly in Sichuan since the late 1960s, because timber quotas have consistently been set above sustainable levels, and forest has been cleared for cultivation and pasture. The province's forest cover is estimated to have declined from 19% to 12.6% between the early 1950s and 1988, mature natural forest being particularly affected (Smil 1984,

1993). Five of the restricted-range bird species are listed as threatened because they have particularly small ranges, and are therefore most likely to be vulnerable to this loss of habitat. A more widespread threatened species which occurs in the EBA is Wood Snipe *Gallinago nemoricola* (classified as Vulnerable). The only known wild population of Crested Ibis *Nipponia nippon* (listed as Critical), a species which formerly ranged widely in eastern Asia, is in the foothills of the Qinling Shan.

The location and extent of this EBA closely matches the current distribution of giant panda *Ailuropoda melanoleuca* (MacKinnon *et al.* 1989), for, like the restricted-range birds, this mammal occurs in temperate-zone forests with a bamboo understorey. The 13 reserves which have been established for giant panda, and for other large mammals such as takin *Budorcas taxicolor* and golden monkey *Rhinopithecus roxellanae*, contain large areas of habitat suitable for the restricted-range birds of this EBA, although their distribution and abundance within these protected areas is poorly known. Omei Shan is protected by its status as one of China's five sacred mountains (Robson 1989), although development for tourism there is causing some localized forest loss (M. J. Crosby pers. obs. 1991).

138 West Sichuan mountains

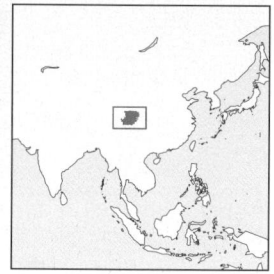

PRIORITY
URGENT

Key habitats Coniferous and mixed forest, rhododendron

Main threats Major habitat loss (e.g. due to commercial logging, overgrazing), hunting

Biological importance ● ● ●
Current threat level ● ● ●

Area 180,000 km² **Altitude** 2,700–4,900 m
Countries China

Restricted-range species	Threatened	Total
Confined to this EBA	3	3
Present also in other EBAs, SAs	0	0
Total	3	3

■ General characteristics

This Chinese EBA is in the eastern part of the Qinghai–Tibetan plateau and falls within central and western Sichuan, south-east Qinghai and southern Gansu provinces and extreme eastern Tibet autonomous region; it includes the Qionglai Shan, Min Shan, Daxue Shan and Shaluli Shan ranges. The restricted-range birds occur in the subalpine and upper temperate zones of these mountains, between about 2,700 and 4,900 m, and the boundary to the

Status and habitat of restricted-range species

Species (ordered taxonomically)	Global status	Other EBAs (and SAs)	Altitude (m)	Habitat
Chinese Monal *Lophophorus lhuysii*	VU	—	c.3,000–4,900, to 2,800 in winter	Coniferous forest immediately below treeline, rhododendrons, alpine meadows, cliffs and rocky areas above treeline
Sichuan Wood-owl *Strix davidi*	VU	—	c.2,700–4,200	Open coniferous and mixed broadleaf–coniferous forest
Sichuan Jay *Perisoreus internigrans*	VU	—	c.3,050–4,300	Dense coniferous forest with poorly developed understorey

Global status (see p. 679 for definitions)
EX Extinct
EW Extinct in the Wild } with year of last record
CR Critical
EN Endangered } threatened species
VU Vulnerable
cd Conservation Dependent
nt Near Threatened
lc Least Concern
DD Data Deficient
NE Not Evaluated

Other EBAs (and SAs) (see p. 77 for locations): bracketed numbers are Secondary Areas; ˣ extinct in that EBA or SA.

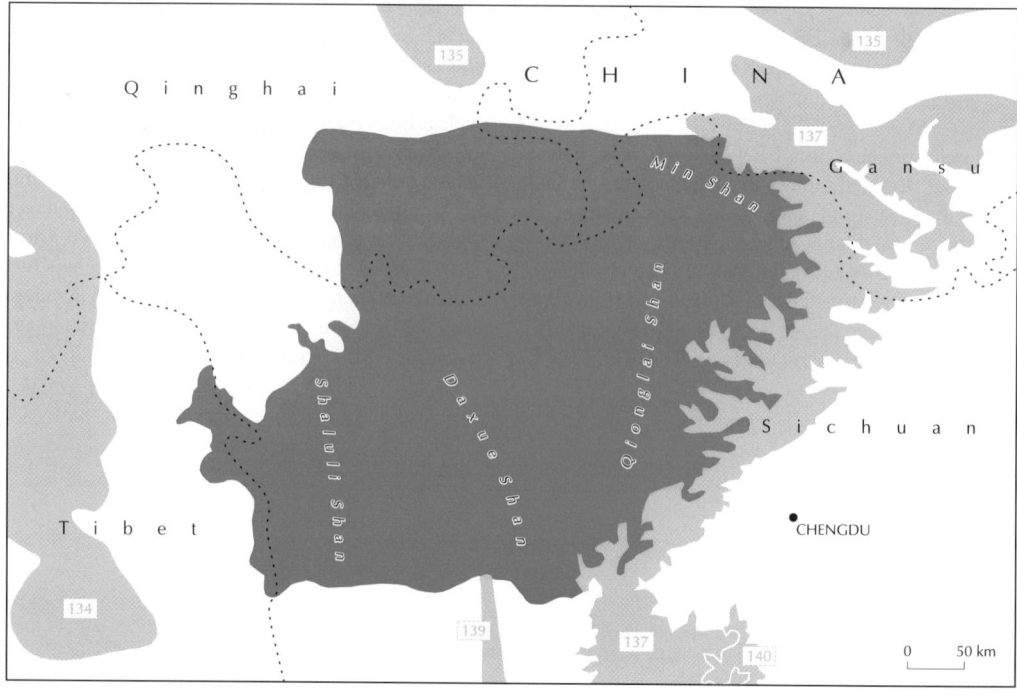

The endemic birds of this EBA occur in subalpine coniferous forest and in more open habitats above the treeline.

M. J. Crosby

EBA has been drawn only approximately, based upon the documented records of the birds and their altitudinal limits. However, detailed contour data are not available for most of the region, and much of the land within this boundary is above 4,900 m and unsuitable for the restricted-range species.

In the Qionglai Shan and Min Shan there is geographical overlap between this EBA and the Central Sichuan mountains (EBA 137), but the restricted-range birds of that EBA tend to occur at lower altitudes, in the temperate zone. The Yunnan mountains (EBA 139) are adjacent to the southern part of the West Sichuan mountains but there is probably no geographical overlap and the birds of that EBA also tend to occur at lower altitudes.

■ Restricted-range species

Of the three species present, *Perisoreus internigrans* and *Strix davidi* are found in subalpine coniferous forest, and *Lophophorus lhuysii* in rhododendron scrub and open areas above the treeline. The first two appear to be associated with relatively dry coniferous forest having a poorly developed understorey, in contrast to the restricted-range birds of the Central Sichuan mountains which occur in wetter forests with a dense understorey, typically of bamboo. All three species are known from the Qionglai Shan and Min Shan ranges (although *P. internigrans* only appears to be present in the north of the Qionglai

Shan), but their ranges are incompletely documented in the western part of the EBA, where they are all known by no more than a few widely scattered records.

■ Threats and conservation

The forests in the Daxue Shan and Shaluli Shan are part of the second most important timber-producing region in China, and are being rapidly exploited. Forest cover in Sichuan province is estimated to have been reduced from 19% to 12.6% between the early 1950s and 1988, with mature natural forest being particularly affected (Smil 1984, 1993). All three of the restricted-range species are classified as threatened: the two forest species because of this rapid rate of habitat loss, and *Lophophorus lhuysii* because of hunting and habitat degradation caused by overgrazing (McGowan and Garson 1995). A more widespread threatened species which occurs in the EBA is White Eared-pheasant *Crossoptilon crossoptilon* (classified as Vulnerable).

The restricted-range birds of this EBA occur in several of the reserves established for the conservation of giant panda *Ailuropoda melanoleuca* in the Qionglai Shan and Min Shan ranges (see IUCN 1992d, 1993), although *Perisoreus internigrans* appears to have been recorded in only two of these reserves in the Min Shan. There are no protected areas in the western part of the EBA.

139 Yunnan mountains

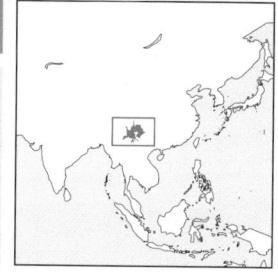

Key habitats Coniferous and mixed forest, bamboo, scrub

Main threats Major habitat loss (e.g. due to commercial logging, agriculture)

Biological importance ● ○ ○
Current threat level ● ● ○

Area 190,000 km²   **Altitude** 1,500–4,000 m

Countries China, Myanmar

Restricted-range species	Threatened	Total
Confined to this EBA	2	3
Present also in other EBAs, SAs	0	0
Total	2	3

■ General characteristics

This EBA is centred around the Hengduan Shan (mountains) of northern Yunnan province in south-central China, but the ranges of some of the restricted-range birds extend into south-west Sichuan and western Guizhou provinces, south-east Tibet autonomous region and north-east Myanmar. Several large rivers cut through the EBA, producing a pattern of high mountain ridges separated by deep valleys. The restricted-range birds are patchily distributed on the ridges and valley slopes in a variety of habitats including coniferous forest and bamboo thickets. There is minor geographical overlap between the Yunnan mountains EBA and the Eastern Himalayas (EBA 130) in extreme western Yunnan, north-east Myanmar and south-east Tibet. This EBA is also adjacent to the Central Sichuan mountains (EBA 137) and West Sichuan mountains (EBA 138), but probably does not overlap geographically with either of them.

■ Restricted-range species

The three restricted-range species vary in their habitat requirements and distributions. *Sitta yunnanensis* breeds in pine forest above 2,440 m; it is relatively widely distributed within the EBA and is the only one of the species to have been recorded from western Guizhou and south-east Tibet. *Paradoxornis brunneus* has a relatively wide altitudinal range and occurs in a variety of habitats; it is also widely distributed within the EBA and is the only species recorded from north-east Myanmar. *Garrulax bieti* is associated with bamboo in forested areas at altitudes above 3,050 m, and is known from only a few localities in the border region between Yunnan and Sichuan.

■ Threats and conservation

The forests of Yunnan are part of China's second most important region for forestry. However, loss of forest land here appears to be by far the worst in

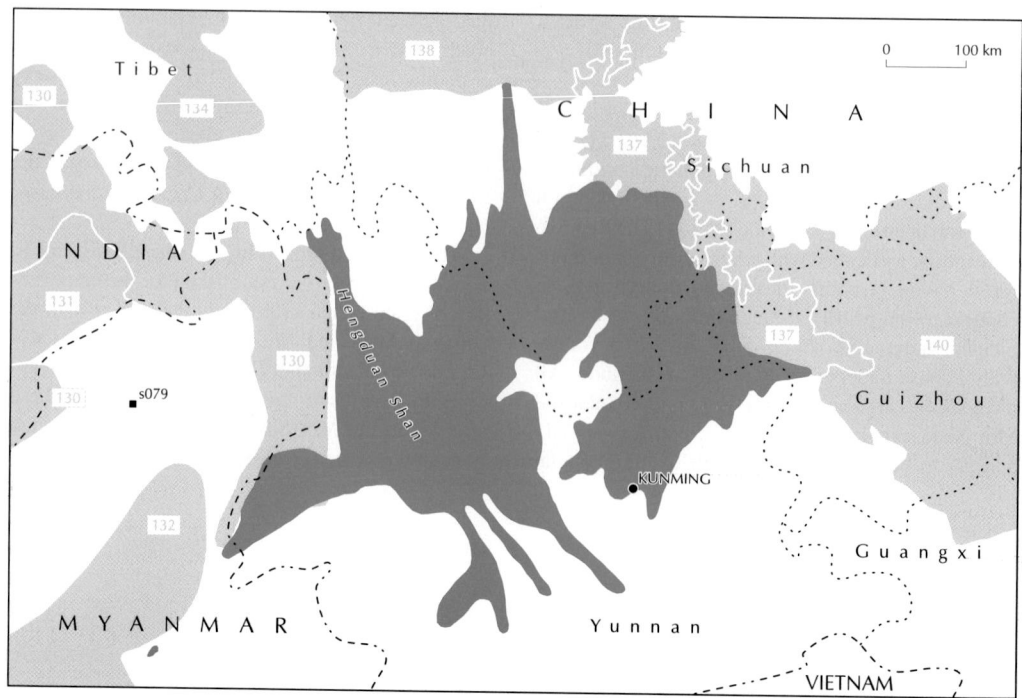

Status and habitat of restricted-range species

Species (ordered taxonomically)	Global status	Other EBAs (and SAs)	Altitude (m)	Habitat
White-speckled Laughingthrush *Garrulax bieti*	VU	—	c.3,050–3,650	Bamboo thickets in coniferous and mixed broadleaf–coniferous forest
Brown-winged Parrotbill *Paradoxornis brunneus*	nt	—	c.1,500–3,650	Bamboo thickets, long grass, scrub, agricultural land
Yunnan Nuthatch *Sitta yunnanensis*	VU	—	c.2,440–3,960, lower in winter	Open pine forest with little undergrowth

Global status (see p. 679 for definitions)	EX Extinct EW Extinct in the Wild	with year of last record	CR Critical EN Endangered VU Vulnerable	threatened species	cd Conservation Dependent nt Near Threatened lc Least Concern	DD Data Deficient NE Not Evaluated

Other EBAs (and SAs) (see p. 77 for locations): bracketed numbers are Secondary Areas; ˣ extinct in that EBA or SA.

China, and forest cover in the province is estimated to have declined from c.55% in the early 1950s to c.30% in 1975, with annual consumption of wood being approximately double its growth rate (Smil 1984). *Garrulax bieti* is listed as threatened because of habitat loss within its highly restricted range, and *Sitta yunnanensis* because it is confined to pine forest, although it does appear able to adapt to degraded and secondary forest (M. Beaman *in litt.* 1993). More widespread threatened species which occur in the EBA are Giant Nuthatch *Sitta magna* (classified as Vulnerable; another pine forest specialist but with a relatively wide altitudinal range of 1,200–3,400 m) and White Eared-pheasant *Crossoptilon crossoptilon* (Vulnerable; found at slightly higher altitudes than the restricted-range species).

There are 14 or so protected areas in this EBA (IUCN 1992d, IUCN 1993), at least eight of which may contain suitable habitat for the restricted-range bird species. However, there appears to be little published information on the occurrence of birds in these protected areas, and it is unclear whether *Garrulax bieti* occurs in any protected area. The Baima Snow Mountain and Haba Mountain Nature Reserves were established to conserve the threatened Yunnan snub-nosed monkey *Rhinopithecus bieti* (Li Wenhua and Zhao Xian-jing 1989, Long and Kirkpatrick 1991) which has a similar range and habitat requirements to the birds of the EBA, so these reserves are likely to be important for their conservation as well.

140 Chinese subtropical forests

PRIORITY CRITICAL

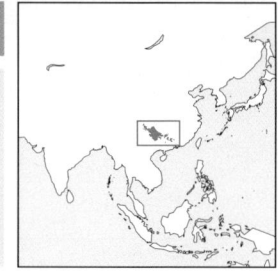

Key habitats Subtropical broadleaf forest

Main threats Severe habitat loss (e.g. due to commercial logging, agriculture)

Biological importance ● ● ●
Current threat level ● ● ●

Area 160,000 km² **Altitude** 300–2,200 m

Countries China

Restricted-range species	Threatened	Total
Confined to this EBA	4	5
Present also in other EBAs, SAs	0	0
Total	4	5

■ General characteristics

The restricted-range species of this Chinese EBA have been recorded in subtropical forest in the mountains to the south-west of the Sichuan basin in south-central Sichuan province and adjacent north-east Yunnan, and a few scattered localities in the mountains of Guizhou and northern Guangdong provinces and northern Guangxi autonomous region. Their distributions are exceptionally poorly known, and most natural forest in the lowlands and foothills has been cleared, so an approximate boundary to the EBA has been drawn to include all land between c.900 and c.1,500 m within their known ranges.

In Sichuan, this EBA overlaps geographically with the southern part of the Central Sichuan mountains (EBA 137), but the birds of that EBA breed mainly at higher altitudes in the temperate zone. In Guangdong and Guangxi, this EBA overlaps with the western part of the South-East Chinese mountains (EBA 141); most of the birds of that EBA are also associated with subtropical broadleaf forest, but for both regions the available information is not good enough to determine whether the birds of the two

EBAs are separated ecologically, or occur together in the same habitats.

■ Restricted-range species

The restricted-range species are recorded only from a small number of scattered localities, where they have been found in broadleaf forest in the subtropical zone below about 2,000 m. *Arborophila rufipectus* is only known from southern Sichuan and almost certainly in adjacent parts of north-east Yunnan where calls considered attributable to this species were heard in 1997 (King 1989a,b, He Fen-qi 1992, Dowell 1995, S. D. Dowell *in litt.* 1997). *Liocichla omeiensis* has been found on Omei Shan (Mt Emei) and other nearby mountains, and in the Daliang Shan (Dai Bo 1996). *Alcippe variegaticeps* and *Oriolus mellianus* are recorded from Sichuan and a few mountain ranges in the provinces to the south-east (Cheng Tso-hsin 1987, King 1989b, Crosby 1991, Wu Zhikang *et al.* 1994). *Phylloscopus emeiensis* was described from Omei Shan in Sichuan by Alström and Olsson (1995), but has also been recorded on Fanjing Shan in Guizhou (Crosby in prep.) and was

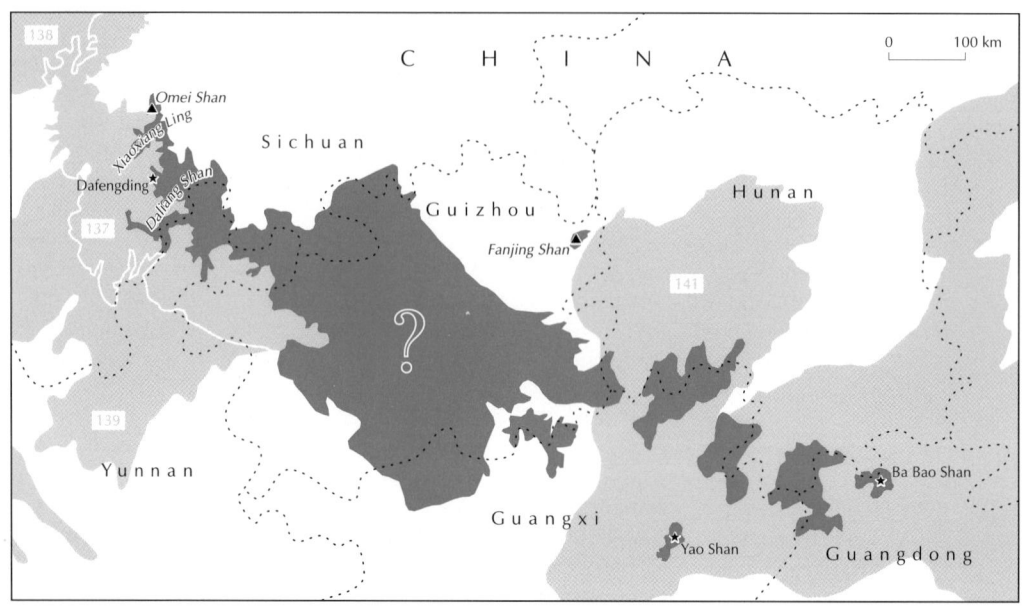

Status and habitat of restricted-range species

Species (ordered taxonomically)	Global status	Other EBAs (and SAs)	Altitude (m)	Habitat
Sichuan Partridge *Arborophila rufipectus*	CR	—	c.1,000–2,200	Broadleaf evergreen forest, bamboo thickets
Omei Shan Liocichla *Liocichla omeiensis*	VU	—	c.1,000–2,200	Dense undergrowth in broadleaf and mixed broadleaf–coniferous forest
Gold-fronted Fulvetta *Alcippe variegaticeps*	VU	—	c.700–1,900	Bamboo in broadleaf forest
Emei Leaf-warbler *Phylloscopus emeiensis*[1]	NE	—	c.1,000–1,900	Deciduous broadleaf forest with dense undergrowth
Silver Oriole *Oriolus mellianus*[2]	VU	—	c.300–1,700	Broadleaf forest

Global status (see p. 679 for definitions)

EX Extinct } with year
EW Extinct in } of last
the Wild } record
CR Critical
EN Endangered } threatened
VU Vulnerable } species
cd Conservation Dependent
nt Near Threatened
lc Least Concern
DD Data Deficient
NE Not Evaluated

Other EBAs (and SAs) (see p. 77 for locations)
Bracketed numbers are Secondary Areas. [x] Extinct in that EBA or SA.

Notes
[1] Newly described by Alström and Olsson (1995).
[2] Migratory, winters in Thailand and Cambodia (King *et al.* 1975).

Distribution patterns of restricted-range species

Species (ordered geographically)	Omei Shan	Xiaoxiang Ling, Daliang Shan	Guizhou mts	Northern Guangxi mts	Northern Guangdong mts	Other EBAs, SAs
Liocichla omeiensis	●	●	–	–	–	–
Phylloscopus emeiensis	●	–	●	–	?	–
Alcippe variegaticeps	●	●	–	●	–	–
Oriolus mellianus	–	●	●	●	●	–
Arborophila rufipectus	–	●	–	–	–	–
Total	3	4	2	2	1	

● Present   ? Present?   Threatened spp. shown in **bold** } see 'Status and habitat'
○ Extinct?   R Reintroduced

found to be common in the Daliang Shan and adjacent northern Yunnan in 1997 (R. Williams *in litt.* 1997).

■ Threats and conservation

Much natural forest in this EBA has already been cleared or degraded, and many of the remaining areas are under pressure. Thus, forest cover in Sichuan was estimated to have been reduced from 19% to 12.6% between the early 1950s and 1988 (Smil 1993), and the relatively accessible, low-altitude subtropical forests have been disproportionately badly affected. Four of the EBA's restricted-range species are threatened because of this continuing loss and fragmentation of their forest habitat. One, *Arborophila rufipectus*, is classified as Critical because of its highly restricted range, where it is recorded from a few forest fragments, all of them unprotected and under pressure from human activities (Dai Bo 1996).

Several protected areas are known or suspected to support populations of the restricted-range birds. Although *Arborophila rufipectus* has not yet been found in any protected area, it could occur in Dafengding Nature Reserve in Sichuan, where *Alcippe variegaticeps* has been recorded (King 1989b).

A. variegaticeps and *Oriolus mellianus* are historically known from the Yao Shan (Dayao Shan) range in Guangxi, where there is a reserve, although there are apparently no records of these species from there since it was gazetted, and this area has suffered two decades of rapid deforestation due to conversion of forest to agricultural land, with large additional areas destroyed by uncontrolled fires (Smil 1984, Lewthwaite 1996). *Liocichla omeiensis* is not recorded in any protected area, but this species, *Phylloscopus emeiensis* and *A. variegaticeps* have been recorded on Omei Shan, which, as one of China's five sacred mountains (Robson 1989), has not been subject to forest clearance—although development for tourism is causing some localized forest loss there, particularly in the subtropical zone (M. J. Crosby pers. obs. 1991). *P. emeiensis* also occurs in Fanjing Shan Nature Reserve. *Oriolus mellianus* has been recorded in Tuoda Forest Nature Reserve in Guizhou, but only in September, so it may be a passage migrant there.

Li Wenhua and Zhao Xian-jing (1989) describe several protected areas in Guizhou, Guangxi and Guangdong as containing subtropical broadleaf forest, but there appear to have been no documented ornithological surveys of these sites. It is likely that unprotected remnants of natural forest also support important populations of some of the restricted-range species, and the location and survey of these forests is required before conservation priorities can be established for this exceptionally poorly known area.

141 South-east Chinese mountains

Key habitats Subtropical broadleaf forest, mixed broadleaf–coniferous forest, coniferous forest

Main threats Severe habitat loss (e.g. due to agriculture), hunting

Biological importance ● ● ●
Current threat level ● ● ●

Area 610,000 km²   **Altitude** 300–1,900 m

Countries China

Restricted-range species	Threatened	Total
Confined to this EBA	4	4
Present also in other EBAs, SAs	1	1
Total	5	5

■ General characteristics

This EBA includes the hills and mountains of most of south-east China, in southern Anhui, southern Jiangsu, Zhejiang, Fujian, Jiangxi, Hunan, northern Guangdong and eastern Guizhou provinces, and Guangxi autonomous region (and possibly adjacent northern Vietnam). The natural vegetation here is subtropical broadleaf forest, with some coniferous and mixed forest in the mountains, and a zone of tropical lowland rain forest in the south. However, the human population density of this region has been high for the past several hundred years (Institute of Geography *et al.* 1994), and much of the natural forest cover had been cleared well before ornithological recording began. The bird species of the region which are treated here as having restricted ranges are thus those which are considered to have occupied areas of 50,000 km² or less throughout the period for which data exist, although the original ranges of some of

them are likely to have been larger than this threshold; all are forest birds. As virtually all level lowland forest in this part of China has been cleared, the EBA is represented on the map by all the land above 300 m, although only a small percentage of this area actually supports natural forest.

In Guizhou, Guangdong and Guangxi, this EBA overlaps with the eastern part of the Chinese subtropical forests (EBA 140). The birds of that EBA are also associated with subtropical broadleaf forest, but the available information on that region is not good enough to determine whether the birds of the two EBAs are separated ecologically, or occur together in the same habitats.

■ Restricted-range species

The restricted-range species vary in their habitat requirements and distributions, and some recent major extensions in their known ranges suggest that

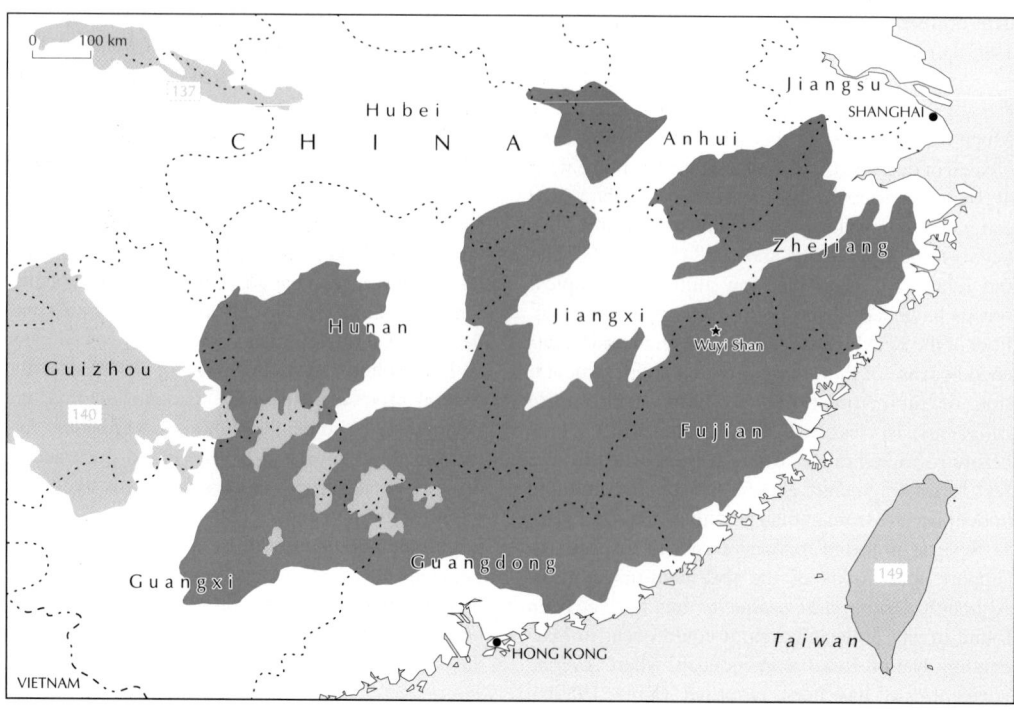

Status and habitat of restricted-range species

Species (ordered taxonomically)	Global status	Other EBAs (and SAs)	Altitude (m)	Habitat
White-eared Night-heron *Gorsachius magnificus*	CR	142	Foothills	Well-watered, densely forested areas, inc. bamboo
White-necklaced Partridge *Arborophila gingica*	VU	—	c.500–1,900	Broadleaf and mixed broadleaf-coniferous forest, scrub at the treeline
Cabot's Tragopan *Tragopan caboti*	VU	—	c.800–1,400	Broadleaf evergreen and mixed broadleaf-coniferous forest, bamboo
Elliot's Pheasant *Syrmaticus ellioti*	VU	—	c.300–1,500	Coniferous and mixed broadleaf-coniferous forest, scrub
Brown-chested Jungle-flycatcher *Rhinomyias brunneata*[1]	VU	—	Lowlands to c.1,100	Broadleaf evergreen forest, bamboo thickets

| Global status (see p. 679 for definitions) | EX Extinct ⎱ with year
EW Extinct in ⎰ of last
     the Wild ⎰ record
CR Critical ⎱
EN Endangered ⎰ threatened
VU Vulnerable ⎰ species | cd Conservation
     Dependent
nt Near Threatened
lc Least Concern
DD Data Deficient
NE Not Evaluated | Other EBAs (and SAs) (see p. 77 for locations)

Notes | Bracketed numbers are Secondary Areas.
ˣ Extinct in that EBA or SA.

[1] Migratory; non-breeding records from Thailand, Malaysia, Singapore and Nicobar Islands (EBA 126). |

much remains to be learned (see e.g. He Fen-qi and Lu Tai-chun 1991, Zheng Guang-mei and Zhang Zheng-wang 1993). *Gorsachius magnificus* is known historically (in this EBA) from Anhui, Zhejiang, Fujian and Guangxi, but the only recent records are from Guangxi (Zhou Fang *in litt.* 1993); a record from northern Vietnam (Vo Quy 1983) suggests that the boundary of the EBA should perhaps be extended to include part of that country. *Tragopan caboti* and *Arborophila gingica* apparently have a more southerly distribution than the other species, in southern Zhejiang, Fujian, southern Jiangxi, Guangdong, Guangxi and south-east Hunan, and range to higher altitudes (see Li Xiao-liu *et al.* 1990, Young *et al.* 1991, Ding Chang-qing and Zheng Guang-mei 1993). *Syrmaticus ellioti* breeds between 500 and 1,000 m (Ding Ping and Zhuge Yang 1990), and is the only species recorded from eastern Guizhou at the western extreme of the EBA (He Fen-qi and Lu Tai-chun 1991). *Rhinomyias brunneata* occurs in lowland forest, and is the only species recorded from southern Jiangsu.

■ Threats and conservation

This EBA is in one of the most densely populated regions in the world, and most of the natural forest has been cleared or modified as a result of the demands for agricultural land and timber. Rapid forest lost has taken place in most provinces in the EBA in the past fifty years, for example in Fujian, where timber reserves declined by 50% between 1949 and 1980 (Smil 1984). All five of the restricted-range species are listed as threatened, mainly as a result of this continuing loss and fragmentation of their habitat, but *Tragopan caboti* and *Syrmaticus ellioti* are also hunted for food (McGowan and Garson 1995). More widespread threatened forest species which breed in this EBA are Fairy Pitta *Pitta nympha* and Short-tailed Parrotbill *Paradoxornis davidianus* (both classified as Vulnerable). The threatened Yellow Bunting *Emberiza sulphurata*, which breeds in the Central Honshu montane forests (Secondary Area s090), is a non-breeding visitor to south-east China.

There are at least 40 protected areas within this EBA, most of which apparently have some suitable habitat for the restricted-range birds (Li Wenhua and Zhao Xian-jing 1989, IUCN 1992d). However, these reserves tend to be relatively small and isolated, and it is not clear how many of them contain large enough areas of suitable forest to support viable populations of these birds. The large Wuyi Shan Nature Reserve (565 km²) in Fujian is likely to be especially important for their long-term survival.

142 Hainan

Key habitats Montane evergreen forest, lowland evergreen rain forest

Main threats Severe habitat loss (e.g. due to timber extraction, agriculture, fuelwood collection)

Biological importance ● ● ●
Current threat level ● ● ●

Area 13,000 km² **Altitude** 600–1,800 m

Countries China

Restricted-range species	Threatened	Total
Confined to this EBA	2	2
Present also in other EBAs, SAs	2	2
Total	4	4

■ General characteristics

The island of Hainan (which constitutes a Chinese province) lies some 20 km off the southern tip of the Chinese mainland. Its natural vegetation is tropical evergreen rain forest (Whitmore 1984), but the lowlands are now almost completely deforested. The restricted-range species are found in the remaining areas of forest in the mountains in the centre and south-west of the island, so an approximate boundary to the EBA has been defined using the 300 m contour.

■ Restricted-range species

The habitat requirements, altitudinal ranges and distributions of the restricted-range species are not well documented. All are forest birds, and mostly recorded from montane altitudes, but it is unclear whether any of them ever ranged into the lowlands in the past. There are recent records of three of these

U. Olsson/BirdLife International

The recently described Hainan Leaf Warbler *Phylloscopus hainanus* is locally common at several localities in the mountains of Hainan.

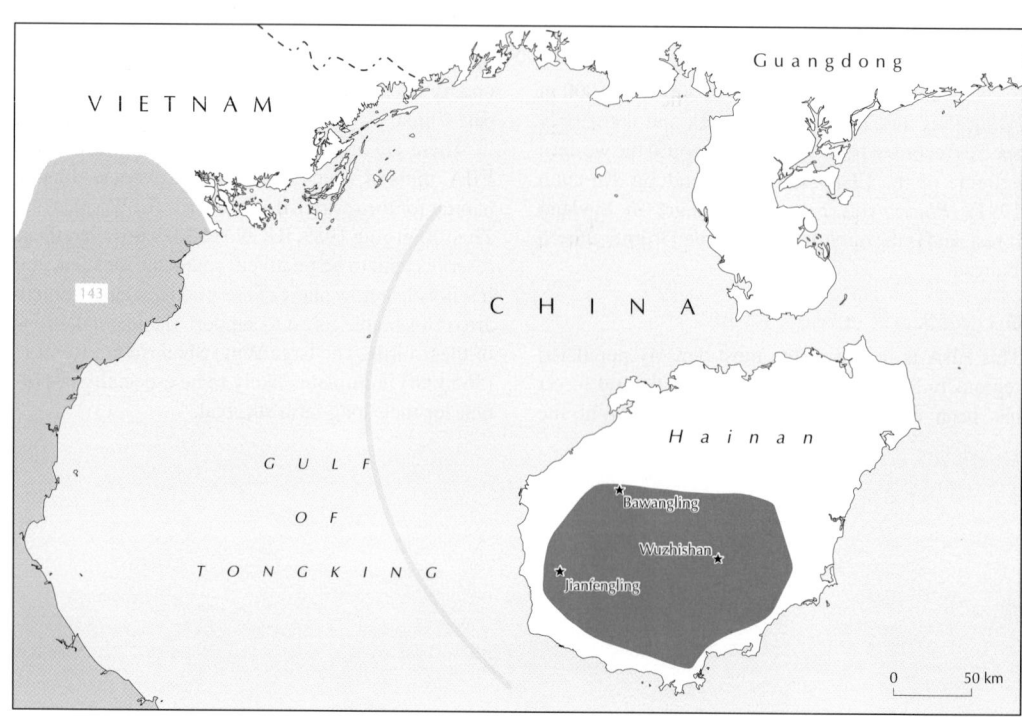

Status and habitat of restricted-range species

Species (ordered taxonomically)	Global status	Other EBAs (and SAs)	Altitude (m)	Habitat
White-eared Night-heron Gorsachius magnificus	CR	141	Foothills	Well-watered, densely forested areas, inc. bamboo
Hainan Partridge Arborophila ardens	EN	—	c.750–1,200	Evergreen forest, bamboo
Hainan Leaf-warbler Phylloscopus hainanus[1]	VU	—	>600	Evergreen forest and secondary growth at forest edge
Yellow-billed Nuthatch Sitta solangiae	VU	145 (s082)	c.700–1,100	Montane evergreen forest

Global status (see p. 679 for definitions)	EX Extinct	} with year of last record	cd Conservation Dependent	**Other EBAs (and SAs)** (see p. 77 for locations)	Bracketed numbers are Secondary Areas.
	EW Extinct in the Wild		nt Near Threatened		X Extinct in that EBA or SA.
	CR Critical	} threatened species	lc Least Concern	**Notes**	[1] Newly described by Olsson et al.
	EN Endangered		DD Data Deficient		(1993).
	VU Vulnerable		NE Not Evaluated		

four species, including the recently described *Phylloscopus hainanus* (Olsson *et al.* 1993), from a small number of localities in the mountains (see Xu Long-hui *et al.* 1983, King and Liao Wei-ping 1989, McGowan *et al.* 1995), but *Gorsachius magnificus* appears not to have been recorded on Hainan since two were sighted during surveys in the 1960s (Zhou Fang *in litt.* 1993, Xu Weishu verbally 1996).

There are about 46 subspecies of bird endemic to Hainan (Cheng Tso-hsin 1987, Howard and Moore 1991), several of which may be better treated as full species (Olsson *et al.* 1993), for example the endemic subspecies of Grey Peacock-pheasant *Polyplectron* (*bicalcaratum*) *katsumatae* and Black-browed Barbet *Megalaima* (*oorti*) *faber*.

■ Threats and conservation

Forest loss is the major threat to the EBA. Zhou Guang-yi (1994) estimates that the area of natural tropical forest on Hainan has decreased from 16,920 km² in 1943 to 3,000 km² in 1994, mainly as a result of excessive timber extraction, the replacement of forest by rubber plantations, slash-and-burn

agriculture and the unrestricted cutting of wood for fuel and other uses (see also Smil 1984, Collins *et al.* 1991). Much of the remaining forest is probably disturbed and not of full stature, so is not capable of supporting many of the specialized forest birds (W. Bleisch *in litt.* 1993). All four of the restricted-range bird species are threatened because of this continuing loss of their habitat, and *Arborophila ardens* also because of hunting (McGowan *et al.* 1995). More widespread threatened forest birds which occur on Hainan are Pale-capped Pigeon *Columba punicea* (classified as Vulnerable) and Blyth's Kingfisher *Alcedo hercules* (Vulnerable).

There are 28 protected areas on Hainan (IUCN 1992d), but it is unclear how many of these contain suitable habitat for the restricted-range birds. There are recent records of some of these species from Bawangling, Jianfengling and Wuzhishan Nature Reserves, which all include substantial areas of natural forest. Many of the other protected areas are small and isolated, and unlikely to support viable populations of any of the birds (W. V. Bleisch *in litt.* 1993).

143 Annamese lowlands

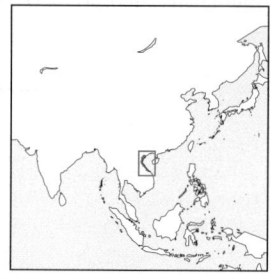

Key habitats Lowland evergreen rain forest

Main threats Severe habitat loss (e.g. due to agriculture, warfare, commercial logging), hunting

Biological importance ● ● ●
Current threat level ● ● ●

Area 51,000 km²   **Altitude** 0–1,000 m
Countries Laos, Vietnam

Restricted-range species	Threatened	Total
Confined to this EBA	5	5
Present also in other EBAs, SAs	2	4
Total	7	9

■ General characteristics

The Annamese lowlands cover the lowlands and foothills of north-central Vietnam (in southern Ninh Binh, Thanh Hoa, Nghe Anh, Ha Tinh, Quang Binh, Quang Tri and Thu Thien Hue provinces) and part of adjacent central Laos.

The natural vegetation of this region is tropical lowland evergreen and semi-evergreen rain forest below c.1,000 m, with tropical montane rain forest above this altitude. However, the coastal lowlands had been deforested almost entirely by 1945, and the forest in the foothills is now highly fragmented and degraded, with few substantial areas of good-quality forest remaining (Collins *et al.* 1991). The EBA has been represented on the map by all land below c.1,000 m within the known historical distributions of the restricted-range species.

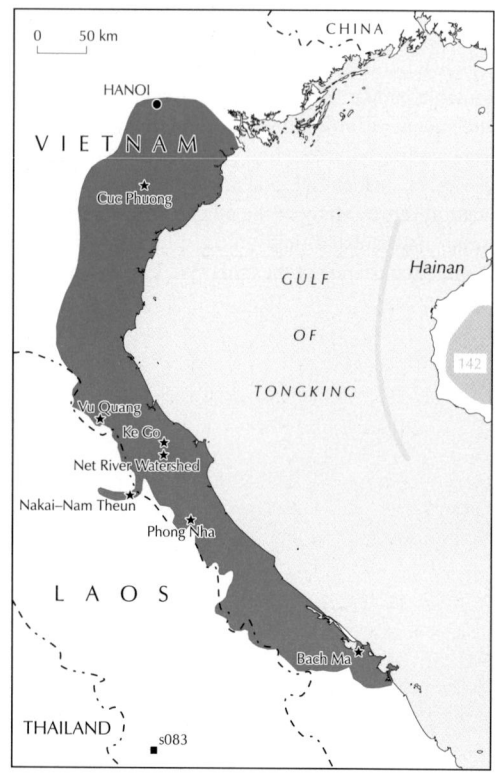

■ Restricted-range species

This part of Indo-China had, until recently, received relatively little ornithological coverage (see ICBP 1992), and the distributions and habitat requirements of the restricted-range species were poorly known. However, surveys by BirdLife International and scientists from the Institute for Ecology and Biological Resources and from the Forest Inventory and Planning Institute are now rapidly improving the quality of the available information (see Robson *et al.* 1991, 1993a,b, Eames *et al.* 1992, 1994, 1995a, Lambert *et al.* 1994).

All of the restricted-range species are found in lowland rain forest, although the distribution of *Rheinardia ocellata* also extends upwards into montane forest and *Garrulax vassali* is principally a lower montane species of only marginal occurrence in this EBA. The three *Lophura* pheasants appear to be extreme lowland forest specialists, as they have not definitely been recorded above about 300 m. *Jabouilleia danjoui* occurs in lowland forest in this EBA, but is a montane forest bird in the Da Lat plateau (EBA 145). *Stachyris herberti* is a specialist of forest on limestone.

Several of the restricted-range species are known from just a few localities. The only recent records of *Arborophila merlini* are from Bach Ma National Park, where it is common. *Lophura imperialis* is known by one old record and a male trapped in 1990 near Cat Bin (Ke Go) on the border between Ha Tinh and Quang Binh provinces. *L. edwardsi* was historically known from at least eight localities in the southern part of the EBA, and was feared extinct in the wild (as it had not been recorded since about 1930) until a pair were captured near Bach Ma National Park in 1996 (Anon. 1996). *L. hatinhensis* occurs to the north of the range of *L. edwardsi* (and may be conspecific with it: Vuilleumier *et al.* 1992), with recent records near Cat Bin (Ke Go) (Ha Tinh province) in 1990 and in a nearby area of primary forest in the Net river watershed (Quang Binh province) in 1994. *Stachyris herberti* is known from specimens collected at two localities in central Laos in the 1920s and sightings in Phong Nha Nature

Status and habitat of restricted-range species

Species (ordered taxonomically)	Global status	Other EBAs (and SAs)	Altitude (m)	Habitat
Annam Partridge *Arborophila merlini*	EN	—	Lowlands to 600	Lowland evergreen forest
Imperial Pheasant *Lophura imperialis*	CR	—	Lowlands to c.200	Lowland evergreen forest
Edwards's Pheasant *Lophura edwardsi*	CR	—	Lowlands to 300(-600)	Lowland evergreen forest
Vietnamese Pheasant *Lophura hatinhensis*	EN	—	Lowlands to c.200	Lowland evergreen forest
Crested Argus *Rheinardia ocellata*	VU	145,158 (s084)	Lowlands to 1,500	Lowland evergreen forest
White-cheeked Laughingthrush *Garrulax vassali*	lc	145 (s083,s084)	600 to c.900	Evergreen forest edge, secondary growth, scrub, grassland, borders of agricultural land
Short-tailed Scimitar-babbler *Jabouilleia danjoui*	VU	145	50 to c.900	Undergrowth in lowland evergreen forest, bamboo
Sooty Babbler *Stachyris herberti*	VU	—	c.200	Forest on limestone outcrops
Grey-faced Tit-babbler *Macronous kelleyi*	nt	144 (s083,s084)	50–700	Lowland evergreen forest, bamboo

Global status (see p. 679 for definitions)
EX Extinct
EW Extinct in the Wild } with year of last record
CR Critical
EN Endangered
VU Vulnerable } threatened species
cd Conservation Dependent
nt Near Threatened
lc Least Concern
DD Data Deficient
NE Not Evaluated

Other EBAs (and SAs) (see p. 77 for locations): bracketed numbers are Secondary Areas; ˣ extinct in that EBA or SA.

Reserve in Bo Trach district in 1994 and Minh Hoa district in Quang Binh province in 1996 (J. C. Eames *in litt.* 1996). *Jabouilleia danjoui* and *Macronous kelleyi* have recently been recorded in Cuc Phuong National Park (Crosby 1995, J. C. Eames *in litt.* 1996), considerably further north than any previous record of any of the EBA's restricted-range species.

■ Threats and conservation

All the coastal plain forest in this EBA has already been cleared, and the only suitable habitat remaining for the lowland species is in small valleys and on the lower slopes of the hills. Causes of deforestation in the past include clearance for agriculture to feed a rapidly increasing population, warfare and logging. The remaining forests are subject to commercial logging, further clearance for permanent agriculture and settlements, and degradation as a result of fuelwood collection, shifting agriculture and fire (Collins *et al.* 1991, Eames *et al.* 1992).

Seven of the restricted-range bird species are classified as threatened, including all five of those which are confined to this EBA. More widespread threatened forest birds which occur are Siamese Fireback *Lophura diardi*, Green Peafowl *Pavo muticus*, Blyth's Kingfisher *Alcedo hercules* and Red-collared Woodpecker *Picus rabieri* (all classified as Vulnerable). The major threat to all of these species is deforestation, although the pheasants are also hunted for food.

At least seven gazetted protected areas within the EBA contain suitable habitat for the restricted-range species. Bach Ma National Park supports populations of several, but of these only *Arborophila merlini* is endemic to the EBA (Eames *et al.* 1992). Two restricted-range species have been recorded in Nakai-Nam Theun National Biodiversity Conservation Area in central Laos (Poole 1994), two in Cuc Phuong National Park and two or three in Vu Quang Nature Reserve (Eames *et al.* 1994), but none of these are endemics. Phong Nha Nature Reserve supports *Stachyris herberti* and *Macronous kelleyi*, and possibly some of the other endemic species. Pu Mat Nature Reserve, Bin En National Park and Pu Huong proposed nature reserve could also be important for some of these birds, but none has been recorded in any of them yet (Eames *et al.* 1994).

Two of the lowland specialists, *Lophura imperialis* and *L. hatinhensis*, have been recorded at Ke Go, although the forest here is degraded and illegal logging persists (Eames *et al.* 1994, Lambert *et al.* 1994); the Ke Go Nature Reserve was established for their protection by the Vietnamese government in December 1996 (Anon. 1997a). Surveys in 1994 located another important area of lowland forest nearby in the Net river watershed in Quang Binh province, which supports at least one of the species endemic to the EBA, and Lambert *et al.* (1994) recommend that a new protected area needs to be established here.

144 South Vietnamese lowlands

Key habitats Lowland semi-evergreen rain forest

Main threats Major habitat loss (e.g. due to agriculture, commercial logging)

Biological importance ● ● ○
Current threat level ● ● ●

Area 30,000 km² **Altitude** 0–1,000 m

Countries Vietnam

Restricted-range species	Threatened	Total
Confined to this EBA	2	2
Present also in other EBAs, SAs	0	1
Total	2	3

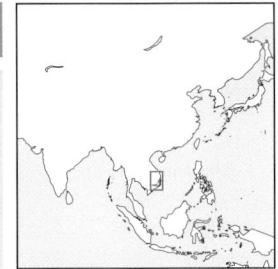

■ General characteristics

The South Vietnamese lowlands are considered here to include the lowlands and foothills of Dong Nai, Song Be and southern Lam Dong provinces, probably extending also into Binh Thuan, Ninh Tuan and Khanh Hoa provinces.

The natural vegetation of this part of the country is tropical semi-evergreen rain forest below c. 1,000 m, with tropical montane rain forest above that altitude—but most of the lowland forest in this region of Vietnam has been cleared. Where this EBA extends onto the slopes of the Da Lat plateau (EBA 145) there is a small overlap in the altitudinal ranges of the birds of the two EBAs.

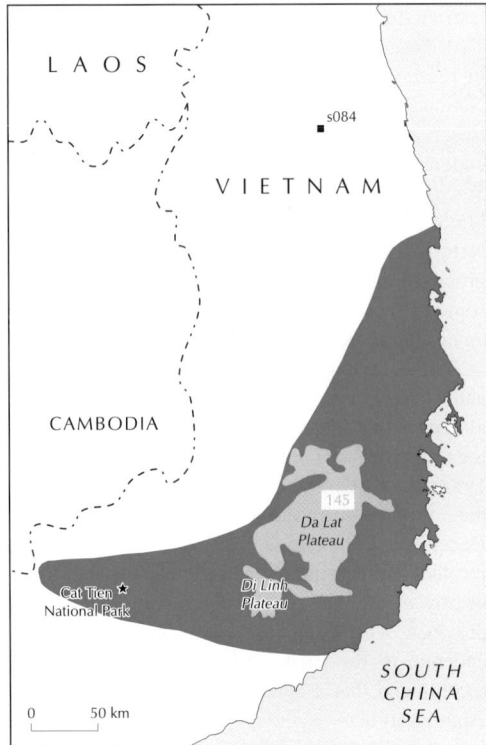

Habitat of the threatened White-winged Duck *Cairina scutulata* in Cat Tien National Park.

■ Restricted-range species

The distributions and habitat requirements of the restricted-range species in this EBA are poorly known, but much new information has been gathered during recent surveys by BirdLife International and others (see Eames *et al.* 1992, Robson *et al.* 1993a,b). It is only possible to draw a tentative boundary to the EBA, based on the known distribution of *Polyplectron germaini*, as all records (in this EBA) of the other two species fall within its range. *Arborophila davidi* was known until recently only from the type-specimens collected at Nu Kroai (Bu Croi) in Song Be province and from several recent sight records in Cat Tien National Park (C. R. Robson *in litt.* 1994), but a survey in 1997 found it to be common in Cat Loc

Status and habitat of restricted-range species

Species (ordered taxonomically)	Global status	Other EBAs (and SAs)	Altitude (m)	Habitat
Orange-necked Partridge *Arborophila davidi*	CR	—	Lowlands to c.250	Evergreen forest, bamboo, scrub
Germain's Peacock-pheasant *Polyplectron germaini*	VU	—	Lowlands to 1,200(-1,500)	Lowland evergreen and semi-evergreen forest, locally in montane evergreen forest
Grey-faced Tit-babbler *Macronous kelleyi*	nt	143 (s083,s084)	50–700	Lowland evergreen forest, bamboo

Global status (see p. 679 for definitions)	EX Extinct EW Extinct in the Wild	} with year of last record	CR Critical EN Endangered VU Vulnerable	} threatened species	cd Conservation Dependent nt Near Threatened lc Least Concern	DD Data Deficient NE Not Evaluated

Other EBAs (and SAs) (see p. 77 for locations): bracketed numbers are Secondary Areas; ˣ extinct in that EBA or SA.

proposed nature reserve (Anon. 1997b). *Macronous kelleyi* has only been recorded (in this EBA) in Cat Tien National Park and adjacent Cat Loc proposed nature reserve. All three species are found in lowland rain forest, and *Polyplectron germaini* has also been recorded locally in montane forest above 1,000 m.

Forest guards in Cat Tien National Park—the key site for conservation in this EBA.

BirdLife Vietnam Programme

■ Threats and conservation

The major threat to the EBA is deforestation, as the lowlands have been almost completely cleared for agriculture and settlement, and extensive forests only remain on the slopes where they continue to be cleared by commercial logging and agricultural en-croachment (Eames *et al.* 1992). Both of the re-stricted-range bird species which are confined to this EBA are threatened. More-widespread threatened species which have been recorded in or near the EBA include forest birds such as Siamese Fireback *Lophura diardi* and Green Peafowl *Pavo muticus* (both classi-fied as Vulnerable), and wetland birds such as Lesser Adjutant *Leptoptilos javanicus* (Vulnerable), White-shouldered Ibis *Pseudibis davisoni* (Endangered) and White-winged Duck *Cairina scutulata* (Endan-gered).

Cat Tien National Park is the key protected area in this EBA, as it includes extensive lowland forest, and supports populations of all three restricted-range bird species and several of the more-widespread threat-ened species (Eames *et al.* 1992). There are several other (mainly small) protected areas in this part of Vietnam (IUCN 1992c), but it is not clear whether any of them have suitable habitat for the restricted-range species. Cat Loc proposed nature reserve, which is adjacent to Cat Tien National Park, supports substantial populations of all three restricted-range species (Eames *et al.* 1992, Anon. 1997b), and Bui Gia Map proposed nature reserve may also prove to be important for the restricted-range species, al-though none has been recorded there yet (Nguyen Cu *in litt.* 1996).

145 | Da Lat plateau

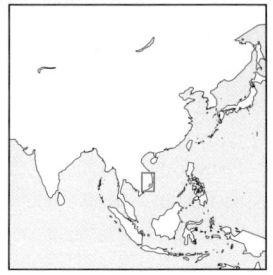

Key habitats Montane evergreen forest, pine forest

Main threats Moderate habitat loss (e.g. due to agriculture, commercial logging, fuelwood collection)

Biological importance ● ● ●
Current threat level ● ● ●

Area 6,000 km² **Altitude** 800–2,400 m

Countries Vietnam

Restricted-range species	Threatened	Total
Confined to this EBA	3	4
Present also in other EBAs, SAs	3	4
Total	6	8

■ General characteristics

This EBA includes the southern part of Vietnam's western highlands which lie within the country's Lam Dong province and adjacent parts of Dak Lak and (probably) Ninh Tuan provinces. Several of the mountains in this area rise to over 2,000 m, the highest being Chu Yang Sin at 2,442 m.

The natural vegetation types of the region are tropical montane evergreen forest and pine forest. The northern part of the South Vietnamese lowlands (EBA 144) lies immediately adjacent to the Da Lat plateau, but the birds of that EBA occur mainly at lower altitudes, in lowland semi-evergreen forest on the flanks of the mountains.

■ Restricted-range species

Recent surveys by BirdLife International and others have produced much new information on distribution

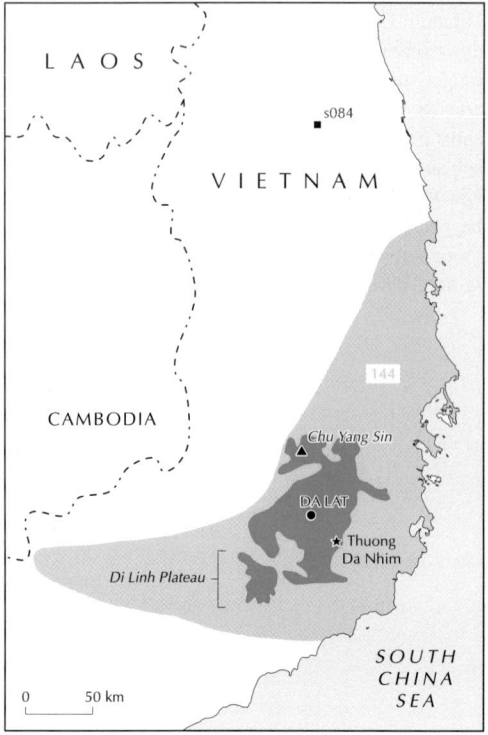

and habitat requirements of restricted-range birds in this EBA (see Eames *et al.* 1992, Robson *et al.* 1993a,b, Eames 1995). The restricted-range species are all found in tropical montane broadleaf evergreen forest, except for *Carduelis monguilloti* which is usually found in pine forest. The other three species which are confined to the EBA all appear to have restricted altitudinal ranges: *Garrulax milleti* occurs at relatively low altitudes up to 1,650 m, and *Crocias langbianis* has only been recorded up to 1,450 m, though it is known by just a small number of specimens and recent sight records (Eames *et al.* 1995b); *Garrulax yersini* is only recorded from upper montane forest above 1,500 m on the higher peaks.

■ Threats and conservation

Shifting cultivation has greatly modified the extent, composition and quality of evergreen forest in the EBA and is resulting in increasing habitat fragmentation. The frequent use of fire by shifting cultivators prevents the regeneration of evergreen forest and has promoted the growth of a fire-climax dominated by *Pinus kesiya*. Logging continues to be a major activity in the EBA, and much of the pine forest is allocated to production forest where logging is permitted. A government-planned resettlement programme has led to thousands of people emigrating annually into the region, causing the degradation of evergreen forests in some areas through increased fuelwood collection and charcoal production, particularly in Dak Lak province. This has also significantly reduced the biological importance of Nui Ba near Da Lat city (Eames 1995).

Six of the restricted-range birds are threatened, principally because of habitat loss and degradation, including three of the four species which are confined to this EBA. Although endemic to the EBA, *Carduelis monguilloti* is not considered to be globally threatened, because it may actually have benefited from the increase in the area of pine forest (Eames *et al.* 1992). A more widespread threatened forest bird which has been recorded in this EBA is Pale-capped Pigeon *Columba punicea* (classified as Vulnerable).

Status and habitat of restricted-range species

Species (ordered taxonomically)	Global status	Other EBAs (and SAs)	Altitude (m)	Habitat
Crested Argus *Rheinardia ocellata*	VU	143,158 (s084)	c.1,700–1,900	Montane evergreen forest
Black-hooded Laughingthrush *Garrulax milleti*	VU	—	800–1,650	Montane evergreen forest
White-cheeked Laughingthrush *Garrulax vassali*	lc	143 (s083,s084)	c.900–1,900	Montane evergreen forest edge, secondary growth, scrub, grassland, borders of agricultural land
Collared Laughingthrush *Garrulax yersini*	VU	—	1,500–2,440	Dense undergrowth in montane evergreen forest
Short-tailed Scimitar-babbler *Jabouilleia danjoui*	VU	143	800–2,000	Undergrowth in montane evergreen forest, bamboo
Grey-crowned Crocias *Crocias langbianis*	CR	—	c.1,000–1,450	Montane evergreen forest
Yellow-billed Nuthatch *Sitta solangiae*	VU	142 (s082)	1,100–2,100	Montane evergreen forest
Vietnam Greenfinch *Carduelis monguilloti*	nt	—	1,050–1,950	Pine forest, mixed pine and montane evergreen forest, agricultural land

Global status (see p. 679 for definitions)								
EX	Extinct	with year of last record	CR	Critical	threatened species	cd	Conservation Dependent	DD Data Deficient
EW	Extinct in the Wild		EN	Endangered		nt	Near Threatened	NE Not Evaluated
			VU	Vulnerable		lc	Least Concern	

Other EBAs (and SAs) (see p. 77 for locations): bracketed numbers are Secondary Areas; ˣ extinct in that EBA or SA.

Logging continues to be a major activity in this EBA, such as here at Thuong Da Nhim. However, large areas of forest are protected within nature reserves at this site and on Chu Yang Sin.

BirdLife International

There are three gazetted protected areas within the EBA (IUCN 1992c). The most important are Chu Yang Sin and Thuong Da Nhim Nature Reserves, which support populations of all the restricted-range species and include over 10% of the EBA's total area—and most of its best remaining areas of ever-green forest. The forests on Chu Yang Sin extend in altitude from 500 m up to its peak at 2,442 m (Eames and Nguyen Cu 1994). Eames *et al.* (1992) recommend a faunal survey and feasibility study of the Nui Ta Dung area with a view to affording this site reserve status.

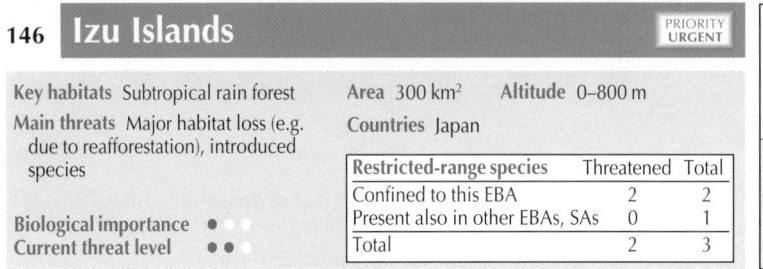

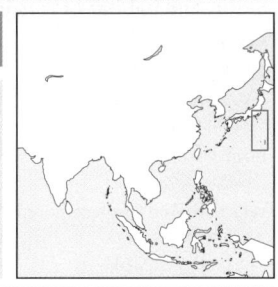

146 Izu Islands

PRIORITY
URGENT

Key habitats Subtropical rain forest

Main threats Major habitat loss (e.g. due to reafforestation), introduced species

Biological importance ● ● ●
Current threat level ● ● ●

Area 300 km² **Altitude** 0–800 m

Countries Japan

Restricted-range species	Threatened	Total
Confined to this EBA	2	2
Present also in other EBAs, SAs	0	1
Total	2	3

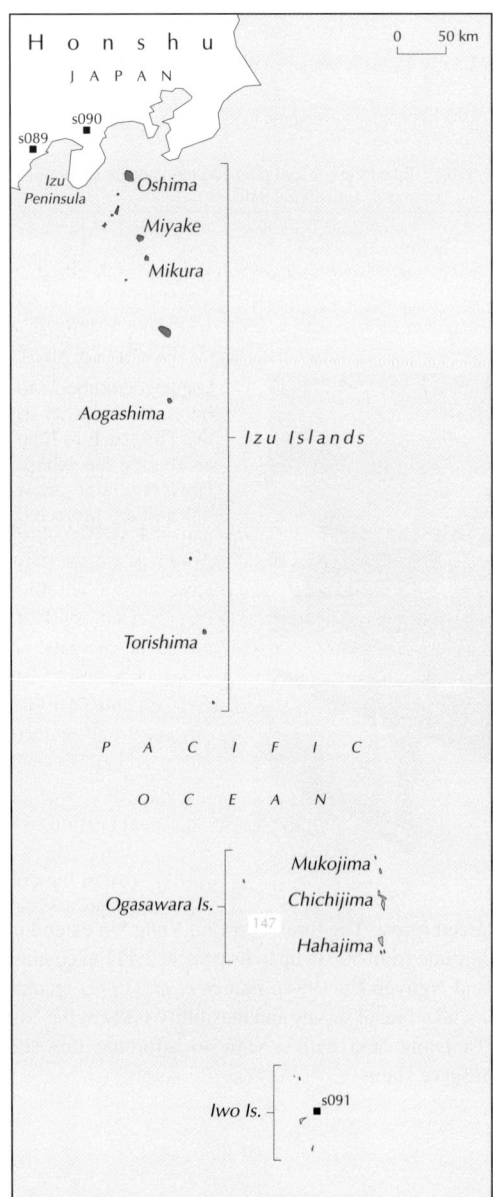

Honshu
JAPAN
s090
s089
Izu Peninsula
Oshima
Miyake
Mikura
Aogashima
Izu Islands
Torishima
PACIFIC
OCEAN
Mukojima
Ogasawara Is.
Chichijima
147
Hahajima
Iwo Is.
s091

0   50 km

■ General characteristics

Situated along the border of the Philippine and Pacific tectonic plates south of the Izu peninsula of Honshu (Japan), the volcanic Izu Islands make up the northernmost archipelago of the so-called Izu–Ogasawara–Mariana Arc (see also EBAs 147 and 189, and Secondary Area s091). The Izu Islands EBA includes Oshima (which has the highest point at 854 m) in the north and Torishima in the south, and all islands between. Native vegetation of the islands is subtropical rain forest.

■ Restricted-range species

The distribution patterns of the EBA's restricted-range species vary slightly, with *Columba janthina* breeding on all the islands from Oshima to Torishima, and *Turdus celaenops* and *Phylloscopus ijimae* on Oshima to Aogashima only.

The two species which are endemic to this EBA, namely *Turdus celaenops* and *Phylloscopus ijimae*, have recently been recorded breeding in the northern Nansei Shoto (EBA 148) c.1,000 km away (Kawaji *et al.* 1989, Higuchi and Kawaji 1989), but because these records are so distant from the species' core ranges in the Izu Islands, and because the numbers of birds involved are very small, the Izu Islands have been treated as an EBA in their own right.

Gorsachius goisagi used to breed commonly on Miyake and Mikura, but no nests have been located since the early 1970s, although recent sightings at Miyake suggest the possibility that the species may still breed in a relatively inaccessible forested area high on the northern slope of that island (J. T. Moyer *in litt.* 1996). Yellow Bunting *Emberiza sulphurata*, a threatened restricted-range species from central Honshu (Secondary Area s090), has also been recorded on the Izu Islands (on Miyake and Mikura) in winter (Brazil 1991).

■ Threats and conservation

Although both of the EBA's endemic species remain locally abundant, there are a number of threats which have caused declines. For example, on Miyake much of the forest has been replaced with the fast-growing

Status and habitat of restricted-range species

Species (ordered taxonomically)	Global status	Other EBAs (and SAs)	Habitat
Japanese Night-heron *Gorsachius goisagi*[1]	VU	(s089)	Heavily forested areas inc. evergreen forest with watercourses and damp areas
Japanese Wood-pigeon *Columba janthina*	nt	147,148 (s091[x],s092)	Mature forest
Izu Thrush *Turdus celaenops*[2,3]	VU	—	Dense forest, secondary growth, orchards, gardens
Ijima's Leaf-warbler *Phylloscopus ijimae*[2,4]	VU	—	Subtropical forest

Global status (see p. 679 for definitions)

EX	Extinct	with year of last record	cd Conservation Dependent
EW	Extinct in the Wild		nt Near Threatened
CR	Critical	threatened species	lc Least Concern
EN	Endangered		DD Data Deficient
VU	Vulnerable		NE Not Evaluated

Notes

[1] Exint in this EBA in 1970s.

[2] Very small numbers recorded breeding in northern Nansei Shoto (EBA 148).

[3] Occasionally winters on mainland of Honshu.

[4] Winters in Luzon, Philippines (EBA 151).

Other EBAs (and SAs) (see p. 77 for locations)
Bracketed numbers are Secondary Areas.
[x] Extinct in that EBA or SA.

softwood *Cryptomeria japonica* for timber, and on Oshima much of the natural forest has been destroyed (Brazil 1991). This removal of valuable breeding habitat, and threats acting in the wintering areas of *Phylloscopus ijimae*, notably deforestation in Luzon in the Philippines (EBA 151), will continue to have an effect.

An additional threat on Miyake, to which has been attributed the rapid decline of *Turdus celaenops* on that island, is predation by weasels *Mustela sibirica*, which were introduced in the early 1970s and again in 1982 to control rats (Takagi and Higuchi 1992, Moyer 1993). However, predation by Jungle Crows *Corvus macrorhynchos*—which have increased immensely owing to the availability of food from raw garbage—may be a more significant factor. A survey in 1992 found that all of a sample of 22 *T. celaenops* nests failed: 19 were destroyed by crows, one by weasels, one by domestic cats and one by an unknown predator. It is likely that the decline of *Gorsachius goisagi* is also attributable to predation by weasels (J. T. Moyer *in litt.* 1996).

As well as being important for restricted-range species, the Izu Islands are particularly notable for seabirds. For example, Short-tailed Albatross *Diomedea albatrus* (classified as Endangered) once bred in huge numbers on islands in the Izu–Ogasawara chain, but exploitation for feathers from the late nineteenth century onwards almost wiped out most populations by 1930, and today it only breeds on a few islands, the most important of which is Torishima in this EBA. Its breeding success has been improved there owing to grass transplantation to stabilize the nesting areas, but the population (c.500 birds) remains susceptible to volcanic eruptions (Hasegawa 1984, 1991).

Another seabird with significant breeding colonies in this EBA is Japanese Murrelet *Synthliboramphus wumizusume* (classified as Vulnerable) which breeds on small islands and stacks in southern Japan and South Korea. The recent increase in popularity of sport-fishing is a particular worry for this species as fishermen discard unwanted fish on isolated reefs, attracting crows and Black-tailed Gulls *Larus crassirostris*. During periods of bad weather when the reefs are inaccessible (and no sport-fishing takes place) these birds eat the eggs and nestlings of *S. wumizusume* instead (J. T. Moyer *in litt.* 1996).

The national government has designated the entire Izu archipelago a 'protected area', and several valuable places have been designated as 'special protected areas'. However, there are no rangers to enforce the protection, and destruction and alteration of habitat continue.

147 Ogasawara Islands

Key habitats Lowland secondary
  subtropical forest
Main threats Major habitat loss (e.g.
  due to cultivation, grazing),
  introduced species
Biological importance ● ● ●
Current threat level ● ● ○

Area 73 km² **Altitude** 0–400 m
Countries Japan

Restricted-range species	Threatened	Total
Confined to this EBA	1	1
Present also in other EBAs, SAs	0	0
Total	1	1

■ General characteristics

The volcanic islands of Ogasawara (or Bonin) lie in
the north Pacific Ocean, c.1,000 km south of Honshu
(Japan), and south of the Izu Islands (EBA 146; see
p. 454 for map). The largest of the 20 islands,
Chichijima and Hahajima—the only ones which are
inhabited—are a little over 20 km² in area, and were
once covered in subtropical evergreen forest.

■ Restricted-range species

The Ogasawara Islands have been identified as an
EBA on the basis of one extant endemic species and
a further three extinct endemic species.

Apalopteron familiare survives only on the
Hahajima group, having become extinct on
Chichijima (although there were reports in 1987 that
it may still exist there, or, more likely, have been
reintroduced) and apparently also on Mukojima (Brazil 1991). Recent molecular work indicates that this
species belongs to the white-eye family (Zosteropidae)
rather than being a honeyeater (Meliphagidae) as
formerly believed and as indicated by its English
name (Springer *et al*. 1995).

■ Threats and conservation

The islands were uninhabited until 1830 but today
the human population stands at c.2,000, the result of
transmigration from the Japanese mainland and the
archipelago has now been widely deforested and

cultivated and the natural vegetation destroyed by
the grazing of goats (WWF/IUCN 1994–1995,
Tomiyama and Susuki 1996).

All the restricted-range species will have been
affected by this habitat loss within their small ranges
and it is likely that cats and rats, which escaped from
whaling boats pulled ashore for repair (Greenway
1967), also contributed to their demise, and that
hunting was a further factor.

Although the one surviving restricted-range species, *Apalopteron familiare*, is common and widespread on Hahajima itself in a variety of different
habitats and in modified forest at higher elevations, it
is considered threatened because of its tiny range and
consequent permanent vulnerability to chance events.
The fact that this species has already been extirpated
from at least two islands is testimony to this.

Plans to construct a new airport on the island of
Anijima (a tiny and relatively intact island 500 m
from Chichijima), which could have increased the
chance of invasion by additional exotic species
(Tomiyama and Suzuki 1996), have been halted but
are under consideration for the main island of
Chichijima (J. Minton *in litt*. 1996).

In 1972, 61 km² of the islands were designated as
a national park and an active conservation programme is underway including the propagation and
reintroduction of threatened native plants (WWF/
IUCN 1994–1995).

Status and habitat of restricted-range species

Species (ordered taxonomically)	Global status	Other EBAs (and SAs)	Habitat
Japanese Wood-pigeon *Columba janthina*[1]	nt	148,146 (s091[X],s092)	Forest
Bonin Wood-pigeon *Columba versicolor*	EX (1889)	—	Forest
Bonin Thrush *Zoothera terrestris*	EX (1828)	—	Forest
Bonin Honeyeater *Apalopteron familiare*	VU	—	Secondary forest, forest edge, bushes, plantations, gardens
Bonin Grosbeak *Chaunoproctus ferreorostris*	EX (1828)	—	Forest

Global status (see p. 679 for definitions)
EX Extinct } with year of last record
EW Extinct in the Wild
CR Critical } threatened species
EN Endangered
VU Vulnerable

cd Conservation Dependent
nt Near Threatened
lc Least Concern
DD Data Deficient
NE Not Evaluated

Other EBAs (and SAs) (see p. 77 for locations)

Notes

Bracketed numbers are Secondary Areas.
[X] Extinct in that EBA or SA.

[1] Extinct in this EBA during early 1880s (Brazil 1991).

148 Nansei Shoto

PRIORITY
CRITICAL

Key habitats Subtropical hill forest, mixed forest

Main threats Major habitat loss (e.g. due to cultivation, settlements, plantations), introduced species

Biological importance ●
Current threat level ● ● ●

Area 4,500 km²   **Altitude** 0–1,900 m

Countries Japan

Restricted-range species	Threatened	Total
Confined to this EBA	5	7
Present also in other EBAs, SAs	0	3
Total	5	10

■ General characteristics

Included within this EBA are all islands lying between Kyushu (the southernmost main island of Japan) and Taiwan (EBA 149). There are over 100 islands, belonging to Japan and divisible into several distinct groups including Danjo, Osumi and Takara in the north, Amami and Okinawa in the middle, Sakishima (main island Ishigaki) and Yaeyama (main island Iriomote) in the south, and Daito to the east. The archipelago is sometimes called the Ryukyu Islands, but there is some ambiguity concerning the correct usage of this term (see Brazil 1991), and thus Nansei Shoto is used here in preference.

The northern islands' characteristic vegetation is temperate forest, while south of Amami subtropical evergreen forest predominates. However, altitude is also influential, and a broad cross-section of habitats can be found on single islands. Thus, on Yakushima, which reaches 1,935 m (the highest point in this EBA), there is subtropical forest on the lower slopes, mixed deciduous and coniferous forest at higher altitudes, and alpine habitats on mountain peaks.

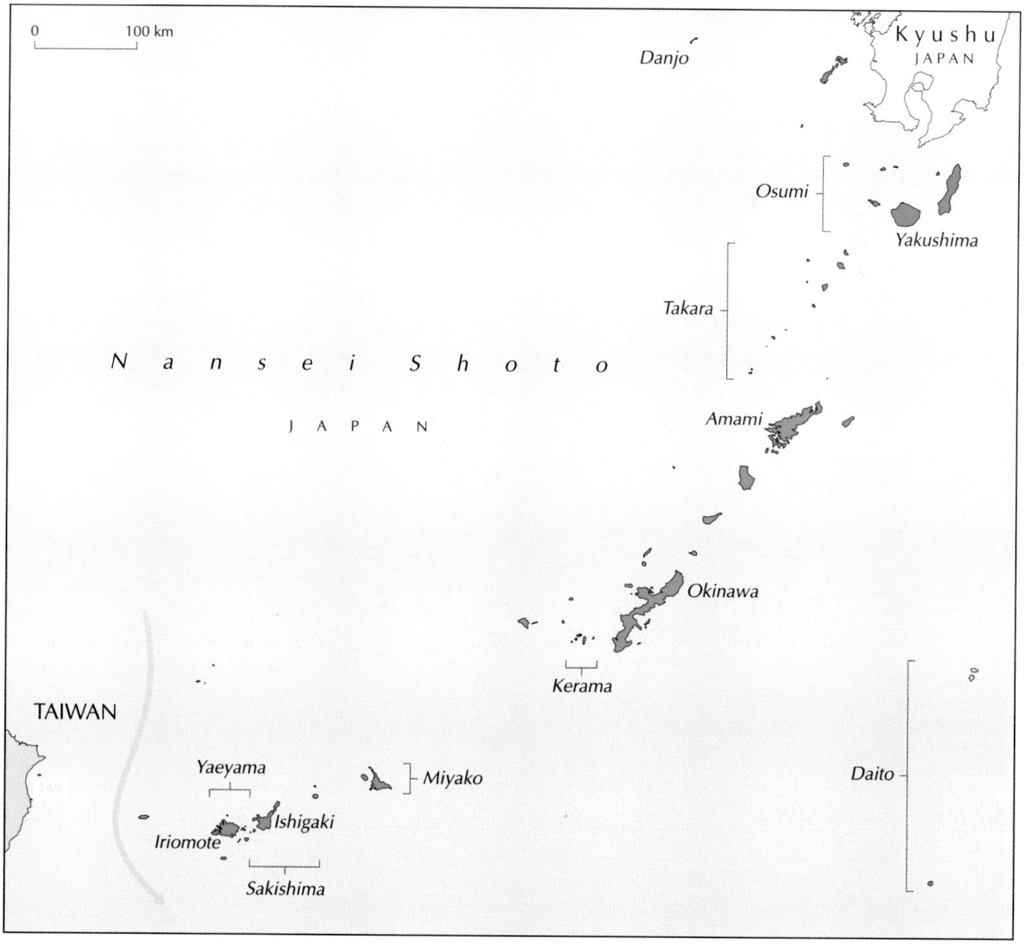

Status and habitat of restricted-range species

Species (ordered taxonomically)	Global status	Other EBAs (and SAs)	Habitat
Okinawa Rail *Gallirallus okinawae*	EN	—	Hill forest, forest edges, scrub, agricultural land
Amami Woodcock *Scolopax mira*	VU	—	Hill forest, sugar-cane fields (winter)
Japanese Wood-pigeon *Columba janthina*	nt	146,147 (s091[X],s092)	Mature forest on coasts and small islands
Ryukyu Pigeon *Columba jouyi*	EX (1936)	—	Forest
Whistling Green-pigeon *Treron formosae*	nt	149 (s093,s094)	Forest and gardens at all altitudes
Elegant Scops-owl *Otus elegans*	lc	(s093,s094)	Forest and forest edge at all altitudes
Micronesian Kingfisher *Todirhamphus cinnamominus*[1]	lc	189[X],190,192	Presumably forest
Okinawa Woodpecker *Sapheopipo noguchii*	CR	—	Mature hill forest
Ryukyu Minivet *Pericrocotus tegimae*	lc	—	Forest and scrub at all altitudes
Amami Thrush *Zoothera major*	CR	—	Uncut primary hill forest, old selectively logged forest (100–400 m)
Ryukyu Robin *Erithacus komadori*	nt	—	Hill forest
Lidth's Jay *Garrulus lidthi*	VU	—	Hill forest, around cultivation and habitation

Global status (see p. 679 for definitions)

EX Extinct } with year
EW Extinct in } of last
     the Wild } record
cd Conservation Dependent
nt Near Threatened
CR Critical }
EN Endangered } threatened species
VU Vulnerable }
lc Least Concern
DD Data Deficient
NE Not Evaluated

Other EBAs (and SAs) (see p. 77 for locations)
Bracketed numbers are Secondary Areas. [X] Extinct in that EBA or SA.

Notes
[1] Known from a single specimen (1887), which may have been of a vagrant, a bird brought in as a pet, or mislabelled (Brazil 1991). Assumed to be extinct in this EBA.

The northern limit of the Oriental faunal region and the southern limit of the Palearctic intergrade in the Nansei Shoto which consequently harbour birds (often endemic races) from both these regions as well as their own unique species. The islands are also important for migrating and wintering birds (see 'Restricted-range species', below) and for colonies of breeding seabirds (WWFJ 1984, 1985, Brazil 1991; see 'Threats and conservation', below).

■ Restricted-range species

All the restricted-range species are forest birds, several also being recorded from secondary and man-made habitats. Five species are confined to Amami and Okinawa only. Ryukyu Serpent-eagle *Spilornis* (*cheela*) *perplexus*, endemic to Sakishima and Yaeyama, is sometimes treated as a full species (e.g. Brazil 1991), but has not been included here.

Two restricted-range species from the Izu Islands, Izu Thrush *Turdus celaenops* and Ijima's Leaf-warbler *Phylloscopus ijimae*, have recently been

Distribution patterns of restricted-range species

Species (ordered geographically)	Danjo	Osumi	Takara	Amami	Okinawa	Kerama	Miyako	Sakishima	Yaeyama	Daito	Other EBAs, SAs
Erithacus komadori	●	●	●	●	●	●	W	W	W	–	–
Columba janthina	●	●	–	●	●	●	W	●	●	–	●
Treron formosae	–	●	–	●	●	–	W	●	●	–	●
Pericrocotus tegimae	–	●	–	●	●	–	–	●	●	●	–
Otus elegans	–	●	–	●	●	–	–	●	●	●	●
Zoothera major	–	–	–	●	–	–	–	–	–	–	–
Garrulus lidthi	–	–	–	●	–	–	–	–	–	–	–
Scolopax mira	–	–	–	●	●	–	–	–	–	–	–
Gallirallus okinawae	–	–	–	–	●	–	–	–	–	–	–
Sapheopipo noguchii	–	–	–	–	●	–	–	–	–	–	–
Columba jouyi	–	–	–	–	X	X	–	–	–	X	–
Todirhamphus cinnamominus	–	–	–	–	–	–	–	X	–	–	●
Total	2	5	1	8	8	2	1	4	4	2	

● Present
○ Extinct?
X Extinct
? Present?
R Reintroduced
W Winter only
Threatened spp. shown in **bold** } see 'Status and habitat' table
Other EBAs, SAs }

recorded breeding in the Takara Islands in this EBA (Higuchi and Kawaji 1989, Kawaji *et al.* 1989), but because the records are c.1,000 km from the species' core ranges, and the numbers involved are very small, the Izu Islands have been treated as a separate EBA (146). A further two restricted-range species are recorded in the Nansei Shoto as non-breeding visitors: Japanese Night-heron *Gorsachius goisagi* and Yellow Bunting *Emberiza sulphurata* (both from central Honshu, Secondary Areas s089 and s090).

Both Okinawa Rail *Gallirallus okinawae* (above) and Amami Woodcock *Scolopax mira* (below) are threatened by the loss of their forest habitat and by predation by introduced species such as mongooses.

■ Threats and conservation

This EBA has already suffered the extinction of one bird species: *Columba jouyi* was last seen on Okinawa in 1904 and on the Daito Islands in 1936, but its full range was never documented and its demise remains inexplicable. Today, five species are considered threatened owing to deforestation within their small ranges, as, on some islands, much of the native subtropical vegetation has been cleared for agriculture, settlement and plantations of pine and pineapple.

The two Okinawa endemics, *Gallirallus okinawae* and *Sapheopipo noguchii*, are restricted to the mountainous northern third of Okinawa (known as Yambaru) where the main threats are: dam construction and associated road-building, forest cutting to make chipboard, and clearance for cultivation, especially of fruit. *G. okinawae*, a flightless species only discovered in 1978, is estimated to number 1,800 birds, and *S. noguchii* c.100 birds in less than 15 km^2 of suitable undisturbed habitat. The two Amami endemics, *Zoothera major* and *Garrulus lidthi*, also have very restricted distributions because much mature forest has been clear-felled in the last few decades; *Z. major* is estimated to be below 100 individuals and *G. lidthi* c.5,800.

Predation by mongooses, introduced to Amami and Okinawa to control poisonous snakes, may prove a serious threat to the endemics, and already appears to have caused a population decline of *Scolopax mira* in part of Amami. Introduced predators are a threat to the Japanese Murrelet *Synthliboramphus wumizusume* (classified as Vulnerable), a seabird only known to breed on small islands/stacks in southern Japan and South Korea. In this EBA, it breeds in the Danjo Islands, where the destruction of nesting habitat and disturbance by fishermen landing at breeding sites may be an additional problem.

All the threatened species have been designated as 'Natural Monuments', which gives them a degree of protection from some threats (e.g. hunting, which was a significant threat to *Garrulus lidthi*). However, this does not automatically lead to the protection or conservation of forest and there is only one reasonably sized protected area on Iriomote. On Okinawa, a key island for the conservation of restricted-range species, only small parts of Mt Yonaha, Mt Ibu and Mt Nishime are designated as protected areas by the government (Ichida in press). However, the US Air Force has a large base in Yambaru, covering some of the best areas of forest, and it is hoped that some of this can be designated as a national park.

149 Taiwan

PRIORITY HIGH

Key habitats Subtropical forest, coniferous and mixed forest

Main threats Major habitat loss (e.g. due to cultivation, plantations)

Biological importance ● ● ○
Current threat level ● ● ○

Area 36,000 km²   **Altitude** 0–3,900 m

Countries Taiwan

Restricted-range species	Threatened	Total
Confined to this EBA	0	14
Present also in other EBAs, SAs	0	1
Total	0	15

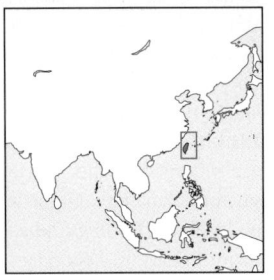

■ General characteristics

Taiwan (formerly known as Formosa) is situated between temperate Japan to the north, subtropical southern China to the west and the tropical Philippines to the south. A ridge with many peaks higher than 3,000 m runs north to south along the central axis of the island and includes Mt Yushan which, at 3,952 m, is the highest mountain in north-east Asia. The mountains fall steeply to the coast in the east and more gently to a wide, densely populated and highly developed agricultural plain in the west. The island's great range of altitudes produces a broad diversity of ecosystems (tropical, subtropical, temperate and alpine habitats) and a wildlife which is correspondingly rich.

The native vegetation includes tropical evergreen rain forest in the lowlands (largely destroyed), subtropical broadleaf evergreen forest at medium altitudes (c.700–1,800 m), and temperate mixed and coniferous forest between c.1,800 and 3,600 m. Wetlands include tidal mudflats, mangrove swamps and saltmarshes, primarily along the west coast.

In addition to its importance for endemic birds, Taiwan lies on the main flyway for birds migrating between Japan and the Philippines, and is therefore of considerable importance for migrants from Japan, mainland China and areas further to the north, including many threatened wetland species (see 'Threats and conservation', below).

■ Restricted-range species

The majority of the EBA's restricted-range species are forest birds and are (now) restricted to uplands, with four species being largely found in the coniferous and mixed forests of higher altitudes, namely *Syrmaticus mikado*, *Tarsiger johnstoniae*, *Garrulax morrisonianus* and *Regulus goodfellowi*. Most species are found widely on the island within their preferred altitudinal range, but *Pycnonotus taivanus* has a rather local distribution (as well as being restricted to coastal lowlands), perhaps owing to competition with the widespread Light-vented Bulbul *P. sinensis* (Wang *et al.* 1991).

Other restricted-range species also occur as non-breeding visitors in Taiwan: Japanese Night-heron *Gorsachius goisagi* (breeds in Central Honshu, Secondary Area s089; has been reported as breeding in Taiwan, but see Sykes 1996), Nordmann's Greenshank *Tringa guttifer* (Sakhalin, Secondary Area s088), Spoon-billed Sandpiper *Eurynorhynchus pygmeus* (Chukotski peninsula, Secondary Area s087) and Yellow Bunting *Emberiza sulphurata* (Central Honshu, Secondary Area s090).

■ Threats and conservation

Today almost all level land (especially in the northern and western plains) and an increasing area on the

Status and habitat of restricted-range species

Species (ordered taxonomically)	Global status	Other EBAs (and SAs)	Altitude (m)	Habitat
Taiwan Partridge *Arborophila crudigularis*	nt	—	700–2,300	Broadleaf forest
Swinhoe's Pheasant *Lophura swinhoii*	nt	—	200–2,300	Primary broadleaf forest, mature secondary forest
Mikado Pheasant *Syrmaticus mikado*	nt	—	1,000–3,850	Broadleaf forest, coniferous and mixed forest, secondary habitats
Whistling Green-pigeon *Treron formosae*	nt	148 (s093,s094)	Up to 2,000	Broadleaf forest, gardens
Styan's Bulbul *Pycnonotus taivanus*	nt	—	Coastal lowlands	Secondary growth, scrub, agricultural areas, gardens
Formosan Whistling-thrush *Myiophonus insularis*	lc	—	600–2,400	Broadleaf forest near streams
Collared Bush-robin *Tarsiger johnstoniae*	lc	—	2,000–3,300	Coniferous and mixed forest edge, scrub
White-whiskered Laughingthrush *Garrulax morrisonianus*	lc	—	2,000–3,500	Coniferous and mixed forest, thickets, bamboo, rhododendron
Steere's Liocichla *Liocichla steerii*	lc	—	900–2,500	Forest, secondary growth
Formosan Barwing *Actinodura morrisoniana*	lc	—	1,200–1,800, lower in winter	Broadleaf forest
White-eared Sibia *Heterophasia auricularis*	lc	—	900–2,800	Broadleaf forest, secondary growth
Formosan Yuhina *Yuhina brunneiceps*	lc	—	500–3,800	Forest, secondary growth
Flamecrest *Regulus goodfellowi*	lc	—	>2,500, lower in winter	Coniferous and mixed forest
Yellow Tit *Parus holsti*	nt	—	700–2,500	Broadleaf forest, sometimes secondary growth
Formosan Magpie *Urocissa caerulea*	lc	—	200–1,800	Broadleaf forest, sometimes secondary growth

Global status (see p. 679 for definitions)
EX Extinct — with year of last record
EW Extinct in the Wild — with year of last record
CR Critical — threatened species
EN Endangered — threatened species
VU Vulnerable — threatened species
cd Conservation Dependent
nt Near Threatened
lc Least Concern
DD Data Deficient
NE Not Evaluated

Other EBAs (and SAs) (see p. 77 for locations): bracketed numbers are Secondary Areas; [x] extinct in that EBA or SA.

lower slopes (up to 1,000 m, but especially between 100 and 500 m) is intensively cultivated (Patel and Lin 1989). Forest still covers c.50% of the total land area, but large tracts are exotic monocultures, which have replaced native species, and are therefore of little wildlife value.

Several of Taiwan's endemic bird species have been identified as being Near Threatened, largely because of the threat that they face from continuing forest destruction—which is also a threat to two of the restricted-range non-breeding visitors, *Gorsachius goisagi* and *Emberiza sulphurata* (see 'Restricted-range species', above), both of which are classified as Vulnerable. Heavy hunting pressure has been a particular problem for the endemic pheasants in the past, but it is not a serious threat today (L. L. Severinghaus *in litt.* 1996). *Tringa guttifer* (classified as Endangered) and *Eurynorhynchus pygmeus* (Vul-

nerable; see above) are threatened by wetland destruction.

Many widespread threatened species occur in Taiwan, including Fairy Pitta *Pitta nympha* (Vulnerable; uncommon in forest), and, as non-breeding visitors only (to wetlands), Chinese Egret *Egretta eulophotes* (Endangered), Oriental Stork *Ciconia boyciana* (Endangered), Black-faced Spoonbill *Platalea minor* (Critical; c.200 birds in winter, more than two-thirds of the known world population), Swan Goose *Anser cygnoides* (Vulnerable), Baikal Teal *Anas formosa* (Vulnerable), Baer's Pochard *Aythya baeri* (Vulnerable) and Saunders's Gull *Larus saundersi* (Endangered).

Some 11% of the island is protected. This area includes six national parks, 18 nature reserves and eight wildlife sanctuaries (P. K. D. Perng *in litt.* 1996).

150 Mindoro

Key habitats Lowland and montane forest, mossy forest

Main threats Severe habitat loss (e.g. due to logging, cultivation, marble mining)

Biological importance ● ● ●
Current threat level ● ● ●

Area 9,800 km² **Altitude** 0–2,000 m

Countries Philippines

Restricted-range species	Threatened	Total
Confined to this EBA	5	5
Present also in other EBAs, SAs	3	5
Total	8	10

■ General characteristics

The whole island of Mindoro, which lies to the south-west of Luzon in the Philippines (EBA 151), is included within this EBA. The island has a broad, rugged, central spine of mountains, rising to c.2,500 m at Mt Halcon in the north and at Mt Baco in the south.

Mindoro would once have been entirely forested, including tropical lowland evergreen rain forest on plains and lower slopes of hills to c.400 m (occasionally higher), giving way to open forest at c.650–1,000 m and above, with mossy forest in the cloud-belt, usually over 1,200 m (Collins *et al.* 1991, Dickinson *et al.* 1991). Stands of Mindoro pine *Pinus merkusii* occur at 600 m or less in the north of the island.

■ Restricted-range species

All the EBA's restricted-range species are forest birds and a few have been recorded from secondary forest. Their altitudinal requirements vary but the birds can be split into predominantly montane species (*Ducula mindorensis*, *Otus mindorensis*, *Lanius validirostris* and *Rhyacornis bicolor*) and lowland ones (the remaining six).

The Mindoro race of Philippine Hawk-owl *Ninox philippensis mindorensis*, recently rediscovered, is very divergent from other races in both call and plumage (Brooks *et al.* 1995a). It appears that this form and the races on Tablas, Sibuyan, Cebu and Camiguin Sur (*spilonata*) and the Sulus (*reyi*) together comprise a species (*N. reyi*), which is probably threatened (N. J. Collar verbally 1997).

■ Threats and conservation

This EBA has been almost totally deforested. According to satellite data from 1988, only 8.5% of land on Mindoro is forested (less than 120 km²) and only about a quarter of this is closed-canopy (Dickinson *et al.* 1991). Pine forest occupies an area of c.60 km².

Although a ban on logging for commercial purposes was introduced in the mid-1970s in Philippine provinces having less than 40% forest cover, logging for domestic use continues in many areas, e.g. along the lower borders (at altitude 750–950 m) of remaining forest on Mt Halcon (Dutson *et al.* 1992, L. A. Ruedas *in litt.* 1993). Encroaching slash-and-burn cultivation (known as 'kaingin') poses an additional serious threat to the few remaining lowland forest fragments, and the mining of marble in the north of the island contributes to forest destruction (Diesmos and Pedregosa 1995).

Not surprisingly all but one of the restricted-range species which occur on Mindoro are classified as threatened or Near Threatened, including all the endemics. Two lowland species, *Gallicolumba platenae* and *Centropus steerii* (both classified as Critical), are under immediate threat of extinction through continuing forest clearance and fragmentation. *Dicaeum retrocinctum* is present at higher population densities over a wider altitudinal range,

Status and habitat of restricted-range species

Species (ordered taxonomically)	Global status	Other EBAs (and SAs)	Altitude (m)	Habitat
Mindoro Bleeding-heart *Gallicolumba platenae*	CR	—	30–300	Lowland forest, secondary forest
Mindoro Imperial-pigeon *Ducula mindorensis*	EN	—	700–1,700+	Mid-mountain and montane forest, mossy forest, forest edge
Black-hooded Coucal *Centropus steerii*	CR	—	0–760	Lowland forest
Mindoro Scops-owl *Otus mindorensis*	VU	—	>870	Montane forest, mossy forest
Mindoro Hornbill *Penelopides mindorensis*	EN	—	Lowlands to 1,070	Forest with big trees for feeding and breeding; can also occur in small forest patches and forest edge
Mountain Shrike *Lanius validirostris*	nt	151,154	>500	Clearings in montane and pine forest, forest edge, open secondary growth, scrub in grasslands
Ashy Thrush *Zoothera cinerea*	VU	151	200–1,100	Forest, selectively logged forest
Luzon Water-redstart *Rhyacornis bicolor*[1]	EN	151	300+	Rocky banks along fast flowing mountain streams in montane and pine forest
Green-backed Whistler *Pachycephala albiventris*	lc	151	300–1,000	Lowland forest, montane forest, mossy forest, secondary forest, forest edge
Scarlet-collared Flowerpecker *Dicaeum retrocinctum*	CR	152	Lowlands to 1,200	Forest, forest edge; poorly tolerant of degraded forest

Global status (see p. 679 for definitions)

EX	Extinct	with year of last record	cd	Conservation Dependent
EW	Extinct in the Wild		nt	Near Threatened
CR	Critical	threatened species	lc	Least Concern
EN	Endangered		DD	Data Deficient
VU	Vulnerable		NE	Not Evaluated

Other EBAs (and SAs) (see p. 83 for locations)
Bracketed numbers are Secondary Areas.   ˣ Extinct in that EBA or SA.

Notes
[1] Two previously unpublished specimens from the 1960s in the Philippines National Museum (Collar *et al.* in press).

but its status is also considered Critical since it tolerates degraded forest only poorly, and deforestation is likely to reach all altitudes in the near future. It has been speculated that new records of this species from Negros and Panay (EBA 152) may reflect recent faunal changes—the result, at least in part, of the massive destruction of Philippine forests (Curio *et al.* 1996).

This endangered bovid, the tamaraw *Bubalus mindorensis*, lives in dense forest but grazes in open areas, close to water for wallowing. Protection of its habitat will also benefit some of the restricted-range bird species in this EBA.

Several other widespread threatened forest birds occur (or have been recorded) on Mindoro: Philippine Hawk-eagle *Spizaetus philippensis* (Vulnerable), Spotted Imperial-pigeon *Ducula carola* (Vulnerable), Philippine Cockatoo *Cacatua haematuropygia* (Critical), Blue-naped Parrot *Tanygnathus lucionensis* (Endangered) and Black-bibbed Cicadabird *Coracina mindanensis* (Vulnerable).

The Mts Iglit–Baco area has been proposed as a national park (754 km²), primarily to protect an endemic threatened bovid, the tamaraw *Bubalus mindorensis*. The area is largely fire-maintained grassland but includes unsurveyed areas of montane forest and small fragments of lowland forest (G. Dutson *in litt.* 1993), which could be important for birds. Other potential protected areas include the Mt Halcon range, which is critically important for the survival of the EBA's endemic montane species, and lowland forest fragments in west-central Mindoro (e.g. near Sablayan and Malpalon). Before other areas can be proposed for protection, there is a need for further field surveys to ascertain whether surviving forest remnants in the south and west of the island still support viable populations of endemic birds (Dutson *et al.* 1992, see Brooks *et al.* 1995a).

151 Luzon

PRIORITY
CRITICAL

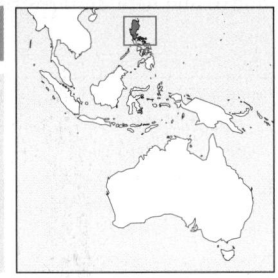

Key habitats	Lowland and montane forest, mossy forest, pine forest

Main threats Major habitat loss (e.g. due to logging, cultivation)

Area 110,000 km² **Altitude** 0–2,700 m

Countries Philippines

Biological importance ● ● ●
Current threat level ● ● ○

Restricted-range species	Threatened	Total
Confined to this EBA	11	24
Present also in other EBAs, SAs	7	16
Total	18	40

■ General characteristics

This EBA includes the lowlands and mountains of Luzon—at over 100,000 km² the largest of the Philippine islands—and the associated islands of Polillo, Marinduque and Catanduanes. The Batanes and Babuyanes Islands to the north of Luzon are treated separately as a Secondary Area (s094). On Luzon there are three main mountain ranges which are important for restricted-range birds: in the west, the Cordillera Central (including Mts Puguis, Polis, Data and Pulog—the highest peak at 2,930 m) and the Zambales Mountains, and in the east the Sierra

Madre; other isolated mountains of note include Mts Banahaw and Isarog further south.

Various different forest types can be recognized in the Philippines including tropical lowland evergreen rain forest which is rich in dipterocarps; this grows best on good soils and therefore is (or was) prevalent on well-watered plains and the lower slopes of hills up to c.400 m, occasionally higher, giving way to a more open, dipterocarp-dominated, montane rain forest at c.650–1,000 m and upwards. Mossy forest, where the trees are dwarf, moss-covered and laden with ferns, orchids and liverworts, occurs in the

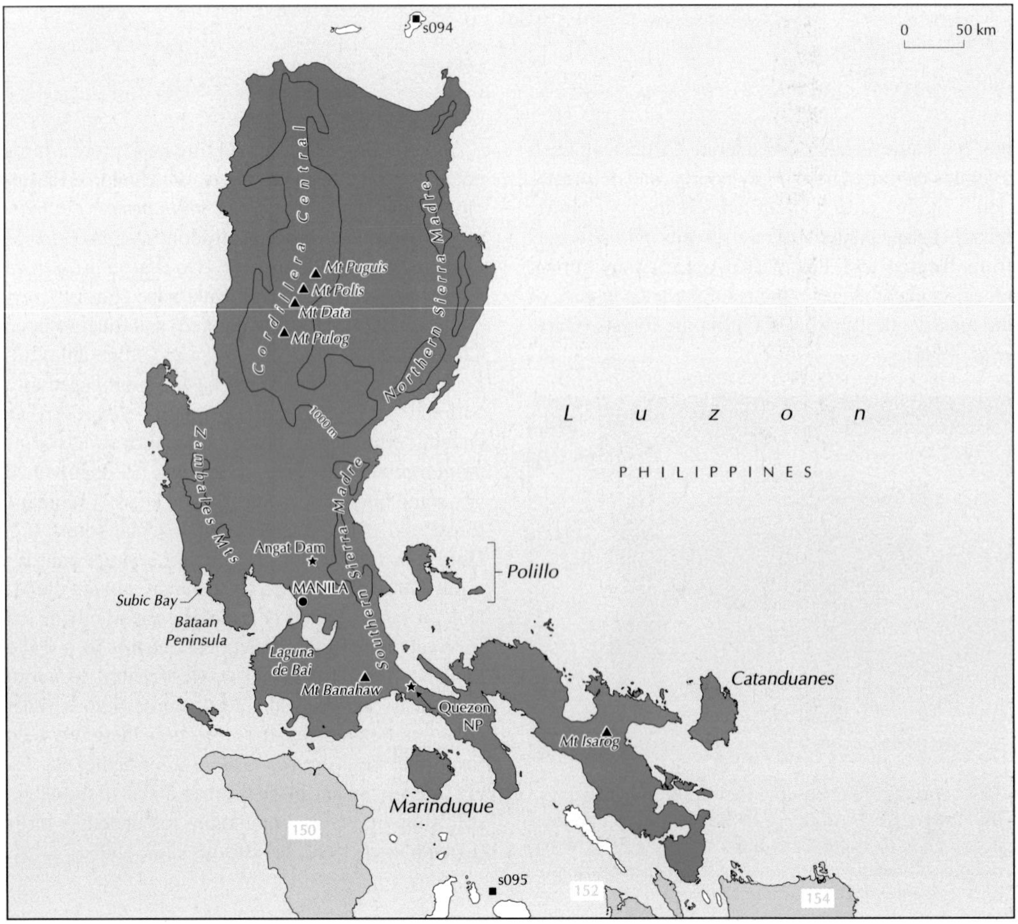

Status and habitat of restricted-range species

Species (ordered taxonomically)	Global status	Other EBAs (and SAs)	Altitude (m)	Habitat
Spotted Buttonquail *Turnix ocellata*	nt	152[1]	Lowlands to 1,800+	Brushy grassland, ravine edges
Worcester's Buttonquail *Turnix worcesteri*	VU	—	Non-breeding records 750–2,270	Grasslands?
Brown-banded Rail *Lewinia mirificus*	EN	154	Non-breeding records 550–1,350	Grasslands?
Luzon Bleeding-heart *Gallicolumba luzonica*	nt	—	0–1,000+	Forest, montane forest, secondary forest
Flame-breasted Fruit-dove *Ptilinopus marchei*	VU	—	(500–) 1,000–2,600	Montane forest, mossy forest
Cream-bellied Fruit-dove *Ptilinopus merrilli*	nt	—	0–1,300	Forest, selectively logged forest
Luzon Racquet-tail *Prioniturus montanus*	VU	—	700+	Montane forest, mossy forest
Green Racquet-tail *Prioniturus luconensis*	EN	—	100–700	Forest, forest edge, secondary growth, cultivated areas
Red-crested Malkoha *Phaenicophaeus superciliosus*	lc	—	0–750	Forest, selectively logged forest, sometimes cogon grasslands
Scale-feathered Malkoha *Phaenicophaeus cumingi*	lc	—	<2,000	Forest
Rufous Coucal *Centropus unirufus*	nt	—	0–1,200	Forest (esp. where interlaced with climbing bamboo), selectively logged forest, forest edge
Luzon Scops-owl *Otus longicornis*	VU	—	350–1,800 (–2,200)	Montane forest, pine forest
Whitehead's Swiftlet *Collocalia whiteheadi*	VU	154	1,200+	Forested mountains for feeding; caves for breeding
Luzon Hornbill *Penelopides manillae*	nt	—	0–1,350	Forest
Whiskered Pitta *Pitta kochi*	VU	—	1,000+	Montane forest, mossy forest; forages where forest floor rooted by pigs
Blackish Cuckoo-shrike *Coracina coerulescens*	nt	153[X]	0–1,100	Forest, degraded forest, secondary forest
Mountain Shrike *Lanius validirostris*	nt	150,152,154	1,000+	Clearings in montane/pine forest, forest edge, open secondary growth, scrub in grasslands
Ashy Thrush *Zoothera cinerea*	VU	150	200–1,100	Forest, selectively logged forest
Luzon Water-redstart *Rhyacornis bicolor*	EN	150	300+	Rocky banks along fast-flowing mountain streams in montane and pine forest
Rabor's Wren-babbler *Napothera rabori*	VU	—	0–1,000	Forest, secondary forest
Golden-crowned Babbler *Stachyris dennistouni*	nt	—	0–1,150	Forest, selectively logged and degraded forest, forest edge
Chestnut-faced Babbler *Stachyris whiteheadi*	nt	—	(100–)800+	Forest, pine forest, mossy forest, secondary forest, scrub
Luzon Striped-babbler *Stachyris striata*	VU	—	Lowlands to 1,000	Forest (inc. bamboo), forest edge, degraded forest, secondary forest
Philippine Bush-warbler *Cettia seebohmi*	lc	—	800+	Pine forest, forest with extensive understorey, dense vegetation in agricultural areas
Long-tailed Bush-warbler *Bradypterus caudatus*	nt	154	700–2,750	Montane forest, mossy forest, forest edge, dense secondary forest
Grey-backed Tailorbird *Orthotomus derbianus*	lc	156[1]	0–750	Forest, forest edge, dense secondary forest, thickets
White-browed Jungle-flycatcher *Rhinomyias insignis*	EN	—	950+	Montane forest, mossy forest, secondary forest, small open areas

cont.

Status and habitat of restricted-range species (cont.)

Species (ordered taxonomically)	Global status	Other EBAs (and SAs)	Altitude (m)	Habitat
Ashy-breasted Flycatcher *Muscicapa randi*	EN	152[1]	Lowlands to 1,200	Forest, degraded forest
Furtive Flycatcher *Ficedula disposita*[2]	EN	—	250–760	Forest, selectively logged and degraded forest, secondary forest
Blue-breasted Flycatcher *Cyornis herioti*	nt	—	100–1,200	Forest, selectively logged forest
Short-crested Monarch *Hypothymis helenae*	nt	154	<1,000	Forest, selectively logged forest
Celestial Monarch *Hypothymis coelestis*	EN	152,154,155 (s095)	100–1,000	Forest, forest edge, secondary forest (may be a riverine specialist)
Green-backed Whistler *Pachycephala albiventris*	lc	150	<2,000	Forest, montane forest, mossy forest, secondary forest, forest edge
White-fronted Tit *Parus semilarvatus*	nt	154	<1,000	Forest, forest edge, secondary forest
Long-billed Rhabdornis *Rhabdornis grandis*	nt	—	<1,250	Forest, selectively logged forest, secondary forest
Flame-crowned Flowerpecker *Dicaeum anthonyi*	nt	154	800–2,100	Montane forest, mossy forest, forest edge, secondary forest
White-cheeked Bullfinch *Pyrrhula leucogenis*	nt	154	1,250–2,600	Mossy forest, forest edge, secondary forest
Green-faced Parrotfinch *Erythrura viridifacies*	EN	152	Prob. 1,000+, occas. lowlands	Forest, forest edge, bamboo, grassland
White-lored Oriole *Oriolus albiloris*	lc	—	0–1,200	Forest, selectively logged and degraded forest
Isabela Oriole *Oriolus isabellae*	CR	—	Lowlands, foothills	Forest (esp. bamboo forest), forest edge

Global status (see p. 679 for definitions)
EX Extinct
EW Extinct in the Wild
} with year of last record

CR Critical
EN Endangered
VU Vulnerable
} threatened species

cd Conservation Dependent
nt Near Threatened
lc Least Concern
DD Data Deficient
NE Not Evaluated

Other EBAs (and SAs) (see p. 83 for locations) Bracketed numbers are Secondary Areas.
X Extinct in that EBA or SA.

Notes [1] In these EBAs, known from single records only.
[2] Taxonomy according to Dutson (1993).

cloud belt where there is constant high humidity, usually over 1,200 m, but also on exposed summits and ridges at lower elevations, and as low as 700 m in the eastern Sierra Madre where it is wettest. Extensive stands of Benguet pine *Pinus kesiya* occur in the western Cordillera Central and Zambales Mountains between 450 and 2,450 m where it is drier (Dickinson *et al.* 1991, Collins *et al.* 1991).

In some parts of Luzon there are large areas of dense 'cogon' grassland; these areas are maintained by fire during the dry season and are all thought to have replaced original forest (Dickinson *et al.* 1991).

■ Restricted-range species

The majority of the restricted-range species occur in forest, with three being (or likely to be) grassland birds. The forest species can be divided into those which tend to occur in lowland and hill forest (largely below 1,000 m) and those which tend to occupy montane and mossy forest (largely above 1,000 m); see 'Habitat associations' table. Although only 'low-

land' species are found on the smaller islands, nearly all of the restricted-range species occur in the Cordillera Central and/or the Sierra Madre (see 'Distribution patterns' table). Because of these distributional similarities and some altitudinal overlap between those birds classified as 'lowland' and those as 'montane', all restricted-range species occurring on Luzon have been included within this single EBA (contra ICBP 1992); a similar treatment has been applied to Mindanao (EBA 154), the second largest island in the Philippines.

The distributions of most species in this EBA appear to be patchy but this is largely because of forest fragmentation and it is likely that ranges were once more widespread and contiguous even in historical times. In addition, recorded distributions are dependent on observer coverage (which is still incomplete), and present-day ranges for some species may be larger in reality than is currently apparent. Because it has been difficult to determine which species genuinely qualify as having ranges of less

Habitat associations of restricted-range species

Lowland and hill forest	Montane forest, mossy forest, pine forest
Gallicolumba luzonica	*Ptilinopus marchei*
Ptilinopus merrilli	**Prioniturus montanus**
Prioniturus luconensis	*Phaenicophaeus cumingi*
Phaenicophaeus	**Otus longicornis**
superciliosus	**Collocalia whiteheadi**
Centropus unirufus	**Pitta kochi**
Penelopides manillae	*Lanius validirostris*
Coracina coerulescens	**Rhyacornis bicolor**
Zoothera cinerea	*Stachyris whiteheadi*
Napothera rabori	*Cettia seebohmi*
Stachyris dennistouni	*Bradypterus caudatus*
Stachyris striata	**Rhinomyias insignis**
Orthotomus derbianus	*Pachycephala albiventris*
Muscicapa randi	*Dicaeum anthonyi*
Ficedula dispositа	*Pyrrhula leucogenis*
Cyornis herioti	**Erythrura viridifacies**
Hypothymis helenae	
Hypothymis coelestis	Grasslands
Parus semilarvatus	*Turnix ocellata*
Rhabdornis grandis	**Turnix worcesteri** ?
Oriolus albiloris	**Lewinia mirificus** ?
Oriolus isabellae	

Threatened species (Critical, Endangered, Vulnerable) are shown in **bold**; see 'Status and habitat' table.

than 50,000 km², all species which are endemic to Luzon (apart from one—Lowland White-eye *Zosterops meyeni*, a widespread habitat generalist) have been included as restricted-range, despite the large size of this island.

Knowledge of some species has been improved by recent surveys: one in the Sierra Madre recorded three very poorly known birds—*Rhabdornis grandis*, *Napothera rabori* and *Pitta kochi* (Danielsen *et al.* 1991, see also Mallari and Jensen 1993)—and another in Mount Pulog National Park in the Cordillera Central found that area probably to be a stronghold for *Rhyacornis bicolor* (Andersen *et al.* 1992). Two species which remain, however, very little known are

Scale-feathered Malkoha *Phaenicophaeus cumingi* is the only restricted-range bird species which has been recorded widely in this EBA.

Lewinia mirificus and *Turnix worcesteri*, with records of these appearing mostly to be individuals involved in post breeding-dispersal or on migration.

In addition to its many resident restricted-range species, four restricted-range species occur on Luzon as wintering birds: Japanese Night-heron *Gorsachius goisagi* from the lowland forests of central Honshu in Japan (Secondary Area s089), Ijima's Leaf-warbler *Phylloscopus ijimae* from the Izu Islands of Japan (EBA 146), Streaked Reed-warbler *Acrocephalus sorghophilus* from China (breeding grounds unknown), and Yellow Bunting *Emberiza sulphurata* from the montane forests of central Honshu (Secondary Area s090).

■ Threats and conservation

This EBA was once completely forested but satellite data from 1988 show forest covering just 24% of Luzon, 3% of Marinduque and 26% of the Catanduanes (Dickinson *et al.* 1991). The Sierra Madre has one of the largest remaining forest blocks (and one of the richest avifaunas yet known from any forest area in the Philippines) but even there much forest has been lost: it has been estimated that 40,000 km² of primary lowland forest remained in the 1930s, but this has been reduced to only 6,850 km² (17%), and most areas are under logging concessions (Mallari and Jensen 1993, Poulsen 1995).

Upland mossy forests, though more secure than lowland ones, are subject to threat, especially in the Cordillera Central where local people have recently accepted modern technology and are growing temperate and semi-temperate vegetable crops on bench terraces after clearance of native montane habitats (Penafiel 1993).

Several restricted-range species in this EBA are hunted for food or for the cage-bird trade, but the main threat to birds comes inevitably from continuing forest loss and fragmentation. For example, *Oriolus isabellae*, which may be close to extinction. This species was known only from the Bataan peninsula and Isabela province, with one of the last records from a site in the Sierra Madre in 1961—where there is now virtually no forest (Danielsen *et al.* 1994); more recently there have been records from two further sites in the Sierra Madre in Quirino and Cagayan provinces, although the former was in a small fragmented forest area of less than 100 km² (Gamauf and Tebbich 1995, van der Linde 1995).

Overall, no other Asian island has as many threatened bird species as Luzon, for—as well as the 18 threatened restricted-range species which breed there, and the four threatened restricted-range species (from other EBAs and Secondary Areas) which occur as winter visitors (all classified as Vulnerable; see 'Restricted-range species', above)—there are nine

Distribution patterns of restricted-range species

Species (ordered geographically)	Cordillera Cent.	Sierra Madre	Bataan pen./Zambales Mts	Laguna de Bai/Mt Banahaw	Polillo Islands	Marinduque I.	Mt Isarog/Southern Luzon	Catanduanes I.	Other EBAs, SAs
Turnix worcesteri	?	–	–	–	–	–	–	–	–
Lewinia mirificus	?	–	–	–	–	–	–	–	●
Cettia seebohmi	●	–	–	–	–	–	–	–	●
Prioniturus montanus	●	●	–	–	–	–	–	–	–
Stachyris dennistouni	●	●	–	–	–	–	–	–	–
Rhinomyias insignis	●	●	–	–	–	–	–	–	●
Lanius validirostris	●	●	–	–	–	–	–	–	●
Rhyacornis bicolor	●	●	–	–	–	–	–	–	●
Bradypterus caudatus	●	●	–	–	–	–	–	–	●
Dicaeum anthonyi	●	●	–	–	–	–	–	–	●
Pyrrhula leucogenis	●	●	–	●	–	–	–	–	●
Ptilinopus marchei	●	●	–	●	–	–	–	–	●
Rhabdornis grandis	●	●	–	●	–	–	–	–	–
Zoothera cinerea	●	●	–	●	–	–	–	–	●
Muscicapa randi	●	●	–	●	–	–	–	–	●
Oriolus albiloris	●	●	●	●	–	–	–	–	–
Turnix ocellata	●	●	●	●	–	–	–	–	●
Prioniturus luconensis	●	●	●	●	–	●	–	–	–
Otus longicornis	●	●	●	●	–	–	●	–	–
Pitta kochi	●	●	●	●	–	–	●	–	–
Napothera rabori	●	●	–	●	–	–	●	–	–
Stachyris whiteheadi	●	●	–	●	–	–	●	–	–
Pachycephala albiventris	●	●	–	●	–	–	●	–	●
Collocalia whiteheadi	●	–	–	–	–	–	●	–	●
Gallicolumba luzonica	●	●	–	●	●	–	●	●	–
Phaenicophaeus cumingi	●	●	●	●	●	●	●	●	–
Hypothymis helenae	●	●	–	–	●	–	●	●	–
Stachyris striata	–	●	●	–	–	–	–	–	–
Ficedula disposita	–	●	●	–	–	–	–	–	–
Oriolus isabellae	–	●	●	–	–	–	–	–	–
Hypothymis coelestis	–	●	●	●	–	–	–	–	●
Erythrura viridifacies	–	●	●	●	–	–	–	–	●
Parus semilarvatus	–	●	●	–	–	–	●	–	●
Penelopides manillae	–	●	●	●	●	●	●	–	–
Ptilinopus merrilli	–	●	●	●	●	–	●	●	–
Centropus unirufus	–	●	●	●	●	–	●	●	–
Cyornis herioti	–	●	–	●	–	–	●	●	–
Phaenicophaeus superciliosus	–	●	●	●	●	–	●	●	●
Coracina coerulescens	–	●	●	●	–	●	●	●	X
Orthotomus derbianus	–	–	–	●	–	–	●	●	●
Total	25	35	14	24	7	5	17	9	

● Present ? Present?
○ Extinct? R Reintroduced
X Extinct I Introduced

Threatened spp. shown in **bold** } see 'Status and habitat' table
Other EBAs, SAs }

additional widespread threatened species found in Luzon's forests. These latter include the Philippine Eagle *Pithecophaga jefferyi* (classified as Critical, with the forests of the Sierra Madre representing the species' largest single remaining stronghold: Danielsen *et al.* 1992), Philippine Hawk-eagle *Spizaetus philippensis* (Vulnerable), Spotted Imperial-pigeon *Ducula carola* (Vulnerable), Philippine Cockatoo *Cacatua haematuropygia* (Critical), Blue-naped Parrot *Tanygnathus lucionensis* (Endangered), Philippine Eagle-owl *Bubo philippensis* (Endangered), Philippine Kingfisher *Ceyx melanurus* (Vulnerable) and Black-bibbed Cicadabird *Coracina mindanensis* (Vulnerable).

There are several protected areas which cover the main mountain ranges in Luzon (e.g. Mts Data, Pulog, Banahaw–San Cristobal and Isarog). The Northern Sierra Madre Protected Area (which includes the Palanan Wilderness Area) has recently been established under the Integrated Protected Areas System (IPAS) and is a critical extension of this network. The watershed at Angat dam (which is not gazetted) and Quezon National Park are two lowland sites which are of prime importance to bird conservation (Lambert 1993a), and the lowland forest in the Subic Bay protected area, also established under IPAS, is another important tract.

152 Negros and Panay

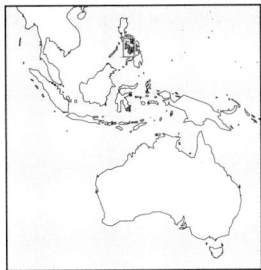

Key habitats Lowland and montane forest, mossy forest

Main threats Severe habitat loss (e.g. due to logging, cultivation)

Biological importance ●
Current threat level ● ● ●

Area 29,000 km² **Altitude** 0–2,000 m

Countries Philippines

Restricted-range species	Threatened	Total
Confined to this EBA	10	10
Present also in other EBAs, SAs	4	7
Total	14	17

■ General characteristics

This EBA covers the central Philippine islands of Negros, Guimaras and Panay, which are all politically part of the Visayas (see also EBAs 153 and 154). The smaller islands of Masbate and Ticao are also included because—although only one restricted-range species, *Penelopides panini*, occurs or occurred there (and they could, therefore, have been treated as a Secondary Area)—there are many sub-species endemic to this group of islands as a whole (Brooks *et al.* 1992). However, Sibuyan, Romblon and Tablas in the north and Siquijor in the south are treated as Secondary Areas (s095 and s096) because their biogeographic affinities are less clear.

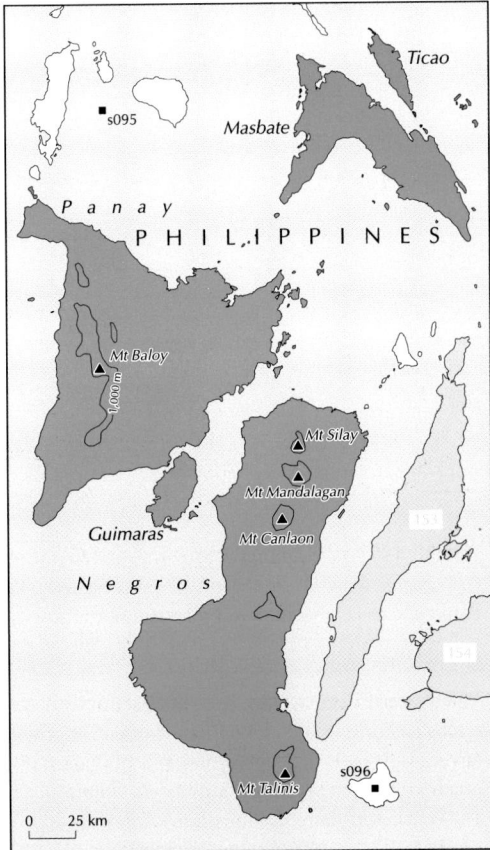

■ Restricted-range species

The islands would once have been completely covered in forest including tropical lowland evergreen rain forest to c.400 m, giving way to a more open forest at 650–1,000 m and upwards, with mossy forest usually over 1,200 m (Collins *et al.* 1991, Dickinson *et al.* 1991).

All the EBA's restricted-range species are forest birds and a few have been recorded from degraded or secondary forest. Most species occur below 1,200 m, apart from *Stachyris latistriata* and *S. nigrorum* which only occur above 1,000 m.

The restricted-range species show a variety of distribution patterns between the islands (see 'Distribution patterns' table), with the recently discovered *Stachyris latistriata* being present on Panay only (Gonzales and Kennedy 1990) and two species—*Ptilinopus arcanus* and *S. nigrorum*—present on

Distribution patterns of restricted-range species

Species (ordered geographically)	Panay	Guimaras	Negros	Masbate, Ticao	Other EBAs, SAs
Stachyris latistriata	●	–	–	–	–
Lanius validirostris	●	–	–	–	●
Gallicolumba keayi	●	–	●	–	–
Stachyris speciosa	●	–	●	–	–
Dicaeum retrocinctum	●	–	●	–	●
Erythrura viridifacies	●	–	○	–	●
Aceros waldeni	●	○	●	–	–
Coracina ostenta	●	○	●	–	–
Rhinomyias albigularis	●	○	●	–	–
Dicaeum haematostictum	●	○	●	–	–
Penelopides panini	●	○	●	○	–
Ptilinopus arcanus	–	–	○ᶜ	–	–
Stachyris nigrorum	–	–	●ᵀ	–	–
Turnix ocellata	–	–	●	–	●
Mearnsia picina	–	–	●	–	●
Muscicapa randi	–	–	○	–	●
Hypothymis coelestis	–	–	○	–	●
Total	11	5	15	1	

● Present　? Present?　Threatened spp. shown in **bold**　⎫ see 'Status
○ Extinct?　R Reintroduced　　　　　　　　　　 ⎬ and habitat'
X Extinct　I Introduced　Other EBAs, SAs ⎭ table
ᶜ Mt Canlaon only　ᵀ Mt Talinis only (if an unrepeated record from Mt Canlaon is discounted)

Status and habitat of restricted-range species

Species (ordered taxonomically)	Global status	Other EBAs (and SAs)	Altitude (m)	Habitat
Spotted Buttonquail *Turnix ocellata*[1]	nt	151	Lowlands to 1,800+	Brushy grassland, ravine edges
Negros Bleeding-heart *Gallicolumba keayi*	CR	—	<1,200	Forest
Negros Fruit-dove *Ptilinopus arcanus*[2]	CR	—	c.1,200, perhaps lower	Mid-montane forest
Philippine Needletail *Mearnsia picina*	lc	153,154,155	<1,250	Forest, clearings
Visayan Hornbill *Penelopides panini*	CR	—	Lowlands to 1,200	Forest, secondary forest
Writhed-billed Hornbill *Aceros waldeni*	CR	—	<1,200	Forest
White-winged Cuckoo-shrike *Coracina ostenta*	VU	—	<1,200, perhaps higher	Forest; scarce in montane forest, forest edge, degraded forest
Mountain Shrike *Lanius validirostris*	nt	150,151,154	1,000+	Clearings in montane forest, forest edge, open secondary growth, scrub in grasslands
Flame-templed Babbler *Stachyris speciosa*	EN	—	Lowlands to 1,100	Forest with thick undergrowth, degraded forest, sometimes secondary growth
Panay Striped-babbler *Stachyris latistriata*	VU	—	1,200–1,900	Montane forest, mossy forest
Negros Striped-babbler *Stachyris nigrorum*	EN	—	>1,000	Montane forest, mossy forest, degraded forest
White-throated Jungle-flycatcher *Rhinomyias albigularis*	CR	—	<1,100	Lowland forest, mid-montane forest, tall secondary forest
Ashy-breasted Flycatcher *Muscicapa randi*	EN	151	<1,200	Forest, degraded forest
Celestial Monarch *Hypothymis coelestis*	EN	151,154,155 (s095)	<1,000	Forest, forest edge, secondary growth (may be a riverine specialist)
Visayan Flowerpecker *Dicaeum haematostictum*[3]	EN	—	400–1,250	Forest, scrub
Scarlet-collared Flowerpecker *Dicaeum retrocinctum*	CR	150	Lowlands to 1,200	Forest, forest edge; poorly tolerant of degraded forest
Green-faced Parrotfinch *Erythrura viridifacies*	EN	151	Probably 1,000+, occas. lowlands	Forest, forest edge, bamboo, grassland

Global status (see p. 679 for definitions)

EX	Extinct ⎱ with year	cd Conservation Dependent
EW	Extinct in ⎰ of last the Wild ⎰ record	
		nt Near Threatened
CR	Critical ⎱	lc Least Concern
EN	Endangered ⎰ threatened species	DD Data Deficient
VU	Vulnerable ⎰	NE Not Evaluated

Other EBAs (and SAs) (see p. 83 for locations)
Bracketed numbers are Secondary Areas.
[x] Extinct in that EBA or SA.

Notes

[1] Known from a single specimen in 1987 in this EBA (Dickinson *et al.* 1991).

[2] Known from a single female collected (and a sighting of another bird) in 1953 (Dickinson *et al.* 1991), but existence as a species is in doubt.

[3] Taxonomy according to Brooks *et al.* (1992).

Negros only. Four species may be extinct on Negros (*Ptilinopus arcanus* last seen in 1953, *Muscicapa randi* in 1877, *Hypothymis coelestis* in 1959 and *Erythrura viridifacies* in 1965), and it is likely that the five restricted-range species which have been recorded on Guimaras are also extinct on this island. Recent range extensions include *Dicaeum retrocinctum* (previously treated as endemic to Mindoro, EBA 150), which has been sighted twice on Negros during 1993–1994 and nine times on Panay in 1992 (Curio 1994, Curio *et al.* 1996, N. A. D. Mallari verbally 1995), and *Lanius validirostris* and *Erythrura viridifacies* which have recently been recorded from Panay (N. A. D. Mallari verbally 1996).

■ Threats and conservation

The western Visayas have been almost totally deforested. According to satellite data from 1988, forest covers only 4% of Negros and 8% of Panay (but much of this is montane and mossy forest above 1,000 m), and there are no significant areas left on Masbate, Ticao or Guimaras (Dickinson *et al.* 1991,

Brooks *et al.* 1992). There are, however, forest remnants (which may not show up on satellite maps) on hill-tops, e.g. along the whole of Ticao where *Penelopides panini* may yet survive (E. Curio *in litt.* 1993). Although logging for commercial purposes is illegal in this EBA, clearance of forest for subsistence agriculture (known as 'kaingin') and small-scale logging for domestic use still continue (Brooks *et al.* 1992).

Inevitably, all the restricted-range species in this EBA are extremely threatened by further loss and fragmentation of forest, with hunting exacerbating the situation for some birds: five endemic species are classified as Critical (the highest number in any EBA in the south-east Asian region). For example, *Aceros waldeni* which appears to have been hunted out from large parts of Panay (Curio *et al.* 1996), is presumed extinct from Guimaras (given the near-total forest clearance), and was recorded in 1991 on Negros for the first time in 80 years—though only one pair at a single locality.

Several other widespread forest threatened species occur (or have been recorded) in the EBA: Philippine Hawk-eagle *Spizaetus philippensis* (Vulnerable), Spotted Imperial-pigeon *Ducula carola* (Vulnerable), Philippine Cockatoo *Cacatua haematuropygia* (Critical), Blue-naped Parrot *Tanygnathus lucionensis* (Endangered) and Rufous-lored Kingfisher *Todirhamphus winchelli* (Endangered).

There is one protected area—at Mt Canlaon on Negros—but its national park status has not prevented the total clearance of the lower slopes, and there is only one sector of forest, Mambucal, which reaches down to 750 m (Brooks *et al.* 1992, Lambert 1993a). Brooks *et al.* (1992) propose protection of the remaining forest at Ban-ban (for the preservation of *Rhinomyias albigularis* in particular) and suggest additional field surveys in a number of areas includ-

G. C. L. Dutson

Flame-templed Babbler *Stachyris speciosa* is a bird of dense forest understorey and more open growth, and is at considerable risk from continuing habitat clearance, although it can survive in some degraded forest.

ing Mts Mandalagan and Silay in northern Negros, and Mt Talinis (and the nearby Lake Balinsasayao area) in the south. On Panay, Mts Madja-as and Baloy are important sites which will be covered by the proposed Panay Mountains National Park (J. Hornbuckle *in litt.* 1996). Further recommendations are in Curio (1994).

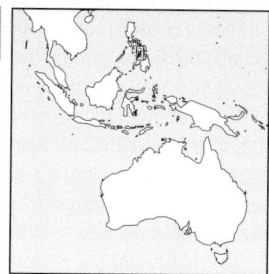

153 Cebu

PRIORITY
CRITICAL

Key habitats Degraded and secondary forest, scrub, bamboo thickets

Main threats Severe habitat loss (e.g. due to sugar-cane plantations)

Biological importance ● ● ○
Current threat level ● ● ●

Area 4,500 km² **Altitude** 0–1,000 m

Countries Philippines

Restricted-range species	Threatened	Total
Confined to this EBA	2	2
Present also in other EBAs, SAs	0	0
Total	2	2

■ General characteristics

The Philippine island of Cebu is one of the Visayan islands which also include Negros and Panay to the west (EBA 152), and Samar, Leyte and Bohol to the east (EBA 154). Deep-water channels dissect this geopolitical grouping, separating Masbate and Ticao (also part of EBA 152) from southern Luzon (EBA 151), and Cebu from Leyte and Bohol. Relatively recently, therefore, there was a land-bridge between Cebu and the other islands in the Western Visayas (EBA 152) and they would thus have had a shared fauna. Although this pattern is still shown by the

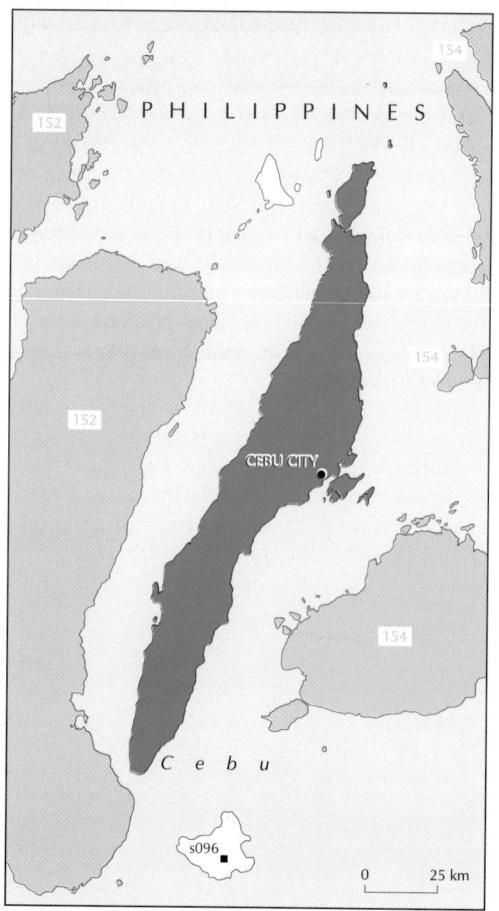

Remnant forest at Tabunan, believed to be the largest remaining area on Cebu. Protection of this forest is critical for the survival of Cebu Flowerpecker *Dicaeum quadricolor*.

mammals (five are endemic to this group of islands: W. L. R. Oliver *in litt.* 1996), it is not apparent in the distributions of today's restricted-range bird species, and Cebu is treated as an EBA in its own right because of its two endemic birds.

It is assumed that the island was once covered in tropical evergreen rain forest as in the other Philippine islands.

■ Restricted-range species

Of the six restricted-range species which are known to have occurred on Cebu, only two are extant, both of them having been thought in the past to be extinct. All the restricted-range species are or were originally forest birds.

Status and habitat of restricted-range species

Species (ordered taxonomically)	Global status	Other EBAs (and SAs)	Habitat
Philippine Needletail *Mearnsia picina*[1]	lc	152,154,155	Forest, clearings
Blackish Cuckoo-shrike *Coracina coerulescens*[1]	nt	151	Forest, degraded forest, secondary forest
Streak-breasted Bulbul *Ixos siquijorensis*[1]	EN	(s095,s096)	Forest, forest edge, secondary forest, scrub
Philippine Leafbird *Chloropsis flavipennis*[1]	EN	154	Forest, forest edge, secondary forest
Black Shama *Copsychus cebuensis*	EN	—	Forest, secondary forest, scrub, bamboo thickets, plantations
Cebu Flowerpecker *Dicaeum quadricolor*	CR	—	Forest, degraded forest

Global status (see p. 679 for definitions)

EX	Extinct	with year of last record	cd	Conservation Dependent
EW	Extinct in the Wild		nt	Near Threatened
CR	Critical	threatened species	lc	Least Concern
EN	Endangered		DD	Data Deficient
VU	Vulnerable		NE	Not Evaluated

Other EBAs (and SAs) (see p. 83 for locations) — Bracketed numbers are Secondary Areas. [X] Extinct in that EBA or SA.

Notes [1] Extinct in this EBA.

Two of the restricted-range species—*Coracina coerulescens altera* and *Ixos siquijorensis monticola*—were represented by endemic subspecies, and a further 10 subspecies of more-widespread species are or were endemic to the island.

■ Threats and conservation

Cebu's relatively low profile (a central ridge reaching a maximum of 1,018 m on Mt Cabalasan) and the early development of Cebu City, the country's second largest conurbation, have contributed to the destruction of most of Cebu's natural forests to make way for sugar-cane plantations: c.99% of the original forest cover has totally gone and even the most degraded secondary habitats are now scarce. This almost complete deforestation has already caused a mass extinction of birds on the island: half of the forest bird species formerly resident on the island, have gone (39 species lost altogether, including four restricted-range species and a further five endemic subspecies) (Brooks *et al.* 1995b; see also Dutson *et al.* 1993).

Dicaeum quadricolor, considered extinct since 1906, was rediscovered in 1992 in a remnant patch of largely degraded forest, believed to be the largest remaining forest area (possibly less than 15 ha of closed-canopy habitat); the area lies to the west of the Mt Manunggal massif, near the village of Tabunan, within the Central Cebu National Park—although this affords it little, if any, protection. Observations in 1994 showed that the species also occurred in open-canopy forest and that interspecific competition with the very common and aggressive Red-striped Flowerpecker *D. australe* may also have contributed to its decline, although this must presumably be a significant problem only where habitat modification has begun to favour the commoner species.

Copsychus cebuensis is now known to survive in a considerable number of localities, but in rather small numbers at each, e.g. sightings are usually of one to five individuals.

The best sites for the threatened bird species (e.g. the forest patch critical for *D. quadricolor*) are under pressure from clearance and development (Dutson *et al.* 1993). If this habitat destruction is allowed to continue, it will ultimately contribute to the extinction of the remaining taxa which are endemic to Cebu (Magsalay 1993, Magsalay *et al.* 1995).

154   Mindanao and the Eastern Visayas   PRIORITY CRITICAL

Key habitats	Lowland and montane rain forest, mossy forest

Main threats   Major habitat loss (e.g. due to logging)

ArEa   120,000 km²   **Altitude**   0–2,700 m

Countries   Philippines

Biological importance   ● ● ●
Current threat level   ● ●

Restricted-range species	Threatened	Total
Confined to this EBA	19	39
Present also in other EBAs, SAs	3	12
Total	22	51

■ General characteristics

The major part of this EBA is the lowlands and mountains of Mindanao, at just under 100,000 km² the second largest Philippine island after Luzon (EBA 151); also included are the islands of Samar, Leyte and Bohol (which are politically part of the Visayas; see also EBAs 152, 153), and associated islands such as Biliran, Dinagat, Siargao, Camiguin Sur and Basilan.

The mountain ranges of Mindanao form three main uplands: those east of the Agusan river including Mt Hilong Hilong in the Diuta range and Mt Mayo in the south-east; the central uplands with major peaks such as Mts Katanglad, Apo and Matutum; and the mountains of the Zamboanga peninsula including Mts Malindang and Sugarloaf.

Various different forest types can be recognized, including lowland evergreen rain forest up to c.400 m, which gives way to a more open forest at higher elevations between c.650 and 1,000 m; in the cloud belt above, usually at over 1,200 m, is mossy forest (Collins *et al.* 1991, Dickinson *et al.* 1991). These vegetational zones can vary, e.g. on Mt Katanglad where they appear to be significantly higher.

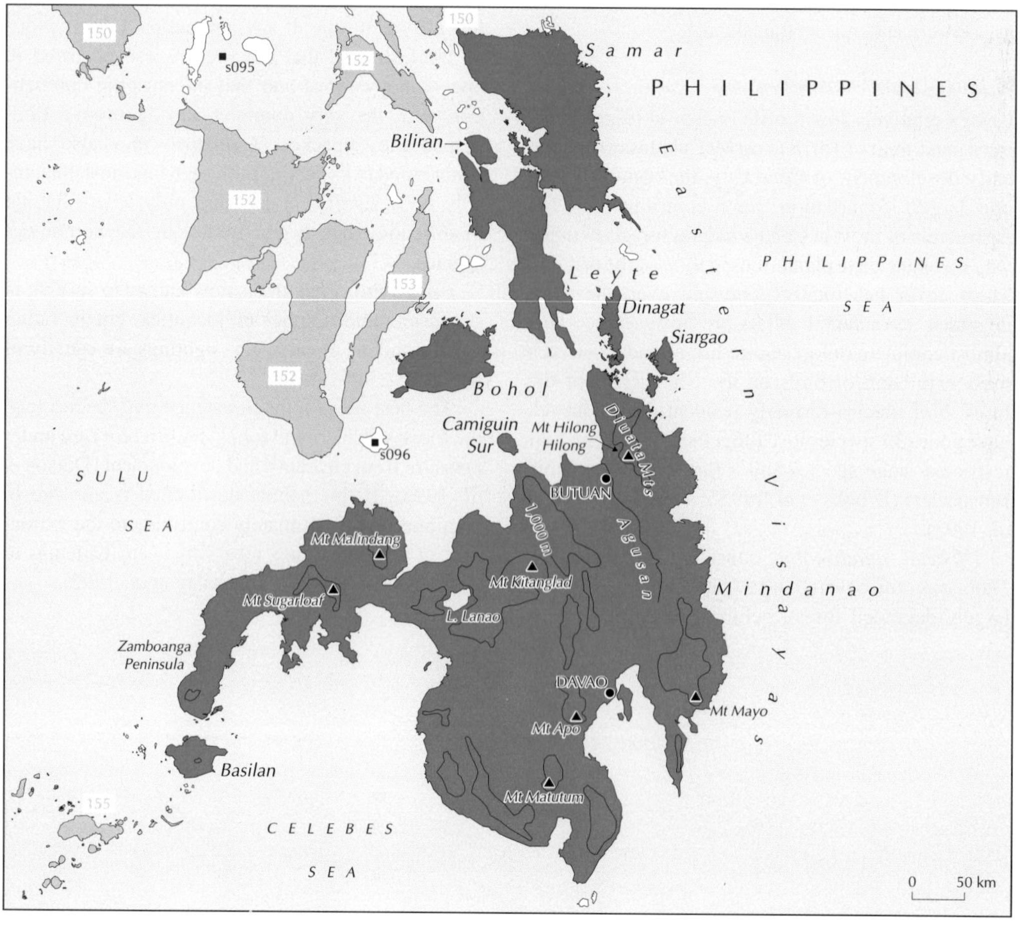

[Map of Mindanao and the Eastern Visayas showing: s095, 150, 152, Samar, PHILIPPINES, Biliran, Leyte, PHILIPPINES SEA, Dinagat, Siargao, 153, Bohol, Camiguin Sur, Mt Hilong Hilong, Diuta Mts, s096, BUTUAN, SULU SEA, 1,000 m, Agusan, Mt Malindang, Mt Kitanglad, Mindanao, Mt Sugarloaf, L. Lanao, Zamboanga Peninsula, DAVAO, Mt Mayo, Basilan, Mt Apo, Mt Matutum, CELEBES SEA, 155, Eastern Visayas, 0 50 km]

Status and habitat of restricted-range species

Species (ordered taxonomically)	Global status	Other EBAs (and SAs)	Altitude (m)	Habitat
Brown-banded Rail *Lewinia mirificus*[1]	EN	151	No data	Grassland?
Mindanao Bleeding-heart *Gallicolumba criniger*	VU	—	0–1,250	Forest, secondary forest
Mindanao Brown-dove *Phapitreron brunneiceps*[2]	NE	—	150–1,500, perhaps higher	Forest
Mindanao Lorikeet *Trichoglossus johnstoniae*	VU	—	1,000–2,500	Montane forest, mossy forest, forest edge (inc. logged and degraded areas)
Mindanao Racquet-tail *Prioniturus waterstradti*	VU	—	>1,000	Forest (apparently makes rapid daily vertical migrations)
Mindanao Scops-owl *Otus mirus*	VU	—	Mountains	Montane forest, mossy forest
Lesser Eagle-owl *Mimizuku gurneyi*[1]	EN	—	Lowlands to 1,300	Forest
Whitehead's Swiftlet *Collocalia whiteheadi*	VU	151	>1,200	Forested mountains for feeding; caves for breeding
Philippine Needletail *Mearnsia picina*	lc	152,153[X],155	<1,250	Forest, clearings
Silvery Kingfisher *Alcedo argentata*	EN	—	0–1,250	Streamside banks and pools in forest
Blue-capped Kingfisher *Actenoides hombroni*	VU	—	800–2,400	Forest, secondary forest
Samar Hornbill *Penelopides samarensis*	nt	—	<1,000	Forest
Mindanao Hornbill *Penelopides affinis*	nt	—	<1,100	Forest, forest edge; relatively tolerant of secondary forest
Writhed Hornbill *Aceros leucocephalus*	EN	—	0–1,200	Forest (trees in clearings), logged forest
Wattled Broadbill *Eurylaimus steerii*	VU	—	0–1,250	Forest, secondary forest
Visayan Broadbill *Eurylaimus samarensis*[3]	NE	—	100–750	Forest (esp. on limestone)
Azure-breasted Pitta *Pitta steerii*	VU	—	<1,000	Forest, secondary forest (esp. mixed forest on limestone)
McGregor's Cuckoo-shrike *Coracina mcgregori*	VU	—	>1,000	Montane forest, mossy forest, forest edge, degraded forest
Zamboanga Bulbul *Ixos rufigularis*	lc	—	<1,700	Forest, forest edge
Yellowish Bulbul *Ixos everetti*	nt	155	Lowlands	Forest, forest edge; not particularly tolerant of secondary/degraded forest
Philippine Leafbird *Chloropsis flavipennis*	EN	153[X]	0–1,500	Forest, forest edge, secondary forest
Mountain Shrike *Lanius validirostris*	nt	150,151	>1,000	Clearings in montane and pine forest, forest edge, open secondary forest, scrub in grassland
Bagobo Babbler *Trichastoma woodi*	VU	—	>1,000	Montane forest, mossy forest
Striated Wren-babbler *Ptilocichla mindanensis*	nt	—	<1,000	Forest, scrubby secondary forest (esp. mixed forest on limestone)
Pygmy Babbler *Stachyris plateni*	nt	—	<1,100	Forest, forest edge, secondary forest
Rusty-crowned Babbler *Stachyris capitalis*	nt	—	<1,050	Forest, forest edge, secondary forest
Miniature Tit-babbler *Micromacronus leytensis*	VU	—	<1,300	Forest, forest edge
Long-tailed Bush-warbler *Bradypterus caudatus*	nt	151	700–2,750	Montane forest, mossy forest, forest edge, dense secondary forest

cont.

Status and habitat of restricted-range species (cont.)

Species (ordered taxonomically)	Global status	Other EBAs (and SAs)	Altitude (m)	Habitat
Rufous-headed Tailorbird *Orthotomus heterolaemus*	lc	—	>800	Montane forest, forest edge, degraded forest, secondary forest
Yellow-breasted Tailorbird *Orthotomus samarensis*	nt	—	<750	Forest, forest edge
Black-headed Tailorbird *Orthotomus nigriceps*	nt	—	Lowlands	Forest, forest edge; usually closed-canopy forest, rarely open forest
White-eared Tailorbird *Orthotomus cinereiceps*	lc	—	<1,150	Forest, forest edge, dense secondary forest
Slaty-backed Jungle-flycatcher *Rhinomyias goodfellowi*	VU	—	>1,000	Mossy forest
Little Slaty Flycatcher *Ficedula basilanica*	VU	—	<1,200	Forest, forest edge, secondary forest
Cryptic Flycatcher *Ficedula crypta*[4]	VU	—	<1,500	Montane forest, mossy forest, secondary forest
Short-crested Monarch *Hypothymis helenae*	nt	151	<1,000	Forest, selectively logged forest, secondary forest
Celestial Monarch *Hypothymis coelestis*	EN	151,152,155 (s095)	<1,000	Forest, forest edge, secondary forest (may be a riverine specialist)
Black-and-cinnamon Fantail *Rhipidura nigrocinnamomea*	lc	—	>1,000	Montane forest, mossy forest
White-fronted Tit *Parus semilarvatus*	nt	151	<1,000	Forest, forest edge, secondary forest
Whiskered Flowerpecker *Dicaeum proprium*	VU	—	>900	Forest, forest edge, secondary forest
Olive-capped Flowerpecker *Dicaeum nigrilore*	lc	—	>900	Montane forest, mossy forest
Flame-crowned Flowerpecker *Dicaeum anthonyi*	nt	151	800–2,100	Montane forest, mossy forest, forest edge, secondary forest
Grey-hooded Sunbird *Aethopyga primigenius*	lc	—	>1,000	Montane forest, mossy forest, forest edge
Apo Sunbird *Aethopyga boltoni*	nt	—	(1,100–) 1,500+	Montane forest, mossy forest, scrub
Lina's Sunbird *Aethopyga linaraborae*[5]	NE	—	(>1,130) >1,200	Mossy forest
Black-masked White-eye *Lophozosterops goodfellowi*	lc	—	>1,000	Montane forest, mossy forest, forest edge, degraded forest
Cinnamon Ibon *Hypocryptadius cinnamomeus*	lc	—	>900	Montane forest, mossy forest, forest edge
Mountain Serin *Serinus estherae*	lc	158,160,166	>1,500	Montane forest, forest edge, alpine scrub and meadows, conifer plantations
White-cheeked Bullfinch *Pyrrhula leucogenis*	nt	151	1,250–2,600	Mossy forest, forest edge, secondary forest
Red-eared Parrotfinch *Erythrura coloria*	VU	—	>1,000	Forest, forest edge, secondary forest, grassy areas
Apo Myna *Basilornis miranda*	nt	—	>1,250	Mossy forest, forest edge

Global status (see p. 679 for definitions)

EX Extinct — with year of last record
EW Extinct in the Wild
CR Critical — threatened species
EN Endangered
VU Vulnerable

cd Conservation Dependent
nt Near Threatened
lc Least Concern
DD Data Deficient
NE Not Evaluated

Other EBAs (and SAs) (see p. 83 for locations)
Bracketed numbers are Secondary Areas.
x Extinct in that EBA or SA.

Notes

[1] Specimens from Samar are in the Philippines National Museum (N. J. Collar verbally 1996).

[2] Treated (as a threatened species) separately from Tawitawi Brown-dove *P. cinereiceps* by Collar *et al.* (in press).

[3] Taxonomy follows Lambert and Woodcock (1996).

[4] Taxonomy according to Dutson (1993).

[5] New species (Kennedy *et al.* 1997).

■ Restricted-range species

All the restricted-range species of this EBA are forest birds. Although some have been recorded from degraded or selectively logged or secondary forest, the long-term survival of all is likely to depend on proximity to primary habitat.

Species can be divided into those which tend to occur in lowland and hill forest (largely below 1,000 m), and those which prefer montane and mossy forest (largely above 1,000 m). Although only 'lowland' species occur on the smaller islands (with three species being confined to Samar, Leyte and Bohol only), there are many distributional similarities and some altitudinal overlap on Mindanao between those species classified as 'lowland' and those as 'montane', and thus all these restricted-range species have been included within this single EBA (contra ICBP 1992; a similar treatment has been applied to Luzon, the Philippines' largest island, see EBA 151).

Habitat associations of restricted-range species

Lowland and hill forest	Montane forest, mossy forest
Gallicolumba criniger	**Trichoglossus johnstoniae**
Phapitreron brunneiceps	**Prioniturus waterstradti**
Mimizuku gurneyi	**Otus mirus**
Mearnsia picina	**Collocalia whiteheadi**
Alcedo argentata	**Actenoides hombroni**
Penelopides samarensis	**Coracina mcgregori**
Penelopides affinis	Ixos rufigularis
Aceros leucocephalus	Lanius validirostris
Eurylaimus steerii	**Trichastoma woodi**
Eurylaimus samarensis	Bradypterus caudatus
Pitta steerii	Orthotomus heterolaemus
Ixos everetti	**Rhinomyias goodfellowi**
Chloropsis flavipennis	**Ficedula crypta**
Ptilocichla mindanensis	Rhipidura nigrocinnamomea
Stachyris plateni	**Dicaeum proprium**
Stachyris capitalis	Dicaeum nigrilore
Micromacronus leytensis	Dicaeum anthonyi
Orthotomus samarensis	Aethopyga primigenius
Orthotomus nigriceps	Aethopyga boltoni
Orthotomus cinereiceps	Aethopyga linaraborae
Ficedula basilanica	Lophozosterops goodfellowi
Hypothymis helenae	Hypocryptadius
Hypothymis coelestis	cinnamomeus
Parus semilarvatus	Serinus estherae
	Pyrrhula leucogenis
Unknown	**Erythrura coloria**
Lewinia mirificus	Basilornis miranda

Threatened species (Critical, Endangered, Vulnerable) are shown in **bold**; see 'Status and habitat' table.

For many species, the distribution in this EBA appears to be patchy (see 'Distribution patterns' table) but, for some species at least, this may be because recorded distributions are dependent on observer coverage (which is still incomplete), and actual ranges may therefore be larger and more contiguous than is apparent from published sightings.

Because of the difficulty in determining range size all species which are endemic to Mindanao have been included as having restricted ranges.

■ Threats and conservation

The islands of this EBA were originally completely forested but satellite data from 1988 show forest covering only 33% of Samar, 14% of Leyte, 6% of Bohol, and 29% of Mindanao (Dickinson et al. 1991). These figures are, however, likely to be overestimates (T. Fisher per G. C. L. Dutson in litt. 1993), and most of the accessible (=lowland) forest estate outside the protected area system is leased to private timber companies for logging (Collins et al. 1991). Aerial surveys of Basilan in 1992 revealed that old-growth forest had been reduced to only c.2 km² (less than 0.2% of the island), indicating a further massive reduction from the 180 km² (14%) estimated from the 1988 satellite data (W. L. R. Oliver in litt. 1996).

Many species have undoubtedly undergone rapid and continuing declines with the loss of their habitat, particularly those species which rely on primary lowland forest, and consequently the majority of the EBA's restricted-range species are classified as threatened (22 in all, a greater number than in any other EBA of the south-east Asian island region) or Near Threatened. Many species appear to be very scarce having been recorded very little in recent years, e.g. Aceros leucocephalus and Alcedo argentata.

Species which occur in mossy forest are more secure as these forests are often found in extremely rugged and inaccessible mountains that contain few commercial tree species and are generally too steep for agricultural purposes. However, the recent discovery of gold in the mountains of eastern Mindanao could be a serious threat, with some of the lower slopes having already been totally destroyed (Kennedy et al. 1997).

Other widespread threatened forest birds which occur in this EBA include the Philippine Eagle Pithecophaga jefferyi (Critical; found in rain forest on the islands of Luzon, Samar, Leyte and Mindanao), Philippine Hawk-eagle Spizaetus philippensis (Vulnerable), Spotted Imperial-pigeon Ducula carola (Vulnerable), Philippine Cockatoo Cacatua haematuropygia (Critical), Blue-naped Parrot Tanygnathus lucionensis (Endangered), Philippine Eagle-owl Bubo philippensis (Endangered), Philippine Kingfisher Ceyx melanurus (Vulnerable), Rufous-lored Kingfisher Todirhamphus winchelli (Endangered) and Black-bibbed Cicadabird Coracina mindanensis (Vulnerable).

There are several protected areas within the EBA including the Rajah Sikatuna National Park on Bohol (90 km², an important site which includes most of the

Distribution patterns of restricted-range species

Species (ordered geographically)	Samar	Leyte	Bohol	Dinagat	Siargao	Diuta pen./mts	Mt Mayo pen./mts	Mt Kitanglad, Lake Lanao	Mt Apo/Davao	Mt Matutum	Mt Malindang	Zamboanga pen.	Basilan	Other EBAs, SAs
Lewinia mirificus	•	–	–	–	–	–	–	–	–	–	–	–	–	•
Penelopides samarensis	•	•	•	–	–	–	–	–	–	–	–	–	–	–
Eurylaimus samarensis	•	•	•	–	–	–	–	–	–	–	–	–	–	–
Orthotomus samarensis	•	•	•	–	–	–	–	–	–	–	–	–	–	–
Hypothymis helenae	•	–	–	•	•	•	–	–	–	–	–	–	–	•
Ixos everetti	•	•	–	•	•	•	–	–	–	–	–	–	–	•
Stachyris plateni	•	•	–	–	–	•	–	•	•	•	•	–	–	–
Pitta steerii	•	•	•	–	–	–	–	–	–	–	–	•	–	–
Micromacronus leytensis	•	•	–	–	–	–	–	•	•	–	–	•	–	–
Mimizuku gurneyi	•	–	–	•	•	•	–	–	–	–	–	•	–	–
Mearnsia picina	•	•	–	–	–	•	–	–	–	–	–	–	–	•
Ficedula basilanica	•	•	–	•	–	•	–	–	–	–	•	–	•	–
Ptilocichla mindanensis	•	•	•	–	–	•	–	•	•	–	–	–	•	–
Gallicolumba criniger	•	•	•	•	–	•	–	–	–	–	–	–	•	–
Alcedo argentata	•	•	•	•	•	•	•	–	–	–	–	–	•	–
Eurylaimus steerii	•	•	•	•	•	•	–	–	–	–	–	–	•	–
Hypothymis coelestis	•	–	–	•	–	–	–	–	–	–	–	–	•	•
Chloropsis flavipennis	–	•	–	•	–	•	•	–	–	–	–	–	–	X
Penelopides affinis	–	–	–	•	•	•	•	–	–	–	–	–	–	–
Orthotomus nigriceps	–	–	–	•	•	•	•	–	–	–	–	–	–	–
Aceros leucocephalus	–	–	–	•	–	•	–	•	•	–	–	–	–	–
Stachyris capitalis	–	–	–	•	–	•	–	•	•	–	•	–	•	–
Otus mirus	–	–	–	–	–	•	–	•	•	–	–	–	•	–
Aethopyga primigenius	–	–	–	–	–	•	–	•	•	–	–	–	–	–
Ficedula crypta	–	–	–	–	–	•	•	–	•	–	•	–	–	–
Rhipidura nigrocinnamomea	–	–	–	–	–	•	•	•	•	–	–	–	–	–
Dicaeum nigrilore	–	–	–	–	–	•	•	•	•	–	–	–	–	–
Lophozosterops goodfellowi	–	–	–	–	–	•	•	•	•	–	–	–	–	–
Hypocryptadius cinnamomeus	–	–	–	–	–	•	•	•	•	–	–	–	–	–
Pyrrhula leucogenis	–	–	–	–	–	–	•	•	•	–	–	–	–	•
Actenoides hombroni	–	–	–	–	–	–	•	•	•	–	•	–	–	–
Orthotomus cinereiceps	–	–	–	–	–	–	•	•	–	–	•	–	•	–
Phapitreron brunneiceps	–	–	–	–	–	–	•	•	–	–	•	–	•	–
Aethopyga linaraborae	–	–	–	–	–	–	•	•	•	–	–	–	–	–
Prioniturus waterstradti	–	–	–	–	–	–	•	•	•	–	•	–	–	–
Dicaeum proprium	–	–	–	–	–	–	•	•	•	–	•	–	–	–
Orthotomus heterolaemus	–	–	–	–	–	–	–	•	•	–	–	–	–	–
Rhinomyias goodfellowi	–	–	–	–	–	–	–	•	•	–	–	–	–	–
Erythrura coloria	–	–	–	–	–	–	–	•	•	–	–	–	–	–
Basilornis miranda	–	–	–	–	–	–	–	•	•	–	–	–	–	–
Collocalia whiteheadi	–	–	–	–	–	–	–	•	•	–	–	–	–	•
Serinus estherae	–	–	–	–	–	–	–	•	•	–	–	–	–	•
Coracina mcgregori	–	–	–	–	–	–	–	•	•	–	•	–	–	–
Trichastoma woodi	–	–	–	–	–	–	–	•	•	–	•	–	–	–
Aethopyga boltoni	–	–	–	–	–	–	–	•	•	–	•	–	–	–
Lanius validirostris	–	–	–	–	–	–	–	•	•	–	•	–	–	•
Bradypterus caudatus	–	–	–	–	–	–	–	•	•	–	•	–	–	•
Dicaeum anthonyi	–	–	–	–	–	–	–	•	•	–	•	–	–	•
Trichoglossus johnstoniae	–	–	–	–	–	–	–	•	•	•	–	•	–	–
Parus semilarvatus	–	–	–	–	–	–	–	•	•	–	–	•	–	•
Ixos rufigularis	–	–	–	–	–	–	–	–	–	–	•	•	•	–
Total	17	14	8	12	7	25	13	35	32	11	20	15	10	

• Present
○ Extinct?
X Extinct

? Present?
R Reintroduced
I Introduced

Threatened spp. shown in **bold**
Other EBAs, SAs

see 'Status and habitat' table

remaining natural forest on the island: Lambert 1993a, Brooks *et al.* 1995c). On Mindanao, there are national parks at Mts Apo (720 km²) and Malindang (534 km²) which have rain forest within their boundaries. As well as being important for restricted-range species, these parks harbour small populations of *Pithecophaga jefferyi*. However, there is no effective management of the Mt Apo National Park, and massive human encroachment, even into the uplands, has destroyed large areas of both lowland and

Once Mindanao was completely forested. Today less than 29% remains.

A. Long

montane forest such that probably over 50% of the original park is now deforested; similar problems affect the Mt Malindang National Park (Lewis 1988, Collins *et al.* 1991; see also Myers 1988b). The construction of a geothermal power station and access road has also threatened the integrity of the Mt Apo National Park. On Basilan, there is a national park (31 km²) but, given the recent reduction in forest, this has afforded no protection. There are no recent data on the status of birds (or other wildlife) owing to the intensification of political insurgency on the island, which seems destined to lose most of its endemic taxa if action is not taken in the near future (W. L. R. Oliver *in litt.* 1996).

Siargo, Agusan Marsh and Mt Katanglad have recently been protected under the Integrated Protected Areas System (IPAS). Mt Katanglad has been identified as one of the most important sites for endemic birds in Mindanao and has one of the richest Philippine avifaunas yet documented, despite the fact that observations in 1993 indicated that the Katanglad range rarely has forest below 1,000 m, and in many place no forest below 1,400 m. The park is under threat from illegal commercial logging, clearing for slash-and-burn agriculture ('kaingin'), and overhunting and collecting of wildlife (Heaney *et al.* 1993, Lambert 1993a).

Many lowland species are still in good numbers in commercial logging concessions of, for example, PICOP Resources Inc. (formerly the Paper Industries Corporation of the Philippines) near Bislig, and, if these areas remain intact, they may be the best hope for these species' survival (T. Fisher per G. C. L. Dutson *in litt.* 1993).

155 Sulu archipelago

Key habitats Lowland rain forest

Main threats Major habitat loss (e.g. due to oil-palm plantations)

Area 1,500 km² **Altitude** 0–700 m

Countries Philippines

Biological importance ● ● ●
Current threat level ● ● ●

Restricted-range species	Threatened	Total
Confined to this EBA	3	4
Present also in other EBAs, SAs	2	5
Total	5	9

■ General characteristics

The 400 or so islands of the Sulu archipelago stretch south-west from the southern Philippine island of Mindanao to Borneo. The EBA covers the main islands of Sulu (or Jolo), Tawitawi and Sibutu, and many smaller offshore islands. Basilan, north-east of the archipelago, is included with Mindanao (EBA 154). The Sulu islands were once covered in forest, including lowland rain forest, beach forest, scrub forest and mangroves, but today much native habitat has been replaced by cultivation.

■ Restricted-range species

All the EBA's restricted-range species are forest birds, and, although their patterns of distribution between the islands vary, almost every species occurs on Tawitawi.

Of several subspecies endemic to the EBA, Sulu Woodpecker *Dendrocopos* (*maculatus*) *ramsayi* is

Distribution patterns of restricted-range species

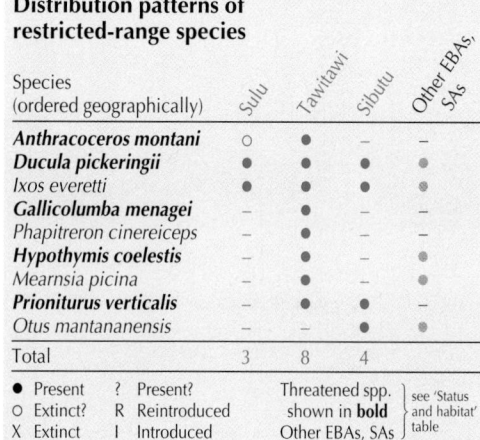

Species (ordered geographically)	Sulu	Tawitawi	Sibutu	Other EBAs, SAs
Anthracoceros montani	O	●	–	–
Ducula pickeringii	●	●	●	●
Ixos everetti	●	●	●	●
Gallicolumba menagei	–	●	–	–
Phapitreron cinereiceps	–	●	–	–
Hypothymis coelestis	–	●	–	●
Mearnsia picina	–	●	–	●
Prioniturus verticalis	–	●	●	–
Otus mantananensis	–	–	●	●
Total	3	8	4	

● Present   ? Present?   Threatened spp. shown in **bold**
O Extinct?   R Reintroduced
X Extinct   I Introduced   Other EBAs, SAs

see 'Status and habitat' table

most distinctive and a candidate for elevation to species rank, and Sulu Hanging-parrot *Loriculus*

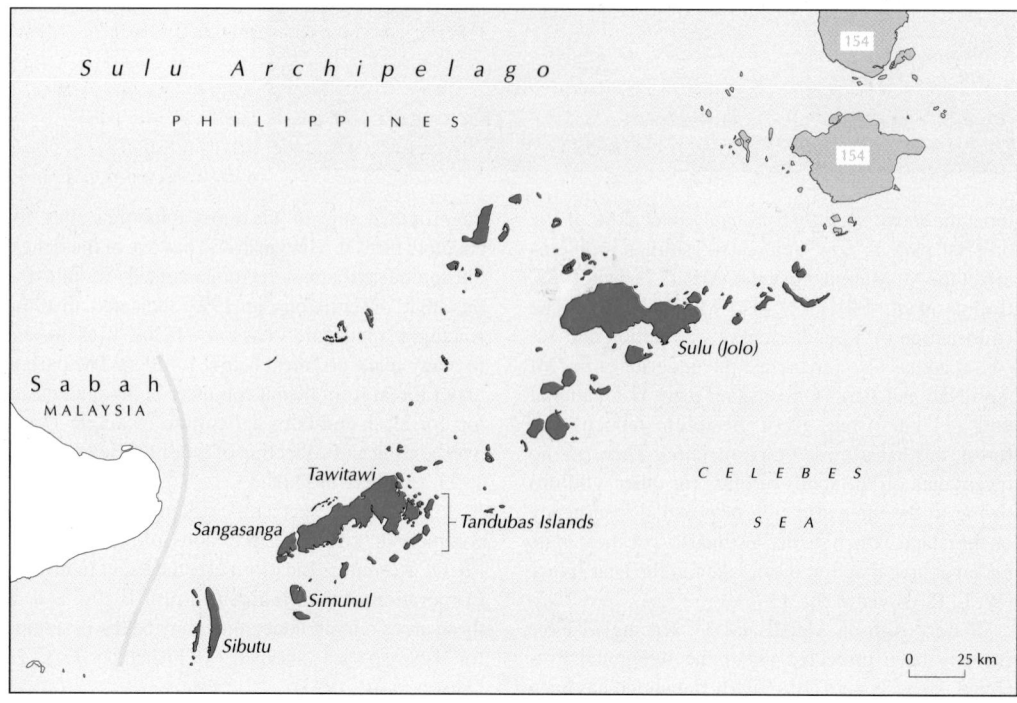

Status and habitat of restricted-range species

Species (ordered taxonomically)	Global status	Other EBAs (and SAs)	Habitat
Sulu Bleeding-heart *Gallicolumba menagei*	CR	—	Forest, secondary forest
Tawitawi Brown-dove *Phapitreron cinereiceps*[1]	NE	—	Forest
Grey Imperial-pigeon *Ducula pickeringii*	VU	156,167 (s097)	Forest on small islands
Blue-winged Racquet-tail *Prioniturus verticalis*	EN	—	Forest, mangroves
Mantanani Scops-owl *Otus mantananensis*	lc	156 (s095,s097)	Forest, coconut plantations
Philippine Needletail *Mearnsia picina*	lc	152,153[X],154	Forest, clearings
Sulu Hornbill *Anthracoceros montani*	CR	—	Forest
Yellowish Bulbul *Ixos everetti*	nt	154	Forest, forest edge, sometimes secondary/degraded forest
Celestial Monarch *Hypothymis coelestis*	EN	151,152,154 (s095)	Forest, logged forest

Global status (see p. 679 for definitions)					Other EBAs (and SAs) (see p. 83 for locations)	
	EX	Extinct	with year of last record	cd	Conservation Dependent	Bracketed numbers are Secondary Areas.
	EW	Extinct in the Wild		nt	Near Threatened	[X] Extinct in that EBA or SA.
	CR	Critical	threatened species	lc	Least Concern	**Notes** [1] Treated as a threatened species by
	EN	Endangered		DD	Data Deficient	Collar *et al.* (in press).
	VU	Vulnerable		NE	Not Evaluated	

(*philippensis*) *bonapartei* is also a possible split. Sulu Hawk-owl *Ninox philippensis reyi*, apart from being clearly distinct from *N. philippensis*, almost certainly represents the nominate form of a species which occurs on other small islands (see under Mindoro, EBA 150) (N. J. Collar verbally 1997).

■ Threats and conservation

In 1991 observations made from the air indicated that virtually no forest remained on Sulu, and that on Tawitawi only the eastern part of the island supported any substantial tracts (Lambert 1993a). In 1994 primary forest on Tawitawi was being rapidly cleared, although there were still large areas of very degraded forest, mostly recently logged (T. M. Brooks and G. C. L. Dutson *in litt.* 1994). In 1996 there were plans to replace some of the most extensive areas of the remaining forest with oil-palm plantations. The smaller islands of Sibutu and Simunul have both been largely cleared and although forest is regenerating, the islands are dry and coralline and it will take a long time before the habitat becomes again of value to forest-dependent species, which, in the meantime, may be lost (D. Allen *in litt.* 1996).

Loss of habitat is thus the main threat to the birds of this EBA, and further losses associated with the economic development of Tawitawi in particular

need careful monitoring (D. Allen verbally 1997).

Not surprisingly, all the endemics are considered highly threatened, especially *Gallicolumba menagei* and *Anthracoceros montani*, which have few recent records from the main islands. However, both these species are reported by local people from three small islands in the Tandubas group which still have small tracts (<10 km²) of lowland forest and which may therefore be very important for their survival. Small-scale logging does take place on these islands and, although at a slow pace, will have a great impact on the already low density of the reported populations (Diesmos and Pedregosa 1995). It is clear that more fieldwork is necessary to establish the nature of remaining habitat on islands in this important EBA.

Other widespread threatened species which occur in the EBA include Blue-naped Parrot *Tanygnathus lucionensis* (Endangered), Rufous-lored Kingfisher *Todirhamphus winchelli* (Endangered; Tawitawi may be a stronghold) and Black-bibbed Cicadabird *Coracina mindanensis* (Vulnerable). The Sulu archipelago is also considered a stronghold for the Philippine Cockatoo *Cacatua haematuropygia* (Critical; once found throughout the Philippines); several hundred still survive on Tawitawi but the species is declining as a result of illegal logging and shooting (Lambert 1992).

156 Palawan

PRIORITY
URGENT

Key habitats Lowland and montane rain forest

Main threats Moderate habitat loss (e.g. due to logging, mining, cultivation)

Biological importance ● ● ●
Current threat level ● ● ●

Area 14,000 km² **Altitude** 0–2,000 m

Countries Philippines

Restricted-range species	Threatened	Total
Confined to this EBA	7	17
Present also in other EBAs, SAs	1	3
Total	8	20

■ General characteristics

This EBA includes the Philippine island of Palawan, the Calamian group in the north, Balabac in the south, and various other smaller offshore islands. These islands constitute the easternmost extension of the Asian continental (Sunda) shelf, and thus some of their more widespread fauna and flora are shared with the island of Borneo to which they were once connected. Because this EBA forms a link between Mindoro (EBA 150) and Borneo, it is an important route for avian migration.

The vegetation on Palawan is one of the most diverse of any island within the Philippines and includes tropical lowland evergreen rain forest, lowland semi-deciduous (seasonal/monsoon) forest, montane forest at 800–1,500 m, and forests over limestone in the south (WWF/IUCN 1994–1995).

■ Restricted-range species

All the restricted-range species occur in forest, mostly in the lowlands. All species occur on Palawan and four are confined to this island alone. *Stachyris hypogrammica* has a very limited distribution, only being recorded from the Mantalingajan range above 1,000 m (Dickinson *et al.* 1991).

■ Threats and conservation

Palawan is the most forested island in the Philippines with satellite data from 1988 showing 54% of land forested (Dickinson *et al.* 1991). However, forest is steadily giving way to logging, mining and agriculture owing to immigration of people from other more crowded parts of the country (Quinnell and Balmford 1988, Collins *et al.* 1991). Consequently some of the restricted-range species, mostly lowland birds which do not appear to tolerate degraded forest or second-

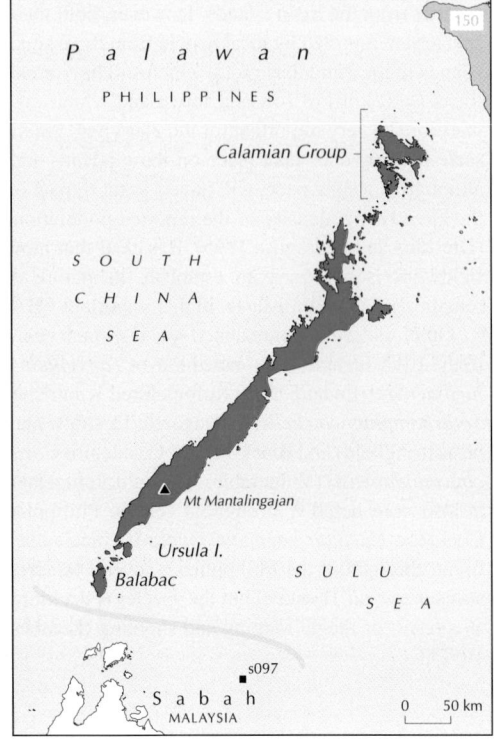

Distribution patterns of restricted-range species

Species (ordered geographically)	Calamian group	Palawan	Balabac	Other EBAs, SAs
Ixos palawanensis	●	●	–	–
Terpsiphone cyanescens	●	●	–	–
Ducula pickeringii	●	●ⁱ	–	●
Otus mantananensis	●	●ⁱ	–	●
Prioniturus platenae	●	●	●	–
Anthracoceros marchei	●	●	●	–
Chloropsis palawanensis	●	●	●	–
Copsychus niger	●	●	●	–
Cyornis lemprieri	●	●	●	–
Parus amabilis	●	●	●	–
Prionochilus plateni	●	●	●	–
Polyplectron emphanum	–	●	–	–
Otus fuliginosus	–	●	–	–
Collocalia palawanensis	–	●	–	–
Stachyris hypogrammica	–	●	–	–
Orthotomus derbianus	–	●	–	●
Malacocincla cinereiceps	–	●	●	–
Malacopteron palawanense	–	●	●	–
Ficedula platenae	–	●	●	–
Ptilocichla falcata	–	●	–	–
Total	11	20	10	

● Present   ? Present?
○ Extinct?   R Reintroduced
ⁱ Small islands off south coast

Threatened spp. shown in **bold**
Other EBAs, SAs

see 'Status and habitat' table

Status and habitat of restricted-range species

Species (ordered taxonomically)	Global status	Other EBAs (and SAs)	Habitat
Palawan Peacock-pheasant *Polyplectron emphanum*	EN	—	Lowland and hill forest, forest edge; less common in logged forest
Grey Imperial-pigeon *Ducula pickeringii*	VU	155,167 (s097)	Forest on small islands
Blue-headed Racquet-tail *Prioniturus platenae*	VU	—	Lowland forest, nearby cultivation
Mantanani Scops-owl *Otus mantananensis*	lc	155 (s095,s097)	Forest on small islands, coconut palms
Palawan Scops-owl *Otus fuliginosus*	VU	—	Lowland forest, trees in mixed cultivation
Palawan Swiftlet *Collocalia palawanensis*	lc	—	Lowland forest and grassland for feeding; caves for breeding
Palawan Hornbill *Anthracoceros marchei*	lc	—	Lowland and hill forest
Sulphur-bellied Bulbul *Ixos palawanensis*	lc	—	Montane forest, forest edge, secondary forest
Yellow-throated Leafbird *Chloropsis palawanensis*	lc	—	Lowland forest, forest edge, secondary forest, scrub
White-vented Shama *Copsychus niger*	lc	—	Lowland forest, forest edge, secondary forest, scrub
Ashy-headed Babbler *Malacocincla cinereiceps*	lc	—	Lowland forest, secondary forest, scrub
Melodious Babbler *Malacopteron palawanense*	EN	—	Lowland and hill forest, forest edge, secondary forest
Falcated Wren-babbler *Ptilocichla falcata*	EN	—	Lowland and hill forest
Palawan Striped-babbler *Stachyris hypogrammica*	VU	—	Montane forest
Grey-backed Tailorbird *Orthotomus derbianus*[1]	lc	151	Lowland and hill forest, forest edge, dense secondary forest, thickets
Palawan Flycatcher *Ficedula platenae*	EN	—	Lowland and hill forest
Palawan Blue-flycatcher *Cyornis lemprieri*	lc	—	Lowland and hill forest, secondary forest
Blue Paradise-flycatcher *Terpsiphone cyanescens*	nt	—	Lowland forest, forest edge, secondary forest, thickets
Palawan Tit *Parus amabilis*	lc	—	Lowland and montane forest, forest edge, secondary forest
Palawan Flowerpecker *Prionochilus plateni*	lc	—	Lowland forest, secondary forest, gardens

Global status (see p. 679 for definitions)

EX	Extinct	with year of last record	
EW	Extinct in the Wild		
CR	Critical	threatened	
EN	Endangered		

cd	Conservation Dependent
nt	Near Threatened
lc	Least Concern
DD	Data Deficient

Other EBAs (and SAs) (see p. 83 for locations) — Bracketed numbers are Secondary Areas. ˣ Extinct in that EBA or SA.

Notes — [1] Known from a single specimen on Palawan in 1958 (Dickinson *et al.* 1991).

ary habitats, are classified as threatened. Three widespread threatened birds—Philippine Hawk-eagle *Spizaetus philippensis* (Vulnerable), Philippine Cockatoo *Cacatua haematuropygia* (Critical) and Blue-naped Parrot *Tanygnathus lucionensis* (Endangered)—also occur on Palawan, which is a stronghold for these species.

The entire province of Palawan has been declared a Fauna and Flora Watershed Reserve, and, within this, there are other kinds of protected areas including the St Paul Subterranean National Park (which is important for threatened species including *Polyplectron emphanum*) and the El Nido area (which has been proposed for protection under the Integrated Protected Areas System). Ursula Island (17 ha), 20 km south-east of the southern tip of Palawan is an important roosting and nesting site for pigeons in-

cluding *Ducula pickeringii* and the widespread Nicobar Pigeon *Caloenas nicobarica* (Near Threatened). It was established as a bird sanctuary in 1960, but there has been a significant decline in the numbers of roosting pigeons, from an estimated 150,000 to a few thousand birds over the last 60 years, perhaps owing to the effects of introduced species and human disturbance (Gonzalez 1996).

A survey of Palawan concluded that a network of protected areas would not be sufficient to prevent environmental deterioration, mainly because it would not receive the support of the local communities. Instead, in 1990 a network of Environmentally Critical Areas was established over the whole island; this is a graded system of protected management, varying from strict control in certain areas to buffer areas where regulated use is allowed (Castañeda 1993).

157 Bornean mountains

PRIORITY
URGENT

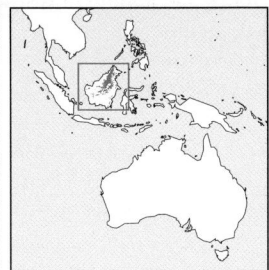

Key habitats	Tropical montane rain forest, hill dipterocarp forest
Main threats	Limited habitat loss

Area 130,000 km² **Altitude** 500–3,700 m

Countries Brunei, Indonesia, Malaysia

Restricted-range species	Threatened	Total
Confined to this EBA	0	24
Present also in other EBAs, SAs	0	5
Total	0	29

Biological importance ● ● ●
Current threat level ● ○ ○

■ General characteristics

The EBA includes the mountain ranges in the interior of Borneo, the largest of the Greater Sunda Islands. These mountains extend into the territories of three different countries: the Indonesian provinces of Kalimantan Barat, Kalimantan Tengah, Kalimantan Timur and Kalimantan Selatan; the East Malaysian states of Sabah and Sarawak; and the nation of Brunei. The highest mountains present are those in Sabah in the north of the island, and these include Mt Kinabalu

which rises to 4,094 m. High ranges with peaks of over 2,000 m extend southwards from here into southern Sarawak and northern and central Kalimantan.

The natural vegetation virtually throughout Borneo is tropical rain forest, and the restricted-range birds are mainly found in montane forest above c.1,000 m, although several occur below this altitude in hill dipterocarp forest on the lower mountain slopes (Wells 1985; see Whitmore 1984). The lower

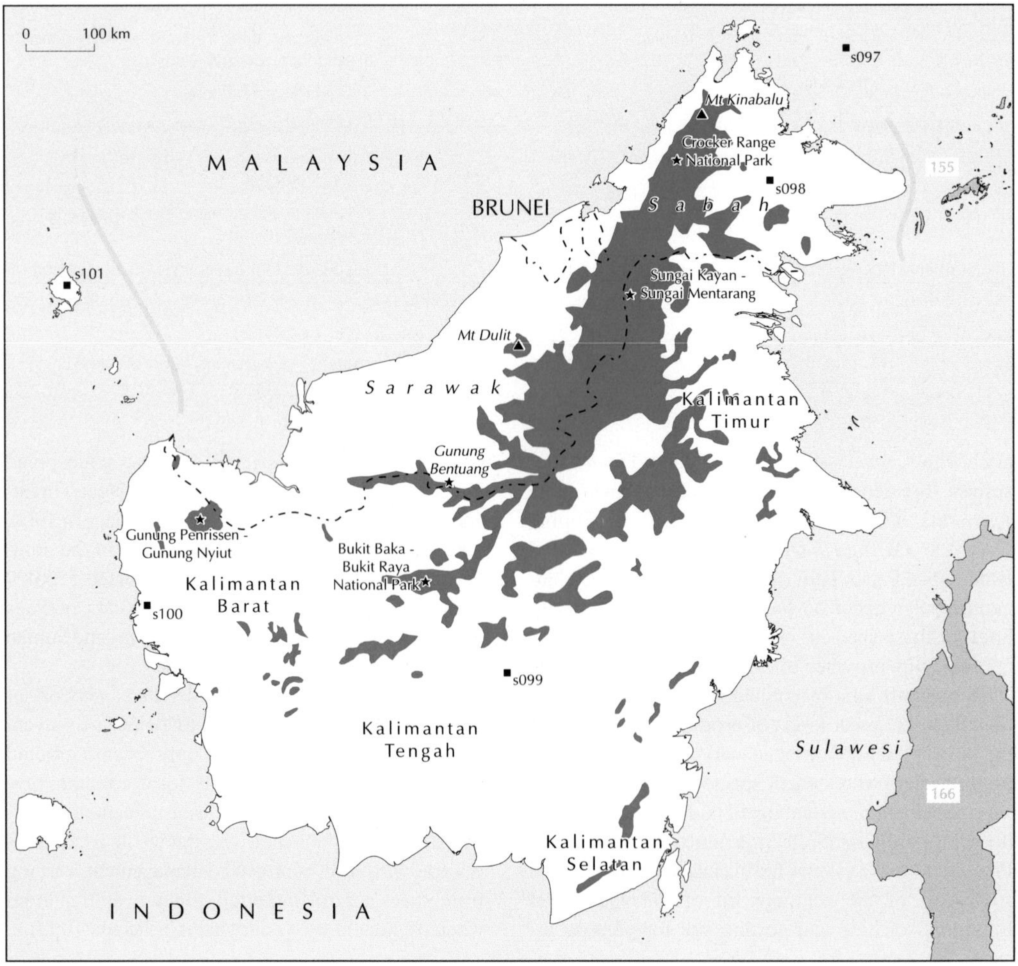

Status and habitat of restricted-range species

Species (ordered taxonomically)	Global status	Other EBAs (and SAs)	Altitude (m)	Habitat
Mountain Serpent-eagle *Spilornis kinabaluensis*	DD	—	(1,000–) 1,600+	Montane forest
Red-breasted Partridge *Arborophila hyperythra*	lc	—	600–3,000	Montane forest, bamboo
Crimson-headed Partridge *Haematortyx sanguiniceps*	lc	—	(200–) 600–3,050	Montane forest
Rajah Scops-owl *Otus brookii*	lc	158	Mountains	Montane forest
Dulit Frogmouth *Batrachostomus harterti*	DD	—	300–1,500	Hill and lower montane forest
Short-tailed Frogmouth *Batrachostomus poliolophus*[1]	DD	158	c.600–1,400	Lower montane forest
Whitehead's Trogon *Harpactes whiteheadi*	lc	—	>1,000	Montane forest
Mountain Barbet *Megalaima monticola*	lc	—	900–2,200	Montane forest
Golden-naped Barbet *Megalaima pulcherrima*	lc	—	(1,000–) 1,500–3,000	Montane forest
Bornean Barbet *Megalaima eximia*	lc	—	(500–) 1,000–2,100	Montane forest
Hose's Broadbill *Calyptomena hosii*	lc	—	Up to 1,000, locally higher	Lowland and lower montane forest
Whitehead's Broadbill *Calyptomena whiteheadi*	lc	—	1,000+	Montane forest
Black-breasted Fruit-hunter *Chlamydochaera jefferyi*	lc	—	900–2,800	Montane forest
Blue-wattled Bulbul *Pycnonotus nieuwenhuisii*	DD	158	Up to c.700	Lowland forest, secondary scrub in agricultural land
Everett's Thrush *Zoothera everetti*	nt	—	1,200–2,300	Montane forest
Sunda Laughingthrush *Garrulax palliatus*	lc	158	(300–) 850–2,200	Montane forest
Bare-headed Laughingthrush *Garrulax calvus*	lc	—	900–2,000	Montane forest
Mountain Wren-babbler *Napothera crassa*	lc	—	1,000–3,050	Montane forest, bamboo
Chestnut-crested Yuhina *Yuhina everetti*	lc	—	900–2,600, locally lower	Montane forest
Bornean Stubtail *Urosphena whiteheadi*	lc	—	(500–) 900–2,600	Montane forest
Friendly Bush-warbler *Bradypterus accentor*	lc	—	2,100–3,650	Montane forest
Eyebrowed Jungle-flycatcher *Rhinomyias gularis*	lc	—	900–3,300	Montane forest
Bornean Whistler *Pachycephala hypoxantha*	lc	—	900–2,900	Montane forest
Black-sided Flowerpecker *Dicaeum monticolum*	lc	—	(500–) 800–2,100	Montane forest
Whitehead's Spiderhunter *Arachnothera juliae*	lc	—	950–3,000	Montane forest
Black-capped White-eye *Zosterops atricapillus*	lc	158	900–2,100	Montane forest
Pygmy White-eye *Oculocincta squamifrons*	lc	—	Up to 2,100	Hill and montane forest

cont.

Status and habitat of restricted-range species (cont.)

Species (ordered taxonomically)	Global status	Other EBAs (and SAs)	Altitude (m)	Habitat
Mountain Blackeye *Chlorocharis emiliae*	lc	—	(1,300–) 1,700–3,650	Montane forest, upper montane scrub near treeline
Black Oriole *Oriolus hosii*	nt	—	900–2,000	Montane forest

Global status (see p. 679 for definitions)

EX Extinct ⎫ with year
EW Extinct in ⎬ of last
the Wild ⎭ record
CR Critical ⎫
EN Endangered ⎬ threatened species
VU Vulnerable ⎭

cd Conservation Dependent
nt Near Threatened
lc Least Concern
DD Data Deficient
NE Not Evaluated

Other EBAs (and SAs) (see p. 83 for locations)

Bracketed numbers are Secondary Areas.   ˣ Extinct in that EBA or SA.

Notes

[1] *Batrachostomus (poliolophus) mixtus* of Borneo and *B. (poliolophus) poliolophus* of Sumatra are here treated as conspecific following Andrew (1992).

altitudinal limit of the EBA has been defined as the 500-m contour.

■ Restricted-range species

The Bornean mountains are rich in restricted-range species, and their distinctive avifauna includes four endemic genera, *Haematortyx*, *Chlamydochaera*, *Oculocincta* and *Chlorocharis*. A further 13 species are endemic to Borneo (Andrew 1992; see Collar and Long 1996), but all of these occur too widely in the lowlands to be treated as restricted-range species, other than *Microhierax latifrons* and *Malacocincla perspicillata* whose ranges define Secondary Areas s098 and s099 respectively.

Habitat associations of restricted-range species

Hill dipterocarp and lower montane forest

Batrachostomus harterti
Batrachostomus poliolophus
Calyptomena hosii
Pycnonotus nieuwenhuisii
Oculocincta squamifrons

Hill dipterocarp forest and lower and upper montane forest

Arborophila hyperythra
Haematortyx sanguiniceps
Garrulax palliatus
Yuhina everetti
Urosphena whiteheadi
Dicaeum monticolum

Lower and upper montane forest

Otus brookii
Harpactes whiteheadi
Megalaima monticola
Megalaima eximia
Calyptomena whiteheadi
Chlamydochaera jefferyi
Zoothera everetti
Garrulax calvus
Napothera crassa
Rhinomyias gularis
Pachycephala hypoxantha
Arachnothera juliae
Zosterops atricapillus
Oriolus hosii

Upper montane forest

Spilornis kinabaluensis
Megalaima pulcherrima
Bradypterus accentor
Chlorocharis emiliae

Threatened species (Critical, Endangered, Vulnerable) are shown in **bold**; see 'Status and habitat' table.

Many of the mountains on Borneo are ornithologically unexplored or poorly known, particularly those in Kalimantan, so knowledge of the habitat requirements and distributions of the restricted-range

birds within the EBA is inevitably incomplete (see Smythies 1981, Mann 1987, Davison 1992). Most of these species are found in both lower and upper montane forest, and some also range down into hill dipterocarp forest below 1,000 m. *Batrachostomus harterti*, *Calyptomena hosii*, *Pycnonotus nieuwenhuisii* and *Oculocincta squamifrons* were categorized as lowland-forest-slope specialists by Wells (1985), although most of them occur in lower montane forest as well as hill dipterocarp forest.

Several species appear to have particularly restricted ranges on Borneo, but in most cases this is probably a reflection of the uneven ornithological coverage of the island. *Spilornis kinabaluensis*, *Otus brookii* (in this EBA), *Zoothera everetti*, *Garrulax calvus*, *Bradypterus accentor* and *Oriolus hosii* are only recorded from East Malaysia (and *Spilornis kinabaluensis* in Brunei) in the northern and western parts of the EBA. However, some of these species probably occur also in Kalimantan, where recent survey work has resulted in the first Indonesian records of *Harpactes whiteheadi*, *Megalaima pulcherrima*, *Rhinomyias gularis* and *Arachnothera juliae*, and the first record of *Zosterops atricapillus* in Kalimantan (Robson 1993b, S. van Balen per Rudyanto *in litt.* 1996). Four species are not recorded from Sabah: *Otus brookii*, which is only known (in this EBA) from Mt Dulit in Sarawak, *Batrachostomus harterti*, *Pycnonotus nieuwenhuisii*, which is only known (in this EBA) by one specimen from Kalimantan and recent sightings in Brunei (and could be an extremely rare morph of another species, or be of hybrid origin: Williams in prep.), and *Oriolus hosii*, which is only recorded from Sarawak. None of the restricted-range birds has been recorded in the mountains of Kalimantan Selatan in the southeast of the EBA, but some of them are likely to occur in the montane forests there.

■ Threats and conservation

None of the restricted-range birds of this EBA is classified as threatened, although four are treated as

Forest on the slopes of Mt Kinabalu in northern Sabah. This is the highest mountain between the Himalayas and New Guinea, and it has the full range of habitat-types found in the EBA.

K. D. Bishop

Data Deficient, three of these because they are only known from a small number of records from relatively low altitudes, and the fourth, *Spilornis kinabaluensis*, because it probably has a small population and may be sensitive to minor degradation of its habitat. Thirteen more-widespread threatened species occur in the forests of Borneo, but these are mainly birds of the lowlands, and only in hill dipterocarp forest do they overlap in distribution with the restricted-range species which characterize the EBA—although Bulwer's Pheasant *Lophura bulweri* (classified as Vulnerable) also occurs in lower montane forest. The concentration of threatened species in the lowlands is a reflection of the fact that most forest loss and degradation on Borneo has taken place there, whereas the montane forests remain relatively untouched as yet (Collins *et al.* 1991).

Protected areas have been gazetted in all parts of this EBA, with several reserves in each of Kalimantan, Sabah, Sarawak and Brunei. Many of these contain large areas of montane and hill dipterocarp forest, and together they include well over 10% of the EBA. Crocker Range National Park and Kinabalu Park in Sabah are notable because they include the full range of habitat types found in the EBA, and therefore support populations of almost all of the restricted-range species. Several of the reserves in Kalimantan include very large areas of montane habitats within their boundaries, notably Sungai Kayan-Sungai Mentarang Nature Reserve, Gunung Penrissen-Gunung Nyiut Game Reserve, Gunung Bentuang Nature Reserve and Bukit Baka-Bukit Raya National Park.

158 Sumatra and Peninsular Malaysia

PRIORITY URGENT

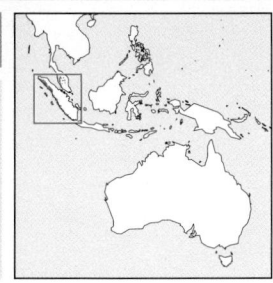

Key habitats Tropical montane rain forest, hill dipterocarp forest

Main threats Moderate habitat loss (e.g. due to agriculture, commercial logging, settlement)

Biological importance ● ● ●
Current threat level ● ○ ○

Area 89,000 km² **Altitude** 500–3,500 m
Countries Indonesia, Malaysia

Restricted-range species	Threatened	Total
Confined to this EBA	6	20
Present also in other EBAs, SAs	1	18
Total	7	38

General characteristics

This EBA includes mountains on the Indonesian island of Sumatra (in the provinces of Aceh, Sumatera Utara, Sumatera Barat, Jambi, Bengkulu, Sumatera Selatan and Lampung) and in Peninsular Malaysia. The Barisan range runs the entire length of western Sumatra, and has several peaks of over 3,000 m, the highest being Mt Kerinci at 3,805 m. These mountains were formed by uplift of sedimentary deposits, although they also include 15 or more volcanoes, of which at least nine are active (Whitten *et al.* 1987b, van Marle and Voous 1988). In Peninsular Malaysia, the restricted-range birds occur on the Main Range, which runs from north to south in the western part of

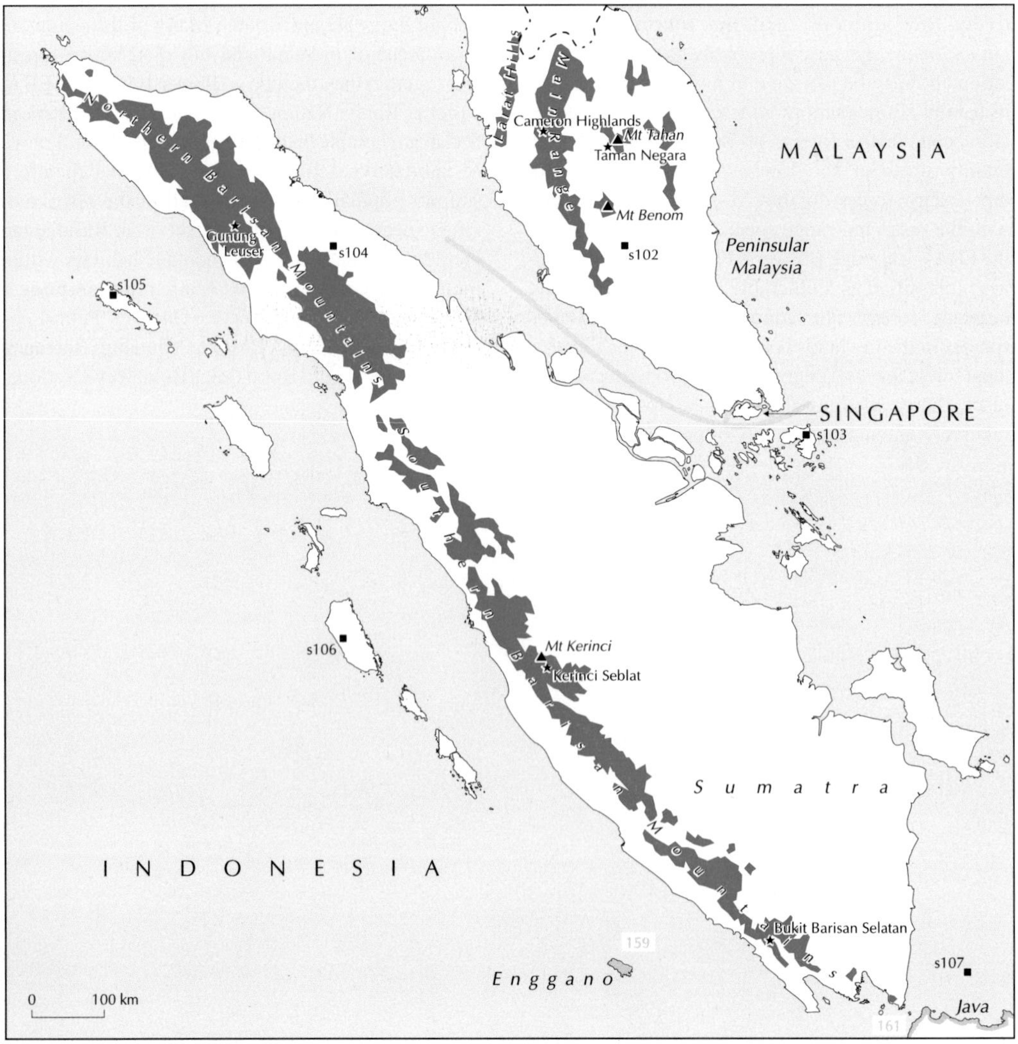

Northern Barisan Mountains
Gunung Leuser
s104
s105
Larut Hills
Main Range
Cameron Highlands
Mt Tahan
Taman Negara
Mt Benom
s102
MALAYSIA
Peninsular Malaysia
SINGAPORE
s103
Southern Barisan Mountains
Mt Kerinci
Kerinci Seblat
s106
Sumatra
INDONESIA
Bukit Barisan Selatan
159
s107
Enggano
Java
161
0 100 km

Status and habitat of restricted-range species

Species (ordered taxonomically)	Global status	Other EBAs (and SAs)	Altitude (m)	Habitat
Red-billed Partridge *Arborophila rubrirostris*	lc	—	900–2,500	Montane forest
Sumatran Pheasant *Lophura hoogerwerfi*	VU	—	600–2,000	Montane forest with little undergrowth
Salvadori's Pheasant *Lophura inornata*	VU	—	1,000–2,200	Montane forest
Bronze-tailed Peacock-pheasant *Polyplectron chalcurum*	nt	—	800–2,400	Montane forest, mature coniferous plantations
Mountain Peacock-pheasant *Polyplectron inopinatum*	VU	—	900–2,000	Montane forest
Crested Argus *Rheinardia ocellata*	VU	143,145 (s084)	670–1,200	Hill forest
Sumatran Green-pigeon *Treron oxyura*	nt	160	350–1,800	Hill and montane forest
Pink-headed Fruit-dove *Ptilinopus porphyreus*	lc	160	1,400–2,200	Montane forest
Sumatran Ground-cuckoo *Carpococcyx viridis*[1]	NE	—	300–1,700	Hill and lower montane forest
Rajah Scops-owl *Otus brookii*	lc	157	1,200–2,400	Montane forest
Short-tailed Frogmouth *Batrachostomus poliolophus*[2]	DD	157	c.600–1,400	Lower montane forest
Salvadori's Nightjar *Caprimulgus pulchellus*	DD	160	c.1,350–2,200	Montane forest; also possible lowland record
Waterfall Swift *Hydrochrous gigas*	nt	160	c.500–2,400	Hill and montane forest, open country
Blue-tailed Trogon *Harpactes reinwardtii*	lc	160	900–2,500	Montane forest
Fire-tufted Barbet *Psilopogon pyrolophus*	lc	—	500–2,200	Hill and montane forest
Schneider's Pitta *Pitta schneideri*	VU	—	900–2,400	Montane forest
Black-crowned Pitta *Pitta venusta*[3]	NE	—	400–1,400	Hill and lower montane forest
Sunda Minivet *Pericrocotus miniatus*	lc	160	1,200–2,700	Montane forest, coniferous plantations
Cream-striped Bulbul *Pycnonotus leucogrammicus*	lc	—	800–1,200 (–2,200)	Lower montane forest, coffee plantations
Spot-necked Bulbul *Pycnonotus tympanistrigus*	VU	—	600–1,400	Hill and lower montane forest
Blue-wattled Bulbul *Pycnonotus nieuwenhuisii*	DD	157	Lowlands to c.700	Lowland forest, secondary scrub in agricultural land
Orange-spotted Bulbul *Pycnonotus bimaculatus*	lc	160	800–3,000	Montane forest, plantations, alpine scrub
Green-winged Bulbul *Hypsipetes virescens*	lc	160	850–2,400	Montane forest, alpine scrub
Blue-masked Leafbird *Chloropsis venusta*	nt	—	600–1,500	Hill and lower montane forest
Shiny Whistling-thrush *Myiophonus melanurus*	lc	—	800–3,300	Hill and montane forest, often near water
Malayan Whistling-thrush *Myiophonus robinsoni*	nt	—	600–1,770	Hill and montane forest, usually near water
Sunda Robin *Cinclidium diana*	lc	160	1,100–1,950	Montane forest

cont.

Status and habitat of restricted-range species (cont.)

Species (ordered taxonomically)	Global status	Other EBAs (and SAs)	Altitude (m)	Habitat
Sunda Forktail *Enicurus velatus*	lc	160	(0–)600–2,000	Near streams in hill and montane forest
Sumatran Cochoa *Cochoa beccarii*	VU	—	1,000–1,700	Lower montane forest
Sunda Laughingthrush *Garrulax palliatus*	lc	157	(300–)850–2,200	Montane forest
Black Laughingthrush *Garrulax lugubris*	lc	—	500–1,600	Hill and lower montane forest
Rusty-breasted Wren-babbler *Napothera rufipectus*	lc	—	900–2,500	Montane forest
Marbled Wren-babbler *Napothera marmorata*	nt	—	700–2,000	Hill and montane forest
Sunda Warbler *Seicercus grammiceps*	lc	160	1,400–2,200	Montane forest
Rufous-vented Niltava *Niltava sumatrana*	lc	—	1,000 to treeline	Montane forest
Black-capped White-eye *Zosterops atricapillus*	lc	157	700–3,000	Montane forest, alpine scrub
Mountain Serin *Serinus estherae*	lc	154,160, 166	c.1,900–3,500	Montane forest, forest edge, alpine scrub and meadows, conifer plantations
Sumatran Drongo *Dicrurus sumatranus*	nt	—	800–1,500	Hill and lower montane forest

Global status (see p. 679 for definitions)

EX Extinct ⎫ with year
EW Extinct in ⎬ of last
      the Wild ⎭ record
CR Critical ⎫ threatened
EN Endangered ⎬ species
VU Vulnerable ⎭

cd Conservation Dependent
nt Near Threatened
lc Least Concern
DD Data Deficient
NE Not Evaluated

Other EBAs (and SAs) (see p. 83 for locations)
Bracketed numbers are Secondary Areas.
ˣ Extinct in that EBA or SA.

Notes

[1] Treated as a separate species from Bornean Ground-cuckoo *Carpococcyx radiatus*, following Collar and Long (1996).

[2] *Batrachostomus (poliolophus) mixtus* of Borneo and *Batrachostomus (poliolophus) poliolophus* of Sumatra are here treated as conspecific following Andrew (1992).

[3] Treated as a species separate from Garnet Pitta *Pitta granatina* which is endemic to Sumatra following Andrew (1992), contra the distribution given in van Marle and Voous (1988) and Sibley and Monroe (1990, 1993).

the peninsula, and on the outlying Larat Hills, Mt Tahan and Mt Benom; these are all relatively low, reaching a maximum of 2,189 m at Mt Tahan.

The natural vegetation of Sumatra and Peninsular Malaysia is tropical rain forest, characterized by high temperatures and rainfall which vary little over the year. The restricted-range birds occur in montane forest, although many are also found in hill dipterocarp forest (see Whitmore 1984) down to c.500 m (this contour defines the lower altitudinal limit of the EBA), with a few in the alpine zone above the treeline. The transitions between these vegetation zones tend to occur at higher altitudes on Sumatra than in Peninsular Malaysia: on Sumatra, the transition between hill dipterocarp forest and lower montane forest is at c.1,000 m, and that from lower to upper montane forest is at c.2,000 m, but in Peninsular Malaysia these transitions occur at c.750 and 1,500 m

B. Simpson

Sumatran Cochoa *Cochoa beccarii* is known from just four specimens and a handful of recent records.

Distribution patterns of restricted-range species

Species (ordered geographically)	Larat hills	Main Range	Mt Tahan	Mt Benom	N Barisan mts	S Barisan mts	Other EBAs, SAs
Psilopogon pyrolophus	●	●	–	●	●	●	–
Napothera marmorata	●	●	–	●	●	●	–
Myiophonus robinsoni	–	●	–	–	–	–	–
Polyplectron inopinatum	–	●	●	●	–	–	–
Niltava sumatrana	–	●	–	–	●	●	–
Garrulax lugubris	–	●	–	●	●	●	–
Hydrochrous gigas	–	●	–	–	–	●	●
Rheinardia ocellata	–	–	●	●	–	–	●
Lophura hoogerwerfi	–	–	–	–	●	–	–
Pycnonotus nieuwenhuisii	–	–	–	–	●	–	●
Serinus estherae	–	–	–	–	●	–	●
Arborophila rubirostris	–	–	–	–	●	●	–
Polyplectron chalcurum	–	–	–	–	●	●	–
Pitta schneideri	–	–	–	–	●	●	–
Pitta venusta	–	–	–	–	●	●	–
Pycnonotus leucogrammicus	–	–	–	–	●	●	–
Pycnonotus tympanistrigus	–	–	–	–	●	●	–
Chloropsis venusta	–	–	–	–	●	●	–
Myiophonus melanurus	–	–	–	–	●	●	–
Cochoa beccarii	–	–	–	–	●	●	–
Napothera rufipectus	–	–	–	–	●	●	–
Dicrurus sumatranus	–	–	–	–	●	●	–
Treron oxyura	–	–	–	–	●	●	●
Otus brookii	–	–	–	–	●	●	●
Batrachostomus poliolophus	–	–	–	–	●	●	●
Harpactes reinwardtii	–	–	–	–	●	●	●
Pericrocotus miniatus	–	–	–	–	●	●	●
Pycnonotus bimaculatus	–	–	–	–	●	●	●
Hypsipetes virescens	–	–	–	–	●	●	●
Cinclidium diana	–	–	–	–	●	●	●
Enicurus velatus	–	–	–	–	●	●	●
Garrulax palliatus	–	–	–	–	●	●	●
Zosterops atricapillus	–	–	–	–	●	●	●
Lophura inornata	–	–	–	–	–	●	–
Carpococcyx viridis	–	–	–	–	–	●	–
Ptilinopus porphyreus	–	–	–	–	–	●	●
Caprimulgus pulchellus	–	–	–	–	–	●	●
Seicercus grammiceps	–	–	–	–	–	●	●
Total	2	7	2	5	29	32	

● Present	? Present?	Threatened spp. shown in **bold**	see 'Status and habitat' table
○ Extinct?	R Reintroduced		
X Extinct	I Introduced	Other EBAs, SAs	

respectively (and lower still on the outlying ranges) (Whitmore 1984, van Marle and Voous 1988).

■ Restricted-range species

The mountains of Sumatra and Peninsular Malaysia are defined as comprising a single EBA because they share more restricted-range species than are endemic to the mountains of Peninsular Malaysia alone. Of the 20 species confined to this EBA, 14 are endemic to Sumatra and two to Peninsular Malaysia, and four are shared, including the monotypic endemic genus *Psilopogon*. This EBA has affinities with the other Greater Sunda montane EBAs, sharing 12 restricted-range species with the Javan and Bali forests (EBA 160), and five with the Bornean mountains (EBA 157).

The mountains of Peninsular Malaysia are relatively well known ornithologically (e.g. Medway and Wells 1976, Yatim 1993), but those of Sumatra are less well studied (see van Marle and Voous 1988, Holmes 1996) and much remains to be learned about the habitat requirements and distributions of that island's restricted-range species. All are primarily forest birds, but there is some variation in their altitudinal distribution. Several species appear to be particularly associated with hill dipterocarp and lower montane forest, notably *Rheinardia ocellata* (restricted within this EBA to hill dipterocarp forest in Peninsular Malaysia), *Treron oxyura*, *Carpococcyx viridis*, *Batrachostomus poliolophus*, *Pitta venusta*, *Pycnonotus leucogrammicus*, *P. tympanistrigus*, *P. nieuwenhuisii* (considered to be a lowland-forest-slope specialist by Wells 1985), *Chloropsis venusta*, *Garrulax lugubris*, *Napothera marmorata* and *Dicrurus sumatranus*.

Several species appear to be localized in their distribution on Sumatra, including *Lophura hoogerwerfi*, which is known only from the northern Barisan range, and *L. inornata* and *Carpococcyx viridis*, which have only been recorded in the southern Barisan range.

The montane and hill forests of Sumatra and peninsular Malaysia support 20 unique bird species.

Vanderbilt's Babbler *Malacocincla vanderbilti*, known by a single specimen from northern Sumatra was recognized as a full species by Sibley and Monroe (1990, 1993) but is judged by (Mees 1995) not to be one, and has not been included here.

■ Threats and conservation

The main threat to the birds of this EBA is deforestation. On Sumatra, at least a third of the natural area of montane forest on the island has been lost, and two-thirds to four-fifths of the lowland forest, and natural vegetation is probably being lost faster than in any other part of Indonesia. Agricultural encroachment by shifting cultivators is an important cause of deforestation, which is affecting large areas of hill dipterocarp and lower montane forest, even within gazetted protected areas (Whitten *et al.* 1987b, Collins *et al.* 1991, A. J. Whitten *in litt.* 1993; see Thorsell 1985). In Peninsular Malaysia, the montane forests remain relatively intact, although some logging of lower montane forest and the development of three hill stations has led to localized deforestation, but plans for a road linking these hill stations would pose severe environmental problems if implemented (Collins *et al.* 1991, Kiew 1994, McGowan and Garson 1995).

Seven of the restricted-range birds of this EBA are classified as threatened, including those species which are believed to be most vulnerable to habitat destruc-tion because they have particularly small ranges or are confined to a narrow (and relatively low) altitudinal band. *Carpococcyx viridis* was classified as Vulnerable by Collar *et al.* (1994), who treated it as conspecific with *C. radiatus*, but needs to be re-evaluated (to ascertain whether it qualifies for a higher threatened category) now that it has been given full specific status. Three particularly poorly known species are listed as Data Deficient. Nineteen more widespread threatened species occur on Sumatra and in Peninsular Malaysia, but these are all birds of lowland forest or wetlands which are mainly found outside the EBA, although several of them overlap in distribution with the restricted-range species in hill dipterocarp forest.

There are over 20 protected areas in the Barisan range on Sumatra, and several in the mountains of Peninsular Malaysia, which cover well over 10% of the area of the EBA. Many of these contain large areas of montane and hill dipterocarp forest, and they are spread throughout the entire extent of the EBA and probably include populations of all of the re-stricted-range species. Important protected areas with large areas of montane forest include Taman Negara National Park (which includes Mt Tahan) and Cameron Highlands Wildlife Sanctuary in Peninsu-lar Malaysia, and Gunung Leuser, Kerinci Seblat and Bukit Barisan Selatan National Parks on Sumatra.

159 Enggano

Key habitats Tropical lowland rain forest

Main threats Limited habitat loss (e.g. due to agriculture)

Biological importance ●
Current threat level ●

Area 450 km² **Altitude** 0–300 m

Countries Indonesia

Restricted-range species	Threatened	Total
Confined to this EBA	0	2
Present also in other EBAs, SAs	0	0
Total	0	2

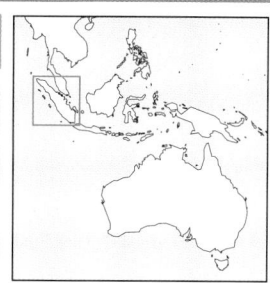

■ General characteristics

The small Indonesian island of Enggano lies c.100 km to the south-west of Sumatra, in the province of Bengkulu (see p. 488 for map). It has probably never had a land connection to the mainland (Whitten *et al.* 1987b), and has an impoverished avifauna typical of an oceanic island. The island has high rainfall which varies very little through the year, and the natural vegetation is tropical lowland evergreen rain forest (Whitmore 1984, van Marle and Voous 1988).

■ Restricted-range species

The two species which are endemic to this EBA are both found in a variety of forested habitats. *Zosterops salvadorii* is described as abundant, and *Otus enganensis* is also probably common, as several were seen during a short visit to the island in 1983 (van Marle and Voous 1988).

■ Threats and conservation

The natural habitats of Enggano have been little disturbed, thanks to the island's sparse population and poor communications (D. A. Holmes *in litt.* 1993), and deforestation appears to be restricted to narrow strips along the few roads (N. Bostock verbally 1993). However, agricultural investments have been tentatively proposed, so there is a risk of drastic habitat changes in the future, and there is therefore a need to develop a protected-area network on the island (D. A. Holmes *in litt.* 1993).

At present, the only protected area on Enggano is Nanuua Hunting Park, a status which does not ensure full protection for the forest and its wildlife. It has therefore been recommended that a change in status to Game Reserve or Nature Reserve be considered (Sujatnika *et al.* 1995).

Status and habitat of restricted-range species

Species (ordered taxonomically)	Global status	Other EBAs (and SAs)	Habitat
Enggano Scops-owl *Otus enganensis*[1]	lc	—	Forest
Enggano White-eye *Zosterops salvadorii*	lc	—	Forest, coconut plantations

Global status (see p. 679 for definitions)	EX Extinct EW Extinct in the Wild } with year of last record		CR Critical EN Endangered VU Vulnerable } threatened species	cd Conservation Dependent nt Near Threatened lc Least Concern DD Data Deficient NE Not Evaluated	**Other EBAs (and SAs)** (see p. 83 for locations)	Bracketed numbers are Secondary Areas. ˣ Extinct in that EBA or SA.
					Notes	[1] Treated here as a full species following Andrew (1992).

160 Java and Bali forests

PRIORITY
CRITICAL

Key habitats Tropical montane and lowland rain forest, monsoon forest

Main threats Severe habitat loss (e.g. due to agriculture), trapping for the cage-bird trade

Biological importance ● ● ●
Current threat level ● ● ○

Area 18,000 km²   **Altitude** 0–3,000 m

Countries Indonesia

Restricted-range species	Threatened	Total
Confined to this EBA	6	20
Present also in other EBAs, SAs	0	14
Total	6	34

■ General characteristics

The Indonesian islands of Java and Bali are both mountainous, rising to maximum altitudes of 3,676 m at Mt Semeru in eastern Java and 3,142 m at Mt Agung on Bali. There are numerous active and extinct volcanoes on the islands, and the fertile volcanic soils support some of the most intensive agriculture in the world—and c.60% of Indonesia's total population (FAO 1982a, RePPProT 1990).

The western half of Java, except for the northern coastal strip, has very high rainfall through most of the year and the natural vegetation is tropical rain forest. Bali and the eastern half of Java are affected by the Australian rain-shadow, and many areas have more seasonal rainfall, and the natural vegetation is deciduous monsoon forest. However, the south-facing sides of the mountains receive relatively high rainfall from the onshore winds, so there are isolated pockets of rain forest in the highlands of central and eastern Java and Bali, and locally in the lowlands along the south coast of Java (Whitmore 1984, A. J. Whitten *in litt.* 1993).

Most of the restricted-range bird species of this EBA are associated with rain forest, principally montane forest, but some occur in the lowlands and in drier forest types. They occur in the provinces of Jawa Barat (West Java), Jawa Tengah (Central Java), Jawa Timur (East Java) and Bali, and probably Yogyakarta. As montane forest above 1,000 m is the

Tree ferns *Cyathea* on Mt Gede in West Java: aggressive early colonists of disturbed montane forest.

most important habitat of this EBA, and much of the forest below this altitude has been cleared, the 1,000 m contour has been used to delineate the EBA, but important lowland localities for the restricted-range bird species are also shown individually on the map. This EBA is adjacent to the Javan coastal zone (EBA 161), but the birds of that EBA are restricted to coastal (mainly non-forest) habitats, and there is little actual overlap between the two.

■ Restricted-range species

The restricted-range species of this EBA include two monotypic endemic genera, *Psaltria*, which is en-

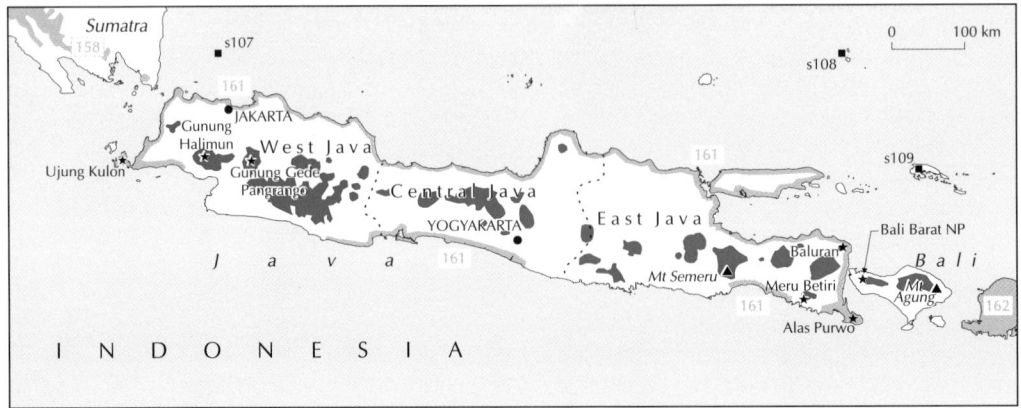

Status and habitat of restricted-range species

Species (ordered taxonomically)	Global status	Other EBAs (and SAs)	Altitude (m)	Habitat
Javan Hawk-eagle *Spizaetus bartelsi*	EN	—	200–1,200 (0–3,000)	Lowland and montane forest
Chestnut-bellied Partridge *Arborophila javanica*	lc	—	1,000–3,000	Montane forest
Sumatran Green-pigeon *Treron oxyura*	nt	158	c.600–3,000	Hill and montane forest
Pink-headed Fruit-dove *Ptilinopus porphyreus*	lc	158	c.900–3,000	Montane forest
Dark-backed Imperial-pigeon *Ducula lacernulata*	lc	162	1,200–3,000	Montane forest
Javan Scops-owl *Otus angelinae*	VU	—	1,000–1,900	Montane forest
Salvadori's Nightjar *Caprimulgus pulchellus*	DD	158	c.1,350–2,200	Montane forest; also possible lowland record
Waterfall Swift *Hydrochrous gigas*	nt	158	c.500–2,400	Hill and montane forest, open country
Volcano Swiftlet *Collocalia vulcanorum*	VU	—	Nests at c.2,200–3,000	Peaks and ridges of volcanoes, nests in rock crevices
Blue-tailed Trogon *Harpactes reinwardtii*	lc	158	1,000–2,500	Montane forest
Brown-throated Barbet *Megalaima corvina*	nt	—	c.900–2,600	Montane forest
Flame-fronted Barbet *Megalaima armillaris*	lc	—	<900–2,500	Forest
Sunda Minivet *Pericrocotus miniatus*	lc	158	<1,200–2,700	Montane forest, coniferous plantations
Orange-spotted Bulbul *Pycnonotus bimaculatus*	lc	158	800–3,000	Montane forest, plantations, alpine scrub
Green-winged Bulbul *Hypsipetes virescens*	lc	158	850–2,400	Montane forest, alpine scrub
Sunda Robin *Cinclidium diana*	lc	158	1,000–2,400	Montane forest
Sunda Forktail *Enicurus velatus*	lc	158	(0–)600–2,000	Near streams in hill and montane forest
Javan Cochoa *Cochoa azurea*	VU	—	900–3,000	Montane forest
Rufous-fronted Laughingthrush *Garrulax rufifrons*	nt	—	1,000–2,400	Montane forest
White-breasted Babbler *Stachyris grammiceps*	VU	—	Lowlands to 1,000(–1,400)	Lowland and hill forest
White-bibbed Babbler *Stachyris thoracica*	lc	—	600–1,800	Hill and montane forest
Crescent-chested Babbler *Stachyris melanothorax*	lc	—	(0–)500–2,500	Hill and montane forest
Grey-cheeked Tit-babbler *Macronous flavicollis*	lc	(s109)	0–c.1,000	Open forest; lowland scrub, particularly dry coastal scrub
Javan Fulvetta *Alcippe pyrrhoptera*	lc	—	>1,000	Montane forest
Spotted Crocias *Crocias albonotatus*	nt	—	c.900–2,400	Montane forest
Javan Tesia *Tesia superciliaris*	lc	—	1,000–3,000	Montane forest
Sunda Warbler *Seicercus grammiceps*	lc	158	800–2,500	Montane forest

cont.

Status and habitat of restricted-range species (cont.)

Species (ordered taxonomically)	Global status	Other EBAs (and SAs)	Altitude (m)	Habitat
Rufous-tailed Fantail *Rhipidura phoenicura*	lc	—	1,000–2,500	Montane forest
White-bellied Fantail *Rhipidura euryura*	nt	—	c.900–2,600	Montane forest
Pygmy Tit *Psaltria exilis*	lc	—	>1,000	Montane forest, coniferous plantations
White-flanked Sunbird *Aethopyga eximia*	lc	—	>1,200	Montane forest, alpine scrub
Javan Grey-throated White-eye *Lophozosterops javanicus*	lc	—	c.900–3,000	Montane forest
Mountain Serin *Serinus estherae*	lc	154,158,166	>1,350	Montane forest, forest edge, alpine scrub and meadows, conifer plantations
Bali Starling *Leucopsar rothschildi*	CR	—	Lowlands	Monsoon forest

Global status (see p. 679 for definitions)	EX Extinct EW Extinct in the Wild	} with year of last record	CR Critical EN Endangered VU Vulnerable	} threatened species	cd Conservation Dependent nt Near Threatened lc Least Concern	DD Data Deficient NE Not Evaluated

Other EBAs (and SAs) (see p. 83 for locations): bracketed numbers are Secondary Areas; [x] extinct in that EBA or SA.

demic to Java, and *Leucopsar*, which is endemic to Bali. There are close affinities with the Sumatra and Peninsular Malaysia (EBA 158), with which 12 restricted-range species are shared. An additional six

The wild population of Bali Starling *Leucopsar rothschildi* is confined to a tiny area within Bali Barat National Park.

species are endemic to Java and Bali, and several more are near-endemic (see Andrew 1992), but these are non-forest birds, or forest birds which have adapted to man-modified habitats, and occur in too wide a range of habitats to be treated as restricted-range.

Most of the restricted-range species are now virtually confined to montane forest, although there are historical records of several of them from the lowlands, which suggests that before extensive lowland deforestation took place they may also have occurred (at least locally) in lowland forest. *Stachyris grammiceps* and *Macronous flavicollis* are mainly found in the lowlands below 1,000 m, *S. grammiceps* mainly in remnant forest patches but *M. flavicollis* also in a variety of non-forest habitats. *Leucopsar rothschildi* is confined to a small area of lowland monsoon forest in western Bali.

All of the restricted-range species apart from *L. rothschildi* have been recorded in West Java, and several are known only from this part of the island, which may be a natural pattern related to the very high rainfall and relatively extensive areas of rain forest found there. However, West Java has been more intensively studied than the rest of the island, and some species may yet prove to be more widespread than is currently known. Recent fieldwork has, for example, extended the known ranges of *Megalaima corvina* and *Psaltria exilis* into Central Java (Robson 1994).

The form of Javan Frogmouth *Batrachostomus javensis* which is endemic to Java (and a restricted-range taxon confined to this EBA) was treated as a full species by Sibley and Monroe (1990, 1993), but

Distribution patterns of restricted-range species

Species (ordered geographically)	West Java	Central Java	East Java	Bali	Other EBAs, SAs
Collocalia vulcanorum	●	–	–	–	–
Cochoa azurea	●	–	–	–	–
Alcippe pyrrhoptera	●	–	–	–	–
Crocias albonotatus	●	–	–	–	–
Treron oxyura	●	–	–	–	●
Hydrochrous gigas	●	–	–	–	●
Harpactes reinwardtii	●	–	–	–	●
Cinclidium diana	●	–	–	–	●
Megalaima corvina	●	●	–	–	–
Garrulax rufifrons	●	●	–	–	–
Tesia superciliaris	●	●	–	–	–
Rhipidura phoenicura	●	●	–	–	–
Psaltria exilis	●	●	–	–	–
Spizaetus bartelsi	●	●	●	–	–
Arborophila javanica	●	●	●	–	–
Otus angelinae	●	?	●	–	–
Stachyris grammiceps	●	●	●	–	–
Stachyris thoracica	●	●	●	–	–
Rhipidura euryura	●	?	●	–	–
Aethopyga eximia	●	●	●	–	–
Caprimulgus pulchellus	●	?	●	–	●
Pericrocotus miniatus	●	●	●	–	●
Hypsipetes virescens	●	●	●	–	●
Enicurus velatus	●	●	●	–	●
Macronous flavicollis	●	●	●	–	●
Seicercus grammiceps	●	●	●	–	●
Serinus estherae	●	●	●	–	●
Megalaima armillaris	●	●	●	●	–
Stachyris melanothorax	●	●	●	●	–
Lophozosterops javanicus	●	●	●	●	–
Ptilinopus porphyreus	●	●	●	●	●
Ducula lacernulata	●	?	●	●	●
Pycnonotus bimaculatus	●	●	●	●	●
Leucopsar rothschildi	–	–	–	●	–
Total	33	21	20	7	

● Present	? Present?	Threatened spp. shown in **bold**	see 'Status and habitat' table
O Extinct?	R Reintroduced		
X Extinct	I Introduced	Other EBAs, SAs	

is here considered as part of a more widespread species which includes Blyth's Frogmouth *B. (javensis) affinis* (following Andrew 1992).

■ Threats and conservation

Closed-canopy forest now covers less than 10% of the land area of Java and Bali (Collins *et al.* 1991). Most of this forest is montane, although several important areas of lowland forest are included in protected areas. Loss of forest cover has now virtually ceased, but degradation of the remaining habitats continues to be a threat, and the hunting and trapping of birds is widespread (MacKinnon and Phillipps 1993, D. A. Holmes *in litt.* 1993). West Java is the most extensively forested part of the EBA, and in Central and East Java and on Bali the natural forest is mostly confined to the upper slopes of the isolated volcanoes and other mountains.

Six of the EBA's restricted-range bird species are threatened, several because they are particularly restricted in range and therefore vulnerable to habitat loss; of the others, *Spizaetus bartelsi* is listed because it occurs at very low densities and prefers forest on the lower mountain slopes, *Stachyris grammiceps* because it is mainly confined to lowland forest, and *Leucopsar rothschildi* because it has a tiny range and population, and continues to be illegally trapped for the cage-bird trade (van Balen and Gepak 1994). More widespread threatened birds which occur on Java include: Green Peafowl *Pavo muticus* (classified as Vulnerable), which has declined throughout its large Asian range and whose relict populations on Java are now all scattered and threatened (van Balen and Holmes 1993); Java Sparrow *Padda oryzivora* (Vulnerable), formerly abundant throughout Java, Bali and the Kangean islands but now much reduced in numbers, apparently due entirely to massive capture for the cage-bird trade; and Straw-headed Bulbul *Pycnonotus zeylanicus* (Vulnerable), which has also declined rapidly as a result of excessive trapping.

Most of the remaining forest on Java and Bali is in the mountains, and much of it is already included in gazetted protected areas. Gunung Gede Pangrango National Park and Gunung Halimun Nature Reserve in West Java are notable, because they probably support populations of all of the restricted-range species—except for *Leucopsar rothschildi*, whose entire range is included within the Bali Barat National Park. Important areas of lowland rain forest are protected in Ujung Kulon, Alas Purwo, Baluran and Meru-Betiri National Parks (Ujung Kulon supports one of only two known populations of the critically endangered Javan rhinoceros *Rhinoceros sondaicus*).

Given the extensive forest loss and fragmentation which has taken place on Java and Bali, the following 21 forest areas are recommended as new reserves (FAO 1982a, Sujatnika and Jepson 1995): Jatiluhur/Sanggabuana, Ciogong, Cikencreng, Cipatujah, Gunung Limbung, Gunung Kencana, Gunung Masigit, Gunung Masigit-Kareumbi and Cimapang in West Java; Gunung Muryo, Pegunungan Pembarisan, Gunung Slamat and Gunung Perahu in Central Java; Teluk Lenggasana (Lebakharjo), Gunung Beser, Gunung Ringgit, Gunung Jagatamu, Gunung Liman Wilis, Gunung Raung, Gunung Kawi/Kelud and Maelang in East Java; extensions are recommended to Bali Barat National Park and Gunung Batukahu Nature Reserve.

161 Javan coastal zone

PRIORITY
HIGH

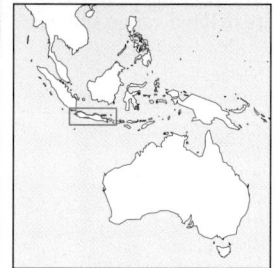

Key habitats Coastal wetlands, grassland, mangroves, scrub, beaches, mudflats

Main threats Severe habitat loss (e.g. due to agriculture, aquaculture)

Biological importance ● ○ ○
Current threat level ● ○ ○

Area 11,000 km²   **Altitude** 0 m

Countries Indonesia

Restricted-range species	Threatened	Total
Confined to this EBA	1	1
Present also in other EBAs, SAs	0	2
Total	1	3

■ General characteristics

This EBA includes the coastal zone of Java and Madura in Indonesia, falling within the provinces of Jawa Barat (West Java), Jakarta, Jawa Tengah (Central Java), Yogyakarta and Jawa Timur (East Java), and the restricted-range birds occur (or formerly occurred) here in a variety of coastal habitats. The lowlands of Java have been densely populated for several hundred years, and there had been considerable destruction and modification of these coastal habitats before ornithological exploration began, so the original distributions of the restricted-range bird species present are unlikely ever to be fully known. The EBA is defined here as comprising those sections of the coast with extensive level lowlands, where coastal wetlands and grassland are likely to have been present in the past.

The birds of the adjacent Java and Bali forests (EBA 160) are found mainly in the remaining natural forests on the mountains and foothills, so there is probably no overlap with the Javan coastal zone.

Status and habitat of restricted-range species

Species (ordered taxonomically)	Global status	Other EBAs (and SAs)	Habitat
Javan Plover *Charadrius javanicus*	nt	(s109)	Sandy beaches, mudflats
Javanese Lapwing *Vanellus macropterus*	EX (c.1940)	—	Grassland adjacent to coastal marshes and river deltas
Sunda Coucal *Centropus nigrorufus*	VU	—	Mangroves and associated swamp vegetation
Javan White-eye *Zosterops flavus*	nt	(s100)	Mangroves, coastal scrub, relict coastal forest

Global status (see p. 679 for definitions)   EX Extinct / EW Extinct in the Wild } with year of last record   CR Critical / EN Endangered / VU Vulnerable } threatened species   cd Conservation Dependent / nt Near Threatened / lc Least Concern   DD Data Deficient / NE Not Evaluated

Other EBAs (and SAs) (see p. 83 for locations): bracketed numbers are Secondary Areas; ˣ extinct in that EBA or SA.

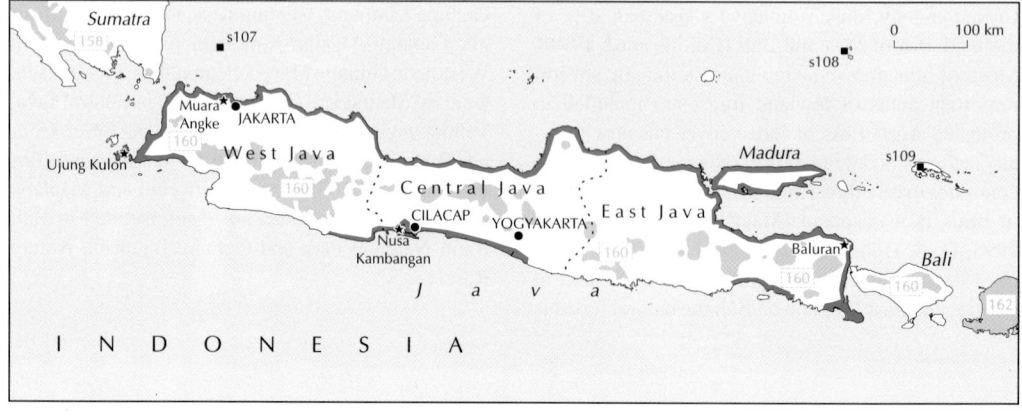

Most of Java's coastal lowlands have been converted to agriculture, and little natural habitat remains.

BirdLife International

Restricted-range species

The restricted-range bird species differ somewhat in their habitat requirements and known distributions. The coastally occurring *Charadrius javanicus* is extremely difficult to distinguish from Kentish Plover *C. alexandrinus* (a non-breeding visitor to Java) and is thus a poorly known species. *Vanellus macropterus* was found in moist grassland along the north coast of western Java and the south coast of eastern Java (and doubtfully from Timor and Sumatra: King 1978–1979), but is almost certainly now extinct. *Centropus nigrorufus* is known from mangroves and adjacent swamp vegetation on Java (and possibly also Sumatra: Collar *et al.* 1994), but an old record from teak forest well inland and recent sightings in scrub away from the coastal wetlands (S. van Balen *in litt.* 1994) suggest that it may not be entirely confined to the remnant coastal wetlands. *Zosterops flavus* is a bird of mangroves and coastal scrub, known from this EBA and coastal Borneo.

Threats and conservation

Java is by far the most industrialized and developed island in Indonesia, with most industry along the north coast and around Cilacap on the south-central coast (Whitten and Whitten 1992). Large areas along the coast have also been converted to agricultural land, and extensive areas of mangrove have been replaced by aquacultures (D. A. Holmes *in litt.* 1993, S. van Balen *in litt.* 1994). As a result, the natural

habitats of this EBA are much reduced in area, and seriously fragmented and degraded.

Centropus nigrorufus is classified as threatened because of this continuing destruction and disturbance of its habitat. More widespread threatened species found in this EBA are Milky Stork *Mycteria cinerea* (classified as Vulnerable), which is only known to breed at one locality there, Lesser Adjutant *Leptoptilos javanicus* (Vulnerable), which is becoming increasingly rare on Java and is not now known to breed there (S. van Balen *in litt.* 1994), and White-winged Duck *Cairina scutulata* (Endangered), which formerly occurred in western and central Java, but is now almost certainly extinct there (Green and Crosby 1992).

There are only a few small areas of coastal wetland in the protected-area system in Java. These include the coastal parts of Ujung Kulon and Baluran National Parks, and Muara Angke, Nusa Kambangan and Wijaya Kusuma Nature Reserves. Additional areas which have been recommended for establishment as new reserves are Muara Gembong, Muara Cimanuk, Tanjung Sedari and Muara Bobos (FAO 1982a, Sujatnika and Jepson 1995). Sujatnika *et al.* (1995) have called for survey work to be carried out to identify more areas of coastal habitat suitable for protection, and there is a need for the maintenance and extension of rehabilitation programmes that local government is conducting on mangroves and coastal areas.

162 Northern Nusa Tenggara

PRIORITY
HIGH

Key habitats Monsoon forest, tropical semi-evergreen rain forest, tropical montane rain forest	Area 39,000 km²	Altitude 0–2,400 m

Countries Indonesia

Main threats Major habitat loss (e.g. due to agriculture, grazing, burning)

Biological importance ● ● ●
Current threat level ● ● ●

Restricted-range species	Threatened	Total
Confined to this EBA	3	17
Present also in other EBAs, SAs	0	12
Total	3	29

■ General characteristics

This EBA comprises the northern chain of the Lesser Sunda islands from Lombok to Alor, in Nusa Tenggara Barat and Nusa Tenggara Timur provinces of Indonesia. These are mountainous islands with numerous volcanoes, many of which are active. Mt Rinjani on Lombok at 3,726 m is by far the highest mountain in the Lesser Sundas, and the mountains on Sumbawa and Flores rise to well over 1,000 m.

The Lesser Sunda Islands are relatively dry (in comparison to the rest of Indonesia) because they lie in the rain-shadow of the Australian continent and receive little rain in the south-east monsoon between April and November; most rain falls during the westerly monsoon in December to March. As a result, the natural vegetation of much of the EBA is deciduous monsoon forest. However, the south-facing sides of the mountains receive moderately high rainfall from onshore winds, and support isolated pockets of tropical semi-evergreen rain forest (Whitmore 1984). Montane forest is present above c.800 m (see map).

■ Restricted-range species

The restricted-range species of this EBA—which include the monotypic endemic genus *Caridonax*—are almost all forest birds, but their precise habitat requirements are not fully understood. The results of recent fieldwork on Sumbawa and Flores by Butchart *et al.* (1996) have, however, added considerably to current knowledge.

Eight species appear to be mainly confined to the lowlands below c.1,000 m, including *Corvus flor-*

G. C. L. Dutson

Pockets of semi-evergreen rain forest are found on several mountain ranges in this EBA, such as here on Mt Olet Sangenges on Sumbawa.

ensis, which is known only from the western half of Flores. *Todirhamphus australasia* and *Dicaeum maugei* have an unusual disjunct distribution, being

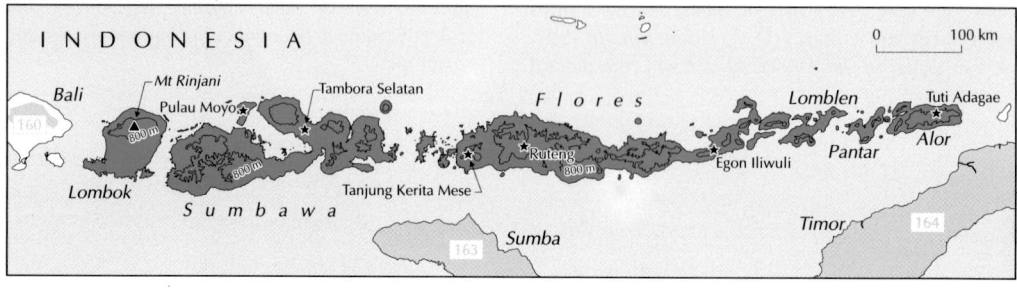

INDONESIA

Bali — Mt Rinjani — Tambora Selatan — *F l o r e s* — Lomblen — Tuti Adagae
Pulau Moyo — Alor
Pantar
Egon Iliwuli
Lombok — Ruteng
S u m b a w a — Tanjung Kerita Mese — Timor
Sumba

0   100 km

Habitat associations of restricted-range species

Lowland forest

Macropygia magna
Treron floris
Ducula rosacea
Trichoglossus euteles
Todirhamphus australasia
Nectarinia solaris
Zosterops wallacei
Corvus florensis

Semi-evergreen rain forest

Ducula lacernulata
Loriculus flosculus
Otus silvicola
Coracina dohertyi
Zoothera dohertyi
Rhinomyias oscillans
Monarcha sacerdotum
Pachycephala nudigula
Lophozosterops dohertyi

Lowland and montane forest

Caridonax fulgidus
Pericrocotus lansbergei
Tesia everetti
Rhipidura diluta
Dicaeum annae
Dicaeum igniferum
Dicaeum maugei
Heleia crassirostris
Lichmera lombokia

Montane forest

Otus alfredi
Phylloscopus presbytes
Lophozosterops
   superciliaris

Threatened species (Critical, Endangered, Vulnerable) are shown in **bold**; see 'status and habitat' table.

found in this EBA only on the western island of Lombok, but also to the east and the south in the other Lesser Sunda EBAs (163–165). Nine species appear to be particularly associated with the pockets of semi-evergreen rain forest found on the mountain slopes of Lombok, Sumbawa and Flores. These include *Loriculus flosculus* and *Monarcha sacerdotum*, which are endemic to Flores and known only from Tanjung Kerita Mese in the west of the island, and the former also from Mt Egon in the east, where

Distribution patterns of restricted-range species

Species (ordered geographically)	Lombok	Sumbawa	Flores	Lomblen	Pantar	Alor	Other EBAs, SAs
Todirhamphus australasia	●	–	–	–	–	–	●
Dicaeum maugei	●	–	–	–	–	–	●
Caridonax fulgidus	●	●	●	–	–	–	–
Lichmera lombokia	●	●	●	–	–	–	–
Ducula lacernulata	●	●	●	–	–	–	●
Zoothera dohertyi	●	●	●	–	–	–	●
Treron floris	●	●	●	●	●	●	–
Otus silvicola	–	●	●	–	–	–	–
Pericrocotus lansbergei	–	●	●	–	–	–	–
Tesia everetti	–	●	●	–	–	–	–
Pachycephala nudigula	–	●	●	–	–	–	–
Lophozosterops superciliaris	–	●	●	–	–	–	–
Lophozosterops dohertyi	–	●	●	–	–	–	–
Heleia crassirostris	–	●	●	–	–	–	–
Coracina dohertyi	–	●	●	–	–	–	●
Rhinomyias oscillans	–	●	●	–	–	–	●
Rhipidura diluta	–	●	●	●	–	–	–
Zosterops wallacei	–	●	●	●	–	–	●
Dicaeum annae	–	●	●	–	–	●	–
Nectarinia solaris	–	●	●	–	–	●	●
Dicaeum igniferum	–	●	●	–	●	●	–
Ducula rosacea	–	●	●	–	●	●	●
Loriculus flosculus	–	–	●	–	–	–	–
Otus alfredi	–	–	●	–	–	–	–
Monarcha sacerdotum	–	–	●	–	–	–	–
Corvus florensis	–	–	●	–	–	–	–
Phylloscopus presbytes	–	–	●	●	–	–	●
Trichoglossus euteles	–	–	–	●	●	●	●
Macropygia magna	–	–	–	–	–	●	●
Total	7	20	25	5	4	7	

● Present   ? Present?   Threatened spp.   ⎫
○ Extinct?   R Reintroduced   shown in **bold**   ⎬ see 'Status
X Extinct   I Introduced   Other EBAs, SAs   ⎭ and habitat' table

Status and habitat of restricted-range species

Species (ordered taxonomically)	Global status	Other EBAs (and SAs)	Altitude (m)	Habitat
Dusky Cuckoo-dove *Macropygia magna*	lc	164,165 (s110)	0–800	Monsoon forest, agricultural land
Flores Green-pigeon *Treron floris*	nt	—	0–800	Monsoon forest, rarely semi-evergreen rain forest
Pink-headed Imperial-pigeon *Ducula rosacea*	lc	164,165 (s107, s108,s109, s110,s111)	0–600	Forest, scrub and agricultural land on small islands
Dark-backed Imperial-pigeon *Ducula lacernulata*	lc	160	400–1,700	Semi-evergreen rain forest, montane forest
Olive-headed Lorikeet *Trichoglossus euteles*	lc	164,165	Lowlands	Mostly on rather arid islands with little forest, sometimes forest and agricultural land
Wallace's Hanging-parrot *Loriculus flosculus*	VU	—	(450–) 850–1,000	Semi-evergreen rain forest with fig trees
Flores Scops-owl *Otus alfredi*[1]	NE	—	c.1,050	Montane forest
Wallace's Scops-owl *Otus silvicola*	nt	—	350–1,600	Semi-evergreen rain forest, lower montane forest, rarely monsoon forest and agricultural land
Cinnamon-banded Kingfisher *Todirhamphus australasia*	nt	163,164,165	Lowlands to 700+	Monsoon forest

cont.

Status and habitat of restricted-range species (cont.)

Species (ordered taxonomically)	Global status	Other EBAs (and SAs)	Altitude (m)	Habitat
White-rumped Kingfisher *Caridonax fulgidus*	lc	—	0–1,500	Semi-evergreen rain forest, lower montane forest, monsoon forest, scrub, agricultural land
Sumba Cicadabird *Coracina dohertyi*	nt	163	200–1,400	Semi-evergreen rain forest, lower montane forest, rarely monsoon forest
Flores Minivet *Pericrocotus lansbergei*	lc	—	0–1,820	Semi-evergreen rain forest, lower montane forest, monsoon forest, riverine forest
Chestnut-backed Thrush *Zoothera dohertyi*	lc	163,164	400–1,700	Semi-evergreen rain forest, lower montane forest
Russet-capped Tesia *Tesia everetti*	lc	—	0–2,140	Semi-evergreen rain forest, montane forest, scarce in monsoon/riverine forest, agricultural land
Timor Leaf-warbler *Phylloscopus presbytes*	lc	164	1,000–2,140	Montane forest
Russet-backed Jungle-flycatcher *Rhinomyias oscillans*	nt	163	370–1,500	Semi-evergreen rain forest, lower montane forest
Flores Monarch *Monarcha sacerdotum*	EN	—	350–1,000	Semi-evergreen rain forest
Brown-capped Fantail *Rhipidura diluta*	lc	—	0–2,140	Semi-evergreen rain forest, montane forest, monsoon forest
Bare-throated Whistler *Pachycephala nudigula*	lc	—	200–2,400	Semi-evergreen rain forest, montane forest
Golden-rumped Flowerpecker *Dicaeum annae*	lc	—	0–1,800	Semi-evergreen rain forest, lower montane forest, rarely monsoon forest
Black-fronted Flowerpecker *Dicaeum igniferum*	lc	—	0–1,730	All forest types (but commonest outside closed-canopy forest), agricultural land, gardens
Red-chested Flowerpecker *Dicaeum maugei*	lc	164,165 (s110)	0–2,000	Open forest
Flame-breasted Sunbird *Nectarinia solaris*	lc	164	0–1,100	Semi-evergreen rain forest, monsoon forest, scrub with scattered trees
Yellow-spectacled White-eye *Zosterops wallacei*	lc	163	0–800	Forest edge, degraded forest, scrub
Yellow-browed White-eye *Lophozosterops superciliaris*	lc	—	1,000–2,140	Montane forest
Crested White-eye *Lophozosterops dohertyi*	nt	—	200–1,400	Semi-evergreen rain forest, lower montane forest
Thick-billed White-eye *Heleia crassirostris*	lc	—	50–1,800	Semi-evergreen rain forest, lower montane forest, monsoon forest
Scaly-crowned Honeyeater *Lichmera lombokia*	lc	—	800–2,140 (lower on Lombok)	Montane forest; lowland forest, agricultural land and gardens on Lombok
Flores Crow *Corvus florensis*	VU	—	0–950	Semi-evergreen rain forest, monsoon forest

Global status (see p. 679 for definitions)

EX	Extinct	cd	Conservation
EW	Extinct in		Dependent
	the Wild	nt	Near Threatened
CR	Critical	lc	Least Concern
EN	Endangered	DD	Data Deficient
VU	Vulnerable	NE	Not Evaluated

EX Extinct, EW Extinct in the Wild — with year of last record. CR Critical, EN Endangered, VU Vulnerable — threatened species.

Other EBAs (and SAs) (see p. 83 for locations)

Bracketed numbers are Secondary Areas.   ˣ Extinct in that EBA or SA.

Notes

[1] Here treated as a full species following Andrew (1992), contra Sibley and Monroe (1993) who considered it to be the red phase of *O. magicus*.

they have been recorded below c.1,000 m. Nine species occur in both lowland and montane forest. The remaining three species are confined (in this EBA) to montane forests above c.1,000 m on Sumbawa and Flores. One of these, *Otus alfredi*, is known by three specimens collected at c.1,050 m on Flores in 1896, and was considered a form of the widespread Moluccan Scops-owl *O. magicus* by Sibley and Monroe (1993).

■ Threats and conservation

Forest clearance, carried out largely to permit shifting cultivation, and the practice of burning in the dry season have had a major impact on the natural vegetation of this EBA, and much of the region's landscape now consists of grassy hills, with forest surviving only in steep valleys and on the highest peaks (FAO 1982c). Lomblen, Pantar and Alor are described as having been devastated by cultivation (White and Bruce 1986), but some extensive areas of forest, including lowland semi-evergreen rain forest, remain on Lombok, Sumbawa and Flores (RePPProT 1990, Collins *et al.* 1991, Butchart *et al.* 1996). The forests in parts of south-west Sumbawa are threatened by a new gold and copper mine (Jepson and Monk 1995).

Flores Monarch *Monarcha sacedorum* is only known from primary semi-evergreen rain forest in Tanjung Kerita Mese in western Flores.

Mining activities are leading to localized forest loss in parts of Sumbawa.

The three restricted-range species which are endemic to Flores are classified as threatened, because they all have particularly small ranges and are vulnerable to habitat loss. A more widespread threatened species (found throughout much of Wallacea) which occurs in the EBA is Yellow-crested Cockatoo

Cacatua sulphurea (classified as Endangered), which is declining throughout its range because of a combination of habitat loss and unsustainable levels of trapping for the bird trade. The world's largest lizard, the Komodo dragon *Varanus komodoensis*, is endemic to this EBA, being found on Komodo, Padar and Rinca islands between Flores and Sumbawa, and very locally on Flores.

There are gazetted protected areas in most parts of this EBA, the most important for the restricted-range birds being the large Gunung Rinjani National Park on Lombok, Tambora Selatan and Pulau Moyo Hunting Reserves on Sumbawa, Ruteng Nature Reserve on Flores, which protects an important area of montane forest, and Tuti Adagae Recreation Forest on Alor. However, the total area protected is well below 10%, and some habitat types are not adequately represented, most notably semi-evergreen rain forest, but also montane forest and lowland monsoon forest. Several new protected areas have been proposed, the most important being Tanjung Kerita Mese and Egon Iliwuli because these include the only areas of semi-evergreen rain forest where two of the Flores endemic birds have been recorded. The other proposed areas are Selalu Legini, Puncak Ngenges (Gunung Olet Sangenges), Gunung Tambora Utara and Kompleks Hutan Dompu on Sumbawa (see Jepson and Monk 1995), and Gunung Ambulombo and Hutan Lewotobi on Flores (FAO 1982c, Sujatnika and Jepson 1995).

163 Sumba

PRIORITY
HIGH

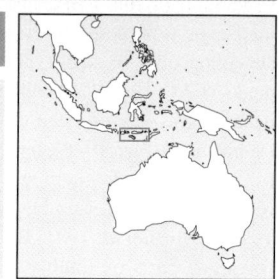

Key habitats Monsoon forest, tropical semi-evergreen rain forest, montane forest, grassland	Area 11,000 km²	Altitude 0–1,200 m

Countries Indonesia

Restricted-range species	Threatened	Total
Confined to this EBA	4	7
Present also in other EBAs, SAs	0	5
Total	4	12

Main threats Major habitat loss (e.g. due to agriculture, grazing, burning)

Biological importance ● ○ ○
Current threat level ● ○ ○

■ General characteristics

The Lesser Sunda island of Sumba, like the Northern Nusa Tenggara EBA (EBA 162), is in Nusa Tenggara Timur province of Indonesia. It is a hilly island, with deeply dissected plateaus, but there is little land above 1,000 m and the highest peak only reaches 1,225 m. Sumba has a seasonal climate because it lies in the rain-shadow of the Australian continent and receives little rain in the south-east monsoon between April and November.

The major natural vegetation type is deciduous monsoon forest, but there are pockets of tropical semi-evergreen rain forest where the south-facing sides of the hills receive moderately high rainfall from onshore winds, some evergreen gallery forest in wet depressions and gullies, and montane forest above c.800 m (FAO 1982c, Whitmore 1984). Much of the island is now covered in dry grassland and savanna woodland as a result of forest clearance and the practice of burning in the dry season (FAO 1982c).

■ Restricted-range species

Turnix everetti is found in open grassland, but otherwise the restricted-range species are all birds of forest or woodland. Recent ornithological survey work on Sumba by Jones *et al.* (1995a) has greatly improved knowledge of the habitat requirements and conservation status of these species. Most of them were found in all forest types, in both primary and secondary forest, and were estimated to have large populations on the island. The exceptions are *Ptilinopus dohertyi* (a Sumba endemic) and *Zoothera dohertyi*, which are associated with primary forest in the higher parts of the island, and *Aceros everetti* (a Sumba endemic), which prefers primary and mature secondary semi-evergreen rain forest in the lowlands. Two further Sumba endemics, *Turnix everetti* and *Ninox rudolfi*, were not recorded frequently enough during the survey work to permit a full assessment of their habitat requirements and conservation status.

Two taxa which are confined to this EBA, Sumba Brown Flycatcher *Muscicapa segregata* and Sumba Myzomela *Myzomela dammermani* were treated as full species by Sibley and Monroe (1990, 1993) but are considered in this study to be forms of the more widespread Asian Brown Flycatcher *M. dauurica* and Red-headed Myzomela *M. erythrocephala* respectively, following Andrew (1992).

■ Threats and conservation

The area of forest on Sumba has declined significantly during the twentieth century, mainly through

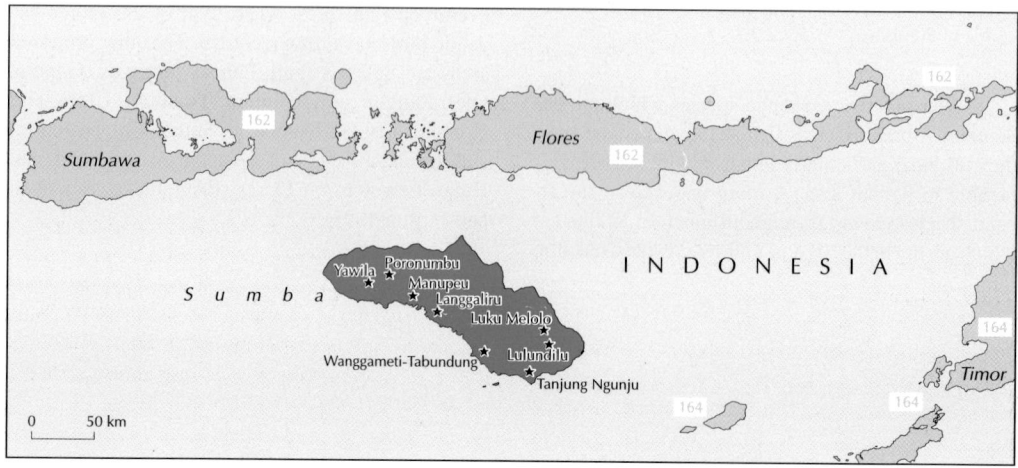

Status and habitat of restricted-range species

Species (ordered taxonomically)	Global status	Other EBAs (and SAs)	Altitude	Habitat
Sumba Buttonquail *Turnix everetti*	VU	—	Lowlands	Grassland and sparse scrub
Sumba Green-pigeon *Treron teysmannii*	nt	—	All altitudes	Open forest, particularly disturbed areas where large trees remain
Red-naped Fruit-dove *Ptilinopus dohertyi*	VU	—	Mainly above 200 m	Undisturbed forest with fruiting trees
Sumba Boobook *Ninox rudolfi*	VU	—	Lowlands to 1,000 m	Forest
Cinnamon-banded Kingfisher *Todirhamphus australasia*	nt	162,164,165	Lowlands to 700 m, sometimes higher	Monsoon forest
Sumba Hornbill *Aceros everetti*	VU	— ·	Mainly low altitudes	Semi-evergreen rain forest
Sumba Cicadabird *Coracina dohertyi*	nt	162	All altitudes	Closed-canopy forest of all types
Chestnut-backed Thrush *Zoothera dohertyi*	lc	162,164	Higher altitudes	Forest
Russet-backed Jungle-flycatcher *Rhinomyias oscillans*	nt	162	All altitudes, prefers higher	Forest
Sumba Flycatcher *Ficedula harterti*	nt	—	All altitudes	All forest types
Apricot-breasted Sunbird *Nectarinia buettikoferi*	lc	—	All altitudes, mostly low	All forest types, scrub in agricultural land
Yellow-spectacled White-eye *Zosterops wallacei*	lc	162	All altitudes	All forest types, scrub

Global status (see p. 679 for definitions): EX Extinct / EW Extinct in the Wild } with year of last record; CR Critical / EN Endangered / VU Vulnerable } threatened species; cd Conservation Dependent; nt Near Threatened; lc Least Concern; DD Data Deficient; NE Not Evaluated

Other EBAs (and SAs) (see p. 83 for locations): bracketed numbers are Secondary Areas; ˣ extinct in that EBA or SA.

the clearance and repeated burning of vegetation to provide land for grazing and cultivation and because of unsustainable levels of utilization of fuelwood and other minor forest products. Closed-canopy forest now covers c.10% of the island and is mainly confined to relatively small and isolated pockets, although some more extensive areas remain along the south coast. Sumba has no logging industry, but some trees are removed for local use (Jones *et al.* 1995a, Jepson *et al.* 1996).

Four of Sumba's endemic restricted-range birds are classified as threatened: *Ptilinopus dohertyi* and *Aceros everetti* because their populations are each estimated to be below 10,000 individuals and their specialized habitat requirements make them vulnerable to further deforestation, and *Turnix everetti* and *Ninox rudolfi* because they appear to be scarce and they may also be vulnerable to loss of their habitat. However, the ecology of *T. everetti* remains very poorly understood, and this species may actually have benefited from the replacement of forest by open grassland.

A more widespread threatened species (found throughout much of Wallacea), Yellow-crested Cockatoo *Cacatua sulphurea* (classified as Endangered), is represented on Sumba by the endemic subspecies *citrinocristata* (which perhaps warrants full specific status: D. A. Holmes *in litt.* 1993); it is declining throughout its range because of a combination of habitat loss and unsustainable levels of trapping for the bird trade.

The only gazetted protected area on Sumba is Langgaliru Nature Reserve. The PHPA/BirdLife International Sumba Forest Conservation Project has proposed the gazetting of a network of seven key forest sites which include the largest remaining areas of forest on the island and would adequately cover all of the important habitats of the EBA: top priority are Wanggameti-Tabundung and Langgaliru-Manupeu (an extension to the existing protected area, to include the largest single population of *Aceros everetti*); high priority are Luku Melolo, Yawila and Poronumbu; and important additional areas are Lulundilu and Tanjung Ngunju (Jepson *et al.* 1996).

164 Timor and Wetar

Key habitats Monsoon forest and woodland, semi-evergreen rain forest, montane forest, scrub

Main threats Major habitat loss (e.g. due to agriculture, grazing, burning)

Biological importance ● ●
Current threat level ● ○ ○

Area 34,000 km²   **Altitude** 0–2,600 m

Countries Indonesia

Restricted-range species	Threatened	Total
Confined to this EBA	5	23
Present also in other EBAs, SAs	0	12
Total	5	35

■ General characteristics

The EBA comprises Timor and its associated islands of Sawu, Roti and Semau (in eastern Nusa Tenggara Timur and Timor Timur provinces of Indonesia), and Wetar (in south-east Maluku province). Wetar is volcanic, and lies off the eastern end of the main chain of the Lesser Sunda Islands, whereas the other islands lie to the south of the main chain and are not volcanic. Both the main islands are mountainous, rising to 2,960 m (Timor) and 1,407 m (Wetar).

As it lies directly in the Australian rain-shadow, this is the driest part of Indonesia, with a dry season which lasts from April to November. The natural vegetation of the islands is deciduous monsoon forest, woodland and savanna, with some isolated patches of semi-evergreen rain forest on the south-facing sides of the mountains where the land receives

rain from the onshore winds, and montane forest above c.900 m on the higher mountains (Whitmore 1984).

■ Restricted-range species

The 23 species which are endemic to this EBA include the monotypic genus *Buettikoferella*. The habitat requirements, altitudinal ranges and abundance of the region's restricted-range birds are, in general, poorly documented. There has been a survey undertaken recently of some of the remnant forest patches in the west of Timor (see Noske and Saleh 1993, Noske 1995), but there is little information on eastern Timor, and Wetar appears to have been visited only once by ornithologists since 1910—and then only for a few hours (White and Bruce 1986, Robson 1990).

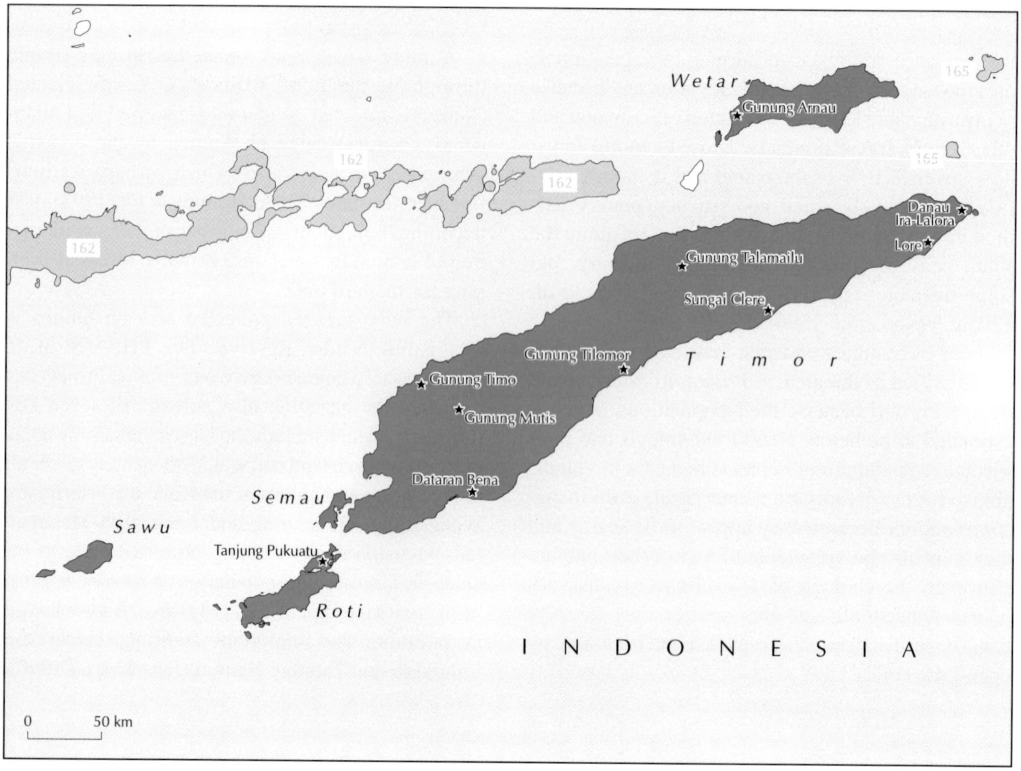

Wetar

Gunung Arnau

162

162

165

165

Danau Ira-Lalora

Lore

Gunung Talamailu

Sungai Clere

Gunung Tilomor   *T i m o r*

Gunung Timo

Gunung Mutis

Dataran Bena

Semau

Sawu

Tanjung Pukuatu

Roti

I N D O N E S I A

0   50 km

Status and habitat of restricted-range species

Species (ordered taxonomically)	Global status	Other EBAs (and SAs)	Altitude (m)	Habitat
Dusky Cuckoo-dove *Macropygia magna*	lc	162,165 (s110)	0–800	Monsoon forest, agricultural land
Black Cuckoo-dove *Turacoena modesta*	VU	—	0–1,100	Monsoon forest, open areas
Wetar Ground-dove *Gallicolumba hoedtii*	VU	—	No data	Forest
Timor Green-pigeon *Treron psittacea*	VU	—	0–600	Monsoon forest
Pink-headed Imperial-pigeon *Ducula rosacea*	lc	162,165,171 (s107, s108,s109,s110,s111)	0–600	Forest, scrub and agricultural land
Timor Imperial-pigeon *Ducula cineracea*	VU	—	1,000–2,200	Montane forest
Olive-headed Lorikeet *Trichoglossus euteles*	lc	162,165	0–2,300	Mostly rather arid islands with little forest, sometimes agricultural land
Iris Lorikeet *Psitteuteles iris*	VU	—	0–1,500	Monsoon forest, flowering trees
Olive-shouldered Parrot *Aprosmictus jonquillaceus*	nt	—	0–2,600	Monsoon forest, *Acacia* savanna
Cinnamon-banded Kingfisher *Todirhamphus australasia*	nt	162,163,165	Lowlands to 700+	Monsoon forest
Chestnut-backed Thrush *Zoothera dohertyi*	lc	162,163	1,050–2,300	Montane forest
Orange-banded Thrush *Zoothera peronii*	nt	165	0–1,200	Monsoon forest
White-bellied Bushchat *Saxicola gutturalis*	nt	—	0–1,200	Monsoon forest
Timor Stubtail *Urosphena subulata*	nt	165	0–1,900	Monsoon forest, scrub, long grass
Timor Leaf-warbler *Phylloscopus presbytes*	lc	162	0–2,300	All forest types
Buff-banded Grassbird *Buettikoferella bivittata*	nt	—	Lowlands	Monsoon forest, scrub, grassland
Plain Gerygone *Gerygone inornata*	lc	—	Lowlands	Monsoon forest, scrub
Black-banded Flycatcher *Ficedula timorensis*	nt	—	0–1,200	Monsoon forest
Timor Blue-flycatcher *Cyornis hyacinthinus*	lc	—	0–2,000	Monsoon forest
Fawn-breasted Whistler *Pachycephala orpheus*	nt	—	0–1,200	Monsoon forest
Red-chested Flowerpecker *Dicaeum maugei*	lc	162,165 (s110)	0–1,200	Open forest
Flame-breasted Sunbird *Nectarinia solaris*	lc	162	0–1,000	Monsoon forest, scrub
Spot-breasted White-eye *Heleia muelleri*	nt	—	0–1,300	Monsoon forest
Crimson-hooded Myzomela *Myzomela kuehni*	DD	—	Lowlands	Monsoon forest, flowering trees, gardens
Red-rumped Myzomela *Myzomela vulnerata*	nt	—	0–1,200	Monsoon forest
White-tufted Honeyeater *Lichmera squamata*	lc	165	Lowlands	Mangroves, forest, scrub, agricultural land
Yellow-eared Honeyeater *Lichmera flavicans*	lc	—	0–2,000	Monsoon forest

cont.

Status and habitat of restricted-range species (cont.)

Species (ordered taxonomically)	Global status	Other EBAs (and SAs)	Altitude (m)	Habitat
Black-chested Honeyeater *Lichmera notabilis*	DD	—	Lowlands	Monsoon forest
Streaky-breasted Honeyeater *Meliphaga reticulata*	nt	—	0–1,200	Monsoon forest
Plain Friarbird *Philemon inornatus*	nt	—	0–2,200	Monsoon forest
Tricoloured Parrotfinch *Erythrura tricolor*	lc	165	0–1,200	Monsoon forest, thickets
Timor Sparrow *Padda fuscata*	nt	—	0–800	Agricultural land, grassland, savanna woodland, scrub
Olive-brown Oriole *Oriolus melanotis*	lc	—	0–1,600	Monsoon forest
Wetar Figbird *Sphecotheres hypoleucus*	DD	—	Lowlands	Monsoon forest, scrub
Timor Figbird *Sphecotheres viridis*[1]	lc	—	Lowlands	Monsoon forest, scrub

Global status (see p. 679 for definitions)

EX Extinct } with year
EW Extinct in } of last
    the Wild } record
CR Critical } threatened
EN Endangered } species
VU Vulnerable }

cd Conservation Dependent
nt Near Threatened
lc Least Concern
DD Data Deficient
NE Not Evaluated

Other EBAs (and SAs) (see p. 83 for locations)
Bracketed numbers are Secondary Areas. ˣ Extinct in that EBA or SA.

Notes
[1] The Timor form is here treated as a full species following Andrew (1992), contra Sibley and Monroe (1990, 1993) who considered it to be a form of the widespread Australasian *Sphecotheres viridis* complex.

The main habitats of the restricted-range species are deciduous monsoon forest and woodland and semi-evergreen rain forest; the exception to this is *Padda fuscata* which is mainly a bird of open country areas. Some of the forest birds appear to be restricted to closed-canopy habitat, but many occur additionally in open woodland, savanna, scrub and agricultural land. Most of them occupy a wide altitudinal range, but a few seem to be confined to the lowlands, and *Ducula cineracea* and *Zoothera dohertyi* are restricted to montane forest. Most of the restricted-range species have been recorded on Timor, and seven are endemic to that island, but three species are confined to the smaller island of Wetar.

R. Noske

Black-banded Flycatcher *Ficedula timorensis* is one of seven species which are known only from the island of Timor.

■ Threats and conservation

On Timor, most forest in the coastal lowlands and in broad valleys has already been cleared, and denuded grassy areas now extend far into the hills (FAO 1982c, White and Bruce 1986). The monsoon forests are reduced to scattered patches (RePPProT 1990, Collins *et al.* 1991), with large areas converted to savanna, as a result of clearance for agriculture and fires (either deliberate or accidental) which increase fodder production for livestock (Whitten and Whitten 1992). In western Timor there are about seven significant forest remnants, all relatively small (the largest is c.90 km²), isolated and unmanaged, and most are grazed by cattle and other ungulates (Noske and Saleh 1993). Several areas of montane forest remain, for example on Mt Mutis, although some deforestation has occurred there (N. Bostock *in litt.* 1993). However, it is possible that forest cover on Timor may now largely have stabilized (D. A. Holmes *in litt.* 1993), although forest does continue to be degraded. Extensive forests remain in the north-west of Wetar, but the status of habitats elsewhere on the island is unknown (K. D. Bishop *in litt.* 1990, F. R. Lambert *in litt.* 1994).

Most of the restricted-range species must have declined as a result of this widespread forest loss, but many of them appear able to maintain healthy populations in the remaining forest fragments in western Timor or are adaptable to man-modified habitats. Five of the restricted-range species are classified as

Distribution patterns of restricted-range species

Species (ordered geographically)	Sawu	Roti	Semau	Timor	Wetar	Other EBAs, SAs
Dicaeum maugei	●	●	●	●	–	●
Gerygone inornata	●	●	–	●	●	–
Treron psittacea	–	●	●	●	●	–
Saxicola gutturalis	–	●	●	●	–	–
Padda fuscata	–	●	●	●	–	–
Aprosmictus jonquillaceus	–	●	–	●	●	–
Oriolus melanotis	–	●	●	●	●	–
Nectarinia solaris	–	●	●	●	●	●
Meliphaga reticulata	–	–	●	●	●	–
Cyornis hyacinthinus	–	–	●	●	●	–
Ducula rosacea	–	–	●	●	●	●
Buettikoferella bivittata	–	–	–	●	–	–
Ficedula timorensis	–	–	–	●	–	–
Heleia muelleri	–	–	–	●	–	–
Myzomela vulnerata	–	–	–	●	–	–
Lichmera flavicans	–	–	–	●	–	–
Philemon inornatus	–	–	–	●	–	–
Sphecotheres viridis	–	–	–	●	–	–
Zoothera dohertyi	–	–	–	●	–	●
Phylloscopus presbytes	–	–	–	●	–	●
Turacoena modesta	–	–	–	●	●	–
Gallicolumba hoedtii	–	–	–	●	●	–
Ducula cineracea	–	–	–	●	●	–
Psitteuteles iris	–	–	–	●	●	–
Pachycephala orpheus	–	–	–	●	●	–
Macropygia magna	–	–	–	●	●	●
Trichoglossus euteles	–	–	–	●	●	●
Todirhamphus australasia	–	–	–	●	●	●
Zoothera peronii	–	–	–	●	●	●
Urosphena subulata	–	–	–	●	●	●
Erythrura tricolor	–	–	–	●	●	●
Myzomela kuehni	–	–	–	–	●	–
Lichmera notabilis	–	–	–	–	●	–
Sphecotheres hypoleucus	–	–	–	–	●	–
Lichmera squamata	–	–	–	–	●	●
Total	2	8	9	31	21	

● Present	? Present?	Threatened spp. shown in **bold**	see 'Status and habitat' table
O Extinct?	R Reintroduced	Other EBAs, SAs	
X Extinct	I Introduced		

Orange-banded Thrush *Zoothera peronii* occurs in monsoon forest in this EBA and on several of the Banda Sea islands (EBA 165).

species endemic to Wetar are treated as Data Deficient because of the paucity of information on their conservation status. A more widespread threatened species (found throughout much of Wallacea) which occurs in the EBA is Yellow-crested Cockatoo *Cacatua sulphurea* (classified as Endangered), which is declining throughout its range because of a combination of habitat loss and unsustainable levels of trapping for the bird trade.

There are several gazetted protected areas on Timor, but all are relatively small, and there are no reserves on Wetar or the other islands. Proposed protected areas are Gunung Timo, Dataran Bena, Gunung Mutis, Gunung Tilomor, Gunung Talamailu, Sungai Clere, Lore and Danau Ira Lalora–Pulau Yaco on Timor, Tanjung Pukuatu/Bakauherlu on Roti, and Gunung Arnau on Wetar (FAO 1982c, Sujatnika and Jepson 1995); however, these proposals are based on field surveys carried out 15 years ago, so new surveys are a high priority. Gunung Mutis is currently in the process of being established as a reserve under a PHPA/WWF project (Sujatnika *et al.* 1995). The forests at Bipolo, Buraen, Camplong and Soe in western Timor are also important for many of the restricted-range bird species (Noske and Saleh 1993).

threatened, including those which appear to be particularly rare or to have declined as a result of the forest clearance and fragmentation, and possibly also hunting for food (Noske and Saleh 1993). The three

165 Banda Sea islands

PRIORITY
HIGH

Key habitats Monsoon forest, tropical semi-evergreen rain forest, mangroves, scrub

Main threats Unquantified habitat loss (e.g due to agriculture)

Biological importance ● ●

Current threat level ●

Area 7,100 km² **Altitude** 0–850 m

Countries Indonesia

Restricted-range species	Threatened	Total
Confined to this EBA	1	18
Present also in other EBAs, SAs	0	23
Total	1	41

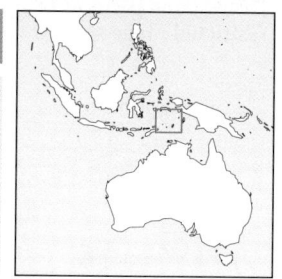

■ General characteristics

This EBA includes the many small, scattered, oceanic islands and island groups which span almost 1,000 km of the eastern edge of the Banda Sea in southern Maluku province of Indonesia. There are two main chains of islands: one runs south-eastwards from near Seram (EBA 170) to the Kai and Tanimbar islands, and from there westwards towards Timor (EBA 164), including Babar, Sermata and Leti; the second is a chain of volcanic islands known as the Banda arc, which runs south-westwards from the

Banda Islands (which lie to the south of Seram) towards Wetar (also EBA 164), including Damar and Romang. Unlike the volcanic Banda arc, the Tanimbar and Kai islands are composed of limestone, and almost flat, with the exception of Kai Besar which is long, narrow and hilly. Many of the islands in the Banda arc are mountainous, but they reach a maximum altitude of only c.850 m (on Damar).

This part of Indonesia is affected by the Australian rain-shadow, so the climate is relatively dry, with markedly seasonal rainfall. The natural vegetation

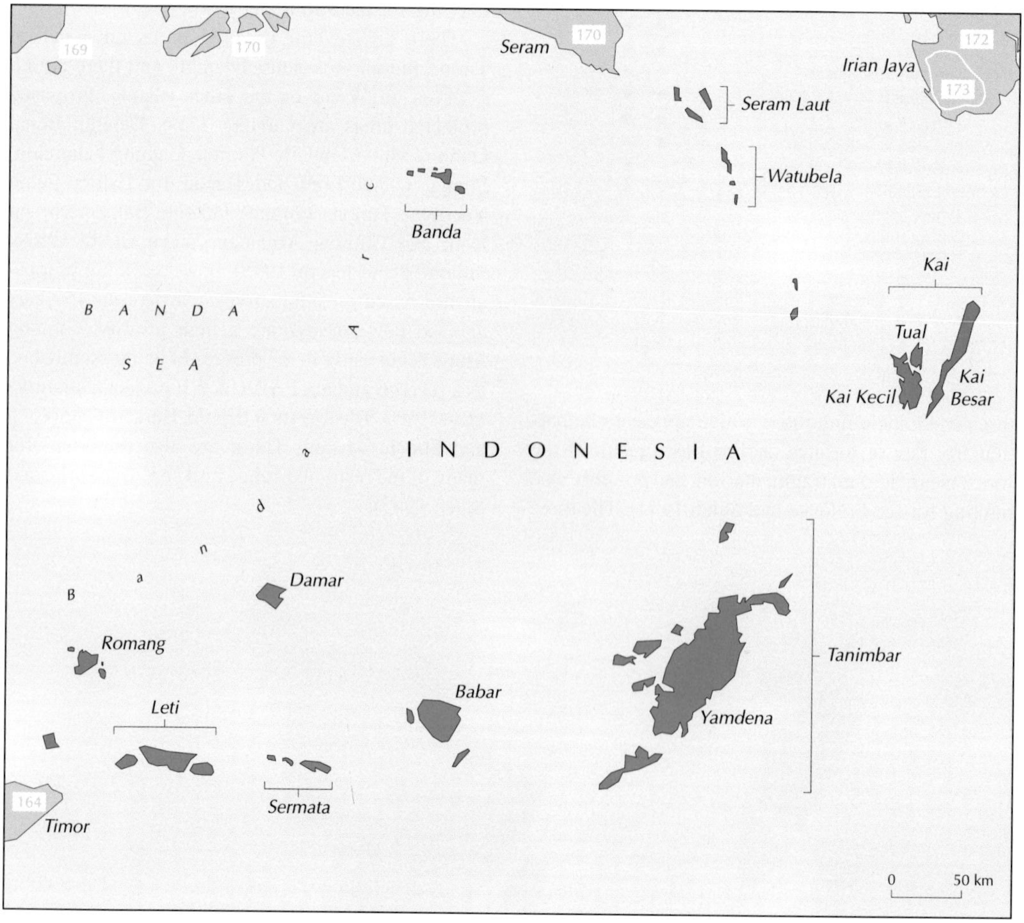

Status and habitat of restricted-range species

Species (ordered taxonomically)	Global status	Other EBAs (and SAs)	Habitat
Dusky Cuckoo-dove *Macropygia magna*	lc	162,164 (s110)	Monsoon forest, agricultural land
Wallace's Fruit-dove *Ptilinopus wallacii*	lc	179 (s112)	Forest, scrub, agricultural land
Elegant Imperial-pigeon *Ducula concinna*	lc	166,167,169,170, 172 (s110,s111,s112)	Forest on small islands
Pink-headed Imperial-pigeon *Ducula rosacea*	lc	162,164,171 (s107, s108,s109,s110,s111)	Forest, scrub and agricultural land on small islands
Red Lory *Eos bornea*	lc	169,170	Forest, mangroves, flowering trees
Blue-streaked Lory *Eos reticulata*[1]	nt	—	Forest, coconut plantations, mangroves
Olive-headed Lorikeet *Trichoglossus euteles*	lc	162,164	Mostly on rather arid islands with little forest, sometimes agricultural land
Tanimbar Cockatoo *Cacatua goffini*	nt	—	Forest, agricultural land
Green-cheeked Bronze-cuckoo *Chrysococcyx rufomerus*	DD	—	Small islands
Pied Bronze-cuckoo *Chrysococcyx crassirostris*[2]	lc	—	Small islands
Kai Coucal *Centropus spilopterus*	nt	—	Open forest, grassland, agricultural land
Lesser Masked-owl *Tyto sororcula*	DD	169	Presumably forest
Moluccan Hawk-owl *Ninox squamipila*	lc	169,170,171	Forest, thickets
Cinnamon-banded Kingfisher *Todirhamphus australasia*	nt	162,163,164	Monsoon forest
Kai Cicadabird *Coracina dispar*	nt	—	Forest on small islands
Slaty-backed Thrush *Zoothera schistacea*	nt	—	Forest
Orange-banded Thrush *Zoothera peronii*	nt	164	Forest
Fawn-breasted Thrush *Zoothera machiki*	nt	—	Forest, scrub
Timor Stubtail *Urosphena subulata*	nt	164	Forest, scrub, long grass
Tanimbar Bush-warbler *Cettia carolinae*	nt	—	Forest
Rufous-sided Gerygone *Gerygone dorsalis*	lc	(s110)	Forest, dry scrub, mangroves, agricultural land
Golden-bellied Flyrobin *Microeca hemixantha*	nt	—	Forest, mangroves
Cinnamon-chested Flycatcher *Ficedula buruensis*	lc	169,170	Forest
Damar Flycatcher *Ficedula henrici*	VU	—	Presumably forest
White-naped Monarch *Monarcha pileatus*	lc	169,171	Forest
Black-bibbed Monarch *Monarcha mundus*	nt	—	Forest, mangroves
White-tailed Monarch *Monarcha leucurus*	nt	—	Forest

cont.

Status and habitat of restricted-range species (cont.)

Species (ordered taxonomically)	Global status	Other EBAs (and SAs)	Habitat
Dark-grey Flycatcher *Myiagra galeata*	lc	169,170,171	Mangroves, forest, scrub, coconut plantations
Cinnamon-tailed Fantail *Rhipidura fuscorufa*	nt	—	Forest, mangroves, agricultural land
Long-tailed Fantail *Rhipidura opistherythra*	nt	—	Forest, mangroves, thickets
Island Whistler *Pachycephala phaionotus*	lc	171,172,174 (s112)	Mangroves, coastal scrub
Drab Whistler *Pachycephala griseonota*	lc	168,169,170, 171	Forest, mangroves
Ashy Flowerpecker *Dicaeum vulneratum*	lc	170	Forest, plantations, agricultural land, gardens
Red-chested Flowerpecker *Dicaeum maugei*	lc	162,164 (s110)	Open forest
Pearl-bellied White-eye *Zosterops grayi*	nt	—	Forest
Golden-bellied White-eye *Zosterops uropygialis*	nt	—	Forest, cleared land with scattered trees
White-tufted Honeyeater *Lichmera squamata*	lc	164	Mangroves, forest, scrub, agricultural land
Black-faced Friarbird *Philemon moluccensis*	lc	169	Forest, mangroves, agricultural land
Tricoloured Parrotfinch *Erythrura tricolor*	lc	164	Agricultural land, thickets
Tanimbar Starling *Aplonis crassa*	nt	—	Forest, mangroves
Black-eared Oriole *Oriolus bouroensis*	lc	169	Forest, mangroves

Global status (see p. 679 for definitions)

EX	Extinct	cd	Conservation Dependent
EW	Extinct in the Wild	nt	Near Threatened
CR	Critical	lc	Least Concern
EN	Endangered	DD	Data Deficient
VU	Vulnerable	NE	Not Evaluated

EX Extinct / EW Extinct in the Wild — with year of last record

CR Critical / EN Endangered / VU Vulnerable — threatened species

Other EBAs (and SAs) (see p. 83 for locations)
Bracketed numbers are Secondary Areas.
x Extinct in that EBA or SA.

Notes

[1] There is a possible sight record from Wetar (EBA 164) (White and Bruce 1986).

[2] The limits of the breeding range and the migratory movements of this species are not fully understood; there are unconfirmed records from Northern Maluku (EBA 171) and a single record from western New Guinea (White and Bruce 1986).

includes both semi-evergreen rain forest and monsoon forest, with mangroves along the coast (Whitmore 1984, White and Bruce 1986).

■ Restricted-range species

The small oceanic islands in this EBA are generally poor in diversity of birds, but the level of endemism is remarkably high. The patterns in the distribution of the restricted-range species are complex, perhaps reflecting the random element in their colonization of the islands in the past. Although they are included in this single EBA, it should be noted that several parts of the EBA are important in their own right, as they support their own endemic species, most notably the Tanimbar and Kai island groups. More than half of the restricted-range species of this EBA are shared with other EBAs and Secondary Areas in Maluku and the Lesser Sunda Islands.

The distribution and habitat requirements of the birds of this EBA are poorly known, as some of the smaller islands have seldom, if ever, been visited by ornithologists, and even the larger island groups have only been visited on a handful of occasions. However, it is clear that almost all of the restricted-range species are forest birds, although many of them appear able to adapt to man-modified habitats.

Some of the restricted-range species are confined to single islands or island groups. The seven species which are endemic to the Tanimbar group, including the recently described *Cettia carolinae* (Rozendaal 1987), were all found to be widespread and numerous on the main island of Yamdena by a PHPA/BirdLife International survey team in 1993 (Cahyadin 1993, Y. Cahyadin and N. Brickle verbally 1993),

Distribution patterns of restricted-range species

Species (ordered geographically)	Romang	Leti	Sermata	Babar	Damar	Tanimbar	Kai	Seram Laut, Watubela, Banda	Other EBAs, SAs
Chrysococcyx rufomerus	●	●	●	–	●	–	–	–	–
Zoothera peronii	●	–	–	●	●	–	–	–	●
Dicaeum maugei	●	●	–	●	●	–	–	–	●
Trichoglossus euteles	●	●	●	●	●	–	–	–	●
Erythrura tricolor	●	–	–	●	●	●	–	–	●
Macropygia magna	●	●	●	●	–	–	–	–	●
Todirhamphus australasia	●	●	●	●	●	–	–	–	●
Pachycephala griseonota	●	●	●	●	●	–	–	–	●
Ducula rosacea	●	●	●	●	●	●	–	–	●
Gerygone dorsalis	●	●	●	●	●	●	–	–	●
Lichmera squamata	●	●	●	●	●	●	●	–	●
Coracina dispar	●	–	–	–	●	●	●	●	–
Ducula concinna	●	●	–	●	●	●	●	●	●
Urosphena subulata	–	–	–	●	–	●	–	–	●
Eos reticulata	–	–	–	●	I	●	I	–	–
Rhipidura fuscorufa	–	–	–	–	●	●	–	–	–
Monarcha mundus	–	–	–	●	●	●	–	–	–
Chrysococcyx crassirostris	–	–	●	●	●	●	–	–	●
Ptilinopus wallacii	–	–	–	●	●	●	–	●	●
Ficedula henrici	–	–	–	●	–	–	–	–	–
Cacatua goffini	–	–	–	–	●	●	I	–	–
Zoothera schistacea	–	–	–	–	●	●	–	–	–
Zoothera machiki	–	–	–	–	●	●	–	–	–
Cettia carolinae	–	–	–	–	●	●	–	–	–
Microeca hemixantha	–	–	–	–	●	●	–	–	–
Rhipidura opistherythra	–	–	–	–	●	●	–	–	–
Aplonis crassa	–	–	–	–	●	●	–	–	●
Tyto sororcula	–	–	–	–	●	●	–	–	●
Ninox squamipila	–	–	–	–	●	●	●	–	●
Oriolus bouroensis	–	–	–	–	●	●	●	–	●
Monarcha pileatus	–	–	–	–	●	●	●	–	●
Philemon moluccensis	–	–	–	–	●	●	●	–	●
Centropus spilopterus	–	–	–	–	●	●	–	–	–
Monarcha leucurus	–	–	–	–	–	●	–	–	–
Zosterops grayi	–	–	–	–	–	●k	–	–	–
Zosterops uropygialis	–	–	–	–	–	●B	–	–	–
Ficedula buruensis	–	–	–	–	–	●	–	–	●
Eos bornea	–	–	–	–	–	●	●	I	●
Myiagra galeata	–	–	–	–	–	●	●	–	●
Pachycephala phaionotus	–	–	–	–	–	●	–	●	●
Dicaeum vulneratum	–	–	–	–	–	–	●	–	●
Total	13	10	6	16	14	26	18	5	4

● Present	? Present?	Threatened spp. shown in **bold**
O Extinct?	R Reintroduced	Other EBAs, SAs
X Extinct	I Introduced	
k Kai Kecil only	B Kai Besar and Tual only	

see 'Status and habitat' table

since it was discovered in 1899, and *Chrysococcyx rufomerus*, only known from the small islands in the south-west of this EBA, has probably also not been recorded during the twentieth century.

Five taxa confined to this EBA—White-browed Triller *Lalage (atrovirens) moesta*, Loetoe Monarch *Monarcha (pileatus) castus*, Wallacean Whistler *Pachycephala (griseonota) arctitorquis*, Banda Myzomela *Myzomela (dibapha) boiei* and Grey Friarbird *Philemon (citreogularis) kisserensis*—were considered by Sibley and Monroe (1990, 1993) to be full species but are treated here as forms of more widespread species, as indicated (following Andrew 1992)—though *M. pileatus* remains a restricted-range species. Jones *et al.* (1995b) considered Tanimbar Megapode *Megapodius tenimberensis*, another taxon endemic to the Tanimbar group, to be a full species, but it is here treated as a form of the more widespread Orange-footed Scrubfowl *M. reinwardt*, following Andrew (1992) and Sibley and Monroe (1990, 1993).

■ Threats and conservation

In the Tanimbar group, the main island of Yamdena remains well forested, with clearance for agriculture mainly confined to a narrow strip along the coast, although the south of the island is covered by a logging concession (Cahyadin 1993, Sujatnika *et al.* 1995). In the Kai group, Kai Kecil and Tual are much more developed than Tanimbar, and the narrow, rugged Kai Besar appears to be almost completely covered in coconut plantations; however, a number of patches of natural forest remain on all of these islands, including some substantial blocks in the more remote areas (Lewis 1993, N. Bostock *in litt.* 1993; see Collins *et al.* 1991). Information on the status of the forest on many of the other islands in the EBA is scant, but it is reported that extensive forests remain on Damar (S. van Balen *in litt.* 1994). *Ficedula henrici* is the only species of this EBA which is threatened, because of its tiny range, although two other particularly poorly known species are classified as Data Deficient.

There are several small gazetted protected areas in this EBA, but the only ones which are likely to be important for the restricted-range species are the small Nustaram and Pulau Nuswotar Nature Reserves in the Tanimbar islands, and Gunung Api Banda Nature Reserve. New protected areas which have been proposed to fill important gaps in coverage of this EBA are Yamdena (Jepson 1995), Kai Besar, Pulau Damar and Pulau Babar (FAO 1982d, Sujatnika and Jepson 1995). However, these proposals do not include the island of Kai Kecil, which has an endemic white-eye.

although they did not record *Tyto sororcula*, which is only known from Tanimbar and Buru (EBA 169); however, one was seen on Yamdena in 1996 (Robson 1996). The four species which are endemic to the Kai group—including *Zosterops uropygialis* which is only known from Kai Besar and Tual and *Zosterops grayi* which is confined to Kai Kecil—also appear to be numerous in the remaining forests on the islands, and able to persist in disturbed forest (Lewis 1993, Robson 1994, K. D. Bishop *in litt.* 1989, N. Bostock *in litt.* 1993). *Ficedula henrici*, a single-island endemic on Damar, has apparently not been recorded

166 Sulawesi

PRIORITY HIGH

Key habitats Tropical lowland rain forest, tropical montane forest, scrub

Main threats Moderate habitat loss (e.g. due to agriculture, commercial logging)

Biological importance ● ● ○
Current threat level ● ○ ○

Area 190,000 km²   **Altitude** 0–3,400 m

Countries Indonesia

Restricted-range species	Threatened	Total
Confined to this EBA	5	42
Present also in other EBAs, SAs	1	12
Total	6	54

■ General characteristics

The large Indonesian island of Sulawesi and a few smaller associated islands constitute this EBA, which includes the provinces of Sulawesi Utara, Sulawesi Tengah, Sulawesi Selatan and Sulawesi Tenggara. Sulawesi is a curious shape, with a relatively small central portion from which four long peninsulas

radiate. It is mountainous virtually throughout, with extensive montane areas above 1,000 m on all four peninsulas and in the centre of the island, and few extensive low-lying areas. The highest peak, Mt Rantemario, rises to 3,455 m.

Sulawesi experiences high temperatures and rainfall throughout the year, and the natural vegetation in

Status and habitat of restricted-range species

Species (ordered taxonomically)	Global status	Other EBAs (and SAs)	Altitude (m)	Habitat
Small Sparrowhawk *Accipiter nanus*	nt	—	900–2,000	Montane forest
Maleo *Macrocephalon maleo*	VU	—	0–1,200	Lowland and montane forest; lays eggs in volcanic soil and coastal beaches
Snoring Rail *Aramidopsis plateni*	VU	—	Lowlands, mountains	Forest
Bald-faced Rail *Gymnocrex rosenbergii*	VU	168	0–800	Lowland forest
Isabelline Waterhen *Amaurornis isabellinus*	lc	—	0–800	Mixed scrub and grassland, *Imperata* grassland, agricultural land
Sulawesi Woodcock *Scolopax celebensis*	nt	—	1,700–2,300	Montane forest
Sulawesi Ground-dove *Gallicolumba tristigmata*	lc	—	0–2,250	Lowland and montane forest
Red-eared Fruit-dove *Ptilinopus fischeri*	lc	—	(1,000–) 2,000–3,000	Montane forest
Maroon-chinned Fruit-dove *Ptilinopus subgularis*	lc	168	0–600	Lowland forest
White-bellied Imperial-pigeon *Ducula forsteni*	lc	—	300–1,500 (–2,000)	Lowland and montane forest
Grey-headed Imperial-pigeon *Ducula radiata*	lc	—	<600–2,400	Montane forest
Elegant Imperial-pigeon *Ducula concinna*	lc	165,167,169,170, 172 (s110,s111,s112)	Lowlands	Forest on small islands
White Imperial-pigeon *Ducula luctuosa*	lc	168	0–300	Open lowland forest, woodland, agricultural land
Sombre Pigeon *Cryptophaps poecilorrhoa*	nt	—	1,500–2,000	Montane forest
Yellow-and-green Lorikeet *Trichoglossus flavoviridis*	lc	168	500–2,000	Lowland and montane forest
Yellowish-breasted Racquet-tail *Prioniturus flavicans*	nt	—	0–1,000	Lowland forest
Red-billed Hanging-parrot *Loriculus exilis*	lc	—	0–800	Lowland forest, mangroves, flowering trees
Sulawesi Hawk-cuckoo *Cuculus crassirostris*	lc	—	500–1,400	Lowland and montane forest
Minahassa Masked-owl *Tyto inexspectata*	DD	—	100–1,500	Lowland and montane forest
Ochre-bellied Hawk-owl *Ninox ochracea*	lc	—	0–800	Lowland forest
Satanic Eared-nightjar *Eurostopodus diabolicus*	VU	—	c.250	Presumably forest
Sulawesi Kingfisher *Ceyx fallax*	lc	167	0–1,000	Lowland forest
Lilac-cheeked Kingfisher *Cittura cyanotis*	lc	167	0–1,000	Lowland forest
Green-backed Kingfisher *Actenoides monachus*	lc	—	0–900	Lowland forest
Scaly Kingfisher *Actenoides princeps*	lc	—	(250–) 900–2,000	Montane forest
Purple-bearded Bee-eater *Meropogon forsteni*	lc	—	0–2,000	Lowland and montane forest, forest edge and clearings
Cerulean Cuckoo-shrike *Coracina temminckii*	lc	—	100–2,200	Lowland and montane forest
Pied Cuckoo-shrike *Coracina bicolor*	nt	167	0–500	Lowland forest, scrub, mangroves

cont.

Status and habitat of restricted-range species (cont.)

Species (ordered taxonomically)	Global status	Other EBAs (and SAs)	Altitude (m)	Habitat
Pygmy Cuckoo-shrike *Coracina abbotti*	lc	—	1,500–2,300	Montane forest
Geomalia *Geomalia heinrichi*	nt	—	1,700–3,400	Montane forest
Red-backed Thrush *Zoothera erythronota*	nt	168	0–1,000	Lowland forest
Sulawesi Thrush *Cataponera turdoides*	lc	—	1,100–2,400	Montane forest
Great Shortwing *Heinrichia calligyna*	lc	—	1,500–3,400	Montane forest
Malia *Malia grata*	lc	—	1,100–2,500	Montane forest
Chestnut-backed Bush-warbler *Bradypterus castaneus*	lc	169,170	(500–) 1,000–3,400	Montane forest, grassland
Sulawesi Leaf-warbler *Phylloscopus sarasinorum*	lc	—	>1,100	Montane forest
Rufous-throated Flycatcher *Ficedula rufigula*	nt	—	0–1,000	Lowland forest
Lompobattang Flycatcher *Ficedula bonthaina*	EN	—	>1,000	Montane forest
Matinan Flycatcher *Cyornis sanfordi*	VU	—	>1,400	Montane forest
Blue-fronted Flycatcher *Cyornis hoevelli*	lc	—	1,400–2,000	Montane forest
Rusty-bellied Fantail *Rhipidura teysmanni*	lc	168	(600–) 1,000–2,300	Montane forest
Olive-flanked Whistler *Hylocitrea bonensis*	lc	—	>1,200	Montane forest
Maroon-backed Whistler *Coracornis raveni*	lc	—	1,600–2,200	Montane forest
Sulphur-bellied Whistler *Pachycephala sulfuriventer*	lc	—	1,000–2,500	Montane forest
Crimson-crowned Flowerpecker *Dicaeum nehrkorni*	lc	—	700–2,600	Montane forest
Pale-bellied White-eye *Zosterops consobrinorum*	nt	—	0–800	Lowland forest, woodland, scrub
Lemon-throated White-eye *Zosterops anomalus*	nt	—	0–1,350	Dry scrub, agricultural land
Streaky-headed White-eye *Lophozosterops squamiceps*	lc	—	1,000–2,500	Montane forest
Dark-eared Myza *Myza celebensis*	lc	—	1,300–2,500	Montane forest
White-eared Myza *Myza sarasinorum*	lc	—	1,700–2,800	Montane forest
Mountain Serin *Serinus estherae*	lc	154,158,160	1,900–3,000	Montane forest, forest edge, alpine scrub and meadows, conifer plantations
Sulawesi Myna *Basilornis celebensis*	lc	—	0–1,200	Lowland forest, woodland
Fiery-browed Myna *Enodes erythrophris*	lc	—	500–2,000	Lowland and montane forest
Sulawesi Drongo *Dicrurus montanus*	lc	—	550–1,800	Lowland and montane forest

Global status (see p. 679 for definitions)
EX   Extinct ⎫ with year
EW   Extinct in ⎬ of last
the Wild ⎭ record

CR   Critical ⎫ threatened
EN   Endangered ⎬ species
VU   Vulnerable ⎭

cd   Conservation Dependent
nt   Near Threatened
lc   Least Concern

DD   Data Deficient
NE   Not Evaluated

Other EBAs (and SAs) (see p. 83 for locations): bracketed numbers are Secondary Areas; ˣ extinct in that EBA or SA.

most parts of the island is tropical lowland evergreen or semi-evergreen rain forest below about 1,000 m, tropical lower montane rain forest between about 1,000 and 2,100 m, and tropical upper montane rain forest between about 2,100 and 3,250 m. The boundary between lowland and montane habitats is represented on the map by the 1,000 m contour. There are some extensive areas of forest on ultrabasic soils on the east and south-east peninsulas and forest on limestone in many parts of the island. Monsoon forest is found in a few parts of the EBA, for example near the tip of the south-east peninsula (Whitmore 1984, Whitten *et al.* 1987c).

■ Restricted-range species

Sulawesi has a relatively depauperate avifauna, with about 120 fewer species than the smaller island of Java, but a high degree of endemism, a result of long isolation from continental landmasses (Watling 1983, Andrew 1992). The 42 restricted-range species which are endemic to this EBA include a remarkable total of 12 endemic genera: *Macrocephalon, Aramidopsis, Cryptophaps, Meropogon, Cataponera, Geomalia, Heinrichia, Malia, Hylocitrea, Coracornis, Myza* and *Enodes*, plus *Cittura* which only otherwise occurs on Sangihe (EBA 167). An additional 16 species of birds are endemic to the Sulawesi EBA (see White and Bruce 1986, Andrew 1992), but are not considered to have restricted ranges because they are widely distributed throughout the island and have been recorded in a relatively broad range of habitats, often in both the lowlands and the mountains.

Maroon-backed Whistler *Coracornis raveni* belongs to an endemic genus, found only in the montane forests of Sulawesi.

Almost all of the restricted-range species are forest birds, and they are found at all altitudes on the island. Many of these species appear to be patchily distributed on Sulawesi; this is partly a result of uneven coverage by ornithologists, but also a reflec-

Habitat associations of restricted-range species

Lowland habitats	
Macrocephalon maleo	Tyto inexspectata
Gymnocrex rosenbergii	**Eurostopodus diabolicus**
Amaurornis isabellinus	Meropogon forsteni
Ptilinopus subgularis	Coracina temminckii
Ducula concinna	Zosterops anomalus
Ducula luctuosa	
Prioniturus flavicans	Montane forest
Loriculus exilis	
Ninox ochracea	Accipiter nanus
Ceyx fallax	Scolopax celebensis
Cittura cyanotis	Ptilinopus fischeri
Actenoides monachus	Cryptophaps poecilorrhoa
Coracina bicolor	Actenoides princeps
Zoothera erythronota	Coracina abbotti
Ficedula rufigula	Geomalia heinrichi
Zosterops consobrinorum	Cataponera turdoides
Basilornis celebensis	Heinrichia calligyna
	Malia grata
Hill and montane forest	Bradypterus castaneus
	Phylloscopus sarasinorum
Ducula forsteni	**Ficedula bonthaina**
Ducula radiata	**Cyornis sanfordi**
Trichoglossus flavoviridis	Cyornis hoevelli
Cuculus crassirostris	Rhipidura teysmanni
Dicaeum nehrkorni	Hylocitrea bonensis
Enodes erythrophris	Coracornis raveni
Dicrurus montanus	Pachycephala
	sulfuriventer
Lowland and montane	Lophozosterops
forest (or unknown)	squamiceps
Aramidopsis plateni	Myza celebensis
Gallicolumba tristigmata	Myza sarasinorum
	Serinus estherae

Threatened species (Critical, Endangered, Vulnerable) are shown in **bold**; see 'Status and habitat' table.

tion of local variations in forest type related to altitude, climate, soil and landform. Seventeen of the species are apparently restricted to the lowlands, and 23 are restricted to montane forest, which led to Sulawesi formerly being divided into a lowland and a montane EBA (ICBP 1992, Sujatnika *et al.* 1995). However, for consistency with similar situations elsewhere in the world, Sulawesi is treated in the present global analysis as a single EBA.

Several of the restricted-range species appear to be confined to certain parts of the EBA (see 'Distribution patterns' table). In some cases this may be related to the geological history of Sulawesi, which is believed to be the cause of local endemism within the island among the macaques *Macaca* spp. and some insect groups (Whitten *et al.* 1987c). However, it could also be the result of specialized habitat requirements or competitive exclusion (by other closely related species) or might simply reflect gaps in knowledge (as some parts of Sulawesi are very poorly worked by ornithologists, notably the east and south-east peninsulas). *Eurostopodus diabolicus* is only definitely known by the type-specimen, collected on the Minahassa peninsula, although there is a possible sighting from central Sulawesi (King

517

Distribution patterns of restricted-range species

Species (ordered geographically)	Togian Islands	N Sulawesi islands	Minahassa pen.	Central Sulawesi	East peninsula	South-east pen.	South peninsula	Muna, Buton	Other EBAs, SAs
Ducula concinna	●	–	–	–	–	–	–	–	●
Prioniturus flavicans	●	●	●	–	–	–	–	–	–
Coracina bicolor	●	●	●	●	●	●	●	●	●
Cittura cyanotis	–	●	●	●	●	●	–	–	●
Actenoides monachus	–	●	●	●	●	●	●	–	–
Ceyx fallax	–	●	●	●	–	●	●	–	●
Macrocephalon maleo	–	●	●	●	●	●	–	●	–
Basilornis celebensis	–	●	●	●	–	●	●	●	–
Ducula luctuosa	–	●	●	●	–	–	●	●	●
Cyornis sanfordi	–	–	●	–	–	–	–	–	–
Eurostopodus diabolicus	–	–	●	?	–	–	–	–	–
Tyto inexspectata	–	–	●	●	–	–	–	–	–
Ptilinopus subgularis	–	–	●	●	●	–	–	–	●
Aramidopsis plateni	–	–	●	●	–	●	–	–	–
Amaurornis isabellinus	–	–	●	●	–	●	–	–	–
Cryptophaps poecilorrhoa	–	–	●	●	–	●	–	–	–
Loriculus exilis	–	–	●	●	–	●	–	–	–
Meropogon forsteni	–	–	●	●	–	●	–	–	–
Gymnocrex rosenbergii	–	–	●	●	–	●	–	–	●
Scolopax celebensis	–	–	●	●	–	–	●	–	–
Accipiter nanus	–	–	●	●	–	●	●	–	–
Gallicolumba tristigmata	–	–	●	●	–	●	●	–	–
Ducula forsteni	–	–	●	●	–	●	●	–	–
Ducula radiata	–	–	●	●	–	●	●	–	–
Cuculus crassirostris	–	–	●	●	–	●	●	–	–
Actenoides princeps	–	–	●	●	–	●	●	–	–
Coracina abbotti	–	–	●	●	–	●	●	–	–
Geomalia heinrichi	–	–	●	●	–	●	●	–	–
Heinrichia calligyna	–	–	●	●	–	●	●	–	–
Malia grata	–	–	●	●	–	●	●	–	–
Phylloscopus sarasinorum	–	–	●	●	–	●	●	–	–
Ficedula rufigula	–	–	●	●	–	●	●	–	–
Hylocitrea bonensis	–	–	●	●	–	●	●	–	–
Coracornis raveni	–	–	●	●	–	●	●	–	–
Pachycephala sulfuriventer	–	–	●	●	–	●	●	–	–
Dicaeum nehrkorni	–	–	●	●	–	●	●	–	–
Lophozosterops squamiceps	–	–	●	●	–	●	●	–	–
Myza celebensis	–	–	●	●	–	●	●	–	–
Myza sarasinorum	–	–	●	●	–	●	●	–	–
Enodes erythrophris	–	–	●	●	–	●	●	–	–
Dicrurus montanus	–	–	●	●	–	●	●	–	–
Trichoglossus flavoviridis	–	–	●	●	–	●	●	–	●
Zoothera erythronota	–	–	●	●	–	●	●	–	●
Bradypterus castaneus	–	–	●	●	–	●	●	–	●
Rhipidura teysmanni	–	–	●	●	–	●	●	–	●
Ptilinopus fischeri	–	–	●	●	●	●	●	–	–
Coracina temminckii	–	–	●	●	●	●	●	–	–
Ninox ochracea	–	–	●	●	●	●	–	●	–
Serinus estherae	–	–	–	●	–	–	–	–	●
Cataponera turdoides	–	–	–	●	–	●	●	–	–
Cyornis hoevelli	–	–	–	●	–	●	●	–	–
Zosterops consobrinorum	–	–	–	–	–	●	–	●	–
Ficedula bonthaina	–	–	–	–	–	–	●	–	–
Zosterops anomalus	–	–	–	–	–	–	●	–	–
Total	3	8	47	47	9	44	36	6	

● Present	? Present?	Threatened spp. shown in **bold** — see 'Status and habitat' table
○ Extinct?	R Reintroduced	
X Extinct	I Introduced	Other EBAs, SAs

1994). *Cyornis sanfordi* is only recorded from the Minahassa peninsula, *Prioniturus flavicans* from this peninsula and the nearby islands, *Zosterops consobrinorum* from the south-east peninsula and Buton (Wardill 1995), *Z. anomalus* from the south peninsula and *Ficedula bonthaina* from montane

Large areas of lowland forest have been cleared on Sulawesi such as here in the Besoa valley, in Central Sulawesi. The mountains in the background are Lore-Lindu National Park, one of several important large reserves for restricted-range species.

K. D. Bishop

forest on Mt Lompobattang in the south peninsula (which also supports several endemic subspecies of birds: P. Andrew *in litt.* 1992; see Fraser and Henson 1996). Other species known from only a handful of specimens and sight records are *Tyto inexspectata*, *Aramidopsis plateni* and *Gymnocrex rosenbergii*.

■ Threats and conservation

Large tracts of undisturbed forest remain on Sulawesi, and total forest cover is estimated to have been 56.4% in 1988 (RePPProT 1990, Collins *et al.* 1991), although since then some large areas of lowland forest have been cleared (A. J. Whitten *in litt.* 1993). The extinct volcanoes of the south peninsula, including Mt Lompobattang, have resulted in rich volcanic soils, so the lowlands in that part of the island are densely populated and largely deforested. Land clearance for transmigration settlements (and further illegal clearance by some of the settlers) and agricultural projects such as sugar-cane plantations, as well as unsustainable logging, have led to deforestation of the lowlands in many other parts of the EBA (Whitten *et al.* 1987c, Collins *et al.* 1991), so the group of restricted-range species which are found in lowland forest are under the most immediate pressure. Much of the remaining forest is in the hills and mountains, so the montane avifauna of Sulawesi is currently relatively secure.

Six of the restricted-range bird species are threatened, including three which appear to be rare and confined to the lowlands and are likely to be vulnerable to habitat loss, two montane species with particularly small ranges, and *Macrocephalon maleo*,

which lays communally on beaches and in forest clearings and is vulnerable to disturbance at nesting sites and over-exploitation of its eggs, as well as habitat loss. The particularly poorly known *Tyto inexspectata* is treated as Data Deficient. A more widespread threatened species (found throughout much of Wallacea) which occurs in the EBA is Yellow-crested Cockatoo *Cacatua sulphurea* (classified as Endangered), which is declining throughout its range because of a combination of habitat loss and unsustainable levels of trapping for the bird trade (see Cahyadin *et al.* 1994, Wardill 1995).

There are gazetted protected areas in central Sulawesi and on all four peninsulas, including several large reserves such as Dumoga-Bone, Lore-Lindu and Rawa Aopa Watumohai National Parks and Morowali and Pegunungan Feruhumpenai Nature Reserves. Almost all of the restricted-range species have populations in at least one protected area. However, the following sites, mainly areas of undisturbed forest, have been proposed for protection in order to strengthen the network: Mamaju (which contains lowland and coastal forest), Pegunungan Latimojong, Gunung Lompobattang (the only known locality for *Ficedula bonthaina*), Pegunungan Buol Toli Toli, Gunung Sojol and Pegunungan Palu dan Sekitarnya. As a result of a PHPA/ICBP/WWF Maleo Conservation Project in 1990–1991, the following sites have been recommended to be gazetted to protect nesting grounds of *Macrocephalon maleo*: Bakiriang, Buntalo, Sangkup, Molobog, Torosik, Molonggota and Dehua (Tanjung Panjung) (FAO 1982b, Sujatnika and Jepson 1995).

167 Sangihe and Talaud

PRIORITY
CRITICAL

Key habitats Tropical lowland rain forest, tropical montane rain forest

Main threats Major habitat loss (e.g. due to agriculture), trapping for cage-bird trade

Biological importance ● ● ●
Current threat level ● ● ●

Area 1,700 km² **Altitude** 0–1,700 m

Countries Indonesia

Restricted-range species	Threatened	Total
Confined to this EBA	4	5
Present also in other EBAs, SAs	1	5
Total	5	10

■ General characteristics

This Indonesian EBA extends northwards from near the tip of the Minahassa peninsula of northern Sulawesi (EBA 166) towards the southern tip of Mindanao (EBA 154) in the Philippines; it comprises the Sangihe and Talaud island groups and the tiny island of Miangas, all of which are in Sulawesi Utara province. The Sangihe group are mountainous, rising to 1,784 m on Siau and 1,320 m on the main island of Sangihe, but Talaud and Miangas are relatively low-lying. The natural vegetation of the islands is tropical lowland evergreen rain forest, with tropical montane rain forest at the higher altitudes, and probably some areas of forest on limestone (Whitmore 1984). On Sangihe, however, virtually all of the forest has been replaced by coconut and nutmeg plantations and the secondary vegetation of abandoned gardens (Whitten *et al.* 1987c,d).

■ Restricted-range species

The habitat requirements and distributions of the restricted-range species are incompletely known, because the larger islands in the EBA have only been visited by ornithologists on a few occasions, and some of the smaller islands have seldom, if ever, been studied (see White and Bruce 1986, Bishop 1992).

A survey of the main islands in the Sangihe and Talaud groups in 1995 recorded all five species which are confined to the EBA (Riley 1995). Of the three species which are endemic to the Sangihe group, *Loriculus catamene* and *Aethopyga duyvenbodei* were found to be locally common, and birds believed to be *Eutrichomyias rowleyi* (a monotypic genus endemic to the EBA which was feared extinct: Whitten *et al.* 1987c) were found to survive in small numbers in remnant forest patches and adjacent agricultural land and plantations. *Todirhamphus enigma*, which is endemic to Talaud, was found to be common in the forested interior of the main island. *Eos histrio* was recorded in small numbers in forest

Map labels:
Mindanao
PHILIPPINES
Miangas
0 50 km
154
Karakelong
Talaud Islands
Mt Awu
Sangihe
Mt Sahendaruman
Sangihe Islands
Siau
Halmahera
INDONESIA
166
Sulawesi
171

Distribution patterns of restricted-range species

Species (ordered geographically)	Miangas	Talaud islands	Sangihe islands	Other EBAs, SAs
Ducula pickeringii	●	●	–	●
Eos histrio	●	●	●	–
Todirhamphus enigma	–	●	–	–
Ducula concinna	–	●	●	●
Loriculus catamene	–	–	●ˢ	–
Eutrichomyias rowleyi	–	–	●ˢ	–
Aethopyga duyvenbodei	–	–	●	–
Ceyx fallax	–	–	●	●
Cittura cyanotis	–	–	●	●
Coracina bicolor	–	–	●	●
Total	2	4	8	

● Present   ? Present?   Threatened spp. shown in **bold**   } see 'Status and habitat' table
○ Extinct?   R Reintroduced   Other EBAs, SAs
X Extinct   I Introduced
ˢ Single-island endemic to Sangihe

Status and habitat of restricted-range species

Species (ordered taxonomically)	Global status	Other EBAs (and SAs)	Habitat
Elegant Imperial-pigeon *Ducula concinna*	lc	165,166,169,170, 172 (s110,s111,s112)	Forest on small islands
Grey Imperial-pigeon *Ducula pickeringii*	VU	155,156 (s097)	Forest on small islands
Red-and-blue Lory *Eos histrio*	EN	—	Forest, open country, coconut plantations
Sangihe Hanging-parrot *Loriculus catamene*	EN	—	Open country, coconut plantations, forest
Sulawesi Kingfisher *Ceyx fallax*	lc	166	Forest
Lilac-cheeked Kingfisher *Cittura cyanotis*	lc	166	Forest
Talaud Kingfisher *Todirhamphus enigma*	nt	—	All habitats
Pied Cuckoo-shrike *Coracina bicolor*	nt	166	Lowland forest
Cerulean Paradise-flycatcher *Eutrichomyias rowleyi*	CR	—	Forest
Elegant Sunbird *Aethopyga duyvenbodei*	EN	—	Forest, bamboo, scrub

Global status (see p. 679 for definitions)
EX Extinct
EW Extinct in the Wild
⎱ with year of last record

CR Critical
EN Endangered
VU Vulnerable
⎱ threatened species

cd Conservation Dependent
nt Near Threatened
lc Least Concern

DD Data Deficient
NE Not Evaluated

Other EBAs (and SAs) (see p. 83 for locations): bracketed numbers are Secondary Areas; ˣ extinct in that EBA or SA.

and adjacent plantations on Talaud, and a tiny population was found in plantations adjacent to remnant forest patches on Sangihe, where this species was previously feared to be extinct. A form of shrike-thrush *Colluricincla* from Sangihe was provisionally treated as a subspecies of Rufous Shrike-thrush *C. megarhycha* (by, e.g., White and Bruce 1986), but studies since its rediscovery on Mt Sahendaruman in 1986 suggest that it would be better treated as an endemic species (Rozendaal and Lambert in prep.). In 1996, a new taxon of *Gymnocrex* rail was found on Talaud, and this may also prove to be an endemic species (F. Lambert verbally 1997).

■ Threats and conservation

Most of the islands of the EBA were largely deforested by 1920 (Whitten *et al.* 1987c), and the only extensive natural forest now remaining is on Karakelang, the main island of the Talaud group. In the Sangihe group, the only remaining forest on the main island is in mainly secondary patches on Mt Awu and around the peak of Mt Sahendaruman, while little or no forest is believed to exist on the volcanically very active island of Siau (Bishop 1992, Riley 1995, K. D. Bishop *in litt.* 1993).

Five of the restricted-range species are classified as threatened, including four of the five species endemic to the EBA, and the poorly known small island specialist, *Ducula pickeringii*. The main threat to most of these is continuing habitat loss, particularly on Sangihe, but *Eos histrio* is also threatened by illegal trapping for the wild bird trade (Nash 1993, Riley 1995) and possibly by introduced species of parrot (F. Lambert verbally 1997). A more widespread threatened species which occurs on Talaud is Blue-naped Parrot *Tanygnathus lucionensis* (classified as Endangered), which formerly occurred widely in the Philippines but is threatened by habitat loss and heavy trapping for the wild bird trade.

The only protected area in this EBA is Karakelang Hunting Park on Talaud, where site evaluation is required to define boundaries and management needs, and it has been recommended that its status should be changed to Wildlife Sanctuary. On Sangihe, Mt Sahendaruman has been proposed as a new protected area, as it contains one of the few remaining areas of forest on the main island (Sujatnika and Jepson 1995), and several of the restricted-range species were recorded there in 1995 (Riley 1995). However, the area of forest here is small, and there is a need for surveys of both the main island and the smaller islands of the Sangihe group to locate more areas of forest which may be suitable as reserves.

168 Banggai and Sula Islands

PRIORITY HIGH

Key habitats Tropical lowland rain forest, tropical montane rain forest

Main threats Moderate habitat loss (e.g. due to commercial logging, agriculture)

Biological importance ● ● ●
Current threat level ● ● ●

Area 7,200 km² **Altitude** 0–1,600 m

Countries Indonesia

Restricted-range species	Threatened	Total
Confined to this EBA	2	8
Present also in other EBAs, SAs	1	8
Total	3	16

■ General characteristics

This Indonesian EBA includes Peleng and the Banggai Islands in Sulawesi Tengah province, and the Sula Islands (Taliabu, Mangole and Sanana) in western Maluku province. The islands are hilly, but the only significant area of land above 800 m is on Taliabu.

The natural vegetation is tropical semi-evergreen rain forest, with tropical lowland evergreen rain forest in the wetter areas (e.g. northern Peleng: Indrawan *et al.* 1993) and some forest on limestone (Whitmore 1984, Whitten *et al.* 1987c). Taliabu has a large area of tropical montane rain forest above c.800 m (Davidson *et al.* 1995), and small areas of such habitat presumably exist at this altitude on some of the other islands.

■ Restricted-range species

Until recently, the habitat requirements and conservation status of the restricted-range species were very poorly understood, but surveys of Taliabu (Davidson *et al.* 1995) and Peleng and the Banggai Islands (Indrawan *et al.* 1993) have added considerably to what is known. However, Indrawan *et al.* (1993) did not record *Corvus unicolor* (known by

Distribution patterns of restricted-range species

Species (ordered geographically)	Peleng	Banggai Islands	Taliabu	Mangole	Sanana	Other EBAs, SAs
Gymnocrex rosenbergii	●	–	–	–	–	●
Zoothera erythronota	●	–	●	–	–	●
Ptilinopus subgularis	●	●	●	●	–	●
Megapodius bernsteinii	●	●	●	●	●	–
Coracina schistacea	●	●	●	●	●	–
Rhinomyias colonus	●	?	●	●	●	–
Basilornis galeatus	●	●	●	●	●	–
Ducula luctuosa	●	●	●	●	●	●
Loriculus amabilis	●	●	●	●	●	●
Corvus unicolor	–	●	–	–	–	–
Tyto nigrobrunnea	–	–	●	–	–	–
Rhipidura teysmanni	–	–	●	●	–	●
Coracina sula	–	–	●	●	●	–
Streptocitta albertinae	–	–	●	●	●	–
Trichoglossus flavoviridis	–	–	●	●	●	●
Pachycephala griseonota	–	–	●	●	●	●
Total	9	7	14	11	10	

● Present   ? Present?
○ Extinct?   R Reintroduced
X Extinct   I Introduced

Threatened spp. shown in **bold** — see 'Status and habitat' table
Other EBAs, SAs

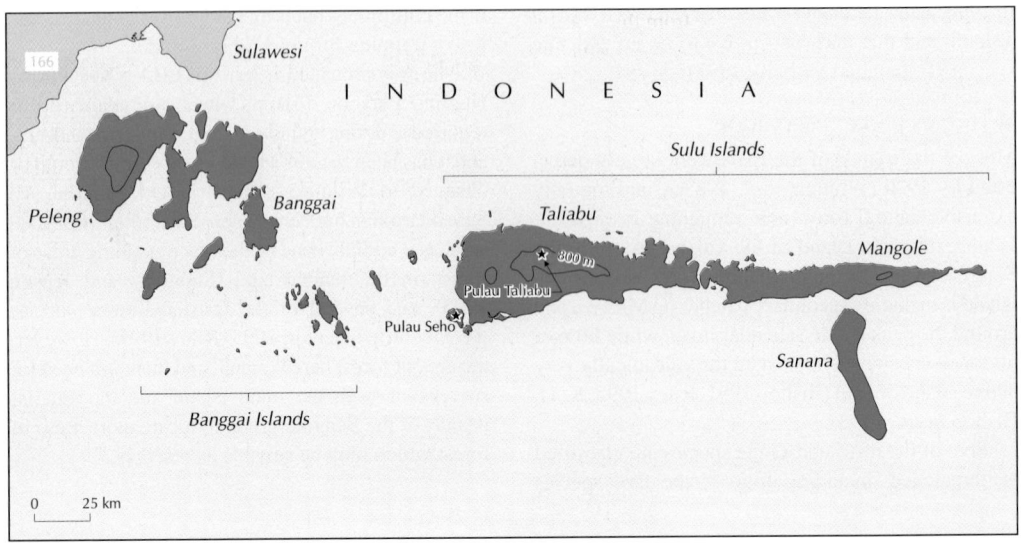

Status and habitat of restricted-range species

Species (ordered taxonomically)	Global status	Other EBAs (and SAs)	Altitude (m)	Habitat
Sula Scrubfowl *Megapodius bernsteinii*	nt	—	Lowlands	Lowland forest, particularly in coastal areas; dense scrub on fringe of agricultural land
Bald-faced Rail *Gymnocrex rosenbergii*	VU	166	Presumably lowlands	Forest
Maroon-chinned Fruit-dove *Ptilinopus subgularis*	lc	166	All altitudes	Lowland forest, less common in montane forest
White Imperial-pigeon *Ducula luctuosa*	lc	166	0–300	Open lowland forest, agricultural land
Yellow-and-green Lorikeet *Trichoglossus flavoviridis*	lc	166	All altitudes	Lowland forest, montane forest
Moluccan Hanging-parrot *Loriculus amabilis*	lc	171	Lowlands	Lowland forest, flowering trees in agricultural land and village gardens
Taliabu Masked-owl *Tyto nigrobrunnea*	VU	—	Lowlands	Lowland forest
Slaty Cuckoo-shrike *Coracina schistacea*	lc	—	All altitudes	Lowland forest, esp. at the edge of agricultural land; much less common in montane forest
Sula Cicadabird *Coracina sula*	lc	—	0–900	Lowland (rarely montane) forest, agricultural land
Red-backed Thrush *Zoothera erythronota*	nt	166	Lowlands	Lowland forest, bamboo in degraded forest
Henna-tailed Jungle-flycatcher *Rhinomyias colonus*	nt	—	0–300	Lowland forest
Rusty-bellied Fantail *Rhipidura teysmanni*	lc	166	Usually >800	Montane forest, very scarce in lowland forest
Drab Whistler *Pachycephala griseonota*	lc	165,169, 170,171	Lowlands	Lowland forest
Helmeted Myna *Basilornis galeatus*	nt	—	0–1,000	Lowland forest, montane forest, tall trees in reedswamps
Bare-eyed Myna *Streptocitta albertinae*	nt	—	0–250	Tall trees in lowland forest and agricultural land
Banggai Crow *Corvus unicolor*	VU	—	No data	No data

Global status (see p. 679 for definitions)	EX EW	Extinct Extinct in the Wild	} with year of last record	CR EN VU	Critical Endangered Vulnerable	} threatened species	cd nt lc	Conservation Dependent Near Threatened Least Concern	DD NE	Data Deficient Not Evaluated

Other EBAs (and SAs) (see p. 83 for locations): bracketed numbers are Secondary Areas; [x] extinct in that EBA or SA.

just two specimens believed to be from the island of Banggai; but see Collar *et al.* 1994) or *Gymnocrex rosenbergii* (known in this EBA by three specimens collected on Peleng). *Tyto nigrobrunnea* is only known from Taliabu by a single specimen collected in 1938 and a sighting in 1991 (Davidson *et al.* 1995).

All the other species are recorded from lowland forest, and some are also found in montane forest on Taliabu; one species, *Rhipidura teysmanni*, is much more common in montane than in lowland forest. Most of these birds can persist in secondary habitats, and some in all but the most degraded areas, including *Coracina schistacea* and *C. sula* (Davidson *et al.* 1995). Of the eight species confined to this EBA, four occur throughout, three are Sula Island endemics, and *Corvus unicolor* is known only from Banggai.

Sula Pitta *Pitta dohertyi*, which is confined to this EBA, was treated as a full species by Sibley and

Sula Scrubfowl *Megapodius bernsteinii* has recently been found to be locally common in lowland forest, particularly near the coast.

Monroe (1990, 1993), but is here considered to be a form of the more widespread Red-bellied Pitta *P. erythrogaster* following Andrew (1992).

■ Threats and conservation

Most of Taliabu retains forest cover, but large-scale logging of lowland forest has taken place, and some areas have been clear-felled for industrial timber production. Most forest below 800 m is now under logging concession, and selective logging has produced a mosaic of different-aged forest stands. There appear to be few, if any, extensive tracts of primary lowland forest left, except perhaps in the central south-west of the island (Davidson *et al.* 1995). Forest on Sanana and Mangole is said to be heavily degraded (Sujatnika *et al.* 1995). On the Banggai Islands (including Peleng), extensive lowland forest remains (RePPProT 1990) but logging has begun in the last areas of primary habitat, which will probably lead to further encroachment of shifting cultivation because of improved access (Indrawan *et al.* 1993).

Three restricted-range species are classified as threatened because they appear particularly rare and are perhaps the most vulnerable to habitat loss. Most of the other restricted-range species survive in logged and secondary forest, but their relative densities and breeding success in primary and secondary lowland forest are still not established, and some may become threatened in the future (Davidson *et al.* 1995).

The only gazetted protected area in the EBA is Pulau Seho Nature Reserve (12.5 km²) on Taliabu. The much larger proposed reserve of Pulau Taliabu (700 km²) would incorporate montane forest in the interior and lowland forest down to the northern shores (FAO 1982d, Sujatnika and Jepson 1995), including populations of all the EBA's endemics except *Corvus unicolor*.

169 Buru

PRIORITY HIGH

Key habitats Tropical lowland rain forest, tropical montane rain forest, monsoon forest

Main threats Limited habitat loss (e.g. due to agriculture, logging)

Biological importance ● ●
Current threat level ●

Area 8,300 km² **Altitude** 0–2,000 m

Countries Indonesia

Restricted-range species	Threatened	Total
Confined to this EBA	5	10
Present also in other EBAs, SAs	1	18
Total	6	28

■ General characteristics

Buru is a mountainous island in Maluku province of Indonesia. It has a rugged topography, and the land is folded into many ridges and deep valleys so that there are several ranges of mountains which rise to heights of over 1,000 m, the tallest being the Kelapatmada range, in the north-west of the island, which has a highest point of 2,429 m.

The island's natural vegetation is largely tropical lowland evergreen and semi-evergreen rain forest, with tropical montane rain forest occurring above an altitude of about 800 m; the exception to this pattern is a distinct zone of monsoon forest in the north and north-east section of the island, where a patchwork of monsoon forest, gallery forest and savannas has developed as a result of repeated burning (Whitmore 1984, White and Bruce 1986, Poulsen in press).

■ Restricted-range species

Ten bird species are endemic to Buru, including the monotypic genus *Madanga*. Until recently ornithologists had rarely visited this EBA, and fewer still had worked the montane regions of the island, but surveys in 1995–1996 by a PHPA/BirdLife International team (sponsored by the British Ornithologists' Union) have added considerably to knowledge of the habitat requirements, altitudinal limits and population densities of the restricted-range species (Poulsen in press). These species have been divided on the basis of habitat as follows: five species which are primarily found in the lowlands, and nine species (including five of the Buru endemics) which are mainly confined to hill and montane forests above about 500 m, plus two species which are too poorly known to classify (see 'Habitat associations' table).

A survey in 1989 recorded six of the Buru endemics, of which *Prioniturus mada*, *Monarcha loricatus*, *Rhipidura superflua* and *Zosterops*

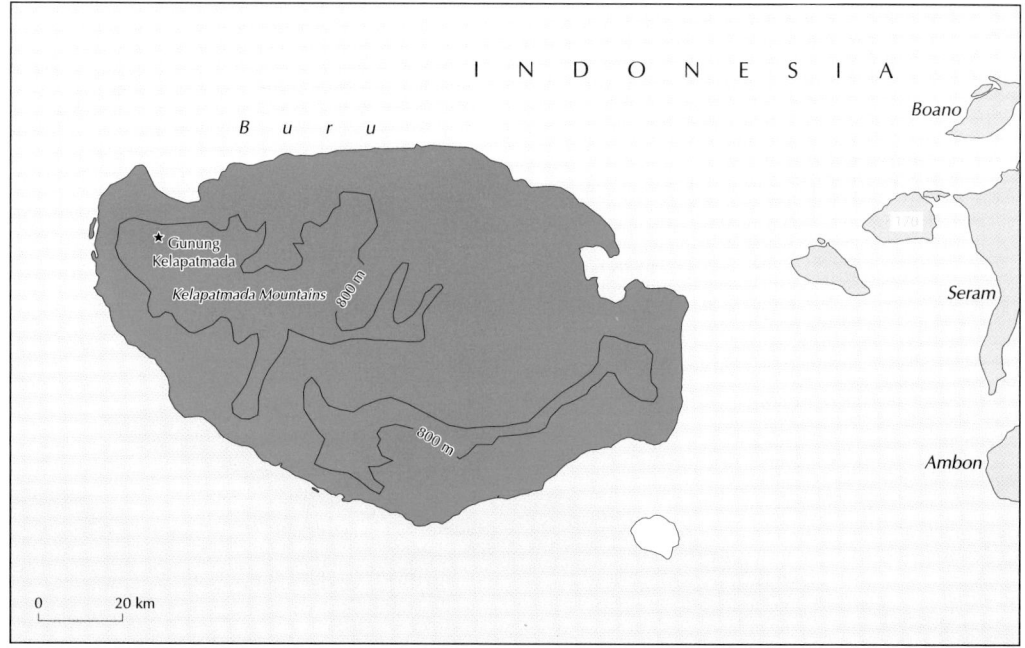

Habitat associations of restricted-range species

Lowland forest	
Ducula concinna	Zosterops buruensis
Ducula perspicillata	Philemon moluccensis
Monarcha pileatus	Oriolus bouroensis
Monarcha loricatus	
Myiagra galeata	**Hill and montane forest**
	Gymnophaps mada
Lowland and montane	***Tanygnathus gramineus***
forest	Zoothera dumasi
Accipiter erythrauchen	Bradypterus castaneus
Megapodius wallacei	***Rhinomyias addita***
Eos bornea	Ficedula buruensis
Prioniturus mada	Rhipidura superflua
Ninox squamipila	***Madanga ruficollis***
Coracina fortis	Lichmera deningeri
Coracina ceramensis	
Pachycephala griseonota	**Unknown**
Dicaeum erythrothorax	***Charmosyna toxopei***
	Tyto sororcula

Threatened species (Critical, Endangered, Vulnerable) are shown in **bold**; see 'Status and habitat' table.

---

buruensis were moderately common, but *Lichmera deningeri* and *Coracina fortis* were uncommon or rare; the other four endemics were not conclusively recorded, mainly because of the limited amount of fieldwork carried out in montane habitats (Jepson 1993). The PHPA/BirdLife International surveys in 1995 and 1996 collected detailed data on the population densities of these species, and recorded two of the other endemic species in the proposed Gunung Kelapatmada Game Reserve in western Buru, both in montane forest and the first records since the 1920s— *Rhinomyias addita* (found to be moderately common) and *Madanga ruficollis* (two birds noted); large parrots heard calling at night in montane forest were almost certainly *Tanygnathus gramineus* (M. K. Poulsen *in litt.* 1995, 1996). The remaining one of the Buru endemics, *Charmosyna toxopei*, was not definitely seen during any of the recent surveys, but interviews with local people suggest that it is probably a lower montane forest species which in some years occurs down in the coastal lowlands (M. K. Poulsen *in litt.* 1996).

Wakolo Myzomela *Myzomela wakoloensis*, a bird which is confined to Buru and Seram (EBA 170), was treated as a full species by Sibley and Monroe (1990, 1993), but it is here considered to be a form of the more widespread Crimson Myzomela *M. dibapha* following Andrew (1992). Another species confined to Buru and Seram, Forsten's Megapode *Megapodius forstenii*, was treated by Jones *et al.* (1995b) as a full species, but is considered here to be a form of the more widespread Orange-footed Scrubfowl *M. reinwardt* following Andrew (1992) and Sibley and Monroe (1990, 1993).

■ Threats and conservation

Most of the coastal lowlands on Buru have now been cleared, and much of the forest surveyed during 1989

Status and habitat of restricted-range species

Speicies (ordered taxonomically)	Global status	Other EBAs (and SAs)	Altitude (m)	Habitat
Rufous-necked Sparrowhawk *Accipiter erythrauchen*	lc	170,171	0–1,400	Lowland and montane forest
Moluccan Scrubfowl *Megapodius wallacei*	VU	170,171	700–1,950 non-breeding	Lowland and montane forest; breeds on coastal beaches
White-eyed Imperial-pigeon *Ducula perspicillata*	lc	170,171	0–1,400	Lowland and montane forest
Elegant Imperial-pigeon *Ducula concinna*[1]	lc	165,166,167,170, 172 (s110,s111,s112)	Lowlands	Forest on small islands
Long-tailed Mountain-pigeon *Gymnophaps mada*	nt	170	<700–2,060	Montane forest
Red Lory *Eos bornea*	lc	165,170	0–1,800	Lowland and montane forest, mangroves, flowering trees
Blue-fronted Lorikeet *Charmosyna toxopei*	VU	—	c.850–1,000	Presumably forest
Buru Racquet-tail *Prioniturus mada*	nt	—	0–1,750	Lowland and montane forest, agricultural land
Black-lored Parrot *Tanygnathus gramineus*	VU	—	600–1,500+	Montane forest
Lesser Masked-owl *Tyto sororcula*	DD	165	Presumably lowlands	Presumably lowland forest
Moluccan Hawk-owl *Ninox squamipila*	lc	165,170,171	0–1,750	Lowland and montane forest, thickets

cont.

Status and habitat of restricted-range species (cont.)

Species (ordered taxonomically)	Global status	Other EBAs (and SAs)	Altitude (m)	Habitat
Buru Cuckoo-shrike *Coracina fortis*	VU	—	0–1,500	Lowland and montane forest, monsoon forest
Pale Cicadabird *Coracina ceramensis*	lc	170,171	0–1,500	Lowland and montane forest, monsoon forest, scrub
Moluccan Thrush *Zoothera dumasi*	DD	170	c.800–1,500	Montane forest
Chestnut-backed Bush-warbler *Bradypterus castaneus*	lc	166,170	>1,000	Montane forest, grassland
Streaky-breasted Jungle-flycatcher *Rhinomyias addita*	VU	—	500–1,500	Lowland and montane forest
Cinnamon-chested Flycatcher *Ficedula buruensis*	lc	165,170	<600–1,500	Lowland and montane forest
White-naped Monarch *Monarcha pileatus*	lc	165,171	Lowlands to 1,100	Lowland and montane forest, transition of swamp forest to agriculture, monsoon forest
Black-tipped Monarch *Monarcha loricatus*	nt	—	0–1,270	Lowland and montane forest, agricultural land
Dark-grey Flycatcher *Myiagra galeata*	lc	165,170,171	0–800	Mangroves, lowland and montane forest, monsoon forest, scrub, coconut plantations
Tawny-backed Fantail *Rhipidura superflua*	nt	—	700–1,750	Montane forest
Drab Whistler *Pachycephala griseonota*	lc	165,168,170, 171	Lowlands to 1,300	Lowland and montane forest, scrub
Flame-breasted Flowerpecker *Dicaeum erythrothorax*	lc	171	0–1,750	Lowland and montane forest, monsoon forest, scrub, riverine habitats, agricultural land
Buru Yellow White-eye *Zosterops buruensis*	lc	—	0–1,750	Lowland and montane forest, scrub
Rufous-throated White-eye *Madanga ruficollis*	VU	—	c.840–1,550	Montane forest
Buru Honeyeater *Lichmera deningeri*	nt	—	800–2,050	Montane forest, scrub
Black-faced Friarbird *Philemon moluccensis*	lc	165	0–1,750	Lowland and montane forest, monsoon forest, mangroves, coconut plantations
Black-eared Oriole *Oriolus bouroensis*	lc	165	0–1,460	Lowland and montane forest, monsoon forest

Global status (see p. 679 for definitions)	EX Extinct EW Extinct in the Wild } with year of last record	cd Conservation Dependent nt Near Threatened	**Other EBAs (and SAs)** (see p. 83 for locations)	Bracketed numbers are Secondary Areas. X Extinct in that EBA or SA.
	CR Critical EN Endangered VU Vulnerable } threatened species	lc Least Concern DD Data Deficient NE Not Evaluated	**Notes**	[1] Only known by a single old record in this EBA, and possibly only a non-breeding visitor (White and Bruce 1986, M. K. Poulsen *in litt.* 1996).

in the northern part of the island had been either selectively logged or disturbed by traditional slash-and-burn agriculture (Jepson 1993) so only a few small patches of primary lowland forest remain (Poulsen in press). The montane forests are still largely undisturbed (FAO 1982d, Poulsen in press).

Six of the restricted-range species of the EBA are classified as threatened: five because they appear to be rare or to have particularly small ranges, and are therefore likely to be vulnerable to habitat loss, and *Megapodius wallacei* because it nests colonially on beaches at a limited number of traditional breeding grounds, and is therefore vulnerable to egg harvest-

ing and disturbance. Two particularly poorly known species are placed in the (non-threatened) Data Deficient category.

There are currently no gazetted protected areas on Buru. The proposed Gunung Kelapatmada Game Reserve in the west of the island includes the Kelapatmada mountains; it extends down to sea-level and up to the highest point on the island (FAO 1982d, Sujatnika and Jepson 1995). The area would contain large areas of both lowland (all now selectively logged) and montane forest which are known to support populations of all except two of Buru's restricted-range species (M. K. Poulsen *in litt.* 1996).

170 Seram

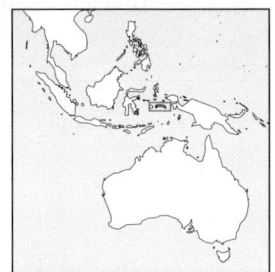

Key habitats Tropical lowland rain forest, tropical montane rain forest

Main threats Limited habitat loss (e.g. due to agriculture), trapping for the cage-bird trade

Biological importance ● ● ○
Current threat level ● ● ○

Area 19,000 km² **Altitude** 0–3,000 m

Countries Indonesia

Restricted-range species	Threatened	Total
Confined to this EBA	4	14
Present also in other EBAs, SAs	1	16
Total	5	30

■ General characteristics

Seram and several smaller associated islands in Maluku province (Indonesia) constitute this EBA. The interior of Seram is mountainous, with several ranges rising to over 1,000 m—and the highest point at Mt Binaiya, part of the central Merkele ridge, reaches 3,027 m (Edwards 1993b). The smaller islands of the EBA are also hilly, but only Ambon rises to an altitude of over 1,000 m. The natural vegetation of Seram is tropical lowland evergreen and semi-evergreen rain forest, with tropical montane rain forest above c.800 m. There are also some areas of forest on limestone and mangroves (Whitmore 1984, Collins *et al.* 1991, Edwards *et al.* 1993).

■ Restricted-range species

The fourteen species which are endemic to this EBA include the monotypic genus *Tephrozosterops*. Survey work during 1987 and 1996 added considerably to knowledge of the habitat requirements and altitudinal limits of most of the restricted-range species, although a few of them remain poorly known, notably *Zoothera dumasi* (Bowler and Taylor 1989, 1993, J. Ekstrom *in litt.* 1997). On habitat they can be subdivided into nine species which are mainly restricted to the lowlands below c.800 m, six which are found in montane forest above c.800 m, 12 which occur in both lowland and montane forest, and a group of three which are mainly recorded from

between about 400 and 1,200 m, where they are presumably associated with the ecotone between lowland and lower montane rain forest.

Eight of the restricted-range species are endemic to Seram alone. *Monarcha boanensis* is only known from Boano, where 5–10 birds were seen in 1994 and the total population was estimated at up to 100–200

Habitat associations of restricted-range species

Lowland forest	
Ducula perspicillata	*Dicaeum vulneratum*
Ducula concinna	*Zosterops kuehni*
Eos bornea	*Myzomela blasii*
Cacatua moluccensis	*Philemon subcorniculatus*
Todirhamphus lazuli	*Oriolus forsteni*
Monarcha boanensis	
Myiagra galeata	**Hill and lower montane forest**
Lichmera argentauris	**Lorius domicella**
Basilornis corythaix	*Ficedula buruensis*
	Tephrozosterops stalkeri
Lowland and montane forest	
Accipiter erythrauchen	**Montane forest**
Megapodius wallacei	*Gymnophaps mada*
Ninox squamipila	*Eos semilarvata*
Coracina atriceps	*Zoothera dumasi*
Coracina ceramensis	*Bradypterus castaneus*
Rhipidura dedemi	*Lophozosterops pinaiae*
Pachycephala griseonota	*Lichmera monticola*

Threatened species (Critical, Endangered, Vulnerable) are shown in **bold**; see 'Status and habitat' table.

Status and habitat of restricted-range species

Species (ordered taxonomically)	Global status	Other EBAs (and SAs)	Altitude (m)	Habitat
Rufous-necked Sparrowhawk *Accipiter erythrauchen*	lc	169,171	0–1,400	Lowland and montane forest
Moluccan Scrubfowl *Megapodius wallacei*	VU	169,171	700–1,950 non-breeding	Lowland and montane forest, breeds on coastal beaches
White-eyed Imperial-pigeon *Ducula perspicillata*	lc	169,171	0–800	Lowland forest
Elegant Imperial-pigeon *Ducula concinna*[1]	lc	165,166,167,169, 172 (s110,s111,s112)	0–850	Lowland forest
Long-tailed Mountain-pigeon *Gymnophaps mada*	nt	169	1,200–2,750	Montane forest
Red Lory *Eos bornea*	lc	165,169	0–900	Lowland forest, mangroves, flowering trees
Blue-eared Lory *Eos semilarvata*	nt	—	(800–)1,200–3,000	Montane forest, tree heath near bare peak
Purple-naped Lory *Lorius domicella*	VU	—	400–1,050	Hill forest
Salmon-crested Cockatoo *Cacatua moluccensis*	VU	—	0–1,100	Lowland forest
Moluccan Hawk-owl *Ninox squamipila*	lc	165,169,171	0–1,750	Lowland and montane forest, thickets
Lazuli Kingfisher *Todirhamphus lazuli*	VU	—	Lowland	Lowland forest, secondary forest in agricultural land
Moluccan Cuckoo-shrike *Coracina atriceps*	lc	171	0–1,200	Lowland and montane forest
Pale Cicadabird *Coracina ceramensis*	lc	169,171	0–1,750	Lowland and montane forest, scrub
Moluccan Thrush *Zoothera dumasi*	DD	169	900–1,280	Montane forest
Chestnut-backed Bush-warbler *Bradypterus castaneus*	lc	166,169	800–1,740	Montane forest, grassland
Cinnamon-chested Flycatcher *Ficedula buruensis*	lc	165,169	(100–)650–850	Montane and lowland forest
Black-chinned Monarch *Monarcha boanensis*	EN	—	c.200–700	Lowland forest
Dark-grey Flycatcher *Myiagra galeata*	lc	165,169,171	0–850	Mangroves, lowland forest, scrub, coconut plantations
Streaky-breasted Fantail *Rhipidura dedemi*	lc	—	100–2,200	Lowland and montane forest
Drab Whistler *Pachycephala griseonota*	lc	165,168, 169,171	0–1,100	Lowland and montane forest
Ashy Flowerpecker *Dicaeum vulneratum*	lc	165	0–1,400 (–2,200)	Lowland and montane forest, plantations, agricultural land, gardens
Ambon Yellow White-eye *Zosterops kuehni*	nt	—	0–500+	Lowland forest, scrub, gardens
Bicoloured White-eye *Tephrozosterops stalkeri*	lc	—	500–1,200	Lowland and montane forest, scrub
Grey-hooded White-eye *Lophozosterops pinaiae*	lc	—	1,100–2,550	Montane forest
Drab Myzomela *Myzomela blasii*	lc	—	0–2,200	Lowland and montane forest, flowering trees
Olive Honeyeater *Lichmera argentauris*	lc	171,172	Coastal lowlands	Flowering and fruiting trees on small islands
Seram Honeyeater *Lichmera monticola*	lc	—	(1,000–)1,200–3,000	Montane forest, alpine zone

cont.

Status and habitat of restricted-range species (cont.)

Species (ordered taxonomically)	Global status	Other EBAs (and SAs)	Altitude (m)	Habitat
Grey-necked Friarbird *Philemon subcorniculatus*	lc	—	0–1,100	Lowland and montane forest, mangroves, coconut plantations
Long-crested Myna *Basilornis corythaix*	lc	—	50–700	Lowland forest, agricultural land, gardens
Grey-collared Oriole *Oriolus forsteni*	lc	—	0–1,100	Lowland and montane forest

Global status (see p. 679 for definitions)
EX Extinct
EW Extinct in the Wild } with year of last record
CR Critical
EN Endangered } threatened species
VU Vulnerable
cd Conservation Dependent
nt Near Threatened
lc Least Concern
DD Data Deficient
NE Not Evaluated

Other EBAs (and SAs) (see p. 83 for locations) Bracketed numbers are Secondary Areas. X Extinct in that EBA or SA.

Notes [1] Only known from this EBA by the records of Bowler and Taylor (1989, 1993), which are at unusually high altitudes for this small-island specialist and require confirmation (M. K. Poulsen *in litt.* 1996)

individuals, confined to the mountainous interior of the island (Moeliker and Heij 1995). *Zosterops kuehni* is only definitely known from forest, scrub and gardens on Ambon, although there is also a doubtful record from Seram (Collar and Andrew 1988) and white-eyes with similar calls and song to this species have recently been recorded on Haruku (M. K. Poulsen *in litt.* 1996).

Drab Whistler *Pachycephala griseonota* (above) is found in all five EBAs in Maluku province in eastern Indonesia. Streaky-breasted Fantail *Rhipidura dedemi* (below) is endemic to Seram, where it is a conspicuous member of mixed species bird flocks in the island's rain forests.

J. M. M. Ekstrom/Wae Bula '96

I. Isherwood/Wae Bula '96

Distribution patterns of restricted-range species

Species (ordered geographically)	Boano	Seram	Ambon	Haruku	Saparua	Other EBAs, SAs
Monarcha boanensis	●	–	–	–	–	–
Coracina ceramensis	●	●	–	–	–	–
Megapodius wallacei	●	●	●	●	–	●
Myiagra galeata	●	●	●	●	–	●
Dicaeum vulneratum	●	●	●	●	–	●
Ducula perspicillata	●	●	●	–	●	●
Eos bornea	●	●	●	●	●	●
Eos semilarvata	–	●	–	–	–	–
Rhipidura dedemi	–	●	–	–	–	–
Tephrozosterops stalkeri	–	●	–	–	–	–
Lophozosterops pinaiae	–	●	–	–	–	–
Lichmera monticola	–	●	–	–	–	–
Philemon subcorniculatus	–	●	–	–	–	–
Basilornis corythaix	–	●	–	–	–	–
Oriolus forsteni	–	●	–	–	–	–
Ducula concinna	–	●	–	–	–	●
Gymnophaps mada	–	●	–	–	–	●
Ninox squamipila	–	●	–	–	–	●
Coracina atriceps	–	●	–	–	–	●
Zoothera dumasi	–	●	–	–	–	●
Bradypterus castaneus	–	●	–	–	–	●
Ficedula buruensis	–	●	–	–	–	●
Pachycephala griseonota	–	●	–	–	–	●
Lichmera argentauris	–	●	–	–	–	●
Lorius domicella	–	●	●	–	–	–
Myzomela blasii	–	●	●	–	–	–
Accipiter erythrauchen	–	●	●	–	–	●
Todirhamphus lazuli	–	●	●	●	–	–
Cacatua moluccensis	–	●	●	●	●	–
Zosterops kuehni	–	?	●	?	–	–
Total	7	28	11	6	3	

● Present
○ Extinct?
X Extinct
? Present?
R Reintroduced
I Introduced

Threatened spp. shown in **bold**
Other EBAs, SAs } see 'Status and habitat' table

Manusela National Park is the largest protected area in Maluku province, and includes extensive areas of montane rain forest.

Wakolo Myzomela *Myzomela wakoloensis*, which is confined to Buru (EBA 169) and Seram, was considered to be a full species by Sibley and Monroe (1990, 1993), but is here treated as a form of the more widespread Crimson Myzomela *M. dibapha* following Andrew (1992). Jones *et al.* (1995b) considered Forsten's Megapode *Megapodius forstenii*, which is also confined to Buru and Seram, to be a full species, but it is here treated as a form of the more widespread Orange-footed Scrubfowl *M. reinwardt* following Andrew (1992) and Sibley and Monroe (1990, 1993). Western Crowned-pigeon *Goura cristata* (see EBA 172) occurs on Seram, where it is assumed to have been introduced (Macdonald 1995).

■ Threats and conservation

Seram is still well forested, although the low-lying areas where the human population is concentrated—along the coast and in the west—have been cleared. At present the potential threats to the EBA are timber extraction, oil drilling, the wild bird trade and the generation of hydroelectricity (see Edwards 1993b). Ambon is densely populated, but *Zosterops kuehni* is able to adapt to man-modified habitats there (M. K. Poulsen *in litt.* 1996). On Boano, trees are cut for timber, but this activity does not seem to focus on the patches of secondary forest where *Monarcha boanensis* still survives (Moeliker and Heij 1995).

Five of the restricted-range species are classified as threatened: *Megapodius wallacei* because it nests colonially on beaches at a limited number of tradi-tional breeding grounds, and is therefore vulnerable to egg harvesting and disturbance; *Lorius domicella* because it is uncommon and is trapped for the local bird trade; *Cacatua moluccensis* principally because of evidence that it has declined in numbers as a result of trapping for the bird trade; *Todirhamphus lazuli* because it appears to be local in the lowlands and may be vulnerable to the removal of dead forest trees suitable for nesting and perching; and *Monarcha boanensis* because of its small, fragmented range and small population. The poorly known *Zoothera dumasi* is treated as Data Deficient.

The key protected area for the conservation of this EBA is Manusela National Park in central Seram. This includes about 10% of the EBA's land area, and contains all of Seram's forest ecosystems from sea-level to the peak of Mt Binaiya (Edwards 1993b), and almost all of the restricted-range bird species occur there. Additional proposed protected areas on Seram include Wae Bula and Gunung Sahuai (FAO 1982d), but Wae Bula has now lost most of its value for conservation; the forests on the highest ridges of eastern Seram are important for several species, including *Lorius domicella* and *Cacatus moluccensis* (J. Ekstrom *in litt.* 1997). There are no reserves on the islands of Boano and Ambon, so the single-island endemic species there are not protected: *Zosterops kuehni* is able to adapt to man-modified habitats, so no special protection may be required, but *Monarcha boanensis* is a forest bird and a new protected area is probably needed on Boano for its conservation.

171 Northern Maluku

Key habitats Tropical lowland rain forest, montane forest, swamp forest

Main threats Limited habitat loss (e.g. due to agriculture, logging), trapping for cage-bird trade

Biological importance ● ● ○
Current threat level ● ● ○

Area 27,000 km²   **Altitude** 0–2,000 m

Countries Indonesia

Restricted-range species	Threatened	Total
Confined to this EBA	5	26
Present also in other EBAs, SAs	1	17
Total	6	43

■ General characteristics

Lying in northern Maluku province of Indonesia, this EBA includes the islands of Halmahera, Morotai, Bacan, Obi, the chain of volcanic islands to the west of Halmahera (which includes Ternate, Tidore, Mare, Moti and Kayoa) and many other small associated islands. The four peninsulas which make up Halmahera are all mountainous, but only reach a maximum altitude of 1,635 m. Morotai (maximum 1,250 m), Bacan (2,111 m) and Obi (1,611 m) are also mountainous.

The natural vegetation of most of the islands is tropical lowland evergreen and semi-evergreen rain forest, with areas of forest on limestone, and tropical montane rain forest above c.700 m. Monsoon forest is reported to exist on the southern peninsula of Halmahera and on Bacan and Obi, but the extent of this forest type is unclear (Whitmore 1984, White and Bruce 1986, Collins *et al.* 1991, MacKinnon *et al.* 1994).

■ Restricted-range species

The avifauna of Northern Maluku is very distinct, and includes the four monotypic endemic genera, *Habroptila*, *Melitograis*, *Lycocorax* and *Semioptera*. Most of the EBA's restricted-range species have been recorded on Halmahera (see 'Distribution patterns' table), and four are known only from this island. Two species are restricted to the southern islands of the EBA: *Ptilinopus granulifrons*, which is known from the lowlands of Obi, and *Scolopax rochussenii*, which is recorded from Obi and Bacan where it appears to be confined to montane forest.

E. Faull

The spectacular Standardwing *Semioptera wallacii* is one of only two species of bird-of-paradise to occur away from New Guinea (and its associated islands), both of which are endemic to this EBA.

The habitat requirements and distribution of the restricted-range species have not formerly been well documented, but survey work on Halmahera since 1994 by PHPA/BirdLife International and others has added considerably to knowledge of their habitat

Status and habitat of restricted-range species

Species (ordered taxonomically)	Global status	Other EBAs (and SAs)	Altitude (m)	Habitat
Moluccan Goshawk *Accipiter henicogrammus*	lc	—	0–1,300	Lowland and montane forest
Rufous-necked Sparrowhawk *Accipiter erythrauchen*	lc	169,170	0–1,400	Lowland and montane forest
Dusky Scrubfowl *Megapodius freycinet*	lc	172,174	0–1,040	Lowland/montane forest, mangroves, sago swamp, dense scrub, plantations, gardens
Moluccan Scrubfowl *Megapodius wallacei*	VU	169,170	700–1,950 non-breeding	Lowland and montane forest, breeds on coastal beaches
Invisible Rail *Habroptila wallacii*	VU	—	Lowlands	Dense swampy thickets, sago swamp
Moluccan Woodcock *Scolopax rochussenii*	VU	—	>500	Probably montane forest
Scarlet-breasted Fruit-dove *Ptilinopus bernsteinii*	lc	—	0–2,000	Lowland and montane forest, agricultural land
Blue-capped Fruit-dove *Ptilinopus monacha*	nt	—	0–750	Lowland forest, mangroves, agricultural land
Grey-headed Fruit-dove *Ptilinopus hyogastra*	lc	—	0–1,000	Lowland and montane forest, agricultural land
Carunculated Fruit-dove *Ptilinopus granulifrons*	VU	—	0–550	Lowland forest, agricultural land
White-eyed Imperial-pigeon *Ducula perspicillata*	lc	169,170	0–1,400	Lowland and montane forest, coconut plantations
Spice Imperial-pigeon *Ducula myristicivora*	lc	172,174 (s113)	Lowlands	Forest on small islands
Pink-headed Imperial-pigeon *Ducula rosacea*	lc	162,164,165 (s107,s108,s109, s110,s111)	0–600	Forest, scrub and agricultural land on small islands
Cinnamon-bellied Imperial-pigeon *Ducula basilica*	lc	—	0–1,050	Lowland and montane forest
Violet-necked Lory *Eos squamata*	lc	172	0–1,250	Lowland and montane forest, coconut plantations, coastal gardens
Chattering Lory *Lorius garrulus*	VU	—	0–1,300	Lowland and montane forest
White Cockatoo *Cacatua alba*	VU	—	0–860	Lowland forest, agricultural land
Moluccan Hanging-parrot *Loriculus amabilis*	lc	168	0–800	Lowland forest, flowering trees in agricultural land and village gardens
Moluccan Cuckoo *Cacomantis heinrichi*	DD	—	c.1,000–1,500, possibly lower	Montane forest, possibly lowland forest
Goliath Coucal *Centropus goliath*	lc	—	0–800	Lowland forest, scrub, agricultural land
Moluccan Hawk-owl *Ninox squamipila*	lc	165,169,170	0–1,750	Lowland and montane forest, thickets
Long-whiskered Owlet-nightjar *Aegotheles crinifrons*	lc	—	0–1,200	Lowland and montane forest, agricultural land
Blue-and-white Kingfisher *Todirhamphus diops*	lc	—	0–650	Lowland forest, agricultural land, coconut plantations, gardens
Sombre Kingfisher *Todirhamphus funebris*	nt	—	0–620	Lowland forest, coconut plantations, bamboo, agricultural land
Purple Roller *Eurystomus azureus*	lc	—	0–465	Lowland forest
Ivory-breasted Pitta *Pitta maxima*	lc	—	0–1,200	Lowland and montane forest

cont.

Status and habitat of restricted-range species (cont.)

Species (ordered taxonomically)	Global status	Other EBAs (and SAs)	Altitude (m)	Habitat
Moluccan Cuckoo-shrike *Coracina atriceps*	lc	170	0–1,200	Lowland and montane forest, mangroves
Halmahera Cuckoo-shrike *Coracina parvula*	lc	—	(150–) 700–900	Lowland and montane forest (probably mainly montane)
Pale Cicadabird *Coracina ceramensis*	lc	169,170	0–1,200	Lowland and montane forest, scrub
Rufous-bellied Triller *Lalage aurea*	lc	—	0–600	Open lowland forest, scrub, agricultural land
White-naped Monarch *Monarcha pileatus*	lc	165,169	0–550	Lowland forest
Dark-grey Flycatcher *Myiagra galeata*	lc	165,169,170	0–850	Lowland forest
Island Whistler *Pachycephala phaionotus*	lc	165,172,174 (s112)	Coastal lowlands	Mangroves, coastal scrub
Drab Whistler *Pachycephala griseonota*	lc	165,168,169, 170	0–1,100	Lowland and montane forest
Flame-breasted Flowerpecker *Dicaeum erythrothorax*	lc	169	0–1,000	Lowland and montane forest, scrub, riverine habitats, agricultural land
Creamy-throated White-eye *Zosterops atriceps*	lc	—	0–1,050	Lowland and montane forest, agricultural land
Olive Honeyeater *Lichmera argentauris*	lc	170,172	Coastal lowlands	Flowering and fruiting trees on small islands
White-streaked Friarbird *Melitograis gilolensis*	lc	—	0–1,600	Lowland and montane forest, mangroves, coconut plantations, agricultural land
Dusky Friarbird *Philemon fuscicapillus*	DD	—	0–600	Lowland forest
Dusky-brown Oriole *Oriolus phaeochromus*	lc	—	0–1,200	Lowland and montane forest, agricultural land
Paradise-crow *Lycocorax pyrrhopterus*	lc	—	0–1,600	Lowland and montane forest, coconut plantations, agricultural land
Standardwing *Semioptera wallacii*	nt	—	0–1,300	Lowland and montane forest
Long-billed Crow *Corvus validus*	lc	—	0–1,150	Lowland/montane forest, coconut plant-ations, agricultural land, *Imperata* grassland

Global status (see p. 679 for definitions)	EX Extinct EW Extinct in the Wild	} with year of last record	CR Critical EN Endangered VU Vulnerable	} threatened species	cd Conservation Dependent nt Near Threatened lc Least Concern	DD Data Deficient NE Not Evaluated

Other EBAs (and SAs) (see p. 83 for locations): bracketed numbers are Secondary Areas; [x] extinct in that EBA or SA.

requirements, altitudinal ranges and population densities (MacKinnon *et al.* 1994, M. K. Poulsen *in litt.* 1996). Most of the restricted-range species which occur on Halmahera were recorded during the surveys, and many were found to be common. All of these species were recorded in lowland rain forest, but many were also found in montane rain forest above c.700 m, and a few were most numerous in that habitat or in forest on limestone. *Cacomantis heinrichi* was not recorded during these surveys; it is a species known only from a handful of specimens collected in montane forest on Halmahera and Bacan, although there is a specimen and recent possible sightings from the lowlands (M. K. Poulsen *in litt.* 1996). One of the four species which are endemic to Halmahera,

the flightless *Habroptila wallacii* which is believed to be confined to sago swamp forests, was recorded only once during the surveys (Anon. 1995).

■ Threats and conservation

The principal long-term threat to the restricted-range species of this EBA is forest loss. Parts of the northern peninsula of Halmahera and the Ternate, Tidore, Mare, Moti and Kayoa islands are volcanic, and the rich volcanic soils have long been intensively cultivated for cloves and other spices (FAO 1982d). Elsewhere, extensive tracts of forest remain, but most of this is included within timber concessions, and there are also plans for agricultural development (RePPProT 1990).

Distribution patterns of restricted-range species

Species (ordered geographically)	Morotai, Rau	Halmahera	Ternate group	Mayu, Tifore	Widi	Bacan	Obi	Other EBAs, SAs
Melitograis gilolensis	●	●	–	–	–	●	–	–
Philemon fuscicapillus	●	●	–	–	–	●	–	–
Accipiter henicogrammus	●	●	●	–	–	●	–	–
Ptilinopus hyogastra	●	●	●	–	–	●	–	–
Pitta maxima	●	●	●	–	–	●	–	–
Zosterops atriceps	●	●	●	–	–	●	●	–
Lycocorax pyrrhopterus	●	●	●	–	–	●	–	–
Accipiter erythrauchen	●	●	●	–	–	●	●	●
Dicaeum erythrothorax	●	●	●	–	–	●	●	●
Ptilinopus monacha	●	●	●	–	–	●	–	–
Ducula basilica	●	●	●	–	–	●	–	–
Centropus goliath	●	●	●	–	–	●	–	–
Todirhamphus diops	●	●	●	–	–	●	–	–
Lalage aurea	●	●	●	–	–	●	–	–
Corvus validus	●	●	●	–	–	●	–	–
Myiagra galeata	●	●	●	–	–	●	–	●
Pachycephala griseonota	●	●	●	–	–	●	–	●
Lorius garrulus	●	●	?	–	●	●	●	–
Ducula perspicillata	●	●	●	–	●	●	●	●
Megapodius freycinet	●	●	●	●T	●	●	●	●
Eos squamata	●	●	●	●M	●	●	●	●
Habroptila wallacii	–	●	–	–	–	–	–	–
Todirhamphus funebris	–	●	–	–	–	–	–	–
Coracina parvula	–	●	–	–	–	–	–	–
Oriolus phaeochromus	–	●	–	–	–	–	–	–
Monarcha pileatus	–	●	–	–	–	–	–	–
Lichmera argentauris	–	●	–	–	–	–	–	●
Cacomantis heinrichi	–	●	–	–	–	●	–	–
Aegotheles crinifrons	–	●	–	–	–	–	–	–
Semioptera wallacii	–	●	–	–	–	–	–	–
Ducula rosacea	–	●	–	–	–	–	–	●
Loriculus amabilis	–	●	–	–	–	–	–	–
Cacatua alba	–	●	●	–	–	●	–	–
Eurystomus azureus	–	●	●	–	–	●	–	–
Megapodius wallacei	–	●	●	–	–	●	–	●
Ninox squamipila	–	●	●	–	–	●	–	●
Coracina atriceps	–	●	●	–	–	●	–	●
Ptilinopus bernsteinii	–	●	●	–	–	–	●	–
Pachycephala phaionotus	–	●	●M	–	–	–	–	●
Ducula myristicivora	–	–	–	–	–	●	●	●
Scolopax rochussenii	–	–	–	–	–	●	●	–
Ptilinopus granulifrons	–	–	–	–	–	–	●	–
Coracina ceramensis	–	–	–	–	–	–	●	●
Total	21	38	21	3	4	33	20	

● Present	? Present?	Threatened spp. shown in **bold**
O Extinct?	R Reintroduced	Other EBAs, SAs
X Extinct	I Introduced	*(see 'Status and habitat' table)*
T Tifore only	M Mayu only	

Six of the restricted-range birds of this EBA are threatened: the two species confined to Obi and Bacan, because they have specialized habitat requirements and are likely to be vulnerable to forest loss; *Megapodius wallacei* because it nests colonially on beaches and is affected by egg-harvesting, habitat loss and hunting; *Cacatua alba* and *Lorius*

garrulus because of a combination of habitat loss and trapping (both legal and illegal) for the cage-bird trade at levels which may not be sustainable (see Lambert 1993b); and the flightless *Habroptila wallacii*, because it is apparently confined to a few areas of swamp forest and is likely to be vulnerable to introduced or feral predators. Two particularly poorly

P. Jepson

Logging operations on Halmahera are focused on the lowland forest, which supports the highest population densities of many of the restricted-range bird species.

known species are treated as Data Deficient.

There are currently no gazetted protected areas within this EBA. A network of representative areas has been proposed, which would include large areas of the key habitats on most of the main islands, and would almost certainly support populations of all of the restricted-range species. The most important proposed protected areas are Lalobata and Aketajawi on Halmahera, Wayabula on Morotai, Gunung Sibela on Bacan and Pulau Obi on Obi (FAO 1982d, Sujatnika and Jepson 1995). The proposals for Lalobata and Aketajawi have recently been revised, and a single new area proposed which covers c.3,550 km² and is representative of all of the forest types on Halmahera (Suherdie *et al.* 1995).

172 West Papuan lowlands

Key habitats Lowland rain forest, swamp forest, mangroves

Main threats Moderate habitat loss (e.g. due to logging, rice growing, settlement, oil exploration)

Biological importance ● ● ●
Current threat level ● ● ●

Area 110,000 km²   **Altitude** 0–1,000 m

Countries Indonesia

Restricted-range species	Threatened	Total
Confined to this EBA	2	9
Present also in other EBAs, SAs	0	10
Total	2	19

■ General characteristics

This EBA is in the Indonesian province of Irian Jaya and includes the west Papuan islands of Waigeo, Batanta, Salawati, Kofiau and Misool, and the lowland rain forests, swamp forests and mangroves of the Vogelkop and Bomberai peninsulas, extending around Geelvink and Etna bays as far east as the Sirowa river in the north and the Mimika river in the south, where it abuts two other lowland Papuan EBAs (176 and 179).

The island of Kofiau (which has two single-island endemics) lies off the Australasian continental (Sahul) shelf and has had no connections with New Guinea in the recent geological past; it does, however, share three restricted-range species with other west Papuan islands and so is included in this EBA.

Most restricted-range bird records from the mainland are from coastal regions, but it is assumed that some birds are likely to occur further inland. The upper limit of this EBA has been defined by the 1,000 m contour which separates it from the West Papuan highlands (EBA 173) and Central Papuan ranges (EBA 178).

■ Restricted-range species

Nearly all the restricted-range species occur in lowland rain forest with several also being recorded in swamp forest and mangroves.

Distribution within the EBA varies considerably (see 'Distribution patterns' table), with nine species occurring on the west Papuan islands only, three on the mainland only and the remaining seven common

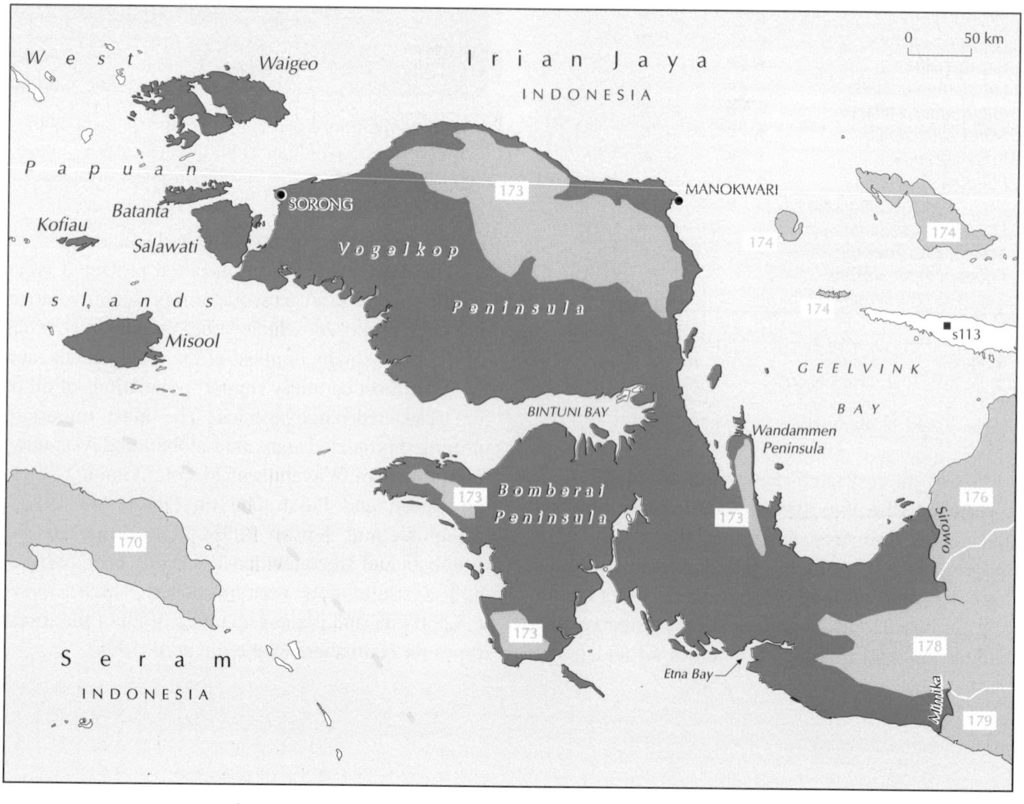

[Map showing West Papuan lowlands region with labels: West Papuan Islands, Waigeo, Irian Jaya, INDONESIA, SORONG, MANOKWARI, Batanta, Kofiau, Salawati, Vogelkop Peninsula, Misool, BINTUNI BAY, GEELVINK BAY, Wandammen Peninsula, Bomberai Peninsula, Seram, INDONESIA, Etna Bay, Sirowo, Mimika. Scale: 0 50 km. Numbered regions: 173, 174, s113, 170, 176, 178, 179.]

Status and habitat of restricted-range species

Species (ordered taxonomically)	Global status	Other EBAs (and SAs)	Altitude (m)	Habitat
Bruijn's Brush-turkey *Aepypodius bruijnii*	VU	—	0–1,000, perhaps higher	Presumably forest on rugged limestone karst
Red-billed Brush-turkey *Talegalla cuvieri*	lc	—	Lowlands to 1,500	Forest
Dusky Scrubfowl *Megapodius freycinet*	lc	171,174	0–1,000	Forest, secondary forest, mangroves, sago swamps, dense scrub
Elegant Imperial-pigeon *Ducula concinna*	lc	165,166,167,169, 170 (s110,s111,s112)	0–850	Forest on small islands (may be a migrant) only
Spice Imperial-pigeon *Ducula myristicivora*	lc	171,174 (s113)	Lowlands	Forest on small islands
Western Crowned-pigeon *Goura cristata*[1]	VU	—	0–150	Undisturbed alluvial forest, hill forest
Black Lory *Chalcopsitta atra*	lc	—	Coasts, lowlands	Forest, swamp forest, savanna, coastal plantations, open grassland
Violet-necked Lory *Eos squamata*	lc	171	0–700	Forest, secondary forest, forest edge, plantations
Kofiau Paradise-kingfisher *Tanysiptera ellioti*	lc	—	Lowlands	Most habitats inc. forest, swamp forest, secondary forest
Red-breasted Paradise-kingfisher *Tanysiptera nympha*	lc	176	Lowlands to 900(–1,500)	Forest, tall secondary forest
Painted Quail-thrush *Cinclosoma ajax*	lc	179,180 (s114)	0–800	Forest, gallery forest, adjoining tall secondary forest
Olive-yellow Robin *Poecilodryas placens*	DD	176,179 (s114)	100–1,450	Forest
Black-backed Monarch *Monarcha julianae*	lc	—	Lowlands	Forest, secondary forest
Island Whistler *Pachycephala phaionotus*	lc	165,171,174 (s112)	Coasts, lowlands	Mangroves, coastal scrub
Olive-crowned Flowerpecker *Dicaeum pectorale*	lc	—	Lowlands	Forest, secondary forest
Olive Honeyeater *Lichmera argentauris*	lc	170,171	Coasts, lowlands	Coconut palms, flowering and fruiting trees on small islands
Wilson's Bird-of-paradise *Cicinnurus respublica*	nt	—	300+	Forest
Red Bird-of-paradise *Paradisaea rubra*	nt	—	0–600	Forest, forest edge, selectively logged and tall secondary forest
Brown-headed Crow *Corvus fuscicapillus*	nt	176 (s112)	0–500	Forest

Global status (see p. 679 for definitions)				**Other EBAs (and SAs)** (see p. 83 for locations)	Bracketed numbers are Secondary Areas. [X] Extinct in that EBA or SA.
	EX Extinct	} with year of last record	cd Conservation Dependent		
	EW Extinct in the Wild		nt Near Threatened		
	CR Critical	} threatened species	lc Least Concern	**Notes**	[1] Reported from Seram (EBA 170) where
	EN Endangered		DD Data Deficient		it was probably introduced
	VU Vulnerable		NE Not Evaluated		(MacDonald 1995).

to both. Of those species which are confined to the west Papuan islands, two are endemic to Kofiau and three to Waigeo plus Batanta. Several species extend their ranges further west into other Indonesian EBAs and some are also found further east in other lowland Papuan EBAs.

■ Threats and conservation

The traditional life style of the tribal groups which live in this EBA has had little impact on the natural ecosystems, with some 86% of the province remaining relatively undisturbed. Indeed the forests of Irian Jaya constitute one of the largest expanses of pristine tropical rain forest in the Asian/Australasian region. However, extensive logging concessions have been granted and there are plans for substantial transmigration schemes (Collins *et al.* 1991). Coastal forests have now been largely logged out around the towns of Sorong and Manokwari, where transmigration settlements have become established.

Distribution patterns of restricted-range species

Species (ordered geographically)	Waigeo	Batanta	Salawati	Kofiau	Misool	Vogelkop	Bomberai	Geelvink/Etna	Other EBAs, SAs
Corvus fuscicapillus	●	–	–	–	–	–	–	–	●
Aepypodius bruijnii	●	?	–	–	–	–	–	–	–
Cicinnurus respublica	●	●	–	–	–	–	–	–	–
Paradisaea rubra	●	●	–	–	–	–	–	–	–
Megapodius freycinet	●	●	–	–	●	–	–	–	●
Eos squamata	●	●	–	–	●	–	–	–	●
Lichmera argentauris	●	–	–	–	●	–	–	–	●
Pachycephala phaionotus	●	–	●	●	●	●	–	–	–
Dicaeum pectorale	●	●	●	●	●	●	–	–	–
Ducula myristicivora	●	●	●	●	●	●	–	–	●
Goura cristata	●	○	●	–	●	●	●	●	–
Chalcopsitta atra	–	●	●	–	●	●	●	–	–
Poecilodryas placens	–	●	–	–	–	●	●	●	–
Talegalla cuvieri	–	–	●	–	●	●	●	–	–
Tanysiptera ellioti	–	–	–	●	–	–	–	–	–
Monarcha julianae	–	–	–	●	–	–	–	–	–
Tanysiptera nympha	–	–	–	–	–	●	●	●	●
Ducula concinna	–	–	–	–	–	–	●	–	●
Cinclosoma ajax	–	–	–	–	–	–	–	●	●
Total	11	9	6	5	9	7	6	4	

● Present   ? Present?   Threatened spp. shown in **bold** — see 'Status and habitat' table
○ Extinct?   R Reintroduced   Other EBAs, SAs
X Extinct   I Introduced

On the west Papuan islands, forest is being destroyed and disturbed by roads built for oil exploration on Salawati, and major forest loss is resulting from logging on Batanta (N. Bostock *in litt.* 1993, R. Burrows *in litt.* 1994, K. D. Bishop *in litt.* 1996). A mining company holds a concession lease on Waigeo (WWF/IUCN 1994–1995).

Swamp forest is also under threat for conversion to rice fields to support increasing populations of settlers, and although it appears that these forests support fewer restricted-range birds compared to lowland rain forest, the limited number of records may reflect the difficulties of surveying these habitats. 'Tambak' (shrimp and fish pond) development, which involves the clear-felling of mangroves and tidal swamp forest, is another pressure, e.g. in Bintuni bay (Sujatnika *et al.* 1995).

The three species which are confined to Waigeo and Batanta (*Aepypodius bruijnii*, *Cicinnurus respublica* and *Paradisaea rubra*) are classified as threatened or Near Threatened because of their vulnerability to any habitat loss. *A. bruijnii* is known with certainty only from specimens obtained on Waigeo by local collectors during the nineteenth century and by one specimen collected in 1939

(Rand and Gilliard 1967). Since that time there have been reports from local people and it was probably sighted on Batanta in 1986 (K. D. Bishop *in litt.* 1987, J. M. Diamond *in litt.* 1987). However, it was not found in 1993 during an 11-day survey of the forests of the south-easternmost part of Waigeo (up to 500 m altitude), possibly because it may be restricted to higher areas by Dusky Scrubfowl *Megapodius freycinet*, or because large forest fires in 1982 have resulted in dense undergrowth and secondary vegetation which may not be suitable for recolonization (Dekker and Argeloo 1993). Although *A. bruijnii* remains almost unknown, it inhabits forest on very rugged limestone karst and may not be as rare as the lack of records suggests.

Hunting is a problem for some species, such as *Goura cristata*, which has been identified as the subject of 'significant' levels of trade (King and Nijboer 1994), and for the widespread Northern Cassowary *Casuarius unappendiculatus* (classified as Vulnerable) and Nicobar Pigeon *Caloenas nicobarica* (Near Threatened), which has important populations on the tiny offshore islands in Geelvink bay (K. D. Bishop *in litt.* 1996; see also Mitchell 1989).

There are nature reserves on all of the west Papuan islands (apart from Kofiau)—Pulau Waigeo (1,530 km² protected), Batanta Barat (100 km²), Salawati Utara (570 km²) and Misool Selatan (840 km²). Although Kofiau has been largely deforested, its two endemics were common and widespread in secondary forest in 1986 (K. D. Bishop *in litt.* 1994), and have not therefore been classified as threatened—but it is, however, critical to establish a reserve on this island to ensure their long-term survival.

On the mainland the isolated Wondiwoi/Wandammen Nature Reserve (730 km²) covers lowland forests in the Wandammen peninsula, and Beriat Nature Reserve (92 km²) covers lowland forests in the Vogelkop peninsula. Additionally, there are five small recreation forests on the coast with a total area of c.35 km². Extensive tracts of lowland forest are included in the proposed nature reserves of Pegunungan Tamrau (c.4,415 km²) in the north of the Vogelkop peninsula, and Pegunungan Fakfak (c.510 km²) and Pegunungan Kumawa (1,180 km²) in the Bomberai peninsula. Consideration should be given to establishing these well-forested areas in order to conserve the restricted-range species of this EBA and its biodiversity in general (Sujatnika *et al.* 1995).

173 West Papuan highlands

Key habitats Lower and upper montane rain forest, wet grassland

Main threats Limited habitat loss (e.g. due to logging, drainage for agriculture)

Biological importance ● ●
Current threat level ●

Area 17,000 km² **Altitude** 1,000–3,000 m

Countries Indonesia

Restricted-range species	Threatened	Total
Confined to this EBA	1	9
Present also in other EBAs, SAs	0	11
Total	1	20

■ General characteristics

The ranges included in this EBA are the Tamrau and Arfak of the Vogelkop peninsula, the Fakfak and Kumawa of the Bomberai peninsula, and the Wandammen of the Wandammen peninsula, which all lie within the Indonesian province of Irian Jaya. The lower limits of the EBA are defined by the 1,000 m contour although some restricted-range birds have been recorded below this, and there may be some overlap with the distributions of the restricted-range species which occur in the West Papuan lowlands (EBA 172).

The vegetation of the region includes lower montane rain forest (up to c.1,500 m) which is dominated by oaks and laurels, giving way to upper montane forest (up to c.2,800 m) which is often

heavily mossed and where the southern beech *Nothofagus* is a conspicuous tree; this merges into high mountain forest (above c.2,400 m) where the trees become stunted and conifers and myrtles predominate, and at the highest altitudes there is alpine shrubbery and grassland (Beehler *et al.* 1986, WWF/IUCN 1994–1995).

This EBA is a poorly known one ornithologically and has been little explored for any purpose. The Kumawa mountains, for example, are uninhabited, and there was no record of anyone ever having entered there before 1983 (Diamond 1985). The limestone mountains of the Fakfak are also extremely inhospitable and difficult of access, with vertical cliffs, sheer-walled fissures and deep sink-holes (Gibbs 1994).

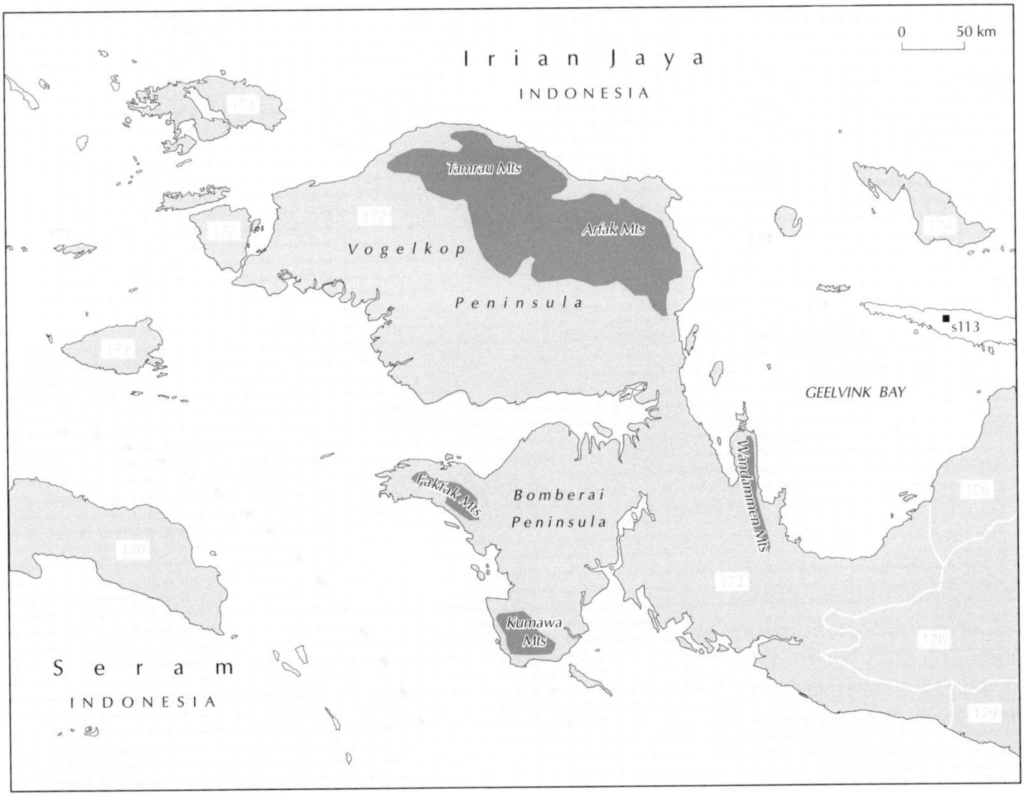

Map showing the West Papuan highlands EBA, Irian Jaya, Indonesia, with the Tamrau Mts, Arfak Mts, Vogelkop Peninsula, Bomberai Peninsula, Fakfak Mts, Kumawa Mts, Wandammen Mts, Geelvink Bay, Seram, and s113.

Status and habitat of restricted-range species

Species (ordered taxonomically)	Global status	Other EBAs (and SAs)	Altitude (m)	Habitat
Chestnut Forest-rail *Rallina rubra*	lc	178	1,500–3,000	Montane forest, mossy forest
White-striped Forest-rail *Rallina leucospila*	DD	—	1,350–1,600	Montane forest
Modest Tiger-parrot *Psittacella modesta*	lc	178	1,700–2,800	Forest, mossy forest, forest edge, secondary growth
Mountain Eared-nightjar *Eurostopodus archboldi*	lc	177,178	(2,200–)2,400–3,000+	Montane forest, stunted cloud forest
Greater Melampitta *Melampitta gigantea*	lc	175,178	650–1,400	Hill forest on rugged limestone karst (may have specialized habitat requirements within this)
Vogelkop Scrubwren *Sericornis rufescens*	lc	—	800–1,800	Forest, forest edge shrubbery
Smoky Robin *Peneothello cryptoleucus*	lc	175,178	1,400–2,500	Forest, forest edge, thickets on ridge-tops
Green-backed Robin *Pachycephalopsis hattamensis*	lc	175,178 (s113)	700–1,650	Hill forest, scrub
Vogelkop Whistler *Pachycephala meyeri*[1]	nt	—	950–1,500	Lower montane forest, thickets
Obscure Berrypecker *Melanocharis arfakiana*[2]	DD	178	950	Forest, forest edge
Rufous-sided Honeyeater *Ptiloprora erythropleura*	lc	178	1,300–2,800	Montane forest, secondary growth, forest edge
Black-backed Honeyeater *Ptiloprora perstriata*	lc	178	1,700–3,000+	Mossy forest, forest edge, subalpine habitats
Cinnamon-browed Melidectes *Melidectes ochromelas*	lc	177,178	1,100–2,000	Forest, forest edge
Vogelkop Melidectes *Melidectes leucostephes*	nt	—	900–1,800	Montane forest, forest edge
Arfak Honeyeater *Melipotes gymnops*	lc	—	1,200–2,700	Montane forest
Grey-banded Munia *Lonchura vana*	VU	—	1,900–2,000	Mid-mountain wet grassland and marshland
Vogelkop Bowerbird *Amblyornis inornatus*	lc	—	1,000–2,000	Forest
Long-tailed Paradigalla *Paradigalla carunculata*	nt	178	1,400–2,200	Montane forest, forest edge
Western Parotia *Parotia sefilata*	lc	—	1,050–1,800	Mid-mountain forest
Arfak Astrapia *Astrapia nigra*	nt	—	1,650–2,500	Montane forest

Global status (see p. 679 for definitions)

EX Extinct	with year of last record	cd	Conservation Dependent
EW Extinct in the Wild			
		nt	Near Threatened
CR Critical	threatened species	lc	Least Concern
EN Endangered		DD	Data Deficient
VU Vulnerable		NE	Not Evaluated

Other EBAs (and SAs) (see p. 83 for locations)
Bracketed numbers are Secondary Areas.   X Extinct in that EBA or SA.

Notes
[1] May also occur in Foya mountains (EBA 175) (Diamond 1985).
[2] In this EBA, known from only a single specimen, in 1867.

■ Restricted-range species

All of the EBA's restricted-range species occur in forested habitats apart from *Lonchura vana* which depends on mid-mountain wet grassland and marshland. Forest species can be divided into three groups according to the habitat types with which they largely associate: lower montane forest (below c.1,500 m), lower–upper montane forest (c.1,000–2,000 m) and upper montane–high mountain forest (above c.1,500 m) (see 'Habitat associations' table).

Nearly all the restricted-range species occur in the Arfak mountains. There are various patterns of distribution between the other mountain ranges (see 'Distribution patterns' table), although this may be due to

Habitat associations of restricted-range species

Lower montane forest	Upper montane and high mountain forest
Rallina leucospila	Rallina rubra
Melampitta gigantea	Psittacella modesta
Pachycephalopsis hattamensis	Eurostopodus archboldi
Pachycephala meyeri	Peneothello cryptoleucus
Melanocharis arfakiana	Ptiloprora erythropleura
	Ptiloprora perstriata
Lower to upper montane forest	Melipotes gymnops
Sericornis rufescens	Paradigalla carunculata
Melidectes ochromelas	Astrapia nigra
Melidectes leucostephes	
Amblyornis inornatus	**Wet grassland/marshland**
Parotia sefilata	**Lonchura vana**

Threatened species (Critical, Endangered, Vulnerable) are shown in **bold**; see 'Status and habitat' table.

poor data, particularly from the higher altitudes. Several species extend their ranges further east into other montane Papuan EBAs.

The inadequacy of exploration in this EBA is illustrated by the fact that in a recent visit to the Fakfak mountains, several taxa potentially new to science were recorded, including two honeyeaters *Ptiloprora* sp. and *Melipotes* sp., a bowerbird *Amblyornis* sp. (possibly *inornatus*) and a paradigalla *Paradigalla* sp. (possibly *carunculata*) (Gibbs 1994). In 1994 and 1995 *Eurostopodus archboldi* was recorded from the Arfak mountains for the first time,

Distribution patterns of restricted-range species

Species (ordered geographically)	Tamrau	Arfak	Fakfak	Kumawa	Wandammen	Other EBAs, SAs
Pachycephala meyeri	●	●	–	–	–	–
Lonchura vana	●	●	–	–	–	–
Astrapia nigra	●	●	–	–	–	–
Psittacella modesta	●	●	–	–	–	●
Sericornis rufescens	●	●	–	●	–	–
Peneothello cryptoleucus	●	●	–	●	–	●
Melidectes leucostephes	●	●	–	●	–	–
Ptiloprora erythropleura	●	●	–	●	–	●
Rallina leucospila	●	●	–	–	●	–
Parotia sefilata	●	●	–	–	–	●
Pachycephalopsis hattamensis	●	●	–	–	●	●
Melidectes ochromelas	●	●	–	–	●	●
Amblyornis inornatus	●	●	●*	●*	●	–
Rallina rubra	–	●	–	–	–	●
Eurostopodus archboldi	–	●	–	–	–	●
Melanocharis arfakiana	–	●	–	–	–	●
Paradigalla carunculata	–	●	●*	–	–	●
Melipotes gymnops	–	●	●	●	–	–
Melampitta gigantea	–	●	●	●	–	●
Ptiloprora perstriata	–	–	–	–	●	●
Total	13	19	6	7	6	

● Present	? Present?	Threatened spp. shown in **bold**	}	see 'Status and habitat' table
O Extinct?	R Reintroduced			
X Extinct	I Introduced	Other EBAs, SAs		
* May be a separate species (see text)				

more than 600 km west of the nearest known records in the Snow mountains (EBA 178) (Gibbs 1996a).

■ Threats and conservation

The extensive montane rain forests of this EBA remain relatively undisturbed due to their geographical isolation, and to the the low density and traditional lifestyle of the human inhabitants. Deforestation is, however, occurring in the hills of the Tamrau and Arfak mountain ranges (Sujatnika *et al.* 1995).

Only one restricted-range species in this EBA, *Lonchura vana*, is currently classified as threatened. Its mid-mountain wet grassland and marshland habitat is very scarce (it is drained for conversion to agriculture) and there are very few recent records. Several other species are classified as Near Threatened, largely because of their limited ranges and apparent rarity. Other widespread threatened species, all classified as Vulnerable, which occur in this EBA include Salvadori's Teal *Salvadorina waigiuensis*, New Guinea Harpy Eagle *Harpyopsis novaeguineae* and Black Sicklebill *Epimachus fastuosus*.

Two restricted-range species are assigned to the non-threatened category, Data Deficient. The apparent extreme rarity and patchy distribution of *Melanocharis arfakiana* (see Status table) suggest either that it may be disappearing, perhaps as a result of competition with ecologically similar congeners, or that it could be an overlooked, canopy-haunting species (Coates 1990). Recent information on the status of *Rallina leucospila* indicates a very patchy distribution (D. Gibbs *in litt.* 1996) but this may be no cause for concern as its habitat is probably largely secure.

Two reserves, which include montane forest, are established in this EBA: the isolated Wondiwoi/Wandammen Nature Reserve (730 km^2) which covers the complete range of lowland through to montane forests in the Wandammen peninsula, and the Pegunungan Arfak Nature Reserve in the north (683 km^2) which covers upper montane forests at altitudes above 1,500 m. As currently gazetted, the latter is considered too small for the maintenance of viable populations of Arfak flora and fauna, and it is proposed that it should be extended to include a greater range of habitats with a change in status to provide indigenous people with the opportunity to continue certain traditional ecologically non-disruptive practices (WWF/IUCN 1994–1995).

In order to have a more comprehensive protected-area network in this EBA, consideration should be given to establishing the well-forested, proposed nature reserves of Pegunungan Tamrau (c.4,415 km^2) in the north of the Vogelkop peninsula, and Pegunungan Fakfak (510 km^2) and Pegunungan Kumawa (1,180 km^2) in the Bomberai peninsula (Sujatnika *et al.* 1995; see also Diamond 1986).

174 Geelvink Islands

PRIORITY
HIGH

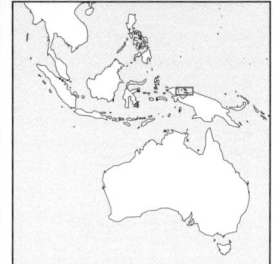

Key habitats Lowland rain forest, mangroves

Main threats Major habitat loss (e.g. due to logging, subsistence farming), trapping for cage-bird trade

Biological importance ● ○ ○
Current threat level ● ○ ○

Area 3,000 km² **Altitude** 0–1,000 m

Countries Indonesia

Restricted-range species	Threatened	Total
Confined to this EBA	3	10
Present also in other EBAs, SAs	0	4
Total	3	14

■ General characteristics

The islands of this EBA, lying in the mouth of Geelvink bay, are all oceanic in origin and are part of the Indonesian province of Irian Jaya. They include the twin islands of Biak and Supiori (separated from each other by a narrow channel), Numfor and Meos Num, and surrounding smaller islands including Rani and the Pandaidori islands. Nearby Yapen, a larger New Guinean land-bridge island, shares only one restricted-range species with this EBA and is treated as a Secondary Area (s113).

Biak and Supiori have extremely rugged limestone mountains, which in the case of Supiori rise steeply from the sea, while the southern part of Biak is a relatively flat plain. The islands were originally forested, with mangroves in sheltered coastal areas.

■ Restricted-range species

This EBA has the most highly endemic avifauna of any of New Guinea's satellite islands (indeed of any single area in the New Guinea region: K. D. Bishop *in litt.* 1996), including c.19 endemic subspecies.

All the restricted-range species are inhabitants of lowland rain forest, some have been recorded from secondary habitats and a few also occur in mangroves. All species occur on Biak-Supiori apart from *Tanysiptera carolinae* which is endemic to Numfor.

Three other taxa, Biak Megapode *Megapodius freycinet geelvinkianus*, Biak Scops-owl *Otus magicus beccarii* and Biak Golden Monarch *Monarcha chrysomela kordensis*, are sometimes considered full species, but have not been treated here as such.

Distribution patterns of restricted-range species

Species (ordered geographically)	Biak-Supiori	Numfor	Meos Num	Other EBAs, SAs
Centropus chalybeus	●	–	–	–
Tanysiptera riedelii	●	–	–	–
Gerygone hypoxantha	●	–	–	–
Monarcha brehmii	●	–	–	–
Zosterops mysorensis	●	–	–	–
Micropsitta geelvinkiana	●	○	–	–
Myiagra atra	●	●	–	–
Aplonis magna	●	●	–	–
Ptilinopus solomonensis	●	●	–	●
Eos cyanogenia	●	○	●	–
Megapodius freycinet	●	●	●	●
Ducula myristicivora	●	●	●	●
Pachycephala phaionotus	●ᴵ	●	●	●
Tanysiptera carolinae	–	●	–	–
Total	13	9	4	

● Present	? Present?	Threatened spp. shown in **bold**	⎫ see 'Status
○ Extinct?	R Reintroduced		⎬ and habitat'
X Extinct	I Introduced	Other EBAs, SAs	⎭ table
ᴵ Tiny offshore islands only			

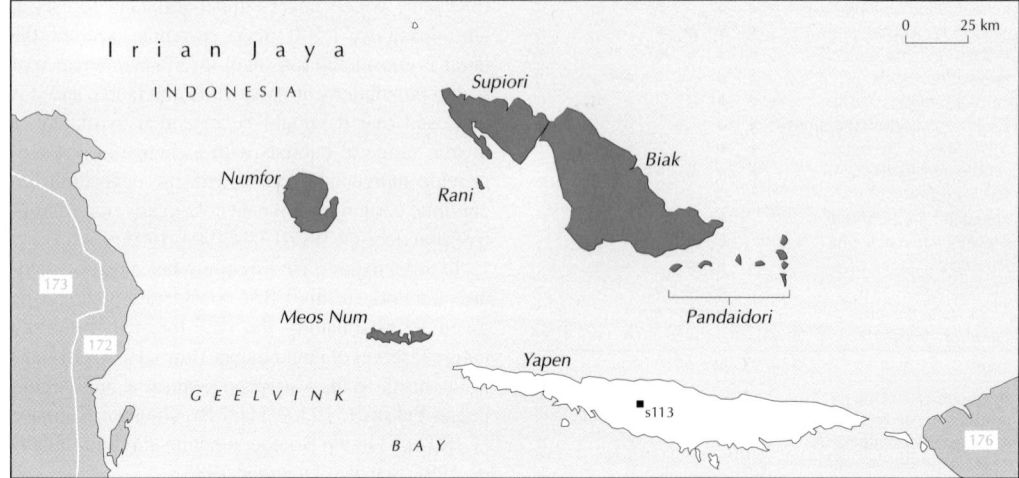

Status and habitat of restricted-range species

Species (ordered taxonomically)	Global status	Other EBAs (and SAs)	Altitude (m)	Habitat
Dusky Scrubfowl *Megapodius freycinet*	lc	171,172	0–1,000	Forest, secondary forest, mangroves, sago swamps, dense scrub
Yellow-bibbed Fruit-dove *Ptilinopus solomonensis*	lc	193,194,195, 198	0–1,400	Forest, shrubs in secondary growth, fruiting trees, gardens
Spice Imperial-pigeon *Ducula myristicivora*	lc	171,172 (s113)	Lowlands	Forest, small islands
Black-winged Lory *Eos cyanogenia*	VU	—	0–460	Forest, mature secondary forest; roosts in coastal habitats inc. coconut plantations
Geelvink Pygmy-parrot *Micropsitta geelvinkiana*	nt	—	0–400 (–1,000)	Forest, secondary forest, edges of wooded gardens
Biak Coucal *Centropus chalybeus*	nt	—	0–300	Forest, sometimes secondary forest
Biak Paradise-kingfisher *Tanysiptera riedelii*	nt	—	0–300 (–600)	Forest, logged forest, tall secondary forest
Numfor Paradise-kingfisher *Tanysiptera carolinae*	lc	—	Lowlands	All habitats inc. forest and beach vegetation
Biak Gerygone *Gerygone hypoxantha*[1]	EN	—	Lowlands	Forest edge, mangroves
Biak Monarch *Monarcha brehmii*	EN	—	0–600	Forest, preferably with a fairly dense middle layer
Biak Flycatcher *Myiagra atra*	nt	—	0–400	Forest, logged forest, secondary forest, occasionally recorded in mangroves
Island Whistler *Pachycephala phaionotus*	lc	165,171,172 (s112)	Coasts, lowlands	Mangroves, coastal scrub
Biak White-eye *Zosterops mysorensis*	nt	—	0–675	Forest, secondary forest, avoids heavily disturbed habitats
Long-tailed Starling *Aplonis magna*	lc	—	0–675	All wooded habitats

Global status (see p. 679 for definitions)

EX Extinct — with year of last record
EW Extinct in the Wild

CR Critical — threatened species
EN Endangered
VU Vulnerable

cd Conservation Dependent
nt Near Threatened
lc Least Concern
DD Data Deficient
NE Not Evaluated

Other EBAs (and SAs) (see p. 83 for locations)
Bracketed numbers are Secondary Areas.
[x] Extinct in that EBA or SA.

Notes [1] Treated as a separate species in Collar *et al.* (1994).

■ Threats and conservation

Much forest on Biak and Numfor has been destroyed or damaged by logging and subsistence farming. The remainder is under pressure, especially in southern Biak and northern Supiori where there is a growing human population of transmigrants. As the islands are almost entirely raised coralline limestone, the forest does not easily regenerate, and Biak's southern plains are now largely stunted woodland and semi-arid scrub (Bishop 1982, K. D. Bishop *in litt.* 1996).

Most species confined to this EBA are considered threatened or Near Threatened because of their forest dependency, small range and rarity. Trapping for the bird trade is an additional threat for *Eos cyanogenia* (and for parrots in general), and hunting is a problem for Victoria Crowned-pigeon *Goura victoria*, a widespread threatened species (classified as Vulnerable), which also occurs on Biak–Supiori.

Overall this is a very important EBA for avian conservation in New Guinea. Although the forests on Supiori rise steeply, they provide suitable lowland habitat up to c.300 m for many restricted-range species (Bishop 1982), and are therefore a vital refuge. However, the destruction of forest in the northern coastlands may well have untold impacts on nomadic species such as pigeons and parrots, which, although nesting in the hills, may need to forage in the lowlands (K. D. Bishop *in litt.* 1996).

Two reserves cover lowland and hill forest on Biak–Supiori (Biak Utara Nature Reserve, 110 km², and Pulau Supiori Nature Reserve, 420 km²). A reserve has also been proposed for Numfor (Diamond 1986), which would cover the habitat of its single-island endemic.

A plan to develop Biak as a tourist resort should carefully balance economic development with biodiversity conservation, ecological impact and the traditions of local people (Sujatnika *et al.* 1995).

175 North Papuan mountains

PRIORITY HIGH

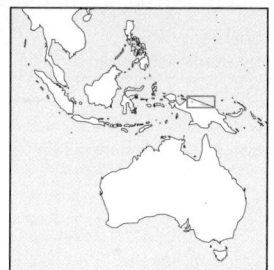

| Key habitats | Montane rain forest |
| Main threats | Possible habitat loss |

Area 4,700 km² **Altitude** 1,000–2,200 m

Countries Indonesia, Papua New Guinea

Biological importance ● ○ ○
Current threat level ● ○ ○

Restricted-range species	Threatened	Total
Confined to this EBA	0	3
Present also in other EBAs, SAs	0	3
Total	0	6

■ General characteristics

The mountain ranges included in this EBA are the Foya (or Gauttier) and Cyclops of the Indonesian province of Irian Jaya, and the North Coastal Range (including the Bewani, Torricelli and Prince Alexander mountains) of Papua New Guinea. The lower limits of the EBA have been defined by the 1,000 m contour although some restricted-range birds have been recorded below this, and there may be some overlap with the distributions of the restricted-range species which occur in the North Papuan lowlands (EBA 176). The natural vegetation is montane rain forest.

This EBA is ornithologically poorly known and little visited. The Foya mountains, for example, are uninhabited and there was no record of anyone ever having entered there for any purpose before 1979 (Diamond 1985).

■ Restricted-range species

All of the EBA's restricted-range species occur in hill and montane forest, but only *Ptiloprora mayri* is common to all three of the disjunct mountain ranges. *Amblyornis flavifrons* has the most limited distribution, being confined to one mountain range (Foya). Three restricted-range species occur more widely in other Papuan montane EBAs.

■ Threats and conservation

Being inaccessible, the EBA is relatively secure. However, *Rallina mayri* was not found on a survey of the Cyclops mountains in 1992 (K. D. Bishop *in litt.* 1994) and so is classified as Data Deficient. *Amblyornis flavifrons* is considered Near Threatened on account of its small range in the Foya mountains and because of this is vulnerable to any possible future change. Black Sicklebill *Epimachus fastuosus* is a widespread threatened species (classified as Vulnerable) which is known from a few localities in the Torricelli and Bewani mountains in this EBA.

Distribution patterns of restricted-range species

Species (ordered geographically)	Foya	Cyclops	N Coastal Range	Other EBAs, SAs
Amblyornis flavifrons	●	–	–	
Peneothello cryptoleucus	●	–	–	●
Pachycephalopsis hattamensis	●	–	–	●
Ptiloprora mayri	●	●	●	–
Rallina mayri	–	●	●	–
Melampitta gigantea	–	–	●	●
Total	4	2	3	

● Present	? Present?	Threatened spp. shown in **bold**
○ Extinct?	R Reintroduced	Other EBAs, SAs
X Extinct	I Introduced	

see 'Status and habitat' table

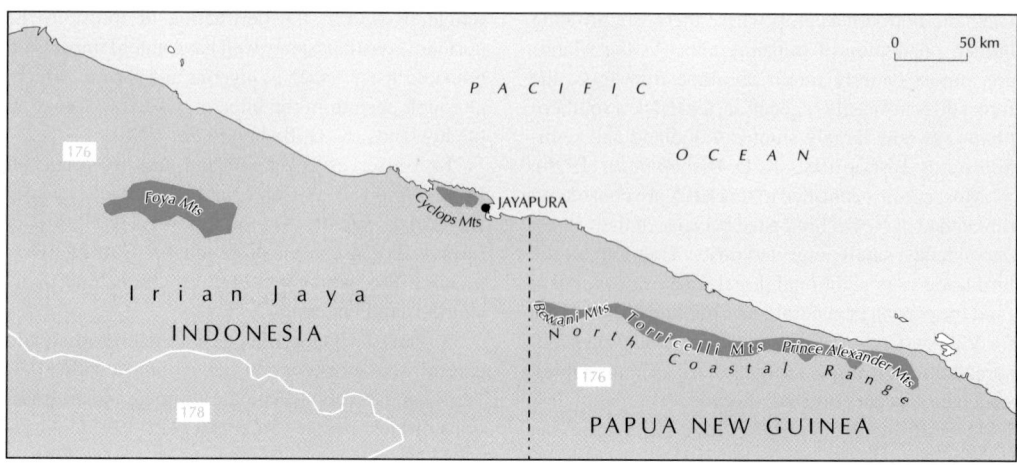

Status and habitat of restricted-range species

Species (ordered taxonomically)	Global status	Other EBAs (and SAs)	Altitude (m)	Habitat
Mayr's Forest-rail *Rallina mayri*	DD	—	1,100–2,200	Forest
Greater Melampitta *Melampitta gigantea*	lc	173,178	650–1,400	Hill/montane forest on rugged limestone karst; roosts in sink holes
Smoky Robin *Peneothello cryptoleucus*	lc	173,178	>1,400	Forest, forest edge
Green-backed Robin *Pachycephalopsis hattamensis*	lc	173,178 (s113)	700–1,650	Hill/montane forest
Mayr's Honeyeater *Ptiloprora mayri*	lc	—	1,200–2,150	Montane forest, mossy forest, secondary forest
Golden-fronted Bowerbird *Amblyornis flavifrons*	nt	—	1,000–2,000	Hill forest

Global status (see p. 679 for definitions)	EX Extinct EW Extinct in the Wild	with year of last record	CR Critical EN Endangered VU Vulnerable	threatened species	cd Conservation Dependent nt Near Threatened lc Least Concern	DD Data Deficient NE Not Evaluated

Other EBAs (and SAs) (see p. 83 for locations): bracketed numbers are Secondary Areas; ˣ extinct in that EBA or SA.

Although the steepness of the terrain in this EBA makes the forests unsuitable for logging, the use of helicopters for timber extraction is becoming more widespread in Papua New Guinea and this practice could conceivably be employed in the future if more readily available supplies are exhausted (WWF/IUCN 1994–1995).

Considerable areas of hill and montane forest are included in the Foya Nature Reserve (10,000 km²), the second largest terrestrial conservation area in Indonesia, and in the Pegunungan Cyclops Nature Reserve (225 km²) (Sujatnika *et al.* 1995; see also Diamond 1986, WWF/IUCN 1994–1995). Never-theless, the lowland forests near the Cyclops mountains are at risk, being so close to Irian Jaya's main town of Jayapura and a large transmigration settlement. It is not known what effects the loss of these lowland forests may have on upper-elevation species that may seasonally depend on food supplies lower down (K. D. Bishop *in litt.* 1996).

The North Coastal Range has been identified as an important area for terrestrial biodiversity in Papua New Guinea, with the Bewani mountains in particular being in need of further survey and research (Beehler 1993).

176 North Papuan lowlands

PRIORITY HIGH

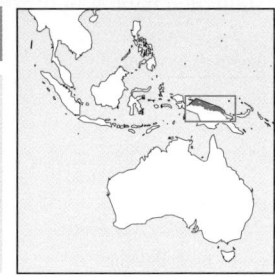

Key habitats Lowland rain forest, swamp/flooded forest, mangroves

Main threats Limited habitat loss (e.g. due to logging, settlement, road-building)

Biological importance ● ● ●
Current threat level ● ● ●

Area 180,000 km²   **Altitude** 0–1,000 m

Countries Indonesia, Papua New Guinea

Restricted-range species	Threatened	Total
Confined to this EBA	1	5
Present also in other EBAs, SAs	0	4
Total	1	9

■ General characteristics

This lowland EBA extends from the south-east of Geelvink bay in the Indonesian province of Irian Jaya to the Huon peninsula in Papua New Guinea. Records of restricted-range birds are very scattered throughout the area but it is assumed to include coastal regions as well as the lower reaches of the Mamberamo–Idenburg– Rouffaer, Sepik–Ramu and Markham–Watut rivers. The EBA is separated from the North Papuan mountains (EBA 175), Adelbert–Huon ranges (EBA 177) and Central Papuan ranges (EBA 178) by the 1,000 m contour; the distributions of some restricted-range species from these different EBAs may overlap at their outer limits.

The habitat of this region is largely lowland rain forest, swamp forest and flooded alluvial forest, with patches of mangrove on the coast, areas of grassland and extensive swampy plains around the river systems, especially those of the Sepik and Ramu. Much of the area remains unexplored.

■ Restricted-range species

All the restricted-range species occur in lowland rain forest and some have been recorded in swamp/floodplain forest and in mangrove habitats. *Philemon brassi* was only discovered in 1939 in a small area of

flooded canegrass and dense secondary forest around a lagoon on the Idenburg river, but has been recorded since from the lower Mamberamo river.

No species occurs throughout this large EBA , but there is sufficient overlap between the species' ranges for the area to qualify as a single EBA. *Poecilodryas placens* is very patchily distributed throughout New Guinea and in this EBA is known only from the Madang area.

Distribution patterns of restricted-range species

Species (ordered geographically)	Mamberamo–Idenberg–Rouffaer	Sepik–Ramu	Adelbert–Huon lowlands	Other EBAs, SAs
Psittaculirostris salvadorii	●	–	–	–
Philemon brassi	●	–	–	–
Epimachus bruijnii	●	–	–	–
Corvus fuscicapillus	●	–	–	●
Pachycephala leucogastra	●	●	–	●
Chalcopsitta duivenbodei	●	●	●	–
Psittaculirostris edwardsii	–	●	●	–
Tanysiptera nympha	–	●	●	●
Poecilodryas placens	–	–	●	●
Total	6	3	4	

● Present	? Present?	Threatened spp. shown in **bold** — see 'Status and habitat' table
○ Extinct?	R Reintroduced	
X Extinct	I Introduced	Other EBAs, SAs

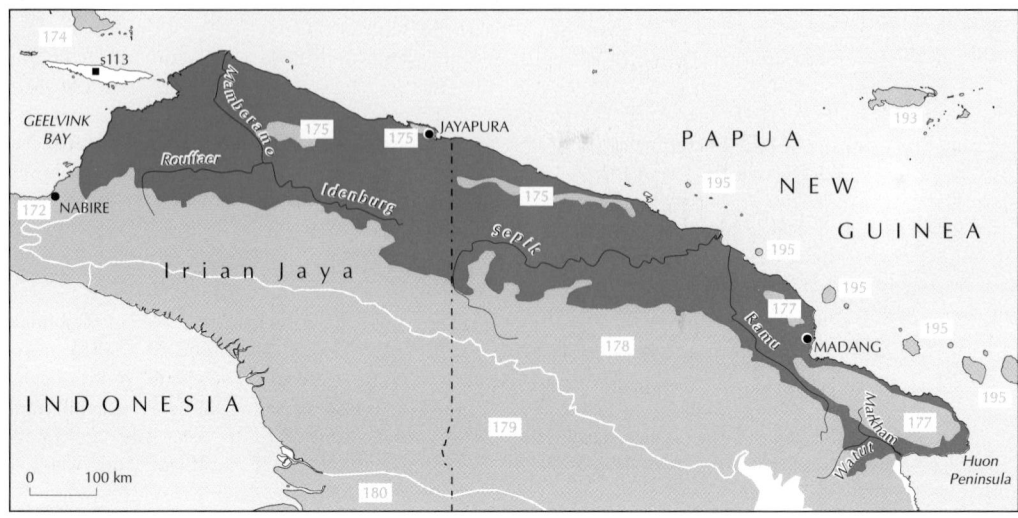

Status and habitat of restricted-range species

Species (ordered taxonomically)	Global status	Other EBAs (and SAs)	Altitude (m)	Habitat
Brown Lory *Chalcopsitta duivenbodei*	lc	—	Lowlands to 200	Forest, alluvial forest, forest edge, coastal clearings close to forest
Edwards's Fig-parrot *Psittaculirostris edwardsii*	lc	—	0–800	Forest, forest edge
Salvadori's Fig-parrot *Psittaculirostris salvadorii*	VU	—	0–400	Forest
Red-breasted Paradise-kingfisher *Tanysiptera nympha*	lc	172	Lowlands to 900(–1,500)	Forest, secondary forest, mangroves
Olive-yellow Robin *Poecilodryas placens*	DD	172,179 (s114)	100–1,450	Forest undergrowth
White-bellied Whistler *Pachycephala leucogastra*	lc	197 (s114)	Lowlands	Mangroves, plantations, scrub, other open coastal habitats
Brass's Friarbird *Philemon brassi*	DD	—	c.50	Flooded cane grass, dense secondary forest
Pale-billed Sicklebill *Epimachus bruijnii*	nt	—	Lowlands to 500	Floodplain forest, limestone hill forest, secondary forest, sometimes forest edge
Brown-headed Crow *Corvus fuscicapillus*	nt	172 (s112)	0–500	Forest, mangroves

Global status (see p. 679 for definitions)	EX Extinct EW Extinct in the Wild	} with year of last record	CR Critical EN Endangered VU Vulnerable	} threatened species	cd Conservation Dependent nt Near Threatened lc Least Concern	DD Data Deficient NE Not Evaluated

Other EBAs (and SAs) (see p. 83 for locations): bracketed numbers are Secondary Areas; ˣ extinct in that EBA or SA.

■ Threats and conservation

Overall this region remains relatively undisturbed as it is inhabited by nomadic hunter-gatherer tribes—as elsewhere in New Guinea. There is, however, local settlement of an immigrant population in trans-migration sites on the Indonesian side of the EBA (e.g. near Nabire and Jayapura, the capital of the province), and associated logging and land clear-

Brass's Friarbird *Philemon brassi*, only recently discovered, appears to have a very small range in the western part of this EBA.

ance. Potential additional threats come from a huge dam, which has been proposed for the Mamberamo gorge, as well as various other major timber and agricultural schemes (K. D. Bishop *in litt.* 1996). The construction of the Trans-Irian Highway, to connect Jayapura and Wamena, will speed up the development of this area by giving improved access (Sujatnika *et al.* 1995).

One species which appears to be particularly susceptible to developing timber schemes and to the depredations of the local parrot trade is *Psittaculirostris salvadorii* (Beehler 1985, K. D. Bishop *in litt.* 1996). Northern Cassowary *Casuarius unappendiculatus*, New Guinea Harpy Eagle *Harpyopsis novaeguineae* and Victoria Crowned-pigeon *Goura victoria* are widespread threatened species (all classified as Vulnerable) which occur in this EBA, and all are susceptible to hunting wherever access to their habitat is increased.

The lowland forest and floodplains of the Mamberamo and Idenburg are within the boundaries of the Foja Nature Reserve, which is Indonesia's second largest terrestrial conservation area, with a total area of c.10,000 km². Additional lowland areas in central-north Irian Jaya are covered by the Jayawijaya Wildlife Sanctuary (8,000 km²) (Sujatnika *et al.* 1995; see also WWF/IUCN 1994–1995).

In Papua New Guinea the middle Sepik, Sepik delta, middle Ramu, Ramu basin, and Watut hills and watershed have been identified by Beehler (1993) as sites which are important for terrestrial and wetland biodiversity.

177 Adelbert and Huon ranges

PRIORITY HIGH

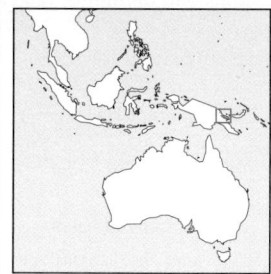

Key habitats Montane rain forest, subalpine forest, alpine grassland

Main threats Unquantified habitat loss (e.g. due to subsistence agriculture, settlement)

Biological importance ● ○ ○
Current threat level ● ○ ○

Area 14,000 km² **Altitude** 1,000–4,100 m

Countries Papua New Guinea

Restricted-range species	Threatened	Total
Confined to this EBA	2	6
Present also in other EBAs, SAs	0	5
Total	2	11

■ General characteristics

Included within this EBA are the Adelbert mountains and also the Finisterre, Saruwaged and Rawlinson ranges of the Huon peninsula in north-east Papua New Guinea. The EBA's lower limits have been defined by the 1,000 m contour although a few of the restricted-range birds may occur below this and might therefore overlap with the ranges of restricted-range species from the North Papuan lowlands (EBA 176).

Habitats include montane and subalpine forest, with alpine grassland above the treeline at c.3,000 m.

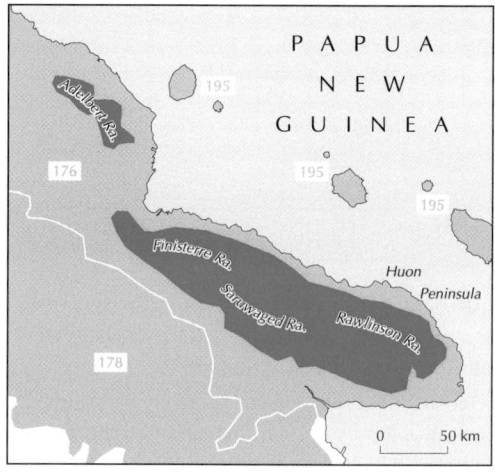

This subalpine forest on Mt Salawaket in the Huon Peninsula is home to Huon Astrapia *Astrapia rothschildi*. These forests are more secure than those at mid-altitudes which are more suitable for subsistence agriculture.

■ Restricted-range species

All of the EBA's restricted-range species occur in forest, apart from *Anthus gutturalis* which occurs at the highest altitudes in alpine grassland.

Locality data for this EBA are generally poor, especially in the Finisterre range, which is virtually unstudied. Of the ten species present in the Huon

Distribution patterns of restricted-range species

Species (ordered geographically)	Adelbert	Huon	Other EBAs, SAs
Sericulus bakeri	●	–	–
Parotia wahnesi	●	●	–
Ptiloprora guisei	●	●	●
Melidectes foersteri	–	●	●
Melipotes ater	–	●	–
Astrapia rothschildi	–	●	–
Paradisaea guilielmi	–	●	–
Eurostopodus archboldi	–	●	●
Anthus gutturalis	–	●	●
Ptiloprora meekiana	–	●	●
Melidectes ochromelas	–	●	●
Total	3	10	

● Present	? Present?	Threatened spp. shown in **bold**	see 'Status and habitat' table
○ Extinct?	R Reintroduced		
X Extinct	I Introduced	Other EBAs, SAs	

Status and habitat of restricted-range species

Species (ordered taxonomically)	Global status	Other EBAs (and SAs)	Altitude (m)	Habitat
Mountain Eared-nightjar *Eurostopodus archboldi*	lc	173,178	(2,200–) 2,400–3,200	Montane forest, stunted cloud forest
Alpine Pipit *Anthus gutturalis*	lc	178	(2,575–) 3,200–4,100	Alpine grassland (often associated with small shrubs), marshes
Olive-streaked Honeyeater *Ptiloprora meekiana*	lc	178	1,500–2,800	Montane forest, secondary forest
Rufous-backed Honeyeater *Ptiloprora guisei*	lc	178	1,300–3,500	Forest (esp. mossy forest), forest edge, secondary forest
Cinnamon-browed Melidectes *Melidectes ochromelas*	lc	173,178	1,100–2,000	Forest, forest edge
Huon Melidectes *Melidectes foersteri*	lc	—	1,600–3,300	Montane forest
Spangled Honeyeater *Melipotes ater*	lc	—	1,200–3,300	Forest, secondary forest, gardens
Fire-maned Bowerbird *Sericulus bakeri*	VU	—	900–1,400	Hill and montane forest; visits food trees in secondary growth at forest edge
Wahnes's Parotia *Parotia wahnesi*	VU	—	1,200–1,800	Mid-montane forest; some records from secondary growth and gardens
Huon Astrapia *Astrapia rothschildi*	lc	—	1,450–3,500	Montane and subalpine forest, secondary forest, gardens
Emperor Bird-of-paradise *Paradisaea guilielmi*	nt	—	500–1,800	Forest, forest edge

Global status (see p. 679 for definitions)
EX Extinct
EW Extinct in the Wild } with year of last record
CR Critical
EN Endangered
VU Vulnerable } threatened species
cd Conservation Dependent
nt Near Threatened
lc Least Concern
DD Data Deficient
NE Not Evaluated

Other EBAs (and SAs) (see p. 83 for locations): bracketed numbers are Secondary Areas; ˣ extinct in that EBA or SA.

peninsula, two extend into the Adelbert mountains, and these two regions thus qualify as a single EBA. One species, *Sericulus bakeri*, is confined to the Adelbert, and thus has one of the most circumscribed distributions known for mainland Papua New Guinea. Five species occur more widely in other Papuan montane EBAs.

Birds not certainly identified but similar to the Obscure Berrypecker *Melanocharis arfakiana* (known only from the Arfak mountains, EBA 173, and the upper Angabunga river, EBA 178) have been recorded from the southern Huon peninsula (B. M. Whitney per P. Gregory *in litt.* 1994).

■ Threats and conservation

As elsewhere in New Guinea, this area is inhabited by a large number of tribal groups who depend on biological resources for sustenance. The optimum altitudes for settlement and subsistence agriculture coincide with the narrow altitudinal preferences of *Sericulus bakeri* and *Parotia wahnesi*, which are therefore considered threatened (see WWF/IUCN

K. D. Bishop

Sweet-potato gardens are present throughout the Adelbert ranges.

1994–1995). Salvadori's Teal *Salvadorina waigiuensis* is a widespread threatened species (classified as Vulnerable) which is also recorded from the Huon mountains, on alpine lakes and fast-flowing streams. The region has been identified by Beehler (1993) as being important for terrestrial biodiversity.

178 Central Papuan mountains

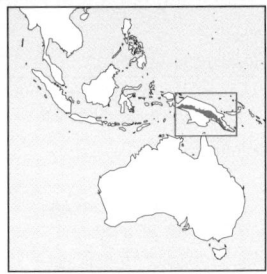

Key habitats Montane and high mountain forest, alpine grasslands

Main threats Moderate habitat loss (e.g. due to logging, mining, road-building), hunting

Biological importance ● ● ●
Current threat level ● ○ ○

Area 190,000 km²   **Altitude** 1,000–4,600 m

Countries Indonesia, Papua New Guinea

Restricted-range species	Threatened	Total
Confined to this EBA	5	39
Present also in other EBAs, SAs	0	14
Total	5	53

■ General characteristics

Upland regions included within this EBA are the Snow mountains (Charles Louis, Weyland and Nassau ranges), Star mountains (Oranje, Star, Victor Emanuel and Hindenburg ranges), Central Highlands (Schrader, Muller and Central ranges), Eastern Highlands (Bismarck, Kubor and Kratke ranges) and the South-east Highlands (Wharton, Herzog and Owen Stanley ranges). These mountain ranges run unbroken from the isthmus of the Vogelkop (EBA 172) in the Indonesian province of Irian Jaya to Milne Bay in Papua New Guinea. Because there are no passes below 1,500 m, lowland species which occur on either side of the mountains are isolated from one another, and separate lowland EBAs are recognized: EBA176 to the north and EBA179 to the south. The lower limit of the present EBA has been defined as the 1,000 m contour, although some of the restricted-range species may occur below this and

there may be some overlap with the distributions of restricted-range species from the adjacent lowland EBAs.

Four different vegetation zones occur in the Papuan mountains: lower montane rain forest (c.500–2,500 m) where the oak *Castanopsis acuminatissima* is predominant; upper montane forest (c.1,500–3,000 m) where the southern beech *Nothofagus* predominates and the forest is often thick with moss; high mountain forest (c.2,500–3,900 m) containing trees of reduced stature, and where conifers (Podocarpaceae) and myrtle (Myrtaceae) increase in importance; and, lastly, alpine shrubbery and grassland above the treeline (Coates 1985, Beehler *et al.* 1986).

■ Restricted-range species

This EBA has the second most restricted-range species of all the EBAs in the south-east Asian island region, as well as a very distinct avifauna, including

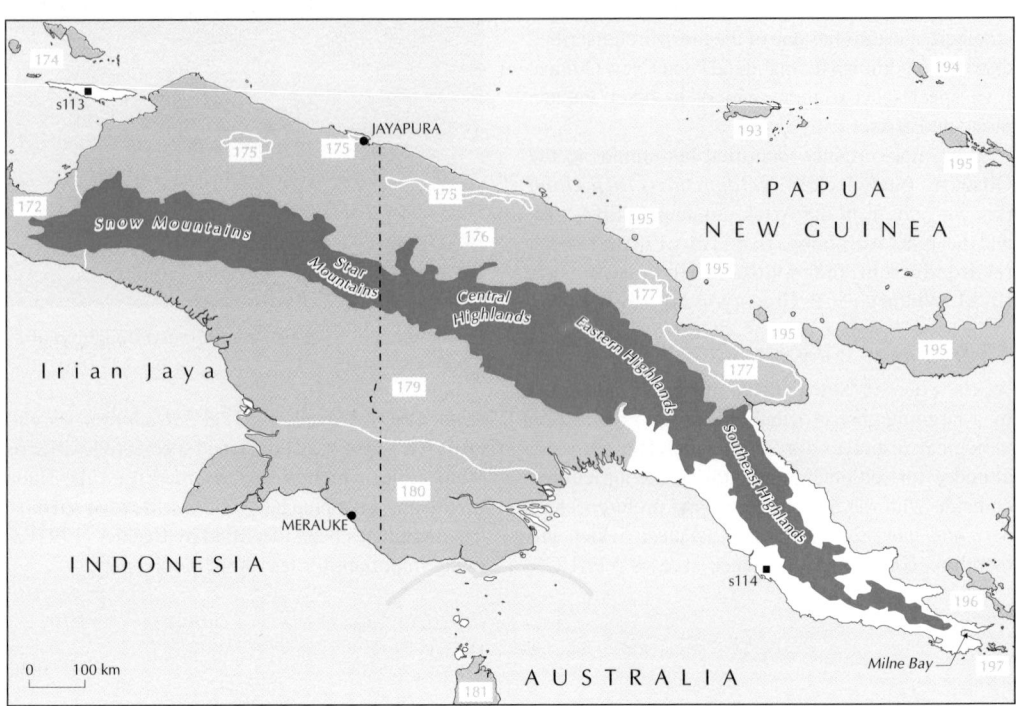

Status and habitat of restricted-range species

Species (ordered taxonomically)	Global status	Other EBAs (and SAs)	Altitude (m)	Habitat
Snow Mountain Quail *Anurophasis monorthonyx*	nt	—	3,100–4,200	Grassland, edge of heavy alpine scrub with trees and brush
Chestnut Forest-rail *Rallina rubra*	lc	173	1,500–3,000	Montane forest, mossy forest
Painted Tiger-parrot *Psittacella picta*	lc	—	(1,370–)2,400 to treeline	Forest, forest edge, secondary forest, alpine shrubbery
Modest Tiger-parrot *Psittacella modesta*	lc	173	1,700–2,800	Forest, forest edge, secondary forest
Archbold's Owlet-nightjar *Aegotheles archboldi*	lc	—	2,100–3,500	Montane forest, mossy forest, subalpine thickets
Mountain Eared-nightjar *Eurostopodus archboldi*	lc	173,177	(2,200–) 2,400–3,200	Montane forest, stunted cloud forest
Bare-legged Swiftlet *Collocalia nuditarsus*	lc	—	<1,500–2,300	Forest, open country for feeding; caves for breeding
Alpine Pipit *Anthus gutturalis*	lc	177	(2,575–) 3,200–4,600	Alpine grassland (often associated with small shrubs), marshes
Greater Ground-robin *Amalocichla sclateriana*	lc	—	2,700–3,900	Montane forest, subalpine habitats
Papuan Whipbird *Androphobus viridis*	DD	—	1,400–3,100+	Montane forest, mossy forest
Greater Melampitta *Melampitta gigantea*	lc	173,175	650–1,400	Hill/montane forest on rugged limestone karst; roosts in sink-holes
Papuan Thornbill *Acanthiza murina*	lc	—	(1,930–) 2,500–3,700	Mossy forest, forest edge
Alpine Robin *Petroica bivittata*	lc	—	2,700–4,000	Forest, alpine shrubbery, forest/alpine grassland edge
Snow Mountain Robin *Petroica archboldi*	DD	—	3,900–4,600	Alpine heaths, rocky tundra above grassland
Smoky Robin *Peneothello cryptoleucus*	lc	173,175	1,400–2,500	Forest, forest edge
Green-backed Robin *Pachycephalopsis hattamensis*	lc	173,175 (s113)	700–1,650	Hill/montane forest, scrub
Lorentz's Whistler *Pachycephala lorentzi*	lc	—	1,800–4,000	Mid-mountain forest, mossy beech forest, alpine scrub
Sooty Shrike-thrush *Colluricincla umbrina*	lc	—	1,400–2,500+	Mid-montane forest, mossy forest, forest shrubbery and thickets
Wattled Ploughbill *Eulacestoma nigropectus*	lc	—	2,000–2,500 (1,650–2,750)	Forest, mossy forest, adjoining disturbed areas, favours thickets of climbing bamboo
Black Sittella *Daphoenositta miranda*	lc	—	2,000–3,700	Upper montane forest, mossy forest, inc. partly cleared areas
Obscure Berrypecker *Melanocharis arfakiana*[1]	DD	173	1,300	Forest, forest edge
Orange-cheeked Honeyeater *Oreornis chrysogenys*	lc	—	(2,600–) 3,250–4,000	Subalpine forest, shrubbery bordering alpine grassland
Leaden Honeyeater *Ptiloprora plumbea*	lc	—	1,000–1,900	Montane forest, forest edge, secondary forest
Olive-streaked Honeyeater *Ptiloprora meekiana*	lc	177	1,500–2,800	Montane forest, secondary forest
Rufous-sided Honeyeater *Ptiloprora erythropleura*	lc	173	1,300–2,800	Montane forest, forest edge, secondary forest
Rufous-backed Honeyeater *Ptiloprora guisei*	lc	177	1,300–2,900	Forest (esp. mossy forest), forest edge, secondary forest
Black-backed Honeyeater *Ptiloprora perstriata*	lc	173	1,700–3,800 (west) 2,500–3,800 (east)	Mossy forest, forest edge, subalpine habitats

cont.

Status and habitat of restricted-range species (cont.)

Species (ordered taxonomically)	Global status	Other EBAs (and SAs)	Altitude (m)	Habitat
Sooty Melidectes *Melidectes fuscus*	lc	—	(2,200–) 3,000–3,700	High mountain and subalpine forest, forest edge, alpine shrubbery
Short-bearded Melidectes *Melidectes nouhuysi*	lc	—	3,200–4,500	Upper limits of forest, forest edge, subalpine shrubbery
Long-bearded Melidectes *Melidectes princeps*	VU	—	3,000–4,200	Mossy forest near treeline, scattered clumps of brush in alpine grassland
Cinnamon-browed Melidectes *Melidectes ochromelas*	lc	173,177	1,100–2,000+	Forest, forest edge
Belford's Melidectes *Melidectes belfordi*	lc	—	1,600–3,800	Mountain forest, forest edge, disturbed areas
Yellow-browed Melidectes *Melidectes rufocrissalis*	lc	—	1,100–2,400	Forest, forest edge, secondary forest, gardens
Mountain Firetail *Oreostruthus fuliginosus*	lc	—	(2,200–) 2,800–3,700	Small openings in montane forest or at treeline, alpine grassland
Black-breasted Munia *Lonchura teerinki*	lc	—	1,100–2,400	Man-made grassland, weedy secondary growth, cultivated edges, gardens
Snow Mountain Munia *Lonchura montana*	lc	—	3,000–3,800 (2,130–4,150)	Alpine grassland (nests in grasses by water), edge of alpine shrubbery, cultivated fields
Alpine Munia *Lonchura monticola*	lc	—	2,700–3,900	Alpine grassland, rock scree on high peaks
Archbold's Bowerbird *Archboldia papuensis*	VU	—	(1,800–) 2,300–2,900	Mixed beech forest, mixed coniferous forest, open frost-disturbed high plateau forest
Streaked Bowerbird *Amblyornis subalaris*	lc	—	1,000–1,400 (700–1,500)	Lower montane forest, tall secondary forest
Yellow-breasted Bird-of-paradise *Loboparadisea sericea*	DD	—	(650–) 1,200–2,100	Montane forest
Crested Bird-of-paradise *Cnemophilus macgregorii*	lc	—	2,300–3,700	Upper montane forest, mossy forest, subalpine shrubbery
Loria's Bird-of-paradise *Cnemophilus loriae*	lc	—	2,000–2,400, (1,450–3,000)	Montane forest, forest edge, secondary forest, gardens
Macgregor's Bird-of-paradise *Macgregoria pulchra*	VU	—	3,200–3,500	Subalpine forest at verge of grassland
Long-tailed Paradigalla *Paradigalla carunculata*	nt	173	1,400–2,200	Mountain forest, forest edge
Short-tailed Paradigalla *Paradigalla brevicauda*	lc	—	1,600–2,800	Montane forest, forest edge, tall trees in secondary growth
Brown Sicklebill *Epimachus meyeri*	lc	—	1,500–3,200	Montane forest, mossy forest, disturbed forest, forest edge
Lawes's Parotia *Parotia lawesii*	lc	—	500–2,300	Mid-montane forest, uncommon at forest edge
Eastern Parotia *Parotia helenae*	lc	—	1,000–1,800	Forest
Splendid Astrapia *Astrapia splendidissima*	lc	—	2,100–2,700 (1,800–3,450)	Montane forest, subalpine forest, forest edge
Ribbon-tailed Astrapia *Astrapia mayeri*	VU	—	2,400–3,400	Upper montane forest, mossy forest, forest edge
Stephanie's Astrapia *Astrapia stephaniae*	lc	—	1,500–2,800	Mountain forest, mossy forest, forest edge, disturbed habitats
King-of-Saxony Bird-of-paradise *Pteridophora alberti*	lc	—	1,500–2,900	High mountain mossy forest, forest edge
Blue Bird-of-paradise *Paradisaea rudolphi*	VU	—	1,400–1,800 (1,000–2,000)	Lower montane forest, forest edge, sometimes gardens

Global status (see p. 679 for definitions)				cd Conservation Dependent	Other EBAs (and SAs) (see p. 83 for locations)	Bracketed numbers are Secondary Areas.
EX	Extinct	with year of last record		nt Near Threatened		ˣ Extinct in that EBA or SA.
EW	Extinct in the Wild			lc Least Concern	Notes	¹ Known in this EBA from a single speci-
CR	Critical	threatened species		DD Data Deficient		men, in 1933.
EN	Endangered			NE Not Evaluated		
VU	Vulnerable					

The male Crested Bird-of-paradise *Cnemophilus macgregorii* (race *macgregorii*) from south-east New Guinea has bright golden-yellow upperparts. This species is an unwary, but inconspicuous, forest-dweller that appears to be largely or entirely frugivorous.

B. Beehler

nine endemic genera: four genera of birds-of-paradise—*Loboparadisea, Cnemophilus, Macgregoria* and *Pteridophora*—together with *Anurophasis, Androphobus, Eulacestoma, Oreornis* and *Oreostruthus*. Most of the restricted-range species occur in forested habitats and these species can be divided into four groups according to the vegetation types with which

they largely associate: lower montane forest, lower–upper montane forest, upper montane–high mountain forest, and high mountain forest. Additionally, six species occur in grasslands only. Because there is overlap between the distributions of birds which

Habitat associations of restricted-range species

Lower montane forest	
Melampitta gigantea	*Ptiloprora meekiana*
Pachycephalopsis	*Ptiloprora erythropleura*
hattamensis	*Ptiloprora guisei*
Melanocharis arfakiana	*Ptiloprora perstriata*
Amblyornis subalaris	*Melidectes fuscus*
Paradisaea rudolphi	*Melidectes belfordi*
	Archboldia papuensis
Lower to upper montane	*Cnemophilus macgregorii*
forest	*Cnemophilus loriae*
Collocalia nuditarsus	*Paradigalla carunculata*
Ptiloprora plumbea	*Paradigalla brevicauda*
Melidectes ochromelas	*Epimachus meyeri*
Melidectes rufocrissalis	*Astrapia splendidissima*
Loboparadisea sericea	**Astrapia mayeri**
Parotia lawesi	*Astrapia stephaniae*
Parotia helenae	*Pteridophora alberti*
Upper montane to high	**High mountain forest to**
mountain forest	**alpine grasslands**
Rallina rubra	*Petroica bivittata*
Psittacella picta	*Melidectes nouhuysi*
Psittacella modesta	**Melidectes princeps**
Aegotheles archboldi	*Oreostruthus fuliginosus*
Eurostopodus archboldi	**Macgregoria pulchra**
Amalocichla sclateriana	
Androphobus viridis	**Alpine grasslands**
Acanthiza murina	*Anurophasis monorthonyx*
Peneothello cryptoleucus	*Anthus gutturalis*
Pachycephala lorentzi	*Petroica archboldi*
Colluricincla umbrina	*Lonchura montana*
Eulacestoma nigropectus	*Lonchura monticola*
Daphoenositta miranda	
Oreornis chrysogenys	**Mid-mountain grasslands**
	Lonchura teerinki

K. D. Bishop

Upper montane forest, here in the Star mountains, is an important habitat for many of this EBA's restricted-range species.

Threatened species (Critical, Endangered, Vulnerable) are shown in **bold**; see 'Status and habitat' table.

have been assigned to these different groups, all restricted-range species occurring in these mountains have been included within a single EBA (contra ICBP 1992).

Distribution patterns of restricted-range species

Species (ordered geographically)	Snow Mts	Star Mts	C & E Highlands	SE Highlands	Other EBAs, SAs
Androphobus viridis	•	?	?	–	–
Petroica archboldi	•	–	–	–	–
Oreornis chrysogenys	•	–	–	–	–
Lonchura teerinki	•	–	–	–	–
Peneothello cryptoleucus	•	–	–	–	○
Ptiloprora erythropleura	•	–	–	–	○
Paradigalla carunculata	•	–	–	–	○
Anurophasis monorthonyx	•	•	–	–	–
Aegotheles archboldi	•	•	–	–	–
Pachycephala lorentzi	•	•	–	–	–
Melidectes nouhuysi	•	•	–	–	–
Lonchura montana	•	•	–	–	–
Astrapia splendidissima	•	•	–	–	–
Archboldia papuensis	•	–	•	–	–
Pachycephalopsis hattamensis	•	–	•	–	○
Colluricincla umbrina	•	–	•	–	–
Paradigalla brevicauda	•	•	•	–	–
Pteridophora alberti	•	•	•	–	–
Rallina rubra	•	•	•	–	○
Psittacella modesta	•	•	•	–	○
Macgregoria pulchra	•	•	•	•	–
Collocalia nuditarsus	•	–	•	•	–
Eurostopodus archboldi	•	–	•	•	○
Ptiloprora meekiana	•	–	•	•	○
Amalocichla sclateriana	•	–	•	•	–
Melampitta gigantea	•	–	–	•	○
Melidectes ochromelas	•	–	•	•	○
Psittacella picta	•	•	•	•	–
Acanthiza murina	•	•	•	•	–
Petroica bivittata	•	•	•	•	–
Eulacestoma nigropectus	•	•	•	•	–
Daphoenositta miranda	•	•	•	•	–
Ptiloprora plumbea	•	•	•	•	–
Melidectes fuscus	•	•	•	•	–
Melidectes belfordi	•	•	•	•	–
Oreostruthus fuliginosus	•	•	•	•	–
Loboparadisea sericea	•	•	•	•	–
Cnemophilus loriae	•	•	•	•	–
Epimachus meyeri	•	•	•	•	–
Anthus gutturalis	•	•	•	•	○
Ptiloprora perstriata	•	•	•	•	○
Melidectes rufocrissalis	–	•	•	•	–
Cnemophilus macgregorii	–	•	•	•	–
Melidectes princeps	–	–	•	–	–
Astrapia mayeri	–	–	•	–	–
Parotia lawesi	–	–	•	•	–
Astrapia stephaniae	–	–	•	•	–
Paradisaea rudolphi	–	–	•	•	–
Ptiloprora guisei	–	–	•	•	○
Melanocharis arfakiana	–	–	?	•	○
Lonchura monticola	–	–	–	•	–
Amblyornis subalaris	–	–	–	•	–
Parotia helenae	–	–	–	•	–
Total	41	28	32	31	

• Present   ? Present?
○ Extinct?   R Reintroduced
X Extinct   I Introduced

Threatened spp. shown in **bold**
Other EBAs, SAs   } see 'Status and habitat' table

The long central mountain ranges of this enormous EBA are a formidable barrier to dispersal and many species are thus limited in their distributions just to certain ranges, e.g. nine species are endemic to the Snow–Star mountains and eight to the Central–South-east Highlands. Several species are very patchily distributed throughout the EBA and it has been difficult to determine which of these genuinely qualify as having ranges of less than 50,000 km^2; *Loboparadisea sericea*, for example, occurs along the length of the Central Ranges, but is often uncommon or absent from seemingly appropriate habitats for reasons unknown (but possibly related to the presence or absence of important food plants: Beehler *et al.* 1986, Coates 1990)—or it may simply be overlooked because it is unobtrusive and inhabits very rugged and rarely visited terrain (K. D. Bishop *in litt.* 1994, 1996).

In general this region is relatively little studied ornithologically and therefore several of the species which appear to be very scarce and/or have disjunct distributions could in reality be more common or have more contiguous ranges. For example, *Androphobus viridis* was formerly known from the Snow mountains only, but since 1990 there have been at least four possible sight records from the Ambua area, near Tari, in the Eastern Highlands, and it may also have been recorded from the Star mountains in 1992. *Melanocharis arfakiana* is known only from one specimen in this EBA (collected in 1933) from the upper Angabunga river in the South-east Highlands, but sightings have been reported from near Tabuli in the Central Highlands, and it could therefore occur more widely. *Petroica archboldi* is known only from the highest peaks of the Snow mountains and there are no recent records.

■ Threats and conservation

The montane rain forests and alpine grasslands of this EBA remain largely undisturbed—even untouched—owing to their very large extent and geographical isolation, combined with the traditional lifestyle and low population density of local people. However, logging (both from large-scale commercial operators and from smaller-scale initiatives which use walkabout sawmills), mining and road-building (e.g. the Trans-Irian Highway from Jayapura to Merauke) are significant local threats, and forest encroachment, illicit logging and wildlife harvesting need to be monitored and controlled (Sujatnika *et al.* 1995, P. Gregory *in litt.* 1994, K. D. Bishop *in litt.* 1996).

Just five species are currently classified as threatened. *Melidectes princeps* is known from only a few mountains in the Eastern Highlands, where it is thinly distributed and suffers disturbance to its limited habitat, which is patchy and dissected. For some species, loss of habitat is exacerbated by hunting, e.g. *Macgregoria pulchra*, which is a popular quarry species, being unwary and site-faithful and therefore easy to kill, and *Astrapia mayeri* and *Paradisaea rudolphi*, which are both hunted for their tail plumes used in local costumes. *Archboldia papuensis* is very patchily distributed, with western and eastern populations appearing to be widely separated; it is generally rare and locally threatened by timber operations. Salvadori's Teal *Salvadorina waigiuensis*, Pesquet's Parrot *Psittrichas fulgidus* and Black Sicklebill *Epimachus fastuosus* are widespread threatened species (all classified as Vulnerable) which also occur in this EBA; all are affected by hunting and *S. waigiuensis* may also suffer locally from the pollution of streams and lakes.

Four restricted-range species are considered Data Deficient because of uncertainties associated with their range size (which may or may not be very small) and lack of records (see 'Restricted-range species', above).

A tribesman from the Central Papuan mountains in traditional dress. The high-altitude forest and grassland in this EBA remain largely undisturbed because there is a low population density of people who largely follow a subsistence lifestyle.

Extensive areas of the habitats of this EBA are contained within three large protected areas on the Irian Jaya side: Gunung Lorentz Nature Reserve (in the Snow mountains, 21,500 km^2), which is Indonesia's largest protected area; Jayawijaya Wildlife Sanctuary (Star mountains, 8,000 km^2); and the Enarotali Nature Reserve (Weyland mountains, 3,000 km^2). However, the montane forests in this last reserve have been degraded, and land around Lake Paniai, at the reserve's centre, is heavily populated; consideration should be given to establishing another reserve to cover a spectrum of habitat types and endemic flora and fauna, and to protect the water catchment (Sujatnika *et al.* 1995). There are proposals to establish a national park (possibly a World Heritage Site) at Lorentz covering 14,300 km^2.

In Papua New Guinea, Mt Scorpion (Star mountains), Doma Peaks and Mt Giluwe (Central Highlands), Crater Mountain (Eastern Highlands), Mt Albert Edward and Mt Suckling (South-east Highlands) have been identified as important areas for terrestrial biodiversity by Beehler (1993).

Forest is the key habitat for the birds of this EBA, but alpine grassland—such as this at c.4,000 m in the Star mountains—also has its own endemics.

179 South Papuan lowlands

PRIORITY HIGH

Key habitats Lowland and hill rain forest, swampy forest

Main threats Limited habitat loss (e.g. due to logging, copper- and gold-mining, road-building)

Biological importance ● ● ●
Current threat level ● ● ●

Area 160,000 km²   **Altitude** 0–1,000 m

Countries Indonesia, Papua New Guinea

Restricted-range species	Threatened	Total
Confined to this EBA	0	3
Present also in other EBAs, SAs	0	3
Total	0	6

■ General characteristics

This EBA includes the south-west lowlands and foothills bordering the Snow and Star mountains from the Mimika river (in the Indonesian province of Irian Jaya) to the drainages of the Kikori and Purari rivers (in Papua New Guinea), including the upper waters of the Fly and Strickland rivers. The northern boundary of the EBA is defined by the 1,000 m contour which divides it from the Central Papuan ranges (EBA 178), and the southern boundary by the coastline and the Trans-Fly (EBA 180).

The vegetation of the region includes lowland, hill and lower montane rain forest with extensive inland swamps following the main river courses.

■ Restricted-range birds

The restricted-range species of this EBA represent a mixed group both in terms of their habitat require-

ments and their distribution. In general data are few and the birds may be more widely distributed in fact than current records indicate. *Ptilinopus wallacii* has been recorded from the Mimika and Noord rivers (but may be an irregular nomad or possibly a vagrant: K. D. Bishop *in litt.* 1996), *Charmosyna multistriata* from the slopes of the Snow mountains east to Mt Bosavi, and *Paradisaea apoda* from Mimika river east to the Strickland river. The remaining species have patchy distributions: *Pitohui incertus* is currently known only from the Noord and upper Fly rivers, *Cinclosoma ajax* (in this EBA) from the upper Fly region including Palmer river to Mt Bosavi, and *Poecilodryas placens* from Mt Bosavi to the Purari River region.

Campbell's Fairywren *Malurus* (*grayi*) *campbelli* from Mt Bosavi and Kiunga is treated as a full species by Schodde and Weatherly (1983) and Sibley and

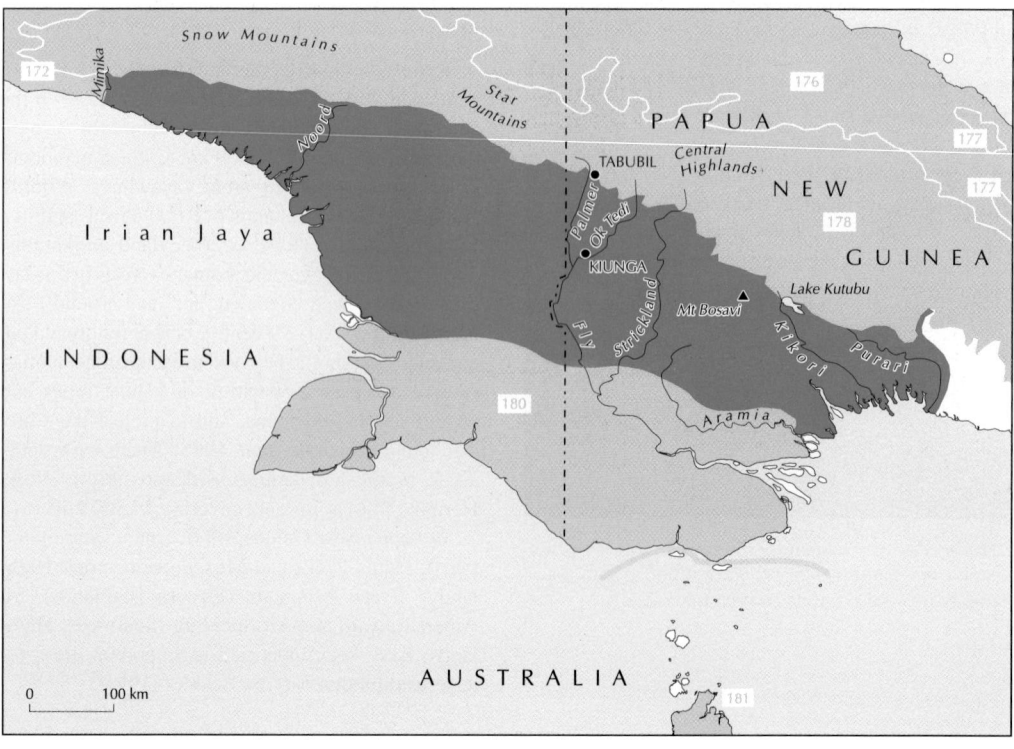

Status and habitat of restricted-range species

Species (ordered taxonomically)	Global status	Other EBAs (and SAs)	Altitude (m)	Habitat
Wallace's Fruit-dove *Ptilinopus wallacii*	lc	165 (s112)	Lowlands	Riverine forest, coastal forest, scrub, agricultural land
Striated Lorikeet *Charmosyna multistriata*	nt	—	80-1,800	Hill and lower montane forest
Painted Quail-thrush *Cinclosoma ajax*	lc	172,180 (s114)	0-500	Forest, monsoon forest, gallery forest, adjoining tall secondary growth
Olive-yellow Robin *Poecilodryas placens*	DD	172,176 (s114)	100-1,450	Forest
White-bellied Pitohui *Pitohui incertus*	lc	—	0-300	Annually flooded alluvial forest with a broken canopy in areas of high rainfall
Greater Bird-of-paradise *Paradisaea apoda*	lc	—	0-950	Forest, forest edge

Global status (see p. 679 for definitions)	EX	Extinct	with year of last record	CR	Critical	threatened species	cd	Conservation Dependent	DD	Data Deficient
	EW	Extinct in the Wild		EN	Endangered		nt	Near Threatened	NE	Not Evaluated
				VU	Vulnerable		lc	Least Concern		

Other EBAs (and SAs) (see p. 83 for locations): bracketed numbers are Secondary Areas; [x] extinct in that EBA or SA.

Monroe (1990, 1993), but is considered by LeCroy and Diamond (1995) to be a subspecies and is not included here.

■ Threats and conservation

Annual observations made during flights over this region since 1985 indicate that there appears to be very little overall change to the status of the forests. Large areas are inaccessible and pristine. However, mining (for copper and gold) and associated logging is a local threat to the wildlife around Tabubil (the mine's township), and logging and road-building are increasing around Kiunga. This permits access to a vast area of forest that would otherwise have been sparsely populated and virtually untouched. Similar mining and logging operations are active in the Snow and Star mountains (K. D. Bishop *in litt.* 1996).

The mining activities of Porgera Joint Venture Ltd and (particularly) Ok Tedi Mining Ltd at Tabubil, have been the focus of significant national and international attention. In some places silt from the mine workings has spread from the riverbanks killing all vegetation. However, an appraisal of the long-term implications of development activities within the whole catchment draws attention to the perhaps more serious threat to biodiversity from large-scale commercial logging operations. Pressure for this will continue to grow as forestry offers an important alternative source of income beyond the life of the mines, which is planned to finish in c.2010 (IUCN 1995).

Although none of the restricted-range species has been identified as threatened, there are other widespread threatened birds which occur in this region: Southern Cassowary *Casuarius casuarius*, Southern Crowned-pigeon *Goura scheepmakeri*, New Guinea Harpy Eagle *Harpyopsis novaeguineae* and Pesquet's Parrot *Psittrichas fulgidus* (all classified as Vulnerable). Despite laws prohibiting the possession of firearms in the Tabubil area, the evidence that they are still in use is apparent in the number of large birds (including some of these threatened species) and mammals that have been shot and are on sale in local markets (K. D. Bishop *in litt.* 1996).

There is one protected area in the south-west which has lowland alluvial and hill rain forest within its boundaries—Gunung Lorentz Nature Reserve, which extends from sea-level into the Central Papuan ranges (EBA 178) and includes the Mimika–Otakwa water catchment. There are recent proposals to upgrade the area to a national park and World Heritage Site (WWF/IUCN 1994–1995). This is probably the single most important reserve in New Guinea.

The old-growth wet rain forests in the upper Fly lowlands, the Mt Bosavi/Aramia watershed, the Kikori Karst/Lake Kutubu area and the Purari basin have all been identified by Beehler (1993) as important areas for terrestrial biodiversity in Papua New Guinea.

180 Trans-Fly

Key habitats Wetlands, savanna, monsoon forest, gallery forest

Main threats Moderate habitat loss (e.g. due to settlement, agriculture), introduced species, hunting

Biological importance ● ● ○

Current threat level ● ○ ○

Area 94,000 km²   **Altitude** 0–90 m

Countries Indonesia, Papua New Guinea

Restricted-range species	Threatened	Total
Confined to this EBA	1	3
Present also in other EBAs, SAs	0	3
Total	1	6

■ General characteristics

Spanning the border between Papua New Guinea and the Indonesian province of Irian Jaya, this EBA encompasses the lowlands south of and bordered by the Digul, Fly and Aramia rivers—one of the most extensive areas of low relief in New Guinea.

The southern region of New Guinea has a strongly seasonal climate and the dominant vegetation types are savanna and monsoon forest which are comparable to those of northern Australia. A wide variety of habitats is present within the EBA including significant expanses of savanna and woodland, seasonally inundated grassland, marsh, reedbeds, monsoon forest, gallery forest, mangroves and tidal mudflats.

■ Restricted-range species

The restricted-range species occur in a variety of wetland, savanna and forest types. Five are confined entirely to this EBA and the Aru Islands (treated separately as Secondary Area s112). The sixth species, *Cinclosoma ajax*, has a very patchy distribution in this EBA and in other EBAs and Secondary Areas.

Megalurus albolimbatus has a particularly small range, being known from a few localities only—including Lake Daviumbu on the middle Fly river, the Bensbach river and Wasur National Park in Irian Jaya—although much potential habitat is unsurveyed and it could therefore occur more widely. It appears to be highly specialized in its wetland habitat requirements, birds in the Wasur National Park being confined during the breeding season to stands of tall, coarse sedges (N. Stronach *in litt.* 1996).

■ Threats and conservation

As with other regions of New Guinea, this EBA is inhabited by a large number of sparsely distributed tribal groups which depend on local biological resources for sustenance. Access is mostly poor and consequently the region has suffered little disturbance overall (WWF/IUCN 1994–1995). However, the population in the Indonesian part of the EBA has been increased through transmigration settlement, and the resulting increase in hunting pressure, trade in birds, conversion of natural habitats for agriculture,

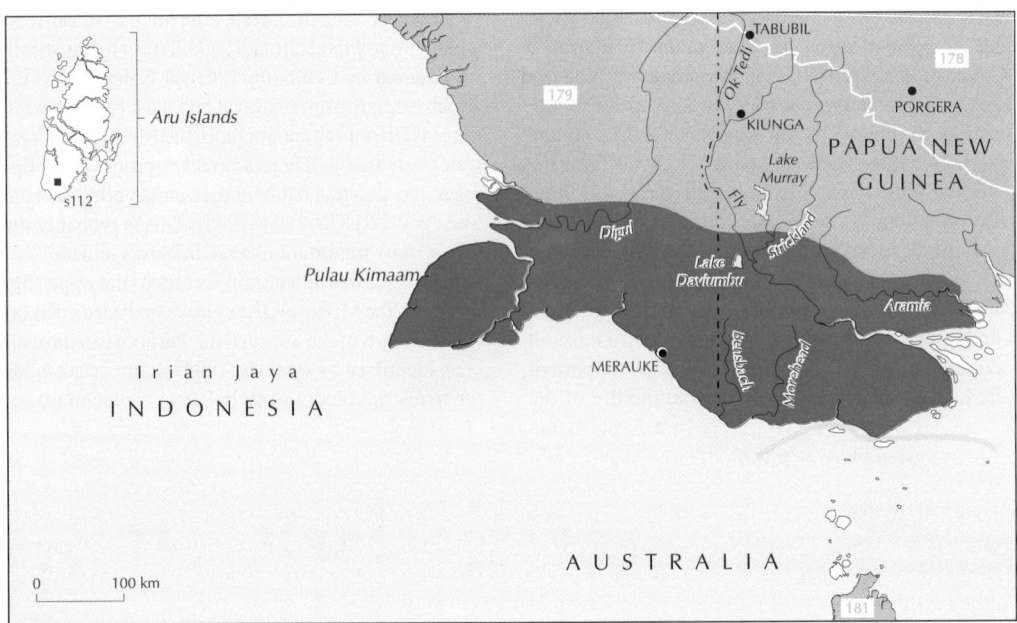

Status and habitat of restricted-range species

Species (ordered taxonomically)	Global status	Other EBAs (and SAs)	Habitat
Spangled Kookaburra *Dacelo tyro*	lc	(s112)	Savanna, gallery forest, thickets on the edge of seasonal swamps
Little Paradise-kingfisher *Tanysiptera hydrocharis*	DD	(s112)	Monsoon forest, gallery forest, tall secondary growth
Painted Quail-thrush *Cinclosoma ajax*	lc	172,179 (s114)	Monsoon forest, gallery forest, adjoining tall secondary growth
Fly River Grassbird *Megalurus albolimbatus*	VU	—	Stands of reeds, sedge, lotus lilies and floating rice grass
Grey-crowned Munia *Lonchura nevermanni*	nt	—	Savanna, marshy grassland, reedbeds
Black Munia *Lonchura stygia*	nt	—	Savanna, reedbeds, inundated grasslands, floating grass mats

Global status (see p. 679 for definitions)	EX Extinct EW Extinct in the Wild } with year of last record	CR Critical EN Endangered VU Vulnerable } threatened species	cd Conservation Dependent nt Near Threatened lc Least Concern	DD Data Deficient NE Not Evaluated

Other EBAs (and SAs) (see p. 83 for locations): bracketed numbers are Secondary Areas; [x] extinct in that EBA or SA.

and unsustainable cutting of forest trees for timber have affected some wildlife habitats in general and as well as reducing populations of particular species (N. Stronach *in litt.* 1993, 1996). The building of new roads into the region, e.g. the Trans-Irian Highway between Jayapura and Merauke, will also result in the local depletion or extinction of some species (K. D. Bishop *in litt.* 1993, P. Gregory *in litt.* 1996).

Additional threats come from introduced rusa deer *Cervus timorensis* which overgraze and trample reedbeds, especially in the Bensbach area—although, according to local people, there has been a recovery of wetland habitats following major reductions in the deer population over the past ten years. Though little studied, the effects of introduced animals are likely to be much wider than just those due to deer. As a further example, grasslands in general appear to be under threat by encroachment of swamp woodland, itself possibly promoted by the activities of both deer and pigs, which cause changes in hydrology favouring tree establishment (N. Stronach *in litt.* 1993, 1996). There are recent rumours of monkeys (presumably macaques) in the lower Fly/Irian border region, probably brought here by Javanese migrants (P. Gregory *in litt.* 1994); if these animals become established they could cause an ecological disaster throughout New Guinea, predating on nests and perhaps even out-competing fruit-eating birds which have evolved in the absence of primates.

The mining activities of Porgera Joint Venture Ltd and (particularly) Ok Tedi Mining Ltd (at Tabubil) have been the focus of significant national and international attention, and an appraisal of the long-term implications of development activities within the whole catchment has been undertaken (IUCN 1995). Although silt from the mine workings at Ok Tedi has spread from the riverbanks killing all vegetation in places, only relatively small areas are affected and fish stocks in the mid and lower Fly appear much as in the past; the situation along the Strickland river, where the gold mine waste from Porgera enters, is less well known, and toxicity may be higher (P. Gregory *in litt.* 1996).

The region has been identified by Beehler (1993) as important for terrestrial and wetland biodiversity in Papua New Guinea. As well as being important for restricted-range species, three widespread threatened birds occur there—Southern Cassowary *Cassuarius cassuarius*, Southern Crowned-pigeon *Goura scheepmakeri* and New Guinea Harpy Eagle *Harpyopsis novaeguineae* (all classified as Vulnerable)—and it is a famous haven for widespread wetland birds, including large numbers of wintering Australian and Palearctic waders and waterfowl. In Australian drought years the Trans-Fly becomes an important refuge for Australian wetland birds.

There is a protected area on the Irian Jayan side, Wasur National Park (3,080 km²), and contiguous with this on the Papua New Guinea side is Tonda Wildlife Management Area (5,900 km²) which includes the floodplains of the Bensback and Morehead rivers. Within Wasur National Park there is pressure to manipulate water-levels by engineering projects, canalization, etc., to supply water to Merauke, and in both protected areas grassland is changing to woodland at a rapid rate (N. Stronach *in litt.* 1996). The Danau Bian Wildlife Sanctuary (694 km²), to the north of Wasur, and Pulau Kimaam (6,000 km²), an island separated from the mainland by a narrow channel, both cover extensive swamps, freshwater lakes and associated marshes, and monsoon and alluvial forests (Scott 1989, Sujatnika *et al.* 1995).

181 | Cape York

Key habitats Eucalypt woodland, lowland rain forest, mangroves

Main threats Moderate habitat loss (e.g. due to fire), trapping, introduced species

Biological importance ● ● ○
Current threat level ● ● ●

Area 99,000 km² **Altitude** 0–500 m

Countries Australia

Restricted-range species	Threatened	Total
Confined to this EBA	2	3
Present also in other EBAs, SAs	0	2
Total	2	5

■ General characteristics

The Cape York EBA embraces the whole of the large north-east peninsula of Australia in the state of Queensland. The region is mostly low-lying with eucalypt woodlands, open grassy plains, rivers, swamps and mangroves, but there are also substantial tracts of tropical lowland rain forest, particularly along the coast between Temple Bay and Princess Charlotte Bay.

Cape York is separated from New Guinea to the north by the Torres Strait (which is c.100 km wide at its narrowest), and this is a major migration route for landbirds to and from northern Australia, with sev-

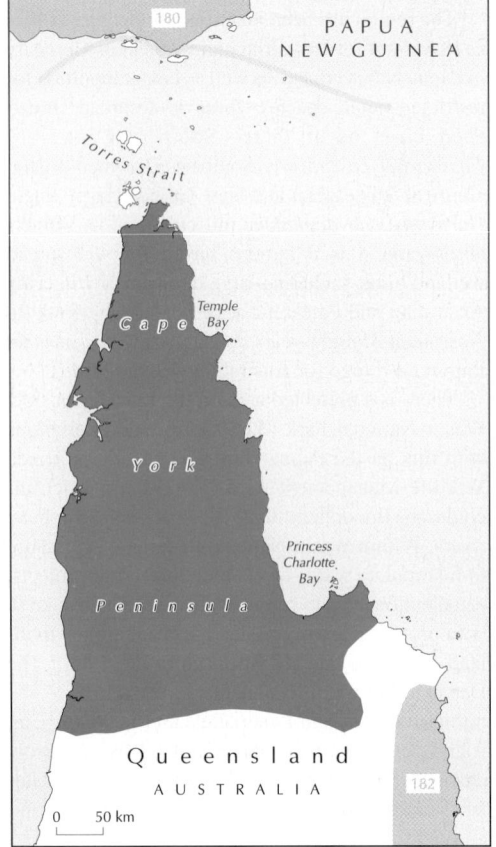

Golden-shouldered Parrot *Psephotus chrysopterygius* is now found in small numbers in a very restricted, and much-reduced, area of savanna woodland in far northern Queensland. The main reasons for its decline are thought to be the alteration of habitat, particularly breeding habitat, by grazing and altered fire regimes, and heavy trapping for the bird trade during the 1950s and 1960s.

eral species breeding on the Cape York peninsula and moving to New Guinea outside the breeding season (see Trans-Fly, EBA 180).

■ Restricted-range species

The EBA's restricted-range species occur in a variety of habitats including rain forest, mangroves, eucalypt woodland, scrub and heathland.

Turnix olivii and *Psephotus chrysopterygius* are both very local in their distributions. *T. olivii* was not

Status and habitat of restricted-range species

Species (ordered taxonomically)	Global status	Other EBAs (and SAs)	Habitat
Buff-breasted Buttonquail *Turnix olivii*	EN	—	Various woodland types; nests in discrete patches of short grass
Golden-shouldered Parrot *Psephotus chrysopterygius*	EN	—	Woodland; nests in termite mounds in waterlogged drainage depressions
Lovely Fairywren *Malurus amabilis*	lc	182	Rain forest edge, woodland, mangroves
White-streaked Honeyeater *Trichodere cockerelli*	lc	—	Woodland, forest along rivers, mangroves, swamps, heath
Yellow-spotted Honeyeater *Meliphaga notata*	lc	182	Rain forest, woodland, coastal scrub, mangroves, farmland

Global status (see p. 679 for definitions)
EX Extinct } with year
EW Extinct in } of last
   the Wild } record
CR Critical } threatened
EN Endangered } species
VU Vulnerable }
cd Conservation Dependent
nt Near Threatened
lc Least Concern
DD Data Deficient
NE Not Evaluated

Other EBAs (and SAs) (see p. 83 for locations): bracketed numbers are Secondary Areas; ˣ extinct in that EBA or SA.

recorded at all during five years of field observations, 1977–1981, and recent records are only of individuals or pairs, while *P. chrysopterygius* now only occupies a 120×225 km strip in the centre of its original range.

Australian Swiftlet *Collocalia terraereginae*, which occurs in this EBA and in the Queensland wet tropics (EBA 182), is treated as a form of the more widespread White-rumped Swiftlet *C. spodiopygia* (following Christidis and Boles 1994, contra Sibley and Monroe 1993), and is therefore not included here as a restricted-range species.

■ Threats and conservation

The two very restricted species endemic to this EBA are considered threatened: *Turnix olivii* is likely to have declined owing to the deliberate burning of woodland patches, especially if this occurs late in the dry season when birds are nesting; *Psephotus chrysopterygius* may also be affected by the burning of seeding grasses, as well as by trapping, predation by feral cats, and disturbance of nests by tourists (Garnett 1993).

Two subspecies of widespread Australian birds have been identified as threatened by Garnett (1993): the Cape York Peninsula form of Rufous Owl *Ninox rufa meesi*, which may be threatened by late dry-season fires, and the white-bellied form of Crimson Finch *Neochmia phaeton evangelinae*, which has disappeared from parts of its range as a result of damage to waterside vegetation by stock and feral pigs. The widespread Southern Cassowary *Casuarius casuarius* of Australia and New Guinea, which is classified as Vulnerable, also occurs in rain forest in this EBA, although there is no information on its numbers.

This region has long been recognized as an important wilderness, and has some of the country's largest national parks, including Lakefield (5,370 km²), Rokeby (2,910 km²), Jardine River (2,530 km²) and Archer Bend (1,660 km²). A recent regional assessment of the conservation value of the area by the Environmental Resources Information Network (ERIN) has identified over 80% of the Cape York peninsula as having natural conservation significance for at least one natural heritage attribute.

182 Queensland wet tropics

PRIORITY
URGENT

Key habitats	Lowland and montane rain forest

Area 32,000 km² **Altitude** 0–1,600 m

Countries Australia

Main threats Moderate habitat loss (e.g. due to sugar-cane plantations, pasture)

Biological importance ● ● ●
Current threat level ● ○ ○

Restricted-range species	Threatened	Total
Confined to this EBA	0	13
Present also in other EBAs, SAs	0	3
Total	0	16

■ General characteristics

Lying largely between Cooktown and Townsville in the north-east of Australia, this EBA comprises mountains and plateaus (the tablelands) which slope steeply to the coast; Hinchinbrook Island is also included within it. The land is (or was) covered in tropical rain forests, fringed and dissected by other habitats including various woodland types, mangroves and swamps.

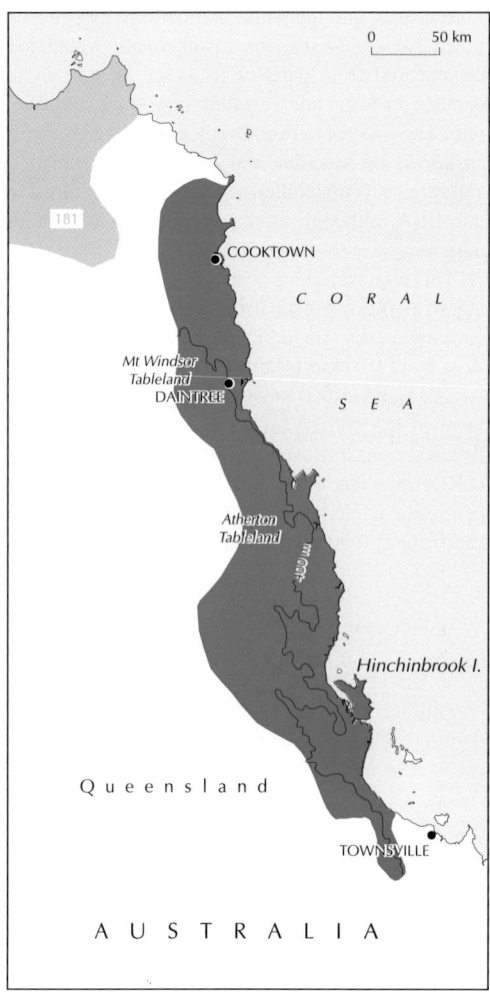

The region has more forest-dependent endemic vertebrates than any other area in Australia, most being confined to the cool, wet rain forests above c.400 m. The EBA has been defined to embrace most of the known records of the restricted-range bird species (from Blakers *et al.* 1984) and their predicted bioclimatic domain (from Nix and Switzer 1991).

■ Restricted-range species

All the restricted-range birds occur in rain forest and eight are restricted to the more temperate highland zone . Although most restricted-range species occur widely within the EBA, the areas occupied by the 13 endemics have been estimated to range from only 1,500 to 10,000 km² (G. N. Harrington *in litt.* 1993).

Australian Swiftlet *Collocalia terraereginae*, which occurs in this EBA and Cape York (EBA 181), is treated as a form of the more widespread White-rumped Swiftlet *C. spodiopygia* (following Christidis and Boles 1994, contra Sibley and Monroe 1993) and is therefore not included here as a restricted-range species.

■ Threats and conservation

Most lowland forest has been cleared for sugar-cane plantations, while the flatter parts of the uplands have been turned into pasture. In total c.20% of the original forest has been felled; remaining forest covers only c.8,000 km², largely on mountains, with remnant patches in the lowlands (Collins *et al.* 1991).

Today c.90% of the remaining forest is protected by the Wet Tropics World Heritage Area (WTWHA), where all logging has been stopped, although the variety of land tenures embraced by the area has resulted in a mosaic of management practices, with only 29% covered by national parks and managed explicitly for conservation. Concerns focus on the very poor representation of relatively undisturbed lowland forest in existing reserves and the fear that further fragmentation could preclude their viability (WWF/IUCN 1994–1995). Conservation challenges and opportunities, such as reforestation and control of non-native species, are outlined by, e.g., Laurance (1993) and Crome (1993).

Status and habitat of restricted-range species

Species (ordered taxonomically)	Global status	Other EBAs (and SAs)	Altitude (m)	Habitat
Lesser Sooty-owl *Tyto multipunctata*	nt	—	0–1,200	Forest, selectively logged forest
Chowchilla *Orthonyx spaldingii*	lc	—	<400–1,200	Forest, selectively logged forest
Lovely Fairywren *Malurus amabilis*	lc	181	Lowlands	Forest edge, woodland, mangroves
Fernwren *Oreoscopus gutturalis*	nt	—	600–1,500	Forest, selectively logged forest
Atherton Scrubwren *Sericornis keri*	cd	—	600–1,500	Forest, forest edge, selectively logged forest
Mountain Thornbill *Acanthiza katherina*	cd	—	450–1,500	Forest, selectively logged forest
Pale-yellow Robin *Tregellasia capito*	lc	183	0–1,500	Forest, selectively logged forest
Grey-headed Robin *Heteromyias cinereifrons*	nt	—	400–1,300	Forest, forest edge, selectively logged forest
Pied Monarch *Arses kaupi*	lc	—	0–1,200	Forest, forest edge, occasionally nearby woodland
Bower's Shrike-thrush *Colluricincla boweri*	nt	—	600–1,300	Forest, selectively logged forest
Yellow-spotted Honeyeater *Meliphaga notata*	lc	181	0–800	Forest, woodland, coastal scrub, mangroves, farmland
Bridled Honeyeater *Lichenostomus frenatus*	nt	—	600–1,500	Forest, selectively logged forest
Macleay Honeyeater *Xanthotis macleayana*	lc	—	0–1,200	Forest, sometimes orchards and gardens
Tooth-billed Catbird *Ailuroedus dentirostris*	nt	—	500–1,600	Forest inc. small remnants bordering agricultural land
Golden Bowerbird *Prionodura newtoniana*	cd	—	600–1,300	Forest, selectively logged rain forest
Victoria's Riflebird *Ptiloris victoriae*	lc	—	<400–1,200	Forest, forest edge, selectively logged rain forest

Global status (see p. 679 for definitions)							
EX	Extinct	with year of last record	CR	Critical	threatened species	cd	Conservation Dependent	DD Data Deficient

Global status (see p. 679 for definitions): EX Extinct, EW Extinct in the Wild } with year of last record; CR Critical, EN Endangered, VU Vulnerable } threatened species; cd Conservation Dependent, nt Near Threatened, lc Least Concern; DD Data Deficient, NE Not Evaluated

Other EBAs (and SAs) (see p. 83 for locations): bracketed numbers are Secondary Areas; ˣ extinct in that EBA or SA.

Outside the WTWHA, there are still important areas of rain forest in private freehold that are likely to be cleared in the future. Notably there is forest at 800–1,200 m on the Atherton tableland (in the Millaa Millaa–Malanda–Ravenshoe area); this is already fragmented, but still retains all the endemic birds. There is also lowland rain forest at Daintree which has been divided into housing blocks but which is still relatively intact. Other sites which have been identified as particularly important within this EBA are Mission Beach, Mt Hypopamee Crater National Park, Mt Lewis, Windsor tableland, Mt Baldy State Forest and Mt Whitfield (G. N. Harrington *in litt.* 1993).

The three endemic species which have the smallest ranges (an area of occupancy estimated to be less than 2,000 km²) have been classified as Conservation Dependent: this non-threatened category is applied where the cessation of a conservation programme (in this case the integrity of the WTWHA) would result in the species qualifying for one of the threatened categories. An additional six species with small ranges (2,000–3,000 km²) have been classified as Near Threatened.

Other species of particular note in this EBA include the endemic eastern subspecies of Rufous Owl *Ninox rufa queenslandica* which is identified as threatened by Garnett (1993), and the widespread Southern Cassowary *Casuarius casuarius* of Australia and New Guinea which is classified as Vulnerable. In this region, *C. casuarius* is estimated to have a population of 1,500–3,000 individuals, but has declined in most areas where rain forest has been cleared or fragmented (Garnett 1993).

183 Eastern Australia

Key habitats Subtropical and temperate rain forest, eucalypt forest and woodland, heath, scrub

Main threats Moderate habitat loss (e.g. due to fire, grazing)

Biological importance ● ● ●
Current threat level ● ● ○

Area 160,000 km² **Altitude** 0–1,200 m

Countries Australia

Restricted-range species	Threatened	Total
Confined to this EBA	3	9
Present also in other EBAs, SAs	0	1
Total	3	10

■ General characteristics

Stretching along the Australian coast from Fraser Island in southern Queensland, through New South Wales to eastern Victoria, this EBA includes the narrow coastal lowlands and the mountains of the Great Dividing Range.

The region's habitats are characterized by patches of rain forest (including subtropical, temperate and dry forest types) but the natural vegetation consists

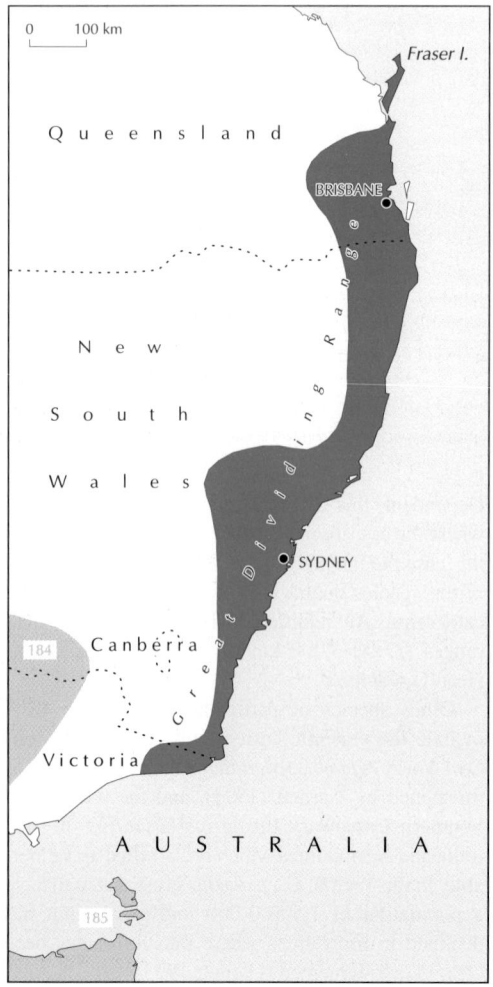

Blue Mountains National Park, west of Sydney, is a spectacular wilderness. Majestic canyons shelter pockets of rain forest, and there are wide expanses of virgin eucalypt forest. Origma *Origma solitaria* occurs here; despite its very small range it is judged only to be Near Threatened, because most of its habitat is protected and it appears in no immediate danger.

mainly of eucalypt forest and woodland. The boundary of the EBA is defined by the restricted-range bird records themselves (from Blakers *et al.* 1984), and the western limits correspond approximately with the 1,000 m contour.

■ Restricted-range species

Most restricted-range species occur in forest, both rain forest and eucalypt.

Distribution patterns within the region vary: five species, *Turnix melanogaster*, *Menura alberti*,

Status and habitat of restricted-range species

Species (ordered taxonomically)	Global status	Other EBAs (and SAs)	Altitude (m)	Habitat
Black-breasted Buttonquail *Turnix melanogaster*	EN	—	Lowlands	Dry rain forest, eucalypt forest; occasionally plantations and lantana thickets
Albert's Lyrebird *Menura alberti*	nt	—	Highlands	Subtropical rain forest, mixed eucalypt and rain forest, palm forest
Rufous Scrub-bird *Atrichornis rufescens*	VU	—	600–1,000+, formerly lowlands	Temperate rain forest, wet eucalypt forest
Eastern Bristlebird *Dasyornis brachypterus*	VU	—	0–1,100	Heath, scrub, tussock grass usually on boundary of forest and woodland
Pilotbird *Pycnoptilus floccosus*	lc	—	Usually 200–500	Temperate rain forest, eucalypt forest, wet woodland
Origma *Origma solitaria*	nt	—	Hills	Rocky gullies, boulders, caves, usually near water
Pale-yellow Robin *Tregellasia capito*	lc	182	0–1,500	Subtropical rain forest, dense vegetation along watercourses
Green Catbird *Ailuroedus crassirostris*	lc	—	Coasts, hills	Rain forest, occasionally eucalypt forest, forest edge
Regent Bowerbird *Sericulus chrysocephalus*	lc	—	Coasts, hills	Rain forest, eucalypt forest, forest edge, secondary growth, coastal scrub, occasionally gardens
Paradise Riflebird *Ptiloris paradiseus*	nt	—	Highlands to 1,200	Rain forest and adjacent eucalypt forest, swamp woodland

Global status (see p. 679 for definitions)

EX	Extinct	with year of last record	CR	Critical	threatened species	cd	Conservation Dependent	DD	Data Deficient
EW	Extinct in the Wild		EN	Endangered		nt	Near Threatened	NE	Not Evaluated
			VU	Vulnerable		lc	Least Concern		

Other EBAs (and SAs) (see p. 83 for locations): bracketed numbers are Secondary Areas; ˣ extinct in that EBA or SA.

Atrichornis rufescens, *Tregellasia capito* and *Ptiloris paradiseus*, occur in south-east Queensland and north-east New South Wales, one species, *Origma solitaria*, is endemic to central-eastern New South Wales (the sandstone areas both north and south of Sydney), and a further two species, *Dasyornis brachypterus* and *Pycnoptilus floccosus*, are confined to the south-east corner of the EBA in south-east New South Wales and eastern Victoria. The overlapping ranges of these birds have therefore defined the overall limits of the EBA. Two species, *Ailuroedus crassirostris* and *Sericulus chrysocephalus*, are found more widely within the area.

In addition to these restricted-range birds, there are a number of species which are largely confined to this EBA, but which are not included because their ranges are judged to exceed 50,000 km²: Wonga Pigeon *Leucosarcia melanoleuca*, Turquiose Parrot *Neophema pulchella*, Superb Lyrebird *Menura novae-hollandiae*, Red-browed Treecreeper *Climacteris erythrops* and Bell Miner *Manorina melanophrys*.

Swift Parrot *Lathamus discolor*, a restricted-range species which breeds in Tasmania (EBA 185), winters in this EBA.

■ Threats and conservation

Much of Eastern Australia's lowland habitat has been cleared for agriculture and consequently three species are classified as threatened. *Turnix melanogaster* has declined drastically in coastal and near coastal areas during the twentieth century and since c.1980 has been recorded from fewer than 50 sites (with less than 10 birds at each), and must also be vulnerable to introduced predators. *Atrichornis rufescens* now occurs in isolated populations in the highlands only, and continues to be threatened by inappropriate burning and forest management practices. *Dasyornis brachypterus* occurs in isolated and scattered populations in coastal regions, where it has suffered from changes in the fire regime (either too frequent with the elimination of tussocks, or too infrequent leading to dense shrubberies unsuitable for nesting) as well as from grazing, introduced exotic plants and animals, land clearance, and some recreational activities (Garnett 1993).

Subspecies of note include the southern form of Coxen's Fig-parrot *Cyclopsitta diophthalma coxeni* and Marbled Frogmouth *Podargus ocellatus plumiferus*, which inhabit subtropical rain forest in south-east Queensland and north-east New South Wales. Both are treated as threatened by Garnett (1993) because of their small and fragmented populations.

The EBA incorporates many protected areas, including seven separate rain forest sites together constituting the East Coast Temperate and Subtropical Rainforest Parks World Heritage Site (2,035 km²).

184 South-east Australia

PRIORITY
CRITICAL

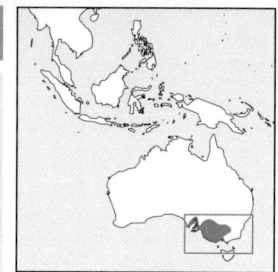

Key habitats Eucalypt woodland (especially mallee)

Main threats Major habitat degradation (e.g. due to fire, grazing), introduced species

Biological importance ● ● ●
Current threat level ● ●

Area 380,000 km²   **Altitude** 0–1,000 m

Countries Australia

Restricted-range species	Threatened	Total
Confined to this EBA	3	6
Present also in other EBAs, SAs	1	1
Total	4	7

■ General characteristics

Falling within the states of South Australia, Victoria and New South Wales, this EBA is characterized by watercourses (including the Murray and Darling rivers) lined with eucalypt woodland, and patches of mallee (a particularly distinct, semi-arid woodland of multi-stemmed eucalypts).

■ Restricted-range species

Four of the restricted-range bird species are mallee specialists, making this habitat a very important one in this EBA.

Of the EBA's seven restricted-range species, three have particularly small ranges: *Psophodes nigrogularis*, which occurs in two isolated populations, with the race *lashmari* on Kangaroo Island and *leucogaster* in a small number of widely scattered localities in southern South Australia and north-west Victoria; *Dasyornis broadbenti*, which occurs in several disjunct populations, with the race *whitei* occurring discontinuously in south-east South Australia and nominate *broadbenti* on the coast in south-west Victoria; and *Manorina melanotis*, which is

now restricted to seven sites in north-west Victoria and one in South Australia.

One species which has been treated here as restricted-range, *Polytelis swainsonii*, is found from northern central New South Wales (beyond the boundary of this EBA) south to northern Victoria, but breeding is apparently confined to the southern part of its distribution (entirely within this EBA), particularly the areas of the Murrumbidgee, Edward and Murray rivers.

Another possible restricted-range species, which is endemic to this EBA, is Yellow Rosella *Platycercus flaveolus*. This taxon is recognized as a species by Sibley and Monroe (1990, 1993) but not by most other recent authors, including Christidis and Boles (1994) (there appears to be extensive hybridization between this form and Crimson Rosella *P. elegans*).

A further two restricted-range species occur in this EBA as winter visitors: Swift Parrot *Lathamus discolor* and Orange-bellied Parrot *Neophema chrysogaster* (both from Tasmania, EBA 185).

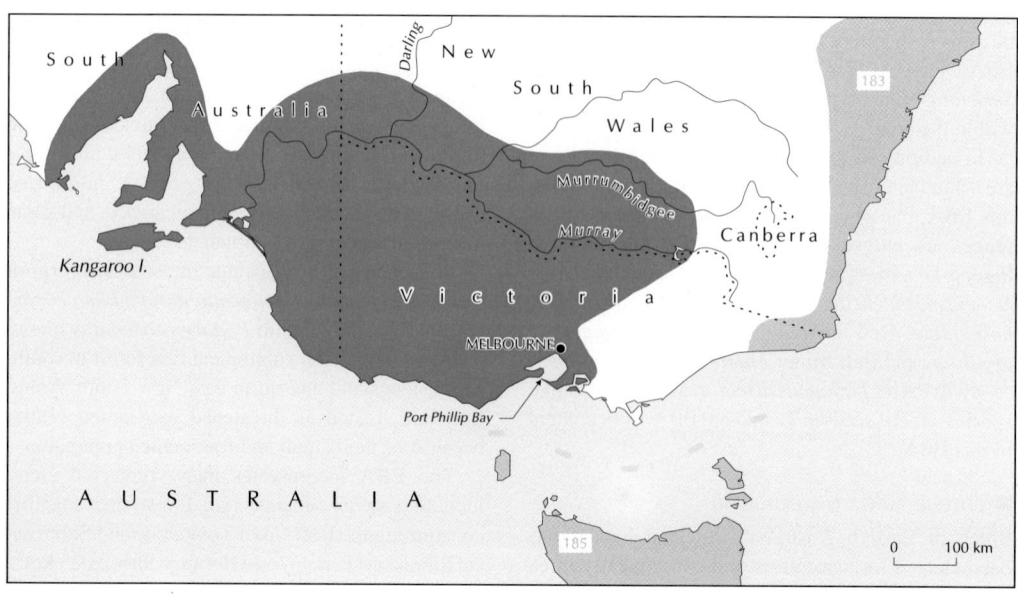

Status and habitat of restricted-range species

Species (ordered taxonomically)	Global status	Other EBAs (and SAs)	Habitat
Kangaroo Island Emu *Dromaius baudinianus*[1]	EX (c.1827)	—	Unknown
Long-billed Corella *Cacatua tenuirostris*	lc	—	Riverine forest, woodland, farmland
Superb Parrot *Polytelis swainsonii*	VU	—	Riparian woodland
Western Whipbird *Psophodes nigrogularis*	VU	186	Mallee-heath, dense thickets
Mallee Emuwren *Stipiturus mallee*	cd	—	Mallee
Rufous Bristlebird *Dasyornis broadbenti*	VU	186[x]	Coastal scrub, thickets
Red-lored Whistler *Pachycephala rufogularis*	cd	—	Mallee
Black-eared Miner *Manorina melanotis*[1]	CR	—	Mature mallee woodland

Global status (see p. 679 for definitions)					Other EBAs (and SAs) (see p. 83 for locations)	Bracketed numbers are Secondary Areas. [x] Extinct in that EBA or SA.
	EX	Extinct	} with year of last record	cd	Conservation Dependent	
	EW	Extinct in the Wild		nt	Near Threatened	
	CR	Critical	} threatened species	lc	Least Concern	**Notes** [1] Taxonomy follows Christidis and Boles (1994).
	EN	Endangered		DD	Data Deficient	
	VU	Vulnerable		NE	Not Evaluated	

■ Threats and conservation

South-east Australia has suffered one extinction, that of *Dromaius baudinianus* from Kangaroo Island, attributed to hunting and excessive burning of habitat (Garnett 1993), and on the mainland clearance of mallee has led to the decline of its specialist birds through habitat fragmentation. The region now has many protected areas which help to conserve surviving populations: those with mallee habitat include Murray–Sunset National Park (6,330 km²), Hattah–Kulkyne National Park (480 km²), Billiat Conservation Park (600 km²), the Big Desert Wilderness (1,135 km²), Wyperfield National Park (1,000 km²) and Ngarkat Conservation Park (2,080 km²). Although habitat degradation through overgrazing by stock (and by kangaroos) and fire remain threats, and bird populations may fluctuate owing to fire patterns, *Stipiturus mallee* and *Pachycephala rufogularis* respond well to management practices which provide them with appropriate habitat (D. Franklin per K. Fitzherbert *in litt.* 1994). As these measures are judged to prevent the species qualifying for threatened status, they are classified as Conservation Dependent (but see Schodde 1990).

Such protection measures are not sufficient, however, for *Manorina melanotis*, which is being genetically swamped by Yellow-throated Miner *M. flavigula* (and is included within that species by Sibley and Monroe 1990, 1993). The opening up of the Murray mallee has favoured *M. flavigula*, and at the start of the 1990s there probably remained fewer than 20 pure individuals of *M. melanotis* (Garnett 1993).

Reduction of saltmarshes around Port Phillip Bay in Victoria, used during the winter by *Neophema chrysogaster* (see 'Restricted-range species', above) is another cause for concern (Garnett 1993), while introduced predators such as feral cats and foxes have been contributory in the decline of many other birds in the EBA, e.g. the threatened, but widespread, Malleefowl *Leipoa ocellata* (Vulnerable) which occurs in mallee and eucalypt woodland.

Other widespread threatened species present include Plains-wanderer *Pedionomus torquatus*, Glossy Black-cockatoo *Calyptorhynchus lathami* (nominate *lathami* in New South Wales and Victoria, *halmaturinus* on Kangaroo Island), Slender-billed Thornbill *Acanthiza iredalei* (race *hedleyi* has a fragmented distribution in north-west Victoria and south-east South Australia), Painted Honeyeater *Grantiella picta* (all Vulnerable) and Regent Honeyeater *Xanthomyza phrygia* (Endangered). Threatened subspecies identified by Garnett (1993) include the eastern form of Regent Parrot *Polytelis anthopeplus anthopeplus*, which is restricted to mallee and riparian woodlands, the south-eastern form of Red-tailed Black-cockatoo *Calyptorhynchus banksii graptogyne*, Helmeted Honeyeater *Lichenostomus melanops cassidix*, which occurs in a small area east of Melbourne in southern Victoria and is the bird emblem for that state, and the South Australian subspecies of White's Thrush *Zoothera dauma halmaturina* from southern South Australia and Kangaroo Island.

185 Tasmania

Key habitats Eucalypt forest, temperate rain forest, sedgeland

Main threats Moderate habitat loss (e.g. due to reafforestation, mining)

Biological importance ● ● ○
Current threat level ● ● ○

Area 68,000 km² **Altitude** 0–1,600 m

Countries Australia

Restricted-range species	Threatened	Total
Confined to this EBA	3	14
Present also in other EBAs, SAs	0	0
Total	3	14

■ General characteristics

This EBA constitutes the Australian state of Tasmania, which includes the islands of the Bass Strait—King Island and the Furneaux Group.

Eucalypt forest is the predominant vegetation, with extensive temperate rain forest in the wetter west of Tasmania. Sedgeland, dominated by buttongrass, often in association with rushes, tea trees, paperbarks and heaths, occurs in the south-west.

■ Restricted-range species

Most restricted-range species occur in eucalypt forest and rain forest, with coastal sedgelands being particularly important for *Neophema chrysogaster*.

Most species are found throughout Tasmania but are included as having restricted ranges because it is assumed that available habitat is less than 50,000 km². Three species have relatively small ranges: *Pardalotus quadragintus*, which was formerly widespread in the eastern half of the island and on King and Flinders Islands, but is now restricted to the coastal south-east in the vicinity of Hobart and to Flinders Island where it has recently been rediscovered (D. J. Baker-Gabb *in litt.* 1996); *Lathamus discolor*, which breeds only in north-east and eastern Tasmania; and *Neophema chrysogaster*, which breeds only in the south-west.

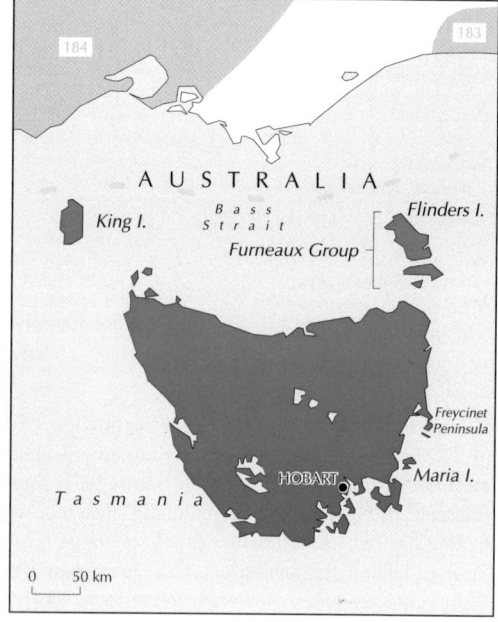

Tasmanian Masked-owl, which is confined to this EBA, is treated here as a race (*castanops*) of the more widespread Masked Owl *T. novaehollandiae* (following Christidis and Boles 1994, contra Sibley and

Freycinet peninsula is an important site for dry eucalypt forest which continues to be lost elsewhere because of clearance, sheep-grazing and subdivision for housing. These developments have allowed invasion by Noisy Miners *Manorina melanocephala* which chase all other birds from their territories.

J. P. Croxall

Status and habitat of restricted-range species

Species (ordered taxonomically)	Global status	Other EBAs (and SAs)	Habitat
King Island Emu *Dromaius ater*[1]	EX (early 19th C)	—	Along shores, near lagoons
Tasmanian Native-hen *Gallinula mortierii*	lc	—	Marshes, riparian vegetation in farmland
Green Rosella *Platycercus caledonicus*	lc	—	Eucalypt forest and woodland, rain forest (breeding); visits heath and farmland (non-breeding)
Orange-bellied Parrot *Neophema chrysogaster*[2]	EN	—	Coastal sedgeland, forest margins (breeding), saltmarshes
Swift Parrot *Lathamus discolor*[3]	VU	—	Eucalypt forest (preferably blue gum during breeding), woodland
Brown Scrubwren *Sericornis humilis*	lc	—	Eucalypt forest, rain forest, wet scrub, coastal heath
Scrubtit *Acanthornis magnus*	lc	—	Wet eucalypt forest, rain forest, fern gullies
Tasmanian Thornbill *Acanthiza ewingii*	lc	—	Wet forest and scrub, preferably wet eucalypt forest and rain forest
Dusky Robin *Melanodryas vittata*	lc	—	Eucalypt forest and woodland, coastal heath
Forty-spotted Pardalote *Pardalotus quadragintus*	VU	—	Dry eucalypt forest dominated by white gum
Yellow-throated Honeyeater *Lichenostomus flavicollis*	lc	—	Eucalypt forest, woodland, coastal heath; visits gardens
Black-headed Honeyeater *Melithreptus affinis*	lc	—	Eucalypt forest, preferably mature dry forest
Strong-billed Honeyeater *Melithreptus validirostris*	lc	—	Eucalypt forest, esp. mature wet forest
Yellow Wattlebird *Anthochaera paradoxa*	lc	—	Mature dry eucalypt forest, woodland; visits orchards and gardens
Black Currawong *Strepera fuliginosa*	lc	—	Eucalypt forest, rain forest (lowland and subalpine), swamp forest, coastal heath, farmland

Global status (see p. 679 for definitions)

EX	Extinct } with year	cd	Conservation
EW	Extinct in } of last		Dependent
	the Wild } record	nt	Near Threatened
CR	Critical } threatened	lc	Least Concern
EN	Endangered } species	DD	Data Deficient
VU	Vulnerable }	NE	Not Evaluated

Other EBAs (and SAs) (see p. 83 for locations)
Bracketed numbers are Secondary Areas. [X] Extinct in that EBA or SA.

Notes
[1] Taxonomy follows Christidis and Boles (1994).
[2] Winters in South-east Australia (EBA 184).
[3] Winters in East Australia (EBA 183) and South-east Australia (EBA 184).

Monroe 1993), and is therefore not included as a restricted-range species.

■ Threats and conservation

Hunting with dogs by seal hunters is thought to have been the principal reason for the disappearance of *Dromaius ater*, and hunting is also likely to have eliminated the Tasmanian subspecies of Emu *D. novaehollandiae diemenensis*. However, the main threats to the species of this EBA today are the destruction of old-growth forest and replacement with short-rotation eucalypt forests and plantations; the destruction, fragmentation and isolation of habitats on private land, particularly dry forest and grassy woodland; mining, both in protected areas and in unprotected rain forest; and the degradation of coastal and wetland habitats (R. Donaghey *in litt*. 1993).

The three species which are classified as threatened have specialist habitat requirements and are the most restricted in their distribution, and thus are the most susceptible to changes in the vegetation.

Subspecies of particular note include the Tasmanian form of Wedge-tailed Eagle *Aquila audax fleayi*, which numbers fewer than 100 breeding pairs and is threatened by land clearance and persecution (Garnett 1993), the Tasmanian forms of Australian Owlet-nightjar *Aegotheles cristatus tasmanicus* and Azure Kingfisher *Alcedo azurea diemenensis*, and the King Island race of Brown Thornbill *Acanthiza pusilla archibaldi*, which are all treated as 'Insufficiently Known' by Garnett (1993).

There are many protected areas in Tasmania, including the Tasmanian Wilderness World Heritage Site (13,836 km²) which protects the breeding habitat of *Neophema chrysogaster* in the south-west. Dry forests are poorly covered by reserves in eastern Tasmania, so sites like the Douglas-Apsley National Park (160 km²), Maria Island (100 km², a refuge for *Pardalotus quadragintus*) and Freycinet (100 km²) are especially important.

186 South-west Australia

PRIORITY
CRITICAL

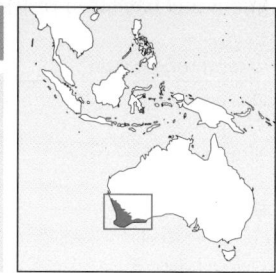

Key habitats Eucalypt forest and woodland, heath

Main threats Major habitat loss (e.g. due to farming, fire)

Biological importance ● ● ●
Current threat level ● ● ○

Area 280,000 km²   **Altitude** 0–400 m

Countries Australia

Restricted-range species	Threatened	Total
Confined to this EBA	3	7
Present also in other EBAs, SAs	1	1
Total	4	8

■ General characteristics

This EBA is in the western part of the state of Western Australia. It is largely low-lying, with eucalypt forest in the hillier and wetter south-west, and eucalypt woodland, including mallee (a particularly distinct, semi-arid woodland of multi-stemmed eucalypts), mallee-heath, heath and thickets elsewhere, where the climate is more Mediterranean.

■ Restricted-range species

Of the eight restricted-range species which occur in this EBA, three have particularly small ranges: *Atrichornis clamosus*, which was largely confined to the Mt Gardner area of the Two Peoples Bay Nature Reserve (47 km²) east of Albany, but is now spread over c.30 km of coastal and near coastal land (Danks and Calver 1993); *Psophodes nigrogularis*, which occurs in two isolated populations, with nominate

nigrogularis in extreme coastal south-west Australia (perhaps only surviving at Two Peoples Bay) and the race *oberon* in eastern south-west Australia (Schodde and Mason 1991), but also occurring in South-east Australia (EBA 184); and *Dasyornis longirostris*, which is now restricted to four localities within the Fitzgerald River National Park and also to the area just east of Albany.

An additional six species are largely confined to this region but are widely dispersed and consequently judged to have breeding ranges of more than 50,000 km², so have not been included as restricted-range species: Slender-billed Black-cockatoo *Calyptorhynchus latirostris*, Western Rosella *Platycercus icterotis*, Red-capped Parrot *Purpureicephalus spurius*, Western Thornbill *Acanthiza inornata*, Western Spinetail *Acanthorhynchus superciliosus* and Little Wattlebird *Anthochaera lunulata*.

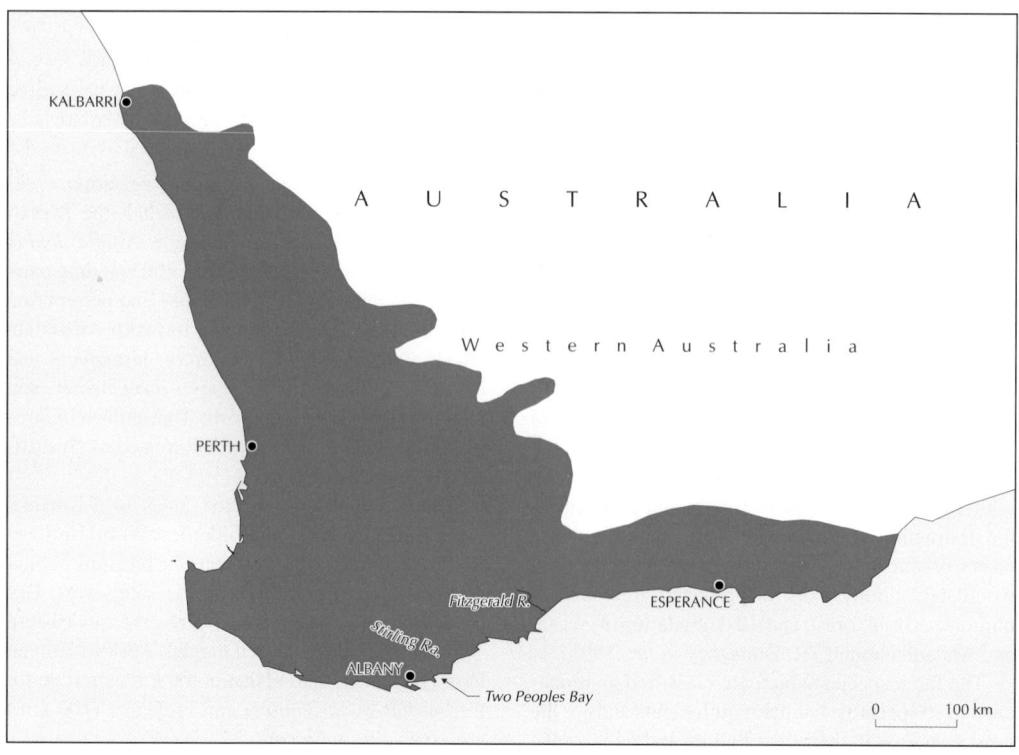

Status and habitat of restricted-range species

Species (ordered taxonomically)	Global status	Other EBAs (and SAs)	Habitat
White-tailed Black-cockatoo *Calyptorhynchus baudinii*	VU	—	Forest; requires hollows in mature eucalypts for breeding
Western Corella *Cacatua pastinator*	nt	—	Woodland, farmland
Noisy Scrub-bird *Atrichornis clamosus*	VU	—	Low forest, dense scrub
Western Whipbird *Psophodes nigrogularis*	VU	184	Mallee-heath, dense thickets
Red-winged Fairywren *Malurus elegans*	lc	—	Forest gullies (usually associated with rank streamside vegetation), margins of freshwater lakes
Western Bristlebird *Dasyornis longirostris*	EN	—	Dense heath
Rufous Bristlebird *Dasyornis broadbenti*[1]	VU	184	Coastal scrub, thickets
White-breasted Robin *Eopsaltria georgiana*	lc	—	Forest, thickets with plenty of litter and a damp environment, heath among dunes
Red-eared Firetail *Stagonopleura oculata*	nt	—	Riparian vegetation in forest, coastal thickets

Global status (see p. 679 for definitions)	EX Extinct EW Extinct in the Wild } with year of last record		cd Conservation Dependent nt Near Threatened	Other EBAs (and SAs) (see p. 83 for locations)	Bracketed numbers are Secondary Areas. ˣ Extinct in that EBA or SA.
	CR Critical EN Endangered VU Vulnerable } threatened species		lc Least Concern DD Data Deficient NE Not Evaluated	Notes	[1] Extinct in this EBA (1906).

■ Threats and conservation

Much of the extreme south-west is still forested, but large areas are extensively farmed, and forest has been cleared leaving only scattered patches, isolated trees, and road- or streamside strips. In total, an estimated 90% of habitat has been removed, and bird populations are thus often too small to be viable or may be too isolated to allow recolonization if the population is lost (Saunders and Ingram 1995).

Fire is a threat to native habitat. Historically, fires were started by Aborigines to encourage new grass, but they also occur naturally in the long dry season. Native plants are fire-adapted, but fragmented ecosystems may be at risk if burning regimes are altered or intensified. Thus, the western race *litoralis* of *Dasyornis broadbenti* is extinct due to destruction of its habitat by frequent burning earlier this century.

The three restricted-range species which have the smallest ranges are considered threatened (despite occurring in protected areas) because of the continuing threat of fire to surviving populations. It is as a result of habitat management (and therefore fire exclusion) and translocation that the range of *Atrichornis clamosus* has been increased, with a consequent improvement in its conservation status.

Other species and races of particular note include the western form of Ground Parrot *Pezoporus wallicus flaviventris*, confined to two populations in Cape Arid and Fitzgerald River National Parks, the southwestern form of Red-tailed Black-cockatoo *Calyptorhynchus banksii naso*, restricted to a sub-coastal strip between Perth and Albany (both treated as threatened by Garnett 1993), *C. latirostris* (Vulnerable; see 'Restricted-range species', above) and Malleefowl *Leipoa ocellata*, a widespread threatened bird (Vulnerable), which occurs in the mallee and eucalypt woodland in the eastern, more arid areas. Overall, it has been estimated that in the wheatbelt of Western Australia nearly 50% of all birds and 88% of resident passerines have declined in range or abundance since European settlement (Robinson and Traill 1996).

There are many protected areas in this EBA including the very important Two Peoples Bay Nature Reserve and the two largest, Fitzgerald River National Park (2,400 km²) and Stirling Range National Park (1,156 km²), which protect some of the threatened restricted-range species. However, it is recognized that for much of the wildlife of this EBA protected areas are not sufficient (or even possible, as most remnants of native habitat are on private land). Rather, land degradation needs to be dealt with at an ecological scale by other means. To this end, over 300 landcare groups have been formed to promote region-wide land conservation measures (see, e.g., Goss and Chatfield 1993). Two urgent priorities are the need to increase the size of woodlands and to re-establish vegetation links between them.

187 North-west Australia

PRIORITY
URGENT

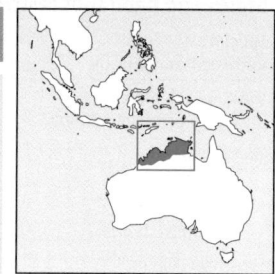

Key habitats	Monsoon rain forest, mangroves, grassy woodland, sandstone areas with spinifex

Area 560,000 km²   **Altitude** 0–1,000 m

Countries Australia

Main threats Moderate habitat degradation (e.g. due to overgrazing)

Biological importance ● ● ●
Current threat level ● ● ●

Restricted-range species	Threatened	Total
Confined to this EBA	1	12
Present also in other EBAs, SAs	0	1
Total	1	13

■ General characteristics

This EBA embraces northern Kimberley in the state of Western Australia, and the Top End in the Northern Territory. The habitats of the region include mangroves, monsoon rain forest (small patches, mainly on the coast) and eucalypt forest and woodland (in inland rugged ranges), but much the greatest part of the land area is, however, covered by variably grassy woodland, with desertic spinifex associations on very shallow substrates. In the north-east there lies a large sandstone escarpment, Arnhem Land, which is Aboriginal land (and is partly included within Kakadu National Park).

The boundary of the EBA has been drawn to include all records of restricted-range species from Blakers *et al.* (1984), and the area thus encompassed is very large. The vast majority of records lie, however, within core areas covering less than half this extent.

■ Restricted-range species

Together, the restricted-range species make use of all the main habitats included in this EBA, but they can be divided on the basis of their preferences: thus five species occur largely in mangroves and rain forest, three in eucalypt forest and grassy woodland, four in sandstone gorges and spinifex, and one in a mixture of different types.

Distribution patterns within the EBA vary, with one species being confined to the Kimberley, six to the Top End and the remaining six shared between the two regions, thereby combining two smaller areas of endemism into one large EBA. Species occurring in both Kimberley and the Top End either just range into one of the areas, or have a few scattered records only in one of the areas, or occur in limited habitat in both areas.

Distribution patterns of restricted-range species

Species (ordered geographically)	Kimberley	Top End	Other EBAs, SAs
Amytornis housei	●	–	–
Turnix castanota	●	●	–
Geophaps smithii	●	●	–
Petrophassa albipennis	●	●	–
Pitta iris	●	●	–
Meliphaga albilineata	●	●	–
Eulabeornis castaneoventris	●	●	●
Petrophassa rufipennis	–	●	–
Ptilinopus alligator	–	●	–
Psephotus dissimilis	–	●	–
Amytornis woodwardi	–	●	–
Pachycephala simplex	–	●	–
Lonchura flaviprymna	–	●	–
Total	7	12	

● Present	? Present?	Threatened spp. shown in **bold**	see 'Status and habitat' table
O Extinct?	R Reintroduced	Other EBAs, SAs	
X Extinct	I Introduced		

There are several other species which are largely confined to this EBA, but which are omitted because their estimated ranges are greater than 50,000 km²: Red-collared Lorikeet *Trichoglossus rubritorquis*, Northern Rosella *Platycercus venustus*, Sandstone Shrike-thrush *Colluricincla woodwardi*, Purple-crowned Fairywren *Malurus coronatus* and Long-tailed Finch *Poephila acuticauda*.

Kimberley Imperial-pigeon *Ducula constans*, which is also confined to this EBA, is treated as a form of the more widespread Pied Imperial-pigeon *D. bicolor* (following Christidis and Boles 1994, contra Sibley and Monroe 1993) and so is not included here as a restricted-range species.

Status and habitat of restricted-range species

Species (ordered taxonomically)	Global status	Other EBAs (and SAs)	Habitat
Chestnut-backed Buttonquail *Turnix castanota*	VU	—	Grassy woodland, particularly on stony hillsides
Chestnut Rail *Eulabeornis castaneoventris*	lc	(s112)	Mangroves
Partridge Pigeon *Geophaps smithii*	nt	—	Open forest, adjacent grassy woodland
White-quilled Rock-pigeon *Petrophassa albipennis*	lc	—	Sandstone gorges; usually on bare rocks, sometimes in grassy woodland
Chestnut-quilled Rock-pigeon *Petrophassa rufipennis*	lc	—	Sandstone gorges, woodland, spinifex, grassland
Black-banded Fruit-dove *Ptilinopus alligator*	nt	—	Monsoon rain forest, marginally into adjacent woodland
Hooded Parrot *Psephotus dissimilis*	nt	—	Open forest, woodland; nests in termite mounds
Rainbow Pitta *Pitta iris*	lc	—	Monsoon rain forest
White-throated Grasswren *Amytornis woodwardi*	nt	—	Sandstone areas with spinifex
Black Grasswren *Amytornis housei*	nt	—	Sandstone areas with spinifex
Brown Whistler *Pachycephala simplex*	lc	—	Mangroves, rain forest
White-lined Honeyeater *Meliphaga albilineata*	lc	—	Monsoon rain forest patches in sandstone gorges
Yellow-rumped Munia *Lonchura flaviprymna*	nt	—	Swamps, reedbeds, savanna, farmland

Global status (see p. 679 for definitions)

EX	Extinct	with year of last record	CR	Critical	threatened species	cd	Conservation Dependent	DD	Data Deficient
EW	Extinct in the Wild		EN	Endangered		nt	Near Threatened	NE	Not Evaluated
			VU	Vulnerable		lc	Least Concern		

Other EBAs (and SAs) (see p. 83 for locations): bracketed numbers are Secondary Areas; ˣ extinct in that EBA or SA.

■ Threats and conservation

The EBA is mostly uninhabited. However, it is farmed with stock, and in some areas there is little or no control over grazing or breeding (and increasing numbers of feral animals including cattle, donkeys, buffalo and pigs), and in consequence grassland is severely degraded. Fire has also degraded plant cover and led to species changes, especially as sustainable Aboriginal burning regimes (to encourage growth of new grass) are often no longer followed (WWF/IUCN 1994–1995). The small size of most patches of monsoon rain forest renders this habitat particularly vulnerable (Russell-Smith and Bowman 1992). Several of the rarer restricted-range species are thus considered Near Threatened, and *Turnix castanota*, whose populations appear to have declined, is classified as Vulnerable. Three subspecies endemic to this EBA are of particular note as all are treated as threatened by Garnett (1993): the Melville Island form of Masked Owl *Tyto novaehollandiae melvillensis*; the western Purple-crowned Fairy-wren *Malurus coronatus coronatus*, from restricted riverine habitat in Kimberley; and the northern Crested Shrike-tit *Falcunculus frontalus whitei*, which occurs at low density throughout the EBA.

The Endangered, but more widespread, Gouldian Finch *Chloebia gouldiae*, is also found in the EBA. Though abundant early in the twentieth century it is now only patchily distributed in north-west Queensland, the northern Northern Territory and the Kimberley region. The main problem appears to be an introduced parasitic mite, found in 60% of Northern Territory birds, which may prevent the population returning to its former numbers (Garnett 1993).

There are many protected areas in the EBA which partly cover the ranges of all its restricted-range species (Woinarski 1992). Particularly noteworthy is Kakadu National Park (18,000 km²), a World Heritage Site. An analysis based on the distributions of all mammals, landbirds and terrestrial reptiles has assigned priorities for the placement of future reserves, including ones in north and south-west Kimberley and eastern Arnhem Land (Woinarski 1992; see also Whitehead *et al.* 1992, Price *et al.* 1995).

188 Christmas Island

PRIORITY
HIGH

Key habitats Lowland rain forest, deciduous forest

Main threats Moderate habitat loss (e.g. due to phosphate mining, settlement), introduced species

Biological importance ● ● ●
Current threat level ● ● ●

Area 140 km² **Altitude** 0–300 m

Countries Christmas Island (to Australia)

Restricted-range species	Threatened	Total
Confined to this EBA	1	2
Present also in other EBAs, SAs	0	0
Total	1	2

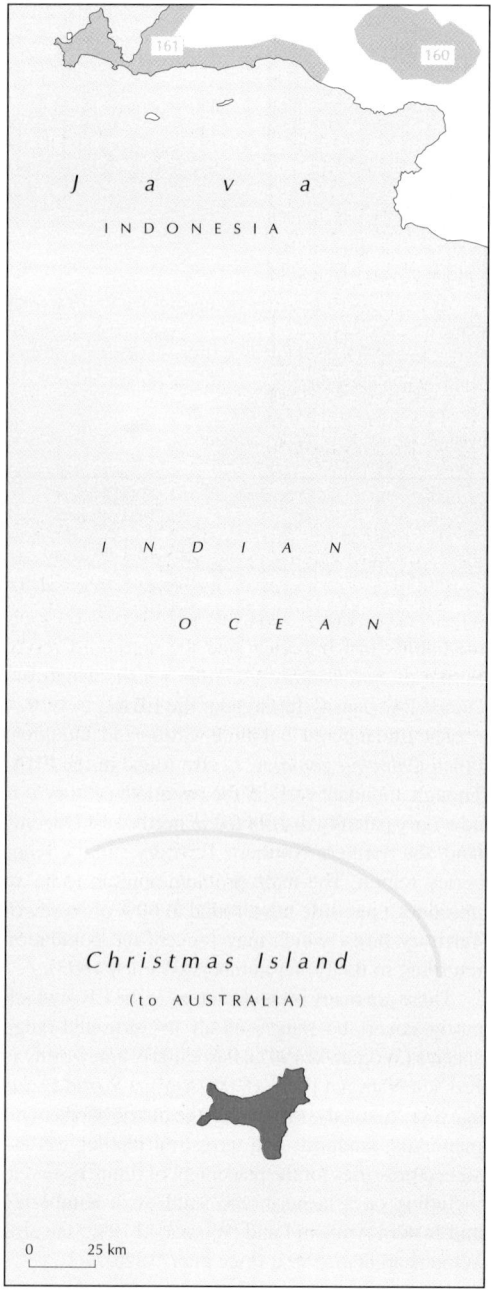

0   25 km

■ General characteristics

Christmas Island, an external territory of Australia, is a raised coral island in the Indian Ocean, c.200 km south of Java in Indonesia (EBAs 160 and 161) and 2,600 km west of Darwin in North-West Australia (EBA 187).

The native vegetation includes mixed closed rain forest above 180 m, occasionally extending down to coastal terraces where deciduous forest predominates (Davis *et al.* 1986).

The best known member of the island's fauna is probably the endemic terrestrial red crab *Gecarcinus lagostomus,* whose estimated 135 million individuals make spectacular annual migrations, which have captured international attention through wildlife documentaries.

■ Restricted-range species

The island is also important for its bird species and, in particular, for its two endemic land birds. These both rely primarily on forest: *Ducula whartoni* is largely restricted to remaining patches, while *Zosterops natalis* occurs more widely in a variety of habitats.

Two seabirds, Abbott's Booby *Papasula abbotti* and Christmas Island Frigatebird *Fregata andrewsi,* are endemic while breeding, and also rely on the remaining forest for nesting sites.

■ Threats and conservation

In 1887 rock specimens collected from Christmas Island were shown to be rich in phosphate, a discovery which led to a century of phosphate mining on the island (stopped in 1987 and recommenced in 1990, but then restricted to previous cleared areas: T. Stokes *in litt.* 1993). The mining and associated settlement has resulted in severe disturbance of the natural environment, including the loss of c.25% of native forest and consequent declines in forest species.

Feral populations of introduced cats, rats and mice have also affected the wildlife, as does (or did) hunting by people (Stokes 1988). The exotic wolf snake *Lycodon aulicus capucius,* is a more recent, but established, introduction (in shipping cargo in 1987), and, as its diet is small animals it may threaten

Status and habitat of restricted-range species

Species (ordered taxonomically)	Global status	Other EBAs (and SAs)	Habitat
Christmas Island Imperial-pigeon *Ducula whartoni*	VU	—	Forest, sometimes secondary growth dominated by the introduced cherry *Muntingia calabura*
Christmas Island White-eye *Zosterops natalis*	nt	—	Forest, most types of native and introduced regrowth

Global status (see p. 679 for definitions)							
EX	Extinct ⎱ with year	CR	Critical ⎱ threatened	cd	Conservation Dependent	DD	Data Deficient
EW	Extinct in ⎰ of last	EN	Endangered ⎰ species	nt	Near Threatened	NE	Not Evaluated
	the Wild ⎰ record	VU	Vulnerable	lc	Least Concern		

Other EBAs (and SAs) (see p. 83 for locations): bracketed numbers are Secondary Areas; [X] extinct in that EBA or SA.

The population of Christmas Island Hawk Owl *Ninox squamipila natalis* has been reduced by forest clearance.

R. Hill

some bird species, especially passerines (T. Stokes *in litt.* 1993), although there is no evidence that this has happened (Rumpff 1992; but see the effects of the introduced brown tree snake *Boiga irregularis* on forest birds in Guam, EBA 189).

Of the two endemic landbird species, *Ducula whartoni* is considered threatened on account of its particularly small range; a widespread introduced shrub, the cherry *Muntingia calabura*, does now provide an alternative food source, but the total area occupied by the bird is still likely to be less than 100 km². Hunting is now illegal and has presumably been reduced, but it continues at an unknown level; *D. whartoni* does remain, however, widespread and common (Garnett 1993, R. Hill *in litt.* 1995).

Two subspecies, both rain forest inhabitants, are classified as threatened by Garnett (1993): the Christmas Island form of Brown Goshawk *Accipiter fasciatus natalis* (population estimated at 50–150 pairs) and Moluccan Hawk-owl *Ninox squamipila natalis* (c.100 pairs). The local race of Emerald Dove *Chalcophaps indica natalis*, also a rain forest bird but tolerant of disturbed habitats, is identified as being a taxon of special concern.

Both endemic seabirds (see 'Restricted-range species', above) are classified as Vulnerable on account of their tiny breeding ranges. The population of *Papasula abbotti* (3,000 pairs in 1991) continues to decline, despite the cessation of new forest clearance, because air turbulence downwind of clearings kills adults and young, and crowding by displaced breeders reduces productivity of pairs breeding elsewhere in the forest (Garnett 1993, Reville and Stokes 1994; see also Yorkston and Green 1997). The population of *Fregata andrewsi* has also declined (currently estimated at 1,600 pairs) and the potential for this slow-breeding species to recover from these losses is low.

There is one protected area, on the south-west of the island, the Christmas Island National Park, which has recently been extended to include c.62% of the island (Garnett 1993), and a new management plan has been developed. This will benefit all the endemic landbirds and the seabirds too, as virtually all nesting sites of *Papasula abbotti* are included within the park and c.20% of mined areas adjacent to nesting sites have been planted in a continuing restoration programme (R. Hill *in litt.* 1994). Two of the three colonies of *Fregata andrewsi* are within the park, though the third, which lies outside, continues to be degraded by phosphate dust from mining activities (R. Hill *in litt.* 1995).

189 Mariana Islands

PRIORITY URGENT

Key habitats Lowland rain forest

Main threats Moderate habitat loss, introduced species (esp. brown tree snake)

Biological importance ● ● ▫
Current threat level ● ● ▫

Area 1,000 km² **Altitude** 0–900 m
Countries Guam (to USA), Northern Mariana Islands (to USA)

Restricted-range species	Threatened	Total
Confined to this EBA	5	7
Present also in other EBAs, SAs	1	5
Total	6	12

■ General characteristics

Some of the islands of this EBA (covering the US dependent territories of the Northern Mariana Islands and Guam) are the peaks of submerged and still-active volcanic mountains, and others, notably Guam, are uplifted coral formations.

Vegetation is varied, with lowland rain forest (mostly man-modified and much reduced) found on limestone areas and old lava flows; fire-adapted grasslands are extensive in southern Guam and on some of the northern islands. *Leucaena leucocephala*, a weedy tree from the American tropics (locally called tangan-tangan), was seeded widely after World

War II, and is now ubiquitous on the larger southern islands where it forms dense thickets.

■ Restricted-range species

Most of the restricted-range species utilize forest and many appear to have adapted to secondary and/or introduced vegetation including tangan-tangan. Some are (or were, as most species have been extirpated from Guam) found on all islands, but a number are confined to the southern ones and thus have tiny world ranges. Several species occur more widely in other Micronesian Endemic Bird Areas (EBAs 190–192).

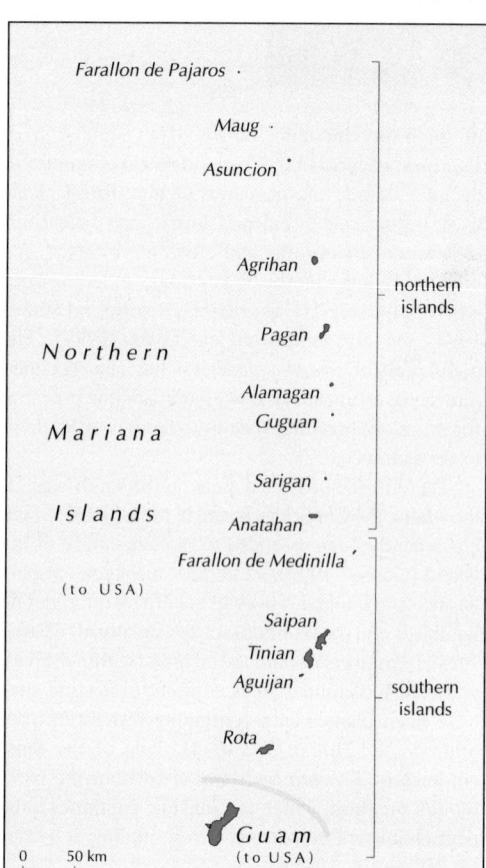

Farallon de Pajaros ·

Maug ·

Asuncion ·

Agrihan ·

Pagan ♪

N o r t h e r n

Alamagan ·

Guguan ·

M a r i a n a

Sarigan ·

I s l a n d s   Anatahan ▬

Farallon de Medinilla ´

(to USA)

northern islands

Saipan

Tinian

Aguijan ▬

southern islands

Rota

G u a m
(to USA)

0   50 km

Distribution patterns of restricted-range species

Species (ordered geographically)	Northern islands	Saipan	Tinian	Aguijan	Rota	Guam	Other EBAs, SAs
Acrocephalus luscinia	●	●	–	○	–	X	–
Megapodius laperouse	●	R	○	●	X	X	●
Gallicolumba xanthonura	●	●	●	●	●	X	●
Myzomela rubratra	●	●	●	●	●	X	●
Aplonis opaca	●	●	●	●	●	●	●
Cleptornis marchei	–	●	–	●	–	–	–
Zosterops saypani	–	●	●	●	–	–	–
Ptilinopus roseicapilla	–	●	●	●	●	X	–
Collocalia inquieta	–	●	X	●	X	●	●
Monarcha takatsukasae	–	–	●	–	–	–	–
Corvus kubaryi	–	–	–	–	●	●	–
Zosterops rotensis	–	–	–	–	●	–	–
Gallirallus owstonii	–	–	–	–	I	X	–
Myiagra freycineti	–	–	–	–	–	X	–
Zosterops conspicillatus	–	–	–	–	–	X	–
Todirhamphus cinnamominus	–	–	–	–	–	X	●
Total	5	9	7	9	6	3	

● Present   R Reintroduced   Threatened spp. } see 'Status
○ Extinct?   I Introduced, not   shown in **bold** } and habitat'
X Extinct   yet established   Other EBAs, SAs } table

■ Threats and conservation

The most important threat to the birds of this EBA is the possible spread of the introduced brown tree snake *Boiga irregularis* (native to Australasia), a most effective colonizer and bird predator (see, e.g., Savidge 1987, Conry 1988, Fritts 1988, Jaffe 1994). Although the snakes on Guam have declined with the

Status and habitat of restricted-range species

Species (ordered taxonomically)	Global status	Other EBAs (and SAs)	Habitat
Micronesian Scrubfowl *Megapodius laperouse*	VU	190	Beaches (breeding), forest, dense coconut plantations
Guam Rail *Gallirallus owstoni*	EW (1987)	—	All habitats except wetlands, inc. forest, scrub, secondary growth, agricultural areas
White-throated Ground-dove *Gallicolumba xanthonura*	nt	191	Forest, secondary growth, plantations
Mariana Fruit-dove *Ptilinopus roseicapilla*	nt	—	Forest, secondary growth
Micronesian Swiftlet *Collocalia inquieta*[1]	lc	192	Caves (breeding), forest, open country
Micronesian Kingfisher *Todirhamphus cinnamominus*[2]	lc	148[X],190,192	Forest, secondary growth
Nightingale Reed-warbler *Acrocephalus luscinia*	VU	—	Forest, tangan-tangan thickets, grassland, wetlands
Tinian Monarch *Monarcha takatsukasae*	VU	—	Forest and all types of shrubby vegetation inc. tangan-tangan thickets
Guam Flycatcher *Myiagra freycineti*	EX (1985)	—	Forest, secondary growth
Guam Bridled White-eye *Zosterops conspicillatus*[3]	EX (1983)	—	Forest, secondary growth, suburban areas
Rota Bridled White-eye *Zosterops rotensis*[3]	CR	—	Forest, secondary growth
Saipan Bridled White-eye *Zosterops saypani*[3]	lc	—	Most habitats, esp. forest, secondary growth
Golden White-eye *Cleptornis marchei*	VU	—	Most habitats, esp. forest and tangan-tangan thickets
Micronesian Myzomela *Myzomela rubratra*	lc	190,191,192	Forest, secondary growth, plantations, urban areas
Micronesian Starling *Aplonis opaca*	lc	190,191,192	Most habitats inc. forest, farmland, urban and suburban areas
Mariana Crow *Corvus kubaryi*	CR	—	Forest, secondary growth

Global status (see p. 679 for definitions)

EX	Extinct	cd	Conservation Dependent
EW	Extinct in the Wild		
		nt	Near Threatened
CR	Critical	lc	Least Concern
EN	Endangered	DD	Data Deficient
VU	Vulnerable	NE	Not Evaluated

EX Extinct } with year / EW Extinct in } of last / the Wild } record — threatened species (CR Critical, EN Endangered, VU Vulnerable)

Other EBAs (and SAs) (see p. 90 for locations)
Bracketed numbers are Secondary Areas. [X] Extinct in that EBA or SA.

Notes
[1] Introduced to Oahu (Central Hawaiian Islands, EBA 217).
[2] Extinct in this EBA c.1988.
[3] Taxonomy according to H. D. Pratt *in litt.* (1994); see also Collar *et al.* (1994).

demise of their bird prey, introduced skinks have proved an alternative food source on which they can persist indefinitely (T. Fritts verbally 1995).

A series of recovery plans has been developed for the birds of this EBA (e.g. USFWS 1990) and efforts are under way to establish an experimental population of *Gallirallus owstoni* on Rota (Witteman *et al.* 1990, Haig *et al.* 1993). However, all bird populations on Rota, and on nearby Tinian and Saipan, are potentially threatened by future snake introductions, as cargo arrives on these islands via Guam.

Despite the absence of brown tree snakes on Rota, some birds, e.g. *Zosterops rotensis* and *Corvus kubaryi*, have also declined on this island, and other threats may be operating (H. D. Pratt *in litt.* 1994),

such as other introduced predators, competitors or diseases; the introduced Black Drongo *Dicrurus macrocercus* has been implicated in the recent rapid decline of *Z. rotensis* (Craig and Taisacan 1994).

In 1993 a National Wildlife Refuge was established on Guam to preserve remaining forest and ensure the continued existence of *Corvus kubaryi*; protection of this habitat will also permit re-establishment and recovery of a variety of bird species should snake control ever take place (Wiles *et al.* 1995). Four remote northern islands (Farallon de Pajaros, Maug, Asuncion and Guguan) are wildlife sanctuaries important for some restricted-range birds and for seabirds (Reichel 1991, G. J. Wiles *in litt.* 1993, D. W. Stinson *in litt.* 1994).

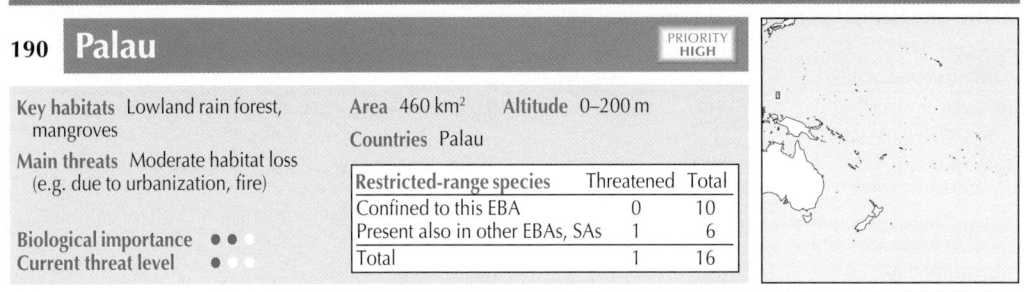

190	Palau		PRIORITY HIGH

Key habitats Lowland rain forest, mangroves

Main threats Moderate habitat loss (e.g. due to urbanization, fire)

Biological importance ● ● ●
Current threat level ● ● ●

Area 460 km²   Altitude 0–200 m

Countries Palau

Restricted-range species	Threatened	Total
Confined to this EBA	0	10
Present also in other EBAs, SAs	1	6
Total	1	16

■ General characteristics

The republic of Palau consists of c.340 islands and islets, of which eight are inhabited. Some islands are of volcanic origin—Babeldaob (the highest island at 218 m and by far the largest, representing more than 75% of Palau's total land area), parts of Koror and a few small islands in the Koror vicinity—while all others (including the Rock Islands, Peleliu and Angaur) are of more recent limestone formation. Six tiny remote islands, 600 km south-west of the main archipelago (the Southwest Islands), are politically part of Palau, but are not included in the EBA as they do not harbour any restricted-range species.

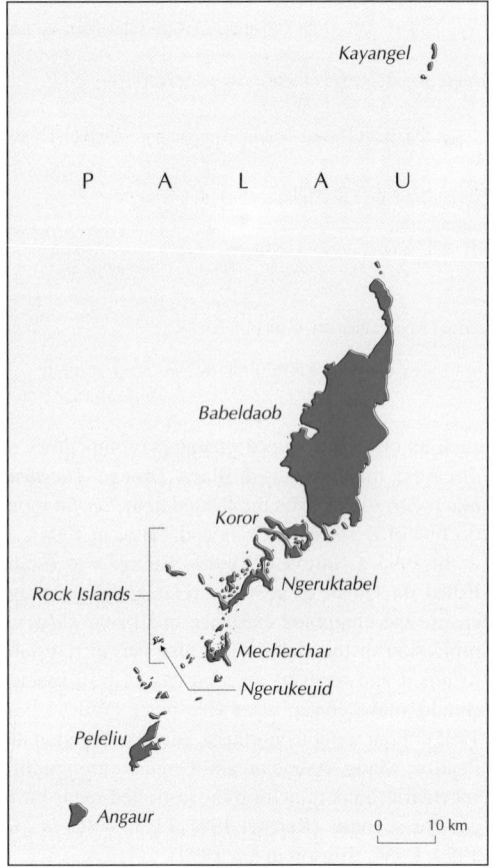

■ Restricted-range species

Dense, tropical, broadleaf forests cover most volcanic and virtually all limestone islands, with the notable exception of Babeldaob, where much of the original forest has been lost and replaced by savanna and grassland, although extensive mangrove forests still remain in protected coastal areas.

■ Restricted-range species

All the restricted-range species are inhabitants of forest and many also forage in mangroves. Most species occur through all of the islands; the exceptions being *Gallicolumba canifrons* (very rare on Babeldaob, commoner on the limestone islands) and *Megazosterops palauensis* (apparently restricted to Peleliu and Ngeruktabel). Several species occur more widely in other Micronesian EBAs (189, 191, 192).

■ Threats and conservation

None of the endemics is currently classified as threatened, but all these species are potentially at risk from introduction of alien forms. Possible future introduction of brown tree snake *Boiga irregularis*, which caused the extinction of many bird species on Guam (see Mariana Islands, EBA 189), is a particular cause for concern, especially to the two species which have the most restricted ranges, and which are consequently classified as Near Threatened.

With the decline in authority of local chiefs, and increasing use of guns and speedboats, certain species of bird, e.g. columbids, seabirds and, notably, *Megapodius laperouse*, have been subject to considerable hunting pressure. Today, however, guns are outlawed, pigeon populations appear to be recovering and nearly all birds on Palau are fully protected by local law. Although densities of *Megapodius laperouse* are low throughout Palau (a population estimate for all islands excluding Kayangel of less than 500 was made in 1991), numbers appear relatively stable with the greatest threat now being tourist use of rock island beaches where the birds nest (Engbring 1988, 1992, H. D. Pratt *in litt.* 1995).

Loss of habitat has adversely affected some birds, particularly on Koror and Babeldaob, which are becoming rapidly built up; on Babeldaob extensive

Status and habitat of restricted-range species

Species (ordered taxonomically)	Global status	Other EBAs (and SAs)	Habitat
Micronesian Scrubfowl *Megapodius laperouse*	VU	189	Beaches (breeding), forest, dense coconut plantations
Palau Ground-dove *Gallicolumba canifrons*	nt	—	Forest, esp. on limestone islands
Palau Fruit-dove *Ptilinopus pelewensis*	lc	—	Forest
Micronesian Imperial-pigeon *Ducula oceanica*	lc	191,192 (s123,s125[x])	Forest on high islands, coconut palms on atolls
Palau Owl *Otus podarginus*	lc	—	All types of forest inc. mangroves
Palau Swiftlet *Collocalia pelewensis*	lc	—	Caves (breeding), forest, open country
Micronesian Kingfisher *Todirhamphus cinnamominus*	lc	148[x],189[x], 192	Forest, secondary growth
Palau Bush-warbler *Cettia annae*	lc	—	Forest, forest edge, secondary vegetation
Mangrove Flycatcher *Myiagra erythrops*	lc	—	Forest, mangroves
Palau Fantail *Rhipidura lepida*	lc	—	Forest, secondary growth
Morningbird *Colluricincla tenebrosa*	lc	—	Forest, secondary growth
Caroline Islands White-eye *Zosterops semperi*	lc	192	Forest, forest edge, scrub, secondary growth
Dusky White-eye *Zosterops finschii*	lc	—	Forest, forest edge, secondary growth, sometimes mangroves
Giant White-eye *Megazosterops palauensis*	nt	—	Forest and *Leucaena* thickets, exclusively on limestone
Micronesian Myzomela *Myzomela rubratra*	lc	189,191,192	Forest, secondary growth, mangroves, gardens, suburban areas
Micronesian Starling *Aplonis opaca*	lc	189,191,192	Most habitats inc. forest, gardens, suburban areas

Global status (see p. 679 for definitions): EX Extinct, EW Extinct in the Wild (with year of last record), CR Critical, EN Endangered, VU Vulnerable (threatened species), cd Conservation Dependent, nt Near Threatened, lc Least Concern, DD Data Deficient, NE Not Evaluated

Other EBAs (and SAs) (see p. 90 for locations): bracketed numbers are Secondary Areas; [x] extinct in that EBA or SA.

areas of native vegetation are burned each year, increasing the size of barren savannas (Engbring 1988). However, the forests on this island grow on very poor soil and harbour few birds compared to the rock island forests (H. D. Pratt *in litt.* 1995), which are more important for the conservation of restricted-range bird species.

Several subspecies which are endemic to Palau qualify as threatened. These include Palau Nicobar Pigeon *Caloenas nicobarica pelewensis* (a subspecies of a widespread globally Near Threatened species), which is conservatively estimated to number c.700 individuals and is most common on the Rock Islands; Palau White-breasted Woodswallow *Artamus leucorhynchus pelewensis*, which may number fewer than 100 birds and is found almost exclusively on the upper savannas of Babeldaob; and Palau Blue-faced

Parrotfinch *Erythrura trichoa pelewensis*, which is virtually restricted to *Casuarina* groves along beaches of the Rock Islands and is estimated to number just over 1,000 individuals (Engbring 1992, H. D. Pratt *in litt.* 1994, 1995).

The EBA's single protected area covers the Ngerukeuid Islands; it is an important pristine reserve where most of the restricted-range species occur (Wiles and Conry 1990). Establishment of other ecological reserves has been recommended, including the protection of forested tracts on Peleliu and Babeldaob, and a Rock Island Reserve covering the largest islands of Ngeruktabel and Mecherchar (Engbring 1992). In a recent conservation education campaign (RARE/Palau Conservation Society) *Ptilinopus pelewensis* was chosen as Palau's national bird.

191 Yap Islands

PRIORITY
HIGH

Key habitats Lowland (secondary) rain forest, mangroves

Main threats Major habitat loss (e.g. due to fire)

Biological importance ●●●
Current threat level ●●●

Area 120 km²   **Altitude** 0–100 m

Countries Micronesia

Restricted-range species	Threatened	Total
Confined to this EBA	1	3
Present also in other EBAs, SAs	0	4
Total	1	7

■ General characteristics

The state of Yap in the western Pacific comprises four main volcanic and metamorphic islands separated by narrow channels: Yap (which has the highest peak at 176 m), Gagil Tomil, Maap and Rumung. The Federated States of Micronesia includes other island states (Truk, Pohnpei and Kosrae) c.1,500 km to the east, but these are treated separately in one EBA, the East Caroline Islands (EBA 192).

At one time broadleaf deciduous forests are thought to have largely covered the Yap islands, but, since the arrival of aboriginal people, this habitat has been destroyed or greatly altered, and now savanna and grassland are common, and virtually all remaining forest is secondary (a mixture of both native and cultivated species) and scrubby in nature (Engbring *et al.* 1990). Mangrove swamps are found around all the islands in sheltered, shallow, coastal situations.

■ Restricted-range species

Most of the restricted-range species occur in a variety of habitats, including all forest types and secondary vegetation, though few native birds use savanna extensively. Four of the restricted-range species occur more widely in the Micronesian region (which includes four EBAs, 189–192), but do not show clear affinities to any one EBA, and thus Yap has been treated as an EBA in its own right.

■ Threats and conservation

Given their small ranges, and despite their large populations, all of the endemic species of this EBA are at risk from introduced species. Main cause for concern is the possible future introduction of the brown tree snake *Boiga irregularis*, which has caused the extinction of many bird species on Guam (see Mariana Islands, EBA 189).

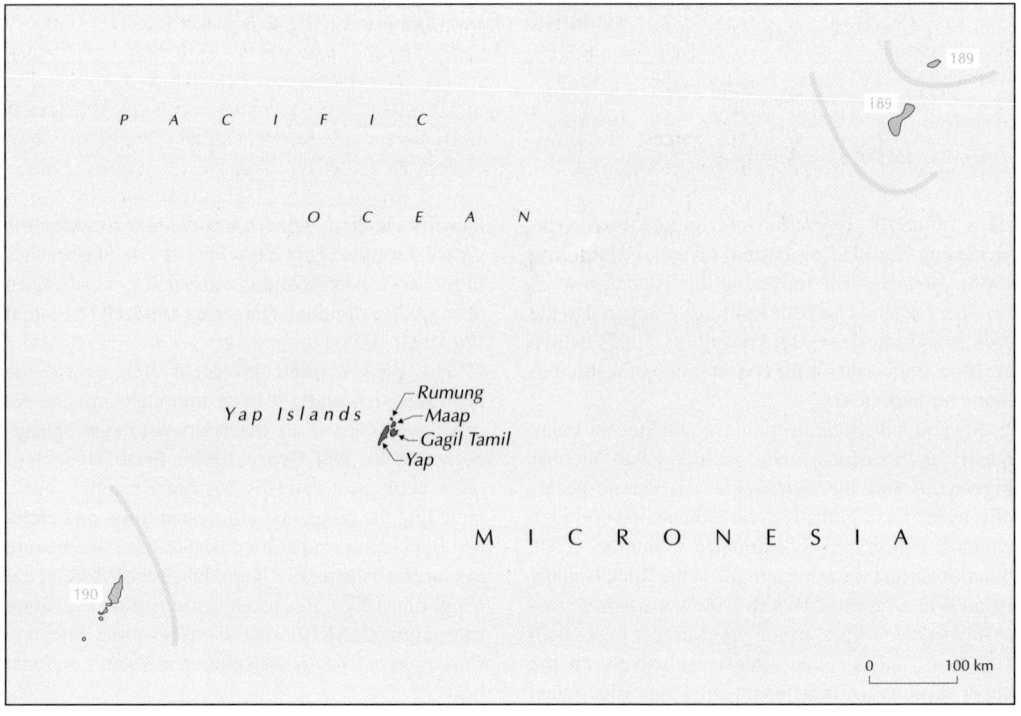

Status and habitat of restricted-range species

Species (ordered taxonomically)	Global status	Other EBAs (and SAs)	Habitat
White-throated Ground-dove *Gallicolumba xanthonura*	nt	189	Forest, gardens
Micronesian Imperial-pigeon *Ducula oceanica*[1]	lc	190,192 (s123,s125[x])	Forest
Yap Monarch *Monarcha godeffroyi*	nt	—	All forest types, inc. mangroves, forest edge
Plain White-eye *Zosterops hypolais*	nt	—	All habitats inc. forest, brushy thickets, open savanna and meadows
Yap Olive White-eye *Zosterops oleagineus*	VU	—	All types of forest and woody vegetation, inc. mangroves
Micronesian Myzomela *Myzomela rubratra*	lc	189,190,192	Forest, mangroves, gardens, urban areas
Micronesian Starling *Aplonis opaca*	lc	189,190,192	Most habitats inc. forest and gardens

| **Global status** (see p. 679 for definitions) | EX Extinct EW Extinct in the Wild } with year of last record | CR Critical EN Endangered VU Vulnerable } threatened species | cd Conservation Dependent nt Near Threatened lc Least Concern DD Data Deficient NE Not Evaluated | **Other EBAs (and SAs)** (see p. 90 for locations) **Notes** | Bracketed numbers are Secondary Areas. [x] Extinct in that EBA or SA. [1] May be introduced from Palau, EBA 190 (H. D. Pratt *in litt.* 1995). |

Concern has also been expressed that the Tree Sparrow *Passer montanus*, introduced in the late 1970s from Eurasia, may carry exotic diseases which could seriously affect the native avifauna (Engbring *et al.* 1990); however, earlier introductions of other bird species have apparently had no drastic effects, and, as Yap receives migrants regularly, continental diseases have probably been present for some time and are unlikely to be a significant threat (H. D. Pratt *in litt.* 1995). Loss of habitat from fire is an additional threat as, during the dry season, large areas of savanna are torched by local people for various reasons (B. Raynor *in litt.* 1995).

Zosterops oleagineus is the scarcest of the endemic species, with a population estimated at less than 20,000 in 1984 and some evidence of a decline since the 1970s; it has therefore been classified as threatened. The two other endemics are regarded as Near Threatened.

Several subspecies endemic to this EBA qualify as threatened. One example is Yap Cicadabird *Coracina tenuirostris nesiotis* (a good candidate for elevation to species rank), which is very rare and thinly distributed in forest (H. D. Pratt *in litt.* 1994). A race of Common Moorhen *Gallinula chloropus* which has nested in small numbers on Yap in recent years is also a threatened subspecies if it has colonized from the Marianas—though not if it has come from Palau or the Asian mainland (see Stinson *et al.* 1991, H. D. Pratt *in litt.* 1995).

Although there are no legally protected areas in this EBA (all land is privately owned), the use of natural resources has been regulated by customary management. However, as elsewhere in the Pacific, such control is likely to be increasingly challenged and to become difficult to maintain. A general policy of regular forest maintenance has therefore been recommended, including standard forestry practices such as controlling fires, and replanting and reclaiming portions of savanna. It is difficult to provide more specific recommendations, such as the identification of specific areas that are of more conservation value than others, because birds are found throughout the remaining forest (Engbring *et al.* 1990).

192   East Caroline Islands

PRIORITY
CRITICAL

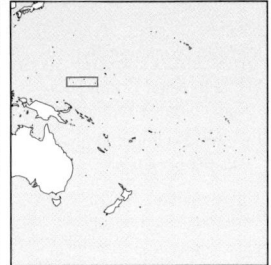

Key habitats Lowland and montane rain forest, mangroves

Main threats Moderate habitat loss (e.g. due to cultivation)

Biological importance ● ● ●
Current threat level ● ● ○

Area 580 km²   **Altitude** 0–700 m

Countries Micronesia

Restricted-range species	Threatened	Total
Confined to this EBA	4	11
Present also in other EBAs, SAs	0	7
Total	4	18

■ General characteristics

This EBA includes the island states of Truk, Pohnpei and Kosrae, each separated from the other by c.500 km, with many tiny atolls between—but it excludes the state of Yap (EBA 191, c.1,500 km to the west though politically also part of the Federated States of Micronesia).

The native vegetation is rain forest, divisible into several different types including lowland and montane forest on the high islands, with cloud forest at the highest elevations on Pohnpei and Kosrae, and mangroves on sheltered coasts.

■ Restricted-range species

Most of the restricted-range species are forest birds occurring at all altitudes (though *Rukia longirostra* and *R. ruki* are typically confined to upper elevations), and several are able to utilize a variety of other habitats including plantations.

The islands have (or had) their own endemics—three species on Truk, five on Pohnpei and two (both extinct) on Kosrae—but they also share restricted-range species, making this a single EBA. Both *Acrocephalus syrinx* and *Aplonis opaca* are widespread within this EBA on atolls as well as on the high islands, and several other species occur more widely in other Micronesian EBAs (189–190).

Mottled Munia *Lonchura hunsteini*, a restricted-range species endemic to New Ireland, Papua New Guinea (EBA 195), was introduced to Pohnpei in the 1920s and is now abundant in the north and east of the island (Pratt *et al.* 1987).

■ Threats and conservation

Loss of forest is a serious problem in some parts of this EBA. For example, on Pohnpei, the lowland forests have been very disturbed and those in the uplands have been seriously affected too, mainly due to the growth of 'sakau' or 'kava' *Piper methysticum*

Distribution patterns of restricted-range species

Species (ordered geographically)	Truk	Pohnpei	Kosrae	Other EBAs, SAs
Myiagra oceanica	●	–	–	–
Metabolus rugensis	●	–	–	–
Rukia ruki	●	–	–	–
Gallicolumba kubaryi	●	●	–	–
Zosterops semperi	●	●	–	●
Acrocephalus syrinx	●	●	X	–
Ptilinopus porphyraceus	●	●	●	●
Ducula oceanica	●	●	●	●
Collocalia inquieta	●	●	●	●
Myzomela rubratra	●	●	●	●
Aplonis opaca	●	●	●	●
Trichoglossus rubiginosus	–	●	–	–
Myiagra pluto	–	●	–	–
Rhipidura kubaryi	–	●	–	–
Rukia longirostra	–	●	–	–
Aplonis pelzelni	–	●	–	–
Todirhamphus cinnamominus	–	●	–	●
Zosterops cinereus	–	●	●	–
Porzana monasa	–	–	X	–
Aplonis corvina	–	–	X	–
Total	11	15	6	

● Present   ? Present?
○ Extinct?   R Reintroduced
X Extinct   I Introduced

Threatened spp. shown in **bold**   } see 'Status and habitat' table
Other EBAs, SAs

M I C R O N E S I A

Truk
Tol
Pohnpei
E a s t
C a r o l i n e
I s l a n d s
Kosrae

0   100 km

Status and habitat of restricted-range species

Species (ordered taxonomically)	Global status	Other EBAs (and SAs)	Habitat
Kosrae Crake *Porzana monasa*	EX (1827)	—	Wet forest, taro patches
Caroline Islands Ground-dove *Gallicolumba kubaryi*	EN	—	Agricultural and native forest, bushy ravines, atoll vegetation, gardens
Purple-capped Fruit-dove *Ptilinopus porphyraceus*	lc	202,203 (s123^X,s127, s128,s129,s130,s131)	Forest, secondary forest
Micronesian Imperial-pigeon *Ducula oceanica*	lc	190,191 (s123,s125^X)	Forest on high islands, coconut palms on atolls
Pohnpei Lory *Trichoglossus rubiginosus*	lc	—	All forest types, coconut plantations
Micronesian Swiftlet *Collocalia inquieta*	lc	189	Caves (breeding), forest, open country
Micronesian Kingfisher *Todirhamphus cinnamominus*	lc	148^X,189^X,190	Variety of forest types, secondary growth, forest edge, plantations
Caroline Islands Reed-warbler *Acrocephalus syrinx*	lc	—	Forest, secondary growth, scrub, gardens
Truk Monarch *Metabolus rugensis*	EN	—	Forest, rarely plantations, well-developed stands of mangroves, atoll vegetation
Oceanic Flycatcher *Myiagra oceanica*	lc	—	Forest, plantations, mangroves, atoll vegetation, gardens
Pohnpei Flycatcher *Myiagra pluto*	lc	—	Forest, plantations, mangroves, secondary growth, bushy savanna
Pohnpei Fantail *Rhipidura kubaryi*	lc	—	Most forest types, forest edge, bushy savanna
Caroline Islands White-eye *Zosterops semperi*	lc	190	Forest, forest edge, scrub, secondary growth
Grey-brown White-eye *Zosterops cinereus*	lc	—	All forest types, secondary growth, brushy vegetation, sometimes grassy fields
Long-billed White-eye *Rukia longirostra*	nt	—	Forest of interior uplands, lowland forest remnants, rarely plantations
Faichuk White-eye *Rukia ruki*	EN	—	Old-growth native (*Semecarpus*) forest at upper , elevationsvisits plantations, mangroves
Micronesian Myzomela *Myzomela rubratra*	lc	189,190,191	Forest, secondary growth, mangroves, plantations, urban areas
Pohnpei Mountain Starling *Aplonis pelzelni*	CR	—	Forest
Kosrae Starling *Aplonis corvina*	EX (1828)	—	Forest
Micronesian Starling *Aplonis opaca*	lc	189,190,191	Most habitats inc. forest and gardens

Global status (see p. 679 for definitions)
EX Extinct
EW Extinct in the Wild } with year of last record
CR Critical
EN Endangered
VU Vulnerable } threatened species
cd Conservation Dependent
nt Near Threatened
lc Least Concern
DD Data Deficient
NE Not Evaluated

Other EBAs (and SAs) (see p. 90 for locations): bracketed numbers are Secondary Areas; ^{X} extinct in that EBA or SA.

as a major cash crop (B. Raynor *in litt.* 1995). On Truk, the only semi-original forest remaining is scattered in tiny remnants on the higher reaches of a few islands, most notably on Tol where the largest tract (0.68 km²) survives.

On Kosrae, however, where two species have become globally extinct, the forests are largely intact, especially in the interior, and it is assumed that the demise of its endemic birds was due to predation by introduced rats (Greenway 1967). Alien species

(including possible future introductions, e.g. brown tree snake *Boiga irregularis*: see Mariana Islands, EBA 189) remain one of the main threats to the birds of this tiny island EBA.

Several unique ecological sites have been identified by Engbring *et al.* (1990). In 1987 51 km² were set aside on Pohnpei in the centre of the island as a watershed reserve and all mangrove forests on the island (55 km²) were established as a protected area (B. Raynor *in litt.* 1995).

193 Admiralty Islands

PRIORITY HIGH

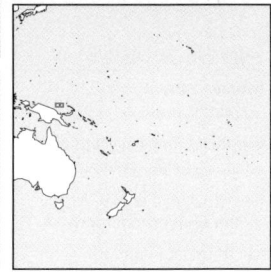

Key habitats Lowland rain forest

Main threats Limited habitat loss (e.g. due to shifting cultivation)

Biological importance ● ● ●
Current threat level ● ● ●

Area 2,000 km²   **Altitude** 0–700 m

Countries Papua New Guinea

Restricted-range birds	Threatened	Total
Confined to this EBA	3	6
Present also in other EBAs, SAs	0	7
Total	3	13

■ General characteristics

The Admiralty Islands, politically part of Papua New Guinea, are often grouped with the St Matthias Islands (EBA 194) and the larger islands of New Britain and New Ireland (EBA 195) into the Bismarck archipelago, but are here treated as an EBA in their own right. The much smaller islands surrounding the main island of Manus also harbour restricted-range species and so are included within the EBA.

The hilly terrain of Manus (reaching 719 m on Mt Dremsel) is covered in rain forest up to its maximum altitude, with an estimated 80% of vegetation being primary forest in 1987 (Kula *et al.* undated).

■ Restricted-range species

All the restricted-range species occur in forest, and a number occur in secondary growth. There are no reported avifaunal changes with altitude.

Of the six species confined to this EBA, four are endemic to Manus, with *Monarcha infelix* and *Rhipidura semirubra* occurring on some of the surrounding islands (there are records from Lou, Fedarb, San Miguel, Rambutyo, Pak and Tong). Several of the more-widespread restricted-range species are small-island birds and occur in other Papuan island and Melanesian EBAs, but do not show clear affinities to any single EBA.

■ Threats and conservation

Manus has no protected areas, and the vulnerability of the island's wildlife was exposed when it was proposed to build a satellite launch site there, but this project is currently shelved (I. Burrows *in litt.* 1994, P. Gregory *in litt.* 1994). Nevertheless, the forest on Manus is being eroded by shifting cultivation, with a number of villages using portable sawmills, taking selected trees for domestic use and for the sale of planks (Buckingham *et al.* 1995). Although this forest loss is still on a relatively small scale and mainly in coastal areas (and is therefore unlikely to be a major threat), three of the Manus endemics are very rare and are classified as threatened on account of their (presumed) tiny populations and distributions.

For example, a tentative population estimate of 1,000 calling birds was made for *Pitta superba* in 1990, but, if the species has specific habitat preferences, this may be an overestimate (Dutson and Newman 1991). Observations in 1994 indicate that it may survive in secondary growth and overgrown gardens, and that bamboo could be an important feature of its habitat requirements (D. Gibbs *in litt.* 1994), perhaps accounting for its apparent rather patchy distribution (P. Gregory *in litt.* 1996).

As with all small islands, introduced mammalian predators may be implicated in the rarity of the

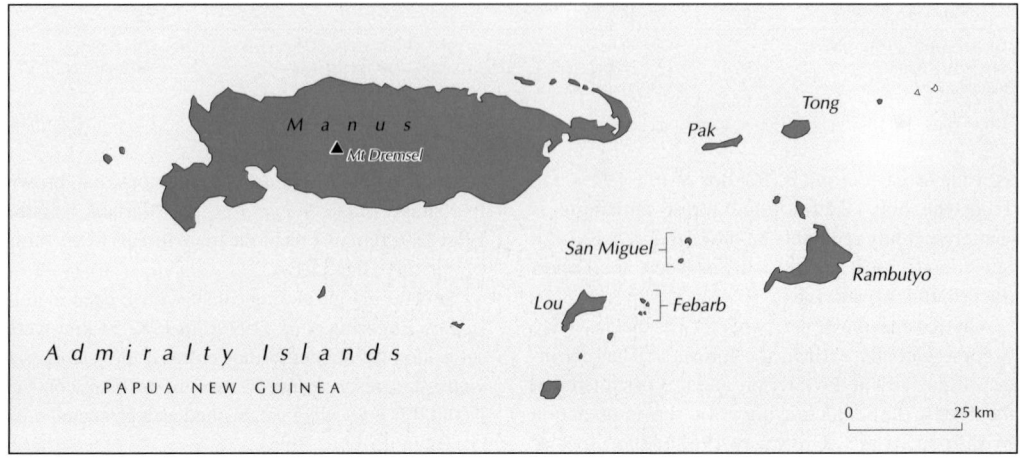

Admiralty Islands

PAPUA NEW GUINEA

0   25 km

Status and habitat of restricted-range species

Species (ordered taxonomically)	Global status	Other EBAs (and SAs)	Habitat
Melanesian Scrubfowl *Megapodius eremita*	lc	194,195, 198	All types of forested habitat, inc. mangroves, coastal scrub
Yellow-bibbed Fruit-dove *Ptilinopus solomonensis*	lc	174,194,195, 198	Forest, shrubs in secondary growth, fruiting trees, gardens
Yellow-tinted Imperial-pigeon *Ducula subflavescens*	lc	195	Mangroves, gallery forest, forest edge, low scrub
Pied Cuckoo-dove *Reinwardtoena browni*	lc	195	Forest
Meek's Pygmy-parrot *Micropsitta meeki*	lc	194	Forest, secondary forest, scrub, trees near habitation
Manus Masked-owl *Tyto manusi*	VU	—	Forest
Manus Hawk-owl *Ninox meeki*	lc	—	Forest, degraded forest, riverine cultivation, areas around villages
Superb Pitta *Pitta superba*	VU	—	Forest, secondary growth, overgrown gardens
Manus Monarch *Monarcha infelix*	nt	—	Forest; less able to tolerate secondary forest, scrub, mangroves
Manus Fantail *Rhipidura semirubra*	VU	—	Forest, scrub, coconut plantations
Black-headed White-eye *Zosterops hypoxanthus*	lc	195	Forest, forest edge, partly cleared areas, secondary growth, gardens
Ebony Myzomela *Myzomela pammelaena*	lc	194,195	Secondary growth, coconut plantations, gardens
White-naped Friarbird *Philemon albitorques*	lc	—	Forest edge, disturbed areas, gardens, coconut plantations

Global status (see p. 679 for definitions)

EX	Extinct	with year of last record	CR	Critical	threatened species	cd	Conservation Dependent	DD Data Deficient
EW	Extinct in the Wild		EN	Endangered		nt	Near Threatened	NE Not Evaluated
			VU	Vulnerable		lc	Least Concern	

Other EBAs (and SAs) (see p. 90 for locations): bracketed numbers are Secondary Areas; [x] extinct in that EBA or SA.

Manus birds, but that island's interior forests are little known and *Tyto manusi* and *Rhipidura semirubra* may simply be overlooked; neither have been recorded there recently, though *R. semirubra* may be common on the surrounding islands (G. C. L. Dutson *in litt.* 1996, D. Gibbs *in litt.* 1996). Islanders say that *R. semirubra* survives on the tiny island of Tong because of the absence of *Philemon albitorques*, which may have undergone a population explosion (detrimental to *R. semirubra*) associated with human colonization and clearance on Manus (D. Gibbs *in litt.* 1994).

A large segment of uninhabited interior forest on Manus, including Mt Dremsel, has been identified as a very important area of terrestrial biodiversity in Papua New Guinea by Beehler (1993).

G. C. L. Dutson

Offshore islets such as this one are important refuges for Manus Fantail *Rhipidura semirubra*.

194 St Matthias Islands

PRIORITY HIGH

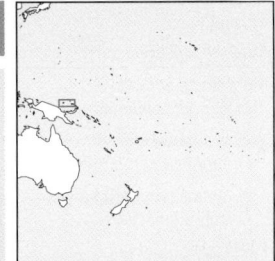

Key habitats	Lowland rain forest

Area 460 km² **Altitude** 0–1,000 m

Main threats	Possible habitat loss

Countries Papua New Guinea

Biological importance ● ● ●
Current threat level ● ● ●

Restricted-range birds	Threatened	Total
Confined to this EBA	0	2
Present also in other EBAs, SAs	0	6
Total	0	8

■ General characteristics

The St Matthias Islands, politically a part of Papua New Guinea, are often grouped together with the Admiralty Islands (EBA 193) and the larger islands of New Britain and New Ireland (EBA 195) into the Bismarck archipelago, but are here treated as an EBA in their own right. The islands involved include the main island, Mussau, which has a central volcanic spine, and the smaller nearby islands of Eloaua and Emirau, which are uplifted reefs.

Mussau is nearly all logged or under concession (G. C. L. Dutson *in litt*. 1997). On the smaller islands only isolated patches of sparser primary forest remain, growing on limestone outcrops too infertile to cultivate (Lepofsky 1992).

■ Restricted-range species

All the restricted-range species are forest birds and occur on Mussau, with the two endemics being confined to just this island. Six of the restricted-range birds are small-island species which occur elsewhere in other Papuan island and Melanesian EBAs, but do not show clear affinities to any one of them, and thus the St Matthias Islands—which host a highly distinctive avifauna, albeit largely at subspecific level (K. D. Bishop *in litt*. 1993)—have been treated as an EBA in their own right.

G. C. L.Dutson

White-breasted Monarch *Monarcha menckei* is a strikingly patterned white and black flycatcher found only on Mussau.

The Mussau subspecies *conjuncta* of Varied Triller *Lalage leucomela* (a species which has many other races elsewhere in New Guinea and the Australian region) is known by only a single male specimen, and has been identified by Coates (1990) as probably being a distinct species.

■ Threats and conservation

There are few recent data on the status of the birds of the St Matthias Islands but, although the two endemics *Monarcha menckei* and *Rhipidura matthiae* (classi-

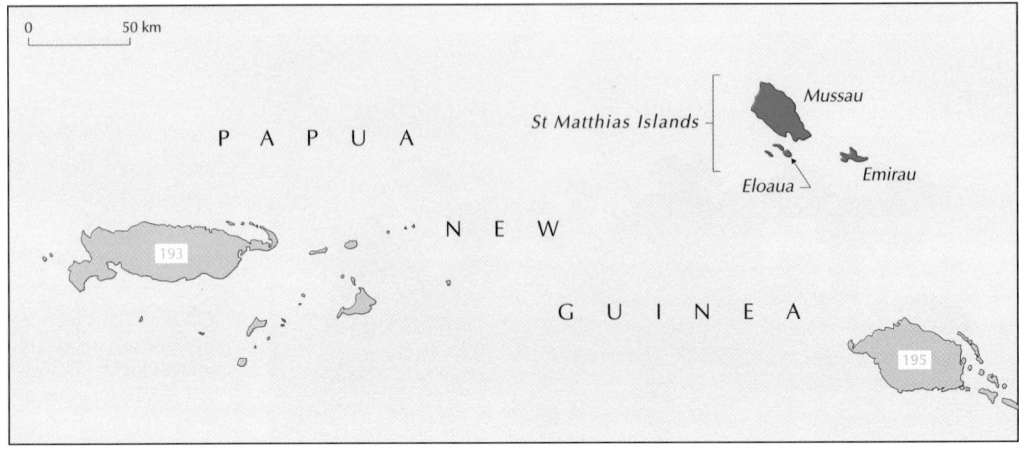

St Matthias Islands

Mussau

Eloaua

Emirau

P A P U A

N E W

G U I N E A

0   50 km

193

195

Status and habitat of restricted-range species

Species (ordered taxonomically)	Global status	Other EBAs (and SAs)	Habitat
Melanesian Scrubfowl *Megapodius eremita*	lc	193,195,198	All types of forested habitat, inc. mangroves, coastal scrub
Yellow-bibbed Fruit-dove *Ptilinopus solomonensis*	lc	174,193,195, 198	Forest, shrubs in secondary growth, fruiting trees, gardens
Knob-billed Fruit-dove *Ptilinopus insolitus*	lc	195	Forest, forest edge, disturbed habitat
Meek's Pygmy-parrot *Micropsitta meeki*	lc	193	Forest, tall secondary growth, trees near habitation
White-breasted Monarch *Monarcha menckei*	DD	—	Forest
Dull Flycatcher *Myiagra hebetior*	lc	195	Forest, forest edge, secondary growth
Matthias Fantail *Rhipidura matthiae*	DD	—	Forest, forest edge
Ebony Myzomela *Myzomela pammelaena*	lc	193,195	Forest, secondary growth, coconut plantations, gardens

Global status (see p. 679 for definitions)
EX Extinct
EW Extinct in the Wild } with year of last record
CR Critical
EN Endangered
VU Vulnerable } threatened species
cd Conservation Dependent
nt Near Threatened
lc Least Concern
DD Data Deficient
NE Not Evaluated

Other EBAs (and SAs) (see p. 90 for locations): bracketed numbers are Secondary Areas; ˣ extinct in that EBA or SA.

G. C. L.Dutson

Matthias Fantail *Rhipidura matthiae* is found only on Mussau. Both of the endemics are little known though apparently not uncommon.

fied as Data Deficient) are fairly common in logged and regrowth forest (Eastwood 1996; G. C. L. Dutson *in litt.* 1997), any future large-scale logging could have a devastating effect (B. J. Coates *in litt.* 1993, 1994).

Mussau has been identified as an important area for terrestrial biodiversity in Papua New Guinea by Beehler (1993) and is clearly a high priority for further biological survey.

195 New Britain and New Ireland

PRIORITY HIGH

Key habitats Lowland and montane rain forest

Main threats Moderate habitat loss (e.g. due to oil-palm and coconut plantations, logging)

Biological importance ● ● ○
Current threat level ● ○ ○

Area 48,000 km² **Altitude** 0–2,200 m

Countries Papua New Guinea

Restricted-range species	Threatened	Total
Confined to this EBA	2	35
Present also in other EBAs, SAs	1	19
Total	3	54

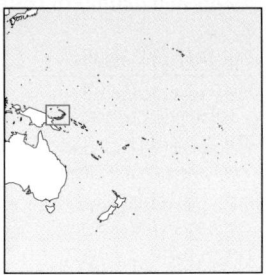

■ General characteristics

This EBA of Papua New Guinea includes New Britain, New Ireland and New Hanover (or Lavongai) and their outliers, from Karkar to Duke of York and from Nauna to Nissan; also the more distant North-western Islands and Schouten Islands. The Admiralty and St Matthias Islands, often grouped with New Britain and New Ireland into the Bismarck archipelago, are treated as separate EBAs (193, 194).

The native vegetation is mainly lowland forest with montane rain forest above c.900 m on the larger islands; mangroves and swamp forest are also common, and man-made grasslands occur locally, especially on New Britain.

■ Restricted-range species

This EBA has more restricted-range species than any other in the Pacific region except for the Solomon group (EBA 198). Most of these species utilize forest, with many also occurring in a range of other habitats. Some species show altitudinal preferences on the larger islands.

There is a complicated pattern of distribution between the islands (see 'Distribution patterns' table) with many species having ranges which extend to other Papuan island and Melanesian EBAs. New Hanover has one endemic species, while New Britain and its surrounding islands have 14 and New Ireland and its islands have seven; however, there are a

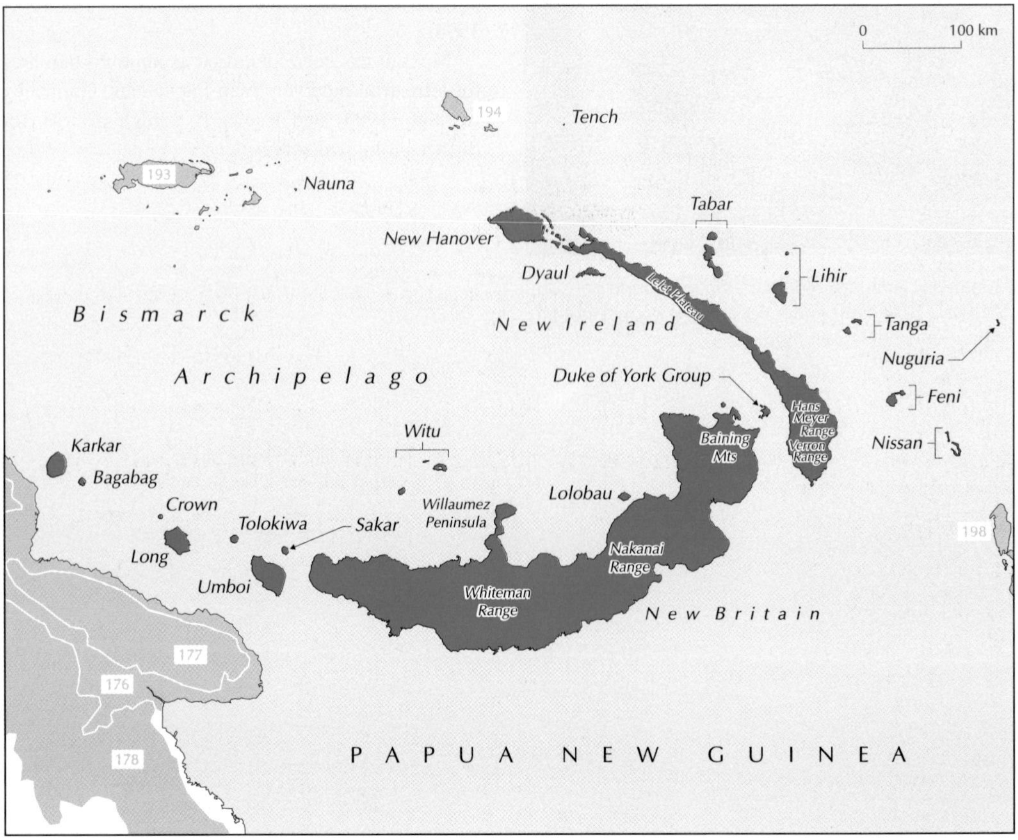

[Map showing the Bismarck Archipelago with New Britain, New Ireland, New Hanover and surrounding islands, scale 0–100 km. Labels include: 194, Tench, 193, Nauna, Tabar, New Hanover, Dyaul, Lelet Plateau, Lihir, Bismarck, New Ireland, Tanga, Archipelago, Duke of York Group, Nuguria, Feni, Witu, Karkar, Baining Mts, Hans Meyer Range, Verron Range, Nissan, Bagabag, Crown, Lolobau, Tolokiwa, Sakar, Willaumez Peninsula, Long, Nakanai Range, 198, Umboi, Whiteman Range, New Britain, 177, 176, 178, PAPUA NEW GUINEA]

Status and habitat of restricted-range species

Species (ordered taxonomically)	Global status	Other EBAs (and SAs)	Altitude (m)	Habitat
Black Honey-buzzard *Henicopernis infuscatus*	nt	—	0–1,000?	Forest, occasionally partly disturbed forest
Pied Goshawk *Accipiter albogularis*	lc	198,200	0–1,800	Forest, forest edge, open secondary growth, gardens, edges of towns, edges of coconut plantations
Slaty-mantled Sparrowhawk *Accipiter luteoschistaceus*	nt	—	0–700?	Forest, forest edge, partly cleared areas
New Britain Goshawk *Accipiter princeps*	nt	—	760–1,430	Montane forest
New Britain Sparrowhawk *Accipiter brachyurus*	VU	—	0–1,000	Forest, forest edge, disturbed forest, partly cleared areas
Melanesian Scrubfowl *Megapodius eremita*	lc	193,194,198	0–300 (–1,800)	All types of forested habitat, inc. degraded forest, secondary growth, mangroves, coastal scrub
New Britain Rail *Gallirallus insignis*	lc	—	0–1,130+	Forest, swamp forest, gallery forest, forest edge
Yellow-legged Pigeon *Columba pallidiceps*	CR	198	0–1,300	Forest, forest edge
Pied Cuckoo-dove *Reinwardtoena browni*	lc	193	0–900+	Forest, forest edge
New Britain Bronzewing *Henicophaps foersteri*	nt	—	Lowlands, lower mts	Forest, inc. swamp forest; also disturbed, logged and mature secondary forest
Yellow-bibbed Fruit-dove *Ptilinopus solomonensis*	lc	174,193,194, 198	0–1,400	Forest, shrubs in secondary growth, fruiting trees, gardens
Knob-billed Fruit-dove *Ptilinopus insolitus*	lc	194	0–1,200	Forest, forest edge, disturbed habitat, swamp forest, mangroves
Red-knobbed Imperial-pigeon *Ducula rubricera*	lc	198	0–1,300	Forest, tall secondary forest, fruiting trees in partly cleared areas, swamp forest, mangroves
Finsch's Imperial-pigeon *Ducula finschii*	nt	—	0–1,850	Forest, swamp forest
Bismarck Imperial-pigeon *Ducula melanochroa*	nt	—	(0–) 1,200–2,000	Forest; seasonally in lowlands in association with fruiting trees
Yellow-tinted Imperial-pigeon *Ducula subflavescens*	lc	193	0–900	Mangroves, swamp forest, gallery forest, forest edge, coastal and tall gallery scrub, savanna
Cardinal Lory *Chalcopsitta cardinalis*	lc	198	0–1,200	Forest, secondary forest, mangroves, coconut plantations, gardens
White-naped Lory *Lorius albidinuchus*	nt	—	250–2,000	Forest, inc. logged forest
Red-chinned Lorikeet *Charmosyna rubrigularis*	lc	—	Lowlands to 1,500+	Forest; seasonally in lowlands with flowering trees
Blue-eyed Cockatoo *Cacatua ophthalmica*	lc	—	0–1,000	Forest, partly cleared areas
Finsch's Pygmy-parrot *Micropsitta finschii*	lc	198,199	0–1,000+	Forest, secondary growth, overgrown gardens, plantations
Singing Parrot *Geoffroyus heteroclitus*	lc	198,199	0–1,760	Forest, secondary forest; less commonly swamp forest, partly cleared areas, gardens
Green-fronted Hanging-parrot *Loriculus tener*	nt	—	Lowlands, lower mts	Forest, secondary forest, forest edge; less commonly partly cleared areas, gardens
Violaceous Coucal *Centropus violaceus*	lc	—	0–1,200	Forest, secondary growth; less commonly swamp forest
Pied Coucal *Centropus ateralbus*	lc	—	0–1,220	Forest, forest edge, secondary growth; rarely in swamp forest, gardens
Bismarck Masked-owl *Tyto aurantia*	VU	—	Lowlands to 1,830+	Forest, forest edge
Bismarck Hawk-owl *Ninox variegata*	lc	—	Lowlands, lower mts	Forest
Russet Hawk-owl *Ninox odiosa*	lc	—	0–1,200	Forest, secondary growth, coconut and oil-palm plantations, occasionally gardens

cont.

Status and habitat of restricted-range species (cont.)

Species (ordered taxonomically)	Global status	Other EBAs (and SAs)	Altitude (m)	Habitat
Mayr's Swiftlet *Collocalia orientalis*	DD	198	Lowlands?, hills	Caves (breeding), forest, open country
Bismarck Kingfisher *Alcedo websteri*	lc	—	Lowlands	Margins of forest streams
New Britain Kingfisher *Todirhamphus albonotatus*	lc	—	0–750	Forest, forest edge and clearings, mature secondary forest
New Britain Thrush *Zoothera talaseae*	nt	198	580–1,500	Montane forest
Bismarck Thicketbird *Megalurulus grosvenori*	DD	—	1,050+	Montane forest, often in places where bamboo present, mossy forest with small trees
Rusty Thicketbird *Ortygocichla rubiginosa*	lc	—	Lowlands to 850	Forest
Black-tailed Monarch *Monarcha verticalis*	lc	—	Lowlands to 1,400+	Forest
Dull Flycatcher *Myiagra hebetior*	lc	194	Lowlands to 1,500	Forest
Bismarck Fantail *Rhipidura dahli*	lc	—	400–1,100+	Montane forest, locally lowland forest
Red-banded Flowerpecker *Dicaeum eximium*	lc	—	0–1,500	Forest, forest edge, secondary growth, partly cleared areas, garden edges
Black-headed White-eye *Zosterops hypoxanthus*	lc	193	Lowlands to 1,760	Forest, forest edge, secondary growth, gardens
Louisiade White-eye *Zosterops griseotinctus*	lc	197	Lowlands	Small islands: forest edge, secondary growth, probably forest
Olive-yellow Myzomela *Myzomela pulchella*	lc	—	500+	Montane forest
Scarlet-bibbed Myzomela *Myzomela sclateri*	lc	—	0–1,830	Small islands: forest, montane shrubbery (Karkar only), secondary growth, coconut plantations
Ebony Myzomela *Myzomela pammelaena*	lc	193,194	0–1,300	Small islands: forest, secondary growth, disturbed areas, coconut plantations, gardens
Black-bellied Myzomela *Myzomela erythromelas*	lc	—	Lowlands to 900+	Forest, forest edge, secondary growth
New Britain Friarbird *Philemon cockerelli*	lc	—	0–1,600	Forest, forest edge, tall secondary forest, disturbed areas, coconut plantations
New Ireland Friarbird *Philemon eichhorni*	lc	—	750–2,200	Montane forest
Bismarck Melidectes *Melidectes whitemanensis*	lc	—	1,050–1,740+	Montane forest
Mottled Munia *Lonchura hunsteini*[1]	lc	—	Lowlands	Grassland, cultivated areas
New Ireland Munia *Lonchura forbesi*	lc	—	Lowlands to 1,000	Grassland
New Hanover Munia *Lonchura nigerrima*	lc	—	Lowlands	Scrubby forest edge, forested streams
Bismarck Munia *Lonchura melaena*	lc	198	0–1,200	Scrubby forest edge, forested streams
Atoll Starling *Aplonis feadensis*	lc	(s126)	Lowlands	Small islands: forest, forest edge, coconut plantations
Ribbon-tailed Drongo *Dicrurus megarhynchus*	lc	—	0–1,800	Mossy montane forest, tall secondary forest
Bismarck Woodswallow *Artamus insignis*	lc	—	Hills to 900	Dead trees in clearings and gardens

Global status (see p. 679 for definitions)	EX Extinct EW Extinct in the Wild } with year of last record CR Critical EN Endangered } threatened species VU Vulnerable	cd Conservation Dependent nt Near Threatened lc Least Concern DD Data Deficient NE Not Evaluated	**Other EBAs (and SAs)** (see p. 90 for locations) **Notes**	Bracketed numbers are Secondary Areas. × Extinct in that EBA or SA. [1] Introduced to Pohnpei (East Caroline Islands, EBA 192).

further 12 species endemic to both New Britain and New Ireland, so these two centres of endemism are combined into one EBA, reflecting the commonest pattern of distribution of the islands' restricted-range species. Four species, *Zosterops griseotinctus*, *Myzomela sclateri*, *M. pammelaena* and *Aplonis feadensis* are only found on tiny islands in this EBA and elsewhere.

The taxonomy of most birds in this EBA has been little studied, and there are undoubtedly undescribed taxa as well as several taxa which are currently lumped with mainland forms by Sibley and Monroe (1990, 1993) that are likely to prove full species. Thus, Coates (1985, 1990) treats the New Britain form of Buff-breasted Paradise-kingfisher *Tanysiptera sylvia nigriceps* and Red-throated Myzomela *Myzomela eques cineracea* as separate species (see also Finch and McKean 1987, Palliser 1992).

▨ Threats and conservation

Much of the north coast of New Britain has been cleared for oil-palm and coconut plantations, and remaining lowland forest has been, or is being, logged (Clay 1994). Despite this, few of the restricted-range species are currently classified as threatened because for many it is not certain whether they are genuinely sparsely distributed or are simply overlooked; depending on the number of recent records, altitudinal preference (and thus vulnerability to habitat destruction) and range size, they have been variously classified as Vulnerable, Near Threatened or Data Deficient. *Columba pallidiceps* is the exception: it is rated as Critical, being apparently uncommon on New Britain in 1959 (Gilliard and LeCroy 1967), with no records from western New Britain during the period 1978–1990 (K. D. Bishop *in litt.* 1989), and only a few additional observations.

Several areas important for terrestrial biodiversity have been identified within the EBA, including the Whiteman range, Nakanai range, Baining mountains and Willaumez peninsula in New Britain, and the Hans Meyer range, Verron range and Lelet plateau in New Ireland. The mountains and lowlands west of New Britain's population centres, the high ranges and southern scarp of central and eastern New Britain, and the highlands of New Ireland have been identified as areas where the present lack of scientific information is particularly serious (Beehler 1993), although many are very difficult of access.

There are a few protected areas, e.g. Pokili and Garu Wildlife Management Areas (98 and 87 km²) on New Britain which are important areas of lowland forest with two major *Megapodius eremita* nesting grounds as well as virtually all the island's lowland and foothill species (K. D. Bishop *in litt.* 1993).

Distribution patterns of restricted-range species

Species (ordered geographically)	Islands close to New Ireland	New Ireland	New Britain	Islands close to New Britain	Other EBAs, SAs
Lonchura nigerrima	●H	–	–	–	–
Accipiter albogularis	●F	–	–	–	◎
Chalcopsitta cardinalis	●	–	–	–	◎
Aplonis feadensis	●	–	–	–	◎
Ninox variegata	●	●	–	–	–
Lonchura hunsteini	●	●	–	–	–
Micropsitta finschii	●	●	–	–	◎
Ptilinopus solomonensis	●	–	●	●	◎
Zosterops griseotinctus	●	–	–	●	◎
Myzomela pammelaena	●	–	–	●	–
Loriculus tener	●	●	●	●	–
Charmosyna rubrigularis	●	●	●	●	–
Alcedo websteri	●	●	●	●	–
Monarcha verticalis	●	●	●	●	–
Dicaeum eximium	●	●	●	●	–
Megapodius eremita	●	●	●	●	◎
Ptilinopus insolitus	●	●	●	●	◎
Ducula rubricera	●	●	●	●	◎
Ducula subflavescens	●	●	●	●	◎
Reinwardtoena browni	●	●	●	●	–
Geoffroyus heteroclitus	●	●	●	●	◎
Myiagra hebetior	●	●	●	●	–
Zosterops hypoxanthus	●	●	●	●	◎
Lorius albidinuchus	–	●	–	–	–
Myzomela pulchella	–	●	–	–	–
Philemon eichhorni	–	●	–	–	–
Lonchura forbesi	–	●	–	–	–
Dicrurus megarhynchus	–	●	–	–	–
Collocalia orientalis	–	●	–	–	◎
Centropus violaceus	–	●	●	–	–
Accipiter luteoschistaceus	–	?	●	●	–
Ducula finschii	–	●	●	●	–
Ducula melanochroa	–	●	●	●	–
Centropus ateralbus	–	●	●	●	–
Rhipidura dahli	–	●	●	●	–
Artamus insignis	–	●	●	●	–
Columba pallidiceps	–	●	●	●	◎
Accipiter princeps	–	–	●	●	–
Accipiter brachyurus	–	–	●	●	–
Gallirallus insignis	–	–	●	●	–
Cacatua ophthalmica	–	–	●	●	–
Tyto aurantia	–	–	●	–	–
Ninox odiosa	–	–	●	–	–
Todirhamphus albonotatus	–	–	●	–	–
Megalurulus grosvenori	–	–	●	–	–
Ortygocichla rubiginosa	–	–	●	–	–
Myzomela erythromelas	–	–	●	–	–
Melidectes whitemanensis	–	–	●	–	–
Lonchura melaena	–	–	●	–	◎
Henicopernis infuscatus	–	–	●	–	–
Henicophaps foersteri	–	–	●	●	–
Philemon cockerelli	–	–	●	●	–
Zoothera talaseae	–	–	●	●	◎
Myzomela sclateri	–	–	–	●	–
Total	23	29	38	28	

● Present   ? Present?   Threatened spp. shown in **bold**   } see 'Status and habitat' table
○ Extinct?   R Reintroduced   Other EBAs, SAs }
X Extinct   I Introduced
H New Hanover only   F Feni only

196 D'Entrecasteaux and Trobriand Islands

Key habitats Lowland and hill rain forest

Main threats Unquantified habitat loss (e.g. due to logging, agriculture)

Biological importance ● ● ●
Current threat level ● ● ●

Area 3,400 km² **Altitude** 0–2,200 m
Countries Papua New Guinea

Restricted-range birds	Threatened	Total
Confined to this EBA	1	2
Present also in other EBAs, SAs	0	0
Total	1	2

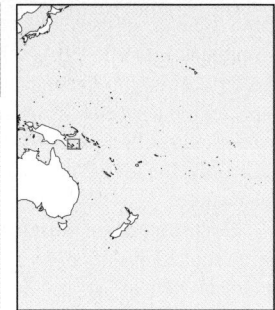

■ General characteristics

There are five principal islands in this EBA: Goodenough (the highest of all of New Guinea's fringing islands, reaching 2,750 m), Fergusson and Normanby (in the D'Entrecasteaux Islands), and Kaileuna and Kiriwina (in the Trobriand Islands). Deep-water channels between these islands and the mainland of Papua New Guinea indicate separation in the late Pleistocene, and differences in their avifaunas reinforce this conclusion.

On Goodenough, the west and south of the island is covered in forest, with secondary growth near villages, and mossy forest at higher altitudes; the plains in the north and east are drier, and burning by local people has resulted in savanna with relict rain forest trees near streams (Bell 1970).

■ Restricted-range species

There are few data on the two species endemic to this EBA, but it is known that *Manucodia comrii* is found on all five islands at all altitudes and will apparently adapt to secondary habitats, while *Paradisaea decora* seems to be confined to primary hill forest on Fergusson and Normanby only.

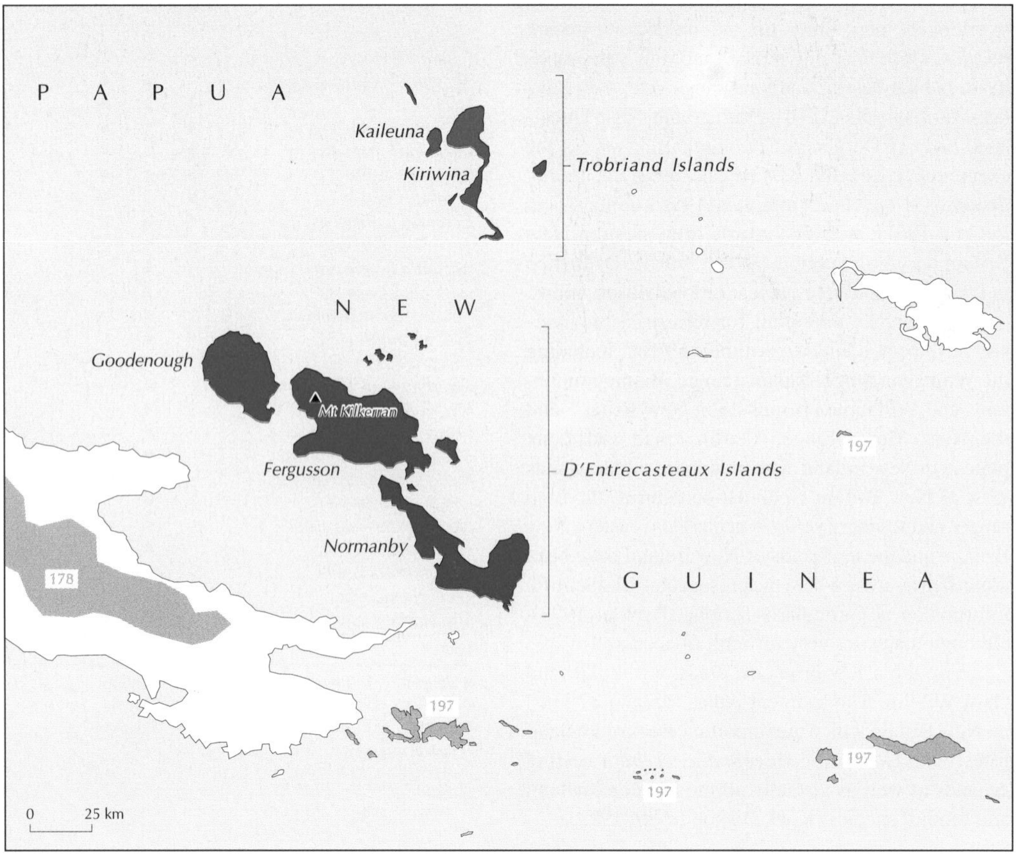

P A P U A

Kaileuna

Kiriwina

Trobriand Islands

N E W

Goodenough

Mt Kilkerran

Fergusson

D'Entrecasteaux Islands

Normanby

178

197

G U I N E A

197

197

197

0   25 km

Status and habitat of restricted-range species

Species (ordered taxonomically)	Global status	Other EBAs (and SAs)	Altitude (m)	Habitat
Curl-crested Manucode *Manucodia comrii*	lc	—	0–2,200	Forest, secondary forest, mangroves, littoral woodland, overgrown gardens
Goldie's Bird-of-paradise *Paradisaea decora*	VU	—	350–700+	Hill forest, forest edge

Global status (see p. 679 for definitions): EX Extinct, EW Extinct in the Wild (with year of last record); CR Critical, EN Endangered, VU Vulnerable (threatened species); cd Conservation Dependent, nt Near Threatened, lc Least Concern; DD Data Deficient, NE Not Evaluated

Other EBAs (and SAs) (see p. 90 for locations): bracketed numbers are Secondary Areas; [X] extinct in that EBA or SA.

■ Threats and conservation

There is little information on the threats to the EBA's birds, although there has recently been a proposal for large-scale agricultural development on Normanby involving logging and clearance, and replanting with cash crops such as maize and rice (Loney 1996). The scheme has yet to be evaluated but would be a grave threat to the island's lowland and hill forests and their birds (P. Gregory *in litt.* 1996), and to *Paradisaea decora* in particular. Though it is fairly common, this species is considered threatened because of its narrow altitudinal range. The species is not known to visit native gardens, even those abandoned and overgrown, so that the preservation of undisturbed forest is likely to be essential to its survival (LeCroy *et al.* 1984).

In 1988 the forest on Fergusson was reputed to be one of the most pristine mosaics of primary rain forest on a relatively large, mountainous island, anywhere on earth. The subsistence economy of local people appeared to be viable, and there was a locally initiated wildlife management area at Lake Lavu (26 km²) in a remote part of the centre of the island. However, it was recognized that a high proportion of the bird species on the island had characteristics which made them particularly vulnerable to logging, road-building and expansion of gardens, particularly below 1,500 m elevation (Ingram 1992). Even in this favourable context, it has still been possible for foreign logging operations to establish without any comprehensive land-use plan that considers local needs, without any decisions on a network of protected areas with representative tracts of primary rain forest, and without mechanisms to channel economic benefit back to local communities (Ingram 1994).

The Goodenough highlands and Fergusson and Normanby islands have all been identified as areas of important terrestrial biodiversity in Papua New Guinea by Beehler (1993), and Mt Kilkerran, a large forested massif on Fergusson, which has never been surveyed zoologically, is considered to be an important area for future study.

197 Louisiade archipelago

PRIORITY
URGENT

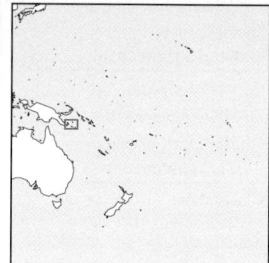

Key habitats Lowland rain forest

Main threats Moderate habitat loss (e.g. due to gold-mining)

Biological importance ● ● ●
Current threat level ● ○ ○

Area 1,600 km²   **Altitude** 0–1,000 m

Countries Papua New Guinea

Restricted-range birds	Threatened	Total
Confined to this EBA	0	5
Present also in other EBAs, SAs	0	2
Total	0	7

General characteristics

Lying off the eastern tip of the Papua New Guinea mainland, the Louisiade archipelago's three main islands are Sudest (the largest and highest island at c.800 km² and c.1,000 m), Misima and Rossel; these are volcanic, but the various smaller islands (including Alcester, to the north of the main group) are mostly coral formations.

The larger islands are forested, and, ever since the Archbold expeditions, the flora of this archipelago has been recognized as one of extreme botanical interest with high rates of local endemism, particularly at the species level (Beehler 1993).

Restricted-range birds

There are few data on the restricted-range species of this EBA and it is presumed that all the endemic species occur in forest habitats.

The distributional patterns of restricted-range species within the EBA vary: *Zosterops meeki*, *Meliphaga vicina* and *Cracticus louisiadensis* are confined to Sudest only, *Dicaeum nitidum* occurs on all three of the main islands, and *Myzomela albigula* is present on Misima and surrounding islands and on Rossel; within this EBA, *Pachycephala leucogastra* is present on Rossel only, and *Zosterops griseotinctus* on Misima, Louisiade outliers and Alcester.

Threats and conservation

The status of all the EBA's birds—and their habitat requirements—are little known, and four of the five endemics are consequently listed as Data Deficient (the highest number of Data Deficient species in any EBA).

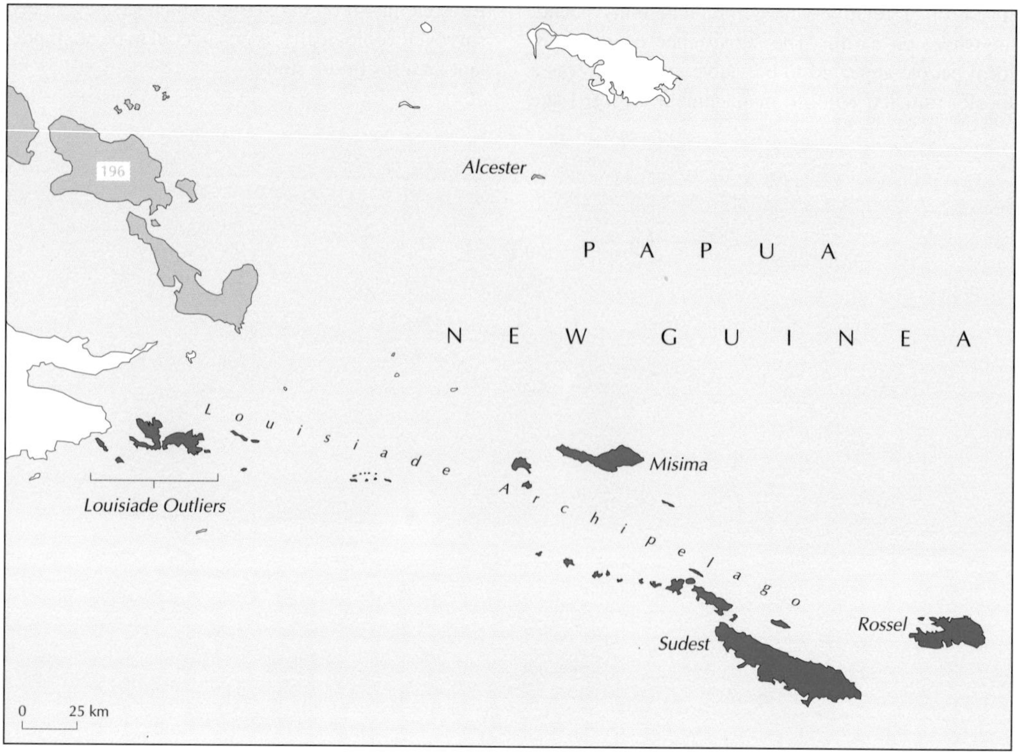

196

Alcester

P A P U A

N E W   G U I N E A

L o u i s i a d e   A r c h i p e l a g o

Louisiade Outliers

Misima

Sudest

Rossel

0   25 km

Status and habitat of restricted-range species

Species (ordered taxonomically)	Global status	Other EBAs (and SAs)	Habitat
White-bellied Whistler *Pachycephala leucogastra*	lc	176 (s114)	Open coastal habitats
Louisiade Flowerpecker *Dicaeum nitidum*	lc	—	Forest, secondary growth
Louisiade White-eye *Zosterops griseotinctus*	lc	195	Forest edge, secondary growth, probably forest
White-throated White-eye *Zosterops meeki*	DD	—	Forest, forest edge
White-chinned Myzomela *Myzomela albigula*	DD	—	Unknown, presumably forest
Tagula Honeyeater *Meliphaga vicina*	DD	—	Forest, forest edge
Tagula Butcherbird *Cracticus louisiadensis*	DD	—	Unknown, presumably forest

Global status (see p. 679 for definitions)
EX Extinct
EW Extinct in the Wild } with year of last record
CR Critical
EN Endangered } threatened species
VU Vulnerable
cd Conservation Dependent
nt Near Threatened
lc Least Concern
DD Data Deficient
NE Not Evaluated

Other EBAs (and SAs) (see p. 90 for locations): bracketed numbers are Secondary Areas; [x] extinct in that EBA or SA.

Large-scale logging could have a devastating effect on the birds of this EBA given their small ranges and the likely reliance, for most species, on forested habitats. The forest of the eastern two-thirds of Sudest is degraded, while gold-mining has had a devastating effect on Misima (Beehler 1993, B. J. Coates *in litt.* 1994)

The islands have been identified as an area of important terrestrial biodiversity in Papua New Guinea by Beehler (1993).

198 Solomon group

PRIORITY
CRITICAL

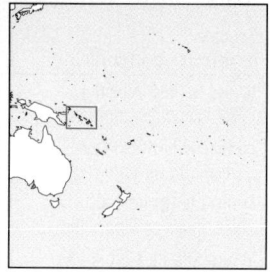

Key habitats Lowland and montane rain forest

Main threats Moderate habitat loss (e.g. due to logging, coconut plantations), introduced species

Biological importance ● ● ●
Current threat level ● ●

Area 34,000 km² **Altitude** 0–2,000 m

Countries Papua New Guinea, Solomon Islands

Restricted-range species	Threatened	Total
Confined to this EBA	13	61
Present also in other EBAs, SAs	1	17
Total	14	78

■ General characteristics

The Solomon group EBA comprises the islands of Bougainville and Buka (politically part of Papua New Guinea), and Choiseul, Isabel, Malaita, the New Georgia group, Guadalcanal and Makira (or San Cristobal), as well as many smaller associated islands (all these belonging to the political Solomon Islands). The EBA does not include Rennell and Bellona (EBA 199), Temotu Province (part of EBA 200), or the atoll of Ongtong Java (Secondary Area s126); these are also all politically part of the Solomons.

The native vegetation is primarily lowland and montane rain forest, with fire-induced grasslands (which are extensive, for example, in the rain-shadow area of northern Guadalcanal and in the Nggela Islands) and mangroves. Montane forest on the highest islands is divisible into a lower montane zone between c.600 and 1,200 m, and an upper zone where the trees are stunted, the canopy is more open, palms

and *Pandanus* abound, and mosses cover much of the ground (Hadden 1981).

■ Restricted-range species

This EBA has more restricted-range bird species than any other. The majority of them inhabit lowland and lower montane forest up to c.1,500 m, with a handful being confined to upper montane forest. Many of the altitudinal ranges given in the 'Status and habitat' table may be correct for the mountainous islands (e.g. Bougainville, Guadalcanal), but the occupied zones might be lower down on the lower islands; on Makira the altitudinal information is largely based on surveys up to 900 m only. Recent information on most of the species can be found in Buckingham *et al.* (1995).

Different species have different patterns of island distribution, and several islands and island groups have their own endemics: Bougainville (four endemic species), Choiseul (one, now extinct), New Georgia

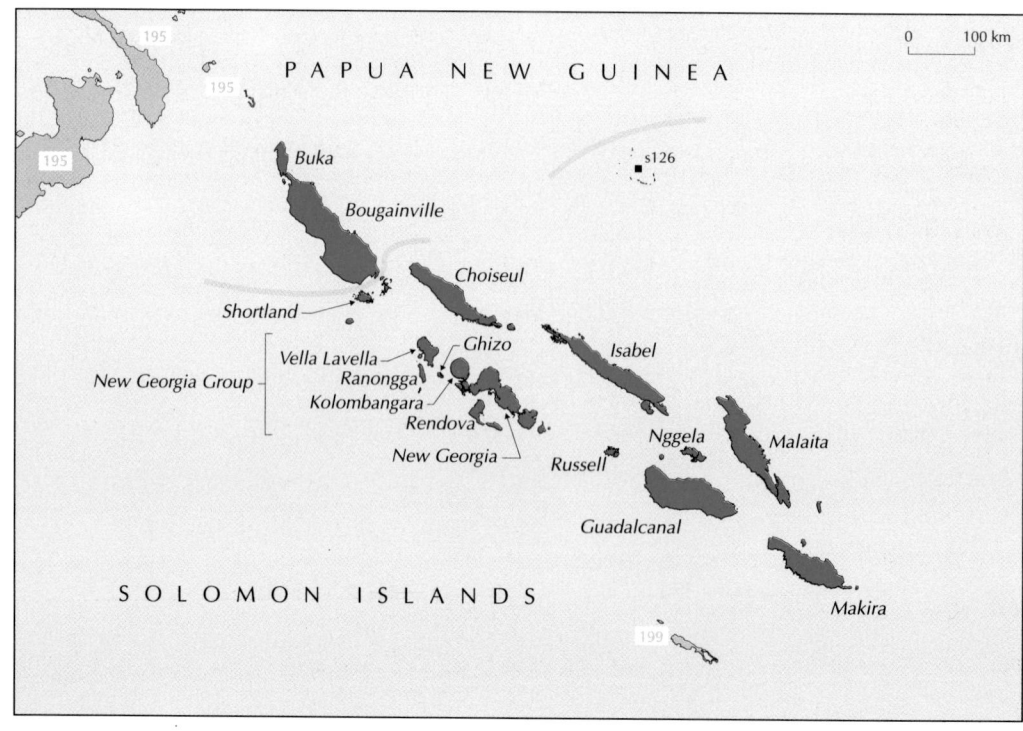

Status and habitat of restricted-range species

Species (ordered taxonomically)	Global status	Other EBAs (and SAs)	Altitude (m)	Habitat
Sanford's Fish-eagle *Haliaeetus sanfordi*	VU	—	0–1,500	Forest, coastal areas
Pied Goshawk *Accipiter albogularis*	lc	195,200	0–1,800	Forest, forest edge, clearings, open secondary growth, gardens, edges of towns
Imitator Sparrowhawk *Accipiter imitator*	EN	—	0–1,000	Forest, tall secondary forest
Melanesian Scrubfowl *Megapodius eremita*	lc	193,194,195	0–1,800	All types of forested habitat inc. mangroves, coastal scrub
Woodford's Rail *Nesoclopeus woodfordi*	EN	—	0–1,000	Forest, old secondary growth, riparian habitats, abandoned gardens
Roviana Rail *Gallirallus rovianae*	nt	—	Lowlands	Scrub, secondary growth (young trees on abandoned cultivation), overgrown coconut plantations
Makira Moorhen *Gallinula silvestris*	CR	—	c.600	Dense undergrowth in lower montane forest
Yellow-legged Pigeon *Columba pallidiceps*	CR	195	0–1,300	Forest, forest edge
Crested Cuckoo-dove *Reinwardtoena crassirostris*	lc	—	0–1,100	Forest, esp. lower montane forest
Thick-billed Ground-dove *Gallicolumba salamonis*	CR	—	0–300	Forest, perhaps swamp forest
Choiseul Pigeon *Microgoura meeki*	EX (1904)	—	Lowlands	Forest, possibly swamp forest
Silver-capped Fruit-dove *Ptilinopus richardsii*	lc	199	Small islands only	Lowland forest, secondary growth
Yellow-bibbed Fruit-dove *Ptilinopus solomonensis*	lc	174,193, 194,195	0–1,400	Forest, shrubs in secondary growth, fruiting trees, gardens
White-headed Fruit-dove *Ptilinopus eugeniae*	nt	—	0–700+	Forest, forest edge, secondary forest, gardens, fruiting trees and groves
Red-knobbed Imperial-pigeon *Ducula rubricera*	lc	195	0–1,100	Forest, tall secondary forest, fruiting trees in partly cleared areas, mangroves
Chestnut-bellied Imperial-pigeon *Ducula brenchleyi*	EN	—	200–700+	Selectively logged foothill forest, lower montane forest
Pale Mountain-pigeon *Gymnophaps solomonensis*	lc	—	0–1,950	Forest, esp. montane forest
Cardinal Lory *Chalcopsitta cardinalis*	lc	195	0–1,200	Forest, secondary forest, mangroves, coconut plantations, gardens
Yellow-bibbed Lory *Lorius chlorocercus*	lc	199	0–900+	Forest, forest edge, secondary growth, coconut plantations
Meek's Lorikeet *Charmosyna meeki*	lc	—	Usually 300–1,800	Forest, esp. montane forest, coconut plantations
Duchess Lorikeet *Charmosyna margarethae*	nt	—	0–1,350	Forest, forest edge, secondary forest, coconut plantations, gardens
Ducorps's Cockatoo *Cacatua ducorpsii*	lc	—	0–1,800	Forest, forest edge, tall secondary forest, gardens
Finsch's Pygmy-parrot *Micropsitta finschii*	lc	195,199	0–1,000+	Forest, secondary growth, overgrown gardens, occasionally coconut palms and casuarinas
Singing Parrot *Geoffroyus heteroclitus*	lc	195,199	0–900+	Forest, partly cleared areas, gardens
Buff-headed Coucal *Centropus milo*	lc	—	0–1,100	Forest, secondary forest
Solomon Islands Hawk-owl *Ninox jacquinoti*	lc	—	0–1,500	Forest, tall secondary forest, gardens
Fearful Owl *Nesasio solomonensis*	VU	—	Lowlands, hills to c.500	Forest, tall secondary forest

cont.

Status and habitat of restricted-range species (cont.)

Species (ordered taxonomically)	Global status	Other EBAs (and SAs)	Altitude (m)	Habitat
Mayr's Swiftlet *Collocalia orientalis*	DD	195	Lowlands?, hills	Caves (breeding), forest, open country
Ultramarine Kingfisher *Todirhamphus leucopygius*	lc	—	0–700	Forest, tall secondary forest, forest edge, clearings, gardens, casuarina groves
Moustached Kingfisher *Actenoides bougainvillei*	VU	—	Lowlands[B], 900–1,325+[G]	Lowland forest, perhaps swamp forest[B], montane forest[G]
Black-faced Pitta *Pitta anerythra*	VU	—	Lowlands, hills to 600	Forest, secondary forest and scrub, abandoned gardens
Melanesian Cuckoo-shrike *Coracina caledonica*	lc	200,201	Lowlands, hills	Forest, secondary forest, mangroves
Solomon Islands Cuckoo-shrike *Coracina holopolia*	lc	—	0–1,000	Forest, forest edge, sometimes secondary forest
Long-tailed Triller *Lalage leucopyga*	lc	200,201, 205[X]	0–600+	Forest, forest edge, secondary growth, plantations, gardens, coastal vegetation
New Britain Thrush *Zoothera talaseae*	nt	195	580–1,500	Montane forest
Makira Thrush *Zoothera margaretae*	nt	—	1,000+[G] 200–700+[M]	Montane forest[G], hill forest[M]
Shade Warbler *Cettia parens*	nt	—	500–900+	Montane forest, forest edge
Makira Leaf-warbler *Phylloscopus makirensis*	nt	—	600–900+	Montane forest
Sombre Leaf-warbler *Phylloscopus amoenus*	VU	—	1,200–1,770	Mossy forest
Bougainville Thicketbird *Megalurulus llaneae*	DD	—	1,140–1,500	Mossy forest
Guadalcanal Thicketbird *Megalurulus whitneyi*	nt	200	700–1,550	Montane forest
Bougainville Monarch *Monarcha erythrostictus*	lc	—	0–1,300	Forest, sometimes nearby secondary forest
Chestnut-bellied Monarch *Monarcha castaneiventris*	lc	—	0–900+	Forest, secondary forest (large islands), coastal forest, coconut plantations, mangroves (small islands)
White-capped Monarch *Monarcha richardsii*	lc	—	0–1,100	Forest, secondary forest
Black-and-white Monarch *Monarcha barbatus*	lc	—	0–1,350	Forest, tall secondary forest
Kolombangara Monarch *Monarcha browni*	nt	—	50–600 (–1,200)	Forest, secondary forest, gardens
White-collared Monarch *Monarcha viduus*	lc	—	0–800+	Forest, secondary forest
Steel-blue Flycatcher *Myiagra ferrocyanea*	lc	—	0–1,500	Forest, forest edge, secondary forest, mangroves, casuarinas
Ochre-tailed Flycatcher *Myiagra cervinicauda*	nt	—	0–600+	Forest, forest edge, secondary forest, gardens
White-winged Fantail *Rhipidura cockerelli*	lc	—	0–1,200	Forest, tall secondary forest
Brown Fantail *Rhipidura drownei*	lc	—	700–1,565	Montane forest
Dusky Fantail *Rhipidura tenebrosa*	nt	—	50–600+	Forest
Malaita Fantail *Rhipidura malaitae*	VU	—	900–1,200	Lower montane forest
Hooded Whistler *Pachycephala implicata*	nt	—	700–1,750+	Montane forest

cont.

Status and habitat of restricted-range species (cont.)

Species (ordered taxonomically)	Global status	Other EBAs (and SAs)	Altitude (m)	Habitat
Midget Flowerpecker *Dicaeum aeneum*	lc	—	0–1,500+	All habitats inc. forest, forest edge, disturbed areas, secondary growth, gardens
Mottled Flowerpecker *Dicaeum tristrami*	lc	—	0–900+	Forest, secondary growth
Banded White-eye *Zosterops vellalavella*	lc	—	Lowlands	Forest, forest edge, scrub, coconut plantations, gardens, disturbed habitats
Ranongga White-eye *Zosterops splendidus*	lc	—	Lowlands	Forest, secondary forest, scrub, coconut plantations, gardens, villages
Ghizo White-eye *Zosterops luteirostris*	VU	—	0–180	Remaining forest in gullies, older secondary growth, scrub
Solomon Islands White-eye *Zosterops kulambangrae*	lc	—	0–400 (–1,000+)	Forest, secondary forest
Hermit White-eye *Zosterops murphyi*	lc	—	350–1,550	Forest
Yellow-throated White-eye *Zosterops metcalfii*	lc	—	Lowlands to 900(–1,200)	Forest, forest edge, secondary forest, gardens, open areas with trees
Grey-throated White-eye *Zosterops rendovae*	lc	—	80–1,950	Forest, forest edge, secondary forest
Malaita White-eye *Zosterops stresemanni*	lc	—	All	Forest, scrub
Cardinal Myzomela *Myzomela cardinalis*	lc	199,200, 201,203	Coastal	Forest, forest edge, secondary forest, mangroves, plantations
Scarlet-naped Myzomela *Myzomela lafargei*	lc	—	0–1,800	Forest, tall secondary forest, forest edge, mangroves, coconut plantations
Yellow-vented Myzomela *Myzomela eichhorni*	lc	—	0–1,550+	Forest, secondary forest, gardens, coconut plantations
Black-headed Myzomela *Myzomela melanocephala*	lc	—	0–950+	Forest, tall secondary forest, forest edge
Red-bellied Myzomela *Myzomela malaitae*	lc	—	All, usually hills	Forest, gardens
Sooty Myzomela *Myzomela tristrami*	lc	—	0–900+	Forest, secondary growth, gardens, coconut plantations
Bougainville Honeyeater *Stresemannia bougainvillei*	lc	—	700–1,950+	Montane forest
Guadalcanal Honeyeater *Guadalcanaria inexpectata*	lc	—	950–1,565	Montane forest, mossy forest
Makira Melidectes *Melidectes sclateri*	lc	—	(0–) 500–900+	Forest, forest edge, tall secondary forest
Bismarck Munia *Lonchura melaena*	lc	195	0–1,200	Forest edge, grassy/swampy areas
Brown-winged Starling *Aplonis grandis*	lc	—	0–1,000	Forest, secondary forest, trees in clearings
Makira Starling *Aplonis dichroa*	lc	—	0–800+	Secondary forest, gardens, less commonly coconut plantations
White-eyed Starling *Aplonis brunneicapilla*	EN	—	0–300	Isolated trees (breeding colonies), forest, swamp forest, gardens cut out of primary forest
Bougainville Crow *Corvus meeki*	nt	—	Lowlands to 1,600+	Forest, partly cleared areas, gardens, coconut plantations
White-billed Crow *Corvus woodfordi*	nt	—	0–900+	Forest, secondary forest, forest edge, abandoned coconut plantations

Global status (see p. 679 for definitions)	EX Extinct EW Extinct in the Wild	} with year of last record	cd Conservation Dependent nt Near Threatened	**Other EBAs (and SAs)** (see p. 90 for locations)	Bracketed numbers are Secondary Areas. ˣ Extinct in that EBA or SA.
	CR Critical EN Endangered VU Vulnerable	} threatened species	lc Least Concern DD Data Deficient NE Not Evaluated	**Notes**	ᴮ Bougainville ᴳ Guadalcanal ᴹ Makira

group (10), Malaita (three), Guadalcanal (two) and Makira (12). Within the New Georgia group, the islands of Vella Lavella, Ranongga and Ghizo each have one endemic species, and Kolombangara has two. The additional 30 restricted-range species endemic to the Solomon group EBA (in various island combinations), and 10 restricted-range species which occur in the group and elsewhere, combine all the islands into one EBA, although it is clear that several islands, notably Makira and the New Georgia group, are important areas of endemism in their own right.

Several of the more-widespread restricted-range species occur in other Papuan island and Melanesian EBAs, both further north into the Bismarck archipelago (EBAs 193–195) and south to Vanuatu (EBA 200) and New Caledonia (EBA 201).

In general the avifauna of this EBA is little known (e.g. *Gallirallus rovianae* was not discovered by ornithologists until 1977 and only described in 1991: Diamond 1991a) and many species had not been seen for decades until recently (Diamond 1987): for example, *Nesoclopeus woodfordi* (not recorded between 1936 and 1985), *Columba pallidiceps* (not recorded in the Solomon Islands after 1928 until re-found in 1987 on Guadalcanal and in 1990 on Makira), *Actenoides bougainvillei* (not reliably reported between 1953 and 1994), *Pitta anerythra* (not reliably recorded 1936–1994) and *Rhipidura malaitae* (not recorded 1930–1990). *Gallinula silvestris* is known only from a 1929 type-specimen and *Gallicolumba salamonis* has not been recorded since 1927, but as Makira's swamps appear never to have been visited by ornithologists, and the primary forest on the south coast not since the 1950s, they have not been classified as extinct. On the other hand, information relating to *Microgoura meeki* (last reliable record 1904) tends to confirm that this highly distinctive species in a monotypic genus is indeed extinct.

The taxonomy of this EBA's birds has been little studied. Some allopatric taxa may be judged full species in the future, e.g. the proposed Guadalcanal Thrush *Zoothera* (*margaretae*) *turipavae* which is treated as a species by Gibbs (1996b).

In addition to the restricted-range land

Distribution patterns of restricted-range species

Species (ordered geographically)	Bougainville	Choiseul	Isabel	New Georgia group	Malaita	Guadalcanal	Makira	Other EBAs, SAs
Megalurulus llaneae	●	–	–	–	–	–	–	–
Monarcha erythrostictus	●	–	–	–	–	–	–	–
Stresemannia bougainvillei	●	–	–	–	–	–	–	–
Corvus meeki	●	–	–	–	–	–	–	–
Zoothera talaseae	●	–	–	–	–	–	–	●
Lonchura melaena	●	–	–	–	–	–	–	●
Accipiter imitator[1]	●	●	●	–	–	–	–	–
Nesasio solomonensis	●	●	●	–	–	–	–	–
Zosterops metcalfii	●	●	●	–	–	–	–	–
Myzomela lafargei	●	●	●	–	–	–	–	–
Pitta anerythra	●	●	●	–	–	–	–	–
Actenoides bougainvillei	●	–	–	–	–	●	–	–
Rhipidura drownei	●	–	–	–	–	●	–	–
Pachycephala implicata	●	–	–	–	–	●	–	–
Todirhamphus leucopygius	●	●	●	–	–	●	–	–
Monarcha barbatus	●	●	●	–	●	●	–	–
Dicaeum aeneum	●	●	●	–	●	●	–	–
Aplonis brunneicapilla	●	●	–	●RE	–	–	–	–
Charmosyna meeki	●	–	●	–	●	●	–	–
Gymnophaps solomonensis	●	–	●	–	●	●	–	–
Coracina caledonica	●	–	●	●	–	●	–	●
Nesoclopeus woodfordi[2]	●	○	●	–	○	○	–	–
Cacatua ducorpsi	●	●	●	●	–	●	–	–
Coracina holopolia	●	●	●	–	●	●	–	–
Myiagra ferrocyanea	●	●	●	●	●	●	–	–
Rhipidura cockerelli	●	●	●	●	●	●	–	–
Aplonis grandis	●	●	●	●	●	●	–	–
Charmosyna margarethae	●	–	●	●	●	●	●	–
Zosterops rendovae	●	–	●	●	–	●	●	–
Haliaeetus sanfordi	●	●	●	●	●	●	●	–
Reinwardtoena crassirostris	●	●	●	●	●	●	●	–
Ninox jacquinoti	●	●	●	?	●	●	●	–
Columba pallidiceps	●	●	–	●	●	●	●	●
Ptilinopus solomonensis	●	–	●	●	●	●	●	●
Accipiter albogularis	●	●	●	●	●	●	●	●
Megapodius eremita	●	●	●	●	●	●	●	●
Ducula rubricera	●	●	●	●	●	●	●	●
Chalcopsitta cardinalis	●	●	●	●	●	●	●	●
Micropsitta finschii	●	●	●	●	●	●	●	●
Geoffroyus heteroclitus	●	●	●	●	●	●	●	●
Microgoura meeki	–	X	–	–	–	–	–	–
Corvus woodfordi	–	●	●	–	●	●	●	–
Monarcha castaneiventris	–	●	●	–	●	●	●	–
Gallirallus rovianae	–	–	–	●	–	–	–	–
Phylloscopus amoenus	–	–	–	●K	–	–	–	–
Monarcha richardsii	–	–	–	●	–	–	–	–
Monarcha browni	–	–	–	●	–	–	–	–
Zosterops vellalavella	–	–	–	●V	–	–	–	–
Zosterops splendidus	–	–	–	●RA	–	–	–	–
Zosterops luteirostris	–	–	–	●G	–	–	–	–
Zosterops kulambangrae	–	–	–	●	–	–	–	–
Zosterops murphyi	–	–	–	●K	–	–	–	–
Myzomela eichhorni	–	–	–	●	–	–	–	–
Centropus milo	–	–	–	●	–	●	–	–
Rhipidura malaitae	–	–	–	–	●	–	–	–
Zosterops stresemanni	–	–	–	–	●	–	–	–
Myzomela malaitae	–	–	–	–	●	–	–	–
Ducula brenchleyi	–	–	–	–	–	●	●	–
Lorius chlorocercus	–	–	–	–	●	●	●	●
Guadalcanaria inexpectata	–	–	–	–	–	●	–	–
Myzomela melanocephala	–	–	–	–	●	●	–	–
Collocalia orientalis	–	–	–	–	–	●	●	–
Megalurulus whitneyi	–	–	–	–	–	●	–	●
Zoothera margaretae	–	–	–	–	–	●	●	–

cont.

Distribution patterns of restricted-range species (cont.)

Species (ordered geographically)	Bougainville	Choiseul	Isabel	New Georgia group	Malaita	Guadalcanal	Makira	Other EBAs, SAs
Gallinula silvestris	–	–	–	–	–	–	●	–
Gallicolumba salamonis	–	–	–	–	–	–	●	–
Ptilinopus eugeniae	–	–	–	–	–	–	●	–
Cettia parens	–	–	–	–	–	–	●	–
Phylloscopus makirensis	–	–	–	–	–	–	●	–
Monarcha viduus	–	–	–	–	–	–	●	–
Myiagra cervinicauda	–	–	–	–	–	–	●	–
Rhipidura tenebrosa	–	–	–	–	–	–	●	–
Dicaeum tristami	–	–	–	–	–	–	●	–
Myzomela tristrami	–	–	–	–	–	–	●	–
Melidectes sclateri	–	–	–	–	–	–	●	–
Aplonis dichroa	–	–	–	–	–	–	●	–
Ptilinopus richardsii	–	–	–	–	–	–	●	◉
Lalage leucopyga	–	–	–	–	–	–	●	◉
Myzomela cardinalis	–	–	–	–	–	–	●	◉
Total	40	27	28	31	27	39	30	

● Present ? Present? Threatened spp. shown in **bold** } see 'Status and habitat' table
○ Extinct? R Reintroduced Other EBAs, SAs
X Extinct I Introduced

K Kolombangara only RA Ranongga only V Vella Lavella only
G Ghizo only RE Rendova only

¹ Also an unconfirmed record from Makira.
² Observations from Kolombangara (in New Georgia group) almost certainly refer to *Gallirallus rovianae* (Gibbs 1996b).

birds, two seabirds suspected of having small breeding ranges are likely to occur within this EBA: Beck's Petrel *Pterodroma becki* is known from two specimens taken at sea in 1928 and, if it survives at all, Bougainville is a likely place for it to breed; Heinroth's Shearwater *Puffinus heinrothi* is known only from a small number of specimens, and could also breed in the Crown Prince range of Bougainville (Hadden 1981), or in the forested mountains of Kolombangara.

■ Threats and conservation

Although montane forest in the Solomon Islands is (at least superficially) mostly intact, large areas of lowland forest below 400 m have been logged for commercial timber extraction or are committed to logging, and much of the coastal area on many islands has been converted to coconut plantations.

It can be argued that all species which occur in lowland and hill primary forest are threatened because of current and proposed logging activities on most of the large islands and on some of the smaller ones (M. C. Garnett *in litt.* 1993, T. Leary *in litt.* 1993). However, some species have been recorded from secondary forest and thus their futures may be relatively secure, but there has been little research on survivorship in these habitats to verify this. The situation is further complicated by the decreasing quality (to wildlife) of regenerating forest because the fallow period between successive gardens is

becoming reduced to increase the availability of land to meet increasing demands for subsistence farming (Buckingham *et al.* 1995).

Terrestrial birds, e.g. *Gallicolumba salamonis*, are additionally under threat from predation by rats, cats, dogs and pigs, and this is likely to worsen as areas are logged, opened up and become populated (G. C. L. Dutson *in litt.* 1993, K. D. Bishop *in litt.* 1996). On Guadalcanal cats have wiped out most native terrestrial mammals (T. Flannery per K. D. Bishop *in litt.* 1994), and cats and rats have been seen at high altitudes on a number of islands (T. Leary *in litt.* 1993).

Some species are considered threatened on account of their tiny ranges, e.g. *Phylloscopus amoenus* (summit of Kolombangara only) and *Zosterops luteirostris* (Ghizo only). Hunting is common and may also become a problem for some species, especially forest pigeons, as village populations increase and habitat is reduced (A. Lees *in litt.* 1993).

Leary (1991) has synthesized information on the state of the Solomon Islands' natural resources, and also gives details of relevant environmental issues. Although most of the land (87%) is under village stewardship rather than government control, there are a few state-protected areas within the islands; Queen Elizabeth National Park on Guadalcanal is one such, but this has been slowly degraded since it was established and is now mostly cleared (G. C. L. Dutson *in litt.* 1993, K. D. Bishop *in litt.* 1996).

In 1990 a survey was undertaken to identify a representative system of protected forest areas, including reserve proposals for each of the main islands (Lees 1991), and progress is now being made to establish forest conservation areas that meet the cultural and economic aspirations of the indigenous forest owners (A. Lees *in litt.* 1993; see also Biliki 1993). A conservation and development programme is currently underway to establish a 630-km² reserve in the central Makira–Bauro highlands. This will protect the last extensive, accessible, lowland forest that remains uncommitted to timber production, along with a complete forested altitudinal transition across the island (Lees 1991, A. Lees *in litt.* 1996).

There is no recent information on the status of birds or forests in Bougainville owing to political unrest; the southern segments of the Crown Prince range, including Mts Takuan and Taraka and Lake Lorolu, have been identified by Beehler (1993) as areas which are important for terrestrial biodiversity.

199 Rennell and Bellona

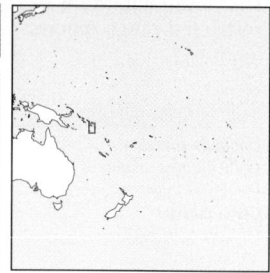

PRIORITY
HIGH

Key habitats Lowland rain forest

Main threats Limited habitat loss (e.g. due to timber extraction), hunting

Biological importance ● ● ●
Current threat level ● ● ●

Area 850 km^2 **Altitude** 0–100 m

Countries Solomon Islands

Restricted-range species	Threatened	Total
Confined to this EBA	0	5
Present also in other EBAs, SAs	0	7
Total	0	12

■ General characteristics

Politically part of the Solomon Islands, Rennell (or Mu Nggava, 825 km^2) and the much smaller Bellona (or Mu Ngiki, 21 km^2) are isolated islands in the south-west Pacific. Their nearest neighbours are Guadalcanal (part of EBA 198) and Makira (EBA 198), c.200 km to the north-east.

The greater part of Rennell is covered in lowland rain forest, though on Bellona there is virtually no forest surviving, the central plateau having been cleared for gardens and coconut plantations (Diamond 1991b, Buckingham *et al.* 1995). Rennell is one of the largest and highest raised coral atolls in the world, and its eastern half is covered by Lake Te Nggano, the largest lake in the Pacific.

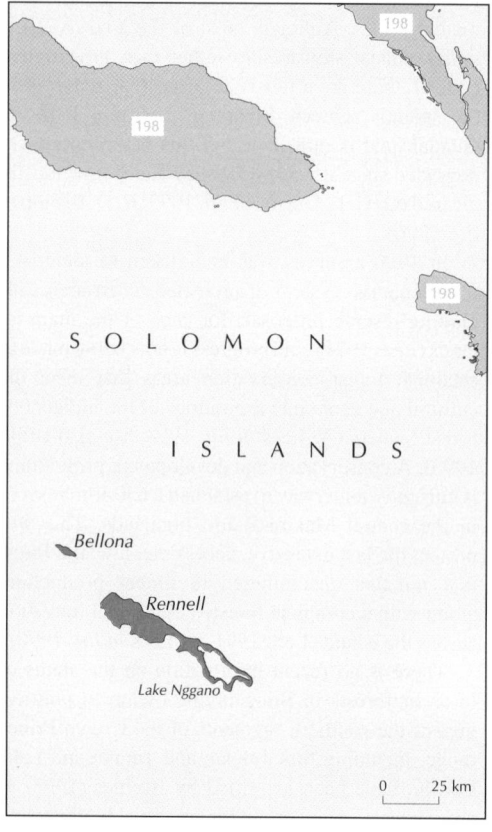

■ Restricted-range species

All the restricted-range species are forest birds and most also occur in secondary habitats.

Rennell is recognized to have a most distinctive avifauna in relation to its size, for as well as five endemic species, it has four endemic subspecies of the more widespread restricted-range species, and a number of endemic subspecies of widespread Austro–Papuan birds. Bellona, on the other hand, being so much smaller, has a depauperate avifauna, but is included in the EBA because two of the restricted-range species which occur on Rennell, *Ptilinopus richardsii* and *Lorius chlorocercus*, have also been recorded there, and a number of subspecies of widespread Austro–Papuan birds are endemic to both Rennell and Bellona, illustrating their avifaunal affinities.

■ Threats and conservation

In the past there have been plans to mine bauxite on Rennell (Diamond 1976) and also to develop a major logging operation, but none of these developments has come to pass, although there is a small milling operation to provide timber for local needs (Lees 1991). Most of the forest (90%) is undisturbed.

Current threats to the restricted-range species include hunting for food and sport by local people (children with catapults take a large number of small birds: B. W. Finch *in litt.* 1993), and capture of nestlings as pets which might perhaps contribute to the rarity of *Lorius chlorocercus* (Diamond 1991b). These threats are, however, relatively minor while the further introduction of exotic species (Pacific rats *Rattus exulans* and cats are already present) could be disastrous to the native avifauna. The restricted-range species are also at risk from natural causes owing to their small ranges and small populations: thus in a recent visit to Rennell, some species (e.g. *Micropsitta finschii*) were found to be scarce, and local people said that their numbers had been greatly reduced by a cyclone in 1992 (H. P. Webb *in litt.* 1996). Because of these various actual and potential threats, the three least-common endemic species are classified as Near Threatened.

Status and habitat of restricted-range species

Species (ordered taxonomically)	Global status	Other EBAs (and SAs)	Habitat
Silver-capped Fruit-dove *Ptilinopus richardsii*	lc	198	Forest, secondary forest
Yellow-bibbed Lory *Lorius chlorocercus*[1]	lc	198	Forest, forest edge, tall secondary forest, rarely coconut plantations
Finsch's Pygmy-parrot *Micropsitta finschii*	lc	195,198	Forest, secondary forest, overgrown gardens, occasionally coconut palms and casuarinas
Singing Parrot *Geoffroyus heteroclitus*	lc	195,198	Forest, partly cleared areas, scrub, gardens
Fan-tailed Gerygone *Gerygone flavolateralis*	lc	200,201	Many habitats inc. forest, secondary growth, scrub, gardens
Rennell Shrikebill *Clytorhynchus hamlini*	nt	—	Forest, secondary forest, edges of old gardens
Melanesian Flycatcher *Myiagra caledonica*	lc	200,201	Forest, forest edge, secondary forest, edges of plantations and gardens
Rennell Fantail *Rhipidura rennelliana*	lc	—	Forest, secondary forest
Rennell White-eye *Zosterops rennellianus*	nt	—	Forest, overgrown gardens
Bare-eyed White-eye *Woodfordia superciliosa*	lc	—	All habitats inc. forest, secondary growth, gardens, coconut plantations
Cardinal Myzomela *Myzomela cardinalis*	lc	198,200,201 203	Forest, forest edge, secondary forest, gardens, plantations
Rennell Starling *Aplonis insularis*	nt	—	Forest, feeds in secondary forest, forest edge, gardens

Global status (see p. 679 for definitions): EX Extinct, EW Extinct in the Wild } with year of last record; CR Critical, EN Endangered, VU Vulnerable } threatened species; cd Conservation Dependent, nt Near Threatened, lc Least Concern; DD Data Deficient, NE Not Evaluated

Other EBAs (and SAs) (see p. 90 for locations): bracketed numbers are Secondary Areas; [x] extinct in that EBA or SA.

There have been several recommendations in the past to establish a protected forest area on Rennell and World Heritage status is currently being investigated.

200 Vanuatu and Temotu

PRIORITY HIGH

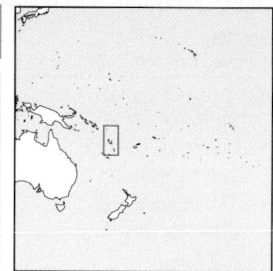

Key habitats Lowland and montane rain forest

Main threats Moderate habitat loss (e.g. due to logging, subsistence farming, pasture)

Biological importance ● ● ○
Current threat level ● ● ○

Area 13,000 km²   **Altitude** 0–1,800 m

Countries Solomon Islands, Vanuatu

Restricted-range species	Threatened	Total
Confined to this EBA	6	15
Present also in other EBAs, SAs	0	15
Total	6	30

■ General characteristics

This EBA includes the Santa Cruz Islands of Temotu province of the Solomon Islands, and the more southerly Torres, Banks and New Hebrides Islands which constitute the political unit of Vanuatu. The land reaches 1,879 m at Mt Tabwemasana on Espiritu Santo and is mostly volcanic in origin. There is still much volcanic activity: Ambrym, for example, suffered extensive new lava flows in 1988.

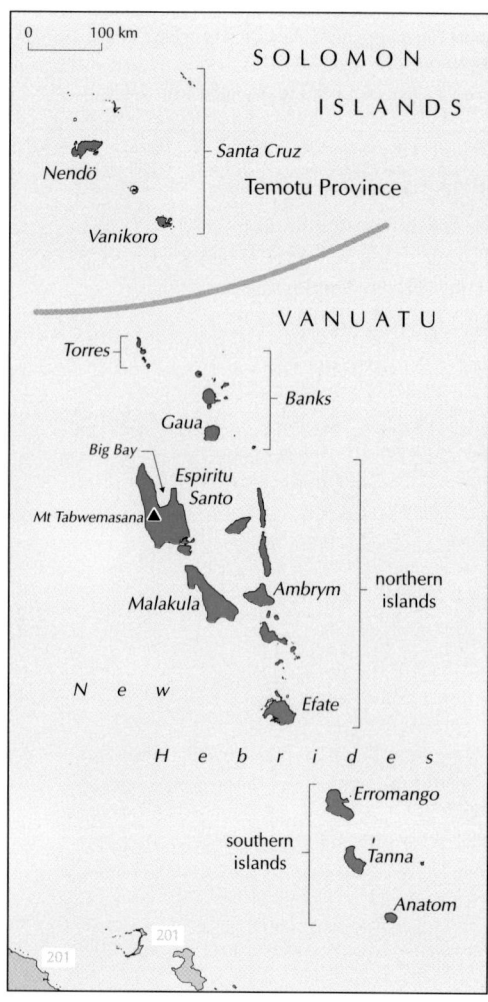

The characteristic vegetation is lowland and montane rain forest; closed conifer forest (dominated by the kauri *Agathis*) is restricted to the western parts of Espiritu Santo, Erromango (which has, or had, the finest remaining stands: Marshall 1973), Anatom and the Santa Cruz Islands. Cloud forest is present on Espiritu Santo and the southern islands, and scattered mangrove forests occur on some islands (Dahl 1980, Davis *et al.* 1986), with those on Malakula being particularly extensive; there are also many freshwater lakes (including Lake Letas on Gaua—one of the largest natural freshwater lakes in the South Pacific) and brackish water and seawater lagoons which are important for resident and migratory birds (H. Bregulla *in litt.* 1993; see also Scott 1993).

Cyclones, earthquakes and associated flooding affect this region. On average, any given area of Vanuatu is struck full-force by a cyclone once in c.30 years, and at such times damage to the forests is enormous (Bregulla 1992); for example, in January 1993 all houses on the Santa Cruz Islands were flattened and as much as 30% of forested areas may have been damaged (T. Leary *in litt.* 1993).

■ Restricted-range species

This EBA lies a faunal crossroads, with the more widespread of its restricted-range bird species having ranges which extend to other Melanesian EBAs: either north to the Solomon Islands (EBAs 198, 199), south to New Caledonia (EBA 201), or in a few cases in both directions; a couple of species also occur eastwards into Central Polynesian EBAs (202, 203).

All the restricted-range species occur in forest and some appear to tolerate partly cleared forest, secondary growth and gardens, perhaps because of adaptation to a cyclone-prone environment. Some species are only found in the highlands or mountains of the larger islands, notably *Aplonis santovestris*, which only occurs above 1,000 m, being confined to the small areas of cloud forest which cover the highest peaks on Espirutu Santo.

Distributional patterns within the EBA vary, although most species occur widely in the archipelago with some gaps along the chain of islands.

Status and habitat of restricted-range species

Species (ordered taxonomically)	Global status	Other EBAs (and SAs)	Altitude (m)	Habitat
Pied Goshawk *Accipiter albogularis*	lc	195,198	0–1,800	Forest, forest edge, clearings, open secondary growth, gardens, edges of towns
Vanuatu Scrubfowl *Megapodius layardi*	VU	—	Lowlands to mid altitudes	Beaches often close to geothermal activity, also near craters (nesting), forest
Santa Cruz Ground-dove *Gallicolumba sanctaecrucis*	VU	—	300–1,000	Forest
Tanna Fruit-dove *Ptilinopus tannensis*	nt	—	Usually lowlands	All wooded habitats inc. forest, savanna, plantations, gardens
Red-bellied Fruit-dove *Ptilinopus greyii*	lc	201	Lowlands to mid altitudes	Forest, secondary growth, savanna woodland, isolated fruit trees in open country
Vanuatu Imperial-pigeon *Ducula bakeri*	VU	—	600+	Forest
Palm Lorikeet *Charmosyna palmarum*	nt	—	Usually >1,000	Montane forest
Chestnut-bellied Kingfisher *Todirhamphus farquhari*	VU	—	Lowlands, hills	Undisturbed or little-disturbed forest, apparently more numerous in hills
Melanesian Cuckoo-shrike *Coracina caledonica*	lc	198,201	Lowlands, hills	Forest, secondary forest, mangroves
Polynesian Triller *Lalage maculosa*	lc	202,203 (s127, s128,s130,s131)	Lowlands, mountains	All habitats inc. forest, forest edge, secondary forest, gardens, parks
Long-tailed Triller *Lalage leucopyga*	lc	198,201,205	Lowlands, mountains	Forest, forest edge, secondary growth, plantations, gardens
Guadalcanal Thicketbird *Megalurulus whitneyi*	nt	198	Usually 700–1,200	Montane forest
Fan-tailed Gerygone *Gerygone flavolateralis*	lc	199,201	0–1,600+	Many habitats inc. forest, secondary growth, savanna woodland, scrub, gardens
Vanikoro Monarch *Mayrornis schistaceus*	nt	—	0–270+	Forest, secondary scrub
Buff-bellied Monarch *Neolalage banksiana*	lc	—	0–1,200	All wooded habitats inc. forest, secondary growth, scrub, overgrown plantations, gardens
Southern Shrikebill *Clytorhynchus pachycephaloides*	lc	201	Lowlands, mountains	Dense forest
Black-throated Shrikebill *Clytorhynchus nigrogularis*	nt	202	0–1,200	Mature wet forest
Melanesian Flycatcher *Myiagra caledonica*	lc	199,201	Usually coastal	Forest, woodland, mangroves, secondary growth, plantations, gardens
Vanikoro Flycatcher *Myiagra vanikorensis*	lc	202	0–1,200	All habitats inc. forest, mangroves, gardens
Streaked Fantail *Rhipidura spilodera*	lc	201,202	0–1,200	Forest, forest edge, thickets
Nendo White-eye *Zosterops sanctaecrucis*	lc	—	Lowlands?	Forest, scrub, gardens
Yellow-fronted White-eye *Zosterops flavifrons*	lc	—	Lowlands, mountains	All habitats with sufficient tree or shrub growth inc. forest, agricultural land, plantations gardens
Sanford's White-eye *Woodfordia lacertosa*	nt	—	Lowlands?	Forest, secondary forest
Cardinal Myzomela *Myzomela cardinalis*	lc	198,199,201 203	All altitudes	Forest, forest edge, secondary growth, mangroves, plantations
Dark-brown Honeyeater *Lichmera incana*	lc	201	Lowlands to mid altitudes	Forest, secondary growth, mangroves, scrub, gardens
New Hebrides Honeyeater *Phylidonyris notabilis*	lc	—	450+	Forest
Royal Parrotfinch *Erythrura regia*	VU	—	Usually mountains	Most types of wooded habitats with fig trees inc. forest, secondary growth, savanna, plantations

cont.

Status and habitat of restricted-range species (cont.)

Species (ordered taxonomically)	Global status	Other EBAs (and SAs)	Altitude (m)	Habitat
Rusty-winged Starling *Aplonis zelandica*	nt	—	Hills, mountains	Forest, sometimes secondary growth, partly cleared areas
Santo Mountain Starling *Aplonis santovestris*	VU	—	1,000+	Cloud forest
Polynesian Starling *Aplonis tabuensis*	lc	202,203 (s127, s128,s129,s130, s131)	0–1,200	Forest, secondary growth, coastal scrub, coconut palms, coral cays

Global status (see p. 679 for definitions)	EX Extinct EW Extinct in the Wild } with year of last record	CR Critical EN Endangered VU Vulnerable } threatened species	cd Conservation Dependent nt Near Threatened lc Least Concern	DD Data Deficient NE Not Evaluated

Other EBAs (and SAs) (see p. 90 for locations): bracketed numbers are Secondary Areas; ˣ extinct in that EBA or SA.

The distribution of *Charmosyna palmarum*, for example, has fluctuated over the last century (in the 1930s it was found on several southern islands but had disappeared from them by the 1960s), perhaps owing to the effects of cyclones (Bregulla 1992).

Distribution patterns of restricted-range species

Species (ordered geographically)	Santa Cruz	Torres and Banks	Northern islands	Southern islands	Other EBAs, SAs
Mayrornis schistaceus	●	–	–	–	–
Zosterops sanctaecrucis	●	–	–	–	–
Woodfordia lacertosa	●	–	–	–	–
Accipiter albogularis	●	–	–	–	●
Clytorhynchus nigrogularis	●	–	–	–	●
Myiagra vanikorensis	●	–	–	–	●
Aplonis tabuensis	●	–	–	–	●
Gallicolumba sanctaecrucis	●	–	●ᴱ	–	–
Lalage maculosa	●	–	●	–	●
Aplonis zelandica	●	●	●	–	–
Charmosyna palmarum	●	●	●	●	–
Ptilinopus greyii	●	●	●	●	●
Myzomela cardinalis	●	●	●	●	●
Ducula bakeri	–	●	●	–	–
Neolalage banksiana	–	●	●	–	–
Phylidonyris notabilis	–	●	●	–	–
Gerygone flavolateralis	–	●	●	●	–
Rhipidura spilodera	–	●	●	–	●
Megapodius layardi	–	●	●	●	–
Ptilinopus tannensis	–	●	●	●	–
Zosterops flavifrons	–	●	●	●	–
Erythrura regia	–	●	●	●	–
Lalage leucopyga	–	●	●	●	●
Clytorhynchus pachycephaloides	–	●	●	●	●
Myiagra caledonica	–	●	●	●	●
Todirhamphus farquhari	–	–	●	–	–
Aplonis santovestris	–	–	●ᴱ	–	–
Megalurulus whitneyi	–	–	●ᴱ	–	●
Coracina caledonica	–	–	●	●	–
Lichmera incana	–	–	●	●	●
Total	13	16	23	12	

● Present   ? Present?
○ Extinct?   R Reintroduced
X Extinct   I Introduced
ᴱ Espiritu Santo only

Threatened spp. shown in **bold** Other EBAs, SAs } see 'Status and habitat' table

There are few data on the three Temotu endemics, *Mayrornis schistaceus* (confined to the island of Vanikoro) and *Woodfordia lacertosa* and *Zosterops sanctaecrucis* (Nendo only) (but see Gibbs 1996b).

■ Threats and conservation

Although most agricultural activity in this EBA is for the production of subsistence food crops, and is typically carried out on the slash-and-burn pattern, there is a growing emphasis on the production of cash crops. Some areas have been cleared for plantations and pastures, particularly on the plateaus of Espiritu Santo and Efate, and all remaining lowland forests are under great pressure from logging companies. The kauri forest on the Santa Cruz Islands has been subject almost throughout to selective logging.

Though the species of this EBA are in no immediate great danger, the status of some may be considered precarious. For example, those birds found on only a few islands and largely dependent on undisturbed forest (e.g. *Gallicolumba sanctaecrucis*, *Todirhamphus farquhari*) are likely to have small populations which are declining as a result of habitat loss, and these are consequently classified as threatened.

Megapodius layardi is one species which is particularly likely to be sensitive to change: although still common, its nesting sites and forest habitat are being destroyed by encroaching agriculture and other development and, while eggs have been collected (from the more accessible sites) as food by village people for centuries with little detrimental effect, any increase in the human population and their mobility may result in over-harvesting (Bregulla 1992). Tebi Beach on the north-west coast of Ambrym is an important nesting area for this species, but a recent survey of egg collectors from 19 villages in the region indicated that its range and numbers have decreased there quite significantly (Bowen 1996).

Another species which is considered threatened is *Aplonis santovestris*. This bird has a tiny range in Espiritu Santo, with records only from 1934, 1961

Habitat destruction—through encroachment of villages, gardens and coconut plantations—has reduced the population of the endemic Vanuatu Scrubfowl *Megapodius layardi*. In addition, the species suffers from over-harvesting of its eggs. Tebi beach on Ambrym, shown here, remains an important nesting site, probably because of its inaccessibility to regular visits.

and 1991 in the Mt Tabwemasana and nearby Peak Santo areas (Reside 1991, Bregulla 1992)—although it may occur more widely than these records suggest as this region is rarely visited by ornithologists.

There have been problems in the past in establishing protected areas on Vanuatu owing to a general failure to address the complex issues associated with custom land rights. However, there have been several recent successful conservation initiatives. One example is the Loru Terrestrial Nature Reserve on Espiritu Santo, officially launched in 1995 and covering c.2 km² of primary lowland forest near the village of Kole One; it is recognized by provincial

and national governments but run by a village-level committee (Bowen 1995, 1997). The Erromango Kauri Reserve has also been officially launched with the signing of a lease agreement (Tacconi and Bennett 1994, L. Tacconi verbally 1995), and a further five areas on Malekula have been proposed for protection (Tacconi 1995). The Big Bay forests on the east coast of Espiritu Santo are the subject of a conservation project, having been identified as important for wildlife (Maturin 1994, Close 1995); lying on the alluvial floodplain of rivers draining the Mt Tabwemasana range, this region is the EBA's largest remaining intact area of lowland forest.

201 New Caledonia

PRIORITY URGENT

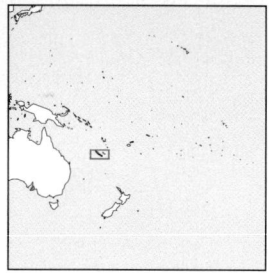

Key habitats Lowland and montane rain forest, dry forest, maquis

Main threats Major habitat loss (e.g. due to logging, agriculture, nickel mining), introduced species

Biological importance ● ● ○
Current threat level ● ● ○

Area 19,000 km² **Altitude** 0–1,600 m

Countries New Caledonia (to France)

Restricted-range species	Threatened	Total
Confined to this EBA	8	22
Present also in other EBAs, SAs	0	9
Total	8	31

■ General characteristics

This EBA comprises the French overseas territory of New Caledonia, which includes the island of New Caledonia itself (Grande Terre, 16,372 km²), the nearby Loyalty Islands of Ouvéa, Lifou and Maré (c.1,970 km² in all), and a number of smaller islands (e.g. Île des Pins). Grande Terre is continental in origin, believed once to have been part of the ancient landmass of Gondwanaland and attached to the Queensland plateau (now in Australia). The Loyalty group consists of raised limestone islands and is of more recent origin.

Grande Terre is by far the most diverse of the islands ecologically, and it has an exceptionally rich flora (c.3,000 species) with high endemism (c.80%) including five endemic plant families (Jaffré et al. 1994, WWF/IUCN 1994–1995). This unique vegetation has led to the island being classified by many botanists as a distinct phytogeographic province (Morat et al. 1984), explicable largely by its long history of isolation (having been separated from Australia in the early Cretaceous period), but also in part by the great variety of its soil types, notably those on ultrabasic rocks where species endemism exceeds 90%.

The predominant vegetation type is a unique scrubland community—known as maquis (typical of regions with a Mediterranean-type climate)—which is largely confined to nutrient-poor ultrabasic soils at varying altitudes. Lowland rain forest, with montane and cloud forest above, is scattered over the central mountain chain (which reaches a maximum altitude of 1,628 m on Mt Panié in the north). These forests are particularly well represented in the east, which is affected during most of the year by the south-east trade winds and has a warm damp tropical climate. Other habitats which are important for some of the restricted-range birds include dry forest (now largely replaced by savanna) along the western, drier, coastal plain from sea-level to 300 m, and mangroves, which occur mostly along the western coastline where the estuaries of the main rivers are wider and deeper than on the steeper east.

The native habitat on the Loyalty Islands is also forest, though, with fewer than plant 400 species, this lacks the main island's great diversity (Jaffré 1993).

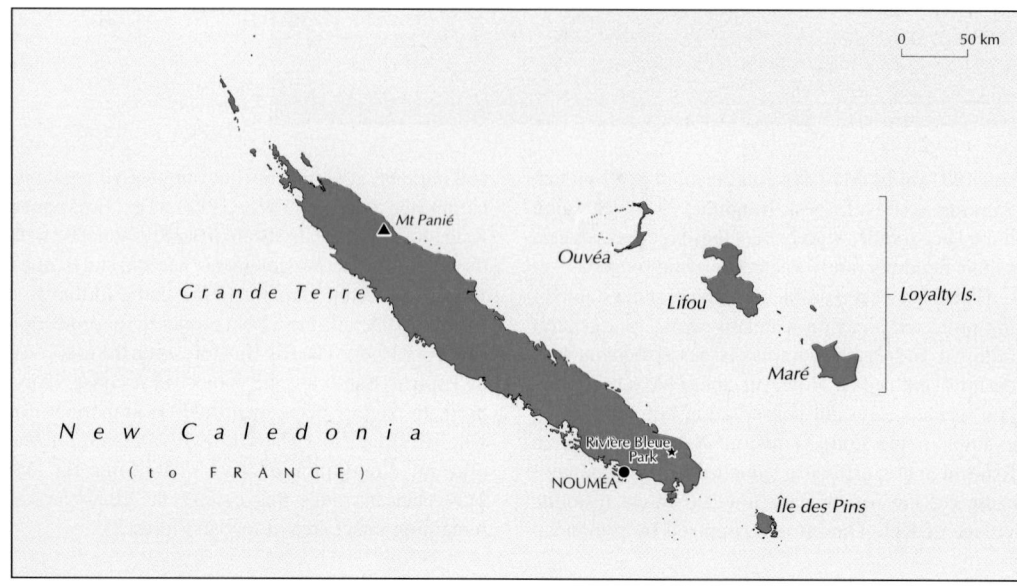

Status and habitat of restricted-range species

Species (ordered taxonomically)	Global status	Other EBAs (and SAs)	Altitude (m)	Habitat
White-bellied Goshawk *Accipiter haplochrous*	lc	—	Lowlands, mid altitudes	Forest, open country
New Caledonian Rail *Gallirallus lafresnayanus*	CR	—	Higher altitudes?	Upper montane forest?, cloud forest?
Kagu *Rhynochetos jubatus*	EN	—	100–1,400	Variety of habitat types from closed-canopy scrub to wet forest
Red-bellied Fruit-dove *Ptilinopus greyii*	lc	200	Lowlands	Coastal forest
Cloven-feathered Dove *Drepanoptila holosericea*	VU	—	Lowlands, mid altitudes	Forest, wooded areas, niaouli savanna
New Caledonian Imperial-pigeon *Ducula goliath*	VU	—	Lowlands, mid altitudes	Forest, esp. riverine forest
New Caledonian Lorikeet *Charmosyna diadema*	EN	—	Higher altitudes?	Cloud forest?
Horned Parakeet *Eunymphicus cornutus*	VU	—	All (*cornutus*); lowlands (*uvaeensis*)	Forest, esp. Kauri pine forest (*cornutus*); forest, secondary growth, gardens (*uvaeensis*)
New Caledonian Owlet-nightjar *Aegotheles savesi*	EN	—	No data	Forest?
Melanesian Cuckoo-shrike *Coracina caledonica*	lc	198,200	Lowlands, mid altitudes	Forest, niaouli savanna, wooded areas
New Caledonian Cuckoo-shrike *Coracina analis*	lc	—	Mid and high altitudes	Forest
Long-tailed Triller *Lalage leucopyga*	lc	198,200 205[X]	Lowlands, mid altitudes	Forest, niaouli savanna, wooded areas, scrub
New Caledonian Grassbird *Megalurulus mariei*	lc	—	Lowlands, mid altitudes	Scrub, grassland
Fan-tailed Gerygone *Gerygone flavolateralis*	lc	199,200	Lowlands, mid altitudes	Forest, niaouli savanna, scrub, wooded areas, gardens
Yellow-bellied Robin *Eopsaltria flaviventris*	lc	—	Lowlands, mid altitudes	Forest, inc. young open forest growing at forest edge
Southern Shrikebill *Clytorhynchus pachycephaloides*	lc	200	Lowlands, mid altitudes	Forest, forest edge
Melanesian Flycatcher *Myiagra caledonica*	lc	199,200	Lowlands, mid altitudes	Forest, forest edge, wooded areas
Streaked Fantail *Rhipidura spilodera*	lc	200,202	Lowlands, mid altitudes	Forest, forest edge, thickets
New Caledonian Whistler *Pachycephala caledonica*	lc	—	Lowlands, mid altitudes	Forest, forest edge
Large Lifou White-eye *Zosterops inornatus*	lc	—	Lowlands	Forest, forest edge, gardens
Green-backed White-eye *Zosterops xanthochrous*	lc	—	Lowlands, mid altitudes	Forest, wooded areas, scrub, gardens
Small Lifou White-eye *Zosterops minutus*	lc	—	Lowlands	Forest, forest edge, gardens
New Caledonian Myzomela *Myzomela caledonica*	lc	—	Lowlands, mid altitudes	Forest, forest edge, wooded areas, scrub
Cardinal Myzomela *Myzomela cardinalis*	lc	198,199 200,203	Lowlands	Forest, forest edge, wooded areas
Dark-brown Honeyeater *Lichmera incana*	lc	200	Lowlands, mid altitudes	Niaouli savanna, scrub, wooded areas, mangroves, gardens
New Caledonian Friarbird *Philemon diemenensis*	lc	—	Lowlands, mid altitudes	Forest, forest edge, wooded areas, scrub, gardens
Crow Honeyeater *Gymnomyza aubryana*	VU	—	All	Forest, forest edge

cont.

Status and habitat of restricted-range species (cont.)

Species (ordered taxonomically)	Global status	Other EBAs (and SAs)	Altitude (m)	Habitat
Barred Honeyeater *Phylidonyris undulata*	lc	—	Lowlands, mid altitudes	Forest, wooded areas, gardens during flowering season
Red-throated Parrotfinch *Erythrura psittacea*	lc	—	Lowlands, mid altitudes	Forest, forest edge, savanna, grassland, scrub, gardens
Striated Starling *Aplonis striata*	lc	—	Lowlands, mid altitudes	Forest, niaouli savanna, wooded areas, gardens
New Caledonian Crow *Corvus moneduloides*	lc	—	Lowlands, mid altitudes	Forest, forest edge, niaouli savanna, wooded areas, grassland

Global status
(see p. 679 for definitions)

EX	Extinct	with year of last record	CR	Critical	threatened species	cd	Conservation Dependent	DD	Data Deficient
EW	Extinct in the Wild		EN	Endangered		nt	Near Threatened	NE	Not Evaluated
			VU	Vulnerable		lc	Least Concern		

Other EBAs (and SAs) (see p. 90 for locations): bracketed numbers are Secondary Areas; ˣ extinct in that EBA or SA.

■ Restricted-range species

New Caledonia is among the Pacific region's top EBAs for the number of endemic restricted-range bird species. Most restricted-range species occur in forest in the lowlands and at mid altitudes, but more precise information on altitudinal and habitat preferences appears to be lacking.

The majority of the endemics are found widely on Grande Terre and its satellite islands, notable exceptions being *Gymnomyza aubryana*, which is apparently confined to the south of Grande Terre, and the two white-eyes *Zosterops*, which are endemic to Lifou. Several of the more-widespread restricted-range birds also occur further north in Melanesia (EBAs 198–200), and a couple occur eastwards into Central Polynesia (EBAs 202, 203).

In general, distributional information on the EBA's restricted-range species is poor. *Gallirallus lafresnayanus*, for example, has not been reliably reported by ornithologists since early in the twentieth century, though local reports suggest that it could still survive in small numbers, perhaps in forest at higher altitudes; *Charmosyna diadema* was last observed in 1913 although islanders again report that it might yet exist in remote cloud forests, and two birds were reported by an experienced bushman in forest west of Mt Panié in 1976; and *Aegotheles savesi*, also assumed to occur in forest, is known only from one specimen collected in 1880 near to the capital Nouméa and one individual reported as having been killed by a hunter in 1960. All these three species have been listed as extinct by some sources (e.g. King 1978–1979).

■ Threats and conservation

On Grande Terre, most of the lowland coastal plains have been cleared for grazing or altered by plantations and agriculture, while logging and open-cast mining (the island has c.50% of the world's known nickel deposits) have destroyed forest and maquis in

Distribution patterns of restricted-range species

Species (ordered geographically)	Grande Terre	Ouvéa	Lifou	Maré	Other EBAs, SAs
Accipiter haplochrous	●	–	–	–	–
Gallirallus lafresnayanus	●	–	–	–	–
Rhynochetos jubatus	●	–	–	–	–
Drepanoptila holosericea	●	–	–	–	–
Ducula goliath	●	–	–	–	–
Charmosyna diadema	●	–	–	–	–
Aegotheles savesi	●	–	–	–	–
Coracina analis	●	–	–	–	–
Megalurulus mariei	●	–	–	–	–
Eopsaltria flaviventris	●	–	–	–	–
Pachycephala caledonica	●	–	–	–	–
Myzomela caledonica	●	–	–	–	–
Gymnomyza aubryana	●	–	–	–	–
Phylidonyris undulata	●	–	–	–	–
Erythrura psittacea	●	–	–	–	–
Clytorhynchus pachycephaloides	●	–	–	–	●
Eunymphicus cornutus	●	●	Iˣ	–	–
Philemon diemenensis	●	–	●	●	–
Rhipidura spilodera	●	–	●	●	●
Zosterops xanthochrous	●	–	–	●	–
Corvus moneduloides	●	–	–	I	–
Aplonis striata	●	●	●	●	–
Ptilinopus greyii	●	●	●	●	●
Coracina caledonica	●	●	●	●	●
Lalage leucopyga	●	●	●	●	●
Gerygone flavolateralis	●	●	●	●	●
Myiagra caledonica	●	●	●	●	●
Lichmera incana	●	●	●	●	●
Myzomela cardinalis	–	●	●	●	●
Zosterops inornatus	–	–	●	–	–
Zosterops minutus	–	–	●	–	–
Total	28	9	12	11	

●	Present	I	Introduced
○	Extinct?	Iˣ	Introduced, but since extinct
X	Extinct		

Threatened spp. shown in **bold**
Other EBAs, SAs
see 'Status and habitat' table

the upper parts of certain massifs (Dupon 1986a), the resulting erosion being some of the worst anywhere in the world. Bush fires, which are started in the dry season to regenerate grazing lands or to clean overgrown cultivated fields, are the principal threat to remaining native vegetation, as they spread into forest edge and maquis.

Today c.50% of the land area of Grande Terre is covered by secondary forest, savanna (dominated mainly by the fire-resistant tree, niaouli *Melaleuca quinquenervia*) and grassland. The most extensive areas of remaining native habitat are rain forest, occupying c.20% of the territory (though only 10% of this forest can be considered undisturbed), and maquis, covering c.24% (Mittermeier *et al.* 1996). Pristine stands of dry forest probably occupy less than 100 km², c.2% of their original extent, with grazing and trampling by cattle and introduced deer preventing regeneration (Bouchet *et al.* 1995).

Although logging is now restricted to a few small areas, even these localized operations can have a significant impact, as forest has already been severely depleted by past activities. Several restricted-range species are likely to have declining populations and are consequently classified as threatened: for example, *Eunymphicus cornutus* which exists as two races, *cornutus* on the mainland (estimated to number 2,000–10,000 individuals) and *uvaeensis* on Ouvéa where the total population is estimated at c.600 birds, with illegal capture for trade an additional threat (Robinet *et al.* 1995, 1996; see also Robinet and Salas 1996). Hunting is another problem for some species—e.g. *Ducula goliath*, the world's largest living arboreal pigeon—as new areas are opened up by logging and prospecting.

Introduced mammalian predators are of particular concern for *Rhynochetos jubatus* (living only on Grande Terre), the sole representative of its family (and New Caledonia's national bird), with eggs being eaten by wild pigs, chicks being killed by dogs, cats and rats (Y. Létocart *in litt.* 1996), and adults being killed by hunting and feral dogs (Hannecart 1988, Hunt *et al.*1996). In 1991–1992, 491 adult *R. jubatus* were censused in unprotected areas; here the species had a patchy, mostly inland distribution in the less-disturbed mountainous parts, with few birds recorded from logged areas or within 4 km of human settlements. This figure, combined with the 163 birds (including juveniles) counted in the Rivière Bleue Park (Létocart 1992), brought the known numbers of *R. jubatus* to 654 in early 1992 (Hunt 1996a).

Increasing fragmentation of habitat is a particular risk for the more sedentary species, e.g. *Rhynochetos jubatus* and *Corvus moneduloides*, where pairs require large, mostly non-overlapping forest territories in which to breed. Localized extinctions may also result in loss of behavioural as well as genetic diversity within species: for example, altitude-related variation exists in the roosting behaviour of *R. jubatus*, and site-specific differences in tool-using behaviour by *C. moneduloides* may be considerable (Hunt 1996 a, b).

Two widespread threatened species also occur on New Caledonia: Australasian Bittern *Botaurus poiciloptilus* (classified as Endangered) and Fairy Tern *Sterna nereis* (Vulnerable), but there are few data on their status in this EBA. Seabirds are likely to be threatened by disturbance, especially as people are able to explore further afield in increasingly sophisticated boats, and reach islands that were previously protected by their isolation (and therefore often important nesting sites) (M. Pandolfi-Benoit per A. Duncan verbally 1996).

There are 26 gazetted terrestrial nature reserves on Grande Terre, including 13 Special Botanical Reserves, five Special Faunal Reserves, two Special Botanical/Faunal Reserves and five Provincial Parks of varying sizes, amounting to c.490 km² or c.3% of the island's total land area. However, the majority of these sites are protected on paper only due to lack of money (Chardonnet and Lartiges 1992); in addition, some are in areas with mining concessions and could therefore be exploited in the future, many of those with rain forest have already been selectively logged, and some may now be so degraded that there may no longer be much justification for their conservation. A notable exception is the Rivière Bleue Park, which is wardened and managed, and is the only site where populations of *Rhynochetos jubatus* are increasing as a result of control of introduced predators (pigs, dogs, etc.). The park covers a very important remnant of forest, selectively exploited until c.20 years ago, and has populations of all the breeding endemic birds.

In addition to nature reserves, there are large areas gazetted for watershed protection, but this designation offers little conservation benefit for fauna and flora (G. R. Hunt *in litt.* 1996). No reserves of any kind have been gazetted in the Loyalty Islands and the existing reserves containing dry forest are considered inadequate by Bouchet *et al.* (1995).

Mittermeier *et al.* (1996) note the fact that New Caledonia is not currently eligible for international biodiversity funds because it is the territory of a developed country rather than being an independent nation, and that conservation has not been a high priority for France or for the regional government. They recommend an assessment of remaining natural areas (focusing particularly on existing protected areas) and a review of existing biological knowledge in order to assess better the geographic priorities for conservation in this extremely important EBA.

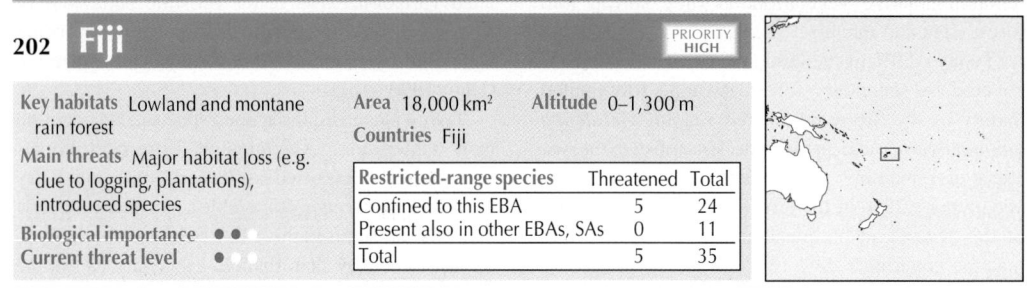

202 Fiji

PRIORITY HIGH

Key habitats Lowland and montane rain forest

Main threats Major habitat loss (e.g. due to logging, plantations), introduced species

Biological importance ● ● ●

Current threat level ● ● ●

Area 18,000 km² Altitude 0–1,300 m

Countries Fiji

Restricted-range species	Threatened	Total
Confined to this EBA	5	24
Present also in other EBAs, SAs	0	11
Total	5	35

■ General characteristics

Included in this EBA are all the Republic of Fiji's islands apart from Rotuma (isolated to the north) which is treated as a Secondary Area (s127). The archipelago comprises high volcanic islands (reaching 1,324 m at Mt Tomanivi on Viti Levu), as well as atolls and raised coral limestone islands.

On the southern and eastern sides of the larger islands, the native vegetation is lowland and montane rain forest, with cloud forest at highest altitudes; on the northern and western sides (which are in the rain shadow), dry forest and open woodland (now largely replaced by fire-climax grassland) formerly occurred at lower elevations. Forest also occurs on some of the smaller islands, though many have been cleared, and mangroves are found to varying extents along many coasts. Cyclones and landslides occur regularly in Fiji and have moulded forests in such a way that

secondary associations are a widespread and integral part of the ecosystems (Collins *et al.* 1991).

■ Restricted-range species

This EBA ranks third for numbers of restricted-range bird species in the Pacific. All the restricted-range species occur in forest and some occur in man-modified habitats. There are few altitudinal limitations to the distribution of the restricted-range birds and, in most cases, any apparent such restriction relates to availability of remaining suitable habitat (D. Watling *in litt.* 1993).

Many species are widely distributed through the islands, but two are confined to Vanua Levu and Taveuni, three to Viti Levu and four to Kadavu. *Mayrornis versicolor* is restricted to Ogea in the Lau archipelago, occurring on the two principal islands—Ogealevu (13 km²) and Ogeadriki (5 km²)—and on

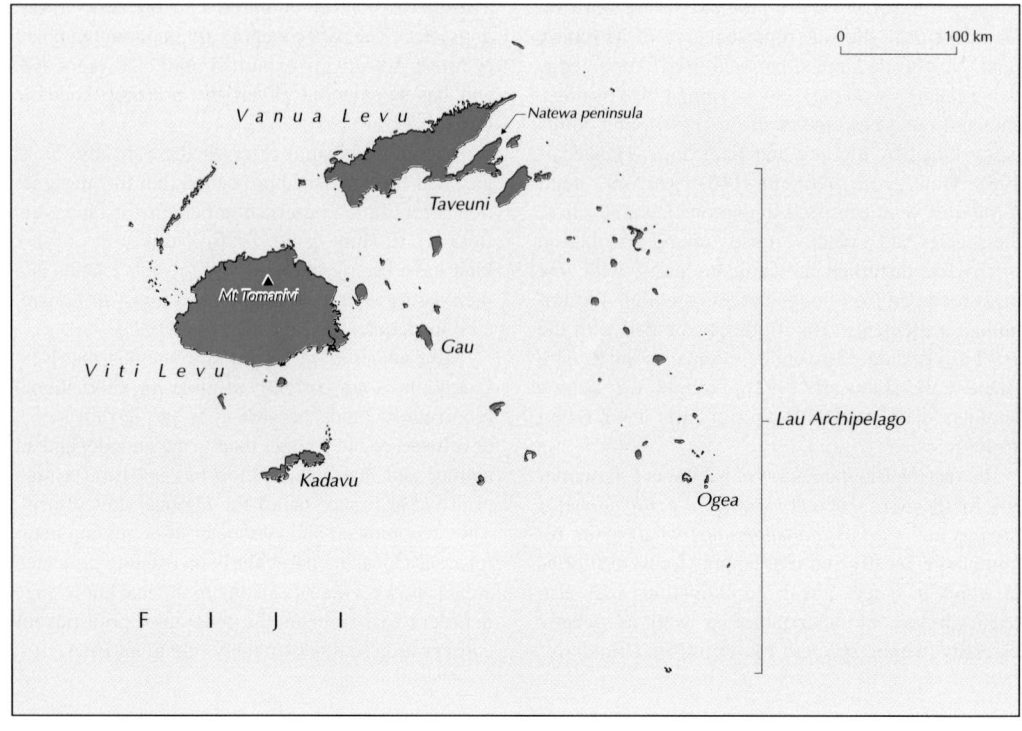

Status and habitat of restricted-range species

Species (ordered taxonomically)	Global status	Other EBAs (and SAs)	Habitat
Fiji Goshawk *Accipiter rufitorques*	lc	—	Many habitats inc. forest, well-wooded agricultural areas, urban parks
Bar-winged Rail *Nesoclopeus poecilopterus*	EX (1973?)	—	Forest, secondary growth, swamps, overgrown plantations, old taro fields
Shy Ground-dove *Gallicolumba stairi*[1]	nt	203 (s128,s130)	Forest inc. bamboo thickets and gallery forest, scrubby bush on small islands
Many-coloured Fruit-dove *Ptilinopus perousii*	lc	203 (s130)	Forest, well developed secondary forest (specialises on fruits of large banyan trees *Ficus* sp.)
Purple-capped Fruit-dove *Ptilinopus porphyraceus*	lc	192,203 (s123[X],s127, s128,s129,s130,s131)	Any wooded habitat inc. forest, secondary forest, plantations
Orange Dove *Ptilinopus victor*	lc	—	Forest, forest edge
Golden Dove *Ptilinopus luteovirens*	lc	—	Forest inc. gallery forest, dense secondary growth
Whistling Dove *Ptilinopus layardi*	nt	—	Forest, forest edge, gardens
Peale's Imperial-pigeon *Ducula latrans*	lc	—	Forest, tall secondary growth, forest edge
Collared Lory *Phigys solitarius*	lc	—	All habitats with suitable flowering trees inc. forest, forest edge, secondary growth, plantations
Blue-crowned Lorikeet *Vini australis*	lc	203 (s128,s129, s130,s131)	All habitats with suitable flowering trees, inc. secondary forest, plantations, urban gardens
Red-throated Lorikeet *Charmosyna amabilis*	VU	—	Forest (usually above 500 m)
Crimson Shining-parrot *Prosopeia splendens*	nt	—	Forest, forest edge
Masked Shining-parrot *Prosopeia personata*	nt	—	Forest, secondary forest, mangroves
Red Shining-parrot *Prosopeia tabuensis*[1]	lc	—	Forest, secondary growth, mangroves, gardens
Polynesian Triller *Lalage maculosa*	lc	200,203 (s127,s128, s130,s131)	All habitats inc. forest, forest edge, secondary forest, gardens, parks
Fiji Bush-warbler *Cettia ruficapilla*	lc	—	Any habitat with thick undergrowth inc. mature forest, secondary bush
Long-legged Thicketbird *Trichocichla rufa*	CR	—	Montane forest
Silktail *Lamprolia victoriae*	VU	—	Forest
Ogea Monarch successional *Mayrornis versicolor*	VU	—	Forest (possibly preferring the more limited and edge habitats)
Slaty Monarch *Mayrornis lessoni*	lc	—	Forest, well-wooded parks and gardens, open areas on small islands
Fiji Shrikebill *Clytorhynchus vitiensis*	lc	203 (s127,s128,s130)	Forest, secondary forest, mangroves, mature scrub
Black-throated Shrikebill *Clytorhynchus nigrogularis*	nt	200	Forest
Vanikoro Flycatcher *Myiagra vanikorensis*	lc	200	All habitats inc. forest, mangroves, gardens, urban parks
Blue-crested Flycatcher *Myiagra azureocapilla*	lc	—	Forest, tall secondary forest
Streaked Fantail *Rhipidura spilodera*	lc	200,201	Forest, forest edge, thickets

cont.

Status and habitat of restricted-range species (cont.)

Species (ordered taxonomically)	Global status	Other EBAs (and SAs)	Habitat
Kadavu Fantail *Rhipidura personata*	nt	—	Forest
Layard's White-eye *Zosterops explorator*	lc	—	Forest, gallery forest, forest edge, well-wooded areas, bush, edges of agricultural land
Orange-breasted Myzomela *Myzomela jugularis*	lc	—	All habitats inc. forest edge, plantations, gardens
Wattled Honeyeater *Foulehaio carunculata*	lc	203 (s128,s130)	All habitats inc. forest, coastal scrub, mangroves, gardens, urban parks
Kadavu Honeyeater *Xanthotis provocator*	nt	—	Mangroves, nearby gardens, forest edge
Giant Honeyeater *Gymnomyza viridis*	lc	—	Forest, forest edge, flowering trees in nearby agricultural areas
Fiji Parrotfinch *Erythrura pealii*	lc	—	Forest, forest edge, grassland, ricefields, parks, gardens
Pink-billed Parrotfinch *Erythrura kleinschmidti*	EN	—	Forest, sometimes secondary forest, dense bush
Polynesian Starling *Aplonis tabuensis*	lc	200,203 (s127,s128, s129,s130,s131)	Forest, secondary growth, coastal scrub, coconut plantations, coral cays
Fiji Woodswallow *Artamus mentalis*	lc	—	Forest edge, open areas with trees, urban parks, roadsides

Global status (see p. 679 for definitions)

EX Extinct ⎫ with year
EW Extinct in ⎬ of last
      the Wild ⎭ record

CR Critical ⎫ threatened
EN Endangered ⎬ species
VU Vulnerable ⎭

cd Conservation Dependent
nt Near Threatened
lc Least Concern
DD Data Deficient
NE Not Evaluated

Other EBAs (and SAs) (see p. 90 for locations)
Bracketed numbers are Secondary Areas.   ˣ Extinct in that EBA or SA.

Notes
[1] Introduced to Abemama, Gilbert Islands (Secondary Area s125).
[2] Introduced to 'Eua, southern Tongan Islands (Secondary Area s130).

the smaller nearby Dakuiyanuya. Several of the more-widespread restricted-range species are shared with the Samoan Islands (EBA 203) and/or other Central Polynesian Secondary Areas (s127–s131), and a few occur to the west in Vanuatu (EBA 200).

The taxonomic treatment of the three *Prosopeia* parrots, *splendens*, *personata* and *tabuensis*, followed here is that of Rinke (1989) and Sibley and Monroe (1990, 1993), although Holyoak and Thibault (in prep.) do not accept Rinke's novel arrangement

and follow the classification of Amadon (1942), as did Forshaw (1989), and recognize only two species, *P. personata* and *P. tabuensis* (the latter having five subspecies, including *splendens*).

In addition to the restricted-range land birds, one seabird, Fiji Petrel *Pterodroma macgillivrayi*, is known only from Gau, where the number of recent observations has risen to eight, but where the breeding grounds, presumed to be in forest, have still to be located (Watling 1986, Watling and Gillison 1993).

H.D.Pratt

Galoa Island, lying off Kadavu. Although only a few of the restricted-range species of this EBA are currently considered threatened, the loss of forest for tourist development and agriculture may be affecting populations of several of the forest-dependent endemics.

Distribution patterns of restricted-range species

Species (ordered geographically)	Vanua Levu	Taveuni	Viti Levu	Kadavu	Lau	Other EBAs, SAs
Ptilinopus victor	●	●	–	–	–	–
Prosopeia tabuensis	●	●	–	–	–	–
Lamprolia victoriae	●	●	–	–	–	–
Trichocichla rufa	●	–	●	–	–	–
Charmosyna amabilis	●	●	●	–	–	–
Myiagra azureocapilla	●	●	●	–	–	–
Gymnomyza viridis	●	●	●	–	–	–
Rhipidura spilodera	●	●	●	–	–	●
Cettia ruficapilla	●	●	●	●	–	–
Zosterops explorator	●	●	●	●	–	–
Erythrura pealii	●	●	●	●	–	–
Artamus mentalis	●	●	●	●	–	–
Clytorhynchus nigrogularis	●	●	●	●	–	●
Foulehaio carunculata	●	●	●	–	●	–
Accipiter rufitorques	●	●	●	●	●	–
Ducula latrans	●	●	●	●	●	–
Phigys solitarius	●	●	●	●	●	–
Mayrornis lessoni	●	●	●	●	●	–
Myzomela jugularis	●	●	●	●	●	–
Gallicolumba stairi	●	●	●	●	●	●
Ptilinopus perousii	●	●	●	●	●	●
Lalage maculosa	●	●	●	●	●	●
Clytorhynchus vitiensis	●	●	●	●	●	●
Myiagra vanikorensis	●	●	●	●	●	●
Aplonis tabuensis	●	●	●	●	●	●
Nesoclopeus poecilopterus	–	–	X	–	–	–
Ptilinopus luteovirens	–	–	●	–	–	–
Prosopeia personata	–	–	●	–	–	–
Erythrura kleinschmidti	–	–	●	–	–	–
Prosopeia splendens	–	–	I	●	–	–
Ptilinopus layardi	–	–	–	●	–	–
Rhipidura personata	–	–	–	●	–	–
Xanthotis provocator	–	–	–	●	–	–
Mayrornis versicolor	–	–	–	–	●	–
Ptilinopus porphyraceus	–	–	–	–	●	●
Vini australis	–	–	–	–	●	●
Total	25	24	25	20	15	

● Present	? Present?	Threatened spp. shown in **bold**	see 'Status and habitat' table
O Extinct?	R Reintroduced	Other EBAs, SAs	
X Extinct	I Introduced		

▓ Threats and conservation

Natural forests of varying quality today cover c.44% of the land area of Fiji with a further 7% covered by softwood and hardwood plantations (D. Watling *in litt.* 1995). On most islands nearly all accessible forest has either been logged or is committed to logging concessions (A. Lees in *litt.* 1993), and Taveuni is the only island with extensive relatively undisturbed forest.

The loss of native forest will have undoubtedly affected populations of the restricted-range species and several are classified as threatened or Near Threatened. An example is *Lamprolia victoriae*, which, although still common in forest on Taveuni (nominate *victoriae*), is very rare on Vanua Levu (race *kleinschmidti*) where it is restricted to the already heavily logged and unprotected Natewa peninsula. The survival of the majority, if not all, of the restricted-range species will depend on the existence of areas of native forest large enough and sufficiently well distributed to negate the localized destruction caused by regular cyclones (D. Watling *in litt.* 1993).

It is likely that predation by introduced mammals (rats, cats and mongooses *Herpestes auropunctatus*) caused the demise of *Nesoclopeus poecilopterus*, which is believed to have been flightless (excepting an unconfirmed 1973 record, the species is not known from the twentieth century and is thought extinct). Predation by feral cats is also a potential threat to *Pterodroma macgillivrayi* (see 'Restricted-range species', above), which is classified as Critical, and to the threatened (Vulnerable) migratory Bristle-thighed Curlew *Numenius tahitiensis*, a restricted range species (see Secondary Area s002) which winters in this EBA and undergoes a flightless moult.

Habitat does remain for *Trichocichla rufa*, *Erythrura kleinschmidti* and *Charmosyna amabilis*, and the cause of their apparent scarcity in it is unclear, although predation may be a contributory factor. However, few observers have sought these species, and the true status of *T. rufa*, which is very skulking with an undescribed song, is more likely to be Data Deficient (D. T. Holyoak *in litt.* 1996).

The threatened status of *Mayrornis versicolor* reflects its tiny range in the Lau archipelago, for it will always remain susceptible to chance catastrophes—though there are no indications that it, or the forests, have been greatly affected by recent cyclones (Watling 1988a).

The state of the environment of Fiji is described in Watling and Chape (1992), which includes a preliminary register of 140 'natural' sites of national significance. At present there are a few small, forested protected areas in this EBA and there are also designated watershed 'protection forests' (about a third of the remaining forest area), but these latter have no legal status and are not inviolate from logging (Watling 1988b), so may not have great conservation value.

A representative national parks and reserves system for Fiji's tropical forests is proposed in Lees (1989) and includes a reserve on Vanua Levu (specifically for *Lamprolia victoriae*) and one on Viti Levu (the Sovi basin) which would protect Fiji's largest remaining area of undisturbed lowland forest (see Cabaniuk *et al.* 1995). There is a commitment within Fiji to establish protected areas, and attention is now being focused on the best way of achieving their conservation within the framework of customary land ownership (A. Lees *in litt.* 1993, 1996).

203 | Samoan Islands

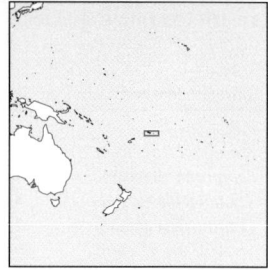

Key habitats Lowland and montane rain forest

Main threats Major habitat loss (e.g. due to logging, agriculture, cyclones), introduced species

Biological importance ● ● ●
Current threat level ● ● ●

Area 3,000 km² **Altitude** 0–1,800 m
Countries American Samoa (to USA), Western Samoa

Restricted-range species	Threatened	Total
Confined to this EBA	5	11
Present also in other EBAs, SAs	0	9
Total	5	20

■ General characteristics

This EBA includes the volcanic islands of Savai'i and 'Upolu and their offshore islands (constituting the political unit of Western Samoa), and the more easterly ones of Tutuila and Manu'a (which make up American Samoa, a US dependent territory).

The native vegetation is largely tropical rain forest which can be subdivided into lowland and montane types, with disturbed forests resulting from the destructive effects of cyclones. Cloud forest occurs above c.1,200 m on Savai'i (which reaches a maximum altitude of 1,848 m at Mt Silisili), and scrubby upland vegetation occurs on peaks and summits. Mangroves are also present and are particularly well developed along the south coast of 'Upolu (see Whistler 1992, 1993).

■ Restricted-range species

All the restricted-range bird species occur in forest but many are also found in plantations and gardens. This use of man-modified environments may be important for the survival of some indigenous species, given the severe loss of native habitat as a result of man's activities and cyclonic storms (see 'Threats and conservation', below; Evans *et al.* 1992b). Some species, however, notably *Didunculus strigirostris* and *Gymnomyza samoensis*, are dependent on remaining patches of primary forest, and conservation of sufficient areas of native habitat thus remains vital.

Although many species are found in upland forest, these may not be their preferred altitudes.

Distributional patterns of species within the EBA vary (see 'Distribution patterns' table), with 10 restricted-range species (now) occurring only in Western Samoa. Two of these are confined to Savai'i: *Zosterops samoensis*, which has a particularly tiny distribution in the unique cloud forest and alpine scrub around Mt Silisili, and *Gallinula pacifica*, which was last recorded in 1873 and consequently is often listed as extinct, but two possible sightings in 1987 in upland forest west of Mt Elietoga (Bellingham and Davis 1988) indicate that it may still survive. *Gallicolumba stairi* also has a very restricted range within this EBA, as it was not found on Savai'i and 'Upolu during a recent lowland survey and may now be restricted to the small offshore Aleipata Islands (which are important nesting sites for many seabird species) (D. J. Butler *in litt.* 1993), while in American Samoa it is only known from Ofu where a single bird was sighted in 1993 (P. W. Trail *in litt.* 1995).

Several of the more widespread restricted-range species are shared with the Fijian Islands EBA (202) and/or occur more widely in Central Polynesian Secondary Areas (s127–s131).

Manu'a Fiji Shrikebill *Clytorhynchus vitiensis powelli* is endemic to the Manu'a Islands in American Samoa and is the most distinctive of the many subspecies of this widespread Polynesian bird, and a

Status and habitat of restricted-range species

Species (ordered taxonomically)	Global status	Other EBAs (and SAs)	Habitat
Samoan Moorhen *Gallinula pacifica*	CR	—	Forest
Shy Ground-dove *Gallicolumba stairi*[1]	nt	202 (s128,s130)	Forest inc. gallery forest and bamboo thickets, scrubby bush on smaller islands
Many-coloured Fruit-dove *Ptilinopus perousii*	lc	202 (s130)	Forest, well-developed secondary forest (specialises on fruits of large banyan trees *Ficus* sp.)
Purple-capped Fruit-dove *Ptilinopus porphyraceus*	lc	192,202 (s123[X], s127,s128,s129, s130,s131)	Any wooded habitat inc. forest, secondary forest
Tooth-billed Pigeon *Didunculus strigirostris*	VU	—	Forest, forest edge at 300–1,400 m; unable to adapt to areas with exotic species that have been logged/replanted
Blue-crowned Lorikeet *Vini australis*	lc	202 (s128,s129, s130,s131)	All habitats with suitable flowering trees, inc. secondary forest, plantations
Flat-billed Kingfisher *Todirhamphus recurvirostris*	lc	—	Forest, forest clearings, along bush tracks and streams, plantations, suburban areas
Polynesian Triller *Lalage maculosa*	lc	200,202 (s127, s128,s130,s131)	All habitats inc. forest, forest edge, secondary forest, gardens, parks
Samoan Triller *Lalage sharpei*	nt	—	Forest, forest edge
Fiji Shrikebill *Clytorhynchus vitiensis*	lc	202 (s127,s128, s130)	Forest, well-developed secondary forest
Samoan Flycatcher *Myiagra albiventris*	VU	—	Forest, forest edge
Samoan Fantail *Rhipidura nebulosa*	lc	—	Forest, secondary growth, roadside brush, edges of fields, gardens
Samoan Whistler *Pachycephala flavifrons*	lc	—	Forest, secondary forest, plantations, gardens
Samoan White-eye *Zosterops samoensis*	VU	—	Montane forest (recorded 780 m and above), forest edge, scrub-like habitat of alpine zone
Cardinal Myzomela *Myzomela cardinalis*	lc	198,199,200,201	Forest, forest edge, secondary growth, mangroves, plantations, gardens, suburban areas
Wattled Honeyeater *Foulehaio carunculata*	lc	202 (s128,s130)	All habitats inc. forest, coastal scrub, mangroves, gardens, suburban areas
Mao *Gymnomyza samoensis*	VU	—	Forest; recorded visiting coconut palms but appears largely dependent on primary forest
Red-headed Parrotfinch *Erythrura cyaneovirens*	lc	—	Forest, well-developed secondary forest
Samoan Starling *Aplonis atrifusca*	lc	—	Forest, plantations, coastal scrub, gardens, suburban areas
Polynesian Starling *Aplonis tabuensis*	lc	200,202 (s127, s128,s129,s130, s131)	Forest, well-developed secondary forest

Global status (see p. 679 for definitions)	EX Extinct EW Extinct in the Wild	} with year of last record	cd Conservation Dependent	**Other EBAs (and SAs)** (see p. 90 for locations)	Bracketed numbers are Secondary Areas. [X] Extinct in that EBA or SA.
			nt Near Threatened		
	CR Critical EN Endangered VU Vulnerable	} threatened species	lc Least Concern DD Data Deficient NE Not Evaluated	**Notes**	[1] Introduced to Abemama, Gilbert Islands (Secondary Area s125).

good candidate for elevation to species status (H. D. Pratt *in litt.* 1994). For the most complete data on American Samoan bird populations before the cyclones of 1991 and 1992, see Engbring and Ramsey (1989), also Amerson *et al.* (1982a,b).

■ Threats and conservation

In Western Samoa, the total remaining forest comprises 23% of the land area of 'Upolu and 47% of Savai'i; most of the original lowland forest has been cleared for agriculture or logged for timber, with perhaps only five tracts remaining and encroachment

Distribution patterns of restricted-range species

Species (ordered geographically)	Savai'i	'Upolu	Tutuila	Manu'a	Other EBAs, SAs
Gallinula pacifica	O	–	–	–	–
Zosterops samoensis	●	–	–	–	–
Didunculus strigirostris	●	●	–	–	–
Todirhamphus recurvirostris	●	●	–	–	–
Lalage sharpei	●	●	–	–	–
Myiagra albiventris	●	●	–	–	–
Rhipidura nebulosa	●	●	–	–	–
Pachycephala flavifrons	●	●	–	–	–
Erythrura cyaneovirens	●	●	–	–	–
Lalage maculosa	●	●	–	–	⊛
Gymnomyza samoensis	●	●	X	–	–
Myzomela cardinalis	●	●	●	–	⊛
Gallicolumba stairi	O	O	–	●	⊛
Vini australis	●	●	–	●	⊛
Aplonis atrifusca	●	●	●	●	–
Ptilinopus perousii	●	●	●	●	⊛
Ptilinopus porphyraceus	●	●	●	●	⊛
Foulehaio carunculata	●	●	●	●	⊛
Aplonis tabuensis	●	●	●	●	⊛
Clytorhynchus vitiensis	–	–	–	●	⊛
Total	19	17	6	8	

● Present ? Present? Threatened spp. shown in **bold** see 'Status and habitat' table
O Extinct? R Reintroduced Other EBAs, SAs
X Extinct I Introduced

inland into montane areas. Following clearance, often only one or two successive crops are grown before the land is abandoned, resulting in heavy erosion and the formation of dense secondary scrub vegetation dominated by weedy species (Davis *et al.* 1986, Taulealo 1993, WWF/IUCN 1994–1995; see also Paulson 1994). On American Samoa about two-thirds of the native vegetation has been disturbed or cleared for settlements or agriculture (Davis *et al.* 1986).

In addition to the severe loss of native habitat through human activities, cyclonic storms can cause extensive damage: tree mortality from this cause was 28% in 1990 and 33% in 1991 (Elmqvist *et al.* 1994). Forests have the capacity to recover rapidly, but damage can be sufficient to allow cattle-grazing and taro-planting in some areas that had previously been little modified (B. D. Bell *in litt.* 1993, H. D. Pratt *in litt.* 1994), and the effects may thus be longer term. Invasion by aggressive exotic weeds is an additional hazard, and on 'Upolu the so-called mile-a-minute vine *Mikania micrantha* still chokes large areas of former forest and may be preventing regeneration (H. D. Pratt *in litt.* 1995), while on Ta'u the weed Koster's curse *Clidema hirta* has spread dramatically and forms nearly impenetrable tangles above c.450 m; this latter may have reduced habitat quality for *Clytorhynchus vitiensis powelli* (P. W. Trail *in litt.* 1995). Furthermore, the rate of forest regeneration may be substantially affected by the large reduction of the whole guild of vertebrate seed-dispersers including two species of flying fox *Pteropus samoensis* and *P. tonganus*, and several species of fruit-pigeons, e.g. Pacific Pigeon *Ducula pacifica* and *Ptilinopus perousii* (Elmqvist *et al.* 1994).

Several of Samoa's restricted-range species are classified as threatened or Near Threatened, largely as the result of deforestation, particularly combined with the severe effects of the recent cyclones, which have caused declines in bird populations (see, e.g., Trail *et al.* 1992). Hunting is an additional pressure which increases as the forest habitat diminishes, especially for the columbids, and notably for the distinctive *Didunculus strigirostris* which has been the subject of a number of studies (e.g. Beichle 1982, 1987) and has recently been chosen as a flagship

This forest on 'Upolu, Western Samoa, has suffered severe damage from the effects of two hurricanes.

H. D. Pratt

species to promote conservation awareness in Western Samoa.

Introduced mammals, such as cats and rats, are thought to have contributed to the decline of *Gallinula pacifica* (which is believed to be almost flightless and will therefore be especially vulnerable to predation) and may also affect other species, including the threatened (Vulnerable) restricted-range Bristle-thighed Curlew *Numenius tahitiensis*, which breeds in Western Alaska (Secondary Area s002) and winters among Pacific islands (including the islands of this EBA) where it undergoes a flightless moult.

The state of the environment in Western Samoa is described in Taulealo (1993) and National Environment and Development Management Strategies are documented in SPREP (1993). A recent lowland forest survey in Western Samoa identified 14 key sites as critically in need of protection to conserve biodiversity, with five identified as being of international significance (Park *et al.* 1992, Sesega and Park 1993). This survey and a later follow-up one (Lovegrove *et al.* 1992) documented the serious impacts of the cyclones on birds.

There are a few protected areas in Western Samoa (see Beichle and Maelzer 1985), including the O Le Pupu Puʻe National Park (28 km²) on ʻUpolu where restricted-range birds are present (Bellingham and Davis 1988), but this park was heavily damaged following recent cyclones, and logging and cattle-farming are continuing threats. Mt Vaea, a small forested ridge on the outskirts of Western Samoa's

SPREP

Billboard in the centre of Apia, the capital of Western Samoa. Tooth-billed Pigeon *Didunculus strigirostris*, a highly distinctive columbid in its own genus, has recently been chosen as a flagship species to promote conservation awareness in the country.

capital, Apia, is also partly protected, although surrounded by an increasingly urbanized landscape. Two areas on Savaiʻi—the Falealupo and Tafua Rainforest Preserves—are protected under local conservation agreements, but both were severely damaged by the recent cyclones and part of Tafua was further destroyed by a forest fire shortly thereafter (Elmqvist 1993, Elmqvist *et al.* 1994, D. J. Butler *in litt.* 1993, P. W. Trail *in litt.* 1993). The National Park of American Samoa was officially established in January 1994 and includes important forest areas on Tuila and Taʻu (P. W. Trail *in litt.* 1995).

204 Lord Howe Island

PRIORITY
CRITICAL

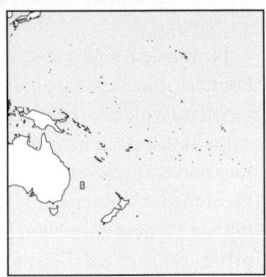

Key habitats Lowland rain forest, palm forest, mossy forest

Main threats Limited habitat loss (e.g. due to farming, settlements), introduced species

Biological importance ● ●

Current threat level ● ● ●

Area 17 km²   Altitude 0–800 m

Countries Australia

Restricted-range species	Threatened	Total
Confined to this EBA	2	2
Present also in other EBAs, SAs	0	0
Total	2	2

■ General characteristics

The small oceanic island of Lord Howe lies 600 km east of the mainland of Australia, to which it belongs politically, being included in the state of New South Wales. There are several small rocky islets around the periphery of the island, including the Admiralty group, Rabbit and Mutton Bird Islands, and Ball's Pyramid, a monolithic spire which rises to c.550 m some 20 km to the south-west.

On Lord Howe, two mountains, Gower (the highest at 875 m) and Lidgbird, dominate the landscape which is covered in forest including evergreen rain forest, palm forest, *Pandanus* forest and mossy forest at higher altitudes; scrub vegetation, small areas of grassland and mangroves also occur (WWF/IUCN 1994–1995). The island is reported to have the world's southernmost coral reef.

■ Restricted-range species

Of all the Pacific's EBAs, Lord Howe Island has the third-greatest number (four) of restricted-range species to have become extinct since 1800 (after the Hawaiian EBAs, 217 and 218).

Both of the extant restricted-range species occur in forest, but *Gallirallus sylvestris* favours palm forests at lower altitudes and mossy forest at higher altitudes (and is rarely found in rain forest), and therefore has a restricted distribution within the island, while *Zosterops tephropleurus* occurs in all wooded habitats and is widespread.

In addition to its restricted-range species, several endemic subspecies occur or occurred on Lord Howe Island, and a couple of seabirds with tiny breeding ranges nest on the island or on small islets nearby (see 'Threats and conservation', below).

■ Threats and conservation

Given that less than 10% of the native vegetation on Lord Howe Island has been cleared for farming and settlements, it is perhaps surprising that four of the six restricted-range birds which occurred there in historical times are extinct and that a number of subspecies have also been extirpated, e.g. White-throated Pigeon *Columba vitiensis godmanae* (last seen in 1853), Kakariki *Cyanoramphus novae-zelandiae subflavescens* (1869), Boobook *Ninox novaeseelandiae albaria* (1950s), Grey Fantail *Rhipidura fuliginosa cervina* (1924) and Vinous-tinted Thrush *Turdus poliocephalus vinitinctus* (1913) (Garnett 1993).

However, several taxa, including *Porphyrio albus*, were eliminated by visiting sailors prior to settlement, and it is likely that the effects of introduced species (cats, rats, dogs, pigs, goats), and particularly predation by introduced black rats *Rattus rattus*, accounted for the rest. *Zosterops strenuus*, for example, was

Lord Howe Island

AUSTRALIA

Admiralty Is.

Rabbit I.

Mutton Bird I.

Mt Lidgbird

Mt Gower

0   1 km

Status and habitat of restricted-range species

Species (ordered taxonomically)	Global status	Other EBAs (and SAs)	Habitat
Lord Howe Island Rail *Gallirallus sylvestris*	EN	—	Mainly mossy forest at higher altitudes, recently reintroduced to lowland palm forest
Lord Howe Island Swamphen *Porphyrio albus*	EX (1834)	—	Presumably swamps
Lord Howe Island Gerygone *Gerygone insularis*	EX (1938)	—	Forest
Lord Howe Island White-eye *Zosterops tephropleurus*	VU	—	All wooded habitats inc. open scrub and secondary growth
Robust White-eye *Zosterops strenuus*	EX (1920)	—	Lowland forest
Norfolk Island Starling *Aplonis fusca*	EX (1923)	205[X]	All forested habitats

Global status (see p. 679 for definitions): EX Extinct, EW Extinct in the Wild (with year of last record); CR Critical, EN Endangered, VU Vulnerable (threatened species); cd Conservation Dependent, nt Near Threatened, lc Least Concern; DD Data Deficient, NE Not Evaluated

Other EBAs (and SAs) (see p. 90 for locations): bracketed numbers are Secondary Areas; [X] extinct in that EBA or SA.

formerly numerous in lowland forest, but disappeared soon after an invasion of rats following a shipwreck in 1918. Various non-native owls, particularly Masked Owl *Tyto novaehollandiae*, which were introduced between 1922 and 1930 to combat the rat plague, resulted in the disappearance of *Ninox novaeseelandiae albaria* (Garnett 1993).

Predator control (including the elimination of feral cats, neutering of domestic ones, and a strict policy of non replacement), and the elimination of pigs and goats, coupled with intensive study, captive breeding and release, has resulted in the improving status of *Gallirallus sylvestris*, which was close to extinction in the 1970s (fewer than 30 birds) but is now much more secure (more than 200 birds). However, predation by introduced *Tyto novaehollandiae* remains an important threat, and was thought to be responsible for a major decline in one population in 1989 (Brouwer and Garnett 1990, Garnett 1993).

Zosterops tephropleurus has apparently adapted successfully to the presence of rats but remains vulnerable on account of its tiny range, as do several extant subspecies which are treated as 'Of Special Concern' in Garnett (1993) including Golden Whistler *Pachycephala pectoralis contempta*, Silvereye *Zosterops lateralis chlorocephala* and Pied Currawong *Strepera graculina crissalis*.

One species and one subspecies of seabird with very restricted breeding ranges occur on Lord Howe Island: Providence Petrel *Pterodroma solandri* (classified as Vulnerable), which nests in burrows and rock crevices on the forested upper slopes of Mts Lidgbird and Gower (and is only known to breed elsewhere on Philip Island near Norfolk Island, EBA 205), and White-bellied Storm Petrel *Fregatta grallaria grallaria*, which was eliminated from rocky outcrops on Lord Howe Island by feral cats and rats about 1913, and is now confined to nearby islets with a small breeding population on the Kermadec Islands north of New Zealand (Marchant and Higgins 1990).

In 1982 the Lord Howe Island group was designated a World Heritage Site.

205 Norfolk Island

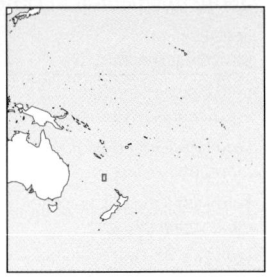

Key habitats Lowland rain forest

Main threats Major habitat loss (e.g. due to agriculture, timber exploitation), introduced species

Biological importance ● ●

Current threat level ● ● ●

Area 35 km² **Altitude** 0–300 m

Countries Norfolk Island (to Australia)

Restricted-range species	Threatened	Total
Confined to this EBA	3	3
Present also in other EBAs, SAs	0	0
Total	3	3

■ General characteristics

Norfolk Island, an Australian external territory, is an isolated, volcanic outcrop (reaching 318 m at Mt Bates) between New Caledonia (EBA 201) and the North Island of New Zealand (EBA 206), some 1,300 km east of mainland Australia. Two other islands, Nepean and the larger Philip Island, complete the Norfolk Island group.

Norfolk Island was originally largely covered in thick subtropical rain forest including pine forest dominated by the endemic Norfolk Island pine *Araucaria heterophylla*, mixed hardwood forest, palm and tree-fern forest.

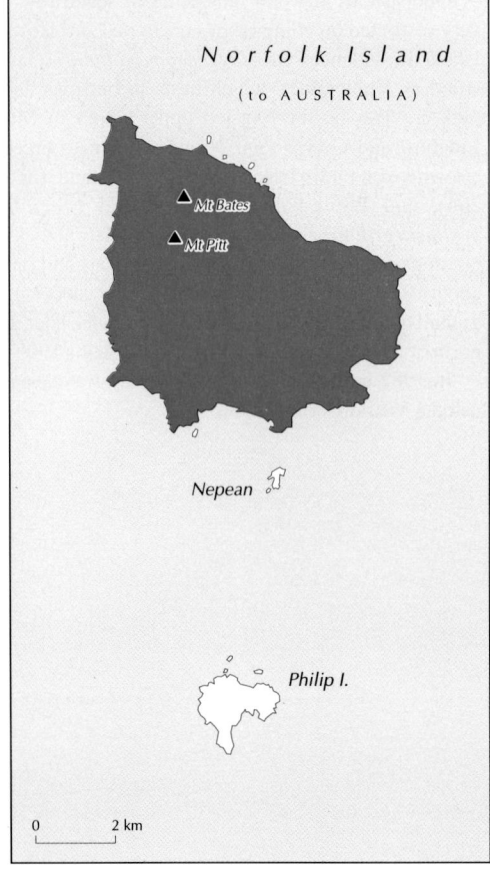

Norfolk Island
(to AUSTRALIA)

△ Mt Bates
△ Mt Pitt

Nepean

Philip I.

0   2 km

■ Restricted-range species

All the extant restricted-range birds occur in forest, with *Gerygone modesta* and *Zosterops tenuirostris* adapting well to secondary habitats (see Schodde *et al.* 1983, Hermes 1985). Norfolk Island has lost three of its restricted-range species: one still occurs elsewhere, but two are globally extinct. An additional extinct species, Norfolk Island Ground-dove *Gallicolumba norfolciensis*, not recorded since 1800, is known only from a drawing and written observations.

Several endemic subspecies also occur or occurred on Norfolk Island, and two seabirds with tiny breeding ranges nest on nearby Philip Island (see 'Threats and conservation', below).

■ Threats and conservation

Forest on Norfolk Island has been greatly reduced by clearance for agriculture and settlement, and has been disturbed by timber exploitation, uncontrolled cattle-grazing and the introduction of a wide range of exotic plant species (many of which have become invasive, e.g. red guava *Psidium guajava* and lantana *Lantana camara* which supplant native species beneath forest canopies).

Native vegetation now exists only in limited areas around Mts Pitt and Bates, and other pockets are so small and isolated as to be almost inconsequential (Schodde *et al.* 1983, WWF/IUCN 1994–1995).

One species largely confined to forest, namely *Zosterops albogularis*, is consequently considered highly threatened. Predation by black rats is also a serious threat to this species, compounded by predation by feral cats and competition from the Silvereye *Z. lateralis* which colonized the island at the beginning of the twentieth century; the last confirmed record of *Z. albogularis* was in 1980 although local people consistently report small numbers of birds fitting its description and it is therefore not treated as extinct (Garnett 1993). Both *Gerygone modesta* and *Z. tenuirostris* are classified as threatened, despite being common, on account of their tiny ranges, which render them forever vulnerable to chance events.

Status and habitat of restricted-range species

Species (ordered taxonomically)	Global status	Other EBAs (and SAs)	Habitat
Norfolk Island Kaka *Nestor productus*	EX (1851)	—	Forest, rocky areas
Long-tailed Triller *Lalage leucopyga*[1]	lc	198,200,201	Forest, forest edge, secondary growth, plantations, gardens, coastal vegetation
Norfolk Island Gerygone *Gerygone modesta*	VU	—	Forest, scrub, gardens
Slender-billed White-eye *Zosterops tenuirostris*	VU	—	Forest, tall secondary growth
White-chested White-eye *Zosterops albogularis*	CR	—	Forest
Norfolk Island Starling *Aplonis fusca*	EX (1923)	204[X]	Forest

Global status (see p. 679 for definitions)	EX Extinct	} with year of last record	cd Conservation Dependent	Other EBAs (and SAs) (see p. 90 for locations)	Bracketed numbers are Secondary Areas. [X] Extinct in that EBA or SA.
	EW Extinct in the Wild		nt Near Threatened		
	CR Critical	} threatened species	lc Least Concern	Notes	[1] Extinct in this EBA (1942).
	EN Endangered		DD Data Deficient		
	VU Vulnerable		NE Not Evaluated		

Several endemic subspecies of birds are listed as threatened or extinct by Garnett (1993), also largely owing to habitat loss and degradation, and the effects of introduced species: New Zealand Pigeon *Hemiphaga novaeseelandiae spadicea* (last recorded in 1900, and treated as extinct), Norfolk Island Boobook *Ninox novaeseelandiae undulata* (a sole surviving female in 1986, but see Olsen 1996), Norfolk Island Parakeet *Cyanoramphus novaezelandiae cookii* (treated as a full species by Sibley and Monroe 1990; c.40 birds in 1991) Scarlet Robin *Petroica multicolor multicolor*, Golden Whistler *Pachycephala pectoralis xanthoprocta* and Grey-headed Blackbird *Turdus poliocephalus poliocephalus* (last seen in 1975 and thought to be probably extinct).

A seabird with a very restricted breeding range (otherwise known to breed only on Lord Howe Island, EBA 204), Providence Petrel *Pterodroma solandri*, was exterminated from Norfolk Island between 1790 and 1800 by hunting and by the effects of introduced pests such as pigs and goats (Marchant and Higgins 1990), but small colonies have recently been reported from Philip Island, as have colonies of White-necked Petrel *P. cervicalis*—which is known to breed elsewhere only on Macauley Island (2 km²) in the Kermadec Islands of New Zealand. Both species are considered threatened (Vulnerable) on account of their tiny breeding ranges.

The declaration in 1986 of the Norfolk Island National Park (formerly the Mount Pitt Reserve), which encompasses the main remaining stands of native forest (4.6 km²), may ensure the long-term survival of the surviving endemic landbirds, especially as steps are being taken to reduce rat and cat predation within the park (Brouwer and Garnett 1990).

206 North Island of New Zealand

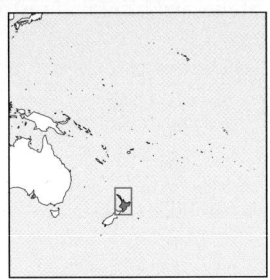

Key habitats Temperate forest (esp. on offshore islands), wetlands

Main threats Major habitat loss (e.g. due to pasture, plantations), introduced species

Biological importance ● ● ●
Current threat level ● ● ●

Area 120,000 km² **Altitude** 0–2,000 m

Countries New Zealand

Restricted-range species	Threatened	Total
Confined to this EBA	2	3
Present also in other EBAs, SAs	0	0
Total	2	3

■ General characteristics

This EBA includes the North Island of New Zealand and its offshore islands, most notably Little Barrier and Kapiti, which are important refuges for many native birds. Mountain ranges extend in a line from Cook Strait to East Cape, with volcanic mountains being prominent landmarks, especially in the centre of the island where some are still active.

The characteristic vegetation is podocarp and mixed hardwood forest, with kauri *Agathis australis* often the dominant tree species in the warmer northern parts. The southern beech *Nothofagus* predominates in forest at higher altitudes, until true forest gives way to a narrow belt of subalpine forest, and ultimately to various scrub and shrubland communities, and tussock grassland.

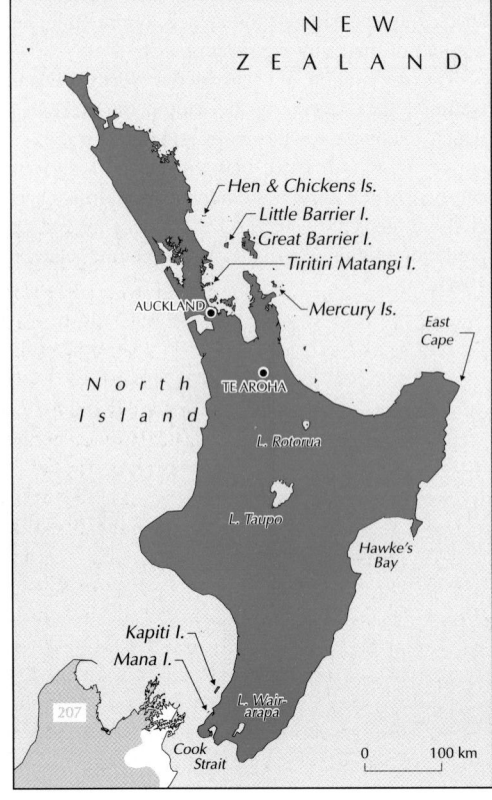

■ Restricted-range species

The historical and current distributions of the restricted-range birds vary considerably. The main breeding population of *Poliocephalus rufopectus* is scattered in north Auckland, Rotorua and Taupo lake districts, Hawkes Bay and Wairarapa, and the west coast dune lakes. *Coenocorypha aucklandica* seems to have survived on Little Barrier Island until c.1870, and a form (known only from subfossils) was widespread on North Island but was probably rare or extinct by the time of Polynesian settlement. *Mohoua albicilla* formerly occurred throughout North Island but is restricted today to forests south of Te Aroha and East Cape, and to the offshore islands of Little Barrier, Kapiti and Tiritiri (where it is introduced). *Notiomystis cincta* was comparatively common in the south of North Island up to the 1870s but declined rapidly thereafter, and only survives on offshore islands including Little Barrier and (as a result of transfers) Hen, Kapiti and Tiritiri; also, following transfer, on Mokoia Island in Lake Rotorua. *Heterolocha acutirostris* was recorded historically from the forests of eastern and southern North Island, with the last generally accepted record in 1907.

An additional two restricted-range species occur in this EBA: Takahe *Porphyrio mantelli*, from South Island (EBA 207), has been introduced to the offshore islands of Kapiti, Tiritiri and Mana; and Wrybill *Anarhynchus frontalis*, also from South Island, winters in the north of North Island.

Four further species are largely confined to or have important breeding populations in this EBA, but are judged to have had historical ranges greater than 50,000 km² and are therefore not treated as having restricted ranges: Little Spotted Kiwi *Apteryx owenii* persists on Kapiti and has been introduced to the islands of Red Mercury, Hen and Tiritiri; Kakapo *Strigops habroptilus* has been introduced to Little Barrier; Kokako *Calleas cinerea* is sporadically distributed in the central and northern forests of North Island and introduced on the islands of Little Barrier and Kapiti; and Saddleback *Philesturnus carunculatus* survives as the result of introductions on some 10 offshore islands.

Status and habitat of restricted-range species

Species (ordered taxonomically)	Global status	Other EBAs (and SAs)	Habitat
New Zealand Dabchick *Poliocephalus rufopectus*	EN	—	Small bodies of fresh water, e.g. sand-dune lakes, lagoons, inland lakes, artificial farm dams
New Zealand Snipe *Coenocorypha aucklandica*[1]	nt	208 (s132,s133)	Damper areas of grassland, tussock, scrub or forest
Whitehead *Mohoua albicilla*	lc	—	Prefers to breed in forest and manuka scrub, can live in exotic pine forest
Stitchbird *Notiomystis cincta*	VU	—	Forest
Huia *Heteralocha acutirostris*	EX (1907)	—	Forest

Global status (see p. 679 for definitions)	EX Extinct EW Extinct in the Wild } with year of last record	cd Conservation Dependent nt Near Threatened	Other EBAs (and SAs) (see p. 90 for locations)	Bracketed numbers are Secondary Areas. [X] Extinct in that EBA or SA.
	CR Critical EN Endangered } threatened species VU Vulnerable	lc Least Concern DD Data Deficient NE Not Evaluated	Notes	[1] Extinct in this EBA c.1870.

■ Threats and conservation

The forests of New Zealand, which once covered most of the islands, have been reduced by Polynesian and European settlers to less than 25% of their former extent, mostly in the mountains, and replaced by scrub, fernland, grassland, pasture and plantations of exotic softwoods. Wetlands have also diminished such that only c.8% of the original now remains (Davis *et al.* 1986, Jones *et al.* 1995c). This habitat destruction (and the resulting fragmentation), coupled with the introduction of a variety of mammals and European birds, has largely caused the extinction and decline in the ranges and numbers of many endemic birds (King 1984).

Two restricted-range species are classified as threatened: *Poliocephalus rufopectus* is considered to be at risk from changes in water quality, destruction of nesting habitat, disturbance, and (especially when nesting) predation by introduced rats and mustelids; *Notiomystis cincta* is thought to have been exterminated from the mainland as a result of predation, disease and collecting. *Mohoua albicilla*, however, remains relatively widespread and is not considered threatened, but has also declined, albeit slowly, being regarded as formerly abundant but now only moderately common.

There are many other threatened landbirds in this EBA, historically widespread, but many now with much reduced ranges, e.g. Brown Kiwi *Apteryx australis* (Vulnerable; the North Island race *mantelli* is treated as a full species by Baker *et al.* 1995), *A. owenii* (Vulnerable; see 'Restricted-range species', above), Australasian Bittern *Botaurus poiciloptilus* (Endangered), Blue Duck *Hymenolaimus malacorhynchus* (Vulnerable), Brown Teal *Anas aucklandica* (Vulnerable; the race *chlorotis* occurs on North Island and Great Barrier Island, and is treated as a full species by Marchant and Higgins 1990), *Porphyrio*

mantelli (Endangered; see above), New Zealand Dotterel *Charadrius obscurus* (Endangered), *Anarhynchus frontalis* (Vulnerable; see above), Black Stilt *Himantopus novaezelandiae* (Critical; part of the population winters in the north of North Island), *Strigops habroptilus* (Extinct in the Wild; see above), New Zealand Kaka *Nestor meridionalis* (Vulnerable), *Callaeas cinerea* (Endangered; see above). *Philesturnus carunculatus* (see above) is classified as Conservation Dependent following successful reintroduction to offshore islands and an increasing population of over 2,000 birds.

Three threatened seabirds, all Vulnerable, are endemic breeders on offshore islands: Cook's Petrel *Pterodroma cookii* (also on Codfish Island off Stewart Island), Pycroft's Petrel *P. pycrofti* and Black Petrel *Procellaria parkinsoni*. Fairy Tern *Sterna nereis*, also Vulnerable but found elsewhere, breeds only on the northern coasts of North Island.

The New Zealand protected-area system is among the most comprehensive in the world, consisting of more than 2,000 individual areas and covering almost 20% of the total land area including many island refuges. However, many areas of native habitat on the mainland continue to be threatened: by the spread of the introduced Australian brush-tailed opossum *Trichosurus vulpecula* (a destructive herbivore, and recently shown to take eggs and chicks of *Callaeas cinerea*: D. Cunningham *in litt.* 1995), by increasing damage by feral goats and deer, by proliferation of exotic plants, and by the spread of wild conifers (IUCN 1992c); predation by introduced mammals also remains a major threat to many bird species. Much conservation effort has been concentrated on the restoration of offshore islands where predator eradication is feasible, and, increasingly, on the temporary control of predators on mainland habitat 'islands' (see, e.g., Ogden 1995).

207 | South Island of New Zealand

PRIORITY
URGENT

Key habitats Temperate forest, subalpine/alpine vegetation, braided rivers

Main threats Moderate habitat loss, introduced species

Biological importance ● ● ●
Current threat level ● ● ●

Area 110,000 km²   **Altitude** 0–2,500 m

Countries New Zealand

Restricted-range species	Threatened	Total
Confined to this EBA	4	6
Present also in other EBAs, SAs	0	0
Total	4	6

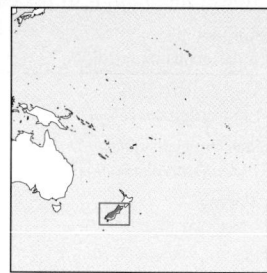

■ General characteristics

This EBA encompasses the Southern Alps and Fiordland of New Zealand's South Island, reaching 3,754 m on Mt Cook and including the upper reaches of eastward-flowing rivers such as the Rakaia and Waitaki. The 1,000 m contour is used to define the eastern boundary of the EBA because most restricted-range birds are thus confined. Offshore islands are also included as they are important refuges for many native birds.

The characteristic vegetation is forest: southern beech *Nothofagus* predominates, with podocarp or mixed forest in some areas including extensive lowland tracts. At higher altitude true forest gives way to a narrow belt of subalpine forest, and ultimately to various scrub and shrub communities, through to tussock grassland.

■ Restricted-range species

Distributions within this EBA vary. *Nestor notabilis*, *Xenicus gilviventris* and *Mohoua ochrocephala* largely occur throughout Fiordland and the Southern Alps, although *M. ochrocephala* has declined considerably in the last 20 years. *Apteryx haastii* is widespread only in north-west Nelson, the Paparoa Range and near Arthur's Pass in the Southern Alps. *Porphyrio mantelli* survives in the Murchison and Stuart mountains of Fiordland, and has an introduced population on the offshore island of Maud. *Anarhynchus frontalis* breeds on some 10 major river systems in Canterbury and northern Otago. *Xenicus lyalli* was discovered on Stephens Island in 1894, but became extinct shortly thereafter.

Two further species are confined to or have important breeding populations in this EBA, but are

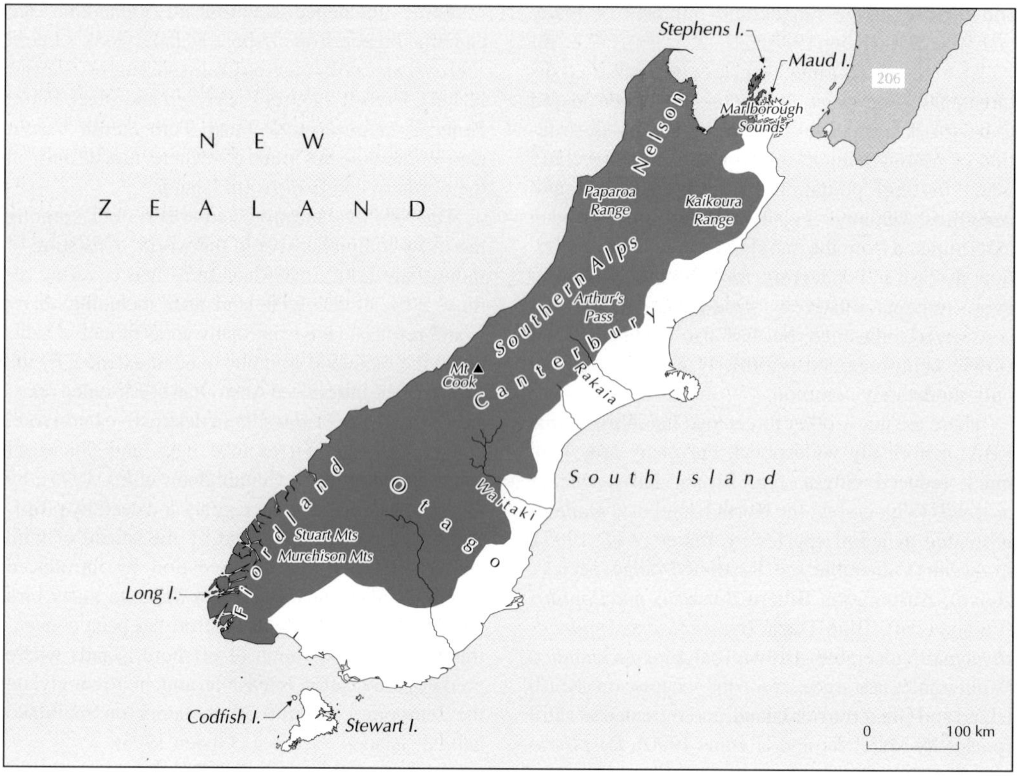

Status and habitat of restricted-range species

Species (ordered taxonomically)	Global status	Habitat
Great Spotted Kiwi *Apteryx haastii*	VU	Mixed beech forest, scrub-covered coastal pasture, subalpine tussock grassland
Takahe *Porphyrio mantelli*[1]	EN	Originally widespread in forest and grass ecosystems, now alpine tussock grassland and fringing beech forest (750–1,200 m)
Wrybill *Anarhynchus frontalis*[2]	VU	Breeds on shingle (braided) riverbeds and deltas, winters on mudflats
Kea *Nestor notabilis*	nt	Forest for nesting (usu. 760+ m), apparently needs alpine scrub above treeline for feeding
South Island Rock Wren *Xenicus gilviventris*	nt	Rocky areas, alpine scrub (usu. 900–2,500 m)
Stephens Island Wren *Xenicus lyalli*	EX (1894)	Presumably rocky areas, scrub
Yellowhead *Mohoua ochrocephala*	VU	Native forest, prefers beech

Global status (see p. 679 for definitions)

EX	Extinct	cd	Conservation Dependent
EW	Extinct in the Wild	with year of last record	
		nt	Near Threatened
CR	Critical	lc	Least Concern
EN	Endangered	threatened species	DD	Data Deficient
VU	Vulnerable	NE	Not Evaluated

Other EBAs (and SAs) (see p. 90 for locations)
Bracketed numbers are Secondary Areas. [x] Extinct in that EBA or SA.

Notes
[1] Introduced to Kapiti, Tiritiri and Mana Islands, North Island (EBA 206).
[2] Winters in North Island (EBA 206).

judged to have had historical ranges greater than 50,000 km²: Black Stilt *Himantopus novaezelandiae* today breeds in the upper Waitaki valley only; Kakapo *Strigops habroptilus* survives within this EBA (following introduction) only on Maud Island.

■ Threats and conservation

All the restricted-range species are considered threatened or Near Threatened, owing largely to introduced predators and competitors. *Porphyrio mantelli* has declined through competition for food from red deer *Cervus elaphus* and predation by stoats *Mustela erminea*. *Apteryx haastii* is declining in some areas owing to predation by introduced mammals (possums, mustelids, cats and dogs). *Mohoua ochrocephala* has periodic population crashes in response to the stoat irruptions that follow major beech-mast production and subsequent mice plagues; it has disappeared from some of the best habitat in northern South Island, perhaps because of introduced wasps which compete for 'honey dew' (an important food source in beech forest). *Anarhynchus frontalis* is subject to predation by stoats and cats, but also suffers from a decline in the quality of nesting habitat owing to encroachment of weeds as hydroelectric schemes reduce seasonal flooding of riverbeds.

The many other threatened landbirds in this EBA were historically widespread, although many have very restricted ranges today. They include Brown Kiwi *Apteryx australis* (Vulnerable; the race *australis* which occurs in Fiordland and on Stewart Island is treated as a full species by Baker *et al.* 1995, Little Spotted Kiwi *A. owenii* (Vulnerable; only Long

Island in this EBA), Australasian Bittern *Botaurus poiciloptilus* (Endangered), Blue Duck *Hymenolaimus malacorhynchus* (Vulnerable), *Himantopus novaezelandiae* (Critical; see 'Restricted-range species', above), New Zealand Kaka *Nestor meridionalis* (Vulnerable) and *Strigops habroptilus* (Extinct in the Wild; see above).

Several threatened seabirds are largely endemic to this EBA when breeding, including Hutton's Shearwater *Puffinus huttoni* (Endangered; Kaikoura Range), Fiordland Penguin *Eudyptes pachyrhynchus* (Vulnerable), Westland Petrel *Procellaria westlandica* (Vulnerable), New Zealand King Shag *Phalacrocorax carunculatus* (Vulnerable; stacks in the Marlborough Sounds) and Black-fronted Tern *Chlidonias albostriatus* (Vulnerable).

There has been much conservation action within this EBA (see, e.g., Lambert and Moritz 1995) and c.40–50% of the total area lies within protected areas, notably Fiordland and Kahurangi national parks. Major conservation programmes involving captive breeding and release, introductions and predator control are targeted at *Porphyrio mantelli*, *Himantopus novaezealandiae* and *Strigops habroptilus* (e.g. Clout and Craig 1995). There is growing concern, however, about the fragmentation of habitat and the impact of this on small relict populations with little or no gene flow between them. Increased tourism is expected to act to the detriment of surviving wild areas, and consequently there is a need to balance the desire for people to enjoy wildlife with the need to protect vulnerable species from excessive disturbance (D. Cunningham *in litt.* 1995).

208 Auckland Islands

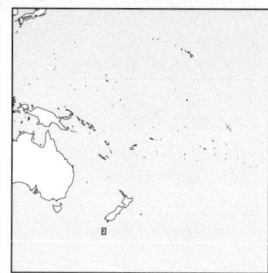

Key habitats Temperate forest, scrub, tussock grassland

Main threats Moderate habitat loss (e.g. due to grazing), introduced species

Biological importance ● ● ●
Current threat level ● ● ●

Area 610 km² **Altitude** 0–600 m

Countries New Zealand

Restricted-range species	Threatened	Total
Confined to this EBA	1	1
Present also in other EBAs, SAs	0	1
Total	1	2

■ General characteristics

This group of seven uninhabited volcanic subantarctic islands belonging to New Zealand lies c.500 km south of the South Island of New Zealand (EBA 207). In descending order of size they are Auckland, Adams, Enderby, Disappointment, Rose, Ewing and Ocean.

On the main island of Auckland, a narrow strip of forest dominated by the southern rata *Metrosideros umbellata* fringes coastal areas to 50 m, above which there is a broad belt of scrub with tussock grassland at c.300 m giving way to upland herbfields and fellfield (of bryophytes, mosses, lichens and sedges) at c.500 m. This basic vegetation pattern varies among the other islands.

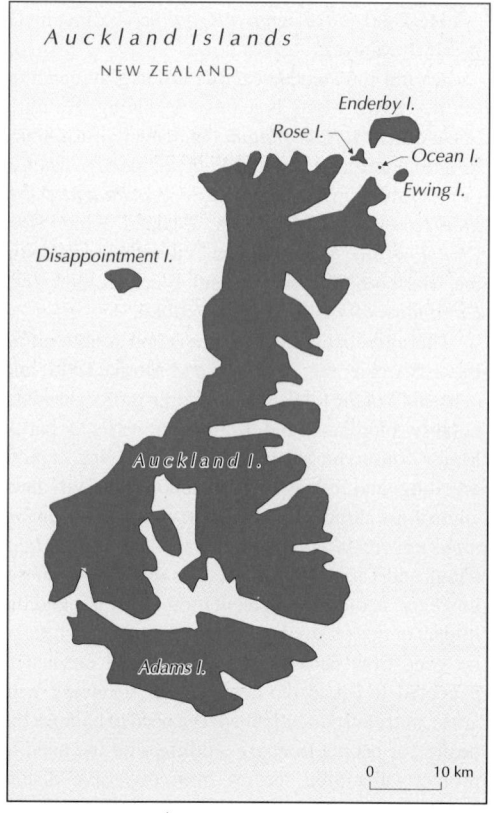

Auckland Islands
NEW ZEALAND

Enderby I.
Rose I.
Ocean I.
Ewing I.
Disappointment I.
Auckland I.
Adams I.

0   10 km

■ Restricted-range species

This EBA has been identified on the basis of its one endemic extant and one endemic extinct species; an additional (extant) restricted-range species also occurs there. The two surviving species, *Lewinia muelleri* (endemic) and *Coenocorypha aucklandica* (nominate race endemic to this EBA), are both found in the same areas of tussock grassland, scrub and forest. *L. muelleri* persists on Adams (with 10% of the island likely to have suitable habitat) and Disappointment only, while *C. aucklandica* is found on all islands apart from Auckland itself.

Interior rata forest on Enderby Island, habitat for New Zealand Snipe *Coenocorypha aucklandica*.

A number of subspecies of more widespread New Zealand birds are also confined to the Auckland Islands: the flightless Auckland Island Brown Teal *Anas aucklandica aucklandica* (treated as a full species in Marchant and Higgins 1990), Auckland Island Double-banded Plover *Charadrius bicinctus exilis* and Auckland Island Tit *Petroica macrocephala marrineri*. Auckland Island Pipit *Anthus novae-seelandiae aucklandicus* occurs in this EBA and on the outer islands of Campbell Island, another New Zealand subantarctic island group to the south.

The islands are very important for seabirds, notably Auckland Islands Shag *Phalacrocorax colensoi* (a breeding endemic confined to the islands of Auckland, Enderby, Ewing and Ocean), Wandering Albatross *Diomedea exulans* and Shy Albatross *D. cauta*

Status and habitat of restricted-range species

Species (ordered taxonomically)	Global status	Other EBAs (and SAs)	Habitat
Auckland Islands Merganser *Mergus australis*	EX (1905)	—	Sheltered inlets, creeks
Auckland Islands Rail *Lewinia muelleri*	VU	—	Scrubby forest, coastal and cliff herbfields, tussock grassland, upland herbfields
New Zealand Snipe *Coenocorypha aucklandica*	nt	206[X] (s132,s133)	Scrubby forest, coastal and cliff herbfields, tussock grassland, upland herbfields

Global status (see p. 679 for definitions)
EX Extinct — with year of last record
EW Extinct in the Wild
CR Critical — threatened species
EN Endangered
VU Vulnerable
cd Conservation Dependent
nt Near Threatened
lc Least Concern
DD Data Deficient
NE Not Evaluated

Other EBAs (and SAs) (see p. 90 for locations): bracketed numbers are Secondary Areas; [X] extinct in that EBA or SA.

Cliff herbfields on Ocean Island, habitat for New Zealand Snipe *Coencorypha aucklandica*, as well as for breeding seabirds such as Yellow-eyed Penguin *Megadyptes antipodes* and Auckland Islands Shag *Phalacrocorax colensoi*.

(Clark and Dingwall 1985), with the subspecies *D. e. gibsoni* and *D. c. steadi* breeding only there (both recognized as full species by Robertson and Nunn in press). Several other species of seabird have endemic races which breed on these islands.

■ **Threats and conservation**

The native vegetation in this EBA has been much modified by introduced mammals, including cattle, goats, rabbits, mice and especially pigs. However, a recent eradication programme has successfully removed introduced mammals from all the islands apart from the largest, Auckland (see Sanson and Dingwall 1995). Adams (100 km²) and Disappointment (4 km²) have never had introduced mammals and are therefore the least disturbed of the islands, Adams being known internationally for its herbaceous flora, and both providing an important refuge for wildlife.

Lewinia muelleri once thought to be extinct, is now known to number c.1,000 individuals (several hundred on Adams and at least 500 on Disappoint-

ment), but is only safe if introduced mammals, especially pigs and cats (still present on Auckland) and rats, fail to reach these islands either by swimming the narrow channel which separates Adams from Auckland or by accidental introduction (Elliott *et al*. 1991). It is likely that introduced predators, plus collecting, caused the demise of *Mergus australis*.

Other threatened birds (all classified as Vulnerable) which occur on the Auckland Islands (see 'Restricted-range species', above), include *Anas aucklandica* (the total population of *A. a. aucklandica* is unlikely to exceed 600), *Phalacrocorax colensoi* (c.4,000 birds) and *Diomedea exulans* (c.9,000 pairs, c.30% of the total world population). The islands are also an important breeding area for the threatened Yellow-eyed Penguin *Megadyptes antipodes* (also Vulnerable, 250–350 pairs, c.20% of the world population).

The Auckland Islands are totally protected and are now visited principally by scientific expeditions, with supervised tourism being permitted only on Auckland and Enderby.

209 Chatham Islands

PRIORITY
CRITICAL

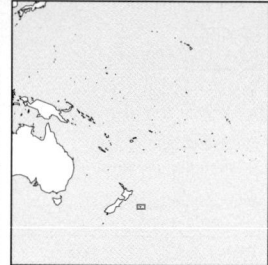

Key habitats Temperate forest, scrub, tussock grassland, rocky shorelines

Main threats Moderate habitat loss (e.g. due to farming, settlement), introduced species

Biological importance ● ●
Current threat level ● ● ●

Area 970 km² **Altitude** 0–200 m

Countries New Zealand

Restricted-range species	Threatened	Total
Confined to this EBA	4	5
Present also in other EBAs, SAs	0	0
Total	4	5

■ General characteristics

The volcanic and sedimentary Chatham Islands lie c.800 km east of the South Island of New Zealand (EBA 207) to which they belong politically. The EBA includes the two main islands of Chatham and Pitt, and the much smaller offshore islands of South East (or Rangatira, c.2 km²), Mangere and Star Keys, all of which are important for restricted-range landbirds.

Native vegetation includes coastal broadleaf forest and scrub and shrubland communities, with tall heath forest inland, interspersed with moorland and bogs.

■ Restricted-range species

Only five endemic landbirds are today extant on the Chatham Islands: two are birds of the shore and three live in forest, scrub and grassland. One, *Thinornis novaeseelandiae*, was recorded from the South Island of New Zealand in 1773 but was quickly exterminated after the arrival of European carnivores; its former alleged distribution on the North Island of New Zealand cannot be verified and is in some doubt (Turbott 1990).

Distribution patterns of restricted-range species

Species (ordered geographically)	Chatham	Pitt	Mangere	South East	Star Keys
Gallirallus dieffenbachii	X	X	–	–	–
Gallirallus modestus	X	X	X	–	–
Megalurus rufescens	X	X	X	–	–
Thinornis novaeseelandiae	X	X	X	●	–
Petroica traversi	X	X	●	●	–
Haematopus chathamensis	●	●	●	●	●
Gerygone albofrontata	●	●	●	●	●
Coenocorypha pusilla	X	X	●	●	●
Total	2	2	4	5	3

● Present ? Present? Threatened spp. shown in
○ Extinct? R Reintroduced **bold** (see 'Status and habitat'
X Extinct I Introduced table)

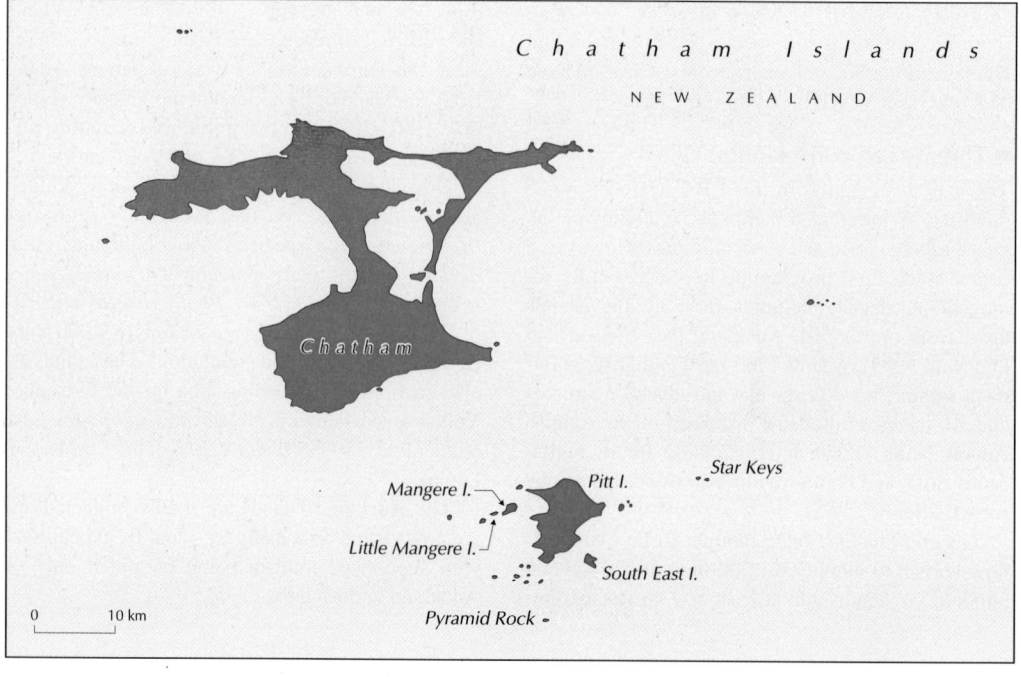

C h a t h a m   I s l a n d s

NEW ZEALAND

Chatham

Mangere I.

Little Mangere I.

Pitt I.

Star Keys

South East I.

0   10 km

Pyramid Rock

Status and habitat of restricted-range species

Species (ordered taxonomically)	Global status	Other EBAs (and SAs)	Habitat
Dieffenbach's Rail *Gallirallus dieffenbachii*	EX (1840)	—	Unknown, perhaps fresh- and saltwater marshes
Chatham Islands Rail *Gallirallus modestus*	EX (1900)	—	Tussock grassland
Chatham Islands Oystercatcher *Haematopus chathamensis*[1]	EN	—	Rocky shorelines
Shore Plover *Thinornis novaeseelandiae*	EN	—	Coastal rock platforms, salt meadows, formerly estuaries and sandy beaches, esp. river mouths
Chatham Islands Snipe *Coenocorypha pusilla*	VU	—	Forest, tall tussock grassland
Chatham Islands Fernbird *Megalurus rufescens*	EX (1900)	—	Forest, scrub, moorland
Chatham Islands Warbler *Gerygone albofrontata*	nt	—	Forest, forest edge, tall scrub
Chatham Islands Robin *Petroica traversi*	EN	—	Forest, scrub

Global status (see p. 679 for definitions)	EX Extinct EW Extinct in the Wild	} with year of last record	cd Conservation Dependent	**Other EBAs (and SAs)** (see p. 90 for locations)	Bracketed numbers are Secondary Areas. ˣ Extinct in that EBA or SA.
	CR Critical EN Endangered VU Vulnerable	} threatened species	nt Near Threatened lc Least Concern DD Data Deficient NE Not Evaluated	**Notes**	¹ Taxonomy follows Turbott (1990).

▧ Threats and conservation

Since Polynesian, European and Maori settlement, much of the Chatham Islands' natural vegetation has been cleared by burning and grazing for farming and development, including on the two small islands, South East and Mangere, which are today protected as reserves. This habitat loss, along with hunting, introduced predators and competitors, have all contributed to the destruction of birdlife on the islands, particularly on Chatham and Pitt (less so on South East and Mangere Islands, which are predator-free, cats having died out naturally on Mangere). In total, of 67 bird species and subspecies recorded, 29 became extinct in pre-European times and eight have died out subsequent to European settlement (Atkinson and Bell 1973), including three species since 1800.

All the endemic landbirds are considered threatened or Near Threatened, including three species which have very small populations and which are thus classified as Endangered: *Thinornis novaeseelandiae* (130 birds in 1993), *Haematopus chathamensis* (c.100 in 1994) and *Petroica traversi* (170 in February 1995: D. V. Merton *in litt.* 1995). This last species became restricted to Little Mangere in the late 1880s and a century later was down to just five birds, including only one viable pair; its recovery represents an amazing conservation success, involving the transfer of the entire remnant population to Mangere and an egg-manipulating, cross-fostering programme (Butler and Merton 1992).

A further four endemic subspecies are also considered priorities for conservation action by Molloy

and Davis (1992) and Tisdall (1994): Chatham Island Pigeon *Hemiphaga novaeseelandiae chathamensis* (may be a full species, c.100 individuals), Forbes's Parakeet *Cyanoramphus auriceps forbesi* (may also be a full species, c.100: see Triggs and Daugherty 1996); Chatham Island Tomtit *Petroica macrocephala chathamensis* (c.1,000 birds) and Chatham Island Tui *Prosthemadera novaeseelandiae chathamensis* (250–350 birds) (B. D. Bell *in litt.* 1993, 1996).

Threatened seabirds, all of which are endemic breeders, include Magenta Petrel *Pterodroma magentae* (Critical; 45–150 birds), Chatham Islands Petrel *P. axillaris* (Critical; c.500), Pitt Shag *Phalacrocorax featherstonii* (Vulnerable; fewer than 2,000) and Chatham Islands Shag *P. onslowi* (Vulnerable; fewer than 1,000). Chatham Albatross *Diomedea cauta eremita* (treated as a full species by Robertson and Nunn in press) is found on Pyramid Rock, where breeding is confined to less than 10 ha, and, although it is fairly numerous (3,200–4,200 pairs) it is suffering from a reduction in the vegetation, probably as a result of climate change.

Conservation programmes are being undertaken for all threatened species and most subspecies. An active programme of reserving and restoring habitat is under way including fencing, controlling herbivores and re-planting, and South East Island has recovered well (B. D. Bell *in litt.* 1993). Recent information is provided by Holdaway (1994) and the conservation of seabirds is discussed in Bell and Robertson (1994).

210 Southern Cook Islands

PRIORITY
URGENT

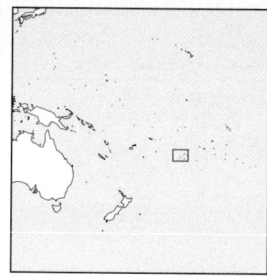

Key habitats Lowland and montane rain forest, makatea forest

Main threats Moderate habitat loss (e.g. due to clearance for agriculture, overgrazing), introduced species

Biological importance ● ● ●
Current threat level ● ● ●

Area 190 km²　**Altitude** 0–600 m

Countries Cook Islands (to New Zealand)

Restricted-range species	Threatened	Total
Confined to this EBA	4	6
Present also in other EBAs, SAs	0	1
Total	4	7

■ General characteristics

This EBA covers the islands of Mitiaro, Atiu, Mauke, Rarotonga and Mangaia. Aitutaki, one of the northernmost islands of the Southern Cook Islands group, is treated separately (Secondary Area s135) as there are no reliable records that restricted-range species have historically been shared between it and the islands of the EBA. The Cook Islands are self-governing but, since 1965, have been in free association with New Zealand.

Rarotonga is the most populated, the largest (67 km²) and the highest island, reaching 652 m at Te Manga; it supports secondary rain forest at lower elevations with almost pristine montane forest above. The other islands consist of much-weathered volcanic centres covered with fernlands and disturbed forests, surrounded by a raised coral limestone platform (the 'makatea') covered with both undisturbed and disturbed forest and scrub. Freshwater marshes and swamps are present on all islands.

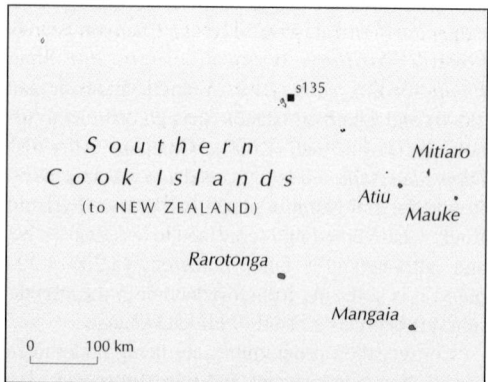

Southern Cook Islands (to NEW ZEALAND)

s135

Mitiaro

Atiu

Mauke

Rarotonga

Mangaia

0　100 km

■ Restricted-range species

Most of the restricted-range species are typically confined to native forest (disturbed and undisturbed) in inland Rarotonga or to the makatea forest of the raised atolls.

The pattern of distribution between the islands is very patchy, but it seems likely that at least some of the species were more widespread in the group prior

to 1800, but were extirpated as a result of the activities of Polynesian settlers (see, e.g., Kirch *et al.* 1992). Kuhl's Lorikeet *Vini kuhlii*, a restricted-range species from Rimatara in French Polynesia (EBA 211), is also likely to have been widespread in this EBA, but was extirpated through exploitation for its red feathers (Steadman 1991, McCormack and Künzle 1993).

Today four species are single-island endemics, being confined to Atiu (one species), Rarotonga (two) and Mangaia (one).

Distribution patterns of restricted-range species

Species (ordered geographically)	Mitiaro	Atiu	Mauke	Rarotonga	Mangaia	Other EBAs, SAs
Acrocephalus kerearako	●	–	–	–	●	–
Collocalia sawtelli	–	●	–	–	–	–
Todirhamphus tuta	–	●	●	–	–	●
Ptilinopus rarotongensis	–	●	X	●	–	–
Aplonis mavornata	–	–	X	–	–	–
Pomarea dimidiata	–	–	–	●	–	–
Aplonis cinerascens	–	–	–	●	–	–
Todirhamphus ruficollaris	–	–	–	–	●	–
Total	1	3	1	3	2	

● Present　? Present?　　　Threatened spp. } see 'Status
○ Extinct?　R Reintroduced　shown in **bold** } and habitat'
X Extinct　　I Introduced　　Other EBAs, SAs } table

■ Threats and conservation

The ranges and densities of all restricted-range species are likely to have been affected by the clearance of forest by man and its degradation through browsing by introduced herbivores—and by the resulting fragmentation of native primary habitat. The four single-island endemics, which have tiny world ranges and small populations, are therefore considered threatened.

Pomarea dimidiata (Rarotonga only) is classified as Critical and was close to extinction in the early 1980s. A remnant population, of a bird recorded as widespread and common on the island in the mid-1800s, survived in 1.5 km² of native forest in the

Status and habitat of restricted-range species

Species (ordered taxonomically)	Global status	Other EBAs (and SAs)	Habitat
Cook Islands Fruit-dove *Ptilinopus rarotongensis*	nt	—	All forest types
Atiu Swiftlet *Collocalia sawtelli*	VU	—	Caves in makatea (breeding), fernlands, mixed horticultural areas
Mangaia Kingfisher *Todirhamphus ruficollaris*	VU	—	Makatea forest, disturbed inland forest
Chattering Kingfisher *Todirhamphus tuta*	lc	213	Makatea forest, disturbed inland forest
Cook Islands Reed-warbler *Acrocephalus kerearako*	lc	—	Forest, gardens, reedbeds
Rarotonga Monarch *Pomarea dimidiata*	CR	—	Mid-elevation montane forest, occasionally in secondary *Hibiscus* thickets at lower elevations
Mysterious Starling *Aplonis mavornata*	EX (1825)	—	Forest
Rarotonga Starling *Aplonis cinerascens*	VU	—	Montane native forest, fringing disturbed forest

Global status (see p. 679 for definitions): EX Extinct / EW Extinct in the Wild (with year of last record); CR Critical / EN Endangered / VU Vulnerable (threatened species); cd Conservation Dependent / nt Near Threatened / lc Least Concern; DD Data Deficient / NE Not Evaluated

Other EBAs (and SAs) (see p. 90 for locations): bracketed numbers are Secondary Areas; [x] extinct in that EBA or SA.

south-east, in the lower foothills and steep V-shaped valleys at 100–250 m. However, suitable habitat was available elsewhere and introduced rats (especially black rat *Rattus rattus* introduced by Europeans) were identified as the main obstacle to successful nesting; subsequent rat control has resulted in an increasing population, starting with a low of 29 birds in 1989, 56 in 1992 and increasing to over 100 in 1995. In August 1997 the population stood at a minimum of 144 birds and, as the numbers have been above 50 birds (all mature birds capable of breeding) for nearly five years, the species is a likely candidate for the down-grading of its threat status—a fitting reflection of the success of this conservation initiative. The site where the species survives—Takitumu Conservation Area—will be managed by the three land-owning families for sustainable development (ecotourism), and the feasibility of transferring the species to an island free of black rats elsewhere in the southern Cook Islands will be assessed (McCormack and Künzle 1990, Robertson *et al.* 1994, Robertson 1995c, G. McCormack *in litt.* 1996, H. Robertson *in litt.* 1996).

It is likely that rats affect other species too and may have contributed to the extinction of *Aplonis mavornata*. This species is based on a single specimen previously of unknown origin (hence its English name), but it has been linked to a description of a 'Sturnus' collected from Mauke in 1825 (the type was then subsequently apparently lost). Observations at the time of the collection of 'quantities of rats', perceived to be similar to brown rat *Rattus*

norvegicus, are thus of considerable interest (Olson 1986).

Common Myna *Acridotheres tristis*, originally introduced to the Cook Islands at the beginning of the twentieth century to control insects, may be detrimental to *Todirhamphus ruficollaris* (Mangaia only), estimated to have a population of 250–450 birds in 1992, as interference with nesting has been observed and there is competition between these two bird species for food; cats and rodents (black rat is present) are also potential predators (Rowe and Empson 1996).

Threats leading to rarity in the other two threatened endemic species are not so apparent. *Aplonis cinerascens* (Rarotonga only) was regarded as abundant early in the twentieth century but is now estimated to number only a few hundred birds, though no reasons for the decline are known. For *Collocalia sawtelli* (Atiu only, where black rat appears to be absent), the major (natural) causes of mortality have been identified as starvation of chicks after falling out of the nest and predation by crabs, although disturbance by tourists could be a problem in the future; a survey in 1995–1996 recorded 175 active nests in the only two caves where it breeds (Tarburton 1990, G. McCormack *in litt.* 1993, 1994, 1996).

Bristle-thighed Curlew *Numenius tahitiensis*, a threatened (Vulnerable) restricted-range species which breeds in Western Alaska (Secondary Area s002), winters among Pacific Islands including the islands of this EBA.

211 Rimatara

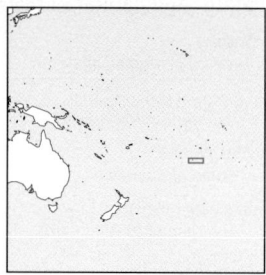

Key habitats Horticultural woodland, makatea forest

Main threats Major habitat loss (e.g. due to coconut plantations)

Biological importance ● ● ●
Current threat level ● ● ●

Area 8 km² **Altitude** 0–80 m

Countries French Polynesia (to France)

Restricted-range species	Threatened	Total
Confined to this EBA	1	2
Present also in other EBAs, SAs	0	0
Total	1	2

■ General characteristics

Rimatara is a raised island in the Austral (or Tubuai) Islands and is the second smallest of all EBAs after Laysan (EBA 216). Other islands in the Austral group include Maria, Rurutu, Tubuai, Raivavae, and, c.300 km to the south-east, Rapa (treated as Secondary Area s136) and Marotiri. All of these islands are politically part of French Polynesia, which is a French overseas territory (see also EBAs 212–214, and Secondary Area s136).

On Rimatara, the centre of the island consists of a once-forested weathered volcanic hill surrounded by a discontinuous ring of swamplands. The raised coral platform ('makatea') forms a coastal rampart around the north-western half of the island and is covered with forest and scrublands, with the south-eastern half being an extensive coastal plain.

■ Restricted-range species

As a result of the recent recognition of the specific status of *Acrocephalus rimatarae* (formerly regarded as a race of *A. vaughani* by Sibley and Monroe 1990, but treated as a species by Graves 1992 and Sibley and Monroe 1993; see EBA 215 and Secondary Area s137), Rimatara, now with two endemic restricted-range species, qualifies as an EBA.

Vini kuhlii, the second restricted-range species occurring in this EBA, is also present on islands in Kiribati (Secondary Area s134), to which it appears to have been introduced, and it is speculated by

Steadman (1991) that the species was spread widely through the Southern Cook Islands prior to 1800 but was extirpated through exploitation by Polynesian settlers.

In general, the Austral Islands are poorly known, and Maria and Marotiri have never been properly investigated by an ornithologist. An unidentified *Acrocephalus* was reported from Raivavae in 1968, but was not found in 1990 (Seitre and Seitre 1991), and could therefore have been a vagrant.

■ Threats and conservation

Today the coastal plains of Rimatara are typically covered in coconut plantations and the upper volcanic slopes with fernlands, grasslands and introduced forestry, while the lower slopes form a horticultural belt which is extensively planted with recently introduced food plants.

This habitat alteration does not, however, appear to be a major threat to the two endemic species. In 1989 *Acrocephalus rimatarae* was found to be common (although no estimate of population was made) and widespread, particularly at lower elevations (Seitre and Seitre 1991). In 1992 *Vini kuhlii* was considered to be common in the belt of mixed horticultural woodland, though less common in the central hills and coastal plains and rare in the extensive makatea forest and scrub (with a total population on Rimatara of c.905 birds) (McCormack and Künzlé 1996).

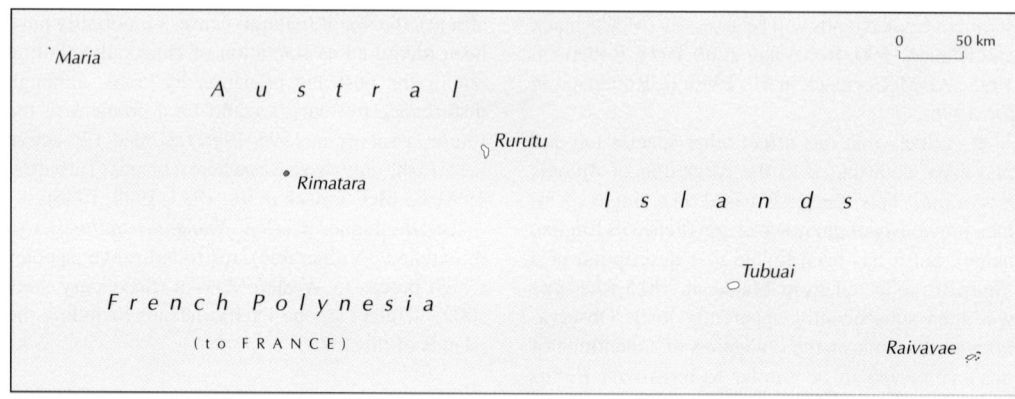

Status and habitat of restricted-range species

Species (ordered taxonomically)	Global status	Other EBAs (and SAs)	Habitat
Kuhl's Lorikeet *Vini kuhlii*[1]	EN	—	Mixed horticultural woodlands, coconut plantations; rarely forest
Rimatara Reed-warbler *Acrocephalus rimatarae*	NE	—	Brushy forest, reedbeds

Global status (see p. 679 for definitions)	EX Extinct EW Extinct in the Wild	} with year of last record	cd Conservation Dependent nt Near Threatened		**Other EBAs (and SAs)** (see p. 90 for locations)	Bracketed numbers are Secondary Areas. ˣ Extinct in that EBA or SA.	
	CR Critical EN Endangered VU Vulnerable	} threatened species	lc Least Concern DD Data Deficient NE Not Evaluated		**Notes**	[1] Introduced to Kiribati (Secondary Area s134).	

The effects of introduced species could, however, be serious, given the tiny ranges of both species; although *Acrocephalus rimatarae* was not evaluated for threatened status by Collar *et al.* (1994), it would certainly qualify as Vulnerable on the basis of its range size. A preliminary rat survey revealed the presence of both Pacific rat *Rattus exulans* and brown rat *R. norvegicus*, but not of black rat *R. rattus*—this latter the most agile tree-climber of the three species of rat in Polynesia, being widely associated with the decline of birds on oceanic islands (Atkinson 1985, Seitre and Seitre 1991), and its absence is perhaps the main reason why *Vini kuhlii* is still relatively abundant on Rimatara. The highest conservation priority should therefore be given to confirming the absence of *R. rattus* on Rimatara and the implementation of a major quarantine programme to ensure that it is not accidentally introduced; reintroduction of *Vini kuhlii* to islands within its former natural range is also recommended (McCormack and Künzlé 1996).

212 | Marquesas Islands

PRIORITY
CRITICAL

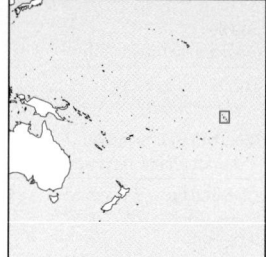

Key habitats Lowland dry forest, montane rain forest

Main threats Major habitat loss (e.g. due to overgrazing, fire), introduced species

Biological importance ● ● ●

Current threat level ● ● ●

Area 1,000 km² **Altitude** 0–1,200 m

Countries French Polynesia (to France)

Restricted-range species	Threatened	Total
Confined to this EBA	7	10
Present also in other EBAs, SAs	0	0
Total	7	10

General characteristics

The Marquesas comprise six main volcanic islands (Nuku Hiva, Ua Huka, Ua Pou, Hiva Oa, Tahuata, Fatu Hiva), four smaller, uninhabited islands (Hatutaa, Eiao, Fatu Huku, Mohotoni) and a few islets. The archipelago is politically part of French Polynesia, an overseas territory of France (see also EBAs 211, 213, 214, and Secondary Area s136).

The islands are very rugged, rising steeply to remarkable heights (reaching 1,232 m on Ua Pou), and consequently have virtually no coastal plains. The larger islands' varied habitats range from dry tropical vegetation (originally dry forest) at lower elevations to montane rain forest above c.600 m, with cloud forest at the highest altitudes (see Dekker 1992).

Restricted-range species

Most of the restricted-range species occur in forest with some in secondary habitats and plantations.

Today their distributions are very restricted, three species being single-island endemics (on Nuku Hiva, Ua Huka and Fatu Hiva) and four occurring in reasonable numbers on two islands only, although subfossils indicate that many species were once widespread in the archipelago (see Steadman 1989).

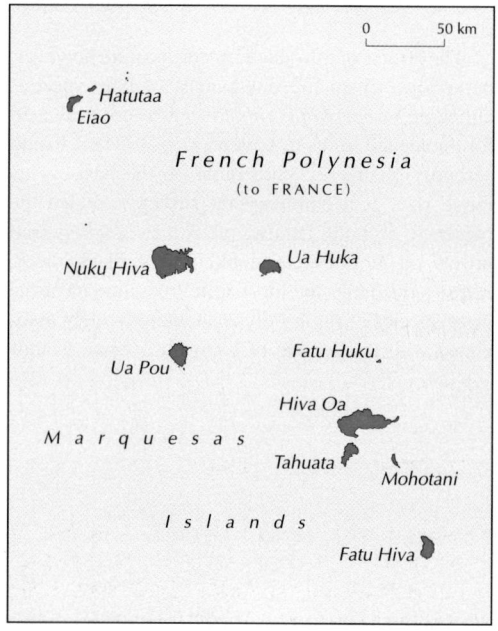

0   50 km

Hatutaa
Eiao

French Polynesia
(to FRANCE)

Nuku Hiva   *Ua Huka*

Fatu Huku
Ua Pou
Hiva Oa
M a r q u e s a s
Tahuata   *Mohotani*

I s l a n d s

Fatu Hiva

Threats and conservation

All the Marquesas islands have been devastated by overgrazing and fire, and much of the original dry forest has been reduced to grassland. Extensive

Distribution patterns of restricted-range species

Species (ordered geographically)	Hatutaa	Eiao	Nuku Hiva	Ua Huka	Ua Pou	Fatu Huku	Hiva Oa	Tahuata	Mohotani	Fatu Hiva
Gallicolumba rubescens	●	–	X	–	–	●	–	–	–	–
Acrocephalus mendanae	●	●	●	●	●	–	●	●	●	●
Pomarea iphis	–	X	–	●	–	–	–	–	–	–
Collocalia ocista	–	●	●	●	●	●	●	●	●	?
Ducula galeata	–	–	●	–	–	–	–	–	–	–
Ptilinopus mercierii	–	–	X	–	–	–	X	–	–	–
Pomarea mendozae	–	–	X	–	●	–	○	X	●	–
Vini ultramarina	–	–	○	R	○	–	–	–	–	R
Ptilinopus dupetithouarsii	–	–	●	●	●	–	●	●	●	●
Todirhamphus godeffroyi	–	–	–	–	–	–	●	●	–	–
Pomarea whitneyi	–	–	–	–	–	–	–	–	–	●
Total	2	2	5	5	5	2	5	4	4	4

● Present	? Present?	Threatened spp. shown in **bold**	see 'Status and habitat' table
○ Extinct?	R Reintroduced		
X Extinct	I Introduced	Other EBAs, SAs	

Status and habitat of restricted-range species

Species (ordered taxonomically)	Global status	Other EBAs (and SAs)	Habitat
Marquesan Ground-dove *Gallicolumba rubescens*	EN	—	Shrubby vegetation
Red-moustached Fruit-dove *Ptilinopus mercierii*	EX (1920s)	—	Forest
White-capped Fruit-dove *Ptilinopus dupetithouarsii*	lc	—	Forest, secondary forest, plantations
Marquesan Imperial-pigeon *Ducula galeata*	CR	—	Remote forested valleys
Ultramarine Lorikeet *Vini ultramarina*	EN	—	All habitats with trees inc. forest, coconut plantations
Marquesan Swiftlet *Collocalia ocista*	lc	—	Cliffs and caves (breeding), forest, forest edge, open country
Marquesan Kingfisher *Todirhamphus godeffroyi*	EN	—	Forest
Marquesan Reed-warbler *Acrocephalus mendanae*	lc	—	Forest, scrub, plantations
Iphis Monarch *Pomarea iphis*	VU	—	All habitats with trees inc. forest, coconut plantations, scrub
Marquesan Monarch *Pomarea mendozae*	EN	—	Forest, degraded forest
Fatuhiva Monarch *Pomarea whitneyi*	VU	—	Forest, wooded thickets

Global status (see p. 679 for definitions): EX Extinct, EW Extinct in the Wild (with year of last record); CR Critical, EN Endangered, VU Vulnerable (threatened species); cd Conservation Dependent, nt Near Threatened, lc Least Concern; DD Data Deficient, NE Not Evaluated

Other EBAs (and SAs) (see p. 90 for locations): bracketed numbers are Secondary Areas; [x] extinct in that EBA or SA.

damage has also been caused to upland forest on the larger islands by feral cattle, horses, goats, sheep and pigs, such that most of the native plants survive only in relict forest patches, and on some small islands little vegetation remains (WWF/IUCN 1994–1995).

Not surprisingly, most of the endemic bird species are considered threatened and *Ptilinopus mercierii* is almost certainly extinct. *Ducula galeata* (150–300 birds in 1993) is also close to extinction, and most other species are declining on at least some islands.

Although all species have suffered from habitat loss and degradation, Seitre and Seitre (1991, 1992) have identified rats (particularly black rat *Rattus rattus*) as the major threat to native birds. Thus they link the decline of *Vini ultramarina* on Ua Pou with an increase in rats following the 1983 hurricane, and they fear that *Pomarea mendozae* may also be susceptible, being now restricted to forest above 550 m where rats are fewer.

Introduced birds—such as the predatory Great Horned Owl *Bubo virginianus* and the very competitive Common Myna *Acridotheres tristis*—are so far restricted to Hiva Oa but are thought to have affected all native species on that island and *Todirhamphus godeffroyi* in particular (although the decline of this species is recent, while the myna was introduced in

1918 and the owl in 1927, and there may thus be other contributory factors). The demise of *Ptilinopus mercierii* on Hiva Oa was speculated to be due to the introduction of the owl (Holyoak and Thibault 1984), but Seitre and Seitre (1991) think that the earlier introduction of cats and rats, and even earlier hunting by Polynesians, may have been significant too. Illegal hunting remains the major threat to *Ducula galeata*, while both *Pomarea iphis* and *P. whitneyi* are considered threatened because of their tiny ranges, despite being relatively common within them.

Thibault (1988) identified the following areas as priorities for native landbird conservation: the high-altitude forests of Crêtes de Toovii on Nuku Hiva; the island of Fatu Huku; and the high-altitude forests of Cirque de Hohoi on Ua Pou. Ua Huka is the main stronghold for *Vini ultramarina* (c.800 individuals in 1991) and is therefore important too; 29 birds were relocated to Fatu Hiva during 1992–1994, and preliminary surveys indicate good survival and possible reproduction (Kuehler 1992, Kuehler *et al.* 1997).

Three islands are protected: Hatutaa, which is free of feral browsing mammals, and Eiao and Mohotoni which are both very degraded by feral sheep and pigs (Thibault 1989, Seitre and Seitre 1991).

213 Society Islands

PRIORITY
URGENT

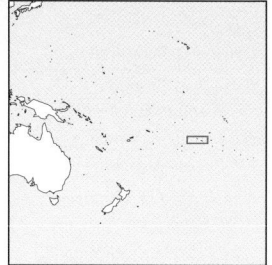

Key habitats Lowland dry forest, montane rain forest

Main threats Major habitat loss (e.g. due to coconut plantations), introduced species

Biological importance ● ● ●
Current threat level ● ● ●

Area 1,400 km²   **Altitude** 0–2,200 m

Countries French Polynesia (to France)

Restricted-range species	Threatened	Total
Confined to this EBA	3	5
Present also in other EBAs, SAs	2	3
Total	5	8

■ General characteristics

The 10 high volcanic islands and five coral atolls comprising the Society Islands can be divided into two main groups, each named after its position relative to the dominant south-east trade winds: the Leeward Islands in the north-west and the Windward Islands in the south-east. The archipelago is a part of French Polynesia, an overseas territory of France (see also EBAs 211, 212, 214, and Secondary Area s136). With a land area of 1,045 km² Tahiti is by far the largest of the islands, and it rises to 2,241 m at Mt Marau.

The native vegetation consists of strand forest with *Cocos* and *Pandanus*, lowland dry forest and extensive montane rain forest with cloud forest on the peaks (Davis *et al.* 1986).

■ Restricted-range species

All the restricted-range birds are forest species, though many occur in secondary habitats and plantations. Five species are restricted to one or two islands but were once more widely distributed. Tahiti supports seven restricted-range species (including three single-islands endemics), while the other islands now have only one or two.

As well as the two extinct endemic species listed in the 'Status and habitat' table, an additional three endemics were collected or seen on Cook's voyage in 1773: Tahiti Rail *Gallirallus pacificus* (Tahiti only), Tahitian Sandpiper *Prosobonia leucoptera* (Moorea

and Tahiti) and Raiatea Parakeet *Cyanoramphus ulietanus* (Raiatea only).

■ Threats and conservation

The Society Islands are perhaps among the most devastated island groups in the whole of the Pacific (Hay 1986). The lowland forest has been greatly modified and all the low atolls have been largely converted to coconut plantations (Davis *et al.* 1986).

Over the last 30 years there has been much habitat modification on Tahiti in particular, with the invasion of an introduced aggressive Neotropical tree *Miconia calvescens* contributing to the progressive disappearance of local trees. It is likely that the replacement of remaining primary forest by this pest (which forms monospecific stands and now dominates forest over 65% of the island) has contributed to the recent decline of *Pomarea nigra* on Mt Marau; this species has apparently been rare throughout the twentieth century but was noted from only four valleys out of 39 visited in 1986–1991 (Monnet *et al.* 1993, Meyer 1996).

The greatest overall threat, however, appears to have come from introduced species, both birds (more than half of the Tahitian avifauna is non-native) and mammals, and it is likely that past extinctions can be linked at least in part to the effects of these introductions. For example, Common Myna *Acridotheres tristis*, one introduced bird pest, is thought to predate the eggs and young of *Collocalia leucophaeus* and

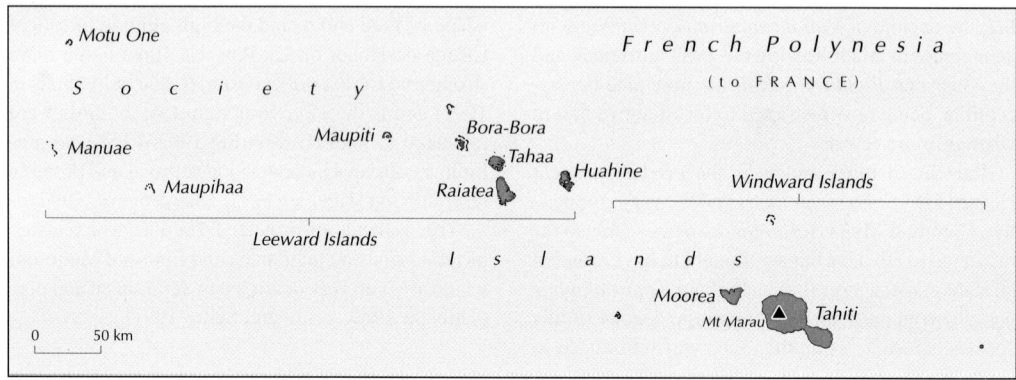

Status and habitat of restricted-range species

Species (ordered taxonomically)	Global status	Other EBAs (and SAs)	Habitat
Polynesian Ground-dove *Gallicolumba erythroptera*[1]	CR	214	Forest
Grey-green Fruit-dove *Ptilinopus purpuratus*	lc	—	Forest, plantations
Polynesian Imperial-pigeon *Ducula aurorae*	VU	214	Forest
Blue Lorikeet *Vini peruviana*	VU	214 (s135)	Forest, coconut plantations, gardens
Black-fronted Parakeet *Cyanoramphus zealandicus*	EX (1844)	—	Presumably forest
Tahiti Swiftlet *Collocalia leucophaeus*	VU	—	Cliffs and caves (nesting), forest, forest edge, open country
Tahiti Kingfisher *Todirhamphus veneratus*	lc	—	Forest, secondary growth, plantations
Chattering Kingfisher *Todirhamphus tuta*	lc	210	Montane stream valleys in forest, secondary forest, old plantations
Tahiti Reed-warbler *Acrocephalus caffer*	VU	—	Secondary forest, bamboo thickets
Tahiti Monarch *Pomarea nigra*	CR	—	Dense primary forest
Maupiti Monarch *Pomarea pomarea*[2]	EX (1823)	—	Presumably forest

Global status (see p. 679 for definitions)					Other EBAs (and SAs) (see p. 90 for locations)	Bracketed numbers are Secondary Areas.
EX	Extinct	} with year of last record	cd	Conservation Dependent		ˣ Extinct in that EBA or SA.
EW	Extinct in the Wild		nt	Near Threatened	**Notes**	[1] Extinct in this EBA (1800s).
CR	Critical	} threatened species	lc	Least Concern		[2] Taxonomy follows Holyoak and Thibault (1984).
EN	Endangered		DD	Data Deficient		
VU	Vulnerable		NE	Not Evaluated		

may compete for food with *Acrocephalus caffer* (Holyoak and Thibault 1984, Seitre and Seitre 1991, 1992).

The species which has suffered the greatest recent range reduction is *Vini peruviana*; its extirpation from many islands correlates very well with the spread of the introduced Swamp Harrier *Circus approximans* (Holyoak and Thibault 1984), and has also been linked to the arrival of black rat *Rattus rattus*, while its recent decline on Manuae is possibly explained by the release of cats there (Seitre and Seitre 1991, 1992).

Thibault (1988) identified the following areas as priorities for native landbird conservation: Mt Marau on Tahiti (for *Pomarea nigra* in particular); vallée de Vaiote on Tahiti; the island of Manuae; the wooded vallée d'Avera on Raiatea; and the lowland humid forest of Oponohu on Moorea. In 1990 the Valley of Fa'aiti Natural Park on Tahiti was established, and a study of Manuae has been proposed to classify the island as a reserve (Drollet 1990), and to explore the feasibility of cat and rat eradication.

Distribution patterns of restricted-range species

Species (ordered geographically)	Motu One	Manuae	Maupihaa	Maupiti	Bora-Bora	Tahaa	Raiatea	Huahine	Moorea	Tahiti	Other EBAs, SAs
Vini peruviana	●	●	X	–	X	X	X	X	X	X	●
Todirhamphus tuta	–	–	–	●	●	●	●	●	–	○	ˣ
Ptilinopus purpuratus	–	–	–	●	●	●	●	●	●	●	–
Pomarea pomarea	–	–	–	X	–	–	–	–	–	–	–
Collocalia leucophaeus	–	–	–	?	–	–	X	V	V	●	–
Acrocephalus caffer	–	–	–	–	–	–	X	X	X	●	–
Todirhamphus veneratus	–	–	–	–	–	–	–	–	●	●	–
Ducula aurorae	–	–	–	–	–	–	–	–	X	●	ˣ
Gallicolumba erythroptera	–	–	–	–	–	–	–	–	X	●	ˣ
Pomarea nigra	–	–	–	–	–	–	–	–	–	●	–
Cyanoramphus zealandicus	–	–	–	–	–	–	–	–	–	X	–
Total	1	1	0	2	2	2	2	2	2	7	

● Present	? Present?	Threatened spp. shown in **bold**	} see 'Status and habitat' table
○ Extinct?	R Reintroduced	Other EBAs, SAs	
X Extinct	V Vagrant		

214 Tuamotu archipelago

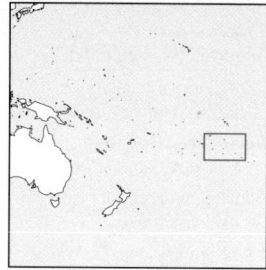

Key habitats Dry forest, atoll/beach forest, scrub

Main threats Moderate habitat loss (e.g. due to coconut plantations), introduced species

Biological importance ● ● ●
Current threat level ● ● ●

Area 690 km² **Altitude** 0–100 m

Countries French Polynesia (to France)

Restricted-range species	Threatened	Total
Confined to this EBA	4	6
Present also in other EBAs, SAs	2	2
Total	6	8

■ General characteristics

The EBA comprises the 78 islands of the Tuamotu archipelago, which stretch over nearly 1,500 km² of ocean, and the nine Gambier Islands to the southeast. All politically part of French Polynesia, which is an overseas territory of France (see also EBAs 211–213, and Secondary Area s136). Makatea and Niau are raised atolls, other islands are low atolls, not more than 7 m above sea-level, while Mangareva and some small islets in the Gambier Islands are volcanic.

The native vegetation, mostly *Pandanus*, *Pisonia* and *Cordia* scrub, has now been largely replaced with coconut plantations on many atolls (Davis *et al.* 1986); the flora of Makatea is rich compared to that of other islands with a dry forest interior.

■ Restricted-range species

Most of the restricted-range species are forest and scrub birds, but a number occur in coconut plantations. *Prosobonia cancellata*, *Gallicolumba erythro-* *ptera* and *Ptilinopus coralensis* were formerly widespread on the low atolls, but only the last of these is now present on more than a few islands. *Vini peruviana* was also widespread in the northern Tuamotus, but now occurs at fewer islands. The three raised islands on the other hand have (or had) localized endemics or near-endemics, with *Ducula aurorae* and *Ptilinopus chalcurus* at Makatea, *Todirhamphus gambieri gertrudae* at Niau and (formerly) *Todirhamphus gambieri gambieri* at Mangareva. Another species, *Lanius gambieranus* (perhaps actually an endemic *Acrocephalus* warbler), from the Gambier Islands was described in 1844, but the specimen is apparently lost (D. T. Holyoak *in litt.* 1996).

In general, information on distribution and population is sparse, as might be expected in an island EBA which covers such a wide region of ocean. Indeed, many of the islands where restricted-range species were recorded by the Whitney Expedition in 1921–1923 have not been visited since, and c.20

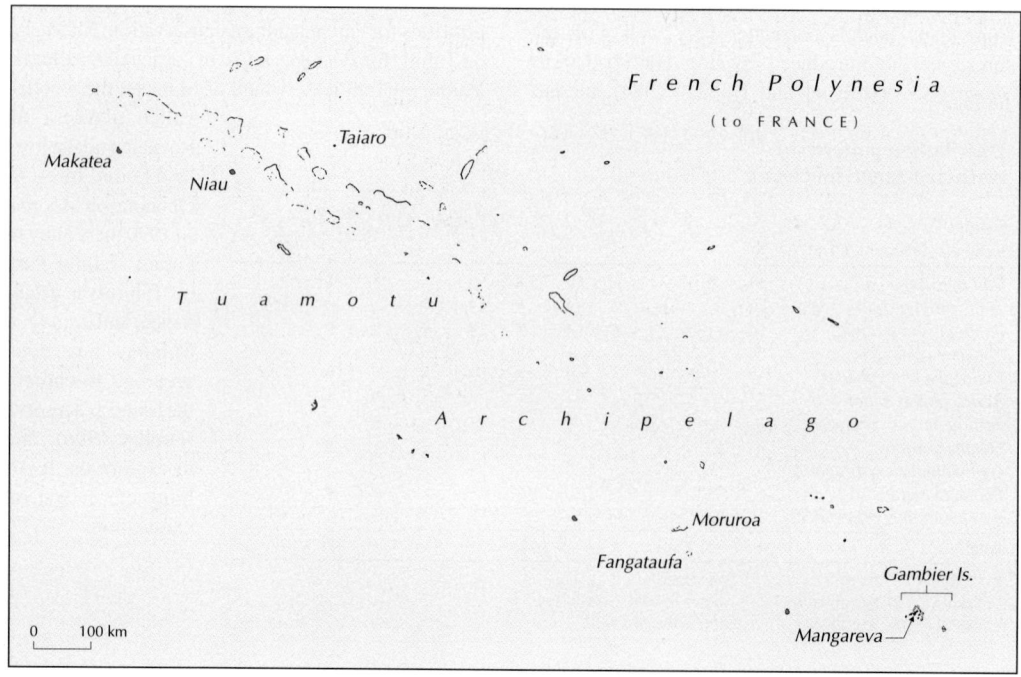

Status and habitat of restricted-range species

Species (ordered taxonomically)	Global status	Other EBAs (and SAs)	Habitat
Tuamotu Sandpiper *Prosobonia cancellata*	EN	(s134[x])	Beaches, shores, scrub
Polynesian Ground-dove *Gallicolumba erythroptera*	CR	213[x]	Forest, scrub
Atoll Fruit-dove *Ptilinopus coralensis*	nt	—	Forest, scrub
Makatea Fruit-dove *Ptilinopus chalcurus*	VU	—	Forest
Polynesian Imperial-pigeon *Ducula aurorae*	VU	213	Forest
Blue Lorikeet *Vini peruviana*	VU	213 (s135)	Forest, scrub, coconut plantations, gardens
Tuamotu Kingfisher *Todirhamphus gambieri*	VU	—	Coconut plantations, gardens, shoreline vegetation, scrub
Tuamotu Reed-warbler *Acrocephalus atyphus*	lc	—	Brushy forest, scrub, coconut plantations

Global status (see p. 679 for definitions): EX Extinct, EW Extinct in the Wild — with year of last record. CR Critical, EN Endangered, VU Vulnerable — threatened species. cd Conservation Dependent, nt Near Threatened, lc Least Concern. DD Data Deficient, NE Not Evaluated

Other EBAs (and SAs) (see p. 90 for locations): bracketed numbers are Secondary Areas; [x] extinct in that EBA or SA.

atolls have never been ornithologically surveyed at all. There is little recent information for *Prosobonia cancellata* and *Gallicolumba erythroptera* in particular.

■ Threats and conservation

The conservation situation in the Tuamotus is perhaps slightly more favourable than that in other French Polynesian archipelagos as a result of their geographic spread, isolation, difficulty of access and low human population. However, a few metres rise in sea levels (as now predicted) will quite likely cause the extinction of the rarer species.

In common with many other small-island areas, predation by introduced rats (particularly black rat *Rattus rattus*) is a current serious threat: for example, *Prosobonia cancellata* is found only on islands free from this pest, and it is also likely that rats have been responsible for the extinction of *Gallicolumba erythroptera* from many islands (Seitre and Seitre 1991).

Habitat destruction was a problem on Makatea, where phosphate mining (1917–1964) had confined the entire populations of *Ducula aurorae* and *Ptilinopus chalcurus* to the remaining inner forest (c.10 km² in total). These species are, however, relatively common today, with stable populations, and it is likely that they will extend their ranges as the

vegetation recovers. The extinction of *Vini peruviana*, a habitat generalist, from Makatea is more likely the result of a particularly violent hurricane and/or the introduction of predators rather than being due to mining activities (Thibault and Guyot 1987), and illustrates the permanent vulnerability of small-island species to chance events.

Mururoa and Fangataufa atolls in the south-east of the Tuamotus have been used by France for nuclear tests since 1966 (most recently in 1995–1996, but subsequently stopped), and it is likely that these activities will have extirpated populations of *Acrocephalus atyphus* on Fangataufa at least (J.-C. Thibault *in litt.* 1996).

The Tuamotus lie within the wintering range of the threatened (Vulnerable), restricted-range Bristle-thighed Curlew *Numenius tahitiensis*, which breeds in Western Alaska (Secondary Area s002). A tentative estimate of c.600 birds was made for the northern Tuamotus in 1989 (Lovegrove *et al.* 1989); as this represents some 6% of the total population, these islands are clearly important sites for the conservation of the species.

Taiaro Atoll was established as a Strict Nature Reserve in 1977; *Ptilinopus coralensis* was seen here in 1972 and *Acrocephalus atyphus* has also been recorded (Holyoak and Thibault 1984).

215 Henderson Island

PRIORITY URGENT

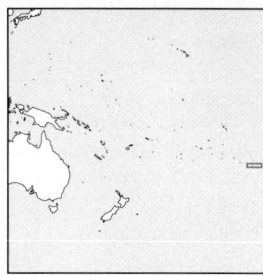

Key habitats Scrub forest	Area 31 km² Altitude 0–30 m		
Main threats Limited habitat loss (e.g. due to wood-cutting), introduced species	Countries Pitcairn Islands (to UK)		

Restricted-range species	Threatened	Total
Confined to this EBA	3	4
Present also in other EBAs, SAs	0	0
Total	3	4

Biological importance ● ● ●
Current threat level ● ●

■ General characteristics

Henderson, a raised island in the south-central Pacific, is one of a group of isolated islands which includes volcanic Pitcairn (the only currently inhabited island, well known as the final refuge for the *Bounty* mutineers, and treated as Secondary Area s137; see 'Restricted-range species', below) and Oeno and Ducie atolls, constituting the political unit of the Pitcairn Islands, a dependent territory of the United Kingdom.

Henderson is covered in dense scrub forest and, with the exception of a few introduced plant species including coconut palms, is one of the few relatively undisturbed elevated limestone islands in the world (see also EBA 099).

■ Restricted-range species

All the restricted-range species occur in the interior forest and a couple are also common in forest edge and surrounding scrub.

Acrocephalus taiti, a Henderson endemic, was formerly treated as a race of *A. vaughani* by Sibley and Monroe (1990), with the two other races *vaughani* on Pitcairn and *rimatarae* on Rimatara in French Polynesia. Consequently this EBA was originally defined as including Pitcairn Island (ICBP 1992) until the three were recognized as separate species (Graves 1992, Sibley and Monroe 1993), resulting in Pitcairn being treated as a Secondary Area (s137) and Rimatara, formerly treated as a Secondary Area but now with two endemic species, as an EBA (211).

Status and habitat of restricted-range species

Species (ordered taxonomically)	Global status	Other EBAs (and SAs)	Habitat
Henderson Crake *Porzana atra*	VU	—	Interior forest and surrounding scrub
Henderson Fruit-dove *Ptilinopus insularis*	VU	—	Interior forest
Henderson Lorikeet *Vini stepheni*	VU	—	Forest, esp. forest edge
Henderson Reed-warbler *Acrocephalus taiti*	NE	—	Forest

Global status (see p. 679 for definitions)	EX Extinct ⎫ with year EW Extinct in ⎬ of last the Wild ⎭ record	CR Critical ⎫ threatened EN Endangered ⎬ species VU Vulnerable ⎭	cd Conservation Dependent nt Near Threatened lc Least Concern	DD Data Deficient NE Not Evaluated

Other EBAs (and SAs) (see p. 90 for locations): bracketed numbers are Secondary Areas; ˣ extinct in that EBA or SA.

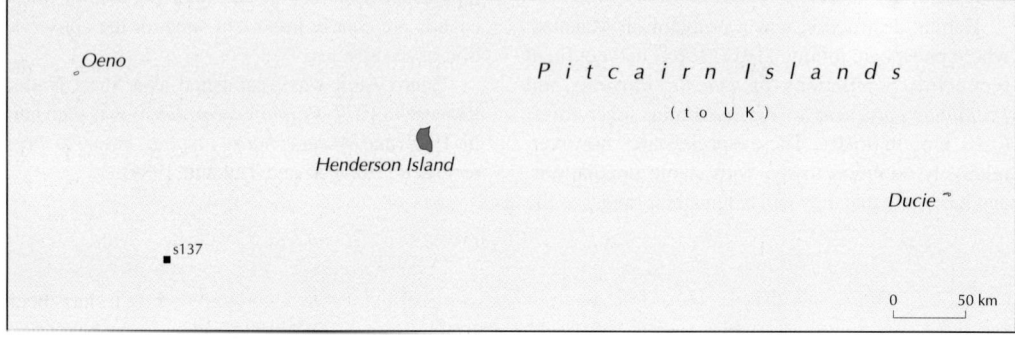

Oeno

P i t c a i r n   I s l a n d s
(t o   U K)

Henderson Island

Ducie

s137

0   50 km

The north-west cliffs of Henderson, one of the few relatively undisturbed elevated limestone islands in the world.

P. J. Jones

A. taiti differs from its two close relatives not only in plumage and vocalization but also in forming breeding groups of unrelated birds, though it has been suggested that this is a direct consequence of Henderson's stable habitat which is at carrying capacity for the species (Brooke and Hartley 1995).

■ Threats and conservation

The vulnerability of Henderson was exposed in 1982–1983 when a millionaire sought (unsuccessfully) to make it his home (Serpell *et al.* 1983). Current threats come from the Pacific rat *Rattus exulans*, introduced by Polynesian settlers, and woodcutting (of miro and tao for carving into curios) by Pitcairners, although present very low levels of clearance apparently make little impact on the avifauna.

Numerically healthy populations of the restricted-range species recorded in 1987 and 1992 indicate that Henderson's surviving landbirds have apparently adapted to the presence of Pacific rat or are at least able to coexist with it. Using different techniques, population estimates are c.3,240 and 6,200 individuals for *Porzana atra*, c.3,420 and 3,400 individuals for *Ptilinopus insularis*, 720–1,820 individuals and 1,200 pairs for *Vini stepheni*, and c.10,800 and 9,500 breeding individuals for *Acrocephalus taiti* (Graves 1992, Brooke and Hartley 1995, Brooke and Jones 1995, Jones *et al.* 1995d, Trevelyan 1995).

Nevertheless all the endemic species are threatened on account of their tiny ranges and their consequent permanent inherent risk of extinction. *Acrocephalus taiti* was not evaluated as a separate species by Collar *et al.* (1994), although it clearly would also qualify for Vulnerable status. The greatest potential danger is the possible accidental introduction of other mammalian predators, especially black rat *R. rattus*, and diseases (e.g. avian malaria and pox). The introduction of some of the exotic

Pitcairn plant species could have very serious consequences for the native Henderson vegetation (Waldren *et al.* 1995) and ultimately for other wildlife.

Henderson is a wintering site of international significance for Bristle-thighed Curlew *Numenius tahitiensis* (40–50 birds in 1991), a threatened (Vulnerable) restricted-range species breeding in Western Alaska (Secondary Area s002) (Brooke 1995a).

Henderson is also important for seabirds (11 breeding species) and, in particular, for three currently recognized gadfly petrels—Kermadec Petrel *Pterodroma neglecta*, Herald Petrel *P. heraldica* and Murphy's Petrel *P. ultima*—which all suffer severely from rat predation with less than 20% of eggs laid yielding fledglings (Brooke 1995b). The two morphs of *P. heraldica*, which both occur on Henderson, are likely to be separate species because they show reproductive isolation, both nesting and courting assortatively in different parts of the island, and having different calls (Brooke and Rowe 1996); Henderson could be the world stronghold for the dark form, the proposed 'Henderson Petrel'. As rat predation severely affects its breeding success and perhaps even its survival on this island, the newly described species will qualify as threatened. Although rat eradication may not be practical on Henderson, it is being considered on Oeno with a view to providing a secure refuge for this bird.

Between January 1991 and March 1992, a detailed survey of the Pitcairn Islands in general and Henderson in particular was carried out by the Sir Peter Scott Commemorative Expedition (see Brooke 1992, Benton and Spencer 1995). This expedition aimed to provide a comprehensive study of the terrestrial and marine biota, the geology, geomorphology and archaeology, and to provide a management plan for Henderson, which has been designated a World Heritage Site.

216 | Laysan Island

PRIORITY
CRITICAL

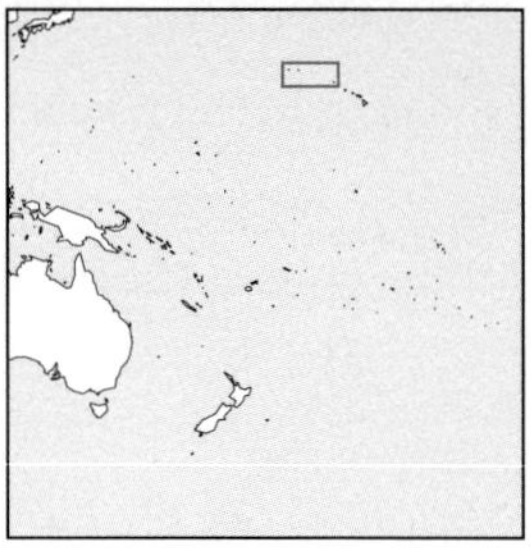

Key habitats Scrub, grassland, saline lagoon

Main threats Possible habitat loss (e.g. due to introduced plants)

Biological importance ● ● ●
Current threat level ● ● ○

Area 4 km² **Altitude** 0–10 m

Countries USA

Restricted-range species	Threatened	Total
Confined to this EBA	2	2
Present also in other EBAs, SAs	0	0
Total	2	2

■ General characteristics

The Hawaiian archipelago (covering EBAs 216–218) constitutes the US state of Hawaii and is a chain of volcanic islands which are gradually sinking and moving north-west, away from the 'hotspot' where they originally erupted. The oldest emergent island is Kure Atoll in the North-western Hawaiian or Leeward Islands and the youngest is the island of Hawaii (EBA 218).

Laysan, now a low-lying coral atoll (reaching only 11 m) with no volcanic rock exposed, is part of the North-western Hawaiian group and, at 3.7 km² in size, is the smallest of all EBAs. The native vegetation is mainly scrub and grass, and c.20% of the atoll is taken up by a central saline lagoon.

One of the restricted-range species extinct in this EBA, *Acrocephalus familiaris*, has a surviving population on Nihoa, but as this island is c.1,000 km south-east of Laysan, and as the two forms (*familiaris* on Laysan and *kingi* on Nihoa) are sometimes regarded as separate species, Nihoa is treated as a Secondary Area (s138). Two other islands in the North-western Hawaiian group—Midway, and Pearl and Hermes—have (or had) populations of some of the restricted-range species of Laysan, but these were all introduced.

■ Restricted-range species

Only two restricted-range species are extant in the EBA. In 1987 *Anas laysanensis* was estimated to number c.500 birds, which probably represents the carrying capacity of the habitat; extreme fluctuations in the population have been noted since the 1950s, but these may just reflect different census methods (Marshall 1992). Between 1960 and 1990 *Telespyza cantans* numbered 5,000–20,000 birds with apparent fluctuations attributable either to unpredictable weather, which has a major influence on breeding success every year, or, again, to variability in census methods (Morin 1992, Morin and Conant 1994). *T. cantans* also persists on Pearl and Hermes Atoll from an introduction in 1967 (but not on Midway Island, where an introduced population succumbed to predation by rats brought in inadvertently as a result of war activities; as did the introduced population of *Porzana palmeri*).

■ Threats and conservation

Previously undisturbed, Laysan was leased to phosphate miners during the period 1890–1904. The removal of guano (produced by the vast numbers of seabirds) was probably not detrimental to the landbirds, but duck-hunting to provide food and

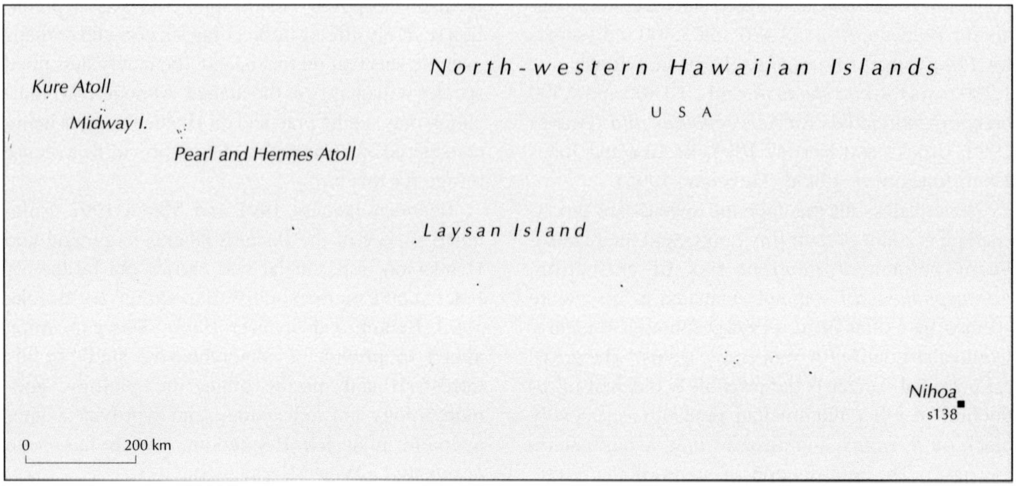

North-western Hawaiian Islands

Kure Atoll
Midway I.
Pearl and Hermes Atoll

U S A

Laysan Island

Nihoa
s138

0   200 km

Status and habitat of restricted-range species

Species (ordered taxonomically)	Global status	Other EBAs (and SAs)	Habitat
Laysan Duck *Anas laysanensis*	VU	—	Central saline lagoon for feeding, surrounding dense stands of shrubs and grasses for nesting
Laysan Crake *Porzana palmeri*[1,2]	EX (1944)	—	Grasses, marginal vegetation
Millerbird *Acrocephalus familiaris*[1]	VU	(s138)	Grasses
Laysan Finch *Telespiza cantans*[3]	VU	—	All plant associations inc. *Scaevola* thickets, low bushy areas; grass tussocks for nesting
'Apapane *Himatione sanguinea*[1]	lc	217,218	Scrub, grasses

Global status (see p. 679 for definitions)
EX Extinct / EW Extinct in the Wild — with year of last record
CR Critical / EN Endangered / VU Vulnerable — threatened species
cd Conservation Dependent
nt Near Threatened
lc Least Concern
DD Data Deficient
NE Not Evaluated

Other EBAs (and SAs) (see p. 90 for locations)
Bracketed numbers are Secondary Areas. [x] Extinct in that EBA or SA.

Notes
[1] Extinct in this EBA (1912–1923).
[2] Introduced and extinct on Midway Island.
[3] Introduced and surviving on Pearl and Hermes Atoll, introduced and extinct on Midway Island.

sport for members of the mining community reduced the population of *Anas laysanensis*. Even greater impact resulted from the introduction of European rabbits *Oryctolagus cuniculus* in 1903–1904 to provide a source of fresh food independent of supply ships. By 1911 the rabbits had caused massive deterioration of the habitat, and three species of bird, deprived of their natural food supply, became extinct. The subsequent removal of these mammals in 1923 allowed regeneration of the vegetation and the recovery of the two surviving species.

The two endemic species are still classified as threatened today because of their very small ranges and, in the case of *Anas laysanensis*, very small population, rendering them both forever at risk of extinction from chance events, such as the effects of severe weather or introduced species, particularly the possible accidental introduction of rats from

passing ships. The aggressive alien plant, *Cenchrus echinatus*, could cause detrimental habitat deterioration, but eradication is under way (K. McDermond *in litt.* 1993).

Laysan is extremely important for seabirds—having some of the greatest nesting colonies in the world, holding 18 species and up to a million breeding pairs (Harrison 1990b)—and is also an important wintering site for Bristle-thighed Curlew *Numenius tahitiensis* (Vulnerable), a migratory, restricted-range species (see Secondary Area s002), with winter counts of 300–350 individuals during 1988–1991 (Marks and Redmond 1994).

Laysan is protected by the Hawaiian Islands National Wildlife Refuge, which includes the Northwestern Hawaiian Islands from Pearl and Hermes Atoll to Nihoa, and is uninhabited except when researchers are present.

217 Central Hawaiian Islands

PRIORITY CRITICAL

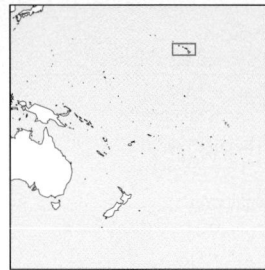

Key habitats Upland rain forest, dry woodland, wetlands

Main threats Major habitat loss (e.g. due to cultivation, grazing, settlement), introduced species

Biological importance ● ● ●
Current threat level ● ● ●

Area 6,300 km² **Altitude** 0–3,000 m

Countries USA

Restricted-range species	Threatened	Total
Confined to this EBA	14	15
Present also in other EBAs, SAs	4	8
Total	18	23

■ General characteristics

As part of the US state of Hawaii, this EBA comprises the islands of Kaua'i, O'ahu, Moloka'i, Lana'i and Maui, but not Hawai'i, which is considered an EBA in its own right (EBA 218; see also EBA 216), nor the two other (smaller) islands in the same group, Ni'ihau and Kaho'olawe, as nothing is known about their ornithological history and neither island is suitable now for native birds; goats were introduced to Ni'ihau in the late 1700s, and sheep and cattle had destroyed the original vegetation before the 1890s (Berger 1972).

Maui, at 1,861 km² the largest island in the EBA, reaches the highest altitude at Haleakala Volcano (3,055 m). The native vegetation is forest and woodland with two distinct types in the uplands, which are important for restricted-range birds: rain forest in the wetter areas (where the myrtaceous tree ohia *Metrosideros polymorpha* is dominant) and open, dry, woodland elsewhere (where koa *Acacia koa* is dominant).

The Hawaiian Islands are renowned for their unique wildlife, with 91% of flowering plants, 100% of land mammals and 81% of birds being endemic at least at subspecies level (Gagné 1988).

■ Restricted-range species

The majority of the restricted-range species of this EBA are taxonomically highly distinct, especially the Hawaiian honeycreepers. This endemic family is a particularly good avian example of adaptive radiation and speciation in an isolated island ecosystem for, from what is believed to have been a single successful colonization by an ancestral species from North America, its members have evolved into a diverse array of species and subspecies, e.g. *Viridonia virens* with a small insectivorous bill, *Dysmorodrepanis munroi* with a woodpecker-like bill and *Vestiaria coccinea* with a large decurved bill for nectar feeding. Five genera are endemic to the EBA—*Dysmorodrepanis, Melamprosops, Palmeria, Paroreomyza* and *Pseudonestor*.

The taxonomy of the species of these islands is still in a state of flux such that populations of *Chasiempis sandwichensis* (which differ strikingly in plumage coloration among the three islands they inhabit) may prove to be separate species, and O'ahu Amakihi *Viridonia virens chloris* and Hawaiian Stilt *Himantopus mexicanus knudseni* are also treated as separate species by some experts (Pratt 1993, H. D. Pratt *in litt.* 1994).

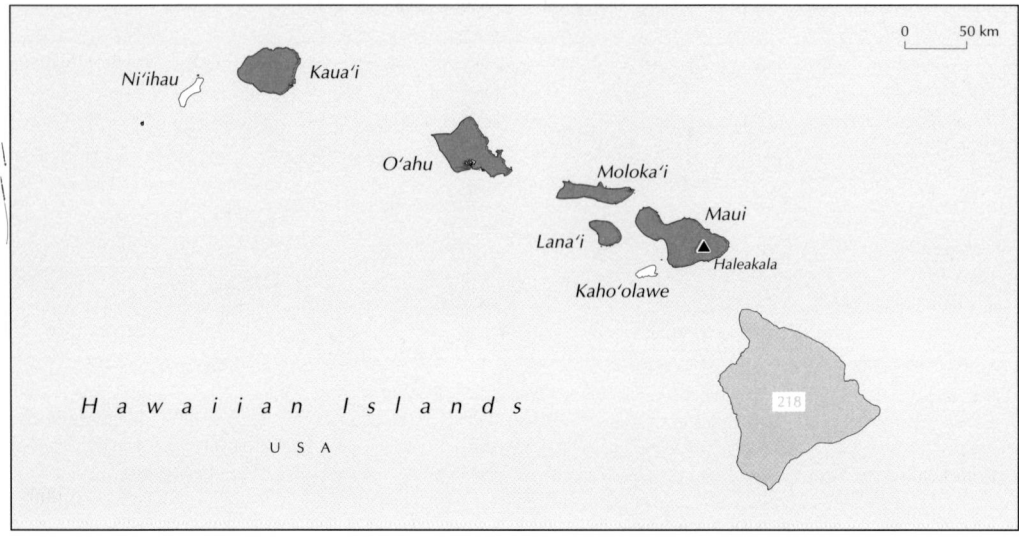

Status and habitat of restricted-range species

Species (ordered taxonomically)	Global status	Other EBAs (and SAs)	Altitude (m)	Habitat
Hawaiian Duck *Anas wyvilliana*	VU	218	Lowlands, mountains	Mountain streams, river valleys, coastal lagoons, ponds, taro fields
Hawaiian Coot *Fulica alai*	VU	218	Lowlands	Any body of water inc. fresh- and saltwater ponds, estuaries, marshes
Kama'o *Myadestes myadestinus*	CR	—	1,100–1,500	Ohia forest
'Amaui *Myadestes oahensis*	EX (1825)	—	No data	Forest
Oloma'o *Myadestes lanaiensis*	CR	—	900–1,100	Ohia forest
Puaiohi *Myadestes palmeri*	CR	—	1,100–1,300	Ohia forest
'Elepaio *Chasiempis sandwichensis*	lc	218	300–3,000	Native and exotic forest, treeless zone
Kaua'i O'o *Moho braccatus*	CR	—	1,100–1,500	Ohia forest
O'ahu O'o *Moho apicalis*	EX (1837)	—	No data	Forest
Bishop's O'o *Moho bishopi*	CR	—	c.1,900	Ohia forest
'O'u *Psittirostra psittacea*	CR	218	700–1,900	Ohia forest
Lana'i Hookbill *Dysmorodrepanis munroi*	EX (1918)	—	No data	Forest
Maui Parrotbill *Pseudonestor xanthophrys*	VU	—	1,200–2,150	Native forest, esp. koa forest
Kaua'i 'Amakihi *Viridonia stejnegeri*	VU	—	1,100–1,500	Ohia forest
Common 'Amakihi *Viridonia virens*	lc	218	100–3,100	Native and exotic forest, treeless zone
'Anianiau *Viridonia parva*	VU	—	0–1,550	Mainly ohia forest, also introduced vegetation
'Akialoa *Hemignathus obscurus*	EX (1969)	218[X]	1,500+	Koa–ohia forest
Nukupu'u *Hemignathus lucidus*	CR	218[X]	1,450–2,000	Ohia, koa–ohia forest with well-developed native understorey
'Akikiki *Oreomystis bairdi*	EN	—	1,100–1,500	Ohia forest
Maui 'Alauahio *Paroreomyza montana*	nt	—	900–2,700	Ohia and koa–ohia forest, exotic forest, treeless zone, savanna, scrubland
Kakawahie *Paroreomyza flammea*	EX (1963)	—	No data	Forest
O'ahu 'Alauahio *Paroreomyza maculata*	CR	—	No data	Forest
'Akeke'e *Loxops caeruleirostris*	EN	—	1,100–1,500	Ohia forest
'Akepa *Loxops coccineus*	EN	218	1,100–2,100	Ohia, koa–ohia forest
'I'iwi *Vestiaria coccinea*	lc	218	300–2,900	Native and exotic forest
Black Mamo *Drepanis funerea*	EX (1907)	—	No data	Forest
'Akohekohe *Palmeria dolei*	VU	—	1,300–2,300	Ohia forest, koa–ohia forest

cont.

Status and habitat of restricted-range species (cont.)

Species (ordered taxonomically)	Global status	Other EBAs (and SAs)	Altitude (m)	Habitat
'Apapane *Himatione sanguinea*	lc	216[X],218	100–2,900	Native (esp. wet ohia) and exotic forest, treeless zone
Po'o-uli *Melamprosops phaeosoma*	CR	—	1,400–2,050	Ohia forest

Global status (see p. 679 for definitions)	EX Extinct EW Extinct in the Wild	} with year of last record	CR Critical EN Endangered VU Vulnerable	} threatened species	cd Conservation Dependent nt Near Threatened lc Least Concern	DD Data Deficient NE Not Evaluated

Other EBAs (and SAs) (see p. 90 for locations): bracketed numbers are Secondary Areas; [X] extinct in that EBA or SA.

Apart from two wetland species, all the restricted-range bird species are forest and/or woodland dwellers (mostly occurring in ohia rain forest), and many are restricted to higher altitudes (largely above 1,000 m), although historically they are likely to have occurred in lowlands too.

The distributional patterns of species vary considerably, with many island extirpations. Extant single-island endemics are found on Kaua'i (seven species), Maui (five), Moloka'i (one) and O'ahu (one), but all these islands are combined into one EBA with Lana'i because of the restricted-range species which are common to them (in various island combinations). Kaua'i and Maui are the most important islands both for their endemics and for the numbers of extant restricted-range species which they support in total (14 on Kaua'i and 11 on Maui).

Many species have tiny distributions within the islands on which they survive, with the Alaka'i Swamp on Kaua'i (a wet montane plateau mostly above 1,000 m) being a very important area, and the north-east slopes of Haleakala and upper Kipahulu valley on Maui being similarly important.

Two restricted-range species have been introduced: Nene *Branta sandvicensis* (from Hawai'i, EBA 218), introduced to Maui (184 birds present in 1989–1990) and Kaua'i (130 in 1995); and Micronesian Swiftlet *Collocalia inquieta* (from the Mariana and East Caroline Islands (EBAs 189, 192), established on O'ahu from a flock introduced in 1962 (the race *bartschi* which is endemic to Guam).

Two seabirds, Hawaiian Petrel *Pterodroma sandwichensis* and Newell's Shearwater *Puffinus newelli*, are, as breeders, largely endemic to this EBA (otherwise likely to breed only, and in very small numbers, on Hawai'i, EBA 218).

■ Threats and conservation

Of all the Pacific EBAs, the Central Hawaiian Islands has the highest number of threatened restricted-range species (18), of threatened endemic restricted-range species (14), and of Critical endemic restricted-range species (eight). Several species with tiny populations have not been seen recently and are therefore likely to be close to extinction: *Myadestes myadestinus* (last seen on Kaua'i in 1989 with an unconfirmed sighting in 1993), *M. lanaiensis* (last seen on Moloka'i in 1988), *Moho braccatus* (last recorded on Kaua'i in 1987), *M. bishopi* (last seen on Maui in 1981 with subsequent reports from the 1980s unconfirmed), *Psittirostra psittacea* (last seen on Kaua'i in 1989) and *Paroreomyza maculata* (last confirmed sighting on O'ahu in 1985) (R. Pyle *in litt.* 1996).

The demise of the avifauna—documented by Pratt (1994) for the period 1893–1993 (see also

Distribution patterns of restricted-range species

Species (ordered geographically)	Kaua'i	O'ahu	Moloka'i	Lana'i	Maui	Other EBAs, SAs
Myadestes myadestinus	○	-	-	-	-	-
Myadestes palmeri	●	-	-	-	-	-
Moho braccatus	○	-	-	-	-	-
Viridonia stejnegeri	●	-	-	-	-	-
Viridonia parva	●	-	-	-	-	-
Oreomystis bairdi	●	-	-	-	-	-
Loxops caeruleirostris	●	-	-	-	-	-
Chasiempis sandwichensis	●	●	-	-	-	●
Hemignathus obscurus	X	X	-	X	-	X
Hemignathus lucidus	○	X	-	-	○	X
Anas wyvilliana	●	R	X	-	X	●
Fulica alai	●	●	●	●	●	●
Psittirostra psittacea	○	X	X	X	X	●
Vestiaria coccinea	●	●	●	X	●	●
Himatione sanguinea	●	●	●	●	●	●
Myadestes oahensis	-	X	-	-	-	-
Moho apicalis	-	X	-	-	-	-
Paroreomyza maculata	-	○	-	-	-	-
Loxops coccineus	-	X	-	-	○	●
Viridonia virens	-	●	●	X	●	●
Paroreomyza flammea	-	-	X	-	-	-
Drepanis funerea	-	-	X	-	-	-
Moho bishopi	-	-	X	-	○	-
Palmeria dolei	-	-	X	-	●	-
Myadestes lanaiensis	-	-	○	X	X	-
Dysmorodrepanis munroi	-	-	-	X	-	-
Paroreomyza montana	-	-	-	X	●	-
Pseudonestor xanthophrys	-	-	-	-	●	-
Melamprosops phaeosoma	-	-	-	-	○	-
Total	14	7	5	2	11	

● Present	? Present?	Threatened spp. shown in **bold**	} see 'Status and habitat' table
○ Extinct?	R Reintroduced	Other EBAs, SAs	
X Extinct	I Introduced		

Jacobi and Atkinson 1995)—has been due to a combination of factors: hunting by early settlers; forest clearance (most of the lowlands have been cleared for cultivation, grazing and settlement, and less than 40% of the land surface is covered with native-dominated vegetation); introduced predators (e.g. rats, cats, dogs and, except on Kaua'i, mongooses *Herpestes auropunctatus*); introduced browsers (e.g. pigs, deer, goats) and plants (such as the invasive neotropical tree *Miconia calvescens*) leading to habitat deterioration; introduced birds and arthropods (e.g. ants and wasps) resulting in increased competition for nesting and food resources; and diseases (especially viral pox and protozoan-caused avian malaria, carried by introduced *Culex* mosquitoes, which are common in wet mid-elevation forests where their populations overlap with highly susceptible native birds).

Since the late 1800s the human population in the Hawaiian Islands has grown exponentially, as has the tourist industry; the direct and indirect impacts of the resulting visitor load on the natural resources of the islands is an additional threat to wildlife (WWF/IUCN 1994–1995), although most native birds survive today in remote refuges where any disturbance is minimal (S. L. Pimm *in litt.* 1996).

These man-related threats can be exacerbated by cyclones, an irregular natural hazard. For example, Hurricane Iniki, which struck Kaua'i with devastating force in 1992, severely altered this legendary 'Garden Isle' by removing most of the forest canopy on exposed ridges. The island's extremely rare native birds, largely surviving in Alaka'i Swamp (and because of habitat alteration no longer able to ride out the storms in lowland valleys), may have been delivered the final death blow by this single event (Pratt 1993), there having been few or no records since.

In recent years the loss of species on Lana'i has accelerated as ecosystems have begun to suffer catastrophic collapse, and this serves as an example of what can happen to small-island systems when native flora and fauna are severely reduced (Hobdy 1993).

In addition to the 18 threatened restricted-range species in this EBA, three subspecies, which may be species—*Chasiempsis sandwichensis ibidis*, *Viridonia virens chloris* and *Himantopus mexicanus knudseni*—also qualify as threatened (H. D. Pratt *in litt.* 1994), and two endemic seabirds—*Pterodroma sandwichensis* and *Puffinus newelli*—(see 'Restricted-range species', above) are classified as threatened (both Vulnerable); *P. sandwichensis* has been reduced to c.900 pairs mainly on Haleakala on Maui, and *P. newelli* to c.8,000 breeding adults (perhaps more) on the mountains of Kaua'i.

There are many important parks and refuges in the Hawaiian Islands—for example, the Haleakala National Park (embracing the Kipahulu valley), which was established on Maui in 1916, and the more recently designated Alaka'i Wilderness Preserve, Koke'e and Waimea Canyon State Parks on Kaua'i—but much of the best remaining forest habitat remains unprotected and vulnerable (Pratt *et al.* 1987), and the long-term survival of native species within protected areas depends on the intensity of management, including programmes such as control of non-native species (IUCN 1992c).

One such programme has successfully controlled feral pigs in Kipahulu valley (Anderson and Stone 1993), an undertaking that has been described as the single most important management action for the protection of the biological diversity of east Maui's rain forests. Another programme is under way to remove *Miconia calvescens* from private and state land on Maui (Loope and Medeiros 1995), and further initiatives and recommendations are described in Stone and Loope (1987) and Medeiros *et al.* (1993). Major new efforts to develop strategies for monitoring transmission of diseases in remote forest habitats and for controlling vector populations are also in progress (Jacobi and Atkinson 1995). A detailed survey of Hawaiian forest birds (1976–1983) has resulted in a mass of distributional, population and habitat data, and in conservation recommendations for specific islands (Scott *et al.* 1986).

218 Hawai'i

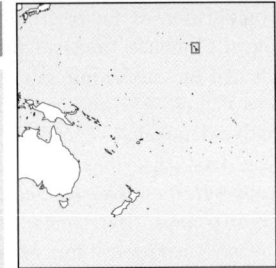

Key habitats Upland rain forest, dry woodland

Main threats Major habitat loss (e.g. due to agriculture, tourist development), introduced species

Biological importance ● ● ●
Current threat level ● ● ●

Area 10,000 km²
Countries USA
Altitude 0–3,100 m

Restricted-range species	Threatened	Total
Confined to this EBA	5	7
Present also in other EBAs, SAs	4	8
Total	9	15

■ General characteristics

The island of Hawai'i is part of the US state of Hawaii (which also includes EBAs 216 and 217) and is larger than all other islands in the archipelago combined. It is the youngest island of the Hawaiian chain, with five volcanoes: Kohala, Mauna Kea (at 4,205 m, the highest mountain), Hualalai, Mauna Loa and Kilauea, the last three having erupted in historic times.

Hawai'i was originally largely covered in forest and woodland, with open areas above the treeline at c.3,000 m and very extensive lava flows where forest survives in small patches (kipukas). Three extant main types of wooded habitat, important for restricted-range species, can be recognized: rain forest in wetter areas (where the myrtaceous tree ohia *Metrosideros polymorpha* is dominant), drier woodland (where koa *Acacia koa* is dominant) and a second type of dry woodland usually at high elevations (where the legume mamane *Sophora chrysophylla* and naio *Myoporum sandwicense* dominate).

J. Jeffrey

Although many of Hawai'i's unique birds are now extinct, 'I'iwi *Vestiaria coccinea*, a brilliant scarlet Hawaiian honeycreeper with a deeply decurved peach-coloured bill, remains common at higher altitudes.

■ Restricted-range species

Hawai'i has a particularly distinctive avifauna with five endemic genera: *Chaetoptila*, *Chloridops*, *Ciridops*, *Loxioides* and *Rhodacanthis*. Most of the restricted-range bird species occur in forest and woodland, and many are found largely above c.500 m, although originally they are likely to have occurred in the lowlands too, e.g. *Psittirostra psittacea* (found only on Mauna Loa) and *Loxioides bailleui* (only on Mauna Kea), which today are confined to upland forest.

A total of 10 restricted-range species (eight extant, one now extinct on Hawai'i, one globally extinct) are shared solely with the Central Hawaiian Islands (EBA 217), but 16 (seven extant, nine globally extinct) are endemic, making Hawai'i an EBA in its own right.

The three separate island populations of *Chasiempsis sandwichensis* differ strikingly in plum-

Hawaiian Islands

USA

Hawai'i

Kohala Mts
Hamakua
Mauna Kea ▲
▲ Hualalai
Kona
Mauna Loa ▲
▲ Kilauea Crater

0   50 km

Status and habitat of restricted-range species

Species (ordered taxonomically)	Global status	Other EBAs (and SAs)	Altitude (m)	Habitat
Nene *Branta sandvicensis*[1]	VU	—	Uplands	Rocky volcanic slopes
Hawaiian Duck *Anas wyvilliana*[2]	VU	217	Lowlands, mountains	Mountain streams, river valleys, coastal lagoons, ponds, taro fields
Hawaiian Hawk *Buteo solitarius*	nt	—	0–2,600	Most habitats inc. virtually all types of forest and orchards, absent from areas with no trees
Hawaiian Crake *Porzana sandwichensis*	EX (1884)	—	No data	Grassy uplands adjacent to forest, forest clearings
Hawaiian Coot *Fulica alai*	VU	217	Lowlands	Any waterbody, inc. fresh- and saltwater ponds, estuaries, marshes
'Oma'o *Myadestes obscurus*	lc	—	300–2,300	Ohia forest, koa–ohia forest, treeless alpine zone
'Elepaio *Chasiempis sandwichensis*	lc	217	300–3,100	Native and exotic forest, treeless zone
Hawai'i O'o *Moho nobilis*	EX (1898)	—	650–1,850	Forest
Kioea *Chaetoptila angustipluma*	EX (1859)	—	No data	Forest
'O'u *Psittirostra psittacea*	CR	217	700–1,900	Ohia forest
Palila *Loxioides bailleui*	EN	—	1,900–3,100	Mamane forest, mamane–naio forest
Lesser Koa-finch *Rhodacanthis flaviceps*	EX (1891)	—	Mountains	Forest, primarily koa
Greater Koa-finch *Rhodacanthis palmeri*	EX (1896)	—	1,000+	Forest, primarily koa
Grosbeak Finch *Chloridops kona*	EX (1894)	—	1,000–1,800	Naio forest on lava flows
Common 'Amakihi *Viridonia virens*	lc	217	100–3,100	Native and exotic forest, treeless zone
Greater 'Amakihi *Viridonia sagittirostris*	EX (1900)	—	800+	Forest, esp. ohia
'Akialoa *Hemignathus obscurus*	EX (1969)	217[X]	1,500+	Koa–ohia forest
Nukupu'u *Hemignathus lucidus*[3]	CR	217	1,450–2,000	Ohia, koa–ohia forest with well-developed native understorey
'Akiapola'au *Hemignathus wilsoni*	EN	—	900–3,100	Koa–ohia forest, mamane–naio forest
Hawai'i Creeper *Oreomystis mana*	EN	—	500–2,300	Koa–ohia forest
'Akepa *Loxops coccineus*	EN	217	1,100–2,100	Ohia, koa–ohia forest
'Ula-'ai-hawane *Ciridops anna*	EX (1890)	—	Mountains	Forest, esp. loulu palm and ohia
'I'iwi *Vestiaria coccinea*	lc	217	300–2,900	Native and exotic forest
Hawai'i Mamo *Drepanis pacifica*	EX (1898)	—	Mountains	Forest, esp. ohia
'Apapane *Himatione sanguinea*	lc	216[X],217	100–2,900	Native (esp. ohia) and exotic forest, treeless zone
Hawaiian Crow *Corvus hawaiiensis*	CR	—	Usually 1,300–1,500	Undisturbed ohia–koa forest

Global status (see p. 679 for definitions)

EX	Extinct	} with year of last record	cd	Conservation Dependent
EW	Extinct in the Wild		nt	Near Threatened
CR	Critical	} threatened species	lc	Least Concern
EN	Endangered		DD	Data Deficient
VU	Vulnerable		NE	Not Evaluated

Other EBAs (and SAs) (see p. 90 for locations)
Bracketed numbers are Secondary Areas.   [X] Extinct in that EBA or SA.

Notes
[1] Introduced to Maui and Kauai (EBA 217).
[2] Reintroduced to Hawaii.
[3] Extinct in this EBA (known only from one nineteenth-century specimen and one questionable record from 1971; see Olson and James 1994).

age coloration and may prove to be separate species; three subspecies are distinguishable on Hawai'i alone (Pratt 1980, 1993). Hawaiian Stilt *Himantopus mexicanus knudseni* is also sometimes recognized as a separate species.

'Apapane *Himatione sanguinea*, perched here on native ohia blossom, is able to utilize exotic forest and treeless habitats and is the most abundant native bird in the Hawaiian Islands.

■ Threats and conservation

This EBA has suffered nine extinctions of endemic species in historic times—more than any other EBA—and many more taxa had become extinct through the actions of Polynesian man before the arrival of European explorers in 1778 (Olson and James 1982).

The demise of the avifauna can be attributed to: forest clearance and degradation for agriculture and forest products (especially in the lowlands; there are now extensive man-made grasslands on the island's drier leeward side); hunting by early settlers; introduced predators; introduced browsers (pigs, goats, sheep, cattle) and plants leading to habitat deterioration; competition from introduced birds; and diseases, especially those carried by introduced mosquitoes (see EBA 217 for more detail).

There are also a number of recently emerging land uses dependent on new technologies (e.g. wood-chipping, geothermal energy, astronomical research) and additional indirect impacts derived from tourist-related, coastal economic development (Juvik *et al.* 1992). Nevertheless, the threatened endemic species are in general less critically imperiled than those of the Central Hawaiian Islands (EBA 217) because

they enjoy more extensive tracts of high-elevation habitat (Pratt 1993).

However, the survival of *Branta sandvicensis* (the state bird) is dependent on releases of captive-bred stock (c.2,100 birds in total during 1960–1990) to maintain numbers—a population of 339 birds on Hawai'i in 1989–1990. Problems identified specifically for this species include inbreeding depression, loss of adaptive skills, disease, poaching, road kills, dietary deficiencies and predation by introduced mammals (Black *et al.* 1991, Marshall and Black 1992).

The endemic *Corvus hawaiiensis*, a primarily fruit-eating, forest-inhabiting crow, is now found only in central Kona (believed to be restricted to one privately-owned ranch) as a result of commercial logging, conversion of forest to agriculture and ranching, and shooting. In 1994 it numbered 31–36 birds in both wild and captive flocks and is the subject of a captive-breeding and release programme (National Research Council 1992).

As well as its nine threatened restricted-range species, three subspecies (important because of potential taxonomic changes; see 'Restricted-range species', above) also qualify as threatened: Mauna Kea 'Elepaio *Chasiempis sandwichensis bryani*, Kona 'Elepaio *C. s. sandwichensis* and *Himantopus mexicanus knudseni* (H. D. Pratt *in litt.* 1994).

Some 10% of Hawai'i is currently included in protected areas, the Hawai'i Volcanoes National Park being world famous (though not established for its biological features, it has recently been expanded to include more forest). However, some important forested areas are still unprotected, notably those of central Kona.

A detailed survey of Hawaiian forest birds (Scott *et al.* 1986) has shown that the native avifauna is most intact in four refugia: the mamane–naio woodlands around Mauna Kea, the ohia forest on the windward Hamakua coast (Hakalau National Wildlife Refuge, recently established there as a consequence of these surveys, houses most rare species and is therefore extremely important: S. L. Pimm *in litt.* 1996), the Kau forest (koa–ohia and ohia forest on the southeast slopes of Mauna Loa), and forests on the north slopes of Hualalai. Conservation priorities include securing ownership or management agreements for several important forest areas, removing feral ungulates and pigs, and controlling introduced plants in essential habitat.

SECONDARY AREAS

A SECONDARY AREA (Figure 1) is an area which supports one or more restricted-range bird species, but does not qualify as an Endemic Bird Area because fewer than two species are entirely confined to it (see p. 20). Typical Secondary Areas include:

- Areas with single restricted-range species which do not overlap in distribution with any other such species, e.g. Rapa in French Polynesia (s136)

which has one endemic bird species only, Rapa Fruit-dove *Ptilinopus huttoni*.

- Areas where there are widely disjunct records of one or more restricted-range species, e.g. South Veracruz coast scrub in Mexico (s005) which supports an isolated population of Mexican Sheartail *Calothorax eliza*, some 650 km from its core range on the Yucatán peninsula (EBA 015).

NORTH AND CENTRAL AMERICA

Eastern Bering Sea islands   s001
This Secondary Area is centred on St Matthew Island (c.600 km²) which lies between St Lawrence Island to the north and the Pribilof Islands to the south, c.350 km west of south-west Alaska, USA. The area has been identified because McKay's Bunting *Plectrophenax hyperboreus* breeds on St Matthew and the much smaller nearby Hall Island. The species also breeds in small numbers on St Lawrence Island, and is regularly reported but rarely nests on St Paul and St George Islands in the Pribilof group (where it appears to hybridize with Snow Bunting *P. nivalis*). This Secondary Area is characterized by rocky coastal areas and upland, rocky tundra and scree slopes. *P. hyperboreus* winters along the coast of western Alaska (Byers *et al.* 1995, Rising 1996).

Seaward peninsula and   s002
Yukon delta
This Secondary Area comprises the mountains (up to c.500 m in elevation) of the west-central Seaward peninsula (the Kougarok mountains) and along eastern Norton Sound, east of the Yukon delta (the southern Nulato hills), in westernmost Alaska, USA. The area holds the only two known breeding populations of the threatened Bristle-thighed Curlew *Numenius tahitiensis* (classified as Vulnerable), which total some 7,000 individuals (although it is possible that small numbers breed at least intermittently on the Chukotka peninsula in Russia: Konyukhov and

McCaffery 1993). This species breeds in various habitats ranging from xeric alpine lichen meadows, through shrub-heath tundra and tussock tundra to wet sedge meadow, and winters throughout the central and southern Pacific (where it suffers predation by introduced animals), including in several oceanic island EBAs and Secondary Areas. The southern Nulato hills portion of this Secondary Area is protected within the Yukon Delta National Wildlife Refuge, although throughout the breeding grounds *N. tahitiensis* is potentially threatened by hunting and by activities associated with gold-mining.

Michigan jack pine savanna   s003
The area is confined to the northern portion of Lower Michigan, USA, and comprises c.1,000 km² of level or gently rolling sandy soil on which the jack pine *Pinus banksiana* occurs naturally. This specialized habitat is the only breeding area of Kirtland's Warbler *Dendroica kirtlandii* (classified as Vulnerable) which is dependent on dense and near-homogeneous stands of jack pine 1.7–5.0 m tall (8–20 years old), such conditions occurring naturally only after extensive fires. Very little of such suitable habitat remains, and *D. kirtlandii* is surviving (there were 692 singing males in 1996) due entirely to intensive management of the remaining forests and control of the parasitic Brown-headed Cowbird *Molothrus ater*. *D. kirtlandii* leaves the area in September to winter in the Bahamas and Turks and Caicos islands (EBA 026).

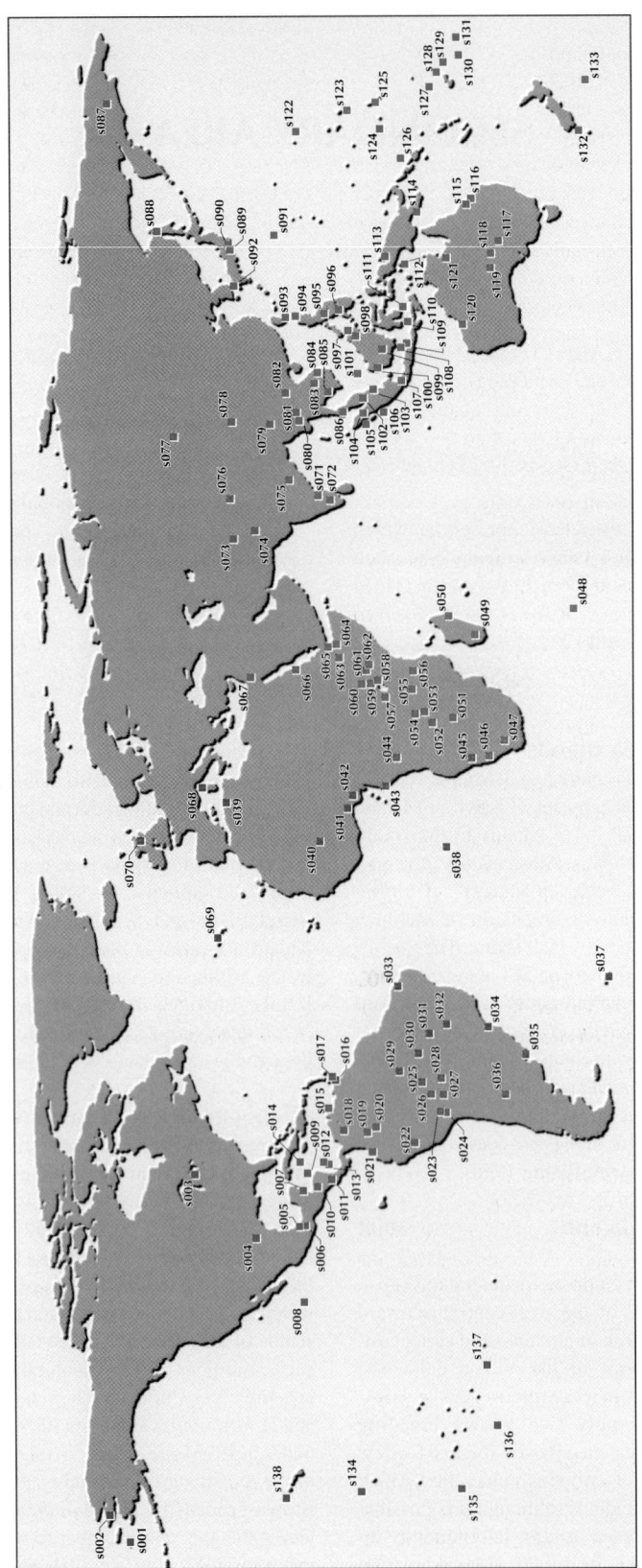

Figure 1. The location of Secondary Areas.

Edwards plateau   s004

Edwards plateau is a large, primarily limestone area of the 'Hill Country' of central Texas, USA (see map, p. 106). The area is characterized by (in the Lampasas Cut plain) low grass-covered hills (generally below 1,000 m) and oak–juniper woodland (although much land has been cleared for grazing), and (in the Balcones canyonlands) steep, narrow canyons with tall deciduous trees (especially Spanish oaks) along the drainage bottoms and a mix of junipers and oaks (especially Texas live oaks) on the slopes. Edwards plateau has been identified as a Secondary Area due to the presence of the threatened Golden-cheeked Warbler *Dendroica chrysoparia* (classified as Endangered), which currently nests in just 30 Texas counties, primarily in the Balcones canyonlands or in nearby areas with similar geology and vegetation. The species is dependent on mature ashe juniper *Juniperus ashei* for nesting, but is equally dependent on a variety of mature oaks for foraging. Urbanization and land-clearance for agriculture have reduced the extent of suitable habitat for *D. chrysoparia* to just 300–1,000 km² (Kroll 1980, Sexton 1992, Kutac and Caran 1994). The species winters in highland pine and pine–oak–madrone habitats in southern Mexico and northern Central America (primarily in the North Central American highlands, EBA 018). The more widespread but equally threatened Black-capped Vireo *Vireo atricapillus* (Endangered) also breeds on Edwards plateau, primarily in regenerating sumac–madrone–oak thickets adjacent to and among the mature oak–juniper woodland utilized by the Golden-cheeked Warbler.

South Veracruz coast scrub   s005

This Secondary Area is defined by a population of Mexican Sheartail *Doricha eliza* in central Veracruz (Mexico) which is disjunct and isolated from the species' main range 650 km to the east along the north coast of the Yucatán peninsula (EBA 015; see map, p. 112). In Veracruz the bird is a fairly common but local resident of arid deciduous scrub from sea-level to 300 m (Howell and Webb 1995a). Dry forest in Veracruz is threatened by agricultural expansion, intensive grazing, firewood-gathering and burning (Dinerstein *et al.* 1995). This population of *D. eliza* is not known to be present in any protected area.

South Mexican karst forests   s006

This Mexican Secondary Area is found between Córdoba town in Veracruz state and Cerro Oro in northern Oaxaca, and is characterized by steep hill country of karst limestone outcrops, which are covered in semi-deciduous and evergreen forest (see map, p. 112). The area embraces the range of Sumichrast's Wren *Hylorchilus sumichrasti*, a cryptic species that espends the majority of its time at or near ground-level, always in closed-canopy forest, foraging in and around cracks and crevices of rocks and vegetation on the limestone outcrops. It is closely related to Nava's Wren *H. navai* (see EBA 013 for discussion of taxonomy). *H. sumichrasti*, is considered threatened (classified as Vulnerable) owing to its tiny range and vulnerability to habitat destruction. Although these forested limestone outcrops are poor for cultivation compared with the surrounding flatter land, and thus have been spared from complete conversion to agriculture, they are threatened by expansion of limestone-quarrying, and in many areas the forest has an understorey of coffee plants. It appears that it is the limestone outcrops rather than the primary forest understorey that are essential for the wren, as it has been found in good numbers in shaded coffee plantations on limestone around Córdoba. Some of the species' habitat has undoubtedly been lost to the extensive Presa Miguel Alemán reservoir in northern Oaxaca, as birds have been recorded on some of the small islands created by the dam (Collar *et al.* 1992). There are currently no protected areas within this Secondary Area.

Eastern Yucatán   s007

This Secondary Area covers much of the range of Yucatán Vireo *Vireo magister*, including the east Caribbean coast of the Yucatán peninsula, mainly eastern Quintana Roo state of Mexico, south through coastal Belize to Ambergris Cay, and also including offshore islands and cays such as Isla Mujeres off Quintana Roo and Belize Cays (Cay Corker, Turneffe Islands, Lighthouse and Glover's reefs) and the Bay Islands of Honduras (Howell and Webb 1995a). *V. magister* is also found on the islands of Cozumel (EBA 016) and Grand Cayman (Secondary Area s014), and through most of its range is a fairly common resident. The dominant vegetation of this coastal Secondary Area is mangrove, semi-deciduous forest and scrub. Some parts, especially in Quintana Roo, have suffered from tourist development, with sizeable areas of native scrub and mangrove destroyed. Large areas do nevertheless remain, some of them in protected areas, the most notable perhaps being the Sian Ka'an Biosphere Reserve (5,282 km²) in Quintana Roo.

Clarión   s008

Clarión (28.4 km²) is one of four oceanic islands comprising the Revillagigedo archipelago in the Pacific Ocean off western Mexico (see EBA 004; also for map). This island lies c.370 km west of the other islands and more than 700 km from the Mexican mainland. Most of the terrain is gently sloping, rising to 335 m. It is arid, and rabbits and feral pigs have caused serious damage to the vegetation. The habitat of Clarión Wren *Troglodytes tanneri*, a species endemic to the island, ranges from rocks on the beaches to shrubbery at the highest elevations, and the bird has a population estimated at 170–180 pairs. It is classified as Vulnerable, as the introduction of an exotic predator remains a possibility (Collar *et al.* 1994) and such an event could have a serious impact on such a tiny population. The threatened seabird, Townsend's Shearwater *Puffinus auricularis* (Vulnerable), which is an endemic breeder to the Revillagigedo Islands, has been almost wiped out on Clarión owing to the feral pigs. Indeed, all burrows found during a survey in 1990 were old, so its current status on the island is unclear. Clarión is now part of the Revillagigedo Islands Biosphere Reserve, which was created as recently as 1994 in recognition of the terrestrial endemic animals and plants and the abundant marine life associated with the archipelago.

Swan Islands   s009
The Swan Islands (part of Honduras) lie in the Caribbean c.200 km due north of Laguna Caratasca in easternmost Honduras and 325 km south-west of Grand Cayman in the West Indies. They comprise two main islands, Big Swan (c.6 km²) and Little Swan, and have been identified as a Secondary Area due to the presence of Vitelline Warbler *Dendroica vitellina*; this, the islands' only resident passerine, occurs also on the Cayman Islands (Secondary Area s014). The population on the Swan Islands constitutes an endemic subspecies, *nelsoni*, and is (or was in the 1960s) common on both islands. Five species of landbird (including *D. vitellina*) have been reported breeding on the islands, including the now locally extinct Red-legged Thrush *Momocichla plumbea*. The islands also support a mixed seabird colony including Red-footed Booby *Sula sula*, Brown Booby *S. leucogaster* and Magnificent Frigatebird *Fregata magnificens* (Monroe 1968).

North Honduran thorn forests   s010
These forests are associated with arid interior valleys such as the Sula and Aguán, on the Atlantic slope of Honduras (see map, p. 135). The vegetation in these valleys comprises (or comprised) arid and mixed scrub, as well as thorn forest which reaches a height of 6–10 m in places and is dominated by Mimosaceae, Cactaceae and Euphorbiaceae (Monroe 1968, Howell and Webb 1989). The threatened Honduran Emerald *Amazilia luciae* (classified as Critical) is endemic to just a few localities in these arid valleys and for years was known from only 11 specimens (the most recent being collected in 1950) until it was rediscovered in 1988 in the upper Aguán valley where it is a common local resident (Howell and Webb 1995a). The rela-

tively small area of preferred habitat is under pressure for conversion to agriculture (cattle grazing and crops such as pineapples) (Collar *et al.* 1992).

Lake Nicaragua marshes   s011
South-west Nicaragua includes two vast freshwater wetlands with sandy shores, extensive permanent marshes and adjacent seasonally flooded marshes (see map, p. 135). The southern edge of Lake Nicaragua (8,270 km², the largest lake in Central America) is adjacent to the border with Costa Rica, and drains into the Caribbean via the San Juan river. The much smaller Lake Managua lies to the north-west and is very important for a wide variety of waterfowl, both breeding and wintering (Scott and Carbonell 1986). Nicaraguan Grackle *Quiscalus nicaraguensis* is found only around the shores of Lake Managua and Lake Nicaragua, associated with open marshy areas, lake shores, riverbanks, wet pastures and scrub (Stiles and Skutch 1989). In recent years the birds have expanded their range, in association with livestock-raising, to the western edge of the Caribbean slope near the source of the San Juan river from Lake Nicaragua and along the nearby Frío river (especially at Lake Caño Negro) into northern Costa Rica (Stiles and Skutch 1989, T. R. Howell *in litt.* 1993).

Providence Island   s012
Politically part of Colombia, this 40-km² island is situated in the Caribbean some 235 km east of the Nicaraguan coast and 100 km north of San Andrés Island (Secondary Area s013; see map, p. 135). Providence is volcanic with steep hills rising to 380 m, mostly forested or devoted to ranching (Hilty and Brown 1986). It has a single restricted-range species, Thick-billed Vireo *Vireo crassirostris*, which also occurs on Cuba (EBA 025), the Bahamas (EBA 026), Hispaniola (EBA 028) and the Cayman Islands (Secondary Area s014).

San Andrés Island   s013
San Andrés Island, politically part of Colombia, lies 200 km east of the Nicaraguan coast and 100 km south of Providence Island (Secondary Area s012; see map, p. 135). It is a sand and limestone island of 52 km², rising to c.100 m, and is densely populated, its northernmost 20% (around the capital San Andrés) being the island's centre for tourism and highly urbanized. During the seventeenth and eighteenth centuries the island apparently supported extensive stands of cedar (possibly *Cedrela odorata*) which were severely reduced by early colonists. The current vegetation cover is mainly coconut palm (covering the southern half of the island) with farmland in between, the native vegetation being restricted to small patches of trees (associated with inland man-

grove swamps) and scrub among the farmland and settlements. Encroachment is caused by urbanization and agriculture, with coastal mangroves being destroyed (on the east coast) by waste oil and the outflow of hot cooling water (Collar *et al.* 1992). The island supports 16 resident landbird species (Hilty and Brown 1986), including two restricted-range species, namely the threatened endemic San Andrés Vireo *Vireo caribaeus* (classified as Critical and now apparently restricted to an area of 17 km^2: Collar *et al.* 1992) and Jamaican Oriole *Icterus leucopteryx* which also occurs on Jamaica (EBA 027) and Grand Cayman (Secondary Area s014).

Cayman Islands   s014

The three Cayman Islands—Grand Cayman, Little Cayman and Cayman Brac—a dependent territory of the UK, lie at the extreme north-west end of the Caribbean island chain, 208 km from Jamaica (EBA 027) and 240 km from Cuba (EBA 025; also for map). Grand and Little Cayman are similar low-lying islands with extensive wetlands of mangrove swamps and associated coastal lagoons and ponds, while on Cayman Brac the wetlands are minimal, and dry forest and scrub are the dominant vegetation types. The Cayman Islands have been identified as a Secondary Area on account of one endemic extinct species (Grand Cayman Thrush *Turdus ravidus*, not recorded since 1938) and the presence of four other restricted-range species (Vitelline Warbler *Dendroica vitellina*, Thick-billed Vireo *Vireo crassirostris*, Yucatán Vireo *Vireo magister* and Jamaican Oriole *Icterus leucopteryx*) which also occur in nearby EBAs and Secondary Areas. Although none of these species is considered threatened, habitats on the Cayman Islands are becoming fragmented owing to the growth of tourism and associated facilities; this is especially the case on Grand Cayman, but more recently also on Little Cayman (Bradley 1995). The widespread but threatened West Indian Whistling-duck *Dendrocygna arborea* (classified as Vulnerable) breeds on all three islands, while the Cuban Parrot *Amazona leucocephala* (Near Threatened) has two endemic subspecies on the islands—*caymanensis* on Grand Cayman and *hesterna* on Cayman Brac.

Netherlands Antilles   s015

The three main islands of this Secondary Area, lying c.50 km off the north-west coast of Venezuela (see map, p. 182), are (from west to east) Aruba (175 km^2), an overseas territory of the Netherlands, and Curaçao (425 km^2) and Bonaire (272 km^2), part of the Netherlands Antilles. The islands are generally covered (to a greater or lesser extent) in xerophytic vegetation, in which a wealth of cacti and thorny *Acacia* predominate, and the avifauna comprises fewer than 150

species of which c.40% are migratory non-breeders (Hummelinck 1957). Two restricted-range species are present: the threatened Yellow-shouldered Amazon *Amazona barbadensis* (Vulnerable, and occurring also in the adjacent mainland, EBA 035) and Pearly-eyed Thrasher *Margarops fuscatus* (found throughout much of the Caribbean). *A. barbadensis* is now, in this Secondary Area, confined to Bonaire (where there are c.400 birds), and became extinct on Aruba (probably) during the 1940s (Collar *et al.* 1992); it is uncertain whether this parrot ever occurred on Curaçao or not. *M. fuscatus* is represented by an endemic subspecies, *bonairensis*, which appears to be almost exclusively confined to the vicinity of Fontein plantation on Bonaire, although it has occurred (but is now apparently extinct) on the Venezuelan island of La Horquilla of the Hermanos Islands (which lie north of Margarita Island and c.350 km east of Bonaire) (Hummelinck 1957).

Trinidad   s016

Trinidad and Tobago (a twin-island nation) are the most southerly of the Caribbean island chain, with Trinidad lying only 12 km from mainland South America (see map, p. 172). Trinidad (4,828 km^2) is relatively flat except for three mountain ranges with a maximum elevation of 940 m and has been identified as a Secondary Area due to the presence of the endemic Trinidad Piping-guan *Pipile pipile* (classified as Critical). This species used to be widespread throughout the island but today is reduced to two small populations in the primary forests of the Northern and Southern ranges, owing to hunting and forest destruction. It inhabits remote primary forest (typically vine- and epiphyte-rich closed-canopy tracts with sparse ground cover) where human disturbance is minimal; areas preferred are hilly (400–900 m) with steep ridges, deep valleys and abundant watercourses (Collar *et al.* 1992).

Tobago   s017

Tobago lies 34 km north-east of Trinidad with which it forms a twin-island nation (see above). At just 295 km^2, it is much the smaller island and is rugged, with a mountain ridge rising to 576 m running two-thirds of its length. White-tailed Sabrewing *Campylopterus ensipennis* (classified as Vulnerable) which is present here is otherwise confined to mainland South America in the Caripe–Paria region (EBA 032). This hummingbird was formerly fairly common in the hill forest along the Main Ridge, but in 1963 Hurricane Flora was thought to have destroyed all suitable habitat. However, the population within the Main Ridge Forest Reserve appears to be re-establishing itself well, with birds recently found in forest at most stages of recovery (Collar *et al.* 1992, Hayes 1996).

SOUTH AMERICA

Lower Río Magdalena   s018

This Secondary Area is centred on Ayacucho, on the lower-middle Río Magdalena in César department of north-central Colombia (see map, p. 188). Ayacucho is the type- (and only known) locality for the threatened Magdalena Tinamou *Crypturellus saltuarius* (classified as Critical), known from just a single male collected in 1943 (taxonomy following Wetmore 1950, Collar *et al*. 1992). The type-locality is (or was) covered by low, dry, deciduous forest and savanna, and the species has therefore not been included within the nearby humid forested Nechí lowlands (EBA 037). The absence of protected areas in this region combined with the widespread clearance of the dry forest for cattle-ranching and farming means that this species, unknown in life, may already be extinct.

Macarena mountains   s019

The isolated Macarena mountains, protected by a national park, are in southern Meta department of Colombia (see map, p. 194), and are geologically distinct from the nearby Andes. Over 100 km in length and 15–25 km wide, they reach c.1,800 m. The west-facing slope is a precipitous cliff towering above the humid forest, while the eastern slope rises gently from the forest floor. Geologically, the Macarenas are related to the isolated table mountains and cerros scattered to the east (including the Sierra de Chiribiquete, Secondary Area s020), and to the Tepuis (EBA 064) of the Guiana shield. This Secondary Area has been identified due to the presence of the Grey-legged Tinamou *Crypturellus duidae*, which also occurs in the Orinoco–Negro white-sand forests (EBA 065). This tinamou is known only in this area from the east side of the Macarena mountains at 400–500 m where it inhabits humid forest and scrubby open woodland (Hilty and Brown 1986). It has been suggested that this disjunct distribution is illusory, with the bird perhaps also occurring on (but as yet unrecorded from) the table mountains of Vaupés department, south-east Colombia. The Macarena mountains were identified as a Key Area for the widespread but threatened Spot-winged Parrotlet *Touit stictoptera* (Vulnerable) and the Speckled Crake *Coturnicops notatus* (Data Deficient) (Wege and Long 1995).

Sierra de Chiribiquete   s020

This isolated range of table-top mountains, protected by a national park, rises from the flat Amazonian lowlands in Guaviare and Caquetá departments of south-east Colombia (see map, p. 194). The sierra consists of an arc of sandstone mesas some 125 km long and 30 km wide rising abruptly from the surrounding flat lowlands; they reach heights of 800–900 m in the north and 600 m in the south, often presenting several levels of terraces separated by vertical cliffs. The thin, sandy soil of the table-tops supports a scrubby vegetation interspersed with areas of naked rock, and the stature of the vegetation reflects the depth of the soil (or its absence) at any given point. The sierra has been identified as a Secondary Area due to the presence of the endemic and recently discovered Chiribiquete Emerald *Chlorostilbon olivaresi* (as described by Stiles 1996), which is a common inhabitant of the scrub and adjacent forests of the middle and upper levels of the sierra, but evidently does not occur in the surrounding lowlands (Stiles 1996). The region is also important for the widespread but threatened Wattled Curassow *Crax globulosa* (classified as Vulnerable) (Wege and Long 1995).

Tumaco and Bocagrande Islands   s021

Tumaco is a small sandy island c.1 km off the Pacific coast of Nariño department in south-west Colombia (see map, p. 198). It is now covered by the city of Tumaco, the second largest port in this region. Bocagrande is c.10 km west of Tumaco, and is similarly a narrow sandy island, now a major holiday resort (Salaman 1995). Tumaco Seedeater *Sporophila insulata* (classified as Critical), the threatened endemic species for which this Secondary Area has been identified, was discovered on Tumaco in 1912, but, despite a number of searches, has not been recorded there since (Collar *et al*. 1992). It was considered possibly extinct until 1994 when it was rediscovered on Bocagrande, six birds being found in a c.4-km stretch of very narrow, raised beach habitat (mainly marram-type grasses and scattered patches of scrub) on the seaward side of the island. Only 1 ha of such habitat was found on Bocagrande, and the development of the Bocagrande tourist resort threatens the species' survival, with regular clearance and burning of scrub for beach cabins having a profound effect on remaining likely habitat (Salaman 1995).

Huallaga valley   s022

The Huallaga valley runs almost south–north, to the east of the Andean Cordillera Central (the North-east Peruvian Cordilleras, EBA 049; also for map) in San Martín and Huánuco departments of north-east Peru. To the east of the valley is a relatively low mountain chain, the Cordillera Azul, which creates a local rainshadow, and the valley is thus relatively dry. The endemic Huallaga Tanager *Ramphocelus melano-gaster* is locally common in shrubby clearings, forest borders and gardens between 500 and 1,000 m (Ridgely and Tudor 1989). It was formerly confined to the Huallaga drainage but is currently extending its range to extreme north-west Ucayali in the Ucayali drainage, east of Tingo María (Isler and Isler 1987).

Upper Inambari valley   s023

The semi-arid upper Inambari valley forms a major biogeographic barrier in southernmost Peru. Situated in northern Puno department, this valley lies at the junction of the Bolivian and Peruvian lower yungas (EBA 054; also for map), the Peruvian East Andean foothills (EBA 053), and the Bolivian and Peruvian upper yungas (EBA 055). The Inambari valley is deep (creating a rainshadow effect), with the narrow floor and steep sides extensively farmed; where not cleared or too rocky, the slopes are covered with dense evergreen shrubs 2–3 m tall (Schulenberg and Binford 1985). The endemic Green-capped Tanager *Tangara meyerdeschauenseei* (classified as Vulnerable on the basis of its very small range) has been found here to be fairly common between 1,750 and 2,180 m in fruiting trees in small garden plots, semi-arid scrub and at the edge of cleared areas (Schulenberg and Binford 1985, Collar *et al.* 1994).

Lake Titicaca   s024

The altiplano, where the Andes reach their maximum width, is an area of inland drainage with enormous lake basins. The whole plain was once covered by one huge lake, Ballivian, now fragmented into the smaller present-day lakes: in the north (at 3,800 m), Lake Titicaca (8,300 km²) drains south via the Desaguadero river and Lake Uru-Uru into the saline Lake Poopó (south of Oruro in Bolivia). Lake Titicaca sits astride the Peru–Bolivia border (see map, p. 239), and is mostly steep-sided and rocky, but parts of the shore are flat with enormous zones of aquatic vegetation extending up to 12 km out into the lake, and with surrounding areas of seasonally inundated puna grassland dotted with other smaller rushy lakes (Scott and Carbonell 1986, Fjeldså and Krabbe 1990). Lake Uru-Uru (280 km²) is a brackish lake supporting extensive beds of emergent vegetation, and is surrounded by heavily grazed puna grassland. Lake Poopó (1,340 km²) is saline with turbid waters and extensive areas of exposed mud (and is particularly important for flamingos); its water-level fluctuates seasonally, but it is in the process of drying out (Scott and Carbonell 1986).

These lakes—Titicaca, Uru-Uru and Poopó—and others nearby have been identified as a Secondary Area due to the presence of the endemic Titicaca Flightless Grebe *Rollandia microptera*. It prefers open lake habitats, often feeding far offshore as long as some vegetation exists at the bottom. Breeding is in rather open mosaic-like parts of wide reed-marshes, in places with easy access to open water. The species is common, but some local populations may disappear in drought years and become re-established in years of extreme flooding (Fjeldså and Krabbe 1990). The lakes of this region are also extremely important for Andean waterfowl and Nearctic waders. Although Titicaca National Reserve protects some of the lake, there is a considerable amount of pollution in the vicinity of Puno from domestic sewage and boat traffic, and excessive utilization of reeds for building, boat construction and handicrafts. Hunting and egg-collection may be a problem in some areas, and many grebes are known to drown in fishing nets (Scott and Carbonell 1986).

Rio Ji-paraná   s025

This Brazilian Secondary Area around Cachoeira Nazaré lies at 100 m elevation near the west bank of the Ji-paraná in north-east Rondônia and is the only known locality for Rondônia Bushbird *Clytoctantes atrogularis*. The area comprises a large tract of mature terra firme forest with some dense vine tangles. The antbird was described to science as recently as 1990 from a single female specimen and from two sightings of males (Lanyon *et al.* 1990). It is classified as Data Deficient but is likely to be very rare as these records were made during many field hours and net-days of study. However, it is thought that the species' range almost certainly includes adjacent parts of Amazonas and Mato Grosso states, because several species endemic to forests between the upper Madeira and Tapajós rivers are also recorded at Cachoeira Nazaré. The area generally supports very rich bird communities, nearly 400 species being found at Cachoeira Nazaré (Lanyon *et al.* 1990). Rapid deforestation (c.4,000 km² per year in the 1980s) and hydroelectric projects in this part of Brazil must be considered threats to this region.

Rio Guaporé   s026

This Secondary Area is defined by the range of Rusty-necked Piculet *Picumnus fuscus*, which is known from fewer than 10 specimens all collected along 500 km of the middle Guaporé river, which follows the border between Brazil (in Rondônia state) and Bolivia (Beni department) between Pimenteiras and Guayaramerin (see map, p. 236). Parker and Rocha (1991) found the piculet to be fairly common in seasonally flooded forest along the Guaporé; the region appeared largely uninhabited and the riverine forest undisturbed. A large portion of this species' range apparently lies within the Guaporé State Biological reserve, in Rondônia (6,000 km²).

Beni lowlands s027

This Secondary Area is based on the range of Blue-throated Macaw *Ara glaucogularis* which is found in a small area of the lowlands of northern Bolivia in the departments of Beni and Santa Cruz (see map, p. 236). There is a mosaic of habitats, but savanna, gallery forest and humid forest dominate. The macaw itself has strict habitat requirements, appearing to be found only in seasonally inundated savanna in which forest is scattered in meandering ribbons and islands, and is dominated by tall palms (*Scheelea princeps* and *Acrocomia totai*) and deciduous trees especially Ebenaceae, Moraceae and *Tabebuia impetiginosa* (Bignoniaceae). This habitat tends to form the transition zone between very open savanna and forest (Hesse and Jammes 1994), with the macaw feeding and nesting in the palms and trees of the forest patches (Brace *et al*. 1995, Hesse 1997). The macaw is threatened (classified as Endangered), a survey in 1995 having estimated a population of as few as 100 birds with all currently occupied areas lying in Beni department. Saving the species from extinction through gaining better understanding of it ecology, educational awareness, and the limiting of trapping is the focus of a long-term project by Fundación Armonía, BirdLife International's Bolivian Partner.

East Bolivian cerrado s028

This Secondary Area is defined by the highly localized and little-known breeding range of Black-and-tawny Seedeater *Sporophila nigrorufa* (classified as Endangered). The seedeater's habits are poorly understood, as it has been found during the breeding season only in a few localities in eastern Santa Cruz department of eastern Bolivia where it is normally the rarest seedeater present (Collar *et al*. 1992, Wege and Long 1995, Pearce-Higgins 1996). There are also a couple of records of it further east from the Pantanal of Mato Grosso do Sul and Mato Grosso states of western Brazil, one of which was of a male associating with a non-breeding flock of seedeaters. The species is most regularly seen (and proved to breed) at three sites of seasonally inundated cerrado grassland at the base of the Serranía de Huanchaca in Noel Kempff Mercado National Park (9,140 km²) (S. Davis *in litt*. 1995). The cerrado grasslands form a mosaic structure with areas of dry and semi-humid forest which show affinities with the chaco region and the main cerrado zone of central Brazil. Agricultural expansion, burning and grazing will pose major threats to this part of eastern Bolivia within the next 10 years (Dinerstein *et al*. 1995).

Borba s029

Borba is located on the right bank of the lower Madeira river in eastern Amazonas state of Brazil

(see map, p. 268). It supports a good representative set of Amazonian habitats (white-water and black-water forest, savanna) and is the type-locality of a number of birds (B. M. Whitney *in litt*. 1995). The site is a Secondary Area because it is the only known locality of Buff-cheeked Tody-flycatcher *Todirostrum senex*, which, until recently rediscovered, was known just from the type-specimen collected in 1830. Fortunately it was found to be fairly common, and an extensive area of forest remains. Although deforestation generally in Amazonas remains slight as yet (Fearnside 1990), the region merits further research as the species has been little-studied biologically, and land on both sides of this important river needs formal protection (B. M. Whitney *in litt*. 1995).

Upper Rio Cururu s030

The headwaters of the Cururu, a right-bank tributary of the upper Tapajós, is located in south-west Pará (Brazil) near the northern rim of the Serra do Cachimbo, a highland area reaching 500 m. This is a Secondary Area through being the only known site of Golden-crowned Manakin *Pipra vilasboasi*, a species which has not been seen since its discovery in 1957 in terra firme rain forest. The extent of deforestation in this particular part of Amazonia is unknown and so the species is considered threatened (Vulnerable). The area probably falls near or inside the Mundurucânia Forest Reserve as the Cururu forms its southern boundary.

Rio Araguaia s031

This area includes the lower and middle region of the Araguaia river in Brazil, from Araguatins in northern Tocantins south to Bananal Island, the largest river island in the world, formed between the Araguaia and the Braço Menor do Rio Araguaia, in southern Tocantins (see map, p. 286). Bananal Antbird *Cercomacra ferdinandi* is confined to this area, inhabiting the lower growth of deciduous and gallery forest, and riparian thickets (Ridgely and Tudor 1994), this vegetation being a transition between the humid Amazon forest to the north and west, and the dry forest of the Brazilian central plateau to the east and south. Much of the northern half of Bananal island falls within the Araguaia National Park (5,623 km²), which holds good numbers of the antbird; in addition, two more-widespread threatened birds have been recorded there—Chestnut-bellied Guan *Penelope ochrogaster* (classified as Vulnerable) andHyacinth Macaw *Anodorhynchus hyacinthinus* (Vulnerable).

Interior southern Brazil s032

This Secondary Area relates to the main part of the range of Brasília Tapaculo *Scytalopus novacapitalis*, the interior of south-central Brazil in the states of

Goiás, the Federal District and Minas Gerais (see map, p. 294). The species has been recorded only locally within this large area, particular sites being Formosa in Goiás, around Brasília, Serra Negra (on the upper Dourados river) and the headwaters of the São Francisco, both in Minas Gerais. There are also a couple of records from Serra do Cipó and Caraça in the hills and tablelands of central Brazil (EBA 073). The habitat of the tapaculo is swampy gallery forest, and birds occasionally colonize disturbed areas near streams with dense secondary growth of bracken *Pteridium aquilinum* (Negret and Cavalcanti 1985). The species is classified as Vulnerable, being under threat from habitat loss around Brasília, but swampy gallery forest, though at considerable risk from fire, has in general escaped clearance, this having primarily affected the adjacent cerrado. *S. novacapitalis* occurs in a number of protected areas, including the Serra da Canastra National Park (720 km^2) on the upper São Francisco river, in which the widespread Brazilian Merganser *Mergus octosetaceus* (Critical) also occurs, and around Brasília in the Brasília National Park (280 km^2), and nearby in two other smaller nature reserves.

Ceará caatinga and serras   s033

This Secondry Area comprises two small ranges of hills in north-east Brazil and the surrounding and intervening area between them (see map, p. 274). The Serra de Baturité runs for c.100 km in north-central Ceará, and the Serra de Ibiapaba runs for c.200 km in the western part of Ceará (reaching up to 900 m). These hills are found in the caatinga dry zone of Brazil, but within them lie semi-deciduous forest as well as the deciduous dry forest more typical of the general region. The area marks the range of Ochraceous Piculet *Picumnus limae*, and part of the range of Buff-breasted Tody-tyrant *Hemitriccus mirandae*, whose main distribution lies within the Atlantic slope of Alagoas and Pernambuco (EBA 071). Both species, classified as Vulnerable, are (poorly) known from only a handful of localities and occur in a region where considerable areas of habitat are being cleared. *H. mirandae* has been recorded in Serra de Baturité State Environment Protection Area (327 km^2), from where a more-widespread threatened species, Moustached Woodcreeper *Xiphocolaptes falcirostris* (Vulnerable), is also known.

Coastal Paraná marshes   s034

This Secondary Area has resulted from the recent discovery of a new species (and genus) of bird from coastal Paraná in south-east Brazil (Bornschein *et al.* 1995; see map, p. 286). Long-billed Antwren *Stymphalornis acutirostris* was discovered only in 1995, and to date is known from taboa *Typha*

dominguensis marshes at Ipacaray and Betares, which are located near the main coastal road between Matinhos and Praia de Leste in Paraná. The little information published indicates that the taxon shows close affinities with *Formicivora* antbirds. There is a great concern regarding the conservation status of this new species because it inhabits marshes which are being steadily encroached upon by human activities. A technical group for the bird's protection has been created in an effort to safeguard its future.

Coastal Uruguay marshes   s035

The marshes of eastern Rio Grande do Sul in south-east Brazil, Uruguay and Buenos Aires in Argentina mark the range of Straight-billed Reedhaunter *Limnornis rectirostris* (see map, p. 298). This species is confined almost exclusively to marshes of spiny sedge *Eryngium*, which is found mainly on the coast but also in the upland plateau zone of eastern Rio Grande do Sul. The species is not currently considered threatened, but has certainly declined in some parts of its range such as coastal Uruguay and in Buenos Aires province of Argentina where marshes are drained for development and agriculture. It is common in Aparados da Serra National Park (123 km^2) and north-east Rio Grande do Sul, and there is a small population in Otamendi Strict Nature Reserve (26 km^2) in north-east Buenos Aires.

Salinas Grandes and Ambargasta   s036

This Secondary Area refers to the range of Salinas Monjita *Xolmis salinarum*, a species described as recently as 1979. The area lies in north-west Córdoba, extreme southern Catamarca, south-west Santiago del Estero and La Rioja provinces of north-west Argentina (see map, p. 242). The landscape comprises semi-open scrubby vegetation on salt-impregnated soil around the extensive Salinas Grande and Salinas Ambargasta (Ridgely and Tudor 1994). During the austral winter the monjita gathers in flocks of up to c.50 birds, but disperses into pairs during the breeding season (Ridgely and Tudor 1994).

South Georgia   s037

South Georgia (3,500 km^2, maximum altitude 2,934 m), together with numerous offshore rocky islands (e.g. Bird Island), are isolated sub-Antarctic islands; characteristic vegetation includes tussock grassland and wet heath. The group is a UK dependent territory with the South Sandwich Islands. South Georgia is a Secondary Area because of one endemic landbird, South Georgia Pipit *Anthus antarcticus*, which breeds mainly on the rat-free offshore islands, notably Bird Island (which is also important for breeding seabirds, especially the Vulnerable Wandering Albatross *Diomedea exulans*).

AFRICA, EUROPE AND THE MIDDLE EAST

St Helena   s038

The island of St Helena covers 122 km² and rises to 823 m. It is a UK dependent territory (see also EBAs 079, 080) in the South Atlantic Ocean, lying some 1,960 km from the nearest point on the south-west coast of Africa and 2,900 km east of South America. The majority of the original vegetation has been almost entirely destroyed, with over 60% of the island now covered by eroded areas of rock or prickly pear, aloe and other exotic species. The island is a Secondary Area on account of its one surviving endemic landbird, the St Helena Plover *Charadrius sanctaehelenae*, which occurs only in the northern flatter parts of the interior. Intensive study during 1988–1989 showed that some 450 birds were then present, at highest densities in relatively dry, flat pasture, and that the only threat appeared to lie in potential land-use changes. However, more recent censuses suggest a steady decline, and the species has been classified as Endangered (Collar *et al.* 1994). The fossil record on St Helena is well represented including evidence of at least four, presumably endemic, landbirds (two flightless rails, a cuckoo and a hoopoe) which were probably present when the island was discovered in 1502, after which they quickly succumbed to the effects of predation by man and his commensal animals and deforestation.

North Algerian mountains   s039

This Secondary Area is defined by the range of the threatened Algerian Nuthatch *Sitta ledanti* (classified as Endangered), which is found in broadleaf and mixed broadleaf–coniferous forest between 350 and 2,000 m (Harrap and Quinn 1996). It is known from four localities (Chalabi 1989, Bellatreche and Chalabi 1990, Bellatreche 1991, Harrap 1992), and, although two of these lie within national parks, the species is threatened throughout by deforestation (Zaimeche 1994).

Upper Niger valley   s040

The Upper Niger valley in south-west Mali has been identified as a Secondary Area on account of the endemic Mali Firefinch *Lagonosticta virata*, which is found in dry grassland and thickets (Hall and Moreau 1970, Sibley and Monroe 1990), although there is a record of this species from outside the Niger watershed in eastern Senegal (Payne 1997). This section of the Niger valley is an important wetland which faces a number of pressures (Hughes and Hughes 1992), but the habitats of the Mali Firefinch are probably not threatened. There are no protected areas in this part of Mali (IUCN 1992b).

South-west Nigeria   s041

This Secondary Area is defined by the range of the threatened Ibadan Malimbe *Malimbus ibadanensis* which is known from several localities within 110 km of the city of Ibadan in south-west Nigeria. However, it may prove to occur more widely as there are possible records from Owerri, east of the Niger river in Nigeria, and from Ghana (Elgood 1992, Morel and Chappuis 1992). It is classified as Critical because of the widespread habitat destruction which has occurred in south-west Nigeria, and it appears to survive only in small numbers in the few remaining forest patches there (Ash 1987, 1991, Elgood 1988).

Lower Niger valley   s042

The lower Niger watershed in southern Nigeria (see map, p. 306) supports one restricted-range species, the threatened Anambra Waxbill *Estrilda poliopareia* (classified as Vulnerable). It is known from only four localities, where it has been found in long grass and herbage along rivers and on lagoon sandbanks, and it may be under pressure from habitat degradation (Ash and Sharland 1986, Ash 1987, 1990).

Gabon–Cabinda coast   s043

This Secondary Area includes a narrow coastal strip in Gabon, Zaïre and Cabinda province of northern Angola (see map, p. 312). It is defined by the range of the threatened Loango Weaver *Ploceus subpersonatus* (classified as Vulnerable), which is found in swamp-forest, landward mangrove edge and savanna, habitats which are being converted to agricultural land in parts of its range. It is not recorded from the Congo, and may be absent because of a lack of appropriate habitats (Dowsett-Lemaire *et al.* 1993).

West Zaïre and north Angola forests   s044

This Secondary Area is defined by the range of the threatened White-headed Robin-chat *Cossypha heinrichi* (classified as Vulnerable), which is known from one site in northern Angola and two sites in western Zaïre. It has been recorded in gallery forest and immediately adjacent savanna, and in forest patches, and is likely to be under pressure from clearance of its habitat.

Namibian escarpment   s045

The mountain slopes and hillsides of the Namibian escarpment extending into extreme southern Angola support the endemic Herero Chat *Namibornis herero* (a monotypic genus), which favours areas of mixed *Acacia* and *Commiphora* trees (Maclean 1984). Part of its range lies close to that of Dune Lark *Certhilauda erythrochlamys* (see Secondary Area s046), but the distributions of the two species do not overlap, and they occur in different habitat types, so the two areas are not considered to comprise an EBA.

Namib desert   s046
This Secondary Area includes part of the Namib desert of southern Namibia (see map, p. 324). It is defined by the range of Dune Lark *Certhilauda erythrochlamys*, which is found in sand-dunes with low scrub or sparse tufts of grass, and sandy inter-dune flats (Maclean 1984, Keith *et al.* 1992).

Karoo   s047
The red sand semi-desert country of north-west Cape Province in South Africa and southern Namibia is a Secondary Area (see map, p. 324), defined by the range of the threatened Red Lark *Certhilauda burra* (classified as Vulnerable). This nomadic species is found on well-vegetated sand-dunes or flats with perennial tussock-grasses, of which only 1,400 km² remain and which are under continuing heavy grazing pressure from domestic livestock (Dean *et al.* 1991).

Kerguelen and Crozet islands   s048
The Kerguelen Islands (7,000 km², maximum altitude 1,960 m; made up of one very big island, Grande Terre, and more than 300 other islands and islets) and the Crozet Islands (500 km², reaching 1,200 m; five islands) are situated in the southern Indian Ocean c.1,500 km apart, both belonging to the French Southern Territories. Vegetation includes shrubland, tussock grassland and moorland, but many high areas are devoid of plants. Several of the islands are part of the Parc National Antarctique Français and are Specially Protected Areas (see Jouventin and Micol 1995). The islands are a major breeding ground for several seabird species, notably Wandering Albatross *Diomedea exulans* (classified as Vulnerable), Sooty Albatross *Phoebetria fusca*, Northern Giant Petrel *Macronectes halli* (both Near Threatened) and Kerguelen Tern *Sterna virgata* (Vulnerable) (see Jouventin *et al.* 1984). The islands are a Secondary Area because of the endemic Eaton's Pintail *Anas eatoni*, which occurs as the race *eatoni* on Kerguelen (population estimated at 5,000–10,000 pairs) and *drygalskyi* on Crozet (1,350 pairs). Introduced Mallard *A. platyrhynchos* are present but seem to form no direct threat to *A. eatoni*, though competition from and predation by feral cats are problems which could arise in the future, especially on Grande Terre, once the cats have depleted the petrels which they currently target as food (Madge and Burn 1988, del Hoyo *et al.* 1992). *A. eatoni eatoni* has also been introduced to the islands of St Paul and Amsterdam

(which are also French Southern Territories). These islands each appear to have been inhabited by their own endemic populations of ducks that were exterminated by humans or by introduced mammals in the past two hundred years. The duck from St Paul is known only from a historical account in 1793, while the abundant bone remains of a duck (a small, teal-sized, flightless species) from Amsterdam Island have been described as a new species, *A. marecula*, by Olson and Jouventin (1996).

Isalo massif   s049
This Secondary Area supports Benson's Rock-thrush *Monticola bensoni*, which was formerly known to breed only from the area between the Mangoky and Onilahy rivers in south-west Madagascar, chiefly in and around the Isalo massif at 700–1,000 m (see map, p. 330). Breeding populations have now also been found in the high-mountain zone of the Andringitra Strict Nature Reserve in the East Malagasy wet forests (EBA 094) west to Ankazoabo in the West Malagasy dry forests (EBA 093) (S. M. Goodman *in litt.* 1996). The characteristic vegetation of the Secondary Area is evergreen, sclerophyllous *Uapaca* woodland, a very restricted vegetation type, which has mostly been replaced by artificial, fire-induced grassland (Du Puy and Moat 1996). However, *M. bensoni* is probably more common in canyons and rocky areas where there is still substantial vegetation, usually either of a western deciduous forest or eastern humid forest type, depending on the substrate and depth of sheltering rock (A. F. A. Hawkins *in litt.* 1996). Although no threats to the species are known, it is listed as Vulnerable: the Isalo National Park in which it occurs is burnt regularly and total numbers of the species may prove to be small (Collar *et al.* 1994).

Ile Sainte-Marie   s050
This 200-km² island (also known as Nosy Boraha) off the north-east coast of Madagascar is a Secondary Area (see map, p. 332) on the basis of its one endemic (extinct) species, Snail-eating Coua *Coua delalandei*, which was last recorded in 1834. Investigations and interviews with local people on the adjacent mainland have failed to indicate that the species ever occurred elsewhere, and it is assumed that deforestation on the island was the principal cause of the species' demise, with hunting and predation by introduced rats *Rattus rattus* also contributing (Goodman 1993).

Southern Zambia   s051
This Secondary Area is defined by the range of the threatened Black-cheeked Lovebird *Agapornis nigrigenis* (classified as Endangered), which is found

in deciduous *Colophospermum mopane* and adjacent *Baikiaea plurijuga* woodland in the Zambezi valley (between the Machili river and Livingstone) and the southern Kafue basin in southern Zambia. A survey in 1994 recorded 2,127 individuals of the species here, and estimated a total population of 10,000 (Dodman 1995). It formerly occurred in the Caprivi Strip of Namibia and northern Zimbabwe, though perhaps only as a vagrant. There is a tiny population inside the Kafue National Park, but elsewhere agricultural encroachment and illegal trapping are possible threats.

North-west Zambia   s052
This Secondary Area is defined by the range of White-chested Tinkerbird *Pogoniulus makawai* (classified as Vulnerable) which is known by just a single specimen from north-west Zambia, collected there at c.1,150 m in 'mavunda' forest, in which *Cryptosepalum* is a dominant tree (Dowsett 1985). It is here treated as a good species, following Fry *et al.* (1988) and Collar *et al.* (1994), but was considered to be an aberrant Yellow-rumped Tinkerbird *P. bilineatus* by Sibley and Monroe (1990, 1993) and by Dowsett and Dowsett-Lemaire (1993). There are extensive mavunda thickets in north-west Zambia and adjacent Angola, and this bird may conceivably persist as a rare relict in this habitat (Fry *et al.* 1988).

Lake Lufira   s053
The swamps bordering Lake Lufira in southern Zaïre are a Secondary Area, defined by the range of the threatened Lake Lufira Weaver *Ploceus ruweti* (classified as Vulnerable). It was common in 1960 within this tiny range, but there is no recent information on its status or on the status of its wetland habitat.

Upemba plains   s054
The area around the Lualaba river and Lake Upemba in southern Zaïre is a Secondary Area, defined by the range of the threatened Black-lored Waxbill *Estrilda nigriloris* (classified as Vulnerable), a species found in level grassy plains with tall grass and bushes—though there have been no records of it since 1950. Much of the Secondary Area lies within Upemba National Park, but it is feared that the grassland there might well be being lost.

South-west Tanzanian swamps   s055
This Secondary Area is defined by the range of Tanzania Masked Weaver *Ploceus reichardi* in southwest Tanzania (Hall and Moreau 1970), and extreme north-east Zambia (Leonard and Beel 1996; see map, p. 358). It is usually found in swamps, and is perhaps entirely restricted to this habitat during the breeding season (Louette and Benson 1982). The wetlands in this region do not appear to be under immediate pressure (Hughes and Hughes 1992), and a substantial area is protected within the Uwanda Game Reserve (IUCN 1992b).

Kilombero floodplain   s056
The geographically isolated wetlands in the Kilombero floodplain in Tanzania (see map, p. 358) constitute a Secondary Area, defined by the range of the threatened Kilombero Weaver *Ploceus burnieri* (classified as Vulnerable). This recently described species breeds in extensive riverine swamp fringed with *Phragmites mauritianus* (Baker and Baker 1990) and is locally common, but recent road-building has destroyed several colony sites. An undescribed cisticola *Cisticola* collected at the same locality may prove to be a full species (N. E. Baker verbally 1994), in which case the Kilombero floodplain would qualify as an EBA. There are currently no protected areas in this region (IUCN 1992b).

Dry woodlands west of   s057
Lake Victoria
These woodlands west of Lake Victoria, in southwest Uganda, eastern Rwanda and extreme northwest Tanzania (see map, p. 364), support the endemic Red-faced Barbet *Lybius rubrifacies*. It is locally common in dry woodland, wooded grassland, gallery forest and open country with cultivation and scattered trees at 1,200–1,550 m (Britton 1980, Fry *et al.* 1988). It can persist in cultivated areas, but excessive habitat clearance has caused its decline in Rwanda, although it survives in Akagera National Park (Collar and Stuart 1985).

Kakamega and Nandi forests   s058
Kakamega and the neighbouring North Nandi and South Nandi forests lie to the west of the Rift Valley in western Kenya (see map, p. 370), in a humid, high-rainfall area; they are at 1,700–2,150 m, and support a mixture of lowland and montane vegetation (Britton 1980, Collar and Stuart 1988, Lewis and Pomeroy 1989). The threatened Chapin's Flycatcher *Muscicapa lendu* (classified as Vulnerable) occurs there, and in montane forest in the Albertine Rift mountains (EBA 106). A more-widespread threatened species which occurs in this Secondary Area is Turner's Eremomela *Eremomela turneri* (classified as Vulnerable).

North Ugandan swamps   s059
This Secondary Area is defined by the range of Fox's Weaver *Ploceus spekeoides* which is confined to a small area of northern Uganda around Lake Kyoga (Hall and Moreau 1970), though there is also a record of a colony at Rhino Camp in north-west Uganda (M. Carswell *in litt.* 1989; see map, p. 372). It is locally

common in bushed and wooded grassland in swampy areas (Britton 1980, Collar and Stuart 1985).

North-east Uganda   s060

This Secondary Area is defined by the range of Karamoja Apalis *Apalis karamojae* (classified as Vulnerable) which occurs in north-east Uganda and the Serengeti plains (EBA 108). In Uganda, it is known from four sites, in riverine *Acacia* in the lowlands. It is threatened by habitat loss in Tanzania, but there is little information on its status or on any threats in the Ugandan part of its range.

North Kenyan short-grass plains   s061

This area is defined by the range of Williams's Lark *Mirafra williamsi* which has two disjunct populations in northern Kenya (see map, p. 380), in the Didi Galgalla desert near Marsabit, and between Isiolo and Garba Tula, where it is found in arid or semi-arid short-grass plains on black lava soils at 600–1,350 m, and well-grazed, grassy areas with scattered bushes on sandy soil (Britton 1980, Keith *et al.* 1992). It is generally rare, but locally common in the Didi Galgalla desert (Zimmerman *et al.* 1996), and is probably not threatened (Collar and Stuart 1985).

Mount Kulal   s062

Northern Kenya's Mt Kulal (see map, p. 380) is a Secondary Area because it is the only locality for the threatened Kulal White-eye *Zosterops kulalensis*. It is here treated as a full species, following Collar *et al.* (1994), though Sibley and Monroe (1990, 1993) and Dowsett and Dowsett-Lemaire (1993) consider it to be a form of the widespread Broad-ringed White-eye *Z. poliogaster*. It is abundant in the mountain forest, but is classified as Critical as by 1980 only 40 km² of the mountain had tree cover, all of which was heavily degraded by cattle (Diamond and Keith 1980).

Northern Ethiopia   s063

This Secondary Area is defined by the range of Sombre Chat *Cercomela dubia*, a poorly known species recorded at a few north Ethiopian localities from the upper Awash valley eastwards (Keith *et al.* 1992), plus a single old record from the mountains of northern Somalia (in EBA 116) where it may possibly prove to be resident (Ash and Miskell 1983). The details of its habitat requirements and altitudinal range are unknown, but there is a recent record from rock- and grass-covered slopes with scattered *Acacia* at 1,625 m (J. S. Ash *in litt.* 1989).

North-west Somalia   s064

This Secondary Area is defined by the range of the threatened Archer's Lark *Heteromirafra archeri* (classified as Endangered). It is known from a small area west of Hargeisa and Buramo in extreme north-west Somalia (see map, p. 390), and was found around Togochale and Teferi Ber on the Ethiopia–Somalia border in 1996 (Webb 1996). It inhabits open, short sparse grassland with rocks and scattered scrub at c.1,500 m on a high plateau (Keith *et al.* 1992), and is threatened because of its exceptionally restricted range and because its habitat may have been seriously disrupted by cultivation and settlement. Another lark which appears to be restricted to the same general area is treated as a full species, Somali Lark *Mirafra sharpii*, by Sibley and Monroe (1990, 1993) but is considered here to be a subspecies of the widespread Rufous-naped Lark *M. africana* following Dowsett and Dowsett-Lemaire (1993).

Djibouti juniper forests   s065

These forests, at 700–1,780 m, support the threatened Djibouti Francolin *Francolinus ochropectus* (see map, p. 390). The main (and probably only viable) site is the 14 km² Forêt du Day National Park. However, the habitat there is being destroyed by overgrazing, clearance, firewood-gathering, army manoeuvres and other developments (Welch and Welch 1988). A second site at Mablas holds a small population (Blot 1985), but the species is judged to be Critical because of the continuing loss of habitat.

North-east Sudan   s066

It is not possible to define the location of this Secondary Area which has been identified on account of the threatened Red Sea Swallow *Hirundo perdita* (classified as Vulnerable), known only by a single specimen found dead at the Sangaheb lighthouse to the north-east of Port Sudan. It has been judged that the swallow is most likely to be found in the Red Sea hills of Sudan or Eritrea (Fry and Smith 1985), inland from where the type-specimen was found. Unidentified cliff swallows possibly of this species have been seen at several localities in Ethiopia, but they are more likely to represent an undescribed taxon (Madge and Redman 1989, Atkins and Harvey 1994, Robertson 1996).

Levantine mountains   s067

This Secondary Area is determined by the range of Syrian Serin *Serinus syriacus*, which breeds in semi-arid Mediterranean woodland of cedar *Cedrus* and juniper *Juniperus* in the Anti-Lebanon mountains of Syria, Lebanon and Israel, and in the Sharrah highlands of Jordan. The greater part of its known breeding population lies within the Dana Nature Reserve in Jordan, which is an Important Bird Area (Evans 1994). During the winter it disperses to lower areas from south-east Turkey and north-west Iraq, south to Sinai. Remaining forest represents barely 5% of the original cover of this region as a result of centuries of clearance for agriculture and overexploitation for timber, and these same processes remain a threat to the forest which is left (WWF/IUCN 1994).

Corsican mountains   s068

The French Mediterranean island of Corsica (covering 8,740 km² and reaching 2,710 m) is a Secondary Area because of its one endemic species, Corsican Nuthatch *Sitta whiteheadi*, which numbers some 4,000–6,000 birds. The key habitat is coniferous mountain forest which today covers only 240 km² of the island. The main threats are forest exploitation and burning, although there is no recent evidence of a significant reduction in the overall population or range of *S. whiteheadi* (Tucker and Heath 1994), which is classified as Near Threatened. Citril Finch *Serinus citrinella* exists on Corsica, Sardinia, Elba and off-lying islands as a very well-marked race *corsicana*, sometimes considered a separate species; if this taxonomic split is recognized, these islands, then with two endemic species, would qualify as an Endemic Bird Area.

Azores   s069

The volcanic North Atlantic archipelago of the Azores is an autonomous region of Portugal lying some 1,500 km west of the mainland. Its nine main islands cover 2,387 km² and reach 2,381 m. The native vegetation has been considerably altered by human activity such that the original laurel forest today covers only 2% of the islands. The archipelago has been identified as a Secondary Area on account of one restricted-range species, Island Canary *Serinus canaria*, which also occurs on Madeira and the Canary Islands (EBA 120). Of the total population of *S. canaria* (60,000–120,000 birds), c.30–40% are found in the Azores, where the species occurs virtually everywhere from open to forested habitats. The Azores Bullfinch *Pyrrhula pyrrhula murina* (a very distinct form of the widespread Eurasian Bullfinch) is endemic to eastern São Miguel. It was a locally abundant pest of fruit orchards in the nineteenth century but, after persecution, became rare in the 1920s; the present population of c.120 pairs is largely confined to remaining native vegetation (a patch of c.5 km²), where the continuing spread of aggressive exotic plants is the main threat (Heredia *et al.* 1996). The Azores are of considerable importance for their breeding seabirds, particularly Cory's Shearwater *Calonectris diomedea* (50,000–100,000 pairs; nearly half the world population) and Roseate Tern *Sterna dougallii* (1,000 pairs; three-quarters of the European population) (Tucker and Heath 1994). Fea's Petrel *Pterodroma feae* (classified as Endangered) may also breed on the islands (see EBAs 078, 120), as suggested by the recent capture there of a single bird (Bibby and del Nevo 1992).

Caledonian pine forest   s070

This Secondary Area in Scotland (UK) is defined by the range of Scottish Crossbill *Loxia scotica*, recently proposed as a full species (e.g. Knox 1990, Sibley and Monroe 1993) having been previously considered conspecific with Common Crossbill *L. curvirostra* which is widespread across the Holarctic. The population of *L. scotica* is estimated at 600–2,600 birds, though it appears to fluctuate, and a true understanding of the species' numbers and distribution is hindered by the extreme difficulties in identification, which causes continuing doubt over its taxonomic validity (hence its status as Data Deficient). Core areas for *L. scotica* (and therefore the most important parts of this Secondary Area) appear to be in the north-west of the Great Glen and in Strathspey and Deeside. The key habitat is native forest of Scots pine *Pinus sylvestris*, which has decreased in area from 15,000 km² a few hundred years ago to just 120 km² today. The remaining forest is no longer being destroyed at the same rate, and is largely protected, though not all receives adequate management, and there has been underplanting with exotic conifers and natural regeneration is prevented by high deer numbers (Tucker and Heath 1994).

CONTINENTAL ASIA

Eastern Andhra Pradesh   s071

The range of Jerdon's Courser *Rhinoptilus bitorquatus* (classified as Endangered) defines this Secondary Area. It is a poorly known nocturnal bird, recorded historically from the Penner and Godaveri valleys in Andhra Pradesh (east-central India; see map, p. 400) and was assumed extinct (King 1978–1979) until its rediscovery in January 1986. It is found in thin scrub on rocky and undulating ground including disturbed areas where regeneration is affected by grazing and firewood collection (Bhushan 1986a,b, Ali and Ripley 1987). Recent records are from an area of c.2,000 km² around the Lankamalai ranges (near the Penner valley) in southern Andhra Pradesh. Two protected areas, Sri Lankamalleswara Wildlife Sanctuary and Sri Venkateswara National Park, have recently been gazetted there, and a third is planned in a nearby area where the courser has been reported (Bhushan 1992).

Southern Deccan plateau   s072

This Secondary Area is defined by the range of Yellow-throated Bulbul *Pycnonotus xantholaemus*, which is recorded from the states of Karnataka, Andhra Praesh, Tamil Nadu, Kerala and possibly Orissa in southern India (see map, p. 400). It is uncommon and patchily distributed on boulder-strewn hills with vegetation ranging from tropical thorn scrub and dry deciduous forest to moist deciduous forest between about 600 and 1,200 m (Ali and Ripley 1987, Subramanya *et al.* 1993, 1995). There is evidence that it has become locally extinct as a result of the total clearance of vegetation and quarrying, while excessive wood-cutting, cattle-grazing and the quarrying of hillocks threaten its survival at other sites, so there is a need to improve protection of its habitats (Subramanya *et al.* 1993, 1995).

Afghanistan mountains   s073

This Secondary Area is defined by the range of Afghan Snowfinch *Montifringilla theresae*, which is only known to breed in the mountains of Afghanistan (see map, p. 412), although there is a non-breeding record from Turkmenistan (Dement'ev and Gladkov 1970). It has been recorded at several scattered localities in the mountains of Afghanistan (Dathe and Neufeldt 1980), where it is found on open rocky or grassy slopes and in precipitous mountain valleys at 2,450–3,100 m (Paludan 1959, Dement'ev and Gladkov 1970). Two Important Bird Areas, Bande Amir and Dashte Nawar, have been identified for its conservation (Evans 1994).

Indus plains   s074

The Indus and its tributaries in Pakistan and small adjacent areas of India and south-east Iran constitute a Secondary Area (see map, p. 412), defined by the range of Sind Sparrow *Passer pyrrhonotus*. The region was formerly considered to be an EBA (ICBP 1992), but taxonomic changes have led to the loss of one restricted-range species: the western (nominate) form of Rufous-vented Prinia *Prinia burnesii* is now treated as conspecific with the eastern form *cinerascens*, following Sibley and Monroe (1993).

The wetlands along the Indus have been subject to rapid change in recent years, as a result of drainage and an increased intensity of cultivation adjacent to the main river banks, which has led to a loss of marshland and riverine forest. New wetlands, often with extensive reedbeds, have been created in some areas by seepage from irrigation canals, particularly around irrigation barrage headwaters. Increased tree-planting along canals and roadsides has created new habitat for a number of species, including *Passer pyrrhonotus* which has increased remarkably (Roberts 1991). However, several more-widespread threat-ened wetland species which occur in this area may have been negatively affected, including breeding Pallas's Fish-Eagle *Haliaeetus leucoryphus*, Jerdon's Babbler *Chrysomma altirostre*, Rufous-vented Prinia *Prinia burnesii*, Bristled Grass-warbler *Chaetornis striatus*, wintering Dalmatian Pelican *Pelecanus crispus*, Marbled Teal *Marmaronetta angustirostris* and White-headed Duck *Oxyura leucocephala* (all classified as Vulnerable). A total of four protected areas lie in or near this Secondary Area, of which at least one, Manglot, has some habitat suitable for the restricted-range and threatened birds (see IUCN 1990, 1992c).

Central Indian forests   s075

This Secondary Area is defined by the range of Forest Owlet *Athene blewitti* (classified as Critical) which occurs (or occurred) in eastern Madhya Pradesh, north-west Maharashtra and north-west Orissa in India, where it was recorded in moist deciduous forest and wild mango groves, sometimes near streams. It is known only from specimens collected before 1884, as the only specimen record during the twentieth century (from Gujarat in 1914) has been proved to be fraudulent, and no sight records or photographs are acceptable (Ripley 1976, Ali and Ripley 1987, Rasmussen and Collar in prep. a,b). There is thus no information on whether it occurs in any protected areas (see IUCN 1992c), or on the extent to which it has been affected by forest loss.

Southern Xinjiang mountains   s076

This Secondary Area has been identified owing to Sillem's Mountain-finch *Leucosticte sillemi*, a re-cently described species (thus not listed by Sibley and Monroe 1990, 1993) known from just two speci-mens collected in 1929 at c.5,125 m on the barren plateau between the upper Kara Kash and the upper Yarkand rivers in southern Xinjiang autonomous region (in an area under Chinese administration but claimed by India; see map, p. 412) (Roselaar 1992, 1994). It is classified as Data Deficient because its current status, habitat requirements and range are unknown.

Mongolian mountains   s077

This Secondary Area is defined by the range of Mongolian Accentor *Prunella koslowi*, a poorly known species which breeds in juniper scrub and grassland on dry mountain slopes (at c.2,000 m) in Mongolia (Stresemann and Portenko 1971, Mauersberger *et al.* 1982). It also occurs in arid scrub in sandy desert in Ningxia autonomous region in northern China, where it is assumed to be a non-breeding visitor (Cheng Tso-hsin 1987, Liu Nai-fa and Zhang Bing-mei 1989, M. J. Crosby pers. obs.

1993). It is not clear whether its habitat is adequately covered by existing protected areas (see IUCN 1992d). A more-widespread threatened species which breeds in the mountains of Mongolia is White-throated Bushchat *Saxicola insignis* (classified as Vulnerable) (Dathe and Neufeldt 1982).

Northern Qinghai–Tibetan plateau   s078

The range of Tibetan Rosefinch *Carpodacus roborowskii* defines this Secondary Area. It has been recorded at a small number of localities in the northern part of the Qinghai–Tibetan plateau in central Qinghai province of China (see map, p. 430), in barren rocky areas and alpine grassland at 4,300–5,200 m (Dathe and Neufeldt 1978, Cheng Tso-hsin 1987). It was classified as Data Deficient because there had been no recent published records, but sightings since 1993 (Otani 1995, Thorpe and Allen 1996, J. Hornskov *in litt.* 1996) suggest that it is unlikely to be threatened. There are no protected areas within its known range (IUCN 1992d).

Northern Myanmar lowlands   s079

This Secondary Area is defined by the range of Chestnut-backed Laughingthrush *Garrulax nuchalis*, which is found in the lowlands and foothills of eastern Arunachal Pradesh, Nagaland and Manipur in India, and in the upper Chindwin and Mali Hka watersheds in northern Myanmar (see map, p. 418). It is found in dense scrub forest on broken ground, in rocky ravines and in tall grass from the foothills to 1,200 m (King *et al.* 1975, Ali and Ripley 1987). Lowland forests are under considerable pressure in north-east India (Collins *et al.* 1991, Katti *et al.* 1992), but this species appears to be adaptable to secondary habitats and is therefore not considered to be threatened. There are several protected areas which could support populations of this species in north-east India, notably the large Namdapha National Park (see IUCN 1992c).

Myanmar–Thailand mountains   s080

This Secondary Area is defined by the range of Burmese Yuhina *Yuhina humilis*, which is known from two localities in north-west Thailand and several localities in southern Shan state, Kayah state and probably Kayin state in east-central Myanmar (see map, p. 424). It is found in hill evergreen forest between about 1,200 and 2,300 m (Boonsong and Round 1991). This area has a large number of hill tribes living in close proximity to the forests, and selective cutting combined with repeated burning continues to degrade most remaining areas of hill evergreen forest, although one of the localities where *Y. humilis* has been recorded in Thailand lies within the large contiguous area protected in Mae Ping National Park and Mae Tuen and Om Koi Wildlife Sanctuaries (Round 1988; see IUCN 1992c).

Doi Chiang Dao   s081

Doi Chiang Dao is a steep limestone massif in northern Thailand which rises to 2,175 m (see map, p. 424). The threatened Deignan's Babbler *Stachyris rodolphei* (classified as Vulnerable) is only known from this mountain, in bamboo forest between 1,000 and 1,700 m (Boonsong and Round 1991). However, it is difficult to distinguish in the field from Rufous-fronted Babbler *S. rufifrons* (with which it may be conspecific: C. R. Robson *in litt.* 1994), and may prove to occur elsewhere. More-widespread threatened species which occur here are Hume's Pheasant *Syrmaticus humiae* and Giant Nuthatch *Sitta magna* (both classified as Vulnerable). Doi Chiang Dao is designated as a Wildlife Sanctuary (IUCN 1992c).

Fan-Si-Pan and northern Laos   s082

Four restricted-range species are recorded from the Fan-Si-Pan range in northern Vietnam: the threatened Ward's Trogon *Harpactes wardi* (classified as Vulnerable; also in EBA 130), Red-winged Laughingthrush *Garrulax formosus* (also in EBA 137), Broad-billed Warbler *Tickellia hodgsoni* (also in EBA 130) and the threatened Yellow-billed Nuthatch *Sitta solangiae* (Vulnerable; also in EBAs 142, 145). *T. hodgsoni* has also been recorded in the mountains of northern Laos, and it is possible that some of these species also occur in the Ailao mountains in southern Yunnan province, China. They are found in broadleaf evergreen forest, scrub and bamboo above c.1,800 m (King *et al.* 1975), although *S. solangiae* has been recorded down to 1,550 m on Fan-Si-Pan (Harrap and Quinn 1996). There has been extensive forest loss around Fan-Si-Pan and in the Ailao mountains (Collins *et al.* 1991). However, there are several protected areas in the Ailao mountains in China (IUCN 1992d), and Nui Hoang Lien Nature Reserve in Vietnam (IUCN 1992c) presumably includes montane habitats suitable for the restricted-range species.

Southern Laos   s083

Two restricted-range species are recorded from southern Laos (see map, p. 448), both also ranging into Vietnam: White-cheeked Laughingthrush *Garrulax vassali* (also EBAs 143 and 145 and Secondary Area s084) and Grey-faced Tit-babbler *Macronous kelleyi* (also EBAs 143 and 144 and Secondary Area s084). In Vietnam, *G. vassali* is found in grassland and scrub on the edge of evergreen forest above c.600 m (Robson *et al.* 1989, 1993a,b), and in Laos it is known from montane forest on the Bolovens plateau, an isolated upland area, where at least four large flocks were seen at Dong Hua Sao in 1993 (Timmins *et al.* 1993). *M. kelleyi* is more widespread in southern Laos, having been recorded in lowland semi-evergreen forest in Dong Hua Sao, Xe Piane and Phou Xang He during surveys in 1992–1993 (Duckworth *et al.* 1993a,b, Timmins *et al.* 1993). Dong Hua Sao, Xe Piane and Phou Xang He were officially declared as protected areas in 1993 (Berkmüller *et al.* 1995).

Kontum plateau   s084

The mountainous region centred around the town of Kontum (or Contum) in Gia Lai-Con Tum and southern Quang Nam-Da Nang provinces of central Vietnam (see map, p. 450) supports at least three restricted-range species, the threatened Crested Argus *Rheinardia ocellata* (classified as Vulnerable; also in EBAs 143 and 145 in Vietnam and 158 in Peninsular Malaysia), White-cheeked Laughingthrush *Garrulax vassali* (also in EBAs 143 and 145 in Vietnam and Secondary Area s083 in Laos) and Grey-faced Tit-babbler *Macronous kelleyi* (also in EBAs 143 and 144 in Vietnam and Secondary Area s083 in Laos). All three species were recorded there during brief surveys of two sites in 1988, including Kong Cha Rang Nature Reserve (Robson *et al.* 1989). In 1996, a survey of the highest mountain in this region, Ngoc Linh (2,598 m), discovered a new form of barwing *Actinodura* (which was common there), similar to Spectacled Barwing *A. ramsayi*, but possibly an undescribed species (J. C. Eames verbally 1996). This mountain lies within the Ngoc Linh nature reserve, and the nearby Kon Kai Kinh and Mom Ray nature reserves may also contain suitable habitat for the restricted-range birds (see IUCN 1992c).

Thailand–Cambodia mountains   s085

This Secondary Area includes the mountains of south-east Thailand and the Cardamom and Elephant mountains in south-west Cambodia. It is defined by the range of the threatened Chestnut-headed Partridge *Arborophila cambodiana* (classified as Vulnerable), which is found in evergreen forest above 700 m. It is represented by the race *diversa* in Thailand and nominate *cambodiana* in Cambodia, these two possibly being better treated as distinct species (McGowan *et al.* 1995). In Thailand, most of this Secondary Area is included in Namtok Phliu National Park and Khao Soi Dao Wildlife Sanctuary, but there are no protected areas in this part of Cambodia. Despite the established protected areas, the partridge is believed to be threatened by forest loss and over-exploitation for food (Round 1988, McGowan *et al.* 1995).

Peninsular Thailand lowland forests   s086

The range of the threatened Gurney's Pitta *Pitta gurneyi* (classified as Critical) defines this Secondary Area. It is found in southern peninsular Thailand and adjacent southern Tenasserim in Myanmar, in level lowland semi-evergreen rain forest below 150 m. Its range appears to correspond to a transitional zone between the everwet tropical rain forests of Peninsular Malaysia and the more seasonal semi-evergreen and monsoon forests found in much of continental south-east Asia (see Whitmore 1984). Level lowland forest has been almost completely lost within its range in Thailand, where intensive survey work has located birds at four localities, but the only possibly viable population is at Khao Nor Chuchi in Krabi province, where 24–34 pairs are estimated; there have been no records from Myanmar since 1914, and it is feared that lowland forests are also rapidly being lost there (Collar *et al.* 1986, Round and Treesucon 1986). Khao Nor Chuchi has been the focus of a BirdLife International/Wild Bird Society of Thailand/Dansk Ornitologisk Forening project since 1990, which is trying to halt deforestation there, but the area of suitable habitat continues to decline gradually and territories are being lost (Gretton *et al.* 1993).

Chukotski peninsula   s087

This Secondary Area is defined by the breeding range of the threatened Spoon-billed Sandpiper *Eurynorhynchus pygmeus* (a monotypic genus endemic to this Secondary Area; classified as Vulnerable), which nests only in north-east Russia, on the Chukotski (or Chukchi) peninsula and the isthmus of the Kamchatka peninsula to the south. It is a long-distance migrant, which has been recorded widely in eastern and southern Asia on passage and in winter. It nests on sea coasts with sparsely vegetated sandy ridges near lakes and marshes, a habitat which is patchily distributed along the narrow coastal zone, especially near to the mouths of some rivers and lagoons and sandy spits. More-widespread threatened species which occur in this area are Lesser White-fronted Goose *Anser erythropus*, Spectacled Eider *Somateria fischeri* and Steller's Eider *Polysticta stelleri* (all classified as Vulnerable). A new protected area on the Chukotski peninsula is under discussion (Tomkovich 1991).

Sakhalin   s088

This Secondary Area has been identified on account of the threatened Nordmann's Greenshank *Tringa guttifer* (classified as Endangered) which is only known to breed on the island of Sakhalin in far-eastern Russia, although it probably also breeds on the Russian mainland along the coast of the Sea of

Okhotsk and possibly on the Kamchatka peninsula and in the lower reaches of the Novy Semyachik river (close to the Kronotsk Reserve). It is a long-distance migrant, recorded widely in eastern and southern Asia on passage and in winter. It nests in lowland swamps and swampy and thinned coniferous forest adjacent to shallow bays on Sakhalin, where the total population is estimated at 30–40 pairs. Some breeding areas have been destroyed by urbanization, and other threats include crow predation, human disturbance and increased hunting pressure (Nechaev 1989).

Central Honshu lowland forests   s089
This Secondary Area is defined by the breeding range of Japanese Night-heron *Gorsachius goisagi*, a very poorly known, shy and retiring nocturnal species, which has declined in the last 30 years such that it appears to have become uncommon everywhere and is consequently classified as Vulnerable. Its breeding range is considered to include the Izu Islands (EBA 146), where it may be extinct, and adjacent parts of central Honshu (see map, p. 454). It has also been recorded from many of the other Japanese islands (including the Nansei Shoto, EBA 148), but with no evidence of breeding (Brazil 1991), and therefore additional (assumed wintering) areas are not covered by this or other Secondary Areas. The main threat in central Honshu is the loss of the species' preferred habitat—subtropical evergreen forest with watercourses and damp areas.

Central Honshu montane forests   s090
The breeding range of Yellow Bunting *Emberiza sulphurata* defines this Secondary Area. The species has a limited distribution largely in the lower mountains and highlands (600–1,500 m) of central Honshu (Japan), especially in the Mt Fuji/Hakone area and in the Japan Alps (see map, p. 454). The key habitat is deciduous and mixed forest, on wooded slopes and in high valleys. Although the species has been recorded elsewhere on Honshu, and on Hokkaido and Kyushu, it is not known to breed in these other areas (Brazil 1991), so these additional (assumed wintering) areas are not covered by this or by other Secondary Areas. There is some evidence that *E. sulphurata* has declined over the past hundred years (and it is consequently classed as Vulnerable), but the causes are unknown.

Iwo Islands   s091
These Japanese islands, which are an extention of the Izu–Ogasawara chain (see map, p. 454), are a Secondary Area because one restricted-range species, Japanese Wood-pigeon *Columba janthina*, occurred on Kita-iwo-jima and Iwo-jima, but became extinct during the early 1980s. The species survives in the Nansci, Izu, Ogasawara and other Japanese and Korean offshore islands (EBAs 146, 147 and 148, and Secondary Area s092).

Japanese and Korean offshore islands   s092
The Japanese islands included in this Secondary Area are those off southern Honshu, Shikoku and Kyushu, and islands in the Korea Strait (Tsushima and the Goto Islands) as far round as the Oki Islands in the Sea of Japan (Brazil 1991); in Korea, also Ullung-do and some of the small islands off the south coast of the mainland (Gore and Won 1971). The area partly covers the breeding range of Japanese Wood-pigeon *Columba janthina* (Near Threatened), which also occurs in the Nansei, Izu and Ogasawara Islands (EBAs 146, 147, 148), and formerly on the Iwo Islands (Secondary Area s091). It has also been recorded on tiny islands off Shandong province in China (Cheng Tso-hsin 1987) and off Taiwan (Wang *et al.* 1991), but, as it is not clear if it breeds here, these islands have not been included within the Secondary Area. The key habitat for the species is dense, mature, subtropical or warm temperate evergreen forest, so any loss or degradation of forest on the tiny islands it favours is a significant threat. Some of the islands in this Secondary Area are also important for seabirds, including Japanese Murrelet *Synthliboramphus wumizusume* (classified as Vulnerable) which is threatened by destruction of nesting habitat, by disturbance from fishermen landing at breeding sites and by introduced predators (Hasegawa 1984, Takeishi 1987).

Lanyu   s093
Lanyu (or Orchid Island), a tiny forested island (46 km^2, reaching a height of 548 m) c.75 km off the south-east coast of Taiwan (see map, p. 460), has been developed for tourism but this is limited to the periphery of the island. Two restricted-range species occur there: Whistling Green-pigeon *Treron formosae* and Elegant Scops-owl *Otus elegans*; both occur also on the Nansei Shoto (EBA 148) and on the Batanes and Babuyan Islands north of the Philippines (Secondary Area s094), and *T. formosae* is also on Taiwan (EBA 149). *T. formosae* was fairly common on Lanyu until 1990 when a major typhoon hit the island and caused extensive damage to the forest (L. L. Severinghaus *in litt.* 1996). *O. elegans botelensis* was listed as threatened by King (1978–1979), and in 1985–1986 the population of this race was estimated at 150–230 birds, surviving in c.18 km^2 of suitable habitat of which only c.5 km^2 was mature forest (Severinghaus 1989). More recently its numbers have been estimated to be stable at 1,000 birds and prospects for its survival appear good if the habitat can be protected (L. L. Severinghaus *in litt.* 1996).

SOUTH-EAST ASIAN ISLANDS, NEW GUINEA AND AUSTRALIA

Batanes and Babuyan Islands   s094
North of Luzon (EBA 151) in the Philippines there is a scattering of small islands, the Batanes and Babuyanes (see map, p. 464), some at least with a volcanic history, lying in the straits between the Philippine archipelago and Taiwan (EBA 149). Present there are two restricted-range species, Whistling Green-pigeon *Treron formosae* and Elegant Scops-owl *Otus elegans*; both occur also on Lanyu (Secondary Area s093) and Nansei Shoto (EBA 148), and *T. formosae* is also on Taiwan (EBA 149), but, as neither species occurs on the mainland of Luzon, the Batanes and Babuyanes are treated as a Secondary Area, separate from the Luzon EBA. *T. formosae filipina* is an uncommon and local resident in forest on Batan, Calayan, Camiguin Norte and Sabtang, and *O. elegans calayensis* is fairly common in forest or forest edge on Batan, Calayan and Sabtang (Dickinson *et al.* 1991).

Tablas, Romblon and Sibuyan   s095
These islands, in the centre of the Philippine archipelago north of Panay (see EBA 152, also for map), have been identified as a Secondary Area on account of three restricted-range species which occur there (and elsewhere, but with no clear affinities to any one other EBA): Mantanani Scops-owl *Otus mantananensis*, also occurring on small islands off Palawan (EBA 156), the Sulus (EBA 155) and Borneo (Secondary Area s097); Streak-breasted Bulbul *Ixos siquijorensis* (classified as Endangered) which is extinct on Cebu (EBA 153) and also occurs on Siquijor (Secondary Area s096); and Celestial Monarch *Hypothymis coelestis* (Endangered), patchily distributed on Luzon (EBA 151) and Mindanao (EBA 154), possibly extinct on Negros (EBA 152) and present in the Sulus (EBA 155). The widespread Rufous-lored Kingfisher *Todirhamphus winchelli* (Endangered) has also been recorded on these islands. There is forest left on Sibuyan (100–150 km², over half of the island's land area); the island rises to a considerable altitude (2,050 m), but logging severely threatens remaining areas of lowland forest (Goodman and Ingle 1993; see also Goodman *et al.* 1995).

Siquijor   s096
This Philippine island (344 km², and reaching 628 m; see map, p. 474) is a Secondary Area on account of one restricted-range species, Streak-breasted Bulbul *Ixos siquijorensis*, possibly numbering several thousand birds there (but classified as Endangered on account of its small and declining range); it also occurs on Romblon and Tablas (Secondary Area

s095) and is extinct on Cebu (EBA 153). The widespread Rufous-lored Kingfisher *Todirhamphus winchelli* (Endangered) and Philippine Cockatoo *Cacatua haematuropygia* (Critical) are (or were) present on the island, but the kingfisher was very scarce and the cockatoo was down to one pair in 1991. Only four significant patches of forest remain, totalling less than 8 km², and, although all are in reserves, there are some signs of continuing degradation (Evans *et al.* 1993).

North-east Bornean islands   s097
There are several small islands off the north and east coasts of Borneo, in the east Malaysian state of Sabah and the Indonesian province of Kalimantan Timur (see map, p. 484), which together constitute a Secondary Area defined by the distribution of Grey Imperial-pigeon *Ducula pickeringii*, a threatened small-island specialist (classified as Vulnerable) which also ranges northwards to the Philippines (EBAs 155, 156) and eastwards to Miangas and Talaud (EBA 167). This species is found in forest on small islands, and is threatened by habitat loss and hunting (Toone *et al.* 1993, D. R. Wells *in litt.* 1994). Another restricted-range small-island specialist, Mantanani Scops-owl *Otus mantananensis*, is common in forest and coconut plantations on the island of Mantanani (MacKinnon and Phillipps 1993) in this Secondary Area, and also ranges northwards to the Philippines (EBAs 155 and 156 and Secondary Area s095).

Sabah lowlands   s098
This Secondary Area includes the lowlands of the state of Sabah in East Malaysia, in the northern part of the island of Borneo (see map, p. 484). It is defined by the range of White-fronted Falconet *Microhierax latifrons*, which is found in lowland and hill forest, forest edge and agricultural land below c.1,200 m (MacKinnon and Phillipps 1993). White-crowned Shama *Copsychus stricklandii*, a restricted-range bird which occurs in lowland forest in this Secondary Area (but also ranges into northern Kalimantan), was treated as a full species by Sibley and Monroe (1990, 1993) but is here considered to be a form of the more widespread White-rumped Shama *C. malabaricus* following Andrew (1992). The Secondary Area is adjacent to the Bornean mountains (EBA 157), but the birds of that EBA mainly occur in higher-altitude montane habitats. The main threat to the Secondary Area is deforestation, as a result of logging and forest fires (Collins *et al.* 1991), but *M. latifrons* appears able to adapt to disturbed habitats, and there are up to

18 protected areas in Sabah which include areas of lowland rain forest (IUCN 1992c). The lowland rain forests of Borneo support several widespread threatened species (Collar *et al.* 1994).

Kalimantan lowlands   s099
This Secondary Area is defined by the range of the threatened Black-browed Babbler *Malacocincla perspicillata* (classified as Vulnerable), known from a single specimen, probably collected near Martapura (3°31′S 114°45′E) (or possibly near Banjarmasin, 3°22′S 114°33′E) (Mees 1995), in the Indonesian province of Kalimantan Selatan (see map, p. 484). It is probably a forest bird, and its habitat is likely to be under pressure from lowland deforestation (see RePPProT 1990, Collins *et al.* 1991). The lowland rain forests of Borneo also support several widespread threatened species (Collar *et al.* 1994). This Secondary Area is adjacent to the Bornean mountains (EBA 157), but the birds of that area mainly occur in montane habitats at higher altitudes.

Bornean coastal zone   s100
The mangroves and coastal scrub and forest along the southern and western coasts of Borneo are included in this Secondary Area, in the provinces of Kalimantan Barat, Kalimantan Tengah and Kalimantan Selatan in Indonesia, and in the East Malaysian state of Sarawak (see map, p. 484). One restricted-range species occurs here, Javan White-eye *Zosterops flavus*, which is otherwise known from the Javan coastal zone (EBA 161). It is common in southern Kalimantan, but only known from a single specimen in Sarawak (MacKinnon and Phillipps 1993).

Natuna Islands   s101
These small islands lie off the western tip of Borneo in the Indonesian province of Kalimantan Barat, and the Secondary Area also includes Burong Island off the mouth of the Lupar river in the state of Sarawak in East Malaysia (see map, p. 484). They support one restricted-range species, the threatened Silvery Wood-pigeon *Columba argentina* (classified as Vulnerable). This is principally a species of forest on small islands, found on islands off Sumatra and Borneo (in Secondary Areas s103, s105, s106), but it is occasionally recorded on the coast of both of these islands and birds suspected (but not confirmed) to be this species were widespread and seen in large numbers in southern Sumatra in 1989 (Verheugt *et al.* 1993). It is believed to be threatened by forest loss, disturbance and hunting.

Malayan peninsula lowlands   s102
The lowland rain forests of Peninsular Malaysia and extreme southern peninsular Thailand are included

in this Secondary Area (see map, p. 488) which is defined by the range of the threatened Malayan Peacock-pheasant *Polyplectron malacense* (classified as Vulnerable), an extreme lowland specialist (Wells 1985) found in rain forest below c.300 m (McGowan and Garson 1995). Its range has been considerably reduced by forest clearance and degradation (see Collins *et al.* 1991), and continuing conversion of land for agriculture could eventually mean that it will be virtually confined to the five protected areas which are known to support populations (McGowan and Garson 1995; see Yatim 1993). The lowland rain forests of the Malayan peninsula also support several widespread threatened species (Collar *et al.* 1994). This Secondary Area is adjacent to Sumatra and Peninsular Malaysia (EBA 158), but the birds of that EBA occur in montane habitats at higher altitudes.

Riau and Lingga islands   s103
These island groups lie off the east coast of Sumatra (and immediately to the south of Singapore at the tip of the Malayan peninsula) in the Indonesian province of Riau (see map, p. 488). The natural vegetation is tropical lowland rain forest (Whitmore 1984). They support one restricted-range species, the threatened Silvery Wood-pigeon *Columba argentina* (classified as Vulnerable; see Secondary Area s101).

North Sumatran lowlands   s104
This Secondary Area is defined by the range of the threatened Rueck's Blue-flycatcher *Cyornis ruckii* (classified as Vulnerable), which is known from two specimens collected in the Indonesian province of Sumatera Utara (see map, p. 488). They were found in exploited forest at an altitude of c.150–200 m (van Marle and Voous 1988) in an area which has now largely been deforested. The species may presumably occur elsewhere in the lowlands of northern Sumatra but is likely to have been affected by the extensive lowland deforestation which has taken place there (see RePPProT 1990). The lowland rain forests on Sumatra also support several widespread threatened species (Collar *et al.* 1994). This Secondary Area is adjacent to Sumatra and Peninsular Malaysia (EBA 158), but the birds of that EBA occur in montane habitats at higher altitudes.

Simeulue   s105
Simeulue lies off the north-west coast of Sumatra, in Aceh province of Indonesia (see map, p. 488). The natural vegetation of the island is tropical lowland rain forest (Whitmore 1984). It supports two restricted-range species, the single-island endemic Simeulue Scops-owl *Otus umbra*, which is found in the forest and forest-edge habitats, and the threatened

Silvery Wood-pigeon *Columba argentina* (classified as Vulnerable; see Secondary Area s101).

Mentawai Islands   s106
The Mentawai Islands lie off the west coast of Sumatra in the Indonesian province of Sumatera Barat, and include the islands of Siberut, Sipura, and North and South Pagai (see map, p. 488). The natural vegetation is tropical lowland rain forest (Whitmore 1984). The islands support two restricted-range species, the threatened Silvery Wood-pigeon *Columba argentina* (classified as Vulnerable; see Secondary Area s101) and Mentawai Scops-owl *Otus mentawi*. The latter is confined to the Mentawai Islands, where its habitat is unknown (van Marle and Voous 1988), but is presumably forest. The Mentawai Islands have 11 endemic species of mammals (Whitten *et al.* 1987b), a remarkably high number considering the relatively low level of endemism in birds.

Seribu Islands   s107
These small Indonesian islands are in the Java Sea, a few kilometres to the north of Jakarta on Java (see map, p. 494). They support one restricted-range species, Pink-headed Imperial-pigeon *Ducula rosacea*, a small-island specialist which is found in forest, scrub and agricultural land on several other islands in the Java Sea (Secondary Areas s108, s109), and in the Moluccas and Lesser Sundas (EBAs 162, 164, 165 and 171 and Secondary Areas s110 and s111).

Masalembu   s108
These small Indonesian islands are in the Java Sea to the north-east of Java (see map, p. 494). They support one restricted-range species, Pink-headed Imperial-pigeon *Ducula rosacea* (see Secondary Area s107). A widespread threatened species, Yellow-crested Cockatoo *Cacatua sulphurea* (classified as Endangered), is represented on the islands by the endemic subspecies *abbotti*, of which only 8–10 individuals could be located in 1993 (Cahyadin and Arif 1994).

Kangean   s109
The Kangean Islands are in the Java Sea, to the north-east of Java in Indonesia (see map, p. 494). They support three restricted-range species: Javan Plover *Charadrius javanicus*, a bird of sandy beaches and mudflats which also occurs in the Javan coastal zone (EBA 161); Pink-headed Imperial-pigeon *Ducula rosacea* (see Secondary Area s107); and Grey-cheeked Tit-babbler *Macronous flavicollis*, a bird of open forest and scrub which also occurs in the Java and Bali forests (EBA 160) and is represented on the Kangean Islands by the endemic subspecies *prillwitzi*.

Salayar and Bonerate Islands   s110
The long, narrow island of Salayar and the scattered islands and islets of the Bonerate group are in the Flores Sea to the south of the southern peninsula of Sulawesi (see EBA 166; also for map) in Indonesia. They support six restricted-range species, including the threatened White-tipped Monarch *Monarcha everetti* (classified as Vulnerable) of Tanahjampea; in 1993 this single-island endemic was found to be quite common in lowland rain forest, which was estimated to cover about half of the island but is potentially under pressure from logging (Dutson 1995). The other restricted-range species are Dusky Cuckoo-dove *Macropygia magna*, which also occurs in the Lesser Sundas (EBAs 162, 164, 165), Elegant Imperial-pigeon *Ducula concinna*, a small-island specialist which also occurs in the Moluccas, Lesser Sundas and Irian Jaya (EBAs 165, 166, 167, 169, 170 and 172 and Secondary Areas s111 and s112), Pink-headed Imperial-pigeon *Ducula rosacea* (see Secondary Area s107), Rufous-sided Gerygone *Gerygone dorsalis*, which also occurs in the Banda Sea islands (EBA 165), and Red-chested Flowerpecker *Dicaeum maugei*, which also occurs in the Lesser Sundas (EBAs 162, 164, 165). All of these species were recorded during a brief visit to the islands in 1993 (Dutson 1995).

Tukangbesi Islands   s111
These islands are in the Banda Sea, off the south-east peninsula of Sulawesi (see EBA 166; also for map), Indonesia. They support two small-island specialist restricted-range species, Elegant Imperial-pigeon *Ducula concinna* (see Secondary Area s110) and Pink-headed Imperial-pigeon *Ducula rosacea* (see Secondary Area s107).

Aru Islands   s112
These Indonesian islands (see map, p. 558) are, at 7,700 km², the largest of the New Guinea satellite islands and have the richest avifauna (c.160 resident species recorded; see Diamond and Bishop 1994). While no bird species is confined to the Arus, there are numerous endemic subspecies and several restricted-range species (recorded in other small-island Indonesian and/or lowland New Guinean EBAs), including Wallace's Fruit-dove *Ptilinopus wallacii*, Elegant Imperial-pigeon *Ducula concinna*, Spangled Kookaburra *Dacelo tyro*, Little Paradise-kingfisher *Tanysiptera hydrocharis*, Island Whistler *Pachycephala phaionotus* and Brown-headed Crow *Corvus fuscicapillus*. Chestnut Rail *Eulabeornis castaneoventris*, a restricted-range species from North-west Australia (EBA 187), also occurs there. The islands support extensive areas of untouched lowland rain forest with good populations of the

above species and of two important widespread species, Southern Cassowary *Casuarius casuarius* (classified as Vulnerable) and Palm Cockatoo *Probosciger aterrimus* (Near Threatened) (K. D. Bishop *in litt.* 1996).

Yapen   s113
Yapen is an island lying in Geelvink bay (see EBA 174; also for map) and is part of the Indonesian province of Irian Jaya. It rises to 1,430 m and was once an outlying range of the New Guinea mainland. It qualifies as a Secondary Area because of the two restricted-range species which occur there but which do not clearly identify it with another single EBA, although each of them occurs in three different EBAs on the mainland: Spice Imperial-pigeon *Ducula myristicivora* and Green-backed Robin *Pachycephalopsis hattamensis*.

South-east Papuan lowlands   s114
This area is defined by the range of its one endemic species, Brown-headed Paradise-kingfisher *Tanysiptera danae*, which occurs only in south-east Papua New Guinea, west in the north to the Waria river and west in the south to the Aroa river (see map, p. 550). The species frequents primary and gallery forest, mainly in hills and foothills up to 800 m, and very locally in the lowlands (Coates 1985). Three other restricted-range species—Painted Quail-thrush *Cinclosoma ajax*, Olive-yellow Robin *Poecilodryas placens* and White-bellied Whistler *Pachycephala leucogastra*, which have disjunct distribtions in five other New Guinea EBAs—also occur there.

Clarke Range   s115
Clarke Range is in central-eastern Queensland (Australia), and has one endemic species, Eungella Honeyeater *Lichenostomus hindwoodi*. The species is classified as Conservation Dependent because it appears to have substantial populations in rain forest which relies for its protection on the existence of the Eungella National Park (496 km²).

East Australian mangroves   s116
This Secondary Area is defined by the range of its one endemic species, Mangrove Honeyeater *Lichenostomus fasciogularis*, which lives in mangroves (frequently visiting flowering shrubs in towns adjacent to mangroves), ranging from Townsville in Queensland to northern New South Wales (Blakers *et al.* 1984).

Bulloo and Diamantina rivers   s117
The Bulloo river is an isolated drainage system in north-west New South Wales and south-west Queensland, and the Diamantina river is in south-west

Queensland and north-east South Australia. These two widely separated localities are home to Grey Grasswren *Amytornis barbatus* (races *barbatus* and *diamantina*), which inhabits patches of seasonally swampy grassland and shrubland. The habitat does not appear to have been degraded by pastoralism, the main land-use, and is under no immediate threat (Garnett 1993).

Simpson and Strzelecki deserts   s118
This Secondary Area in northern South Australia and southern Northern Territory has been identified on account of Eyrean Grasswren *Amytornis goyderi*, a restricted-range species which was long thought to have disappeared but is now known to be abundant in cane grass on sandhills in the region.

South Australian desert   s119
This Secondary Area lies in the semi-arid and arid zones of the state of South Australia, defined by the range of its one endemic species, Chestnut-breasted Whiteface *Aphelocephala pectoralis*, which is widely but locally distributed in fewer than 40 localities. The key habitat is chenopod shrubland in stony environments which, in places, is being destroyed by opal mining and degraded by livestock and rabbit grazing. *A. pectoralis* is classified as Vulnerable because its population is unlikely to exceed 6,000 individuals and there is some evidence of decline (Garnett 1993).

West Australian mangroves   s120
This Secondary Area is defined by the range of its one endemic species, Dusky Gerygone *Gerygone tenebrosa*, which is confined to mangroves (perhaps more abundant on the seaward side of mangrove belts) from King Sound south to Bush bay in Western Australia. At least three populations exist (and three races have been described: north to south, *tenebrosa*, *whitlocki* and *christopheri*), separated at the Eighty Mile Beach, and at the break in mangroves between Pt Cloates and Carnarvon (Blakers *et al.* 1984).

Gulf of Carpentaria   s121
This north Australian Secondary Area is defined by the range of its one endemic species, Carpentarian Grasswren *Amytornis dorotheae*, known from just eight isolated localities in a strip of sandstone country with mature, unburnt tussock grassland, lying inland from the southern coast of the gulf; it runs from the Tawallah range near the Limmen Bight in the Northern Territory to the Gunpowder district north of Mt Isa in Queensland (see map, p. 572). The grasswren is classified as Vulnerable because, although numbers are difficult to assess, it has probably been adversely affected by changes in the fire regime since the arrival of Europcans (Garnett 1993).

PACIFIC ISLANDS

Wake Island   s122

Three tiny, low-lying coral atolls (7 km²) surrounding a lagoon constitute Wake Island, a US unincorporated territory. The atolls are situated c.550 km north of the Marshall Islands (Secondary Area s123) in the north-central Pacific, and are covered by an open scrub forest. The island is a Secondary Area on the basis of its one endemic (extinct) species, Wake Island Rail *Gallirallus wakensis*, which was last seen in 1945. It has been claimed that this flightless species was eaten by Japanese forces occupying the island and that the bird became extinct as a consequence (Greenway 1967).

Marshall Islands   s123

Lying c.500 km east of the Caroline Islands (EBA 192), the Marshall Islands are an archipelago of 31 coral atolls strung out in two chains and totalling 181 km² in area (Ralik and Ratak). Small remnants of atoll/beach and mangrove forest remain, although all the islands have been greatly modified by coconut and breadfruit plantations, and some have been drastically damaged by the testing of atomic weapons (Davis *et al.* 1986). The islands have been identified as a Secondary Area because two restricted-range species which occur in other Micronesian/Polynesian EBAs are or were present there: Purple-capped Fruit-dove *Ptilinopus porphyraceus* is locally extinct on Ebon in the Ralik chain, and Micronesian Imperial-pigeon *Ducula oceanica* is extant on four atolls. The recognition of Gilbert Rail *Gallirallus conditicus*—listed as extinct and known only from the type-specimen supposedly from Ebon (mistakenly taken to be in the Gilbert Islands of Kiribati by Sibley and Monroe 1990, but corrected in Sibley and Monroe 1993)—is probably traceable to an early curatorial error, and the specimen is more likely one of Lord Howe Rail *G. sylvestris* (EBA 204) (Olson 1992). Bristle-thighed Curlew *Numenius tahitiensis* (classified as Vulnerable), a restricted-range species which breeds in western Alaska (Secondary Area s002), winters on islands in the Pacific region including the Marshall Islands.

Nauru   s124

Nauru, an independent nation, is a raised limestone island (21 km²) in the west-central Pacific, and is a Secondary Area on the basis of its single-island endemic, Nauru Reed-warbler *Acrocephalus rehsei*. Vegetation includes mixed plateau forest with a few remaining areas of atoll forest; about two-thirds of the island has been mined for phosphates (Davis *et al.* 1986) but extraction is now carried out on only a small scale. In 1993 *A. rehsei* was found to be relatively common and widely distributed in remnant forest on the steep sides of the escarpment, in gardens on the coastal strip and in regenerating areas on the plateau (B. Fletcher *in litt.* 1995). Although the species does not appear to be under any immediate threat, it is considered threatened (classified as Vulnerable) on account of its tiny range which renders it forever susceptible to chance events such as cyclones or the introduction of alien predators.

Gilbert Islands   s125

The 16 small atolls or limestone islands of this group (278 km² in total) are politically part of Kiribati (see also Secondary Area s134) in the west-central Pacific, south of the Marshall Islands (Secondary Area s123). Most of the scrub vegetation on the larger islands has been replaced by plantations of coconuts and breadfruit (Davis *et al.* 1986). These islands are treated as a Secondary Area because one restricted-range species, Micronesian Imperial-pigeon *Ducula oceanica*, which occurs in other Micronesian EBAs, has been recorded from Kuria and Aranuka, two of the atolls. Shy Ground-dove *Gallicolumba stairii*, a restricted-range species from central Polynesia (EBAs 202, 203), was introduced to nearby Abemama in c.1940, but its present status there is unknown (Pratt *et al.* 1987). Bristle-thighed Curlew *Numenius tahitiensis* (classified as Vulnerable), a restricted-range species which breeds in western Alaska (Secondary Area s002), winters on islands in the Pacific region including the Gilbert Islands.

Ontong Java atoll   s126

This tiny atoll lies c.300 km north-east of the main Solomon Islands, to which it belongs politically (see map, p. 596). It holds a population of Atoll Starling *Aplonis feadensis*, a restricted-range species of forest, forest edge and coconut groves which also occurs on tiny islands in the Bismarck archipelago (EBA 195) to the west (Coates 1990).

Rotuma   s127

The volcanic island of Rotuma (47 km², and rising to 250 m), politically part of Fiji, lies with its few small satellites c.500 km north of the Fijian island of Vanua Levu (EBA 202). Most if not all of its native forest has long since given way to shifting cultivation and to coconut plantations, but, like most of the inhabited Fijian islands, it supports quite extensive secondary bush (Clunie 1984), which provides habitats for native species. Although Rotuma has a similar avifauna to Fiji (albeit a depauperate one), with populations of four central Polynesian restricted-range species (Purple-capped Fruit-dove *Ptilinopus porphyraceus*, Polynesian Triller *Lalage maculosa*, Fiji Shrikebill *Clytorhynchus vitiensis* and Polynesian Starling *Aplonis tabuensis*), it is treated separately as a Secondary Area, on account of its geographical isolation. It has one endemic species, Rotuma Myzomela *Myzomela chermesina* (sometimes considered to be conspecific with Cardinal Honeyeater *M. cardinalis*), which is classified as threatened (Vulnerable) on account of its tiny range.

Wallis and Futuna   s128

These two islands (255 km^2 in total, reaching an altitude of 500 m) are a French overseas territory in the south-west Pacific Ocean. A rapidly increasing human population and resulting agricultural activities have led to clearance of forest and a decrease in bird habitats (Dupon 1986b, Guyot and Thibault 1988). The islands are treated as a Secondary Area because seven central Polynesian restricted-range species occur (Purple-capped Fruit-dove *Ptilinopus porphyraceus*, Shy Ground-dove *Gallicolumba stairii*, Blue-crowned Lorikeet *Vini australis*, Polynesian Triller *Lalage maculosa*, Fiji Shrikebill *Clytorhynchus vitiensis*, Wattled Honeyeater *Foulehaio carunculata* and Polynesian Starling *Aplonis tabuensis*); as all these species also occur on Samoa (EBA 203) to the east and on Fiji (EBA 202) to the west, Wallis and Futuna have no clear affinity with either one EBA rather than the other.

Niuafo'ou   s129

Niuafo'ou (55 km^2), an active volcano which last erupted in 1946, is the northernmost island in the Tongan archipelago, c.500 km north-east of Fiji (EBA 202) and c.300 km south-west of Western Samoa (EBA 203). Today the ridge of the crater surrounds a large lake, the inner slopes of which are mostly forested, as are the islands within the central lake. Villages and plantations are concentrated on the outer slopes of the crater in the north and east, and the western part of the island is characterized by dry open forest. Niuafo'ou is treated as a Secondary Area on account of its single-island endemic, Niuafo'ou Megapode *Megapodius pritchardii*; three central Polynesian restricted-range species also occur on the island (Purple-capped Fruit-dove *Ptilinopus porphyraceus*, Blue-crowned Lorikeet *Vini australis* and Polynesian Starling *Aplonis tabuensis*). The megapode has a small population (fewer than 1,000 birds) and a tiny range within the island (its habit of using hot volcanic ash to incubate its eggs confines its nesting sites to small areas of loose soil close to vents); it is considered threatened (classified as Endangered), mainly through predation by feral cats,

egg harvesting, development plans and volcanic eruption; recently chicks and eggs have been released on the predator-free Tongan islands of Late (in the Vava'u group) and Fonualei (Secondary Area s130)—where the species is not known to have occurred naturally in historical times—with further transfers planned (Rinke 1986a,b, 1991, 1993).

Tonga   s130

This Tongan Secondary Area includes all the islands which make up the political unit of Tonga apart from Niuafo'ou, which is treated as a Secondary Area in its own right (see above). There are c.170 scattered limestone and volcanic islands in total (700 km^2, maximum altitude 1,030 m) including the Vava'u, Ha'apai and Tongatapu groups. Vegetation includes lowland rain forest (which has been much cleared on the larger islands for settlement and cultivation) and coastal scrub (Davis *et al.* 1986). These islands are treated as a Secondary Area on account of the endemic Tongan Whistler *Pachycephala jacquinoti* (sometimes treated as a subspecies of Golden Whistler *P. pectoralis*), which is common and widespread in the Vava'u group. Although Niuafo'ou Megapode *Megapodius pritchardii* has recently been introduced to Late in the same group, and there is thus now an overlap in range between these two restricted-range species, the islands have not been treated as an EBA as there has been no natural overlap in historical times. The occurrence of several central Polynesian restricted-range species in the Ha'apai and Tongatapu island groups (Many-coloured Fruit-dove *Ptilinopus perousii*, Purple-capped Fruit-dove *P. porphyraceus*, Shy Ground-dove *Gallicolumba stairii*, Blue-crowned Lorikeet *Vini australis*, Polynesian Triller *Lalage maculosa*, Fiji Shrikebill *Clytorhynchus vitiensis*, Wattled Honeyeater *Foulehaio carunculata* and Polynesian Starling *Aplonis tabuensis*) extends the boundary of this Secondary Area southwards. Another restricted-range species, Red Shining-parrot *Prosopeia tabuensis*, from Fiji (EBA 202) has been introduced to 'Eua in the Tongatapu group.

Niue   s131

Niue is a raised island (maximum altitude 70 m) of 260 km^2 lying c.500 km south-east of Samoa (EBA 203) and 480 km east of Tonga (see above); it is a self-governing territory in association with New Zealand. Though originally covered by tropical rain forest, shifting cultivation has greatly modified the vegetation over much of the island, and there are now large areas of secondary forest and scrub in the central basin (Davis *et al.* 1986). Niue is treated as a Secondary Area because it holds several central Polynesian restricted-range species (Many-coloured Fruit-dove *Ptilinopus perousii*, Purple-capped Fruit-dove *P. porphyraceus*, Blue-crowned Lorikeet *Vini australis*, Polynesian Triller *Lalage maculosa* and Polynesian Starling *Aplonis tabuensis*) at this, the south-eastern limit of their ranges. Bristle-thighed Curlew *Numenius tahitiensis* (classified as Vulnerable), a restricted-range species which breeds in western Alaska (Secondary Area s002), winters on islands in the Pacific region including Niue.

Snares Islands and Stewart Island islets   s132

The Snares Islands are granitic, uninhabited islands (3.3 km², rising to 150 m) which lie c.100 km south-west of the South Island of New Zealand (EBA 207), and are covered with low forest with tussock grassland around the perimeter (see Clark and Dingwall 1985). The islands are treated as a Secondary Area on account of one restricted-range species, New Zealand Snipe *Coenocorypha aucklandica* (occurring on other New Zealand subantarctic islands, EBA 208 and Secondary Area s133), which has a race, *huegeli*, known only from these islands and listed as a priority for conservation by Tisdall (1994). The Secondary Area also includes islets off Stewart Island because another race of *C. aucklandica*, *iredalei*, occurred there including on South Cape and Jacky Islands (exterminated from South Cape by introduced Weka *Gallirallus australis* and from Jacky by black rats *Rattus rattus*). The Snares Islands and the Stewart Island outliers are important for seabirds, notably Snares Island Penguin *Eudyptes robustus* (classified as Vulnerable), which breeds only on predator-free islands in the group (population estimated at 23,250 pairs in 1985–1986), and Stewart Island Shag *Phalacrocorax chalconotus* (also Vulnerable), which ranges around Stewart Island and south-east South Island, nesting on rocky headlands and small islands, with a population of over c.3,000 birds (Marchant and Higgins 1990). The Snares Islands are protected, and landings are strictly controlled by permit (see Sanson and Dingwall 1995).

Antipodes Islands   s133

These volcanic, uninhabited, subantarctic islands (c.21 km², rising to 400 m) are c.850 km south-east of the South Island of New Zealand (EBA 207), and are managed as a reserve. The predominant vegetation in coastal areas is tussock grassland with scrub, ferns and bogs inland (Clark and Dingwall 1985, Sanson and Dingwall 1995). The Antipodes Islands are treated as a Secondary Area because Antipodes Parakeet *Cyanoramphus unicolor* is endemic to the group; it nests among tall dense tussocks and sedges and, despite having a population estimated at 2,000–3,000 birds, is classified as threatened (Vulnerable) because of its tiny range and the possibility of

accidental introductions of alien species. Another restricted-range species, New Zealand Snipe *Coenocorypha aucklandica*, has a race, *meinertzhagenae*, which is known only from these islands. Antipodean Albatross *Diomedea exulans antipodensis*, which breeds only on Antipodes and Campbell Islands, is treated as a full species by Robertson and Nunn (in press).

Northern Line Islands   s134

These central Pacific islands—Teraina (or Washington Island), Tabuaeran (Fanning Island) and Kiritimati (Christmas Island, 364 km²)—are politically part of Kiribati (see also Secondary Area s125). Native vegetation includes coastal strand vegetation, limited areas of mangroves and relict stands of inland forest. Secondary vegetation and coconut plantations predominate today, and the islands have been further altered as a result of guano extraction and, on Kiritimati, the testing of nuclear weapons. The islands constitute a Secondary Area because a restricted-range species, Bokikokiko *Acrocephalus aequinoctialis*, is endemic to (and common on) the group. A further two restricted-range species are known from the islands: Tuamotu Sandpiper *Prosobonia cancellata* (see EBA 214), which is extinct on Kiritimati where the type-specimen was collected, and Kuhl's Lorikeet *Vini kuhlii* (see EBA 211), which is believed to have been introduced to the islands by early Polynesian voyagers (1,000 birds minimum on Teraina, c.50 on Tabuaeran: Watling 1995). Bristle-thighed Curlew *Numenius tahitiensis* (classified as Vulnerable), a restricted-range species which breeds in western Alaska (Secondary Area s002), winters on islands in the Pacific region including the northern Line Islands.

Aitutaki   s135

Aitutaki (18 km², maximum altitude 120 m) is one of the northernmost of the Southern Cook Islands (see EBA 210; also for map) and is classified as an 'almost-atoll', being composed of a volcanic cone and a ring of small coral islands encircling a lagoon. The entire main island is under cultivation or secondary growth, while the vegetation of the coralline islets is largely native forest. Aitutaki is a Secondary Area because the threatened (Vulnerable) restricted-range species Blue Lorikeet *Vini peruviana* occurs there (as well as in the Society Islands, EBA 213), although, as caged birds may once have been carried between islands by the Polynesians, the species may not be native. Prehistoric records of Kuhl's Lorikeet *V. kuhlii* (today native to Rimatara, EBA 211) from Mangaia, Atiu and Aitutaki suggest that this species was once indigenous to the Southern Cook Islands and it is not known whether two closely related small parrots could have coexisted (Steadman 1991). The population of *V. peruviana* is estimated at c.1,200 birds on the main island of Aitutaki (which is therefore an important stronghold), with none occurring on the smaller reef islands. There is no evidence of a decline on Aitutaki in the last decade, and extensive trapping in March 1994 indicated the absence of black rat *Rattus rattus* (Wilson 1993, G. McCormack *in litt.* 1994, 1996), the most likely cause of the species' disappearance from other islands in its French Polynesian range.

Rapa   s136
Rapa (40 km², maximum altitude 630 m) is in the Austral (or Tubuai) Islands of French Polynesia (see also EBAs 211–214). Vegetation includes tropical and secondary rain forest, and savanna which develops as a result of fires and the browsing of goats and cattle. Rapa is a Secondary Area because of its single-island endemic, Rapa Fruit-dove *Ptilinopus huttoni*, which is confined to less than 3 km² of the remaining fragmented forest, and was estimated to number 274 birds in 1989–1990. The main threat to it is further loss and degradation of habitat, although hunting and predation by cats and/or rats may also have an effect (Thibault and Varney 1991). The species is classified as threatened (Vulnerable) on account of its tiny range and population.

Pitcairn   s137
Volcanic Pitcairn (4.6 km²) is one of a group of four islands (the Pitcairn Islands, a UK dependent territory) which includes Henderson (see EBA 215; also for map). The island was uninhabited when occupied by mutineers of HMS *Bounty* in 1790, although it had been settled by Polynesian travellers previously. The vegetation has been greatly modified by man's activities, and today there are only remnants of rain forest, with scrub and grassland elsewhere. Pitcairn

is a Secondary Area because of the single endemic species it holds, Pitcairn Reed-warbler *Acrocephalus vaughani*, which has recently been afforded specific status (Graves 1992, Sibley and Monroe 1993; see EBAs 211, 215). Casual observation indicates that the species breeds only in pairs, unlike *A. taiti* (from uninhabited Henderson) which forms breeding groups; this possible behavioural difference may be related to the greater disturbance and consequent year-to-year instability of the habitat on Pitcairn (Brooke and Hartley 1995).

Nihoa   s138
Nihoa (0.8 km², 280 m) is the youngest of the Northwestern Hawaiian Islands (see EBA 216; also for map), and is an uninhabited volcanic remnant of a once-high island with very little level ground, and sheer cliffs which drop to the ocean on three sides. Several well-developed valleys are densely vegetated with low shrubs, and grasses are common on most ridges. For its size, Nihoa supports a remarkable endemic flora and fauna, including two restricted-range species, Millerbird *Acrocephalus familiaris* and Nihoa Finch *Telespiza cantans*. The island is treated as a Secondary Area rather than as an EBA because *A. familiaris* is also known from Laysan Island (EBA 216), though it became extinct there some time during 1912–1923; the two races—*familiaris* from Nihoa and *kingi* from Laysan—are, however, sometimes regarded as full species. Both Nihoa's endemics are numerically quite strong (389–1,031 *A. familiaris* and 1,350–3,810 *T. cantans* in 1993) but are treated as threatened (classified Vulnerable) because of their tiny ranges. Although Nihoa is part of the Hawaiian Islands National Wildlife Refuge, the accidental introduction of rats or other predators to the island would doom its endemic species, and would be a serious threat to nesting seabirds.

INCLUDED here are all the landbird species treated as having restricted ranges, listed with the countries in which they breed (but omitting countries in which all populations originate from introductions), the Endemic Bird Areas (and Secondary Areas) in which they occur, the broad habitat-types which they prefer, their status and (for those which are classified as threatened) the major threats which affect them. Some species are of unknown provenance, and these are listed on p. 724.

Habitat codes

F	All forest and woodland types	D	Desert
		R	Rocky areas
S	Scrub	A	Agricultural areas
V	Savanna	X	Introduced vegetation
G	Grassland	Z	Unknown
W	Wetland		

Status

IUCN Red List Categories have been used as applied by Collar *et al.* (1994). Criteria operate at different numerical thresholds associated with each of the threatened categories, covering abundance, range size, and rates of decrease in these (see IUCN/SSC 1994). Brief definitions are as follows.

EX   *Extinct*. A taxon is Extinct when there is no reasonable doubt that its last individual has died.

EW   *Extinct in the Wild*. A taxon is Extinct in the Wild when it is known only to survive in cultivation, in captivity, or as a naturalized population well outside the past range.

CR   *Critically Endangered* (referred to throughout this book as 'Critical'). A taxon is Critical when it is facing an extremely high risk of extinction in the wild in the immediate future, judged to be a probability of 50% in 10 years.

EN   *Endangered*. A taxon is Endangered when it is not Critical but is facing a very high risk of extinction in the wild in the near future, judged to be a probability of 20% in 20 years.

VU   *Vulnerable*. A taxon is Vulnerable when it is not Critical or Endangered but is facing a high risk of extinction in the wild in the medium-term future, judged to be a probability of 10% in 100 years.

cd   *Conservation Dependent*. Taxa which are the focus of a continuing taxon-specific or habitat-specific conservation programme which directly affects the taxon in question, the cessation of which would result in the taxon qualifying for one of the threatened categories above within a period of five years.

nt   *Near Threatened*. Taxa which do not qualify for Conservation Dependent, but which are close to qualifying for Vulnerable.

lc   *Least Concern*. Taxa which do not qualify for Conservation Dependent or Near Threatened.

DD   *Data Deficient*. A taxon is Data Deficient when there is inadequate information to make a direct, or indirect, assessment of its risk of extinction based on its distribution and/or population status.

NE   *Not Evaluated*. A taxon is Not Evaluated when it has not yet been assessed against the criteria.

Threat codes

0   Unknown
1   Loss or alteration of habitat
2   Hunting, persecution, egg-collecting (subsistence)
3   Disturbance (by humans, stock)
4   Pollution, pesticides, poisoning
5   Introduced species (predators, competitors, herbivores, diseases)
6   Trade, egg-collecting (commercial)
7   Natural causes (exacerbated by other influences)
8   Small range or population

Notes

*   Taxonomy deviates from Sibley and Monroe (1990, 1993); see EBA (or Secondary Area) account for further details and references. The relationship of the new genus *Cryptosylvicola* (p. 708) within Sylviinae is unconfirmed, and so it has been placed at the end of that subfamily.

[X]   Extinct in that country or in that EBA/SA.

[1]   Antigua and Barbuda, Dominica, Guadeloupe (to France), Martinique (to France), Montserrat (to UK), Netherlands Antilles (to Netherlands), Puerto Rico (to USA), St Lucia, Virgin Islands (to UK), Virgin Islands (to USA).

[2]   Antigua and Barbuda, Dominica, Guadeloupe (to France), Martinique (to France), Montserrat (to UK), Netherlands Antilles (to Netherlands), St Kitts and Nevis, St Lucia, St Vincent.

[3]   Antigua and Barbuda, Anguilla (to UK), Barbados, Dominica, Grenada, Guadeloupe (to France), Martinique (to France), Montserrat (to UK), Netherlands Antilles (to Netherlands), St Kitts and Nevis, St Lucia, Puerto Rico (to USA), St Vincent, Virgin Islands (to UK), Virgin Islands (to USA).

[4]   Antigua and Barbuda, Anguilla (to UK), Netherlands Antilles, Barbados, Dominica, Grenada, Guadeloupe (to France), St Lucia, Martinique (to France), Montserrat (to UK), Puerto Rico (to USA), St Kitts and Nevis, St Vincent, Virgin Islands (to UK), Virgin Islands (to USA).

[5]   Antigua and Barbuda, Dominica, Guadeloupe (to France), Martinique (to France), Montserrat (to UK), St Kitts and Nevis, St Lucia.

[6]   Dominica, Guadeloupe (to France), Montserrat (to UK), Netherlands Antilles (to Netherlands), St Kitts and Nevis, St Vincent.

[7]   Antigua and Barbuda, Barbados, Dominica, Grenada, Guadeloupe (to France), Martinique (to France), Montserrat (to UK), Netherlands Antilles (to Netherlands), St Lucia.

[8]   Antigua and Barbuda, Anguilla (to UK), Bahamas, Dominica, Dominican Republic, Guadeloupe (to France), Netherlands Antilles (to Netherlands), Martinique (to France), Montserrat (to UK), St Kitts and Nevis, St Lucia, Puerto Rico (to USA), Virgin Islands (to UK), Virgin Islands (to USA).

[9]   Antigua and Barbuda, Anguilla (to UK), Barbados, Dominica, Grenada, Guadeloupe (to France), Martinique (to France), Montserrat (to UK), Netherlands Antilles (to Netherlands), St Kitts and Nevis, St Lucia, St Vincent, Virgin Islands (to USA).

[10]   Antigua and Barbuda, Dominica, Dominican Republic, Grenada, Guadeloupe (to France), Haiti, Martinique (to France), Montserrat (to UK), Netherlands Antilles (to Netherlands), Puerto Rico (to USA), St Lucia, St Vincent.

	Breeding range	EBAs (and SAs)	Habitat codes	Status	Threat codes
Family DROMAIIDAE: Emus					
Kangaroo Island Emu *Dromaius baudinianus* *	Australia[X]	184[X]	Z	EX	—
King Island Emu *Dromaius ater* *	Australia[X]	185[X]	Z	EX	—
Family APTERYGIDAE: Kiwis					
Great Spotted Kiwi *Apteryx haastii*	New Zealand	207	FSG	VU	25000
Family TINAMIDAE: Tinamous					
Black Tinamou *Tinamus osgoodi*	Colombia, Peru	040,053,054	F	DD	—
Berlepsch's Tinamou *Crypturellus berlepschi*	Colombia, Ecuador	041	F	lc	—
Tepuí Tinamou *Crypturellus ptaritepui*	Venezuela	064	F	VU	18
Pale-browed Tinamou *Crypturellus transfasciatus*	Ecuador, Peru	045	FS	nt	—
Chocó Tinamou *Crypturellus kerriae*	Colombia, Panama	023	F	VU	1
Magdalena Tinamou *Crypturellus saltuarius* *	Colombia	(s018)	F	CR	128
Grey-legged Tinamou *Crypturellus duidae*	Brazil, Colombia, Venezuela	065 (s019)	F	lc	—
Barred Tinamou *Crypturellus casiquiare*	Brazil, Colombia, Venezuela	065	F	lc	—
Taczanowski's Tinamou *Nothoprocta taczanowskii*	Peru	051	FSGR	VU	12
Kalinowski's Tinamou *Nothoprocta kalinowskii*	Peru	051	S	CR	08
Chilean Tinamou *Nothoprocta perdicaria*	Chile	060	SGA	lc	—
Family PODICIPEDIDAE: Grebes					
Titicaca Flightless Grebe *Rollandia microptera*	Bolivia, Peru	(s024)	W	lc	—
Alaotra Grebe *Tachybaptus rufolavatus*	Madagascar	095	W	CR	12578
Atitlán Grebe *Podilymbus gigas*	Guatemala[X]	018[X]	W	EX	—
New Zealand Dabchick *Poliocephalus rufopectus*	New Zealand	206	W	EN	135
Colombian Grebe *Podiceps andinus*	Colombia[X]	038[X]	W	EX	—
Junín Grebe *Podiceps taczanowskii*	Peru	050	W	CR	148
Hooded Grebe *Podiceps gallardoi*	Argentina	062	W	nt	—
Family ARDEIDAE: Herons, egrets, bitterns					
Madagascar Heron *Ardea humbloti*	Madagascar	096	FWA	VU	2
Galápagos Heron *Butorides sundevalli*	Ecuador	031	FW	lc	—
White-eared Night-heron *Gorsachius magnificus*	China	141,142	F	CR	18
Japanese Night-heron *Gorsachius goisagi*	Japan	146[X] (s089)	F	VU	1
Family THRESKIORNITHIDAE: Ibises, spoonbills					
Dwarf Olive Ibis *Bostrychia bocagei* *	São Tomé e Príncipe	082	F	CR	18
Family ANATIDAE: Ducks, geese, swans					
Nene *Branta sandvicensis*	USA	218	GR	VU	2578
Ruddy-headed Goose *Chloephaga rubidiceps*	Argentina, Chile, Falkland Islands (to UK)	062	GA	nt	—
Crested Shelduck *Tadorna cristata*	China?, North Korea?	See p. 724	W	CR	08
Falkland Steamerduck *Tachyeres brachypterus*	Falkland Islands (to UK)	062	W	lc	—
Hawaiian Duck *Anas wyvilliana*	USA	217,218	W	VU	158
Laysan Duck *Anas laysanensis*	USA	216	SGW	VU	8
Meller's Duck *Anas melleri*	Madagascar	095,096	W	nt	—
Madagascar Teal *Anas bernieri*	Madagascar	096	W	EN	1238
Eaton's Pintail *Anas eatoni*	French Southern Territories (to France)	(s048)	W	lc	—
Madagascar Pochard *Aythya innotata*	Madagascar	095	W	CR	08
Auckland Islands Merganser *Mergus australis*	New Zealand[X]	208[X]	W	EX	—
Family ACCIPITRIDAE: Hawks, eagles, harriers, old world vultures					
Black Honey-buzzard *Henicopernis infuscatus*	Papua New Guinea	195	F	nt	—
Sanford's Fish-eagle *Haliaeetus sanfordi*	Papua New Guinea, Solomon Islands	198	F	VU	12
Madagascar Fish-eagle *Haliaeetus vociferoides*	Madagascar	095[X],096	FW	CR	128
Nicobar Serpent-eagle *Spilornis minimus*	India	126	FA	nt	—
Mountain Serpent-eagle *Spilornis kinabaluensis*	Brunei, Malaysia	157	F	DD	—
Andaman Serpent-eagle *Spilornis elgini*	India	125	F	nt	—
Madagascar Serpent-eagle *Eutriorchis astur*	Madagascar	094	F	CR	1238
Nicobar Sparrowhawk *Accipiter butleri*	India	126	F	nt	—
Pied Goshawk *Accipiter albogularis*	Papua New Guinea, Solomon Islands	195,198,200	F	lc	—
Fiji Goshawk *Accipiter rufitorques*	Fiji	202	FA	lc	—
White-bellied Goshawk *Accipiter haplochrous*	New Caledonia (to France)	201	F	lc	—
Moluccan Goshawk *Accipiter henicogrammus*	Indonesia	171	F	lc	—
Slaty-mantled Sparrowhawk *Accipiter luteoschistaceus*	Papua New Guinea	195	F	nt	—
Imitator Sparrowhawk *Accipiter imitator*	Papua New Guinea, Solomon Is.	198	F	EN	18
New Britain Goshawk *Accipiter princeps*	Papua New Guinea	195	F	nt	—
Small Sparrowhawk *Accipiter nanus*	Indonesia	166	F	nt	—

	Breeding range	EBAs (and SAs)	Habitat codes	Status	Threat codes
Rufous-necked Sparrowhawk *Accipiter erythrauchen*	Indonesia	169,170,171	F	lc	
New Britain Sparrowhawk *Accipiter brachyurus*	Papua New Guinea	195	F	VU	1
Grey-backed Hawk *Leucopternis occidentalis*	Ecuador, Peru	045	F	EN	18
Hispaniolan Hawk *Buteo ridgwayi*	Dominican Republic, Haiti	028	FX	EN	128
Galápagos Hawk *Buteo galapagoensis*	Ecuador	031	FSR	VU	258
Hawaiian Hawk *Buteo solitarius*	USA	218	FA	nt	—
Javan Hawk-eagle *Spizaetus bartelsi*	Indonesia	160	F	EN	1268
Family FALCONIDAE: Falcons, caracaras					
Carunculated Caracara *Phalcoboenus carunculatus*	Colombia, Ecuador	043	SGA	lc	—
Striated Caracara *Phalcoboenus australis*	Argentina, Chile, Falkland Islands (to UK)	062	GR	nt	—
Guadalupe Caracara *Polyborus lutosus*	Mexico[X]	003[X]	D	EX	—
Plumbeous Forest-falcon *Micrastur plumbeus*	Colombia, Ecuador	041	F	EN	1
White-fronted Falconet *Microhierax latifrons*	Malaysia	(s098)	F	nt	—
Mauritius Kestrel *Falco punctatus*	Mauritius	102	FSX	EN	8
Seychelles Kestrel *Falco araea*	Seychelles	100	FX	VU	258
Family MEGAPODIIDAE: Megapodes					
Bruijn's Brush-turkey *Aepypodius bruijnii*	Indonesia	172	F	VU	178
Red-billed Brush-turkey *Talegalla cuvieri*	Indonesia	172	F	lc	—
Maleo *Macrocephalon maleo*	Indonesia	166	FR	VU	1237
Nicobar Scrubfowl *Megapodius nicobariensis*	India, Myanmar[X]	125[X],126	F	VU	12
Sula Scrubfowl *Megapodius bernsteinii*	Indonesia	168	FS	nt	—
Dusky Scrubfowl *Megapodius freycinet*	Indonesia	171,172,174	FSWX	lc	—
Melanesian Scrubfowl *Megapodius eremita*	Papua New Guinea, Solomon Is.	193,194,195,198	FS	lc	—
Vanuatu Scrubfowl *Megapodius layardi*	Vanuatu	200	FR	VU	125
Micronesian Scrubfowl *Megapodius laperouse*	Guam (to USA)[X], Northern Mariana Islands (to USA), Palau	189,190	FRX	VU	1235
Niuafo'ou Scrubfowl *Megapodius pritchardii*	Tonga	(s129)	F	EN	12578
Moluccan Scrubfowl *Megapodius wallacei*	Indonesia	169,170,171	FR	VU	126
Family CRACIDAE: Curassows, guans, chachalacas					
Rufous-headed Chachalaca *Ortalis erythroptera*	Ecuador, Peru	045	F	VU	12
Rufous-bellied Chachalaca *Ortalis wagleri*	Mexico	005	FS	lc	—
White-bellied Chachalaca *Ortalis leucogastra*	El Salvador, Guatemala, Honduras, Mexico, Nicaragua	017	FS	lc	—
Bearded Guan *Penelope barbata*	Ecuador, Peru	046	F	VU	12
Baudó Guan *Penelope ortoni*	Colombia, Ecuador	041	F	VU	12
Red-faced Guan *Penelope dabbenei*	Argentina, Bolivia	057	F	lc	—
Cauca Guan *Penelope perspicax*	Colombia	040	F	EN	128
White-winged Guan *Penelope albipennis*	Peru	045	F	CR	18
Trinidad Piping-guan *Pipile pipile*	Trinidad and Tobago	(s016)	F	CR	128
Black Guan *Chamaepetes unicolor*	Costa Rica, Panama	020	F	nt	—
Horned Guan *Oreophasis derbianus*	Guatemala, Mexico	018	F	VU	12
Alagoas Curassow *Mitu mitu*	Brazil	071[X]	F	EW	128
Northern Helmeted Curassow *Pauxi pauxi*	Colombia, Venezuela	033,034,038	F	EN	12
Southern Helmeted Curassow *Pauxi unicornis*	Bolivia, Peru	053,054	F	EN	12
Blue-billed Curassow *Crax alberti*	Colombia	036,037	F	CR	128
Red-billed Curassow *Crax blumenbachii*	Brazil	075	F	CR	128
Family TETRAONIDAE: Grouse					
Caucasian Grouse *Tetrao mlokosiewiczi*	Armenia, Azerbaijan, Georgia, Iran, Russia, Turkey	122	FSG	nt	—
Caucasian Snowcock *Tetraogallus caucasicus*	Azerbaijan, Georgia, Russia	122	SGR	lc	—
Family PHASIANIDAE: Francolins, quails, pheasants					
Philby's Partridge *Alectoris philbyi*	Sauda Arabia, Yemen	118	SRA	lc	—
Rusty-necklaced Partridge *Alectoris magna*	China	135	GR	nt	—
Harwood's Francolin *Francolinus harwoodi*	Ethiopia	115	SA	VU	12
Grey-striped Francolin *Francolinus griseostriatus*	Angola	087	F	VU	12
Grey-breasted Spurfowl *Francolinus rufopictus*	Tanzania	108	FG	lc	—
Djibouti Francolin *Francolinus ochropectus*	Djibouti	(s065)	F	CR	138
Handsome Francolin *Francolinus nobilis*	Burundi, Rwanda, Uganda, Zaïre	106	FS	lc	—
Jackson's Francolin *Francolinus jacksoni*	Kenya, Uganda	109	FS	lc	—
Mount Cameroon Francolin *Francolinus camerunensis*	Cameroon	086	F	VU	128
Swierstra's Francolin *Francolinus swierstrai*	Angola	087	FGR	VU	12
Udzungwa Forest-partridge *Xenoperdix udzungwensis* *	Tanzania	105	F	EN	2
Snow Mountain Quail *Anurophasis monorthonyx*	Indonesia	178	SG	nt	—
Manipur Bush-quail *Perdicula manipurensis*	Bangladesh, India	131	SGW	VU	12

	Breeding range	EBAs (and SAs)	Habitat codes	Status	Threat codes
Taiwan Partridge *Arborophila crudigularis*	Taiwan	149	F	nt	—
Chestnut-breasted Partridge *Arborophila mandellii*	Bhutan, China, India	130	F	VU	12
Sichuan Partridge *Arborophila rufipectus*	China	140	F	CR	18
Chestnut-bellied Partridge *Arborophila javanica*	Indonesia	160	F	lc	—
Red-breasted Partridge *Arborophila hyperythra*	Indonesia, Malaysia	157	F	lc	—
White-necklaced Partridge *Arborophila gingica*	China	141	FS	VU	1
Orange-necked Partridge *Arborophila davidi*	Vietnam	144	F	CR	18
Chestnut-headed Partridge *Arborophila cambodiana*	Cambodia, Thailand	(s085)	F	VU	12
Red-billed Partridge *Arborophila rubrirostris*	Indonesia	158	F	lc	—
Hainan Partridge *Arborophila ardens*	China	142	F	EN	12
Annam Partridge *Arborophila merlini*	Vietnam	143	F	EN	1
Crimson-headed Partridge *Haematortyx sanguiniceps*	Indonesia, Malaysia	157	F	lc	—
Sri Lanka Spurfowl *Galloperdix bicalcarata*	Sri Lanka	124	F	lc	—
Himalayan Quail *Ophrysia superciliosa*	India	128	SG	CR	08
Western Tragopan *Tragopan melanocephalus*	India, Pakistan	128	F	VU	1
Blyth's Tragopan *Tragopan blythii*	Bhutan, China, India, Myanmar	130	F	VU	12
Cabot's Tragopan *Tragopan caboti*	China	141	F	VU	12
Sclater's Monal *Lophophorus sclateri*	China, India, Myanmar	130	FSGR	VU	12
Chinese Monal *Lophophorus lhuysii*	China	138	FSGR	VU	12
Sri Lanka Junglefowl *Gallus lafayetii*	Sri Lanka	124	FSX	lc	—
Imperial Pheasant *Lophura imperialis*	Vietnam	143	F	CR	128
Edwards's Pheasant *Lophura edwardsi*	Vietnam	143	F	CR	18
Vietnamese Pheasant *Lophura hatinhensis*	Vietnam	143	F	EN	128
Swinhoe's Pheasant *Lophura swinhoii*	Taiwan	149	F	nt	—
Sumatran Pheasant *Lophura hoogerwerfi*	Indonesia	158	F	VU	1
Salvadori's Pheasant *Lophura inornata*	Indonesia	158	F	VU	1
Tibetan Eared-pheasant *Crossoptilon harmani*	China	133	FSG	VU	12
Brown Eared-pheasant *Crossoptilon mantchuricum*	China	136	FSG	VU	12
Cheer Pheasant *Catreus wallichi*	India, Nepal, Pakistan	128	FSG	VU	12
Elliot's Pheasant *Syrmaticus ellioti*	China	141	FS	VU	12
Mikado Pheasant *Syrmaticus mikado*	Taiwan	149	F	nt	—
Bronze-tailed Peacock-pheasant *Polyplectron chalcurum*	Indonesia	158	FX	nt	—
Mountain Peacock-pheasant *Polyplectron inopinatum*	Malaysia	158	F	VU	1
Germain's Peacock-pheasant *Polyplectron germaini*	Vietnam	144	F	VU	12
Malayan Peacock-pheasant *Polyplectron malacense*	Malaysia, Thailand	(s102)	F	VU	1
Palawan Peacock-pheasant *Polyplectron emphanum*	Philippines	156	F	EN	12
Crested Argus *Rheinardia ocellata*	Laos, Malaysia, Vietnam	143,145,158 (s084)	F	VU	12
Bearded Wood-partridge *Dendrortyx barbatus*	Mexico	012	F	CR	128
Banded Quail *Philortyx fasciatus*	Mexico	008	FSA	lc	—
Black-fronted Wood-quail *Odontophorus atrifrons*	Colombia, Venezuela	036,038	F	nt	—
Chestnut Wood-quail *Odontophorus hyperythrus*	Colombia	040,042	F	nt	—
Dark-backed Wood-quail *Odontophorus melanonotus*	Colombia, Ecuador	041	F	nt	—
Tacarcuna Wood-quail *Odontophorus dialeucos*	Colombia, Panama	024	F	nt	—
Gorgeted Wood-quail *Odontophorus strophium*	Colombia	038	F	EN	12
Venezuelan Wood-quail *Odontophorus columbianus*	Venezuela	033,038	F	nt	—
Black-breasted Wood-quail *Odontophorus leucolaemus*	Costa Rica, Panama	020	F	nt	—
Stripe-faced Wood-quail *Odontophorus balliviani*	Bolivia, Peru	055	F	lc	—
Ocellated Quail *Cyrtonyx ocellatus*	El Salvador, Guatemala, Honduras, Mexico, Nicaragua	018	F	nt	—
Family NUMIDIDAE: Guineafowl					
White-breasted Guineafowl *Agelastes meleagrides*	Ghana, Ivory Coast, Liberia, Sierra Leone	084	F	VU	12
Family MESITORNITHIDAE: Mesites					
White-breasted Mesite *Mesitornis variegata*	Madagascar	093	F	VU	17
Brown Mesite *Mesitornis unicolor*	Madagascar	094	F	VU	1
Subdesert Mesite *Monias benschi*	Madagascar	097	S	VU	125
Family TURNICIDAE: Buttonquails					
Spotted Buttonquail *Turnix ocellata*	Philippines	151,152	GR	nt	—
Black-breasted Buttonquail *Turnix melanogaster*	Australia	183	FX	EN	158
Chestnut-backed Buttonquail *Turnix castanota*	Australia	187	FG	VU	15
Buff-breasted Buttonquail *Turnix olivii*	Australia	181	FG	EN	18
Worcester's Buttonquail *Turnix worcesteri*	Philippines	151	Z	VU	08
Sumba Buttonquail *Turnix everetti*	Indonesia	163	G	VU	18
Family RALLIDAE: Rails, crakes, coots					
Slender-billed Flufftail *Sarothrura watersi*	Madagascar	095	GW	EN	18
Chestnut Forest-rail *Rallina rubra*	Indonesia, Papua New Guinea	173,178	F	lc	—

	Breeding range	EBAs (and SAs)	Habitat codes	Status	Threat codes
White-striped Forest-rail *Rallina leucospila*	Indonesia	173	F	DD	—
Mayr's Forest-rail *Rallina mayri*	Indonesia, Papua New Guinea	175	F	DD	—
Andaman Crake *Rallina canningi*	India	125	FW	VU	15
Rusty-flanked Crake *Laterallus levraudi*	Venezuela	033	GW	VU	148
Junín Rail *Laterallus tuerosi* *	Peru	050	W	EN	148
Galápagos Rail *Laterallus spilonotus*	Ecuador	031	FSW	nt	—
Woodford's Rail *Nesoclopeus woodfordi*	Papua New Guinea, Solomon Is.	198	FA	EN	25
Bar-winged Rail *Nesoclopeus poecilopterus*	Fiji[X]	202[X]	FW	EX	—
New Caledonian Rail *Gallirallus lafresnayanus*	New Caledonia (to France)	201	F	CR	58
Lord Howe Island Rail *Gallirallus sylvestris*	Australia	204	F	EN	58
Okinawa Rail *Gallirallus okinawae*	Japan	148	FSA	EN	18
New Britain Rail *Gallirallus insignis*	Papua New Guinea	195	FW	lc	—
Roviana Rail *Gallirallus rovianae*	Solomon Islands	198	S	nt	—
Guam Rail *Gallirallus owstoni*	Guam (to USA)	189[X]	FSA	EW	58
Wake Island Rail *Gallirallus wakensis*	US minor outlying islands (to USA)[X]	(s122[X])	FS	EX	—
Dieffenbach's Rail *Gallirallus dieffenbachii*	New Zealand[X]	209[X]	W	EX	—
Chatham Islands Rail *Gallirallus modestus*	New Zealand[X]	209[X]	G	EX	—
Plain-flanked Rail *Rallus wetmorei*	Venezuela	035	FW	EN	148
Bogotá Rail *Rallus semiplumbeus*	Colombia	038	GW	EN	148
Madagascar Rail *Rallus madagascariensis*	Madagascar	095	GWA	lc	—
Brown-banded Rail *Lewinia mirificus*	Philippines	151,154	Z	EN	0
Auckland Islands Rail *Lewinia muelleri*	New Zealand	208	FSG	VU	8
Snoring Rail *Aramidopsis plateni*	Indonesia	166	F	VU	15
Inaccessible Rail *Atlantisia rogersi*	St Helena (to UK)	079	FSGR	VU	8
Bald-faced Rail *Gymnocrex rosenbergii*	Indonesia	166,168	F	VU	1
Isabelline Waterhen *Amaurornis isabellinus*	Indonesia	166	GA	lc	—
Sakalava Rail *Amaurornis olivieri*	Madagascar	096	W	CR	158
Laysan Crake *Porzana palmeri*	USA[X]	216[X]	GW	EX	—
Hawaiian Crake *Porzana sandwichensis*	USA[X]	218[X]	FG	EX	—
Kosrae Crake *Porzana monasa*	Micronesia[X]	192[X]	FW	EX	—
Henderson Crake *Porzana atra*	Pitcairn Islands (to UK)	215	FS	VU	8
Zapata Rail *Cyanolimnas cerverai*	Cuba	025	SW	CR	158
Chestnut Rail *Eulabeornis castaneoventris*	Australia	187 (s112)	F	lc	—
Invisible Rail *Habroptila wallacii*	Indonesia	171	FW	VU	15
Lord Howe Island Swamphen *Porphyrio albus*	Australia[X]	204[X]	W	EX	—
Takahe *Porphyrio mantelli*	New Zealand	207	FG	EN	58
Samoan Moorhen *Gallinula pacifica*	Western Samoa	203	F	CR	58
Makira Moorhen *Gallinula silvestris*	Solomon Islands	198	F	CR	258
Gough Moorhen *Gallinula comeri* *	St Helena (to UK)	080	SG	VU	8
Tristan Moorhen *Gallinula nesiotis* *	St Helena (to UK)[X]	079[X]	G	EX	—
Tasmanian Native-hen *Gallinula mortierii*	Australia	185	WA	lc	—
Hawaiian Coot *Fulica alai*	USA	217,218	W	VU	158
Family RHYNOCHETIDAE: Kagu					
Kagu *Rhynochetos jubatus*	New Caledonia (to France)	201	FS	EN	158
Family JACANIDAE: Jacanas					
Madagascar Jacana *Actophilornis albinucha*	Madagascar	095,096	W	lc	—
Family HAEMATOPODIDAE: Oystercatchers					
Canary Islands Oystercatcher *Haematopus meadewaldoi*	Spain[X]	120[X]	W	EX	—
Chatham Islands Oystercatcher *H. chathamensis* *	New Zealand	209	W	EN	1578
Family CHARADRIIDAE: Plovers					
Magellanic Plover *Pluvianellus socialis*	Argentina, Chile	062	W	nt	—
Madagascar Plover *Charadrius thoracicus*	Madagascar	096	GW	VU	07
St Helena Plover *Charadrius sanctaehelenae*	St Helena (to UK)	(s038)	GA	EN	158
Javan Plover *Charadrius javanicus*	Indonesia	161 (s109)	W	nt	—
Shore Plover *Thinornis novaeseelandiae*	New Zealand	209	GW	EN	8
Wrybill *Anarhynchus frontalis*	New Zealand	207	W	VU	15
Javanese Lapwing *Vanellus macropterus*	Indonesia[X]	161[X]	GW	EX	—
Family SCOLOPACIDAE: Woodcocks, snipes, sandpipers					
Amami Woodcock *Scolopax mira*	Japan	148	FA	VU	15
Sulawesi Woodcock *Scolopax celebensis*	Indonesia	166	F	nt	—
Moluccan Woodcock *Scolopax rochussenii*	Indonesia	171	F	VU	8
Madagascar Snipe *Gallinago macrodactyla*	Madagascar	095	GW	lc	—
Chatham Islands Snipe *Coenocorypha pusilla*	New Zealand	209	FG	VU	8

	Breeding range	EBAs (and SAs)	Habitat codes	Status	Threat codes
New Zealand Snipe *Coenocorypha aucklandica*	New Zealand	206^X,208 (s132, s133)	FSG	nt	—
Bristle-thighed Curlew *Numenius tahitiensis*	USA	(s002)	GW	VU	1257
Nordmann's Greenshank *Tringa guttifer*	Russia	149 (s088)	FW	EN	12378
Tuamotu Sandpiper *Prosobonia cancellata*	French Polynesia (to France), Kiribati^X	214 (s134^X)	SW	EN	58
Spoon-billed Sandpiper *Eurynorhynchus pygmeus*	Russia	149 (s087)	W	VU	17

Family GLAREOLIDAE: Coursers, Pratincoles

Jerdon's Courser *Rhinoptilus bitorquatus*	India	(s071)	SR	EN	18

Family COLUMBIDAE: Pigeons, doves

Somali Pigeon *Columba oliviae*	Somalia	116	R	VU	01
Madeira Laurel Pigeon *Columba trocaz*	Portugal	120	F	cd	—
Dark-tailed Laurel Pigeon *Columba bollii*	Spain	120	FSA	VU	125
White-tailed Laurel Pigeon *Columba junoniae*	Spain	120	F	VU	125
Cameroon Olive-pigeon *Columba sjostedti*	Cameroon, Equatorial Guinea, Nigeria	086	F	lc	—
Maroon Pigeon *Columba thomensis*	São Tomé e Príncipe	082	F	VU	128
Comoro Olive-pigeon *Columba pollenii*	Comoros, Mayotte (to France)	098	F	nt	—
Nilgiri Wood-pigeon *Columba elphinstonii*	India	123	F	nt	—
Sri Lanka Wood-pigeon *Columba torringtoni*	Sri Lanka	124	FX	VU	1
Silvery Wood-pigeon *Columba argentina*	Indonesia, Malaysia	(s101,s103,s105, s106)	F	VU	123
Andaman Wood-pigeon *Columba palumboides*	India	125,126	F	nt	—
Japanese Wood-pigeon *Columba janthina*	Japan, South Korea	146,147^X,148 (s091,s092^X)	F	nt	—
Bonin Wood-pigeon *Columba versicolor*	Japan^X	147^X	F	EX	—
Ryukyu Pigeon *Columba jouyi*	Japan^X	148^X	F	EX	—
Yellow-legged Pigeon *Columba pallidiceps*	Papua New Guinea, Solomon Is.	195,198	F	CR	128
Chilean Pigeon *Columba araucana*	Argentina, Chile	061	F	nt	—
Ring-tailed Pigeon *Columba caribaea*	Jamaica	027	F	CR	1278
Peruvian Pigeon *Columba oenops*	Peru	048	F	VU	12
Dusky Pigeon *Columba goodsoni*	Colombia, Ecuador	041	F	lc	—
São Tomé Bronze-naped Pigeon *Columba malherbii*	Equatorial Guinea, São Tomé e Príncipe	081,082,083	FVX	lc	—
Pink Pigeon *Columba mayeri*	Mauritius	102	FX	CR	1578
White-winged Collared-dove *Streptopelia reichenowi*	Ethiopia, Kenya, Somalia	113	F	nt	—
Andaman Cuckoo-dove *Macropygia rufipennis*	India	125,126	F	nt	—
Dusky Cuckoo-dove *Macropygia magna*	Indonesia	162,164,165 (s110)	FA	lc	—
Pied Cuckoo-dove *Reinwardtoena browni*	Papua New Guinea	193,195	F	lc	—
Crested Cuckoo-dove *Reinwardtoena crassirostris*	Papua New Guinea, Solomon Is.	198	F	lc	—
Black Cuckoo-dove *Turacoena modesta*	Indonesia	164	F	VU	12
New Britain Bronzewing *Henicophaps foersteri*	Papua New Guinea	195	F	nt	—
Partridge Pigeon *Geophaps smithii*	Australia	187	FG	nt	—
White-quilled Rock-pigeon *Petrophassa albipennis*	Australia	187	R	lc	—
Chestnut-quilled Rock-pigeon *Petrophassa rufipennis*	Australia	187	R	lc	—
Socorro Dove *Zenaida graysoni*	Mexico	004^X	FS	EW	158
Galápagos Dove *Zenaida galapagoensis*	Ecuador	031	FSR	lc	—
Ecuadorian Ground-dove *Columbina buckleyi*	Ecuador, Peru	045	FS	lc	—
Bare-eyed Ground-dove *Metriopelia morenoi*	Argentina	056	SG	lc	—
Brown-backed Dove *Leptotila battyi*	Panama	021	F	nt	—
Grenada Dove *Leptotila wellsi*	Grenada	030	F	CR	1358
Ochre-bellied Dove *Leptotila ochraceiventris*	Ecuador, Peru	045	FS	VU	1
Tolima Dove *Leptotila conoveri*	Colombia	040	F	EN	1
Purplish-backed Quail-dove *Geotrygon lawrencii*	Costa Rica, Panama	019,021,023	F	lc	—
Veracruz Quail-dove *Geotrygon carrikeri* *	Mexico	013	F	EN	1
Buff-fronted Quail-dove *Geotrygon costaricensis*	Costa Rica, Panama	020	F	lc	—
Crested Quail-dove *Geotrygon versicolor*	Jamaica	027	F	nt	—
Rufous-breasted Quail-dove *Geotrygon chiriquensis*	Costa Rica, Panama	020	F	lc	—
Russet-crowned Quail-dove *Geotrygon goldmani*	Colombia, Panama	024	F	nt	—
Bridled Quail-dove *Geotrygon mystacea*	Caribbean^1 (see p. 679)	029,030	F	nt	—
Luzon Bleeding-heart *Gallicolumba luzonica*	Philippines	151	F	nt	—
Mindoro Bleeding-heart *Gallicolumba platenae*	Philippines	150	F	CR	128
Negros Bleeding-heart *Gallicolumba keayi*	Philippines	152	F	CR	128
Mindanao Bleeding-heart *Gallicolumba criniger*	Philippines	154	F	VU	1
Sulu Bleeding-heart *Gallicolumba menagei*	Philippines	155	F	CR	128
Sulawesi Ground-dove *Gallicolumba tristigmata*	Indonesia	166	F	lc	—

	Breeding range	EBAs (and SAs)	Habitat codes	Status	Threat codes
Caroline Islands Ground-dove *Gallicolumba kubaryi*	Micronesia	192	FSX	EN	28
Polynesian Ground-dove *Gallicolumba erythroptera*	French Polynesia (to France)	213[X],214	FS	CR	58
White-throated Ground-dove *Gallicolumba xanthonura*	Guam (to USA)[X], Micronesia, N Mariana Islands (to USA)	189,191	FX	nt	—
Shy Ground-dove *Gallicolumba stairi*	American Samoa (to USA), Fiji, Tonga, Wallis and Futuna Is. (to France), Western Samoa	202,203 (s128, s130)	FS	nt	—
Santa Cruz Ground-dove *Gallicolumba sanctaecrucis*	Solomon Islands, Vanuatu	200	F	VU	125
Thick-billed Ground-dove *Gallicolumba salamonis*	Solomon Islands	198	F	CR	158
Marquesan Ground-dove *Gallicolumba rubescens*	French Polynesia (to France)	212	S	EN	8
Palau Ground-dove *Gallicolumba canifrons*	Palau	190	F	nt	—
Wetar Ground-dove *Gallicolumba hoedtii*	Indonesia	164	F	VU	1
Choiseul Pigeon *Microgoura meeki*	Solomon Islands[X]	198[X]	F	EX	—
Mindanao Brown-dove *Phapitreron brunneiceps* *	Philippines	154	F	NE	—
Tawitawi Brown-dove *Phapitreron cinereiceps* *	Philippines	155	F	NE	—
Flores Green-pigeon *Treron floris*	Indonesia	162	F	nt	—
Sumba Green-pigeon *Treron teysmannii*	Indonesia	163	F	nt	—
Timor Green-pigeon *Treron psittacea*	Indonesia	164	F	VU	1
São Tomé Green-pigeon *Treron sanctithomae*	São Tomé e Príncipe	082	FX	lc	—
Pemba Green-pigeon *Treron pembaensis*	Tanzania	110	F	nt	—
Sumatran Green-pigeon *Treron oxyura*	Indonesia	158,160	F	nt	—
Whistling Green-pigeon *Treron formosae*	Japan, Philippines, Taiwan	148,149 (s093,s094)	F	nt	—
Pink-headed Fruit-dove *Ptilinopus porphyreus*	Indonesia	158,160	F	lc	—
Red-naped Fruit-dove *Ptilinopus dohertyi*	Indonesia	163	F	VU	1
Black-banded Fruit-dove *Ptilinopus alligator*	Australia	187	FS	nt	—
Flame-breasted Fruit-dove *Ptilinopus marchei*	Philippines	151	F	VU	12
Cream-bellied Fruit-dove *Ptilinopus merrilli*	Philippines	151	F	nt	—
Red-eared Fruit-dove *Ptilinopus fischeri*	Indonesia	166	F	lc	—
Maroon-chinned Fruit-dove *Ptilinopus subgularis*	Indonesia	166,168	F	lc	—
Scarlet-breasted Fruit-dove *Ptilinopus bernsteinii*	Indonesia	171	FA	lc	—
Tanna Fruit-dove *Ptilinopus tannensis*	Vanuatu	200	FVX	nt	—
Wallace's Fruit-dove *Ptilinopus wallacii*	Indonesia	165,179 (s112)	FSA	lc	—
Many-coloured Fruit-dove *Ptilinopus perousii*	American Samoa (to USA), Fiji, Tonga, Western Samoa	202,203 (s130)	F	lc	—
Blue-capped Fruit-dove *Ptilinopus monacha*	Indonesia	171	FA	nt	—
Mariana Fruit-dove *Ptilinopus roseicapilla*	Guam (to USA)[X], Northern Mariana Islands (to USA)	189	F	nt	—
Red-bellied Fruit-dove *Ptilinopus greyii*	New Caledonia (to France), Solomon Islands, Vanuatu	200,201	FV	lc	—
Silver-capped Fruit-dove *Ptilinopus richardsii*	Solomon Islands	198,199	F	lc	—
Purple-capped Fruit-dove *Ptilinopus porphyraceus*	American Samoa (to USA), Fiji, Marshall Is.[X], Micronesia, Niue (to New Zealand), Tonga, Wallis and Futuna Is. (to France), Western Samoa	192,202,203 (s123[X],s127,s128, s129,s130,s131)	FX	lc	—
Palau Fruit-dove *Ptilinopus pelewensis*	Palau	190	F	lc	—
Cook Islands Fruit-dove *Ptilinopus rarotongensis*	Cook Islands (to New Zealand)	210	F	nt	—
Rapa Fruit-dove *Ptilinopus huttoni*	French Polynesia (to France)	(s136)	F	VU	1258
Grey-green Fruit-dove *Ptilinopus purpuratus*	French Polynesia (to France)	213	FX	lc	—
Atoll Fruit-dove *Ptilinopus coralensis*	French Polynesia (to France)	214	FS	nt	—
Makatea Fruit-dove *Ptilinopus chalcurus*	French Polynesia (to France)	214	F	VU	8
Henderson Fruit-dove *Ptilinopus insularis*	Pitcairn Islands (to UK)	215	F	VU	8
Red-moustached Fruit-dove *Ptilinopus mercierii*	French Polynesia (to France)[X]	212[X]	F	EX	—
White-capped Fruit-dove *Ptilinopus dupetithouarsii*	French Polynesia (to France)	212	FX	lc	—
Yellow-bibbed Fruit-dove *Ptilinopus solomonensis*	Indonesia, Papua New Guinea, Solomon Islands	174,193,194,195, 198	F	lc	—
White-headed Fruit-dove *Ptilinopus eugeniae*	Solomon Islands	198	F	nt	—
Grey-headed Fruit-dove *Ptilinopus hyogastra*	Indonesia	171	FA	lc	—
Carunculated Fruit-dove *Ptilinopus granulifrons*	Indonesia	171	FA	VU	1
Knob-billed Fruit-dove *Ptilinopus insolitus*	Papua New Guinea	194,195	F	lc	—
Negros Fruit-dove *Ptilinopus arcanus*	Philippines	152	F	CR	128
Orange Dove *Ptilinopus victor*	Fiji	202	F	lc	—
Golden Dove *Ptilinopus luteovirens*	Fiji	202	FS	lc	—
Whistling Dove *Ptilinopus layardi*	Fiji	202	FS	nt	—
Cloven-feathered Dove *Drepanoptila holosericea*	New Caledonia (to France)	201	FV	VU	12
Comoro Blue-pigeon *Alectroenas sganzini*	Comoros, Mayotte (to France), Seychelles	098,099	FS	lc	—

	Breeding range	EBAs (and SAs)	Habitat codes	Status	Threat codes
Mauritius Blue-pigeon *Alectroenas nitidissima*	Mauritius	102	F	EX	—
Seychelles Blue-pigeon *Alectroenas pulcherrima*	Seychelles	100	F	lc	—
White-bellied Imperial-pigeon *Ducula forsteni*	Indonesia	166	F	lc	—
Mindoro Imperial-pigeon *Ducula mindorensis*	Philippines	150	F	EN	128
Grey-headed Imperial-pigeon *Ducula radiata*	Indonesia	166	F	lc	—
White-eyed Imperial-pigeon *Ducula perspicillata*	Indonesia	169,170,171	FX	lc	—
Elegant Imperial-pigeon *Ducula concinna*	Indonesia	165,166,167,169, 170,172 (s110, s111,s112)	F	lc	—
Micronesian Imperial-pigeon *Ducula oceanica*	Kiribati[X], Marshall Islands, Micronesia, Palau	190,191,192 (s123,s125[X])	FX	lc	—
Polynesian Imperial-pigeon *Ducula aurorae*	French Polynesia (to France)	213,214	F	VU	128
Marquesan Imperial-pigeon *Ducula galeata*	French Polynesia (to France)	212	F	CR	1258
Red-knobbed Imperial-pigeon *Ducula rubricera*	Papua New Guinea, Solomon Is.	195,198	F	lc	—
Spice Imperial-pigeon *Ducula myristicivora*	Indonesia	171,172,174 (s113)	F	lc	—
Christmas Island Imperial-pigeon *Ducula whartoni*	Christmas Island (to Australia)	188	F	VU	28
Pink-headed Imperial-pigeon *Ducula rosacea*	Indonesia	162,164,165,171 (s107,s108,s109, s110,s111)	FSA	lc	—
Grey Imperial-pigeon *Ducula pickeringii*	Indonesia, Malaysia, Philippines	155,156,167 (s097)	F	VU	12
Cinnamon-bellied Imperial-pigeon *Ducula basilica*	Indonesia	171	F	lc	—
Finsch's Imperial-pigeon *Ducula finschii*	Papua New Guinea	195	F	nt	—
Peale's Imperial-pigeon *Ducula latrans*	Fiji	202	F	lc	—
Chestnut-bellied Imperial-pigeon *Ducula brenchleyi*	Solomon Islands	198	F	EN	12
Vanuatu Imperial-pigeon *Ducula bakeri*	Vanuatu	200	F	VU	12
New Caledonian Imperial-pigeon *Ducula goliath*	New Caledonia (to France)	201	F	VU	2
Bismarck Imperial-pigeon *Ducula melanochroa*	Papua New Guinea	195	F	nt	—
Dark-backed Imperial-pigeon *Ducula lacernulata*	Indonesia	160,162	F	lc	—
Timor Imperial-pigeon *Ducula cineracea*	Indonesia	164	F	VU	1
White Imperial-pigeon *Ducula luctuosa*	Indonesia	166,168	FA	lc	—
Yellow-tinted Imperial-Pigeon *Ducula subflavescens*	Papua New Guinea	193,195	FS	lc	—
Sombre Pigeon *Cryptophaps poecilorrhoa*	Indonesia	166	F	nt	—
Long-tailed Mountain-pigeon *Gymnophaps mada*	Indonesia	169,170	F	nt	—
Pale Mountain-pigeon *Gymnophaps solomonensis*	Papua New Guinea, Solomon Is.	198	F	lc	—
Western Crowned-pigeon *Goura cristata*	Indonesia	172	F	VU	126
Tooth-billed Pigeon *Didunculus strigirostris*	Western Samoa	203	F	VU	127

Family PSITTACIDAE: Parrots, cockatoos, lories, macaws

	Breeding range	EBAs (and SAs)	Habitat codes	Status	Threat codes
Black Lory *Chalcopsitta atra*	Indonesia	172	FVGX	lc	—
Brown Lory *Chalcopsitta duivenbodei*	Indonesia, Papua New Guinea	176	F	lc	—
Cardinal Lory *Chalcopsitta cardinalis*	Papua New Guinea, Solomon Is.	195,198	FX	lc	—
Red-and-blue Lory *Eos histrio*	Indonesia	167	FX	EN	16
Violet-necked Lory *Eos squamata*	Indonesia	171,172	FX	lc	—
Red Lory *Eos bornea*	Indonesia	165,169,170	F	lc	—
Blue-streaked Lory *Eos reticulata*	Indonesia	165	FX	nt	—
Black-winged Lory *Eos cyanogenia*	Indonesia	174	F	VU	126
Blue-eared Lory *Eos semilarvata*	Indonesia	170	FS	nt	—
Olive-headed Lorikeet *Trichoglossus euteles*	Indonesia	162,164,165	FA	lc	—
Yellow-and-green Lorikeet *Trichoglossus flavoviridis*	Indonesia	166,168	F	lc	—
Mindanao Lorikeet *Trichoglossus johnstoniae*	Philippines	154	F	VU	1
Pohnpei Lorikeet *Trichoglossus rubiginosus*	Micronesia	192	FX	lc	—
Iris Lorikeet *Psitteuteles iris*	Indonesia	164	F	VU	1
Chattering Lory *Lorius garrulus*	Indonesia	171	F	VU	16
Purple-naped Lory *Lorius domicella*	Indonesia	170	F	VU	6
White-naped Lory *Lorius albidinuchus*	Papua New Guinea	195	F	nt	—
Yellow-bibbed Lory *Lorius chlorocercus*	Solomon Islands	198,199	F	lc	—
Collared Lory *Phigys solitarius*	Fiji	202	FX	lc	—
Blue-crowned Lorikeet *Vini australis*	American Samoa (to USA), Fiji, Niue (to New Zealand), Tonga, Wallis and Futuna Is. (to France), Western Samoa	202,203 (s128, s129,s130,s131)	FX	lc	—
Kuhl's Lorikeet *Vini kuhlii*	French Polynesia (to France)	211	FX	EN	58
Henderson Lorikeet *Vini stepheni*	Pitcairn Islands (to UK)	215	F	VU	8
Blue Lorikeet *Vini peruviana*	Cook Islands (to New Zealand), French Polynesia (to France)	213,214 (s135)	FX	VU	56
Ultramarine Lorikeet *Vini ultramarina*	French Polynesia (to France)	212	FX	EN	58
Palm Lorikeet *Charmosyna palmarum*	Solomon Islands, Vanuatu	200	F	nt	—
Red-chinned Lorikeet *Charmosyna rubrigularis*	Papua New Guinea	195	F	lc	—

	Breeding range	EBAs (and SAs)	Habitat codes	Status	Threat codes
Meek's Lorikeet *Charmosyna meeki*	Papua New Guinea, Solomon Is.	198	F	lc	—
Blue-fronted Lorikeet *Charmosyna toxopei*	Indonesia	169	F	VU	18
Striated Lorikeet *Charmosyna multistriata*	Indonesia, Papua New Guinea	179	F	nt	—
New Caledonian Lorikeet *Charmosyna diadema*	New Caledonia (to France)	201	F	EN	08
Red-throated Lorikeet *Charmosyna amabilis*	Fiji	202	F	VU	58
Duchess Lorikeet *Charmosyna margarethae*	Papua New Guinea, Solomon Is.	198	FX	nt	—
White-tailed Black-cockatoo *Calyptorhynchus baudinii*	Australia	186	F	VU	12
Blue-eyed Cockatoo *Cacatua ophthalmica*	Papua New Guinea	195	F	lc	—
Salmon-crested Cockatoo *Cacatua moluccensis*	Indonesia	170	F	VU	16
White Cockatoo *Cacatua alba*	Indonesia	171	FA	VU	16
Tanimbar Cockatoo *Cacatua goffini*	Indonesia	165	FA	nt	—
Western Corella *Cacatua pastinator*	Australia	186	FGA	nt	—
Long-billed Corella *Cacatua tenuirostris*	Australia	184	FA	lc	—
Ducorps's Cockatoo *Cacatua ducorpsii*	Papua New Guinea, Solomon Is.	198	F	lc	—
Kea *Nestor notabilis*	New Zealand	207	FS	nt	—
Norfolk Island Kaka *Nestor productus*	Norfolk Island[X]	205[X]	FR	EX	—
Geelvink Pygmy-parrot *Micropsitta geelvinkiana*	Indonesia	174	F	nt	—
Meek's Pygmy-parrot *Micropsitta meeki*	Papua New Guinea	193,194	FS	lc	—
Finsch's Pygmy-parrot *Micropsitta finschii*	Papua New Guinea, Solomon Is.	195,198,199	FX	lc	—
Edwards's Fig-parrot *Psittaculirostris edwardsii*	Indonesia, Papua New Guinea	176	F	lc	—
Salvadori's Fig-parrot *Psittaculirostris salvadorii*	Indonesia	176	F	VU	16
Painted Tiger-parrot *Psittacella picta*	Indonesia, Papua New Guinea	178	FS	lc	—
Modest Tiger-parrot *Psittacella modesta*	Indonesia, Papua New Guinea	173,178	F	lc	—
Singing Parrot *Geoffroyus heteroclitus*	Papua New Guinea, Solomon Is.	195,198,199	FS	lc	—
Luzon Racquet-tail *Prioniturus montanus*	Philippines	151	F	VU	126
Mindanao Racquet-tail *Prioniturus waterstradti*	Philippines	154	F	VU	1
Blue-headed Racquet-tail *Prioniturus platenae*	Philippines	156	FA	VU	1
Green Racquet-tail *Prioniturus luconensis*	Philippines	151	FA	EN	16
Blue-winged Racquet-tail *Prioniturus verticalis*	Philippines	155	F	EN	12
Yellowish-breasted Racquet-tail *Prioniturus flavicans*	Indonesia	166	F	nt	—
Buru Racquet-tail *Prioniturus mada*	Indonesia	169	FA	nt	—
Black-lored Parrot *Tanygnathus gramineus*	Indonesia	169	F	VU	8
Crimson Shining-parrot *Prosopeia splendens*	Fiji	202	F	nt	—
Masked Shining-parrot *Prosopeia personata*	Fiji	202	F	nt	—
Red Shining-parrot *Prosopeia tabuensis*	Fiji	202	F	lc	—
Olive-shouldered Parrot *Aprosmictus jonquillaceus*	Indonesia	164	FV	nt	—
Superb Parrot *Polytelis swainsonii*	Australia	184	F	VU	16
Green Rosella *Platycercus caledonicus*	Australia	185	FS	lc	—
Hooded Parrot *Psephotus dissimilis*	Australia	187	FS	nt	—
Golden-shouldered Parrot *Psephotus chrysopterygius*	Australia	181	F	EN	1356
Antipodes Parakeet *Cyanoramphus unicolor*	New Zealand	(s133)	G	VU	8
Black-fronted Parakeet *Cyanoramphus zealandicus*	French Polynesia (to France)[X]	213[X]	Z	EX	—
Horned Parakeet *Eunymphicus cornutus*	New Caledonia (to France)	201	F	VU	16
Orange-bellied Parrot *Neophema chrysogaster*	Australia	185	FGW	EN	1578
Swift Parrot *Lathamus discolor*	Australia	185	F	VU	16
Mascarene Parrot *Mascarinus mascarinus*	Réunion (to France)[X]	101[X]	Z	EX	—
Fischer's Lovebird *Agapornis fischeri*	Tanzania	108	FGA	nt	—
Black-cheeked Lovebird *Agapornis nigrigenis*	Zambia	(s051)	S	EN	128
Sri Lanka Hanging-parrot *Loriculus beryllinus*	Sri Lanka	124	FAX	lc	—
Moluccan Hanging-parrot *Loriculus amabilis*	Indonesia	168,171	FA	lc	—
Sangihe Hanging-parrot *Loriculus catamene*	Indonesia	167	FX	EN	18
Green-fronted Hanging-parrot *Loriculus tener*	Papua New Guinea	195	F	nt	—
Red-billed Hanging-parrot *Loriculus exilis*	Indonesia	166	F	lc	—
Wallace's Hanging-parrot *Loriculus flosculus*	Indonesia	162	F	VU	18
Seychelles Parakeet *Psittacula wardi*	Seychelles[X]	100[X]	F	EX	—
Mauritius Parakeet *Psittacula eques*	Mauritius	102	F	CR	8
Rodrigues Parakeet *Psittacula exsul*	Mauritius[X]	103[X]	F	EX	—
Malabar Parakeet *Psittacula columboides*	India	123	F	lc	—
Layard's Parakeet *Psittacula calthropae*	Sri Lanka	124	F	lc	—
Nicobar Parakeet *Psittacula caniceps*	India	126	F	nt	—
Lear's Macaw *Anodorhynchus leari*	Brazil	070	FSR	CR	1268
Spix's Macaw *Cyanopsitta spixii*	Brazil	070	FS	CR	168
Blue-throated Macaw *Ara glaucogularis*	Bolivia	(s027)	FV	EN	68
Cuban Macaw *Ara tricolor* *	Cuba[X]	025[X]	FX	EX	—
Red-fronted Macaw *Ara rubrogenys*	Bolivia	056	FA	EN	1268
Socorro Parakeet *Aratinga brevipes* *	Mexico	004	F	VU	158

	Breeding range	EBAs (and SAs)	Habitat codes	Status	Threat codes
Pacific Parakeet *Aratinga strenua*	El Salvador, Guatemala, Honduras, Mexico, Nicaragua	014,017	FS	lc	—
Red-masked Parakeet *Aratinga erythrogenys*	Ecuador, Peru	045	FSA	nt	—
Hispaniolan Parakeet *Aratinga chloroptera*	Dominican Republic, Haiti, Puerto Rico (to USA)	028,029	FAX	VU	126
Thick-billed Parrot *Rhynchopsitta pachyrhyncha*	Mexico	006	F	EN	1
Maroon-fronted Parrot *Rhynchopsitta terrisi*	Mexico	010	F	VU	1
Santa Marta Parakeet *Pyrrhura viridicata*	Colombia	036	FS	VU	1
Fiery-shouldered Parakeet *Pyrrhura egregia*	Brazil, Guyana, Venezuela	064	F	lc	—
El Oro Parakeet *Pyrrhura orcesi*	Ecuador	045	F	VU	1
White-necked Parakeet *Pyrrhura albipectus*	Ecuador	044,047	F	VU	1
Flame-winged Parakeet *Pyrrhura calliptera*	Colombia	038	F	VU	1
Red-eared Parakeet *Pyrrhura hoematotis*	Venezuela	033,034	FV	lc	—
Rose-headed Parakeet *Pyrrhura rhodocephala*	Venezuela	034	FG	nt	—
Sulphur-winged Parakeet *Pyrrhura hoffmanni*	Costa Rica, Panama	020	F	lc	—
Slender-billed Parakeet *Enicognathus leptorhynchus*	Chile	061	FA	nt	—
Rufous-fronted Parakeet *Bolborhynchus ferrugineifrons*	Colombia	043	FSG	EN	18
Mexican Parrotlet *Forpus cyanopygius*	Mexico	005	F	lc	—
Pacific Parrotlet *Forpus coelestis*	Ecuador, Peru	045	FSA	lc	—
Yellow-faced Parrotlet *Forpus xanthops*	Peru	048	FS	VU	16
Grey-cheeked Parakeet *Brotogeris pyrrhopterus*	Ecuador, Peru	045	FA	nt	—
Tepui Parrotlet *Nannopsittaca panychlora*	Brazil, Guyana, Venezuela	032,064	F	lc	—
Red-fronted Parrotlet *Touit costaricensis*	Costa Rica, Panama	020	F	nt	—
Brown-backed Parrotlet *Touit melanonota*	Brazil	075	F	EN	18
Rose-faced Parrot *Pionopsitta pulchra*	Colombia, Ecuador	041	F	lc	—
Black-winged Parrot *Hapalopsittaca melanotis*	Bolivia, Peru	049,055	F	lc	—
Rusty-faced Parrot *Hapalopsittaca amazonina*	Colombia, Venezuela	034,038,042	F	EN	1
Fuertes's Parrot *Hapalopsittaca fuertesi*	Colombia	042	F	CR	18
Red-faced Parrot *Hapalopsittaca pyrrhops*	Ecuador, Peru	046	F	EN	18
Yellow-billed Amazon *Amazona collaria*	Jamaica	027	FA	nt	—
Hispaniolan Amazon *Amazona ventralis*	Dominican Republic, Haiti	028	FA	nt	—
Black-billed Amazon *Amazona agilis*	Jamaica	027	FA	VU	1267
Puerto Rican Amazon *Amazona vittata*	Puerto Rico (to USA)	029	F	CR	78
Tucumán Amazon *Amazona tucumana*	Argentina, Bolivia	057	F	lc	—
Red-spectacled Amazon *Amazona pretrei*	Argentina, Brazil	076	F	EN	16
Green-cheeked Amazon *Amazona viridigenalis*	Mexico	011	F	EN	16
Red-tailed Amazon *Amazona brasiliensis*	Brazil	075	F	EN	126
Yellow-shouldered Amazon *Amazona barbadensis*	Aruba (to Netherlands)[X], Netherlands Antilles, Venezuela	035 (s015)	FSD	VU	16
St Lucia Amazon *Amazona versicolor*	St Lucia	030	F	VU	78
Red-necked Amazon *Amazona arausiaca*	Dominica	030	F	VU	78
St Vincent Amazon *Amazona guildingii*	St Vincent	030	F	VU	78
Imperial Amazon *Amazona imperialis*	Dominica	030	F	VU	78
Blue-bellied Parrot *Triclaria malachitacea*	Brazil	075	F	EN	1

Family MUSOPHAGIDAE: Turacos

Fischer's Turaco *Tauraco fischeri*	Kenya, Somalia, Tanzania	105,111	F	nt	—
Knysna Turaco *Tauraco corythaix*	South Africa	089	FS	lc	—
Bannerman's Turaco *Tauraco bannermani*	Cameroon	086	F	VU	1
Prince Ruspoli's Turaco *Tauraco ruspolii*	Ethiopia	114	F	EN	178
Ruwenzori Turaco *Musophaga johnstoni*	Burundi, Rwanda, Uganda, Zaïre	106	F	lc	—

Family CUCULIDAE: Cuckoos, coucals

Sulawesi Hawk-cuckoo *Cuculus crassirostris*	Indonesia	166	F	lc	—
Moluccan Cuckoo *Cacomantis heinrichi*	Indonesia	171	F	DD	—
Green-cheeked Bronze-cuckoo *Chrysococcyx rufomerus*	Indonesia	165	Z	DD	—
Pied Bronze-cuckoo *Chrysococcyx crassirostris*	Indonesia	165	Z	lc	—
Red-faced Malkoha *Phaenicophaeus pyrrhocephalus*	Sri Lanka	124	F	VU	12
Red-crested Malkoha *Phaenicophaeus superciliosus*	Philippines	151	FG	lc	—
Scale-feathered Malkoha *Phaenicophaeus cumingi*	Philippines	151	F	lc	—
Sumatran Ground-cuckoo *Carpococcyx viridis* *	Indonesia	158	F		—
Snail-eating Coua *Coua delalandei*	Madagascar[X]	(s050[X])	F	EX	—
Coquerel's Coua *Coua coquereli*	Madagascar	093,094	F	lc	—
Red-breasted Coua *Coua serriana*	Madagascar	094	F	lc	—
Running Coua *Coua cursor*	Madagascar	097	FS	lc	—
Verreaux's Coua *Coua verreauxi*	Madagascar	097	S	nt	—
Buff-headed Coucal *Centropus milo*	Solomon Islands	198	F	lc	—
Goliath Coucal *Centropus goliath*	Indonesia	171	FSA	lc	—

	Breeding range	EBAs (and SAs)	Habitat codes	Status	Threat codes
Violaceous Coucal *Centropus violaceus*	Papua New Guinea	195	F	lc	—
Pied Coucal *Centropus ateralbus*	Papua New Guinea	195	F	lc	—
Kai Coucal *Centropus spilopterus*	Indonesia	165	FGA	nt	—
Biak Coucal *Centropus chalybeus*	Indonesia	174	F	nt	—
Black-hooded Coucal *Centropus steerii*	Philippines	150	F	CR	178
Brown Coucal *Centropus andamanensis*	India, Myanmar	125	FA	nt	—
Sunda Coucal *Centropus nigrorufus*	Indonesia	161	FW	VU	1
Green-billed Coucal *Centropus chlororhynchus*	Sri Lanka	124	F	EN	1
Rufous Coucal *Centropus unirufus*	Philippines	151	F	nt	—
Cocos Cuckoo *Coccyzus ferrugineus*	Costa Rica	022	FS	VU	158
Chestnut-bellied Cuckoo *Hyetornis pluvialis*	Jamaica	027	F	lc	—
Rufous-breasted Cuckoo *Hyetornis rufigularis*	Dominican Republic, Haiti	028	F	VU	124
Jamaican Lizard-cuckoo *Saurothera vetula*	Jamaica	027	F	lc	—
Hispaniolan Lizard-cuckoo *Saurothera longirostris*	Dominican Republic, Haiti	028	FX	lc	—
Puerto Rican Lizard-cuckoo *Saurothera vieilloti*	Puerto Rico (to USA)	029	FX	lc	—
Banded Ground-cuckoo *Neomorphus radiolosus*	Colombia, Ecuador	041	F	EN	1

Family TYTONIDAE: Barn owls

Lesser Sooty-owl *Tyto multipunctata*	Australia	182	F	nt	—
Minahassa Masked-owl *Tyto inexspectata*	Indonesia	166	F	DD	—
Taliabu Masked-owl *Tyto nigrobrunnea*	Indonesia	168	F	VU	18
Lesser Masked-owl *Tyto sororcula*	Indonesia	165,169	F	DD	—
Manus Masked-owl *Tyto manusi*	Papua New Guinea	193	F	VU	08
Bismarck Masked-owl *Tyto aurantia*	Papua New Guinea	195	F	VU	1
Madagascar Red Owl *Tyto soumagnei*	Madagascar	094	F	EN	18
Ashy-faced Owl *Tyto glaucops*	Dominican Republic, Haiti	028	FSV	lc	—
Congo Bay-owl *Phodilus prigoginei*	Zaïre	106	FG	VU	1

Family STRIGIDAE: Owls

Sokoke Scops-owl *Otus ireneae*	Kenya, Tanzania	105,111	F	VU	8
Andaman Scops-owl *Otus balli*	India	125	FA	nt	—
Simeulue Scops-owl *Otus umbra*	Indonesia	(s105)	F	lc	—
Javan Scops-owl *Otus angelinae*	Indonesia	160	F	VU	8
Flores Scops-owl *Otus alfredi* *	Indonesia	162	F	NE	—
Luzon Scops-owl *Otus longicornis*	Philippines	151	F	VU	1
Mindoro Scops-owl *Otus mindorensis*	Philippines	150	F	VU	18
Mindanao Scops-owl *Otus mirus*	Philippines	154	F	VU	1
São Tomé Scops-owl *Otus hartlaubi*	São Tomé e Príncipe	082	F	nt	—
Elegant Scops-owl *Otus elegans*	Japan, Philippines, Taiwan	148 (s093,s094)	F	lc	—
Mantanani Scops-owl *Otus mantananensis*	Malaysia, Philippines	155,156 (s095,s097)	FX	lc	—
Seychelles Scops-owl *Otus insularis* *	Seychelles	100	F	CR	18
Enggano Scops-owl *Otus enganensis* *	Indonesia	159	F	lc	—
Pemba Scops-owl *Otus pembaensis* *	Tanzania	110	FX	nt	—
Anjouan Scops-owl *Otus capnodes* *	Comoros	098	F	CR	128
Grand Comoro Scops-owl *Otus pauliani*	Comoros	098	F	CR	158
Rajah Scops-owl *Otus brookii*	Indonesia, Malaysia	157,158	F	lc	—
Mentawai Scops-owl *Otus mentawi*	Indonesia	(s106)	F	lc	—
Palawan Scops-owl *Otus fuliginosus*	Philippines	156	FA	VU	1
Wallace's Scops-owl *Otus silvicola*	Indonesia	162	F	nt	—
Bare-shanked Screech-owl *Otus clarkii*	Colombia, Costa Rica, Panama	020,024	F	lc	—
Santa Barbara Screech-owl *Otus barbarus*	Guatemala, Mexico	018	F	nt	—
Colombian Screech-owl *Otus colombianus* *	Colombia, Ecuador	041	F	nt	—
Cinnamon Screech-owl *Otus petersoni* *	Ecuador, Peru	044	F	lc	—
Cloud-forest Screech-owl *Otus marshalli* *	Peru	053	F	VU	1
Puerto Rican Screech-owl *Otus nudipes*	Puerto Rico (to USA), Virgin Is. (to UK), Virgin Is. (to USA)	029	F	lc	—
Palau Owl *Otus podarginus*	Palau	190	F	lc	—
Lesser Eagle-owl *Mimizuku gurneyi*	Philippines	154	F	EN	1
Usambara Eagle-owl *Bubo vosseleri*	Tanzania	105	F	VU	18
Rufous Fishing-owl *Scotopelia ussheri*	Ghana, Guinea, Ivory Coast, Liberia, Sierra Leone	084	FW	EN	14
Fulvous Owl *Strix fulvescens*	El Salvador, Guatemala, Honduras, Mexico	018	F	lc	—
Sichuan Wood-owl *Strix davidi*	China	138	F	VU	1
Tawny-browed Owl *Pulsatrix koeniswaldiana*	Argentina, Brazil, Paraguay	075	F	lc	—
Tamaulipas Pygmy-owl *Glaucidium sanchezi* *	Mexico	012	F	NE	—
Chestnut-backed Owlet *Glaucidium castanonotum*	Sri Lanka	124	F	nt	—
Albertine Owlet *Glaucidium albertinum*	Rwanda, Zaïre	106	F	VU	1

	Breeding range	EBAs (and SAs)	Habitat codes	Status	Threat codes
Long-whiskered Owlet *Xenoglaux loweryi*	Peru	047	F	nt	—
Forest Owlet *Athene blewitti*	India	(s075)	F	CR	18
Sumba Boobook *Ninox rudolfi*	Indonesia	163	F	VU	1
Andaman Hawk-owl *Ninox affinis*	India	125,126	F	nt	—
Ochre-bellied Hawk-owl *Ninox ochracea*	Indonesia	166	F	lc	—
Moluccan Hawk-owl *Ninox squamipila*	Indonesia	165,169,170,171	F	lc	—
Manus Hawk-owl *Ninox meeki*	Papua New Guinea	193	F	lc	—
Bismarck Hawk-owl *Ninox variegata*	Papua New Guinea	195	F	lc	—
Russet Hawk-owl *Ninox odiosa*	Papua New Guinea	195	FX	lc	—
Solomon Islands Hawk-owl *Ninox jacquinoti*	Papua New Guinea, Solomon Is.	198	F	lc	—
Jamaican Owl *Pseudoscops grammicus*	Jamaica	027	FX	lc	—
Fearful Owl *Nesasio solomonensis*	Papua New Guinea, Solomon Is.	198	F	VU	1

Family PODARGIDAE: Frogmouths

Dulit Frogmouth *Batrachostomus harterti*	Indonesia, Malaysia	157	F	DD	—
Short-tailed Frogmouth *Batrachostomus poliolophus* *	Indonesia, Malaysia	157,158	F	DD	—

Family AEGOTHELIDAE: Owlet-nightjars

Long-whiskered Owlet-nightjar *Aegotheles crinifrons*	Indonesia	171	FA	lc	—
New Caledonian Owlet-nightjar *Aegotheles savesi*	New Caledonia (to France)	201	F	EN	08
Archbold's Owlet-nightjar *Aegotheles archboldi*	Indonesia, Papua New Guinea	178	FS	lc	—

Family CAPRIMULGIDAE: Nightjars

Satanic Eared-nightjar *Eurostopodus diabolicus*	Indonesia	166	F	VU	18
Mountain Eared-nightjar *Eurostopodus archboldi*	Indonesia, Papua New Guinea	173,177,178	F	lc	—
Caatinga Nighthawk *Chordeiles vielliardi* *	Brazil	070	S	NE	—
Jamaican Pauraque *Siphonorhis americanus*	Jamaica	027	FS	CR	158
Least Poorwill *Siphonorhis brewsteri*	Dominican Republic, Haiti	028	FV	nt	—
Chocó Poorwill *Nyctiphrynus rosenbergi* *	Colombia, Ecuador	041	F	nt	—
Puerto Rican Nightjar *Caprimulgus noctitherus*	Puerto Rico (to USA)	029	F	CR	1358
Dusky Nightjar *Caprimulgus saturatus*	Costa Rica, Panama	020	F	lc	—
Scrub Nightjar *Caprimulgus anthonyi*	Ecuador, Peru	045,048	FS	lc	—
Roraiman Nightjar *Caprimulgus whitelyi*	Venezuela	064	FS	nt	—
Pygmy Nightjar *Caprimulgus hirundinaceus*	Brazil	070	F	nt	—
Vaurie's Nightjar *Caprimulgus centralasicus*	China	127	D	VU	18
Itombwe Nightjar *Caprimulgus prigoginei*	Zaïre	106	F	VU	1
Nechisar Nightjar *Caprimulgus solala* *	Ethiopia	114	G	NE	—
Ruwenzori Nightjar *Caprimulgus ruwenzorii*	Burundi, Rwanda, Uganda, Zaïre	106	FA	lc	—
Salvadori's Nightjar *Caprimulgus pulchellus*	Indonesia	158,160	F	DD	—

Family APODIDAE: Swifts

Tepui Swift *Cypseloides phelpsi*	Brazil, Guyana, Venezuela	033,064	FGR	lc	—
White-chested Swift *Cypseloides lemosi*	Colombia	039	FSGR	VU	4
Rothschild's Swift *Cypseloides rothschildi*	Argentina, Bolivia	057	FV	nt	—
White-fronted Swift *Cypseloides storeri*	Mexico	006,009	F	DD	—
Waterfall Swift *Hydrochrous gigas*	Indonesia, Malaysia	158,160	F	nt	—
Seychelles Swiftlet *Collocalia elaphra*	Seychelles	100	FWR	VU	138
Mascarene Swiftlet *Collocalia francica*	Mauritius, Réunion (to France)	101,102	FSR	nt	—
Volcano Swiftlet *Collocalia vulcanorum*	Indonesia	160	R	VU	78
Whitehead's Swiftlet *Collocalia whiteheadi*	Philippines	151,154	F	VU	1
Bare-legged Swiftlet *Collocalia nuditarsus*	Indonesia, Papua New Guinea	178	F	lc	—
Mayr's Swiftlet *Collocalia orientalis*	Papua New Guinea, Solomon Is.	195,198	F	DD	—
Palawan Swiftlet *Collocalia palawanensis*	Philippines	156	FG	lc	—
Palau Swiftlet *Collocalia pelewensis*	Palau	190	F	lc	—
Micronesian Swiftlet *Collocalia inquieta*	Guam (to USA), Micronesia, Northern Mariana Is. (to USA)	189,192	F	lc	—
Atiu Swiftlet *Collocalia sawtelli*	Cook Islands (to New Zealand)	210	SRA	VU	8
Tahiti Swiftlet *Collocalia leucophaeus*	French Polynesia (to France)	213	F	VU	58
Marquesan Swiftlet *Collocalia ocista*	French Polynesia (to France)	212	F	lc	—
Schouteden's Swift *Schoutedenapus schoutedeni*	Zaïre	107	FR	VU	1
Philippine Needletail *Mearnsia picina*	Philippines	152,153[X],154,155	F	lc	—
São Tomé Spinetail *Zoonavena thomensis*	São Tomé e Príncipe	082,083	FVX	lc	—
Lesser Antillean Swift *Chaetura martinica*	Dominica, Guadeloupe (to France), St Lucia, Martinique (to France), St Vincent	030	F	lc	—
Pygmy Swift *Tachornis furcata*	Colombia, Venezuela	035	FV	lc	—
Cape Verde Swift *Apus alexandri*	Cape Verde	078	R	lc	—
Plain Swift *Apus unicolor*	Spain, Portugal	120	FSRA	lc	—
Dark-rumped Swift *Apus acuticauda*	Bhutan, India	130	R	VU	8

	Breeding range	EBAs (and SAs)	Habitat codes	Status	Threat codes
Family TROCHILIDAE: Hummingbirds					
Minute Hermit *Phaethornis idaliae*	Brazil	075	FSV	lc	—
Saw-billed Hermit *Ramphodon naevius*	Brazil	075	F	nt	—
Hook-billed Hermit *Glaucis dohrnii*	Brazil	075	F	CR	18
Long-tailed Sabrewing *Campylopterus excellens*	Mexico	013	FX	nt	—
Rufous Sabrewing *Campylopterus rufus*	El Salvador, Guatemala, Mexico	018	FA	lc	—
Rufous-breasted Sabrewing *Campylopterus hyperythrus*	Brazil, Venezuela	064	FS	lc	—
Buff-breasted Sabrewing *Campylopterus duidae*	Brazil, Venezuela	064	FS	lc	—
White-tailed Sabrewing *Campylopterus ensipennis*	Trinidad and Tobago, Venezuela	032 (s017)	F	VU	17
Santa Marta Sabrewing *Campylopterus phainopeplus*	Colombia	036	FSX	nt	—
Napo Sabrewing *Campylopterus villaviscensio*	Ecuador, Peru	044	F	nt	—
Jamaican Mango *Anthracothorax mango*	Jamaica	027	F	lc	—
Antillean Mango *Anthracothorax dominicus*	Dominican Republic, Haiti, Puerto Rico (to USA), Virgin Islands (to USA)	028,029	FSVAX	lc	—
Green Mango *Anthracothorax viridis*	Puerto Rico (to USA)	029	FX	lc	—
Purple-throated Carib *Eulampis jugularis*	Caribbean[2] (see p. 679)	030	FX	lc	—
Green-throated Carib *Eulampis holosericeus*	Caribbean[3] (see p. 679)	029,030	FSX	lc	—
Antillean Crested Hummingbird *Orthorhyncus cristatus*	Caribbean[4] (see p. 679)	029,030	FSX	lc	—
Short-crested Coquette *Lophornis brachylopha*	Mexico	009	F	EN	18
Peacock Coquette *Lophornis pavoninus*	Brazil, Guyana, Venezuela	064	F	lc	—
White-crested Coquette *Lophornis adorabilis*	Costa Rica, Panama	021	F	lc	—
Coppery Thorntail *Popelairia letitiae*	Bolivia	See p. 724	F	DD	—
Cozumel Emerald *Chlorostilbon forficatus* *	Mexico	016	F	lc	—
Brace's Emerald *Chlorostilbon bracei*	Bahamas[X]	026[X]	S	EX	—
Hispaniolan Emerald *Chlorostilbon swainsonii*	Dominican Republic, Haiti	028	FS	lc	—
Puerto Rican Emerald *Chlorostilbon maugaeus*	Puerto Rico (to USA)	029	FSX	lc	—
Chiribiquete Emerald *Chlorostilbon olivaresi* *	Colombia	(s020)	FS	lc	—
Coppery Emerald *Chlorostilbon russatus*	Colombia, Venezuela	036,038	FSA	lc	—
Narrow-tailed Emerald *Chlorostilbon stenura*	Colombia, Venezuela	034,038	FS	lc	—
Green-tailed Emerald *Chlorostilbon alice*	Venezuela	032,033,034	FX	lc	—
Short-tailed Emerald *Chlorostilbon poortmani*	Colombia, Venezuela	034,038	FS	lc	—
Dusky Hummingbird *Cynanthus sordidus*	Mexico	008	FSD	lc	—
Blue-headed Hummingbird *Cyanophaia bicolor*	Dominica, Martinique (to France)	030	F	lc	—
Mexican Woodnymph *Thalurania ridgwayi*	Mexico	005	FX	VU	1
Fiery-throated Hummingbird *Panterpe insignis*	Costa Rica, Panama	020	FG	lc	—
Sapphire-bellied Hummingbird *Lepidopyga lilliae*	Colombia	035	F	CR	148
Xantus's Hummingbird *Hylocharis xantusii*	Mexico	002	FS	lc	—
Violet-capped Hummingbird *Goldmania violiceps*	Colombia, Panama	024	F	lc	—
Rufous-cheeked Hummingbird *Goethalsia bella*	Colombia, Panama	024	F	nt	—
Red-billed Streamertail *Trochilus polytmus* *	Jamaica	027	FX	lc	—
Black-billed Streamertail *Trochilus scitulus* *	Jamaica	027	FX	lc	—
Tepui Goldenthroat *Polytmus milleri*	Venezuela	064	FSG	lc	—
Buffy Hummingbird *Leucippus fallax*	Colombia, Venezuela	035	FSD	lc	—
Tumbes Hummingbird *Leucippus baeri*	Peru	045	FS	lc	—
Spot-throated Hummingbird *Leucippus taczanowskii*	Peru	048,051	FSV	lc	—
Olive-spotted Hummingbird *Leucippus chlorocercus*	Brazil, Colombia, Ecuador, Peru	066	FS	lc	—
Green-and-white Hummingbird *Amazilia viridicauda*	Peru	053	FA	lc	—
Honduran Emerald *Amazilia luciae*	Honduras	(s010)	FS	CR	1
Táchira Emerald *Amazilia distans*	Venezuela	034	FX	EN	1
Charming Hummingbird *Amazilia decora*	Costa Rica, Panama	021	F	lc	—
Purple-chested Hummingbird *Amazilia rosenbergi*	Colombia, Ecuador	041	FS	lc	—
Mangrove Hummingbird *Amazilia boucardi*	Costa Rica	021	F	VU	1
Blue-tailed Hummingbird *Amazilia cyanura*	El Salvador, Guatemala, Honduras, Mexico, Nicaragua	017	FS	lc	—
Chestnut-bellied Hummingbird *Amazilia castaneiventris*	Colombia	037,038	F	EN	1
White-tailed Hummingbird *Eupherusa poliocerca*	Mexico	009	F	EN	1
Oaxaca Hummingbird *Eupherusa cyanophrys*	Mexico	009	F	EN	18
Black-bellied Hummingbird *Eupherusa nigriventris*	Costa Rica, Panama	020	F	lc	—
White-tailed Emerald *Elvira chionura*	Costa Rica, Panama	020	F	lc	—
Coppery-headed Emerald *Elvira cupreiceps*	Costa Rica	020	F	lc	—
Green-throated Mountain-gem *Lampornis viridipallens*	El Salvador, Guatemala, Honduras, Mexico, Nicaragua	018	F	lc	—
Green-breasted Mountain-gem *Lampornis sybillae*	Honduras, Nicaragua	018	F	lc	—
White-bellied Mountain-gem *Lampornis hemileucus*	Costa Rica, Panama	020	F	lc	—
Blossomcrown *Anthocephala floriceps*	Colombia	036,040	F	nt	—

	Breeding range	EBAs (and SAs)	Habitat codes	Status	Threat codes
Ecuadorian Piedtail *Phlogophilus hemileucurus*	Colombia, Ecuador, Peru	044	F	nt	—
Peruvian Piedtail *Phlogophilus harterti*	Peru	053,054	F	nt	—
Empress Brilliant *Heliodoxa imperatrix*	Colombia, Ecuador	041	F	lc	—
Velvet-browed Brilliant *Heliodoxa xanthogonys*	Brazil, Guyana, Venezuela	064	FS	lc	—
Pink-throated Brilliant *Heliodoxa gularis*	Colombia, Ecuador, Peru	044	F	nt	—
Rufous-webbed Brilliant *Heliodoxa branickii*	Peru	053	F	lc	—
Scissor-tailed Hummingbird *Hylonympha macrocerca*	Venezuela	032	F	CR	18
Violet-chested Hummingbird *Sternoclyta cyanopectus*	Venezuela	033,034	FX	lc	—
Black-breasted Hillstar *Oreotrochilus melanogaster*	Peru	050	GR	lc	—
Wedge-tailed Hillstar *Oreotrochilus adela*	Bolivia	056	FS	nt	—
White-tufted Sunbeam *Aglaeactis castelnaudii*	Peru	051	FS	lc	—
Purple-backed Sunbeam *Aglaeactis aliciae*	Peru	048	S	VU	8
Black-hooded Sunbeam *Aglaeactis pamela*	Bolivia	055	FSR	lc	—
Brown Inca *Coeligena wilsoni*	Colombia, Ecuador	041	F	lc	—
Black Inca *Coeligena prunellei*	Colombia	038	F	VU	1
White-tailed Starfrontlet *Coeligena phalerata*	Colombia	036	FS	lc	—
Golden-bellied Starfrontlet *Coeligena bonapartei*	Colombia, Venezuela	034,038	F	lc	—
Blue-throated Starfrontlet *Coeligena helianthea*	Colombia, Venezuela	038	FS	lc	—
Rainbow Starfrontlet *Coeligena iris*	Ecuador, Peru	046	FS	lc	—
Juan Fernández Firecrown *Sephanoides fernandensis*	Chile	059	FS	CR	1578
Velvet-purple Coronet *Boissonneaua jardini*	Colombia, Ecuador	041	F	lc	—
Orange-throated Sunangel *Heliangelus mavors*	Colombia, Venezuela	034,038	FS	lc	—
Mérida Sunangel *Heliangelus spencei*	Venezuela	034	F	lc	—
Gorgeted Sunangel *Heliangelus strophianus*	Colombia, Ecuador	041	F	lc	—
Purple-throated Sunangel *Heliangelus viola*	Ecuador, Peru	046	F	lc	—
Royal Sunangel *Heliangelus regalis*	Peru	047	FS	VU	18
Bogotá Sunangel *Heliangelus zusii* *	Colombia	See p. 679x	F	CR	18
Black-breasted Puffleg *Eriocnemis nigrivestis*	Ecuador	043	FG	CR	18
Turquoise-throated Puffleg *Eriocnemis godini*	Ecuador	041	F	CR	18
Coppery-bellied Puffleg *Eriocnemis cupreoventris*	Colombia, Venezuela	034,038	FS	lc	—
Blue-capped Puffleg *Eriocnemis glaucopoides*	Argentina, Bolivia	057	FS	lc	—
Colourful Puffleg *Eriocnemis mirabilis*	Colombia	041	F	VU	8
Black-thighed Puffleg *Eriocnemis derbyi*	Colombia, Ecuador	042	F	nt	—
Hoary Puffleg *Haplophaedia lugens*	Colombia, Ecuador	041	FS	nt	—
Purple-bibbed Whitetip *Urosticte benjamini*	Colombia, Ecuador	041	F	lc	—
Rufous-vented Whitetip *Urosticte ruficrissa*	Colombia, Ecuador, Peru	040,044	FS	lc	—
Black-backed Thornbill *Ramphomicron dorsale*	Colombia	036	FG	lc	—
Violet-throated Metaltail *Metallura baroni*	Ecuador	043	FS	VU	1
Neblina Metaltail *Metallura odomae*	Ecuador, Peru	043	FS	nt	—
Coppery Metaltail *Metallura theresiae*	Peru	049	FSG	lc	—
Fire-throated Metaltail *Metallura eupogon*	Peru	049	FS	lc	—
Scaled Metaltail *Metallura aeneocauda*	Bolivia, Peru	055	FS	lc	—
Perijá Metaltail *Metallura iracunda*	Colombia, Venezuela	038	FS	nt	—
Olivaceous Thornbill *Chalcostigma olivaceum*	Bolivia, Peru	051,056	FSG	lc	—
Bronze-tailed Thornbill *Chalcostigma heteropogon*	Colombia, Venezuela	038	FGR	lc	—
Bearded Helmetcrest *Oxypogon guerinii*	Colombia, Venezuela	034,036,038,043	SG	lc	—
Grey-bellied Comet *Taphrolesbia griseiventris*	Peru	048,051	FSA	VU	8
Violet-tailed Sylph *Aglaiocercus coelestis*	Colombia, Ecuador	041	F	lc	—
Bearded Mountaineer *Oreonympha nobilis*	Peru	051	FS	lc	—
Hooded Visorbearer *Augastes lumachellus*	Brazil	073	S	nt	—
Hyacinth Visorbearer *Augastes scutatus*	Brazil	073	SGR	nt	—
Marvellous Spatuletail *Loddigesia mirabilis*	Peru	049	FS	VU	1
Magenta-throated Woodstar *Philodice bryantae*	Costa Rica, Panama	020	FS	nt	—
Slender Sheartail *Doricha enicura*	El Salvador, Guatemala, Honduras, Mexico	018	FS	lc	—
Mexican Sheartail *Doricha eliza*	Mexico	015 (s005)	S	lc	—
Beautiful Hummingbird *Calothorax pulcher*	Mexico	008	S	lc	—
Bahama Woodstar *Calliphlox evelynae*	Bahamas, Turks and Caicos Islands (to UK)	026	FS	lc	—
Vervain Hummingbird *Mellisuga minima*	Dominican Republic, Haiti, Jamaica	027,028	FSA	lc	—
Wine-throated Hummingbird *Atthis ellioti*	El Salvador, Guatemala, Honduras, Mexico	018	FS	lc	—
Chilean Woodstar *Eulidia yarrellii*	Chile, Peru	052	SDA	VU	18
Short-tailed Woodstar *Myrmia micrura*	Ecuador, Peru	045	FS	lc	—
Santa Marta Woodstar *Acestrura astreans*	Colombia	036	FS	lc	—
Esmeraldas Woodstar *Acestrura berlepschi*	Ecuador	045	F	EN	18

	Breeding range	EBAs (and SAs)	Habitat codes	Status	Threat codes
Allen's Hummingbird *Selasphorus sasin*	Mexico, USA	001	FS	lc	—
Volcano Hummingbird *Selasphorus flammula*	Costa Rica, Panama	020	FG	lc	—
Scintillant Hummingbird *Selasphorus scintilla*	Costa Rica, Panama	020	FS	lc	—
Glow-throated Hummingbird *Selasphorus ardens*	Panama	020	F	VU	8
Family TROGONIDAE: Quetzals, trogons					
White-tipped Quetzal *Pharomachrus fulgidus*	Colombia, Venezuela	032,033,036	F	lc	—
Hispaniolan Trogon *Priotelus roseigaster*	Dominican Republic, Haiti	028	F	nt	—
Lattice-tailed Trogon *Trogon clathratus*	Costa Rica, Panama	019	F	lc	—
White-eyed Trogon *Trogon comptus*	Colombia, Ecuador	037,041	F	lc	—
Baird's Trogon *Trogon bairdii*	Costa Rica, Panama	021	F	nt	—
Orange-bellied Trogon *Trogon aurantiiventris*	Costa Rica, Panama	020	F	lc	—
Blue-tailed Trogon *Harpactes reinwardtii*	Indonesia	158,160	F	lc	—
Whitehead's Trogon *Harpactes whiteheadi*	Indonesia, Malaysia	157	F	lc	—
Ward's Trogon *Harpactes wardi*	Bhutan, China, India, Myanmar, Vietnam	130 (s082)	F	VU	1
Family ALCEDINIDAE: Kingfishers					
Bismarck Kingfisher *Alcedo websteri*	Papua New Guinea	195	F	lc	—
Silvery Kingfisher *Alcedo argentata*	Philippines	154	F	EN	1
São Tomé Kingfisher *Alcedo thomensis*	São Tomé e Príncipe	082	FVWX	lc	—
Príncipe Kingfisher *Alcedo nais*	São Tomé e Príncipe	083	FWX	lc	—
Sulawesi Kingfisher *Ceyx fallax*	Indonesia	166,167	F	lc	—
Spangled Kookaburra *Dacelo tyro*	Indonesia, Papua New Guinea	180 (s112)	FV	lc	—
Lilac-cheeked Kingfisher *Cittura cyanotis*	Indonesia	166,167	F	lc	—
Blue-and-white Kingfisher *Todirhamphus diops*	Indonesia	171	FAX	lc	—
Lazuli Kingfisher *Todirhamphus lazuli*	Indonesia	170	FA	VU	1
New Britain Kingfisher *Todirhamphus albonotatus*	Papua New Guinea	195	F	lc	—
Ultramarine Kingfisher *Todirhamphus leucopygius*	Papua New Guinea, Solomon Is.	198	FX	lc	—
Chestnut-bellied Kingfisher *Todirhamphus farquhari*	Vanuatu	200	F	VU	1
Flat-billed Kingfisher *Todirhamphus recurvirostris*	Western Samoa	203	FX	lc	—
Micronesian Kingfisher *Todirhamphus cinnamominus*	Guam (to USA)[X], Japan[X], Micronesia, Palau	148[X],189[X],190,192	FX	lc	—
Sombre Kingfisher *Todirhamphus funebris*	Indonesia	171	FAX	nt	—
Talaud Kingfisher *Todirhamphus enigma*	Indonesia	167	F	nt	—
Cinnamon-banded Kingfisher *Todirhamphus australasia*	Indonesia	162,163,164,165	F	nt	—
Tahiti Kingfisher *Todirhamphus veneratus*	French Polynesia (to France)	213	FX	lc	—
Mangaia Kingfisher *Todirhamphus ruficollaris*	Cook Islands (to New Zealand)	210	F	VU	58
Chattering Kingfisher *Todirhamphus tuta*	Cook Islands (to New Zealand), French Polynesia (to France)	210,213	F	lc	—
Marquesan Kingfisher *Todirhamphus godeffroyi*	French Polynesia (to France)	212	F	EN	58
Tuamotu Kingfisher *Todirhamphus gambieri*	French Polynesia (to France)	214	SX	VU	8
White-rumped Kingfisher *Caridonax fulgidus*	Indonesia	162	FSA	lc	—
Moustached Kingfisher *Actenoides bougainvillei*	Papua New Guinea, Solomon Is.	198	F	VU	1
Blue-capped Kingfisher *Actenoides hombroni*	Philippines	154	F	VU	18
Green-backed Kingfisher *Actenoides monachus*	Indonesia	166	F	lc	—
Scaly Kingfisher *Actenoides princeps*	Indonesia	166	F	lc	—
Little Paradise-kingfisher *Tanysiptera hydrocharis*	Indonesia, Papua New Guinea	180 (s112)	F	DD	—
Kofiau Paradise-kingfisher *Tanysiptera ellioti*	Indonesia	172	F	lc	—
Biak Paradise-kingfisher *Tanysiptera riedelii*	Indonesia	174	F	nt	—
Numfor Paradise-kingfisher *Tanysiptera carolinae*	Indonesia	174	FS	lc	—
Red-breasted Paradise-kingfisher *Tanysiptera nympha*	Indonesia, Papua New Guinea	172,176	F	lc	—
Brown-headed Paradise-kingfisher *Tanysiptera danae*	Papua New Guinea	(s114)	F	lc	—
Family TODIDAE: Todies					
Narrow-billed Tody *Todus angustirostris*	Dominican Republic, Haiti	028	FS	nt	—
Puerto Rican Tody *Todus mexicanus*	Puerto Rico (to USA)	029	FSX	lc	—
Jamaican Tody *Todus todus*	Jamaica	027	FX	lc	—
Broad-billed Tody *Todus subulatus*	Dominican Republic, Haiti	028	FS	lc	—
Family MOTMOTIDAE: Motmots					
Blue-throated Motmot *Aspatha gularis*	El Salvador, Guatemala, Honduras, Mexico	018	F	lc	—
Family MEROPIDAE: Bee-eaters					
Purple-bearded Bee-eater *Meropogon forsteni*	Indonesia	166	F	lc	—
Family CORACIIDAE: Rollers, ground-rollers					
Purple Roller *Eurystomus azureus*	Indonesia	171	F	lc	—
Short-legged Ground-roller *Brachypteracias leptosomus*	Madagascar	094	F	VU	1
Scaly Ground-roller *Brachypteracias squamigera*	Madagascar	094	F	VU	125

	Breeding range	EBAs (and SAs)	Habitat codes	Status	Threat codes
Rufous-headed Ground-roller *Atelornis crossleyi*	Madagascar	094	F	VU	1
Long-tailed Ground-roller *Uratelornis chimaera*	Madagascar	097	S	VU	125
Family BUCEROTIDAE: Hornbills					
Malabar Grey-hornbill *Ocyceros griseus*	India	123	F	nt	—
Sri Lanka Grey-hornbill *Ocyceros gingalensis*	Sri Lanka	124	F	lc	—
Palawan Hornbill *Anthracoceros marchei*	Philippines	156	F	lc	—
Sulu Hornbill *Anthracoceros montani*	Philippines	155	F	CR	128
Luzon Hornbill *Penelopides manillae*	Philippines	151	F	nt	—
Mindoro Hornbill *Penelopides mindorensis*	Philippines	150	F	EN	1
Visayan Hornbill *Penelopides panini*	Philippines	152	F	CR	12
Samar Hornbill *Penelopides samarensis*	Philippines	154	F	nt	—
Mindanao Hornbill *Penelopides affinis*	Philippines	154	F	nt	—
Writhed-billed Hornbill *Aceros waldeni*	Philippines	152	F	CR	128
Writhed Hornbill *Aceros leucocephalus*	Philippines	154	F	EN	12
Narcondam Hornbill *Aceros narcondami*	India	125	F	VU	8
Sumba Hornbill *Aceros everetti*	Indonesia	163	F	VU	1
Brown-cheeked Hornbill *Ceratogymna cylindricus*	Ghana, Guinea, Ivory Coast, Liberia, Sierra Leone	084	FAX	nt	—
Family GALBULIDAE: Jacamars					
Dusky-backed Jacamar *Brachygalba salmoni*	Colombia, Panama	023,037	F	lc	—
Three-toed Jacamar *Jacamaralcyon tridactyla*	Brazil	075	F	EN	18
Coppery-chested Jacamar *Galbula pastazae*	Colombia, Ecuador, Peru	044	F	VU	1
Family BUCCONIDAE: Puffbirds					
Sooty-capped Puffbird *Bucco noanamae*	Colombia	023,041	FS	nt	—
Semicollared Puffbird *Malacoptila semicincta*	Bolivia, Brazil, Peru	068	F	lc	—
Brown Nunlet *Nonnula brunnea*	Colombia, Ecuador, Peru	066	F	lc	—
Chestnut-headed Nunlet *Nonnula amaurocephala*	Brazil	067	F	nt	—
Family CAPITONIDAE: Barbets					
Fire-tufted Barbet *Psilopogon pyrolophus*	Indonesia, Malaysia	158	F	lc	—
Brown-throated Barbet *Megalaima corvina*	Indonesia	160	F	nt	—
Yellow-fronted Barbet *Megalaima flavifrons*	Sri Lanka	124	FA	lc	—
Mountain Barbet *Megalaima monticola*	Indonesia, Malaysia	157	F	lc	—
Flame-fronted Barbet *Megalaima armillaris*	Indonesia	160	F	lc	—
Golden-naped Barbet *Megalaima pulcherrima*	Indonesia, Malaysia	157	F	lc	—
Bornean Barbet *Megalaima eximia*	Indonesia, Malaysia	157	F	lc	—
White-chested Tinkerbird *Pogoniulus makawai* *	Zambia	(s052)	V	VU	08
Red-faced Barbet *Lybius rubrifacies*	Rwanda, Tanzania, Uganda	(s057)	FSA	nt	—
Usambiro Barbet *Trachyphonus usambiro*	Kenya, Tanzania	108	FSG	lc	—
Orange-fronted Barbet *Capito squamatus*	Colombia, Ecuador	041	F	nt	—
White-mantled Barbet *Capito hypoleucus*	Colombia	037	F	EN	1
Five-coloured Barbet *Capito quinticolor*	Colombia	041	F	VU	1
Scarlet-hooded Barbet *Eubucco tucinkae*	Bolivia, Peru	068	FS	nt	—
Prong-billed Barbet *Semnornis frantzii*	Costa Rica, Panama	020	F	lc	—
Toucan Barbet *Semnornis ramphastinus*	Colombia, Ecuador	041	F	nt	—
Family INDICATORIDAE: Honeyguides					
Dwarf Honeyguide *Indicator pumilio*	Rwanda, Uganda, Zaïre	106	F	nt	—
Family RAMPHASTIDAE: Toucans					
Yellow-browed Toucanet *Aulacorhynchus huallagae*	Peru	049	F	nt	—
Fiery-billed Aracari *Pteroglossus frantzii*	Costa Rica, Panama	021	F	lc	—
Plate-billed Mountain-toucan *Andigena laminirostris*	Colombia, Ecuador	041	F	nt	—
Hooded Mountain-toucan *Andigena cucullata*	Bolivia, Peru	055	F	nt	—
Chocó Toucan *Ramphastos brevis*	Colombia, Ecuador	041	F	lc	—
Family PICIDAE: Wrynecks, woodpeckers					
Orinoco Piculet *Picumnus pumilus*	Brazil, Colombia, Venezuela	065	FSV	lc	—
Rusty-necked Piculet *Picumnus fuscus*	Bolivia, Brazil	(s026)	F	lc	—
Ecuadorian Piculet *Picumnus sclateri*	Ecuador, Peru	045	FS	lc	—
Speckle-chested Piculet *Picumnus steindachneri*	Peru	044	F	nt	—
Várzea Piculet *Picumnus varzeae*	Brazil	067	F	lc	—
Tawny Piculet *Picumnus fulvescens*	Brazil	070,071	F	VU	1
Ochraceous Piculet *Picumnus limae*	Brazil	(s033)	F	VU	1
Fine-barred Piculet *Picumnus subtilis*	Peru	068	F	nt	—
Greyish Piculet *Picumnus granadensis*	Colombia	039	FS	lc	—
Chestnut Piculet *Picumnus cinnamomeus*	Colombia, Venezuela	035	FS	lc	—
Antillean Piculet *Nesoctites micromegas*	Dominican Republic, Haiti	028	FX	nt	—
Guadeloupe Woodpecker *Melanerpes herminieri*	Guadeloupe (to France)	030	F	nt	—

	Breeding range	EBAs (and SAs)	Habitat codes	Status	Threat codes
Puerto Rican Woodpecker *Melanerpes portoricensis*	Puerto Rico (to USA), Virgin Islands (to USA)	029	FX	lc	—
Golden-naped Woodpecker *Melanerpes chrysauchen*	Colombia, Costa Rica, Panama	021,037	F	lc	—
Hispaniolan Woodpecker *Melanerpes striatus*	Dominican Republic, Haiti	028	FSVAX	lc	—
Jamaican Woodpecker *Melanerpes radiolatus*	Jamaica	027	FX	lc	—
Grey-breasted Woodpecker *Melanerpes hypopolius*	Mexico	008	FSD	lc	—
Knysna Woodpecker *Campethera notata*	South Africa	089	FS	nt	—
Nuttall's Woodpecker *Picoides nuttallii*	Mexico, USA	001	FS	lc	—
Chocó Woodpecker *Veniliornis chocoensis*	Colombia	041	F	nt	—
Yellow-eared Woodpecker *Veniliornis maculifrons*	Brazil	075	F	lc	—
Stripe-cheeked Woodpecker *Piculus callopterus*	Panama	019,023	F	lc	—
Lita Woodpecker *Piculus litae*	Colombia, Ecuador	041	F	lc	—
Andaman Woodpecker *Dryocopus hodgei*	India	125	F	nt	—
Imperial Woodpecker *Campephilus imperialis*	Mexico	006	F	CR	128
Okinawa Woodpecker *Sapheopipo noguchii*	Japan	148	F	CR	18

Family EURYLAIMIDAE: Broadbills

African Green Broadbill *Pseudocalyptomena graueri*	Uganda, Zaïre	106	F	VU	1
Wattled Broadbill *Eurylaimus steerii*	Philippines	154	F	VU	1
Visayan Broadbill *Eurylaimus samarensis* *	Philippines	154	F	NE	—
Hose's Broadbill *Calyptomena hosii*	Indonesia, Malaysia	157	F	lc	—
Whitehead's Broadbill *Calyptomena whiteheadi*	Indonesia, Malaysia	157	F	lc	—

Family FURNARIIDAE: Ovenbirds

Coastal Miner *Geositta peruviana*	Peru	045,052	SDR	lc	—
Dark-winged Miner *Geositta saxicolina*	Peru	050	GR	lc	—
Short-billed Miner *Geositta antarctica*	Argentina, Chile	062	G	lc	—
Thick-billed Miner *Geositta crassirostris*	Peru	052	SRD	lc	—
Bolivian Earthcreeper *Upucerthia harterti*	Bolivia	056	S	nt	—
Striated Earthcreeper *Upucerthia serrana*	Peru	051	FSGR	lc	—
White-throated Earthcreeper *Upucerthia albigula*	Chile, Peru	052	SWD	lc	—
Córdoba Cinclodes *Cinclodes comechingonus*	Argentina	058	SG	lc	—
Long-tailed Cinclodes *Cinclodes pabsti*	Brazil	076	VGRA	lc	—
Olrog's Cinclodes *Cinclodes olrogi*	Argentina	058	WGR	lc	—
Stout-billed Cinclodes *Cinclodes excelsior* *	Colombia, Ecuador	043	SG	lc	—
Royal Cinclodes *Cinclodes aricomae* *	Bolivia, Peru	051,056	FS	CR	18
Surf Cinclodes *Cinclodes taczanowskii*	Peru	045,052	R	lc	—
Blackish Cinclodes *Cinclodes antarcticus*	Argentina, Chile	062	R	lc	—
White-bellied Cinclodes *Cinclodes palliatus*	Peru	050	SGWR	VU	8
Crag Chilia *Chilia melanura*	Chile	060	SG	lc	—
Masafuera Rayadito *Aphrastura masafuerae*	Chile	059	FS	VU	18
Striolated Tit-spinetail *Leptasthenura striolata*	Brazil	076	F	lc	—
Rusty-crowned Tit-spinetail *Leptasthenura pileata*	Peru	051	FS	lc	—
White-browed Tit-spinetail *Leptasthenura xenothorax*	Peru	051	F	CR	18
Araucaria Tit-spinetail *Leptasthenura setaria*	Argentina, Brazil	076	F	nt	—
Perijá Thistletail *Schizoeaca perijana*	Colombia, Venezuela	038	FSG	nt	—
Ochre-browed Thistletail *Schizoeaca coryi*	Venezuela	034	FSG	lc	—
Mouse-coloured Thistletail *Schizoeaca griseomurina*	Ecuador, Peru	043	F	lc	—
Eye-ringed Thistletail *Schizoeaca palpebralis*	Peru	049	FSG	lc	—
Vilcabamba Thistletail *Schizoeaca vilcabambae*	Peru	049	F	lc	—
Puna Thistletail *Schizoeaca helleri*	Peru	055	FS	lc	—
Black-throated Thistletail *Schizoeaca harterti*	Bolivia	055	FS	lc	—
Itatiaia Thistletail *Schizoeaca moreirae*	Brazil	076	FSG	lc	—
Bahia Spinetail *Synallaxis whitneyi* *	Brazil	076	F	NE	—
Apurímac Spinetail *Synallaxis courseni*	Peru	051	FS	VU	8
Plain Spinetail *Synallaxis infuscata*	Brazil	071	F	EN	18
Silvery-throated Spinetail *Synallaxis subpudica*	Colombia	038	FS	lc	—
Blackish-headed Spinetail *Synallaxis tithys*	Ecuador, Peru	045	FS	VU	1
Marañón Spinetail *Synallaxis maranonica*	Peru	048	F	lc	—
Black-throated Spinetail *Synallaxis castanea*	Venezuela	033	F	lc	—
Rusty-headed Spinetail *Synallaxis fuscorufa*	Colombia	036	FS	nt	—
Russet-bellied Spinetail *Synallaxis zimmeri*	Peru	051	FS	EN	1
Necklaced Spinetail *Synallaxis stictothorax*	Ecuador, Peru	045,048	FS	lc	—
White-whiskered Spinetail *Synallaxis candei*	Colombia, Venezuela	035	FSD	lc	—
Hoary-throated Spinetail *Synallaxis kollari*	Brazil, Guyana	063	F	VU	8
Red-shouldered Spinetail *Gyalophylax hellmayri*	Brazil	070	F	VU	1
Pink-legged Graveteiro *Acrobatornis fonsecai* *	Brazil	075	F	NE	—
Tepui Spinetail *Cranioleuca demissa*	Brazil, Guyana, Venezuela	064	F	lc	—

	Breeding range	EBAs (and SAs)	Habitat codes	Status	Threat codes
Streak-capped Spinetail *Cranioleuca hellmayri*	Colombia	036	F	lc	—
Marcapata Spinetail *Cranioleuca marcapatae*	Peru	055	F	lc	—
Light-crowned Spinetail *Cranioleuca albiceps*	Bolivia, Peru	055	F	lc	—
Creamy-crested Spinetail *Cranioleuca albicapilla*	Peru	051	FS	lc	—
Coiba Spinetail *Cranioleuca dissita*	Panama	021	F	nt	—
Scaled Spinetail *Cranioleuca muelleri*	Brazil	067	F	lc	—
Canyon Canastero *Asthenes pudibunda*	Peru	051	FSR	lc	—
Rusty-fronted Canastero *Asthenes ottonis*	Peru	051	FSR	lc	—
Maquis Canastero *Asthenes heterura*	Bolivia	056	FS	VU	1
Cactus Canastero *Asthenes cactorum*	Peru	052	SD	nt	—
Cipó Canastero *Asthenes luizae*	Brazil	073	GR	EN	178
Berlepsch's Canastero *Asthenes berlepschi*	Bolivia	056	SA	VU	8
Chestnut Canastero *Asthenes steinbachi*	Argentina	056	S	VU	1
Dusky-tailed Canastero *Asthenes humicola*	Chile	060	S	lc	—
Line-fronted Canastero *Asthenes urubambensis*	Bolivia, Peru	051,056	FSG	nt	—
Junín Canastero *Asthenes virgata*	Peru	050,051	FSGR	lc	—
Scribble-tailed Canastero *Asthenes maculicauda*	Argentina, Bolivia, Peru	056	SGR	lc	—
Orinoco Softtail *Thripophaga cherriei*	Venezuela	065	FS	VU	8
Striated Softtail *Thripophaga macroura*	Brazil	075	F	VU	1
Russet-mantled Softtail *Thripophaga berlepschi*	Peru	049	F	nt	—
Great Spinetail *Siptornopsis hypochondriacus*	Peru	048	FS	nt	—
Chestnut-backed Thornbird *Phacellodomus dorsalis*	Peru	048	S	nt	—
Red-eyed Thornbird *Phacellodomus erythrophthalmus*	Brazil	075	F	lc	—
Canebrake Groundcreeper *Clibanornis dendrocolaptoides*	Argentina, Brazil, Paraguay	075	F	nt	—
Straight-billed Reedhaunter *Limnornis rectirostris*	Argentina, Brazil, Uruguay	(s035)	GW	nt	—
Equatorial Greytail *Xenerpestes singularis*	Ecuador, Peru	044	F	nt	—
Roraiman Barbtail *Roraimia adusta*	Brazil, Guyana, Venezuela	064	FS	lc	—
White-throated Barbtail *Premnoplex tatei*	Venezuela	032	F	EN	1
Ruddy Treerunner *Margarornis rubiginosus*	Costa Rica, Panama	020	F	lc	—
Fulvous-dotted Treerunner *Margarornis stellatus*	Colombia, Ecuador	041	F	lc	—
Beautiful Treerunner *Margarornis bellulus*	Panama	024	F	nt	—
Pale-browed Treehunter *Cichlocolaptes leucophrus*	Brazil	075	F	lc	—
Guttulated Foliage-gleaner *Syndactyla guttulata*	Venezuela	032,033	F	lc	—
Rufous-necked Foliage-gleaner *Syndactyla ruficollis*	Ecuador, Peru	045	F	VU	1
White-browed Foliage-gleaner *Philydor amaurotis*	Argentina, Brazil, Paraguay	075	F	nt	—
Alagoas Foliage-gleaner *Philydor novaesi*	Brazil	071	F	CR	18
Bolivian Recurvebill *Simoxenops striatus*	Bolivia	054	F	VU	1
Uniform Treehunter *Thripadectes ignobilis*	Colombia, Ecuador	041	F	lc	—
Streak-breasted Treehunter *Thripadectes rufobrunneus*	Costa Rica, Panama	020	F	lc	—
White-throated Foliage-gleaner *Automolus roraimae*	Brazil, Venezuela	064	F	lc	—
Henna-hooded Foliage-gleaner *Hylocryptus erythrocephalus*	Ecuador, Peru	045	F	VU	1

Family FORMICARIIDAE: Antbirds

	Breeding range	EBAs (and SAs)	Habitat codes	Status	Threat codes
Collared Antshrike *Sakesphorus bernardi*	Ecuador, Peru	045,048	FS	lc	—
Black-backed Antshrike *Sakesphorus melanonotus*	Colombia, Venezuela	035	FS	lc	—
White-bearded Antshrike *Biatas nigropectus*	Argentina, Brazil	075	F	VU	1
Chapman's Antshrike *Thamnophilus zarumae* *	Ecuador, Peru	045	FS	lc	—
Black-hooded Antshrike *Thamnophilus bridgesi*	Costa Rica, Panama	021	FS	lc	—
Cocha Antshrike *Thamnophilus praecox*	Ecuador	066	F	nt	—
Upland Antshrike *Thamnophilus aroyae*	Bolivia, Peru	054	F	lc	—
Streak-backed Antshrike *Thamnophilus insignis*	Brazil, Venezuela	064	F	lc	—
Recurve-billed Bushbird *Clytoctantes alixii*	Colombia, Venezuela	037,038	F	EN	1
Rondônia Bushbird *Clytoctantes atrogularis*	Brazil	(s025)	F	DD	—
Speckled Antshrike *Xenornis setifrons*	Colombia, Panama	023	F	VU	1
Spot-breasted Antvireo *Dysithamnus stictothorax*	Argentina, Brazil	075	F	nt	—
Streak-crowned Antvireo *Dysithamnus striaticeps*	Costa Rica, Honduras, Nicaragua	019	F	lc	—
Rufous-backed Antvireo *Dysithamnus xanthopterus*	Brazil	076	F	lc	—
Plumbeous Antvireo *Dysithamnus plumbeus*	Brazil	075	F	VU	1
Bicoloured Antvireo *Dysithamnus occidentalis*	Colombia, Ecuador	041,044	F	VU	1
Klages's Antwren *Myrmotherula klagesi*	Brazil	067	F	nt	—
Yellow-throated Antwren *Myrmotherula ambigua*	Brazil, Colombia, Venezuela	065	F	lc	—
Alagoas Antwren *Myrmotherula snowi* *	Brazil	071	F	CR	18
Star-throated Antwren *Myrmotherula gularis*	Brazil	075	F	lc	—
Rio de Janeiro Antwren *Myrmotherula fluminensis*	Brazil	075	F	VU	1
Salvadori's Antwren *Myrmotherula minor*	Brazil	075	F	VU	1
Ashy Antwren *Myrmotherula grisea*	Bolivia	054	F	VU	1

Appendix 1: Restricted-range Bird Species Listed by Family

	Breeding range	EBAs (and SAs)	Habitat codes	Status	Threat codes
Unicoloured Antwren *Myrmotherula unicolor*	Brazil	075	F	VU	1
Band-tailed Antwren *Myrmotherula urosticta*	Brazil	075	F	VU	1
Ash-throated Antwren *Herpsilochmus parkeri*	Peru	047	F	VU	18
Creamy-bellied Antwren *Herpsilochmus motacilloides*	Peru	053	F	lc	—
Spot-backed Antwren *Herpsilochmus dorsimaculatus*	Brazil, Colombia, Venezuela	065	F	lc	—
Roraiman Antwren *Herpsilochmus roraimae*	Brazil, Guyana, Venezuela	064	F	lc	—
Long-billed Antwren *Stymphalornis acutirostris* *	Brazil	(s034)	W	NE	—
Narrow-billed Antwren *Formicivora iheringi*	Brazil	072	F	VU	1
Serra Antwren *Formicivora serrana*	Brazil	075	FS	nt	—
Black-hooded Antwren *Formicivora erythronotos*	Brazil	075	F	CR	18
Restinga Antwren *Formicivora littoralis* *	Brazil	075	FS	EN	18
Bertoni's Antbird *Drymophila rubricollis*	Argentina, Brazil, Paraguay	075	F	lc	—
Rufous-tailed Antbird *Drymophila genei*	Brazil	076	F	nt	—
Ochre-rumped Antbird *Drymophila ochropyga*	Brazil	076	F	nt	—
Orange-bellied Antwren *Terenura sicki*	Brazil	071	F	VU	18
Yellow-rumped Antwren *Terenura sharpei*	Bolivia, Peru	054	F	VU	1
Rio de Janeiro Antbird *Cercomacra brasiliana*	Brazil	075	F	nt	—
Bananal Antbird *Cercomacra ferdinandi*	Brazil	(s031)	F	lc	—
Rio Branco Antbird *Cercomacra carbonaria*	Brazil, Guyana	063	F	VU	8
Fringe-backed Fire-eye *Pyriglena atra*	Brazil	075	F	EN	18
Slender Antbird *Rhopornis ardesiaca*	Brazil	072	F	EN	1
Black-tailed Antbird *Myrmoborus melanurus*	Peru	066	F	VU	1
Caura Antbird *Percnostola caurensis*	Brazil, Venezuela	064	F	lc	—
White-lined Antbird *Percnostola lophotes*	Bolivia, Peru	068	FX	lc	—
Stub-tailed Antbird *Myrmeciza berlepschi*	Colombia, Ecuador	041	F	lc	—
Scalloped Antbird *Myrmeciza ruficauda*	Brazil	071,075	F	VU	1
White-bibbed Antbird *Myrmeciza loricata*	Brazil	075	F	lc	—
Squamate Antbird *Myrmeciza squamosa*	Brazil	075	F	lc	—
Yapacana Antbird *Myrmeciza disjuncta*	Colombia, Venezuela	065	FS	lc	—
Grey-bellied Antbird *Myrmeciza pelzelni*	Brazil, Colombia, Venezuela	065	F	lc	—
Goeldi's Antbird *Myrmeciza goeldii*	Bolivia, Brazil, Peru	068	F	lc	—
Grey-headed Antbird *Myrmeciza griseiceps*	Ecuador, Peru	045	F	EN	1
White-masked Antbird *Pithys castanea*	Peru	066	F	DD	—
Chestnut-crested Antbird *Rhegmatorhina cristata*	Brazil, Colombia	065	F	lc	—
Rufous-fronted Antthrush *Formicarius rufifrons*	Peru	068	F	VU	1
Schwartz's Antthrush *Chamaeza turdina*	Colombia, Venezuela	033,040	F	lc	—
Such's Antthrush *Chamaeza meruloides*	Brazil	075	F	lc	—
Rufous-tailed Antthrush *Chamaeza ruficauda*	Brazil	076	F	lc	—
Black-crowned Antpitta *Pittasoma michleri*	Colombia, Costa Rica, Panama	019,023	F	lc	—
Rufous-crowned Antpitta *Pittasoma rufopileatum*	Colombia, Ecuador	041	F	lc	—
Giant Antpitta *Grallaria gigantea*	Colombia, Ecuador	042,046	F	VU	1
Great Antpitta *Grallaria excelsa*	Venezuela	033,034,038	F	nt	—
Moustached Antpitta *Grallaria alleni*	Colombia	040	F	EN	18
Táchira Antpitta *Grallaria chthonia*	Venezuela	038	F	VU	18
Ochre-striped Antpitta *Grallaria dignissima*	Colombia, Ecuador, Peru	066	F	lc	—
Elusive Antpitta *Grallaria eludens*	Peru	068	F	nt	—
Cundinamarca Antpitta *Grallaria kaestneri*	Colombia	038	F	VU	8
Santa Marta Antpitta *Grallaria bangsi*	Colombia	036	F	nt	—
Scrub Antpitta *Grallaria watkinsi*	Ecuador, Peru	045	FS	lc	—
Bicoloured Antpitta *Grallaria rufocinerea*	Colombia	042	F	EN	1
Pale-billed Antpitta *Grallaria carrikeri*	Peru	049	F	lc	—
White-throated Antpitta *Grallaria albigula*	Argentina, Bolivia, Peru	054,057	FS	lc	—
Yellow-breasted Antpitta *Grallaria flavotincta*	Colombia, Ecuador	041	F	lc	—
Rusty-tinged Antpitta *Grallaria przewalskii*	Peru	049	F	lc	—
Bay Antpitta *Grallaria capitalis*	Peru	049	F	lc	—
Red-and-white Antpitta *Grallaria erythroleuca*	Peru	055	F	lc	—
Grey-naped Antpitta *Grallaria griseonucha*	Venezuela	034	F	lc	—
Chestnut Antpitta *Grallaria blakei*	Peru	049	F	nt	—
Rufous-faced Antpitta *Grallaria erythrotis*	Bolivia	055	F	lc	—
Brown-banded Antpitta *Grallaria milleri*	Colombia	042	F	EN	18
Brown-breasted Antpitta *Myrmothera simplex*	Brazil, Venezuela	064	FS	lc	—
Scallop-breasted Antpitta *Grallaricula loricata*	Venezuela	033	F	nt	—
Peruvian Antpitta *Grallaricula peruviana*	Ecuador, Peru	044	F	nt	—
Ochre-fronted Antpitta *Grallaricula ochraceifrons*	Peru	047	F	nt	—
Crescent-faced Antpitta *Grallaricula lineifrons*	Colombia, Ecuador	042,046	F	nt	—
Hooded Antpitta *Grallaricula cucullata*	Colombia, Venezuela	038,040	F	VU	1

697

	Breeding range	EBAs (and SAs)	Habitat codes	Status	Threat codes
Family RHINOCRYPTIDAE: Tapaculos					
Chestnut-throated Huet-huet *Pteroptochos castaneus* *	Chile	060	F	lc	—
Black-throated Huet-huet *Pteroptochos tarnii* *	Argentina, Chile	061	F	lc	—
Moustached Turca *Pteroptochos megapodius*	Chile	060	S	lc	—
White-throated Tapaculo *Scelorchilus albicollis*	Chile	060	SR	lc	—
Chucao Tapaculo *Scelorchilus rubecula*	Argentina, Chile	061	F	lc	—
Elegant Crescent-chest *Melanopareia elegans* *	Ecuador, Peru	045	FS	lc	—
Marañón Crescent-chest *Melanopareia maranonica* *	Peru	048	FS	nt	—
Spotted Bamboowren *Psilorhamphus guttatus*	Argentina, Brazil	075	F	nt	—
Slaty Bristlefront *Merulaxis ater*	Brazil	075	F	nt	—
Stresemann's Bristlefront *Merulaxis stresemanni*	Brazil	075	F	CR	18
Ochre-flanked Tapaculo *Eugralla paradoxa*	Argentina, Chile	060,061	FS	lc	—
Large-footed Tapaculo *Scytalopus macropus*	Peru	049	F	lc	—
Tacarcuna Tapaculo *Scytalopus panamensis*	Colombia, Panama	024	F	lc	—
Nariño Tapaculo *Scytalopus vicinior*	Colombia, Ecuador, Panama	024,041	F	lc	—
Silvery-fronted Tapaculo *Scytalopus argentifrons*	Costa Rica, Panama	020	F	lc	—
Diademed Tapaculo *Scytalopus schulenbergi* *	Bolivia, Peru	055	F	lc	—
White-browed Tapaculo *Scytalopus superciliaris*	Argentina, Bolivia	057	FS	lc	—
Brasília Tapaculo *Scytalopus novacapitalis*	Brazil	073 (s032)	F	VU	1
Bahia Tapaculo *Scytalopus psychopompus*	Brazil	075	F	EN	18
Family COTINGIDAE: Cotingas					
Slaty Becard *Pachyramphus spodiurus*	Ecuador, Peru	045,048	F	nt	—
Jamaican Becard *Pachyramphus niger*	Jamaica	027	F	lc	—
Black-and-gold Cotinga *Tijuca atra*	Brazil	076	F	nt	—
Grey-winged Cotinga *Tijuca condita*	Brazil	076	FG	VU	18
Hooded Berryeater *Carpornis cucullatus*	Brazil	075	F	nt	—
Bay-vented Cotinga *Doliornis sclateri*	Peru	049	F	lc	—
Chestnut-bellied Cotinga *Doliornis remseni* *	Colombia, Ecuador, Peru	043	F	VU	1
White-cheeked Cotinga *Zaratornis stresemanni*	Peru	051	F	VU	1
Orange-breasted Fruiteater *Pipreola jucunda*	Colombia, Ecuador	041	F	lc	—
Black-chested Fruiteater *Pipreola lubomirskii*	Colombia, Ecuador, Peru	040,044	F	nt	—
Masked Fruiteater *Pipreola pulchra*	Peru	044	F	lc	—
Handsome Fruiteater *Pipreola formosa*	Venezuela	032,033	F	lc	—
Red-banded Fruiteater *Pipreola whitelyi*	Guyana, Venezuela	064	F	lc	—
Buff-throated Purpletuft *Iodopleura pipra*	Brazil	071,075	F	VU	1
Kinglet Calyptura *Calyptura cristata*	Brazil	075	F	CR	18
Scimitar-winged Piha *Lipaugus uropygialis*	Bolivia, Peru	055	F	lc	—
Rose-collared Piha *Lipaugus streptophorus*	Brazil, Guyana, Venezuela	064	F	lc	—
Turquoise Cotinga *Cotinga ridgwayi*	Costa Rica, Panama	021	F	VU	1
Banded Cotinga *Cotinga maculata*	Brazil	075	F	EN	18
White-winged Cotinga *Xipholena atropurpurea*	Brazil	071,075	F	VU	1
Snowy Cotinga *Carpodectes nitidus*	Costa Rica, Honduras, Nicaragua, Panama	019	F	lc	—
Yellow-billed Cotinga *Carpodectes antoniae*	Costa Rica, Panama	021	F	VU	1
Black-faced Cotinga *Conioptilon mcilhennyi*	Peru	068	F	nt	—
Bare-necked Umbrellabird *Cephalopterus glabricollis*	Costa Rica, Panama	019,020	F	VU	1
Long-wattled Umbrellabird *Cephalopterus penduliger*	Colombia, Ecuador	041	F	VU	126
Family PIPRIDAE: Manakins					
Scarlet-horned Manakin *Pipra cornuta*	Brazil, Guyana, Venezuela	064	F	lc	—
Golden-crowned Manakin *Pipra vilasboasi*	Brazil	(s030)	F	VU	1
Cerulean-capped Manakin *Pipra coeruleocapilla*	Peru	053	F	lc	—
Orange-bellied Manakin *Lepidothrix suavissima*	Brazil, Guyana, Venezuela	064	F	lc	—
Yungas Manakin *Chiroxiphia boliviana*	Bolivia, Peru	053,054	F	lc	—
Club-winged Manakin *Machaeropterus deliciosus*	Colombia, Ecuador	041	F	lc	—
Olive Manakin *Chloropipo uniformis*	Brazil, Guyana, Venezuela	064	F	lc	—
Yellow-headed Manakin *Chloropipo flavicapilla*	Colombia, Ecuador	040,041,044	F	nt	—
Orange-crested Manakin *Heterocercus aurantiivertex*	Ecuador, Peru	066	F	lc	—
Serra do Mar Tyrant-manakin *Neopelma chrysolophum* *	Brazil	073,076	F	NE	—
Black-capped Manakin *Piprites pileatus*	Argentina, Brazil	076	F	VU	1
Grey-headed Piprites *Piprites griseiceps*	Costa Rica, Guatemala, Honduras, Nicaragua	019	F	nt	—
Family TYRANNIDAE: Tyrant-flycatchers					
Inca Flycatcher *Leptopogon taczanowskii*	Peru	049	F	lc	—
Hazel-fronted Pygmy-tyrant *Pseudotriccus simplex*	Bolivia, Peru	054	F	lc	—
White-cheeked Tody-tyrant *Poecilotriccus albifacies*	Peru	068	F	nt	—

	Breeding range	EBAs (and SAs)	Habitat codes	Status	Threat codes
Brown-breasted Bamboo-tyrant *Hemitriccus obsoletus*	Brazil	076	F	lc	—
Yungas Tody-tyrant *Hemitriccus spodiops*	Bolivia	054	F	lc	—
Pelzeln's Tody-tyrant *Hemitriccus inornatus*	Brazil	065	FS	lc	—
Cinnamon-breasted Tody-tyrant *H. cinnamomeipectus*	Ecuador, Peru	047	F	nt	—
Buff-breasted Tody-tyrant *Hemitriccus mirandae*	Brazil	071 (s033)	F	VU	1
Kaempfer's Tody-tyrant *Hemitriccus kaempferi*	Brazil	075	F	EN	18
Fork-tailed Pygmy-tyrant *Hemitriccus furcatus*	Brazil	075	F	VU	1
Buff-cheeked Tody-flycatcher *Todirostrum senex*	Brazil	(s029)	F	lc	—
Ruddy Tody-flycatcher *Todirostrum russatum*	Brazil, Venezuela	064	F	lc	—
Maracaibo Tody-flycatcher *Todirostrum viridanum*	Venezuela	035	FS	nt	—
Golden-winged Tody-flycatcher *T. calopterum*	Colombia, Ecuador, Peru	066	FS	lc	—
Black-backed Tody-flycatcher *T. pulchellum*	Peru	068	FS	lc	—
Grey-capped Tyrannulet *Phyllomyias griseocapilla*	Brazil	076	F	nt	—
Bolivian Tyrannulet *Zimmerius bolivianus*	Bolivia, Peru	053,054	F	lc	—
Red-billed Tyrannulet *Zimmerius cinereicapillus*	Ecuador, Peru	044,053	F	lc	—
Peruvian Tyrannulet *Zimmerius viridiflavus*	Peru	049	FX	lc	—
Cocos Flycatcher *Nesotriccus ridgwayi*	Costa Rica	022	FS	VU	158
Pacific Elaenia *Myiopagis subplacens*	Ecuador, Peru	045	FS	lc	—
Jamaican Elaenia *Myiopagis cotta*	Jamaica	027	F	lc	—
Grey-and-white Tyrannulet *Pseudelaenia leucospodia*	Ecuador, Peru	045	S	lc	—
Noronha Elaenia *Elaenia ridleyana*	Brazil	069	FS	lc	—
Slaty Elaenia *Elaenia strepera*	Argentina, Bolivia	057	F	lc	—
Great Elaenia *Elaenia dayi*	Venezuela	064	FS	lc	—
Greater Antillean Elaenia *Elaenia fallax*	Dominican Republic, Haiti, Jamaica	027,028	F	lc	—
Slender-billed Tyrannulet *Inezia tenuirostris*	Colombia, Venezuela	035	FS	lc	—
Unstreaked Tit-tyrant *Uromyias agraphia*	Peru	049	F	lc	—
Ash-breasted Tit-tyrant *Anairetes alpinus*	Bolivia, Peru	051,056	F	EN	18
Juan Fernández Tit-tyrant *Anairetes fernandezianus*	Chile	059	FS	lc	—
Grey-backed Tachuri *Polystictus superciliaris*	Brazil	073,076	SVGR	nt	—
Venezuelan Bristle-tyrant *Phylloscartes venezuelanus*	Venezuela	033	F	nt	—
Antioquia Bristle-tyrant *Phylloscartes lanyoni*	Colombia	037	F	EN	1
Black-fronted Tyrannulet *Phylloscartes nigrifrons*	Venezuela	064	F	lc	—
Chapman's Tyrannulet *Phylloscartes chapmani*	Brazil, Venezuela	064	F	lc	—
Ecuadorian Tyrannulet *Phylloscartes gualaquizae*	Ecuador, Peru	044	F	lc	—
Minas Gerais Tyrannulet *Phylloscartes roquettei*	Brazil	074	F	EN	18
Oustalet's Tyrannulet *Phylloscartes oustaleti*	Brazil	075	F	nt	—
Serra do Mar Tyrannulet *Phylloscartes difficilis*	Brazil	076	F	nt	—
Alagoas Tyrannulet *Phylloscartes ceciliae*	Brazil	071	F	EN	18
Bahia Tyrannulet *Phylloscartes beckeri* *	Brazil	076	F	NE	—
Restinga Tyrannulet *Phylloscartes kronei* *	Brazil	075	FS	VU	1
Long-crested Pygmy-tyrant *Lophotriccus eulophotes*	Bolivia, Brazil, Peru	068	F	lc	—
Pacific Royal Flycatcher *Onychorhynchus occidentalis* *	Ecuador, Peru	045	F	VU	1
Unadorned Flycatcher *Myiophobus inornatus*	Bolivia, Peru	054	FS	lc	—
Orange-banded Flycatcher *Myiophobus lintoni*	Ecuador, Peru	046	F	nt	—
Olive-chested Flycatcher *Myiophobus cryptoxanthus*	Ecuador, Peru	066	F	lc	—
Grey-breasted Flycatcher *Lathrotriccus griseipectus*	Ecuador, Peru	045,048	F	VU	1
Tawny-chested Flycatcher *Aphanotriccus capitalis*	Costa Rica, Nicaragua	019	F	nt	—
Black-billed Flycatcher *Aphanotriccus audax*	Colombia, Panama	023,037	F	nt	—
Belted Flycatcher *Xenotriccus callizonus*	El Salvador, Guatemala, Mexico	018	F	nt	—
Pileated Flycatcher *Xenotriccus mexicanus*	Mexico	008	S	nt	—
Dark Pewee *Contopus lugubris*	Costa Rica, Panama	020	F	lc	—
Ochraceous Pewee *Contopus ochraceus*	Costa Rica, Panama	020	F	nt	—
Jamaican Pewee *Contopus pallidus* *	Jamaica	027	FX	lc	—
Hispaniolan Pewee *Contopus hispaniolensis* *	Dominican Republic, Haiti	028	FX	lc	—
Lesser Antillean Pewee *Contopus latirostris*	Dominica, Guadeloupe (to France), Martinique (to France), Puerto Rico (to USA), St Lucia	029,030	FX	lc	—
Black-capped Flycatcher *Empidonax atriceps*	Costa Rica, Panama	020	F	lc	—
Piura Chat-tyrant *Ochthoeca piurae*	Peru	045	S	nt	—
Tumbes Tyrant *Ochthoeca salvini*	Peru	045	FS	nt	—
Santa Marta Bush-tyrant *Myiotheretes pernix*	Colombia	036	FS	VU	1
Rufous-bellied Bush-tyrant *Myiotheretes fuscorufus*	Bolivia, Peru	049,055	F	nt	—
Salinas Monjita *Xolmis salinarum*	Argentina	(s036)	W	nt	—
Chocolate-vented Tyrant *Neoxolmis rufiventris*	Argentina, Chile	062	SG	lc	—
Brazilian Black-tyrant *Knipolegus franciscanus* *	Brazil	074	F	NE	—
Rufous Flycatcher *Myiarchus semirufus*	Peru	045	FS	lc	—

	Breeding range	EBAs (and SAs)	Habitat codes	Status	Threat codes
Sad Flycatcher *Myiarchus barbirostris*	Jamaica	027	F	lc	—
Sooty-crowned Flycatcher *Myiarchus phaeocephalus*	Ecuador, Peru	045,048	F	lc	—
Apical Flycatcher *Myiarchus apicalis*	Colombia	039	FS	lc	—
Grenada Flycatcher *Myiarchus nugator*	Grenada, St Vincent	030	F	lc	—
Large-billed Flycatcher *Myiarchus magnirostris*	Ecuador	031	FS	lc	—
Rufous-tailed Flycatcher *Myiarchus validus*	Jamaica	027	F	lc	—
Stolid Flycatcher *Myiarchus stolidus*	Dominican Republic, Haiti, Jamaica	027,028	FS	lc	—
Puerto Rican Flycatcher *Myiarchus antillarum*	Puerto Rico (to USA), Virgin Is. (to UK), Virgin Is. (to USA)	029	FS	lc	—
Lesser Antillean Flycatcher *Myiarchus oberi*	Caribbean[5] (see p. 679)	030	FX	lc	—
Golden-bellied Flycatcher *Myiodynastes hemichrysus*	Costa Rica, Panama	020	F	lc	—
Baird's Flycatcher *Myiodynastes bairdii*	Ecuador, Peru	045	FS	lc	—

Family PHYTOTOMIDAE: Plantcutters

Peruvian Plantcutter *Phytotoma raimondii*	Peru	045	S	CR	18

Family PITTIDAE: Pittas

Schneider's Pitta *Pitta schneideri*	Indonesia	158	F	VU	1
Gurney's Pitta *Pitta gurneyi*	Myanmar, Thailand	(s086)	F	CR	18
Ivory-breasted Pitta *Pitta maxima*	Indonesia	171	F	lc	—
Superb Pitta *Pitta superba*	Papua New Guinea	193	F	VU	8
Azure-breasted Pitta *Pitta steerii*	Philippines	154	F	VU	1
Whiskered Pitta *Pitta kochi*	Philippines	151	F	VU	12
Black-crowned Pitta *Pitta venusta* *	Indonesia	158	F	NE	—
Rainbow Pitta *Pitta iris*	Australia	187	FS	lc	—
Black-faced Pitta *Pitta anerythra*	Papua New Guinea, Solomon Is.	198	F	VU	15

Family ACANTHISITTIDAE: New Zealand wrens

South Island Rock Wren *Xenicus gilviventris*	New Zealand	207	SR	nt	—
Stephens Island Wren *Xenicus lyalli*	New Zealand[X]	207[X]	R	EX	—

Family PHILEPITTIDAE: Asities

Schlegel's Asity *Philepitta schlegeli*	Madagascar	093,094	F	nt	—
Yellow-bellied Asity *Neodrepanis hypoxanthus*	Madagascar	094	F	EN	1

Family MENURIDAE: Lyrebirds

Albert's Lyrebird *Menura alberti*	Australia	183	F	nt	—

Family ATRICHORNITHIDAE: Scrub-birds

Rufous Scrub-bird *Atrichornis rufescens*	Australia	183	F	VU	1
Noisy Scrub-bird *Atrichornis clamosus*	Australia	186	FS	VU	8

Family ALAUDIDAE: Larks

Williams's Lark *Mirafra williamsi*	Kenya	(s061)	G	nt	—
Ash's Lark *Mirafra ashi*	Somalia	112	G	EN	18
Degodi Lark *Mirafra degodiensis*	Ethiopia	113	S	VU	18
Archer's Lark *Heteromirafra archeri*	Somalia	(s064)	G	EN	18
Sidamo Lark *Heteromirafra sidamoensis*	Ethiopia	114	SG	EN	18
Rudd's Lark *Heteromirafra ruddi*	South Africa	091	G	CR	1
Dune Lark *Certhilauda erythrochlamys*	Namibia	(s046)	SD	lc	—
Red Lark *Certhilauda burra*	Namibia, South Africa	(s047)	G	VU	1
Obbia Lark *Spizocorys obbiensis*	Somalia	112	G	nt	—
Botha's Lark *Spizocorys fringillaris*	South Africa	091	G	VU	1
Raso Lark *Alauda razae*	Cape Verde	078	R	EN	8

Family HIRUNDINIDAE: Swallows, martins

White-eyed River-martin *Pseudochelidon sirintarae*	Thailand	See p. 724	W	CR	08
Bahama Swallow *Tachycineta cyaneoviridis*	Bahamas	026	FWA	nt	—
Golden Swallow *Tachycineta euchrysea*	Dominican Republic, Haiti, Jamaica	027,028	FA	nt	—
Black-capped Swallow *Notiochelidon pileata*	El Salvador, Guatemala, Mexico	018	FA	lc	—
White-tailed Swallow *Hirundo megaensis*	Ethiopia	114	SG	VU	1
Red Sea Swallow *Hirundo perdita*	Sudan	(s066)	Z	VU	08
Forest Swallow *Hirundo fuliginosa*	Cameroon, Gabon, Nigeria	085	F	lc	—
Mountain Sawwing *Psalidoprocne fuliginosa*	Cameroon, Equatorial Guinea, Nigeria	086	FGA	nt	—

Family MOTACILLIDAE: Wagtails, pipits

Sharpe's Longclaw *Macronyx sharpei*	Kenya	109	G	nt	—
Yellow-breasted Pipit *Anthus chloris*	Lesotho, South Africa	091	G	VU	1
Mountain Pipit *Anthus hoeschi*	Lesotho, South Africa	090	G	nt	—
Long-tailed Pipit *Anthus longicaudatus* *	South Africa	See p. 724		NE	—

	Breeding range	EBAs (and SAs)	Habitat codes	Status	Threat codes
Berthelot's Pipit *Anthus berthelotii*	Portugal, Spain	120	RA	lc	—
Sokoke Pipit *Anthus sokokensis*	Kenya, Tanzania	111	F	VU	1
Nilgiri Pipit *Anthus nilghiriensis*	India	123	G	lc	—
South Georgia Pipit *Anthus antarcticus*	South Georgia (to UK)	(s037)	G	lc	—
Alpine Pipit *Anthus gutturalis*	Indonesia, Papua New Guinea	177,178	GW	lc	—

Family CAMPEPHAGIDAE: Cuckoo-shrikes

Slaty Cuckoo-shrike *Coracina schistacea*	Indonesia	168	F	lc	—
Moluccan Cuckoo-shrike *Coracina atriceps*	Indonesia	170,171	F	lc	—
Buru Cuckoo-shrike *Coracina fortis*	Indonesia	169	F	VU	1
Melanesian Cuckoo-shrike *Coracina caledonica*	New Caledonia (to France), Papua New Guinea, Solomon Islands, Vanuatu	198,200,201	FV	lc	—
Cerulean Cuckoo-shrike *Coracina temminckii*	Indonesia	166	F	lc	—
Pied Cuckoo-shrike *Coracina bicolor*	Indonesia	166,167	FS	nt	—
Halmahera Cuckoo-shrike *Coracina parvula*	Indonesia	171	F	lc	—
Pygmy Cuckoo-shrike *Coracina abbotti*	Indonesia	166	F	lc	—
New Caledonian Cuckoo-shrike *Coracina analis*	New Caledonia (to France)	201	F	lc	—
Grauer's Cuckoo-shrike *Coracina graueri*	Zaïre	106	F	nt	—
Mauritius Cuckoo-shrike *Coracina typica*	Mauritius	102	F	VU	158
Réunion Cuckoo-shrike *Coracina newtoni*	Réunion (to France)	101	FS	EN	1258
Blackish Cuckoo-shrike *Coracina coerulescens*	Philippines	151,153[X]	F	nt	—
Sumba Cicadabird *Coracina dohertyi*	Indonesia	162,163	F	nt	—
Sula Cicadabird *Coracina sula*	Indonesia	168	FA	lc	—
Kai Cicadabird *Coracina dispar*	Indonesia	165	F	nt	—
Pale Cicadabird *Coracina ceramensis*	Indonesia	169,170,171	FS	lc	—
Solomon Islands Cuckoo-shrike *Coracina holopolia*	Papua New Guinea, Solomon Is.	198	F	lc	—
McGregor's Cuckoo-shrike *Coracina mcgregori*	Philippines	154	F	VU	1
White-winged Cuckoo-shrike *Coracina ostenta*	Philippines	152	F	VU	1
Rufous-bellied Triller *Lalage aurea*	Indonesia	171	FSA	lc	—
Polynesian Triller *Lalage maculosa*	Fiji, Niue (to New Zealand), Solomon Is., Tonga, Wallis and Futuna Is. (to France), Western Samoa, Vanuatu	200,202,203 (s127, s128,s130,s131)	FS	lc	—
Samoan Triller *Lalage sharpei*	Western Samoa	203	F	nt	—
Long-tailed Triller *Lalage leucopyga*	New Caledonia (to France), Norfolk I.[X], Solomon Is., Vanuatu	198,200,201,205[X]	FSVX	lc	—
Western Wattled Cuckoo-shrike *Campephaga lobata*	Ghana, Guinea, Ivory Coast, Liberia, Sierra Leone	084	FX	VU	1
Ryukyu Minivet *Pericrocotus tegimae*	Japan	148	FS	lc	—
Flores Minivet *Pericrocotus lansbergei*	Indonesia	162	F	lc	—
Sunda Minivet *Pericrocotus miniatus*	Indonesia	158,160	FX	lc	—
Black-breasted Fruit-hunter *Chlamydochaera jefferyi*	Indonesia, Malaysia	157	F	lc	—

Family PYCNONOTIDAE: Bulbuls

Cream-striped Bulbul *Pycnonotus leucogrammicus*	Indonesia	158	FX	lc	—
Spot-necked Bulbul *Pycnonotus tympanistrigus*	Indonesia	158	F	VU	1
Grey-headed Bulbul *Pycnonotus priocephalus*	India	123	FS	nt	—
Styan's Bulbul *Pycnonotus taivanus*	Taiwan	149	FSA	nt	—
Blue-wattled Bulbul *Pycnonotus nieuwenhuisii*	Brunei, Indonesia	157,158	FS	DD	—
Orange-spotted Bulbul *Pycnonotus bimaculatus*	Indonesia	158,160	FSX	lc	—
Yellow-throated Bulbul *Pycnonotus xantholaemus*	India	(s072)	FS	nt	—
Yellow-eared Bulbul *Pycnonotus penicillatus*	Sri Lanka	124	FS	nt	—
Cameroon Greenbul *Andropadus montanus*	Cameroon, Nigeria	086	F	nt	—
Grey-throated Greenbul *Andropadus tephrolaemus*	Cameroon, Equatorial Guinea, Nigeria	086	F	lc	—
Green-throated Greenbul *Andropadus chlorigula*	Tanzania	105	F	lc	—
Prigogine's Greenbul *Chlorocichla prigoginei*	Zaïre	106	F	VU	1
Cameroon Olive Greenbul *Phyllastrephus poensis*	Cameroon, Equatorial Guinea, Nigeria	086	F	lc	—
Sassi's Greenbul *Phyllastrephus lorenzi*	Uganda, Zaïre	107	F	nt	—
Grey-headed Greenbul *Phyllastrephus poliocephalus*	Cameroon, Nigeria	086	F	nt	—
Sharpe's Greenbul *Phyllastrephus alfredi*	Malawi, Tanzania, Zambia	105	F	lc	—
Liberian Greenbul *Phyllastrephus leucolepis*	Liberia	084	F	CR	18
Appert's Greenbul *Phyllastrephus apperti*	Madagascar	093	F	VU	18
Dusky Greenbul *Phyllastrephus tenebrosus*	Madagascar	094	F	EN	1
Grey-crowned Greenbul *Phyllastrephus cinereiceps*	Madagascar	094	F	VU	1

	Breeding range	EBAs (and SAs)	Habitat codes	Status	Threat codes
Green-tailed Bristlebill *Bleda eximia*	Ghana, Guinea, Ivory Coast, Liberia, Sierra Leone	084	F	VU	1
Yellow-throated Olive Greenbul *Criniger olivaceus*	Ghana, Guinea, Ivory Coast, Liberia, Sierra Leone	084	F	VU	1
Sulphur-bellied Bulbul *Ixos palawanensis*	Philippines	156	F	lc	—
Zamboanga Bulbul *Ixos rufigularis*	Philippines	154	F	lc	—
Streak-breasted Bulbul *Ixos siquijorensis*	Philippines	153[X] (s095,s096)	FS	EN	1
Yellowish Bulbul *Ixos everetti*	Philippines	154,155	F	nt	—
Green-winged Bulbul *Hypsipetes virescens*	Indonesia	158,160	FS	lc	—
Seychelles Bulbul *Hypsipetes crassirostris*	Seychelles	100	F	lc	—
Comoro Bulbul *Hypsipetes parvirostris*	Comoros	098	F	lc	—
Olivaceous Bulbul *Hypsipetes borbonicus* *	Réunion (to France)	101	F	lc	—
Mauritius Bulbul *Hypsipetes olivaceus* *	Mauritius	102	F	VU	158
Nicobar Bulbul *Hypsipetes nicobariensis*	India	126	F	VU	5

Family IRENIDAE: Leafbirds, fairy-bluebirds

Philippine Leafbird *Chloropsis flavipennis*	Philippines	153[X],154	F	EN	1
Yellow-throated Leafbird *Chloropsis palawanensis*	Philippines	156	FS	lc	—
Blue-masked Leafbird *Chloropsis venusta*	Indonesia	158	F	nt	—

Family LANIIDAE: Shrikes

Mountain Shrike *Lanius validirostris*	Philippines	150,151,152,154	FS	nt	—
São Tomé Fiscal *Lanius newtoni*	São Tomé e Príncipe	082	F	CR	18
Uhehe Fiscal *Lanius marwitzi*	Tanzania	105	GA	lc	—
Orange-breasted Bush-shrike *Laniarius brauni*	Angola	087	F	EN	18
Gabela Bush-shrike *Laniarius amboimensis*	Angola	087	F	EN	18
Bulo Burti Bush-shrike *Laniarius liberatus*	Somalia	113	FS	CR	18
Yellow-breasted Boubou *Laniarius atroflavus*	Cameroon, Nigeria	086	FS	lc	—
Fuelleborn's Boubou *Laniarius fuelleborni*	Malawi, Tanzania, Zambia	105	FA	lc	—
Mount Kupe Bush-shrike *Telophorus kupeensis*	Cameroon	086	F	CR	8
Green-breasted Bush-shrike *Malaconotus gladiator*	Cameroon, Nigeria	086	F	VU	1
Monteiro's Bush-shrike *Malaconotus monteiri*	Angola, Cameroon	086,087	F	EN	18
Uluguru Bush-shrike *Malaconotus alius*	Tanzania	105	F	CR	18
Grey-crested Helmet-shrike *Prionops poliolophus*	Kenya, Tanzania	108	FSG	VU	1
Yellow-crested Helmet-shrike *Prionops alberti*	Zaïre	106	F	VU	1
Gabela Helmet-shrike *Prionops gabela*	Angola	087	FSA	EN	18

Family VANGIDAE: Vangas

Red-shouldered Vanga *Calicalicus rufocarpalis* *	Madagascar	097	S	NE	—
Lafresnaye's Vanga *Xenopirostris xenopirostris*	Madagascar	097	S	lc	—
Van Dam's Vanga *Xenopirostris damii*	Madagascar	093	F	VU	18
Pollen's Vanga *Xenopirostris polleni*	Madagascar	094	F	VU	1
Bernier's Vanga *Oriolia bernieri*	Madagascar	094	F	VU	1
Helmet Vanga *Euryceros prevostii*	Madagascar	094	F	nt	—
Nuthatch Vanga *Hypositta corallirostris*	Madagascar	094	F	lc	—

Family BOMBYCILLIDAE: Waxwings

Long-tailed Silky-flycatcher *Ptilogonys caudatus*	Costa Rica, Panama	020	F	lc	—
Black-and-yellow Silky-flycatcher *Phainoptila melanoxantha*	Costa Rica, Panama	020	F	lc	—

Family DULIDAE: Palmchats

Palmchat *Dulus dominicus*	Dominican Republic, Haiti	028	FVA	lc	—

Family CINCLIDAE: Dippers

Rufous-throated Dipper *Cinclus schulzi*	Argentina, Bolivia	057	W	VU	14

Family TROGLODYTIDAE: Wrens

Yucatán Wren *Campylorhynchus yucatanicus*	Mexico	015	S	lc	—
Giant Wren *Campylorhynchus chiapensis*	Mexico	017	FSA	lc	—
Grey-barred Wren *Campylorhynchus megalopterus*	Mexico	006,012	F	lc	—
Sumichrast's Wren *Hylorchilus sumichrasti* *	Mexico	(s006)	F	VU	1
Nava's Wren *Hylorchilus navai* *	Mexico	013	F	VU	1
Apolinar's Wren *Cistothorus apolinari*	Colombia	038	GW	EN	18
Mérida Wren *Cistothorus meridae*	Venezuela	034	SGW	lc	—
Socorro Wren *Thryomanes sissonii*	Mexico	004	FS	nt	—
Zapata Wren *Ferminia cerverai*	Cuba	025	VW	CR	158
Black-throated Wren *Thryothorus atrogularis*	Costa Rica, Nicaragua, Panama	019	F	lc	—
Inca Wren *Thryothorus eisenmanni*	Peru	055	F	lc	—
Riverside Wren *Thryothorus semibadius*	Costa Rica, Panama	021	F	lc	—
Niceforo's Wren *Thryothorus nicefori*	Colombia	038	S	CR	18
Superciliated Wren *Thryothorus superciliaris*	Ecuador, Peru	045	FS	lc	—

	Breeding range	EBAs (and SAs)	Habitat codes	Status	Threat codes
Cobb's Wren *Troglodytes cobbi* *	Falkland Islands (to UK)	062	G	VU	158
Clarión Wren *Troglodytes tanneri*	Mexico	(s008)	SR	VU	8
Rufous-browed Wren *Troglodytes rufociliatus*	El Salvador, Guatemala, Honduras, Mexico	018	F	lc	—
Ochraceous Wren *Troglodytes ochraceus*	Costa Rica, Panama	020	F	lc	—
Santa Marta Wren *Troglodytes monticola*	Colombia	036	FSG	lc	—
Tepui Wren *Troglodytes rufulus*	Brazil, Venezuela	064	FSV	lc	—
Timberline Wren *Thryorchilus browni*	Costa Rica, Panama	020	F	lc	—
Bar-winged Wood-wren *Henicorhina leucoptera*	Ecuador, Peru	047,049	F	nt	—
Flutist Wren *Microcerculus ustulatus*	Brazil, Guyana, Venezuela	064	F	lc	—
Family MIMIDAE: Thrashers, mockingbirds					
Blue-and-white Mockingbird *Melanotis hypoleucus*	El Salvador, Guatemala, Honduras, Mexico	018	FS	lc	—
Bahama Mockingbird *Mimus gundlachii*	Bahamas, Cuba, Jamaica, Turks and Caicos Is. (to UK)	025,026,027	FS	lc	—
Chilean Mockingbird *Mimus thenca*	Chile	060	S	lc	—
Galápagos Mockingbird *Nesomimus parvulus*	Ecuador	031	FSG	lc	—
Floreana Mockingbird *Nesomimus trifasciatus*	Ecuador	031	FSG	EN	78
Hood Mockingbird *Nesomimus macdonaldi*	Ecuador	031	FSG	lc	—
San Cristóbal Mockingbird *Nesomimus melanotis*	Ecuador	031	FSG	lc	—
Socorro Mockingbird *Mimodes graysoni*	Mexico	004	FS	EN	158
Cozumel Thrasher *Toxostoma guttatum*	Mexico	016	F	nt	—
California Thrasher *Toxostoma redivivum*	Mexico, USA	001	S	lc	—
Brown Trembler *Cinclocerthia ruficauda*	Caribbean[6] (see p. 679)	030	F	lc	—
Grey Trembler *Cinclocerthia gutturalis*	Martinique (to France), St Lucia	030	F	lc	—
White-breasted Thrasher *Ramphocinclus brachyurus*	Martinique (to France), St Lucia	030	F	EN	158
Scaly-breasted Thrasher *Margarops fuscus*	Caribbean[7] (see p. 679)	030	F	lc	—
Pearly-eyed Thrasher *Margarops fuscatus*	Caribbean[8] (see p. 679)	026,028,029,030 (s015)	FS	lc	—
Family PRUNELLIDAE: Accentors					
Yemen Accentor *Prunella fagani*	Sauda Arabia, Yemen	118	SR	nt	—
Mongolian Accentor *Prunella koslowi*	Mongolia	(s077)	SR	lc	—
Subfamily TURDINAE: Thrushes, robins, chats					
Greater Ground-robin *Amalocichla sclateriana*	Indonesia, Papua New Guinea	178	F	lc	—
Rufous Rockjumper *Chaetops frenatus*	South Africa	088	R	nt	—
Orange-breasted Rockjumper *Chaetops aurantius*	Lesotho, South Africa	090	SGR	nt	—
Forest Rock-thrush *Monticola sharpei*	Madagascar	094	F	nt	—
Benson's Rock-thrush *Monticola bensoni*	Madagascar	093,094 (s049)	FS	VU	18
Littoral Rock-thrush *Monticola imerinus*	Madagascar	097	S	lc	—
Sri Lanka Whistling-thrush *Myiophonus blighi*	Sri Lanka	124	FR	EN	18
Shiny Whistling-thrush *Myiophonus melanurus*	Indonesia	158	F	lc	—
Malayan Whistling-thrush *Myiophonus robinsoni*	Malaysia	158	F	nt	—
Formosan Whistling-thrush *Myiophonus insularis*	Taiwan	149	F	lc	—
Geomalia *Geomalia heinrichi*	Indonesia	166	F	nt	—
Slaty-backed Thrush *Zoothera schistacea*	Indonesia	165	F	nt	—
Moluccan Thrush *Zoothera dumasi*	Indonesia	169,170	F	DD	—
Red-backed Thrush *Zoothera erythronota*	Indonesia	166,168	F	nt	—
Chestnut-backed Thrush *Zoothera dohertyi*	Indonesia	162,163,164	F	lc	—
Ashy Thrush *Zoothera cinerea*	Philippines	150,151	F	VU	12
Orange-banded Thrush *Zoothera peronii*	Indonesia	164,165	F	nt	—
Everett's Thrush *Zoothera everetti*	Malaysia	157	F	nt	—
Kivu Ground-thrush *Zoothera tanganjicae*	Burundi, Rwanda, Uganda, Zaïre	106	F	nt	—
Forest Ground-thrush *Zoothera oberlaenderi*	Uganda, Zaïre	107	F	nt	—
Spot-winged Thrush *Zoothera spiloptera*	Sri Lanka	124	FX	nt	—
Amami Thrush *Zoothera major*	Japan	148	F	CR	18
Fawn-breasted Thrush *Zoothera machiki*	Indonesia	165	FS	nt	—
New Britain Thrush *Zoothera talaseae*	Papua New Guinea	195,198	F	nt	—
Makira Thrush *Zoothera margaretae*	Solomon Islands	198	F	nt	—
Bonin Thrush *Zoothera terrestris*	Japan[X]	147[X]	F	EX	—
Sulawesi Thrush *Cataponera turdoides*	Indonesia	166	F	lc	—
Tristan Thrush *Nesocichla eremita*	St Helena (to UK)	079	FSGR	nt	—
Forest Thrush *Cichlherminia lherminieri*	Dominica, Guadeloupe (to France), Montserrat (to UK), St Lucia	030	F	nt	—
Kama'o *Myadestes myadestinus*	USA	217	F	CR	58
'Amaui *Myadestes oahensis*	USA[X]	217[X]	F	EX	—

	Breeding range	EBAs (and SAs)	Habitat codes	Status	Threat codes
Oloma'o *Myadestes lanaiensis*	USA	217	F	CR	58
'Oma'o *Myadestes obscurus*	USA	218	FS	lc	—
Puaiohi *Myadestes palmeri*	USA	217	F	CR	578
Rufous-throated Solitaire *Myadestes genibarbis*	Dominica, Dominican Republic, Haiti, Jamaica, Martinique (to France), St Lucia, St Vincent	027,028,030	F	lc	—
Black-faced Solitaire *Myadestes melanops*	Costa Rica, Panama	020	F	lc	—
Varied Solitaire *Myadestes coloratus*	Colombia, Panama	024	F	lc	—
Black Solitaire *Entomodestes coracinus*	Colombia, Ecuador	041	F	lc	—
Black-billed Nightingale-thrush *Catharus gracilirostris*	Costa Rica, Panama	020	F	lc	—
São Tomé Thrush *Turdus olivaceofuscus*	São Tomé e Príncipe	082,083	FVX	nt	—
Somali Thrush *Turdus ludoviciae* *	Somalia	116	F	EN	1
Taita Thrush *Turdus helleri* *	Kenya	105	F	CR	18
Yemen Thrush *Turdus menachensis*	Sauda Arabia, Yemen	118	FSRA	VU	1
Comoro Thrush *Turdus bewsheri*	Comoros	098	FX	lc	—
Grey-sided Thrush *Turdus feae*	China	136	F	VU	1
Izu Thrush *Turdus celaenops*	Japan	146	FX	VU	5
White-chinned Thrush *Turdus aurantius*	Jamaica	027	FAX	lc	—
Grand Cayman Thrush *Turdus ravidus*	Cayman Islands (to UK)ˣ	(s014ˣ)	FS	EX	—
Sooty Thrush *Turdus nigrescens*	Costa Rica, Panama	020	FSG	lc	—
Plumbeous-backed Thrush *Turdus reevei*	Ecuador, Peru	045	FS	lc	—
Marañon Thrush *Turdus maranonicus*	Peru	048	FS	lc	—
Ecuadorian Thrush *Turdus maculirostris*	Ecuador, Peru	045	F	lc	—
White-eyed Thrush *Turdus jamaicensis*	Jamaica	027	F	lc	—
Grayson's Thrush *Turdus graysoni*	Mexico	005	FX	nt	—
La Selle Thrush *Turdus swalesi*	Dominican Republic, Haiti	028	F	VU	1
Rufous-collared Robin *Turdus rufitorques*	El Salvador, Guatemala, Honduras, Mexico	018	FA	lc	—
Rusty-bellied Shortwing *Brachypteryx hyperythra*	China, India	130	F	VU	1
White-bellied Shortwing *Brachypteryx major*	India	123	F	nt	—
Great Shortwing *Heinrichia calligyna*	Indonesia	166	F	lc	—
Red-throated Alethe *Alethe poliophrys*	Burundi, Rwanda, Uganda, Zaïre	106	F	lc	—
Thyolo Alethe *Alethe choloensis*	Malawi, Mozambique	105	F	VU	1
Swynnerton's Robin *Swynnertonia swynnertoni*	Mozambique, Tanzania, Zimbabwe	104,105	F	VU	1
Sharpe's Akalat *Sheppardia sharpei*	Malawi, Tanzania, Zambia	105	F	lc	—
Gabela Akalat *Sheppardia gabela*	Angola	087	F	EN	18
Usambara Akalat *Sheppardia montana*	Tanzania	105	F	VU	1
Iringa Akalat *Sheppardia lowei*	Tanzania	105	F	VU	1
Ryukyu Robin *Erithacus komadori*	Japan	148	F	nt	—
Rufous-headed Robin *Luscinia ruficeps*	China	137	F	VU	1
Black-throated Blue Robin *Luscinia obscura*	China	137	FS	VU	1
Collared Bush-robin *Tarsiger johnstoniae*	Taiwan	149	FS	lc	—
Mountain Robin-chat *Cossypha isabellae*	Cameroon, Nigeria	086	F	lc	—
Archer's Robin-chat *Cossypha archeri*	Burundi, Rwanda, Uganda, Zaïre	106	FS	lc	—
Chorister Robin-chat *Cossypha dichroa*	South Africa, Swaziland	089	F	lc	—
White-headed Robin-chat *Cossypha heinrichi*	Angola, Zaïre	(s044)	F	VU	1
Angola Cave-chat *Xenocopsychus ansorgei*	Angola	087	R	nt	—
Brown Scrub-robin *Cercotrichas signata*	Mozambique, South Africa	089	F	lc	—
Herero Chat *Namibornis herero*	Angola, Namibia	(s045)	SR	nt	—
Seychelles Magpie-robin *Copsychus sechellarum*	Seychelles	100	FX	CR	8
White-vented Shama *Copsychus niger*	Philippines	156	FS	lc	—
Black Shama *Copsychus cebuensis*	Philippines	153	FSX	EN	18
Ala Shan Redstart *Phoenicurus alaschanicus*	China	135	SR	nt	—
Luzon Water-redstart *Rhyacornis bicolor*	Philippines	150,151	F	EN	124
Sunda Robin *Cinclidium diana*	Indonesia	158,160	F	lc	—
Sunda Forktail *Enicurus velatus*	Indonesia	158,160	F	lc	—
Sumatran Cochoa *Cochoa beccarii*	Indonesia	158	F	VU	1
Javan Cochoa *Cochoa azurea*	Indonesia	160	F	VU	16
Fuerteventura Chat *Saxicola dacotiae*	Spain	120	SRA	nt	—
Réunion Stonechat *Saxicola tectes*	Réunion (to France)	101	F	lc	—
White-bellied Bushchat *Saxicola gutturalis*	Indonesia	164	F	nt	—
Cyprus Wheatear *Oenanthe cypriaca*	Cyprus	121	FAX	lc	—
Sombre Chat *Cercomela dubia*	Ethiopia, Somalia	(s063)	SR	nt	—
Rüppell's Chat *Myrmecocichla melaena*	Eritrea, Ethiopia	115	R	lc	—
Spot-throat *Modulatrix stictigula*	Malawi, Tanzania	105	F	lc	—
Dappled Mountain robin *Modulatrix orostruthus*	Mozambique, Tanzania	105	F	VU	1

	Breeding range	EBAs (and SAs)	Habitat codes	Status	Threat codes
Chowchilla *Orthonyx spaldingii*	Australia	182	F	lc	—
Papuan Whipbird *Androphobus viridis*	Indonesia, Papua New Guinea	178	F	DD	—
Western Whipbird *Psophodes nigrogularis*	Australia	184,186	S	VU	15
Painted Quail-thrush *Cinclosoma ajax*	Indonesia, Papua New Guinea	172,179,180 (s114)	F	lc	—
Greater Melampitta *Melampitta gigantea*	Indonesia, Papua New Guinea	173,175,178	F	lc	—
Subfamily TIMALIINAE: Babblers					
Dohrn's Thrush-babbler *Horizorhinus dohrni*	São Tomé e Príncipe	083	FX	lc	—
Malia *Malia grata*	Indonesia	166	F	lc	—
Ashy-headed Laughingthrush *Garrulax cinereifrons*	Sri Lanka	124	F	VU	1
Sunda Laughingthrush *Garrulax palliatus*	Brunei, Indonesia, Malaysia	157,158	F	lc	—
Rufous-fronted Laughingthrush *Garrulax rufifrons*	Indonesia	160	F	nt	—
Black Laughingthrush *Garrulax lugubris*	Indonesia, Malaysia	158	F	lc	—
Bare-headed Laughingthrush *Garrulax calvus*	Malaysia	157	F	lc	—
Black-hooded Laughingthrush *Garrulax milleti*	Vietnam	145	F	VU	1
Chestnut-backed Laughingthrush *Garrulax nuchalis*	India, Myanmar	(s079)	FSG	nt	—
White-cheeked Laughingthrush *Garrulax vassali*	Laos, Vietnam	143,145 (s083, s084)	FSG	lc	—
Wynaad Laughingthrush *Garrulax delesserti*	India	123	FS	nt	—
Snowy-cheeked Laughingthrush *Garrulax sukatschewi*	China	137	F	VU	1
Barred Laughingthrush *Garrulax lunulatus*	China	137	F	nt	—
White-speckled Laughingthrush *Garrulax bieti*	China	139	F	VU	1
Rufous-breasted Laughingthrush *Garrulax cachinnans*	India	123	FS	nt	—
Grey-breasted Laughingthrush *Garrulax jerdoni*	India	123	FS	nt	—
Striped Laughingthrush *Garrulax virgatus*	India, Myanmar	130	FS	nt	—
Brown-capped Laughingthrush *Garrulax austeni*	India, Myanmar	130	F	DD	—
White-whiskered Laughingthrush *G. morrisonianus*	Taiwan	149	FS	lc	—
Collared Laughingthrush *Garrulax yersini*	Vietnam	145	F	VU	1
Red-winged Laughingthrush *Garrulax formosus*	China, Vietnam	137 (s082)	F	nt	—
Omei Shan Liocichla *Liocichla omeiensis*	China	140	F	VU	16
Steere's Liocichla *Liocichla steerii*	Taiwan	149	F	lc	—
Bagobo Babbler *Trichastoma woodi*	Philippines	154	F	VU	1
Black-browed Babbler *Malacocincla perspicillata*	Indonesia	(s099)	F	VU	18
Ashy-headed Babbler *Malacocincla cinereiceps*	Philippines	156	FS	lc	—
Marsh Babbler *Pellorneum palustre*	Bangladesh, India	131	SGW	VU	1
Brown-capped Babbler *Pellorneum fuscocapillum*	Sri Lanka	124	FSX	lc	—
Melodious Babbler *Malacopteron palawanense*	Philippines	156	F	EN	1
Rufous-winged Illadopsis *Illadopsis rufescens*	Ghana, Guinea, Ivory Coast, Liberia, Sierra Leone	084	F	nt	—
Short-tailed Scimitar-babbler *Jabouilleia danjoui*	Laos, Vietnam	143,145	F	VU	1
Striated Wren-babbler *Ptilocichla mindanensis*	Philippines	154	FS	nt	—
Falcated Wren-babbler *Ptilocichla falcata*	Philippines	156	F	EN	1
Rusty-breasted Wren-babbler *Napothera rufipectus*	Indonesia	158	F	lc	—
Marbled Wren-babbler *Napothera marmorata*	Indonesia, Malaysia	158	F	nt	—
Mountain Wren-babbler *Napothera crassa*	Indonesia, Malaysia	157	F	lc	—
Rabor's Wren-babbler *Napothera rabori*	Philippines	151	F	VU	1
Nepal Wren-babbler *Pnoepyga immaculata*	Nepal	129	F	nt	—
Rufous-throated Wren-babbler *Spelaeornis caudatus*	Bhutan, India, Nepal	130	F	VU	1
Rusty-throated Wren-babbler *Spelaeornis badeigularis*	India	130	F	VU	18
Tawny-breasted Wren-babbler *S. longicaudatus*	India	130	F	VU	1
Wedge-billed Wren-babbler *Sphenocichla humei*	China, India, Myanmar	130	F	nt	—
Wedge-tailed Jery *Hartertula flavoviridis*	Madagascar	094	F	nt	—
Deignan's Babbler *Stachyris rodolphei*	Thailand	(s081)	F	VU	8
Pygmy Babbler *Stachyris plateni*	Philippines	154	F	nt	—
Golden-crowned Babbler *Stachyris dennistouni*	Philippines	151	F	nt	—
Rusty-crowned Babbler *Stachyris capitalis*	Philippines	154	F	nt	—
Flame-templed Babbler *Stachyris speciosa*	Philippines	152	F	EN	1
Chestnut-faced Babbler *Stachyris whiteheadi*	Philippines	151	FS	nt	—
Luzon Striped-babbler *Stachyris striata*	Philippines	151	F	VU	1
Panay Striped-babbler *Stachyris latistriata*	Philippines	152	F	VU	1
Negros Striped-babbler *Stachyris nigrorum*	Philippines	152	F	EN	1
Palawan Striped-babbler *Stachyris hypogrammica*	Philippines	156	F	VU	8
White-breasted Babbler *Stachyris grammiceps*	Indonesia	160	F	VU	1
Sooty Babbler *Stachyris herberti*	Laos, Vietnam	143	F	VU	1
Snowy-throated Babbler *Stachyris oglei*	India	130	FSR	VU	1
White-bibbed Babbler *Stachyris thoracica*	Indonesia	160	F	lc	—
Crescent-chested Babbler *Stachyris melanothorax*	Indonesia	160	F	lc	—
Grey-cheeked Tit-babbler *Macronous flavicollis*	Indonesia	160 (s109)	FS	lc	—

	Breeding range	EBAs (and SAs)	Habitat codes	Status	Threat codes
Grey-faced Tit-babbler *Macronous kelleyi*	Laos, Vietnam	143,144 (s083, s084)	F	nt	—
Miniature Tit-babbler *Micromacronus leytensis*	Philippines	154	F	VU	1
Spiny Babbler *Turdoides nipalensis*	Nepal	129	S	lc	—
Iraq Babbler *Turdoides altirostris*	Iran, Iraq	119	WAX	nt	—
White-throated Babbler *Turdoides gularis*	Myanmar	132	SA	lc	—
Rufous Babbler *Turdoides subrufus*	India	123	FS	lc	—
Orange-billed Babbler *Turdoides rufescens*	Sri Lanka	124	FS	lc	—
Hinde's Pied-babbler *Turdoides hindei*	Kenya	109	FS	EN	18
Giant Babax *Babax waddelli*	China, India	133	FS	nt	—
Tibetan Babax *Babax koslowi*	China	134	FS	nt	—
Hoary-throated Barwing *Actinodura nipalensis*	Bhutan, China, India, Nepal	129,130	F	lc	—
Streak-throated Barwing *Actinodura waldeni*	China, India, Myanmar	130	F	lc	—
Formosan Barwing *Actinodura morrisoniana*	Taiwan	149	F	lc	—
Gold-fronted Fulvetta *Alcippe variegaticeps*	China	140	F	VU	1
Ludlow's Fulvetta *Alcippe ludlowi*	Bhutan, China, India	130	F	lc	—
Javan Fulvetta *Alcippe pyrrhoptera*	Indonesia	160	F	lc	—
Bush Blackcap *Lioptilus nigricapillus*	South Africa	089	FS	nt	—
White-throated Mountain-babbler *Kupeornis gilberti*	Cameroon, Nigeria	086	F	VU	1
Red-collared Mountain-babbler *Kupeornis rufocinctus*	Burundi, Rwanda, Zaïre	106	F	nt	—
Chapin's Mountain-babbler *Kupeornis chapini*	Zaïre	106	F	nt	—
Grey-crowned Crocias *Crocias langbianis*	Vietnam	145	F	CR	18
Spotted Crocias *Crocias albonotatus*	Indonesia	160	F	nt	—
Grey Sibia *Heterophasia gracilis*	China, India, Myanmar	130	F	nt	—
White-eared Sibia *Heterophasia auricularis*	Taiwan	149	F	lc	—
Beautiful Sibia *Heterophasia pulchella*	China, India, Myanmar	130	F	lc	—
Chestnut-crested Yuhina *Yuhina everetti*	Indonesia, Malaysia	157	F	lc	—
White-naped Yuhina *Yuhina bakeri*	Bangladesh, Bhutan, China, India, Myanmar, Nepal	130	F	lc	—
Burmese Yuhina *Yuhina humilis*	Myanmar, Thailand	(s080)	F	nt	—
Formosan Yuhina *Yuhina brunneiceps*	Taiwan	149	F	lc	—
Madagascar Yellowbrow *Crossleyia xanthophrys*	Madagascar	094	F	VU	1
Subfamily PANURINAE: Parrotbills					
Three-toed Parrotbill *Paradoxornis paradoxus*	China	137	F	lc	—
Black-breasted Parrotbill *Paradoxornis flavirostris*	Bangladesh, India, Nepal[X]	131	SGW	VU	1
Brown-winged Parrotbill *Paradoxornis brunneus*	China, Myanmar	139	SGA	nt	—
Grey-hooded Parrotbill *Paradoxornis zappeyi*	China	137	F	VU	1
Rusty-throated Parrotbill *Paradoxornis przewalskii*	China	137	F	VU	1
Subfamily PICATHARTINAE: Rockfowl					
White-necked Rockfowl *Picathartes gymnocephalus*	Ghana, Guinea, Ivory Coast, Liberia, Sierra Leone	084	F	VU	126
Grey-necked Rockfowl *Picathartes oreas*	Cameroon, Equatorial Guinea, Gabon, Nigeria	085,086	FR	VU	12
Subfamily POLIOPTILINAE: Gnatcatchers					
Cuban Gnatcatcher *Polioptila lembeyei*	Cuba	025	S	nt	—
Subfamily SYLVIINAE: Old world Warblers					
Canary Islands Kinglet *Regulus teneriffae*	Spain	120	F	lc	—
Flamecrest *Regulus goodfellowi*	Taiwan	149	F	lc	—
Brown-backed Cisticola *Cisticola discolor*	Cameroon, Nigeria	086	SG	lc	—
Hunter's Cisticola *Cisticola hunteri*	Kenya, Tanzania, Uganda	109	S	lc	—
Black-lored Cisticola *Cisticola nigriloris*	Malawi, Tanzania, Zambia	105	FS	lc	—
Tana River Cisticola *Cisticola restrictus*	Kenya	111	S	DD	—
Churring Cisticola *Cisticola njombe*	Malawi, Tanzania, Zambia	105	SG	nt	—
Aberdare Cisticola *Cisticola aberdare*	Kenya	109	G	lc	—
Socotra Cisticola *Cisticola incanus*	Yemen	117	FS	lc	—
Island Cisticola *Cisticola haesitatus*	Yemen	117	SG	VU	8
São Tomé Prinia *Prinia molleri*	São Tomé e Príncipe	082	FVX	lc	—
White-eyed Prinia *Prinia leontica*	Guinea, Ivory Coast, Liberia, Sierra Leone	084	FS	VU	1
Briar Warbler *Prinia robertsi*	Mozambique, Zimbabwe	104	FS	lc	—
Green Longtail *Urolais epichlora*	Cameroon, Equatorial Guinea, Nigeria	086	FGX	lc	—
Collared Apalis *Apalis ruwenzorii*	Burundi, Rwanda, Uganda, Zaïre	106	F	lc	—
Taita Apalis *Apalis fuscigularis* *	Kenya	105	F	CR	18
Namuli Apalis *Apalis lynesi* *	Mozambique	105	F	VU	8

	Breeding range	EBAs (and SAs)	Habitat codes	Status	Threat codes
White-winged Apalis *Apalis chariessa*	Kenya, Malawi, Mozambique, Tanzania	105,111	F	VU	1
Black-faced Apalis *Apalis personata*	Burundi, Rwanda, Uganda, Zaïre	106	F	lc	—
Rudd's Apalis *Apalis ruddi*	Malawi, Mozambique, Swaziland, South Africa	092	F	lc	—
Sharpe's Apalis *Apalis sharpei*	Ghana, Guinea, Ivory Coast, Liberia, Sierra Leone	084	F	lc	—
Kungwe Apalis *Apalis argentea*	Burundi, Rwanda, Tanzania, Zaïre	106	F	VU	1
Bamenda Apalis *Apalis bamendae*	Cameroon	086	F	VU	1
Kabobo Apalis *Apalis kaboboensis*	Zaïre	106	F	DD	—
Chapin's Apalis *Apalis chapini*	Malawi, Tanzania, Zambia	105	F	lc	—
Chirinda Apalis *Apalis chirindensis*	Mozambique, Zimbabwe	104	F	lc	—
Karamoja Apalis *Apalis karamojae*	Tanzania, Uganda	108 (s060)	S	VU	1
Javan Tesia *Tesia superciliaris*	Indonesia	160	F	lc	—
Russet-capped Tesia *Tesia everetti*	Indonesia	162	FA	lc	—
Timor Stubtail *Urosphena subulata*	Indonesia	164,165	FSG	nt	—
Bornean Stubtail *Urosphena whiteheadi*	Indonesia, Malaysia	157	F	lc	—
Philippine Bush-warbler *Cettia seebohmi*	Philippines	151	FA	lc	—
Palau Bush-warbler *Cettia annae*	Palau	190	F	lc	—
Shade Warbler *Cettia parens*	Solomon Islands	198	F	nt	—
Fiji Bush-warbler *Cettia ruficapilla*	Fiji	202	F	lc	—
Tanimbar Bush-warbler *Cettia carolinae*	Indonesia	165	F	nt	—
Dja River Warbler *Bradypterus grandis*	Cameroon, Gabon	085	FGW	DD	—
Grauer's Swamp-warbler *Bradypterus graueri*	Burundi, Rwanda, Uganda, Zaïre	106	W	VU	1
Knysna Scrub-warbler *Bradypterus sylvaticus*	South Africa	089	FS	lc	—
Bangwa Forest Warbler *Bradypterus bangwaensis* *	Cameroon, Nigeria	086	FSGX	nt	—
Victorin's Scrub-warbler *Bradypterus victorini*	South Africa	088	SGR	lc	—
Sri Lanka Bush-warbler *Bradypterus palliseri*	Sri Lanka	124	FS	nt	—
Long-tailed Bush-warbler *Bradypterus caudatus*	Philippines	151,154	F	nt	—
Friendly Bush-warbler *Bradypterus accentor*	Malaysia	157	F	lc	—
Chestnut-backed Bush-warbler *Bradypterus castaneus*	Indonesia	166,169,170	FG	lc	—
Brown Emu-tail *Dromaeocercus brunneus*	Madagascar	094	F	nt	—
Black-capped Rufous Warbler *Bathmocercus cerviniventris*	Ghana, Guinea, Ivory Coast, Liberia, Sierra Leone	084	F	VU	1
Mrs Moreau's Warbler *Bathmocercus winifredae*	Tanzania	105	F	VU	1
Aldabra Warbler *Nesillas aldabrana*	Seychelles[X]	099[X]	S	EX	—
Anjouan Brush-warbler *Nesillas longicaudata*	Comoros	098	FVA	lc	—
Lantz's Brush-warbler *Nesillas lantzii* *	Madagascar	097	S	NE	—
Grand Comoro Brush-warbler *Nesillas brevicaudata*	Comoros	098	FS	lc	—
Moheli Brush-warbler *Nesillas mariae*	Comoros	098	F	nt	—
Thamnornis Warbler *Thamnornis chloropetoides*	Madagascar	093,097	FS	lc	—
Streaked Reed-warbler *Acrocephalus sorghophilus*	China	See p. 724	WAZ	VU	1
Basra Reed-warbler *Acrocephalus griseldis*	Iraq	119	W	nt	—
Nightingale Reed-warbler *Acrocephalus luscinia*	Guam (to USA)[X], Northern Mariana Islands (to USA)	189	FGWX	VU	1457
Caroline Islands Reed-warbler *Acrocephalus syrinx*	Micronesia	192	FS	lc	—
Nauru Reed-warbler *Acrocephalus rehsei*	Nauru	(s124)	S	VU	18
Millerbird *Acrocephalus familiaris*	USA	216[X] (s138)	SG	VU	8
Bokikokiko *Acrocephalus aequinoctialis*	Kiribati	(s134)	S	lc	—
Tahiti Reed-warbler *Acrocephalus caffer*	French Polynesia (to France)	213	FS	VU	158
Marquesan Reed-warbler *Acrocephalus mendanae*	French Polynesia (to France)	212	FSX	lc	—
Tuamotu Reed-warbler *Acrocephalus atyphus*	French Polynesia (to France)	214	FSX	lc	—
Cook Islands Reed-warbler *Acrocephalus kerearako*	Cook Islands (to New Zealand)	210	FW	lc	—
Rimatara Reed-warbler *Acrocephalus rimitarae*	French Polynesia (to France)	211	FW	NE	—
Pitcairn Reed-Warbler *Acrocephalus vaughani*	Pitcairn Islands (to UK)	(s137)	S	NE	—
Henderson Reed-warbler *Acrocephalus taiti*	Pitcairn Islands (to UK)	215	F		—
Cape Verde Warbler *Acrocephalus brevipennis*	Cape Verde	078	SAX	VU	178
Rodrigues Warbler *Acrocephalus rodericanus*	Mauritius	103	S	CR	1578
Seychelles Warbler *Acrocephalus sechellensis*	Seychelles	100	FS	VU	8
African Tailorbird *Orthotomus metopias*	Mozambique, Tanzania	105	F	lc	—
Long-billed Tailorbird *Orthotomus moreaui*	Mozambique, Tanzania	105	F	CR	1
Rufous-headed Tailorbird *Orthotomus heterolaemus*	Philippines	154	F	lc	—
Grey-backed Tailorbird *Orthotomus derbianus*	Philippines	151,156	FS	lc	—
Yellow-breasted Tailorbird *Orthotomus samarensis*	Philippines	154	F	nt	—
Black-headed Tailorbird *Orthotomus nigriceps*	Philippines	154	F	nt	—
White-eared Tailorbird *Orthotomus cinereiceps*	Philippines	154	F	lc	—

	Breeding range	EBAs (and SAs)	Habitat codes	Status	Threat codes
White-tailed Warbler *Poliolais lopezi*	Cameroon, Equatorial Guinea, Nigeria	086	FS	lc	—
Grauer's Warbler *Graueria vittata*	Burundi, Rwanda, Uganda, Zaïre	106	F	lc	—
Chapin's Crombec *Sylvietta chapini*	Zaïre	106	F	lc	—
Neumann's Warbler *Hemitesia neumanni*	Burundi, Rwanda, Uganda, Zaïre	106	F	lc	—
Pulitzer's Longbill *Macrosphenus pulitzeri*	Angola	087	F	EN	1
São Tomé Short-tail *Amaurocichla bocagii*	São Tomé e Príncipe	082	F	VU	18
Red-faced Woodland-warbler *Phylloscopus laetus*	Burundi, Rwanda, Uganda, Zaïre	106	FX	lc	—
Black-capped Woodland-warbler *Phylloscopus herberti*	Cameroon, Equatorial Guinea, Nigeria	086	F	lc	—
Caucasian Chiffchaff *Phylloscopus lorenzii*	Armenia, Azerbaijan, Georgia, Iran, Russia, Turkey	122	FS	lc	—
Brooks's Leaf-warbler *Phylloscopus subviridis*	Afghanistan, India, Pakistan	128	F	lc	—
Tytler's Leaf-warbler *Phylloscopus tytleri*	Afghanistan, India, Pakistan, Nepal	128	FS	nt	—
Ijima's Leaf-warbler *Phylloscopus ijimae*	Japan	146	F	VU	01
Emei Leaf-warbler *Phylloscopus emeiensis* *	China	140	F	NE	—
Hainan Leaf-warbler *Phylloscopus hainanus* *	China	142	F	VU	1
Yellow-vented Warbler *Phylloscopus cantator*	Bhutan, India, Nepal	130	F	nt	—
Sulawesi Leaf-warbler *Phylloscopus sarasinorum*	Indonesia	166	F	lc	—
Timor Leaf-warbler *Phylloscopus presbytes*	Indonesia	162,164	F	lc	—
Makira Leaf-warbler *Phylloscopus makirensis*	Solomon Islands	198	F	nt	—
Sombre Leaf-warbler *Phylloscopus amoenus*	Solomon Islands	198	F	VU	578
Sunda Warbler *Seicercus grammiceps*	Indonesia	158,160	F	lc	—
Broad-billed Warbler *Tickellia hodgsoni*	China, India, Laos, Myanmar, Nepal, Vietnam	130 (s082)	FS	nt	—
Grey Emu-tail *Amphilais seebohmi*	Madagascar	095	FSGWA	lc	—
Fly River Grassbird *Megalurus albolimbatus*	Papua New Guinea	180	W	VU	58
Chatham Islands Fernbird *Megalurus rufescens*	New Zealand[X]	209[X]	FS	EX	—
Buff-banded Grassbird *Buettikoferella bivittata*	Indonesia	164	FSG	nt	—
New Caledonian Grassbird *Megalurulus mariei*	New Caledonia (to France)	201	SG	lc	—
Bismarck Thicketbird *Megalurulus grosvenori*	Papua New Guinea	195	F	DD	—
Bougainville Thicketbird *Megalurulus llaneae*	Papua New Guinea	198	F	DD	—
Guadalcanal Thicketbird *Megalurulus whitneyi*	Solomon Islands, Vanuatu	198,200	F	nt	—
Rusty Thicketbird *Ortygocichla rubiginosa*	Papua New Guinea	195	F	lc	—
Long-legged Thicketbird *Trichocichla rufa*	Fiji	202	F	CR	58
Broad-tailed Grassbird *Schoenicola platyura*	India	123	GW	nt	—
Yemen Warbler *Sylvia buryi*	Sauda Arabia, Yemen	118	FSRA	VU	1
Cyprus Warbler *Sylvia melanothorax*	Cyprus	121	FS	lc	—
Cryptic Warbler *Cryptosylvicola randrianasoloi* *	Madagascar	094	F	NE	—

Subfamily MALURINAE: Australian warblers

	Breeding range	EBAs (and SAs)	Habitat codes	Status	Threat codes
Lovely Fairywren *Malurus amabilis*	Australia	181,182	F	lc	—
Red-winged Fairywren *Malurus elegans*	Australia	186	FW	lc	—
Mallee Emuwren *Stipiturus mallee*	Australia	184	S	cd	—
Grey Grasswren *Amytornis barbatus*	Australia	(s117)	GW	nt	—
White-throated Grasswren *Amytornis woodwardi*	Australia	187	GR	nt	—
Carpentarian Grasswren *Amytornis dorotheae*	Australia	(s121)	G	VU	1
Eyrean Grasswren *Amytornis goyderi*	Australia	(s118)	G	lc	—
Black Grasswren *Amytornis housei*	Australia	187	GR	nt	—
Western Bristlebird *Dasyornis longirostris*	Australia	186	S	EN	18
Eastern Bristlebird *Dasyornis brachypterus*	Australia	183	SG	VU	135
Rufous Bristlebird *Dasyornis broadbenti*	Australia	184,186[X]	S	VU	157
Pilotbird *Pycnoptilus floccosus*	Australia	183	F	lc	—
Origma *Origma solitaria*	Australia	183	R	nt	—
Fernwren *Oreoscopus gutturalis*	Australia	182	F	nt	—
Brown Scrubwren *Sericornis humilis*	Australia	185	FS	lc	—
Atherton Scrubwren *Sericornis keri*	Australia	182	F	cd	—
Vogelkop Scrubwren *Sericornis rufescens*	Indonesia	173	FS	lc	—
Scrubtit *Acanthornis magnus*	Australia	185	F	lc	—
Papuan Thornbill *Acanthiza murina*	Indonesia, Papua New Guinea	178	F	lc	—
Mountain Thornbill *Acanthiza katherina*	Australia	182	F	cd	—
Tasmanian Thornbill *Acanthiza ewingii*	Australia	185	FS	lc	—
Biak Gerygone *Gerygone hypoxantha* *	Indonesia	174	F	EN	18
Dusky Gerygone *Gerygone tenebrosa*	Australia	(s120)	F	lc	—
Plain Gerygone *Gerygone inornata*	Indonesia	164	FS	lc	—
Rufous-sided Gerygone *Gerygone dorsalis*	Indonesia	165 (s110)	FSA	lc	—
Lord Howe Island Gerygone *Gerygone insularis*	Australia[X]	204[X]	F	EX	—
Norfolk Island Gerygone *Gerygone modesta*	Norfolk Island	205	FS	VU	8

	Breeding range	EBAs (and SAs)	Habitat codes	Status	Threat codes
Chatham Islands Warbler *Gerygone albofrontata*	New Zealand	209	FS	nt	—
Fan-tailed Gerygone *Gerygone flavolateralis*	New Caledonia (to France), Solomon Islands, Vanuatu	199,200,201	FSV	lc	—
Chestnut-breasted Whiteface *Aphelocephala pectoralis*	Australia	(s119)	SD	VU	15
Whitehead *Mohoua albicilla*	New Zealand	206	FS	lc	—
Yellowhead *Mohoua ochrocephala*	New Zealand	207	F	VU	5
Silktail *Lamprolia victoriae*	Fiji	202	F	VU	17
Subfamily MUSCICAPINAE: Old world flycatchers					
Golden-bellied Flyrobin *Microeca hemixantha*	Indonesia	165	F	nt	—
Alpine Robin *Petroica bivittata*	Indonesia, Papua New Guinea	178	FS	lc	—
Snow Mountain Robin *Petroica archboldi*	Indonesia	178	SR	DD	—
Chatham Islands Robin *Petroica traversi*	New Zealand	209	FS	EN	8
Dusky Robin *Melanodryas vittata*	Australia	185	FS	lc	—
Pale-yellow Robin *Tregellasia capito*	Australia	182,183	F	lc	—
Yellow-bellied Robin *Eopsaltria flaviventris*	New Caledonia (to France)	201	F	lc	—
White-breasted Robin *Eopsaltria georgiana*	Australia	186	FS	lc	—
Olive-yellow Robin *Poecilodryas placens*	Indonesia, Papua New Guinea	172,176,179 (s114)	F	DD	—
Smoky Robin *Peneothello cryptoleucus*	Indonesia	173,175,178	F	lc	—
Grey-headed Robin *Heteromyias cinereifrons*	Australia	182	F	nt	—
Green-backed Robin *Pachycephalopsis hattamensis*	Indonesia, Papua New Guinea	173,175,178 (s113)	FS	lc	—
Angola Slaty-flycatcher *Dioptrornis brunneus*	Angola	087	F	lc	—
Yellow-eyed Black-flycatcher *Melaenornis ardesiacus*	Burundi, Rwanda, Uganda, Zaïre	106	F	lc	—
Nimba Flycatcher *Melaenornis annamarulae*	Guinea, Ivory Coast, Liberia, Sierra Leone	084	FX	VU	1
Streaky-breasted Jungle-flycatcher *Rhinomyias addita*	Indonesia	169	F	VU	8
Russet-backed Jungle-flycatcher *Rhinomyias oscillans*	Indonesia	162,163	F	nt	—
Brown-chested Jungle-flycatcher *Rhinomyias brunneata*	China	141	F	VU	1
Henna-tailed Jungle-flycatcher *Rhinomyias colonus*	Indonesia	168	F	nt	—
Eyebrowed Jungle-flycatcher *Rhinomyias gularis*	Indonesia, Malaysia	157	F	lc	—
White-browed Jungle-flycatcher *Rhinomyias insignis*	Philippines	151	F	EN	1
White-throated Jungle-flycatcher *R. albigularis*	Philippines	152	F	CR	18
Slaty-backed Jungle-flycatcher *Rhinomyias goodfellowi*	Philippines	154	F	VU	1
Ashy-breasted Flycatcher *Muscicapa randi*	Philippines	151,152	F	EN	1
Chapin's Flycatcher *Muscicapa lendu*	Kenya, Uganda, Zaïre	106 (s058)	F	VU	1
Grand Comoro Flycatcher *Humblotia flavirostris*	Comoros	098	FS	VU	1
Kashmir Flycatcher *Ficedula subrubra*	India, Pakistan	123,124,128	F	VU	1
Rufous-throated Flycatcher *Ficedula rufigula*	Indonesia	166	F	nt	—
Cinnamon-chested Flycatcher *Ficedula buruensis*	Indonesia	165,169,170	F	lc	—
Little Slaty Flycatcher *Ficedula basilanica*	Philippines	154	F	VU	1
Damar Flycatcher *Ficedula henrici*	Indonesia	165	F	VU	8
Sumba Flycatcher *Ficedula harterti*	Indonesia	163	F	nt	—
Palawan Flycatcher *Ficedula platenae*	Philippines	156	F	EN	1
Cryptic Flycatcher *Ficedula crypta* *	Philippines	154	F	VU	1
Furtive Flycatcher *Ficedula disposita* *	Philippines	151	F	EN	18
Lompobattang Flycatcher *Ficedula bonthaina*	Indonesia	166	F	EN	1
Black-and-rufous Flycatcher *Ficedula nigrorufa*	India	123	FX	nt	—
Black-banded Flycatcher *Ficedula timorensis*	Indonesia	164	F	nt	—
Dull-blue Flycatcher *Eumyias sordida*	Sri Lanka	124	FX	nt	—
Nilgiri Flycatcher *Eumyias albicaudata*	India	123	FX	nt	—
Rufous-vented Niltava *Niltava sumatrana*	Indonesia, Malaysia	158	F	lc	—
Matinan Flycatcher *Cyornis sanfordi*	Indonesia	166	F	VU	8
Blue-fronted Flycatcher *Cyornis hoevelli*	Indonesia	166	F	lc	—
Timor Blue-flycatcher *Cyornis hyacinthinus*	Indonesia	164	F	lc	—
Rueck's Blue-flycatcher *Cyornis ruckii*	Indonesia	(s104)	F	VU	18
Blue-breasted Flycatcher *Cyornis herioti*	Philippines	151	F	nt	—
White-bellied Blue-flycatcher *Cyornis pallipes*	India	123	F	nt	—
Palawan Blue-flycatcher *Cyornis lemprieri*	Philippines	156	F	lc	—
Archbold's Newtonia *Newtonia archboldi*	Madagascar	093,097	FS	lc	—
Red-tailed Newtonia *Newtonia fanovanae*	Madagascar	094	F	VU	1
Subfamily PLATYSTEIRINAE: Puffback-flycatchers, wattle-eyes					
Ruwenzori Batis *Batis diops*	Burundi, Rwanda, Uganda, Zaïre	106	FS	lc	—
Gabon Batis *Batis minima*	Cameroon, Gabon	085	F	DD	—
Fernando Po Batis *Batis poensis*	Equatorial Guinea	086	FX	lc	—
Banded Wattle-eye *Platysteira laticincta*	Cameroon	086	F	VU	1
White-fronted Wattle-eye *Platysteira albifrons*	Angola	087	F	nt	—

	Breeding range	EBAs (and SAs)	Habitat codes	Status	Threat codes
Subfamily MONARCHINAE: Monarchs, paradise-flycatchers					
Short-crested Monarch *Hypothymis helenae*	Philippines	151,154	F	nt	—
Celestial Monarch *Hypothymis coelestis*	Philippines	151,152,154,155 (s095)	F	EN	1
Cerulean Paradise-flycatcher *Eutrichomyias rowleyi*	Indonesia	167	F	CR	18
Annobón Paradise-flycatcher *Terpsiphone smithii* *	Equatorial Guinea	081	FA	VU	8
Bedford's Paradise-flycatcher *Terpsiphone bedfordi*	Zaïre	107	F	nt	—
São Tomé Paradise-flycatcher *T. atrochalybeia*	São Tomé e Príncipe	082	FVX	lc	—
Seychelles Paradise-flycatcher *Terpsiphone corvina*	Seychelles	100	F	CR	18
Mascarene Paradise-flycatcher *T. bourbonnensis*	Mauritius, Réunion (to France)	101,102	F	lc	—
Blue Paradise-flycatcher *Terpsiphone cyanescens*	Philippines	156	FS	nt	—
'Elepaio *Chasiempis sandwichensis*	USA	217,218	FSX	lc	—
Rarotonga Monarch *Pomarea dimidiata*	Cook Islands (to New Zealand)	210	F	CR	58
Tahiti Monarch *Pomarea nigra*	French Polynesia (to France)	213	F	CR	1578
Maupiti Monarch *Pomarea pomarea* *	French Polynesia (to France)[X]	213[X]	F	EX	
Iphis Monarch *Pomarea iphis*	French Polynesia (to France)	212	FSX	VU	8
Marquesan Monarch *Pomarea mendozae*	French Polynesia (to France)	212	F	EN	58
Fatuhiva Monarch *Pomarea whitneyi*	French Polynesia (to France)	212	F	VU	8
Ogea Monarch *Mayrornis versicolor*	Fiji	202	F	VU	8
Slaty Monarch *Mayrornis lessoni*	Fiji	202	F	lc	—
Vanikoro Monarch *Mayrornis schistaceus*	Solomon Islands	200	F	nt	—
Buff-bellied Monarch *Neolalage banksiana*	Vanuatu	200	FSX	lc	—
Southern Shrikebill *Clytorhynchus pachycephaloides*	New Caledonia (to France), Vanuatu	200,201	F	lc	—
Fiji Shrikebill *Clytorhynchus vitiensis*	American Samoa (to USA), Fiji, Tonga, Wallis and Futuna Islands (to France)	202,203 (s127, s128,s130)	FS	lc	—
Black-throated Shrikebill *Clytorhynchus nigrogularis*	Fiji, Solomon Islands	200,202	F	nt	—
Rennell Shrikebill *Clytorhynchus hamlini*	Solomon Islands	199	F	nt	—
Truk Monarch *Metabolus rugensis*	Micronesia	192	F	EN	18
Bougainville Monarch *Monarcha erythrostictus*	Papua New Guinea	198	F	lc	—
Chestnut-bellied Monarch *Monarcha castaneiventris*	Solomon Islands	198	FX	lc	—
White-capped Monarch *Monarcha richardsii*	Solomon Islands	198	F	lc	—
White-naped Monarch *Monarcha pileatus*	Indonesia	165,169,171	F	lc	—
Black-bibbed Monarch *Monarcha mundus*	Indonesia	165	F	nt	—
Flores Monarch *Monarcha sacerdotum*	Indonesia	162	F	EN	18
White-tipped Monarch *Monarcha everetti*	Indonesia	(s110)	FS	VU	18
Black-tipped Monarch *Monarcha loricatus*	Indonesia	169	FA	nt	—
Black-chinned Monarch *Monarcha boanensis*	Indonesia	170	F	EN	18
White-tailed Monarch *Monarcha leucurus*	Indonesia	165	F	nt	—
Black-backed Monarch *Monarcha julianae*	Indonesia	172	F	lc	—
Biak Monarch *Monarcha brehmii*	Indonesia	174	F	EN	18
Manus Monarch *Monarcha infelix*	Papua New Guinea	193	FS	nt	—
White-breasted Monarch *Monarcha menckei*	Papua New Guinea	194	F	DD	—
Black-tailed Monarch *Monarcha verticalis*	Papua New Guinea	195	F	lc	—
Black-and-white Monarch *Monarcha barbatus*	Papua New Guinea, Solomon Is.	198	F	lc	—
Kolombangara Monarch *Monarcha browni*	Solomon Islands	198	F	nt	—
White-collared Monarch *Monarcha viduus*	Solomon Islands	198	F	lc	—
Yap Monarch *Monarcha godeffroyi*	Micronesia	191	F	nt	—
Tinian Monarch *Monarcha takatsukasae*	Northern Mariana Is. (to USA)	189	FSX	VU	8
Pied Monarch *Arses kaupi*	Australia	182	F	lc	—
Guam Flycatcher *Myiagra freycineti*	Guam (to USA)[X]	189[X]	F	EX	—
Mangrove Flycatcher *Myiagra erythrops*	Palau	190	F	lc	—
Oceanic Flycatcher *Myiagra oceanica*	Micronesia	192	FX	lc	—
Pohnpei Flycatcher *Myiagra pluto*	Micronesia	192	FSVX	lc	—
Biak Flycatcher *Myiagra atra*	Indonesia	174	F	nt	—
Dark-grey Flycatcher *Myiagra galeata*	Indonesia	165,169,170,171	FSX	lc	—
Steel-blue Flycatcher *Myiagra ferrocyanea*	Papua New Guinea, Solomon Is.	198	FX	lc	—
Ochre-tailed Flycatcher *Myiagra cervinicauda*	Solomon Islands	198	F	nt	—
Melanesian Flycatcher *Myiagra caledonica*	New Caledonia (to France), Solomon Islands, Vanuatu	199,200,201	FV	lc	—
Vanikoro Flycatcher *Myiagra vanikorensis*	Fiji, Solomon Islands	200,202	FS	lc	—
Samoan Flycatcher *Myiagra albiventris*	Western Samoa	203	F	VU	17
Blue-crested Flycatcher *Myiagra azureocapilla*	Fiji	202	F	lc	—
Dull Flycatcher *Myiagra hebetior*	Papua New Guinea	194,195	F	lc	—
Subfamily RHIPIDURINAE: Fantails					
Rufous-tailed Fantail *Rhipidura phoenicura*	Indonesia	160	F	lc	

	Breeding range	EBAs (and SAs)	Habitat codes	Status	Threat codes
Black-and-cinnamon Fantail *R. nigrocinnamomea*	Philippines	154	F	lc	—
White-bellied Fantail *Rhipidura euryura*	Indonesia	160	F	nt	—
Brown-capped Fantail *Rhipidura diluta*	Indonesia	162	F	lc	—
Cinnamon-tailed Fantail *Rhipidura fuscorufa*	Indonesia	165	FA	nt	—
White-winged Fantail *Rhipidura cockerelli*	Papua New Guinea, Solomon Is.	198	F	lc	—
Brown Fantail *Rhipidura drownei*	Papua New Guinea, Solomon Is.	198	F	lc	—
Dusky Fantail *Rhipidura tenebrosa*	Solomon Islands	198	F	nt	—
Rennell Fantail *Rhipidura rennelliana*	Solomon Islands	199	F	lc	—
Streaked Fantail *Rhipidura spilodera*	Fiji, New Caledonia (to France), Vanuatu	200,201,202	FS	lc	—
Kadavu Fantail *Rhipidura personata*	Fiji	202	FS	nt	—
Samoan Fantail *Rhipidura nebulosa*	Western Samoa	203	FS	lc	—
Rusty-bellied Fantail *Rhipidura teysmanni*	Indonesia	166,168	F	lc	—
Tawny-backed Fantail *Rhipidura superflua*	Indonesia	169	F	nt	—
Streaky-breasted Fantail *Rhipidura dedemi*	Indonesia	170	F	lc	—
Long-tailed Fantail *Rhipidura opistherythra*	Indonesia	165	F	nt	—
Palau Fantail *Rhipidura lepida*	Palau	190	F	lc	—
Bismarck Fantail *Rhipidura dahli*	Papua New Guinea	195	F	lc	—
Matthias Fantail *Rhipidura matthiae*	Papua New Guinea	194	F	DD	—
Malaita Fantail *Rhipidura malaitae*	Solomon Islands	198	F	VU	78
Pohnpei Fantail *Rhipidura kubaryi*	Micronesia	192	FSV	lc	—
Manus Fantail *Rhipidura semirubra*	Papua New Guinea	193	FSX	VU	08

Subfamily PACHYCEPHALINAE: Whistlers, popio

	Breeding range	EBAs (and SAs)	Habitat codes	Status	Threat codes
Olive-flanked Whistler *Hylocitrea bonensis*	Indonesia	166	F	lc	—
Maroon-backed Whistler *Coracornis raveni*	Indonesia	166	F	lc	—
Red-lored Whistler *Pachycephala rufogularis*	Australia	184	S	cd	—
Green-backed Whistler *Pachycephala albiventris*	Philippines	150,151	F	lc	—
Island Whistler *Pachycephala phaionotus*	Indonesia	165,171,172,174 (s112)	FS	lc	—
Bornean Whistler *Pachycephala hypoxantha*	Indonesia, Malaysia	157	F	lc	—
Sulphur-bellied Whistler *Pachycephala sulfuriventer*	Indonesia	166	F	lc	—
Vogelkop Whistler *Pachycephala meyeri*	Indonesia	173	FS	nt	—
Brown Whistler *Pachycephala simplex*	Australia	187	F	lc	—
Fawn-breasted Whistler *Pachycephala orpheus*	Indonesia	164	F	nt	—
Lorentz's Whistler *Pachycephala lorentzi*	Indonesia, Papua New Guinea	178	FS	lc	—
New Caledonian Whistler *Pachycephala caledonica*	New Caledonia (to France)	201	F	lc	—
Samoan Whistler *Pachycephala flavifrons*	Western Samoa	203	FX	lc	—
Tongan Whistler *Pachycephala jacquinoti*	Tonga	(s130)	FS	nt	—
Bare-throated Whistler *Pachycephala nudigula*	Indonesia	162	F	lc	—
Hooded Whistler *Pachycephala implicata*	Papua New Guinea, Solomon Is.	198	F	nt	—
Drab Whistler *Pachycephala griseonota*	Indonesia	165,168,169,170, 171	FS	lc	—
White-bellied Whistler *Pachycephala leucogastra*	Papua New Guinea	176,197 (s114)	FSVX	lc	—
Sooty Shrike-thrush *Colluricincla umbrina*	Indonesia, Papua New Guinea	178	F	lc	—
Bower's Shrike-thrush *Colluricincla boweri*	Australia	182	F	nt	—
Morningbird *Colluricincla tenebrosa*	Palau	190	F	lc	—
White-bellied Pitohui *Pitohui incertus*	Indonesia, Papua New Guinea	179	F	lc	—
Wattled Ploughbill *Eulacestoma nigropectus*	Indonesia, Papua New Guinea	178	FS	lc	—

Family AEGITHALIDAE: Long-tailed or bush tits

	Breeding range	EBAs (and SAs)	Habitat codes	Status	Threat codes
White-cheeked Tit *Aegithalos leucogenys*	Afghanistan, India, Pakistan	128	FS	lc	—
White-throated Tit *Aegithalos niveogularis*	India, Nepal, Pakistan	128	FS	nt	—
White-necklaced Tit *Aegithalos fuliginosus*	China	137	F	nt	—
Pygmy Tit *Psaltria exilis*	Indonesia	160	FX	lc	—

Family PARIDAE: Tits

	Breeding range	EBAs (and SAs)	Habitat codes	Status	Threat codes
Rusty-breasted Tit *Parus davidi*	China	137	F	lc	—
Palawan Tit *Parus amabilis*	Philippines	156	F	lc	—
Stripe-breasted Tit *Parus fasciiventer*	Burundi, Rwanda, Uganda, Zaïre	106	FS	lc	—
Yellow Tit *Parus holsti*	Taiwan	149	F	nt	—
White-fronted Tit *Parus semilarvatus*	Philippines	151,154	F	nt	—

Family SITTIDAE: Nuthatches

	Breeding range	EBAs (and SAs)	Habitat codes	Status	Threat codes
Black Sittella *Daphoenositta miranda*	Indonesia, Papua New Guinea	178	F	lc	—
Kashmir Nuthatch *Sitta cashmirensis*	Afghanistan, India, Nepal, Pakistan	128	F	lc	—
White-browed Nuthatch *Sitta victoriae*	Myanmar	130	F	VU	8
Corsican Nuthatch *Sitta whiteheadi*	France	(s068)	F	nt	—
Algerian Nuthatch *Sitta ledanti*	Algeria	(s039)	F	EN	18

	Breeding range	EBAs (and SAs)	Habitat codes	Status	Threat codes
Yunnan Nuthatch *Sitta yunnanensis*	China	139	F	VU	1
Yellow-billed Nuthatch *Sitta solangiae*	China, Vietnam	142,145 (s082)	F	VU	1
Family RHABDORNITHIDAE: Philippine treecreepers					
Long-billed Rhabdornis *Rhabdornis grandis*	Philippines	151	F	nt	—
Family DICAEIDAE: Flowerpeckers					
Forty-spotted Pardalote *Pardalotus quadragintus*	Australia	185	F	VU	17
Palawan Flowerpecker *Prionochilus plateni*	Philippines	156	F	lc	—
Golden-rumped Flowerpecker *Dicaeum annae*	Indonesia	162	F	lc	—
Whiskered Flowerpecker *Dicaeum proprium*	Philippines	154	F	VU	1
White-throated Flowerpecker *Dicaeum vincens*	Sri Lanka	124	FX	nt	—
Olive-capped Flowerpecker *Dicaeum nigrilore*	Philippines	154	F	lc	—
Flame-crowned Flowerpecker *Dicaeum anthonyi*	Philippines	151,154	F	nt	—
Cebu Flowerpecker *Dicaeum quadricolor*	Philippines	153	F	CR	178
Visayan Flowerpecker *Dicaeum haematostictum* *	Philippines	152	FS	EN	1
Scarlet-collared Flowerpecker *Dicaeum retrocinctum*	Philippines	150,152	F	CR	1
Crimson-crowned Flowerpecker *Dicaeum nehrkorni*	Indonesia	166	F	lc	—
Flame-breasted Flowerpecker *Dicaeum erythrothorax*	Indonesia	169,171	FSA	lc	—
Ashy Flowerpecker *Dicaeum vulneratum*	Indonesia	165,170	FAX	lc	—
Olive-crowned Flowerpecker *Dicaeum pectorale*	Indonesia	172	F	lc	—
Louisiade Flowerpecker *Dicaeum nitidum*	Papua New Guinea	197	F	lc	—
Red-banded Flowerpecker *Dicaeum eximium*	Papua New Guinea	195	F	lc	—
Midget Flowerpecker *Dicaeum aeneum*	Papua New Guinea, Solomon Is.	198	F	lc	—
Mottled Flowerpecker *Dicaeum tristrami*	Solomon Islands	198	F	lc	—
Black-fronted Flowerpecker *Dicaeum igniferum*	Indonesia	162	FA	lc	—
Red-chested Flowerpecker *Dicaeum maugei*	Indonesia	162,164,165 (s110)	F	lc	—
Black-sided Flowerpecker *Dicaeum monticolum*	Indonesia, Malaysia	157	F	lc	—
Obscure Berrypecker *Melanocharis arfakiana*	Indonesia, Papua New Guinea	173,178	F	DD	—
Family NECTARINIDAE: Sunbirds					
Amani Sunbird *Anthreptes pallidigaster*	Kenya, Tanzania	105,111	F	VU	1
Banded Sunbird *Anthreptes rubritorques*	Tanzania	105	F	VU	1
Orange-breasted Sunbird *Nectarinia violacea*	South Africa	088	S	lc	—
Príncipe Sunbird *Nectarinia hartlaubii*	São Tomé e Príncipe	083	FX	lc	—
Newton's Sunbird *Nectarinia newtonii*	São Tomé e Príncipe	082	FVX	lc	—
Giant Sunbird *Nectarinia thomensis*	São Tomé e Príncipe	082	F	VU	18
Cameroon Sunbird *Nectarinia oritis*	Cameroon, Equatorial Guinea, Nigeria	086	F	lc	—
Blue-headed Sunbird *Nectarinia alinae*	Burundi, Rwanda, Uganda, Zaïre	106	F	lc	—
Socotra Sunbird *Nectarinia balfouri*	Yemen	117	FS	lc	—
Seychelles Sunbird *Nectarinia dussumieri*	Seychelles	100	F	lc	—
Crimson-backed Sunbird *Nectarinia minima*	India	123	FX	lc	—
Apricot-breasted Sunbird *Nectarinia buettikoferi*	Indonesia	163	FSA	lc	—
Flame-breasted Sunbird *Nectarinia solaris*	Indonesia	162,164	FS	lc	—
Humblot's Sunbird *Nectarinia humbloti*	Comoros	098	F	lc	—
Anjouan Sunbird *Nectarinia comorensis*	Comoros	098	F	lc	—
Mayotte Sunbird *Nectarinia coquerellii*	Mayotte (to France)	098	SX	lc	—
Ursula's Sunbird *Nectarinia ursulae*	Cameroon, Equatorial Guinea	086	F	nt	—
Montane Double-collared Sunbird *N. ludovicensis*	Angola	087	F	lc	—
Stuhlmann's Double-collared Sunbird *N. stuhlmanni*	Zaïre	106	FS	lc	—
Neergaard's Sunbird *Nectarinia neergaardi*	Mozambique, South Africa	092	FS	nt	—
Regal Sunbird *Nectarinia regia*	Burundi, Rwanda, Tanzania, Uganda, Zaïre	106	FS	lc	—
Loveridge's Sunbird *Nectarinia loveridgei*	Tanzania	105	F	nt	—
Moreau's Sunbird *Nectarinia moreaui*	Tanzania	105	F	nt	—
Rockefeller's Sunbird *Nectarinia rockefelleri*	Zaïre	106	FS	VU	8
Rufous-winged Sunbird *Nectarinia rufipennis*	Tanzania	105	F	VU	8
Purple-breasted Sunbird *Nectarinia purpureiventris*	Burundi, Rwanda, Uganda, Zaïre	106	F	lc	—
Pemba Sunbird *Nectarinia pembae* *	Tanzania	110	F	nt	—
Grey-hooded Sunbird *Aethopyga primigenius*	Philippines	154	F	lc	—
Apo Sunbird *Aethopyga boltoni*	Philippines	154	FS	nt	—
Lina's Sunbird *Aethopyga linaraborae* *	Philippines	154	F	NE	—
Elegant Sunbird *Aethopyga duyvenbodei*	Indonesia	167	FS	EN	18
White-flanked Sunbird *Aethopyga eximia*	Indonesia	160	FS	lc	—
Whitehead's Spiderhunter *Arachnothera juliae*	Indonesia, Malaysia	157	F	lc	—

	Breeding range	EBAs (and SAs)	Habitat codes	Status	Threat codes
Family ZOSTEROPIDAE: White-eyes					
Mount Cameroon Speirops *Speirops melanocephalus*	Cameroon	086	FSG	VU	8
Black-capped Speirops *Speirops lugubris*	São Tomé e Príncipe	082	FX	lc	—
Fernando Po Speirops *Speirops brunneus*	Equatorial Guinea	086	FS	VU	8
Príncipe Speirops *Speirops leucophaeus*	São Tomé e Príncipe	083	FX	VU	124
Pemba White-eye *Zosterops vaughani*	Tanzania	110	F	nt	—
Chestnut-sided White-eye *Zosterops mayottensis*	Mayotte (to France), Seychelles[X]	100[X],098	F	lc	—
Kulal White-eye *Zosterops kulalensis* *	Kenya	(s062)	F	CR	18
South Pare White-eye *Zosterops winifredae* *	Tanzania	109	FS	VU	1
Taita White-eye *Zosterops silvanus* *	Kenya	105	F	CR	18
Mount Karthala White-eye *Zosterops mouroniensis*	Comoros	098	FS	CR	18
São Tomé White-eye *Zosterops ficedulinus*	São Tomé e Príncipe	082,083	FVX	VU	1
Annobón White-eye *Zosterops griseovirescens*	Equatorial Guinea	081	FSWA	VU	8
Mascarene Grey White-eye *Zosterops borbonicus*	Réunion (to France), Mauritius	101,102	FS	lc	—
Réunion Olive White-eye *Zosterops olivaceus*	Réunion (to France)	101	FS	lc	—
Mauritius Olive White-eye *Zosterops chloronothos*	Mauritius	102	F	CR	158
Seychelles White-eye *Zosterops modestus*	Seychelles	100	F	CR	158
Sri Lanka White-eye *Zosterops ceylonensis*	Sri Lanka	124	FSX	lc	—
Enggano White-eye *Zosterops salvadorii*	Indonesia	159	FX	lc	—
Guam Bridled White-eye *Zosterops conspicillatus* *	Guam (to USA)[X]	189[X]	F	EX	—
Saipan Bridled White-eye *Zosterops saypani* *	Northern Mariana Is. (to USA)	189	F	lc	—
Rota Bridled White-eye *Zosterops rotensis* *	Northern Mariana Is. (to USA)	189	F	CR	58
Plain White-eye *Zosterops hypolais*	Micronesia	191	FSVA	nt	—
Caroline Islands White-eye *Zosterops semperi*	Micronesia, Palau	190,192	FS	lc	—
Black-capped White-eye *Zosterops atricapillus*	Indonesia, Malaysia	157,158	FS	lc	—
Christmas Island White-eye *Zosterops natalis*	Christmas Island (to Australia)	188	F	nt	—
Javan White-eye *Zosterops flavus*	Indonesia, Malaysia	161 (s100)	FSW	nt	—
Pearl-bellied White-eye *Zosterops grayi*	Indonesia	165	F	nt	—
Golden-bellied White-eye *Zosterops uropygialis*	Indonesia	165	F	nt	—
Pale-bellied White-eye *Zosterops consobrinorum*	Indonesia	166	FS	nt	—
Lemon-throated White-eye *Zosterops anomalus*	Indonesia	166	SA	nt	—
Yellow-spectacled White-eye *Zosterops wallacei*	Indonesia	162,163	FS	lc	—
Creamy-throated White-eye *Zosterops atriceps*	Indonesia	171	FA	lc	—
White-throated White-eye *Zosterops meeki*	Papua New Guinea	197	F	DD	—
Black-headed White-eye *Zosterops hypoxanthus*	Papua New Guinea	193,195	F	lc	—
Biak White-eye *Zosterops mysorensis*	Indonesia	174	F	nt	—
Buru Yellow White-eye *Zosterops buruensis*	Indonesia	169	FS	lc	—
Ambon Yellow White-eye *Zosterops kuehni*	Indonesia	170	FS	nt	—
Louisiade White-eye *Zosterops griseotinctus*	Papua New Guinea	195,197	F	lc	—
Rennell White-eye *Zosterops rennellianus*	Solomon Islands	199	F	nt	—
Banded White-eye *Zosterops vellalavella*	Solomon Islands	198	FSX	lc	—
Ranongga White-eye *Zosterops splendidus*	Solomon Islands	198	FSX	lc	—
Ghizo White-eye *Zosterops luteirostris*	Solomon Islands	198	FS	VU	18
Solomon Islands White-eye *Zosterops kulambangrae*	Solomon Islands	198	F	lc	—
Hermit White-eye *Zosterops murphyi*	Solomon Islands	198	F	lc	—
Yellow-throated White-eye *Zosterops metcalfii*	Papua New Guinea, Solomon Is.	198	F	lc	—
Grey-throated White-eye *Zosterops rendovae*	Solomon Islands	198	F	lc	—
Malaita White-eye *Zosterops stresemanni*	Solomon Islands	198	FS	lc	—
Nendo White-eye *Zosterops sanctaecrucis*	Solomon Islands	200	FS	lc	—
Lord Howe Island White-eye *Zosterops tephropleurus*	Australia	204	FS	VU	8
Robust White-eye *Zosterops strenuus*	Australia[X]	204[X]	F	EX	—
Slender-billed White-eye *Zosterops tenuirostris*	Norfolk Island	205	F	VU	8
White-chested White-eye *Zosterops albogularis*	Norfolk Island	205	F	CR	1578
Large Lifou White-eye *Zosterops inornatus*	New Caledonia (to France)	201	F	lc	—
Layard's White-eye *Zosterops explorator*	Fiji	202	FS	lc	—
Yellow-fronted White-eye *Zosterops flavifrons*	Vanuatu	200	FAX	lc	—
Green-backed White-eye *Zosterops xanthochrous*	New Caledonia (to France)	201	FS	lc	—
Small Lifou White-eye *Zosterops minutus*	New Caledonia (to France)	201	F	lc	—
Samoan White-eye *Zosterops samoensis*	Western Samoa	203	FS	VU	58
Dusky White-eye *Zosterops finschii*	Palau	190	F	lc	—
Grey-brown White-eye *Zosterops cinereus*	Micronesia	192	FSG	lc	—
Yap Olive White-eye *Zosterops oleagineus*	Micronesia	191	F	VU	8
Long-billed White-eye *Rukia longirostra*	Micronesia	192	F	nt	—
Faichuk White-eye *Rukia ruki*	Micronesia	192	F	EN	18
Golden White-eye *Cleptornis marchei*	Northern Mariana Is. (to USA)	189	FX	VU	58
Bicoloured White-eye *Tephrozosterops stalkeri*	Indonesia	170	FS	lc	—
Rufous-throated White-eye *Madanga ruficollis*	Indonesia	169	F	VU	8

	Breeding range	EBAs (and SAs)	Habitat codes	Status	Threat codes
Javan Grey-throated White-eye *Lophozosterops javanicus*	Indonesia	160	F	lc	—
Streaky-headed White-eye *Lophozosterops squamiceps*	Indonesia	166	F	lc	—
Black-masked White-eye *Lophozosterops goodfellowi*	Philippines	154	F	lc	—
Yellow-browed White-eye *Lophozosterops superciliaris*	Indonesia	162	F	lc	—
Grey-hooded White-eye *Lophozosterops pinaiae*	Indonesia	170	F	lc	—
Crested White-eye *Lophozosterops dohertyi*	Indonesia	162	F	nt	—
Pygmy White-eye *Oculocincta squamifrons*	Indonesia, Malaysia	157	F	lc	—
Thick-billed White-eye *Heleia crassirostris*	Indonesia	162	F	lc	—
Spot-breasted White-eye *Heleia muelleri*	Indonesia	164	F	nt	—
Mountain Blackeye *Chlorocharis emiliae*	Indonesia, Malaysia	157	FS	lc	—
Bare-eyed White-eye *Woodfordia superciliosa*	Solomon Islands	199	FSX	lc	—
Sanford's White-eye *Woodfordia lacertosa*	Solomon Islands	200	F	nt	—
Giant White-eye *Megazosterops palauensis*	Palau	190	FS	nt	—
Cinnamon Ibon *Hypocryptadius cinnamomeus*	Philippines	154	F	lc	—
Family MELIPHAGIDAE: Honeyeaters					
Drab Myzomela *Myzomela blasii*	Indonesia	170	F	lc	—
White-chinned Myzomela *Myzomela albigula*	Papua New Guinea	197	F	DD	—
Olive-yellow Myzomela *Myzomela pulchella*	Papua New Guinea	195	F	lc	—
Crimson-hooded Myzomela *Myzomela kuehni*	Indonesia	164	F	DD	—
New Caledonian Myzomela *Myzomela caledonica*	New Caledonia (to France)	201	FS	lc	—
Micronesian Myzomela *Myzomela rubratra*	Guam (to USA)[X], Micronesia, N Mariana Is. (to USA), Palau	189,190,191,192	FX	lc	—
Cardinal Myzomela *Myzomela cardinalis*	American Samoa (to USA), New Caledonia (to France), Solomon Is., Vanuatu, Western Samoa	198,199,200,201, 203	FVX	lc	—
Rotuma Myzomela *Myzomela chermesina*	Fiji	(s127)	F	VU	8
Scarlet-bibbed Myzomela *Myzomela sclateri*	Papua New Guinea	195	FX	lc	—
Ebony Myzomela *Myzomela pammelaena*	Papua New Guinea	193,194,195	FX	lc	—
Scarlet-naped Myzomela *Myzomela lafargei*	Papua New Guinea, Solomon Is.	198	FX	lc	—
Yellow-vented Myzomela *Myzomela eichhorni*	Solomon Islands	198	FX	lc	—
Black-headed Myzomela *Myzomela melanocephala*	Solomon Islands	198	F	lc	—
Red-bellied Myzomela *Myzomela malaitae*	Solomon Islands	198	F	lc	—
Sooty Myzomela *Myzomela tristrami*	Solomon Islands	198	FX	lc	—
Orange-breasted Myzomela *Myzomela jugularis*	Fiji	202	FX	lc	—
Black-bellied Myzomela *Myzomela erythromelas*	Papua New Guinea	195	F	lc	—
Red-rumped Myzomela *Myzomela vulnerata*	Indonesia	164	F	nt	—
Bougainville Honeyeater *Stresemannia bougainvillei*	Papua New Guinea	198	F	lc	—
Scaly-crowned Honeyeater *Lichmera lombokia*	Indonesia	162	FA	lc	—
Olive Honeyeater *Lichmera argentauris*	Indonesia	170,171,172	F	lc	—
Dark-brown Honeyeater *Lichmera incana*	New Caledonia (to France), Vanuatu	200,201	FSV	lc	—
White-tufted Honeyeater *Lichmera squamata*	Indonesia	164,165	FSA	lc	—
Buru Honeyeater *Lichmera deningeri*	Indonesia	169	FS	nt	—
Seram Honeyeater *Lichmera monticola*	Indonesia	170	FS	lc	—
Yellow-eared Honeyeater *Lichmera flavicans*	Indonesia	164	F	lc	—
Black-chested Honeyeater *Lichmera notabilis*	Indonesia	164	F	DD	—
White-streaked Honeyeater *Trichodere cockerelli*	Australia	181	FSW	lc	—
Tagula Honeyeater *Meliphaga vicina*	Papua New Guinea	197	F	DD	—
Yellow-spotted Honeyeater *Meliphaga notata*	Australia	181,182	FSA	lc	—
White-lined Honeyeater *Meliphaga albilineata*	Australia	187	R	lc	—
Streaky-breasted Honeyeater *Meliphaga reticulata*	Indonesia	164	F	nt	—
Guadalcanal Honeyeater *Guadalcanaria inexpectata*	Solomon Islands	198	F	lc	—
Wattled Honeyeater *Foulehaio carunculata*	American Samoa (to USA), Fiji, Tonga, Wallis and Futuna Islands (to France), Western Samoa	202,203 (s128, s130)	FS	lc	—
Bridled Honeyeater *Lichenostomus frenatus*	Australia	182	F	nt	—
Eungella Honeyeater *Lichenostomus hindwoodi*	Australia	(s115)	F	cd	—
Mangrove Honeyeater *Lichenostomus fasciogularis*	Australia	(s116)	F	lc	—
Yellow-throated Honeyeater *Lichenostomus flavicollis*	Australia	185	FS	lc	—
Macleay Honeyeater *Xanthotis macleayana*	Australia	182	F	lc	—
Kadavu Honeyeater *Xanthotis provocator*	Fiji	202	F	nt	—
Orange-cheeked Honeyeater *Oreornis chrysogenys*	Indonesia	178	FS	lc	—
Bonin Honeyeater *Apalopteron familiare*	Japan	147	FSAX	VU	8
Black-headed Honeyeater *Melithreptus affinis*	Australia	185	F	lc	—
Strong-billed Honeyeater *Melithreptus validirostris*	Australia	185	F	lc	—
Stitchbird *Notiomystis cincta*	New Zealand	206	F	VU	8

	Breeding range	EBAs (and SAs)	Habitat codes	Status	Threat codes
White-streaked Friarbird *Melitograis gilolensis*	Indonesia	171	FAX	lc	—
Plain Friarbird *Philemon inornatus*	Indonesia	164	F	nt	—
Brass's Friarbird *Philemon brassi*	Indonesia	176	FW	DD	—
Dusky Friarbird *Philemon fuscicapillus*	Indonesia	171	F	DD	—
Black-faced Friarbird *Philemon moluccensis*	Indonesia	165,169	FAX	lc	—
Grey-necked Friarbird *Philemon subcorniculatus*	Indonesia	170	FX	lc	—
White-naped Friarbird *Philemon albitorques*	Papua New Guinea	193	FX	lc	—
New Britain Friarbird *Philemon cockerelli*	Papua New Guinea	195	FX	lc	—
New Ireland Friarbird *Philemon eichhorni*	Papua New Guinea	195	F	lc	—
New Caledonian Friarbird *Philemon diemenensis*	New Caledonia (to France)	201	FS	lc	—
Leaden Honeyeater *Ptiloprora plumbea*	Indonesia, Papua New Guinea	178	F	lc	—
Olive-streaked Honeyeater *Ptiloprora meekiana*	Indonesia, Papua New Guinea	177,178	F	lc	—
Rufous-sided Honeyeater *Ptiloprora erythropleura*	Indonesia	173,178	F	lc	—
Mayr's Honeyeater *Ptiloprora mayri*	Indonesia, Papua New Guinea	175	F	lc	—
Rufous-backed Honeyeater *Ptiloprora guisei*	Papua New Guinea	177,178	F	lc	—
Black-backed Honeyeater *Ptiloprora perstriata*	Indonesia, Papua New Guinea	173,178	FS	lc	—
Sooty Melidectes *Melidectes fuscus*	Indonesia, Papua New Guinea	178	FS	lc	—
Bismarck Melidectes *Melidectes whitemanensis*	Papua New Guinea	195	F	lc	—
Short-bearded Melidectes *Melidectes nouhuysi*	Indonesia	178	FS	lc	—
Long-bearded Melidectes *Melidectes princeps*	Papua New Guinea	178	FS	VU	1
Cinnamon-browed Melidectes *Melidectes ochromelas*	Indonesia, Papua New Guinea	173,177,178	F	lc	—
Vogelkop Melidectes *Melidectes leucostephes*	Indonesia	173	F	nt	—
Belford's Melidectes *Melidectes belfordi*	Indonesia, Papua New Guinea	178	F	lc	—
Yellow-browed Melidectes *Melidectes rufocrissalis*	Indonesia, Papua New Guinea	178	F	lc	—
Huon Melidectes *Melidectes foersteri*	Papua New Guinea	177	F	lc	—
Makira Melidectes *Melidectes sclateri*	Solomon Islands	198	F	lc	—
Arfak Honeyeater *Melipotes gymnops*	Indonesia	173	F	lc	—
Spangled Honeyeater *Melipotes ater*	Papua New Guinea	177	F	lc	—
Dark-eared Myza *Myza celebensis*	Indonesia	166	F	lc	—
White-eared Myza *Myza sarasinorum*	Indonesia	166	F	lc	—
Giant Honeyeater *Gymnomyza viridis*	Fiji	202	F	lc	—
Mao *Gymnomyza samoensis*	American Samoa (to USA)ˣ, Western Samoa	203	F	VU	17
Crow Honeyeater *Gymnomyza aubryana*	New Caledonia (to France)	201	F	VU	1
Kaua'i O'o *Moho braccatus*	USA	217	F	CR	158
O'ahu O'o *Moho apicalis*	USAˣ	217ˣ	F	EX	—
Bishop's O'o *Moho bishopi*	USA	217	F	CR	158
Hawai'i O'o *Moho nobilis*	USAˣ	218ˣ	F	EX	—
Kioea *Chaetoptila angustipluma*	USAˣ	218ˣ	F	EX	—
Barred Honeyeater *Phylidonyris undulata*	New Caledonia (to France)	201	F	lc	—
New Hebrides Honeyeater *Phylidonyris notabilis*	Vanuatu	200	F	lc	—
Black-eared Miner *Manorina melanotis* *	Australia	184	F	CR	178
Yellow Wattlebird *Anthochaera paradoxa*	Australia	185	FX	lc	—
Cape Sugarbird *Promerops cafer*	South Africa	088	S	lc	—
Subfamily EMBERIZINAE: Buntings					
Slaty Bunting *Latoucheornis siemsseni*	China	137	F	nt	—
Tibetan Bunting *Emberiza koslowi*	China	134	SR	nt	—
Socotra Bunting *Emberiza socotrana*	Yemen	117	SR	VU	78
Yellow Bunting *Emberiza sulphurata*	Japan	141 (s090)	FSA	VU	0
McKay's Bunting *Plectrophenax hyperboreus*	USA	(s001)	R	lc	—
Volcano Junco *Junco vulcani*	Costa Rica, Panama	020	FSG	lc	—
Guadalupe Junco *Junco insularis*	Mexico	003	FS	CR	158
Sierra Madre Sparrow *Xenospiza baileyi*	Mexico	006	G	EN	18
Bridled Sparrow *Aimophila mystacalis*	Mexico	008	FSD	lc	—
Black-chested Sparrow *Aimophila humeralis*	Mexico	008	SD	lc	—
Cinnamon-tailed Sparrow *Aimophila sumichrasti*	Mexico	014	FS	nt	—
Tumbes Sparrow *Aimophila stolzmanni*	Ecuador, Peru	045	FS	lc	—
Oaxaca Sparrow *Aimophila notosticta*	Mexico	008	S	nt	—
Cuban Sparrow *Torreornis inexpectata*	Cuba	025	FS	EN	18
White-throated Towhee *Pipilo albicollis*	Mexico	008	FS	lc	—
Black-capped Sparrow *Arremon abeillei*	Ecuador, Peru	045,048	FS	lc	—
Tocuyo Sparrow *Arremonops tocuyensis*	Colombia, Venezuela	035	FS	lc	—
White-rimmed Brush-finch *Atlapetes leucopis*	Colombia, Ecuador	042,046	F	nt	—
Santa Marta Brush-finch *Atlapetes melanocephalus*	Colombia	036	FS	lc	—
Yellow-headed Brush-finch *Atlapetes flaviceps*	Colombia	040	FS	EN	1
Dusky-headed Brush-finch *Atlapetes fuscoolivaceus*	Colombia	040	FS	nt	—
Moustached Brush-finch *Atlapetes albofrenatus*	Colombia, Venezuela	034,038	F	lc	—

	Breeding range	EBAs (and SAs)	Habitat codes	Status	Threat codes
Bay-crowned Brush-finch *Atlapetes seebohmi*	Ecuador, Peru	045	FS	lc	—
Rusty-bellied Brush-finch *Atlapetes nationi*	Peru	051	FS	lc	—
White-headed Brush-finch *Atlapetes albiceps*	Ecuador, Peru	045	FS	lc	—
Pale-headed Brush-finch *Atlapetes pallidiceps*	Ecuador	045	FSA	CR	18
Rufous-eared Brush-finch *Atlapetes rufigenis*	Peru	051	FS	nt	—
Tepui Brush-finch *Atlapetes personatus*	Brazil, Venezuela	064	FS	lc	—
Yellow-striped Brush-finch *Atlapetes citrinellus*	Argentina	057	FSA	lc	—
Green-striped Brush-finch *Atlapetes virenticeps*	Mexico	006	F	lc	—
Large-footed Finch *Pezopetes capitalis*	Costa Rica, Panama	020	FS	lc	—
Yellow-thighed Finch *Pselliophorus tibialis*	Costa Rica, Panama	020	F	lc	—
Yellow-green Finch *Pselliophorus luteoviridis*	Panama	020	F	VU	8
Sooty-faced Finch *Lysurus crassirostris*	Colombia, Costa Rica, Panama	020,024	F	lc	—
Tanager-finch *Oreothraupis arremonops*	Colombia, Ecuador	041	F	VU	01
Black-backed Bush-tanager *Urothraupis stolzmanni*	Colombia, Ecuador	043	FS	lc	—
Crimson Finch-tanager *Rhodospingus cruentus*	Ecuador, Peru	045	FS	lc	—
Canary-winged Finch *Melanodera melanodera*	Argentina, Chile, Falkland Islands (to UK)	062	GA	nt	—
Peg-billed Finch *Acanthidops bairdii*	Costa Rica, Panama	020	F	nt	—
Grey-crested Finch *Lophospingus griseocristatus*	Argentina, Bolivia	056	SA	lc	—
Gough Bunting *Rowettia goughensis*	St Helena (to UK)	080	S	VU	8
Tristan Bunting *Nesospiza acunhae*	St Helena (to UK)	079	SG	VU	8
Grosbeak Bunting *Nesospiza wilkinsi*	St Helena (to UK)	079	FG	VU	8
Short-tailed Finch *Idiopsar brachyurus*	Argentina, Bolivia, Peru	056	GR	lc	—
Cinereous Finch *Piezorhina cinerea*	Peru	045	FS	lc	—
Slender-billed Finch *Xenospingus concolor*	Chile, Peru	052	SD	VU	18
Great Inca-finch *Incaspiza pulchra*	Peru	051	S	lc	—
Rufous-backed Inca-finch *Incaspiza personata*	Peru	048,051	S	lc	—
Grey-winged Inca-finch *Incaspiza ortizi*	Peru	048,051	S	nt	—
Buff-bridled Inca-finch *Incaspiza laeta*	Peru	048	FS	lc	—
Little Inca-finch *Incaspiza watkinsi*	Peru	048	S	nt	—
Bay-chested Warbling-finch *Poospiza thoracica*	Brazil	076	FS	lc	—
Bolivian Warbling-finch *Poospiza boliviana*	Bolivia	056	FS	lc	—
Plain-tailed Warbling-finch *Poospiza alticola*	Peru	051	FS	EN	18
Rufous-breasted Warbling-finch *Poospiza rubecula*	Peru	051	FS	EN	18
Cochabamba Mountain-finch *Poospiza garleppi*	Bolivia	056	FSA	EN	18
Tucumán Mountain-finch *Poospiza baeri*	Argentina	056	S	VU	18
Chestnut-breasted Mountain-finch *Poospiza caesar*	Peru	051	FS	lc	—
Citron-headed Yellow-finch *Sicalis luteocephala*	Argentina, Bolivia	056	SGA	nt	—
Sulphur-throated Finch *Sicalis taczanowskii*	Ecuador, Peru	045	SG	lc	—
Duida Grass-finch *Emberizoides duidae*	Venezuela	064	G	lc	—
Pale-throated Pampa-finch *Embernagra longicauda*	Brazil	073	SVA	nt	—
Buffy-fronted Seedeater *Sporophila frontalis*	Argentina, Brazil, Paraguay	075	F	EN	16
Temminck's Seedeater *Sporophila falcirostris*	Argentina, Brazil, Paraguay	075	F	EN	16
Dubois's Seedeater *Sporophila ardesiaca*	Brazil	075	SGW	lc	—
Hooded Seedeater *Sporophila melanops*	Brazil	See p. 724	GW	VU	8
Drab Seedeater *Sporophila simplex*	Ecuador, Peru	045,052	SA	lc	—
Black-and-tawny Seedeater *Sporophila nigrorufa*	Bolivia	(s028)	SG	EN	1
Marsh Seedeater *Sporophila palustris*	Argentina, Brazil, Uruguay	077	SGW	EN	16
Chestnut Seedeater *Sporophila cinnamomea*	Argentina, Brazil, Uruguay	077	GW	nt	—
Entre Ríos Seedeater *Sporophila zelichi*	Argentina	077	SGW	CR	168
Black-bellied Seedeater *Sporophila melanogaster*	Brazil	076	SGW	nt	—
Tumaco Seedeater *Sporophila insulata*	Colombia	(s021)	SG	CR	8
Nicaraguan Seed-finch *Oryzoborus nuttingi*	Costa Rica, Nicaragua, Panama	019	SGWA	lc	—
White-naped Seedeater *Dolospingus fringilloides*	Brazil, Colombia, Venezuela	065	FSV	lc	—
Yellow-shouldered Grassquit *Loxipasser anoxanthus*	Jamaica	027	F	lc	—
Puerto Rican Bullfinch *Loxigilla portoricensis*	Puerto Rico (to USA), St Kitts and Nevis[X]	029,030[X]	FX	lc	—
Lesser Antillean Bullfinch *Loxigilla noctis*	Caribbean[9] (see p. 679)	029,030	F	lc	—
St Lucia Black Finch *Melanospiza richardsoni*	St Lucia	030	FSX	nt	—
Large Ground-finch *Geospiza magnirostris*	Ecuador	031	FS	lc	—
Medium Ground-finch *Geospiza fortis*	Ecuador	031	FS	lc	—
Small Ground-finch *Geospiza fuliginosa*	Ecuador	031	FS	lc	—
Sharp-beaked Ground-finch *Geospiza difficilis*	Ecuador	031	FS	lc	—
Common Cactus-finch *Geospiza scandens*	Ecuador	031	FS	lc	—
Large Cactus-finch *Geospiza conirostris*	Ecuador	031	FS	lc	—
Vegetarian Finch *Camarhynchus crassirostris*	Ecuador	031	FS	lc	—
Large Tree-finch *Camarhynchus psittacula*	Ecuador	031	FS	lc	—

	Breeding range	EBAs (and SAs)	Habitat codes	Status	Threat codes
Medium Tree-finch *Camarhynchus pauper*	Ecuador	031	FS	nt	—
Small Tree-finch *Camarhynchus parvulus*	Ecuador	031	FS	lc	—
Woodpecker Finch *Camarhynchus pallidus*	Ecuador	031	FS	lc	—
Mangrove Finch *Camarhynchus heliobates*	Ecuador	031	F	EN	8
Warbler Finch *Certhidea olivacea*	Ecuador	031	FS	lc	—
Cocos Finch *Pinaroloxias inornata*	Costa Rica	022	FS	VU	158

Subfamily CARDINALINAE: Cardinal-grosbeaks

Black-thighed Grosbeak *Pheucticus tibialis*	Costa Rica, Panama	020	F	lc	—
Vermilion Cardinal *Cardinalis phoeniceus*	Colombia, Venezuela	035	SD	lc	—
Crimson-collared Grosbeak *Rhodothraupis celaeno*	Mexico	011	FS	lc	—
Black-cowled Saltator *Saltator nigriceps*	Ecuador, Peru	045	FS	lc	—
Rufous-bellied Saltator *Saltator rufiventris*	Argentina, Bolivia	056	FSA	VU	1
Rose-bellied Bunting *Passerina rositae*	Mexico	014	FS	nt	—

Subfamily THRAUPINAE: Tanagers

Cone-billed Tanager *Conothraupis mesoleuca*	Brazil	See p. 724	F	VU	8
Puerto Rican Tanager *Nesospingus speculiferus*	Puerto Rico (to USA)	029	F	lc	—
Tacarcuna Bush-tanager *Chlorospingus tacarcunae*	Colombia, Panama	024	F	lc	—
Pirre Bush-tanager *Chlorospingus inornatus*	Panama	024	F	lc	—
Dusky Bush-tanager *Chlorospingus semifuscus*	Colombia, Ecuador	041	F	lc	—
Sooty-capped Bush-tanager *Chlorospingus pileatus*	Costa Rica, Panama	020	F	lc	—
Yellow-green Bush-tanager *Chlorospingus flavovirens*	Colombia, Ecuador	041	F	VU	18
Orange-browed Hemispingus *Hemispingus calophrys*	Bolivia, Peru	055	F	lc	—
Parodi's Hemispingus *Hemispingus parodii*	Peru	055	FS	lc	—
Grey-capped Hemispingus *Hemispingus reyi*	Venezuela	034	FS	lc	—
Slaty-backed Hemispingus *Hemispingus goeringi*	Venezuela	034	F	VU	18
Rufous-browed Hemispingus *H. rufosuperciliaris*	Peru	049	F	nt	—
Fulvous-headed Tanager *Thlypopsis fulviceps*	Colombia, Venezuela	032,033,034,038	FS	lc	—
Brown-flanked Tanager *Thlypopsis pectoralis*	Peru	051	FSA	lc	—
Buff-bellied Tanager *Thlypopsis inornata*	Peru	048	FS	lc	—
Black-and-yellow Tanager *Chrysothlypis chrysomelas*	Costa Rica, Panama	019,023	F	lc	—
Scarlet-and-white Tanager *Chrysothlypis salmoni*	Colombia, Ecuador	037,041	FS	lc	—
Cherry-throated Tanager *Nemosia rourei*	Brazil	075	F	CR	18
Black-crowned Palm-tanager *Phaenicophilus palmarum*	Dominican Republic, Haiti	028	FSVAX	lc	—
Grey-crowned Palm-tanager *P. poliocephalus*	Haiti	028	F	lc	—
Chat-tanager *Calyptophilus frugivorus*	Dominican Republic, Haiti	028	FS	VU	1
Olive-backed Tanager *Mitrospingus oleagineus*	Brazil, Guyana, Venezuela	064	F	lc	—
Olive-green Tanager *Orthogonys chloricterus*	Brazil	076	F	lc	—
Slaty Tanager *Creurgops dentata*	Bolivia, Peru	053,054	F	lc	—
Sulphur-rumped Tanager *Heterospingus rubrifrons*	Costa Rica, Panama	019,023	F	lc	—
Sooty Ant-tanager *Habia gutturalis*	Colombia	037	F	nt	—
Black-cheeked Ant-tanager *Habia atrimaxillaris*	Costa Rica	021	F	VU	1
Crested Ant-tanager *Habia cristata*	Colombia	041	F	lc	—
Huallaga Tanager *Ramphocelus melanogaster*	Peru	(s022)	F	lc	—
Azure-shouldered Tanager *Thraupis cyanoptera*	Brazil	075	F	nt	—
Blue-and-gold Tanager *Bangsia arcaei*	Costa Rica, Panama	020,024	F	nt	—
Black-and-gold Tanager *Bangsia melanochlamys*	Colombia	040,041	F	EN	1
Golden-chested Tanager *Bangsia rothschildi*	Colombia, Ecuador	041	F	lc	—
Moss-backed Tanager *Bangsia edwardsi*	Colombia, Ecuador	041	F	lc	—
Gold-ringed Tanager *Bangsia aureocincta*	Colombia	041	F	VU	18
Golden-backed Mountain-tanager *Buthraupis aureodorsalis*	Peru	049	F	VU	8
Masked Mountain-tanager *Buthraupis wetmorei*	Colombia, Ecuador, Peru	043	FS	VU	1
Orange-throated Tanager *Wetmorethraupis sterrhopteron*	Ecuador, Peru	047	F	EN	1
Santa Marta Mountain-tanager *Anisognathus melanogenys*	Colombia	036	F	lc	—
Black-chinned Mountain-tanager *A. notabilis*	Colombia, Ecuador	041	F	lc	—
Purplish-mantled Tanager *Iridosornis porphyrocephala*	Colombia, Ecuador	041	F	nt	—
Golden-collared Tanager *Iridosornis jelskii*	Bolivia, Peru	049,055	FS	lc	—
Yellow-scarfed Tanager *Iridosornis reinhardti*	Peru	049,055	FS	lc	—
Jamaican Euphonia *Euphonia jamaica*	Jamaica	027	FAX	lc	—
Velvet-fronted Euphonia *Euphonia concinna*	Colombia	039	FA	lc	—
Antillean Euphonia *Euphonia musica*	Caribbean [10] (see p. 679)	028,029,030	FS	lc	—
Spot-crowned Euphonia *Euphonia imitans*	Costa Rica, Panama	021	F	lc	—
Yellow-collared Chlorophonia *Chlorophonia flavirostris*	Colombia, Ecuador, Panama	024,041	F	lc	—

	Breeding range	EBAs (and SAs)	Habitat codes	Status	Threat codes
Golden-browed Chlorophonia *Chlorophonia callophrys*	Costa Rica, Panama	020	F	lc	—
Glistening-green Tanager *Chlorochrysa phoenicotis*	Colombia, Ecuador	041	F	lc	—
Multicoloured Tanager *Chlorochrysa nitidissima*	Colombia	040,041	F	VU	1
Azure-rumped Tanager *Tangara cabanisi*	Guatemala, Mexico	018	F	EN	18
Seven-coloured Tanager *Tangara fastuosa*	Brazil	071	F	EN	16
Brassy-breasted Tanager *Tangara desmaresti*	Brazil	076	F	lc	—
Gilt-edged Tanager *Tangara cyanoventris*	Brazil	075	F	lc	—
Blue-whiskered Tanager *Tangara johannae*	Colombia, Ecuador	041	F	nt	—
Lesser Antillean Tanager *Tangara cucullata*	Grenada, St Vincent	030	F	lc	—
Black-backed Tanager *Tangara peruviana*	Brazil	075	FS	EN	1
Green-capped Tanager *Tangara meyerdeschauenseei*	Peru	(s023)	FSA	VU	8
Rufous-cheeked Tanager *Tangara rufigenis*	Venezuela	033	F	lc	—
Spangle-cheeked Tanager *Tangara dowii*	Costa Rica, Panama	020	F	lc	—
Green-naped Tanager *Tangara fucosa*	Colombia, Panama	024	F	nt	—
Sira Tanager *Tangara phillipsi*	Peru	053	F	nt	—
Straw-backed Tanager *Tangara argyrofenges*	Bolivia, Peru	044,053,054	F	lc	—
Turquoise Dacnis *Dacnis hartlaubi*	Colombia	038,040,041	F	VU	1
Black-legged Dacnis *Dacnis nigripes*	Brazil	075	F	VU	16
Viridian Dacnis *Dacnis viguieri*	Colombia, Panama	023	F	nt	—
Scarlet-breasted Dacnis *Dacnis berlepschi*	Colombia, Ecuador	041	F	VU	1
Slaty Flower-piercer *Diglossa plumbea*	Costa Rica, Panama	020	FSG	lc	—
Venezuelan Flowerpiercer *Diglossa venezuelensis*	Venezuela	032	FS	CR	18
Chestnut-bellied Flower-piercer *Diglossa gloriosissima*	Colombia	041	FSG	nt	—
Mérida Flower-piercer *Diglossa gloriosa*	Venezuela	034	FS	lc	—
Grey-bellied Flower-piercer *Diglossa carbonaria*	Argentina, Bolivia	055,056	FS	lc	—
Scaled Flower-piercer *Diglossa duidae*	Brazil, Venezuela	064	FS	lc	—
Greater Flower-piercer *Diglossa major*	Brazil, Venezuela	064	FS	lc	—
Indigo Flower-piercer *Diglossopis indigotica*	Colombia, Ecuador	041	F	lc	—
Orangequit *Euneornis campestris*	Jamaica	027	F	lc	—

Family PARULIDAE: New world warblers

	Breeding range	EBAs (and SAs)	Habitat codes	Status	Threat codes
Colima Warbler *Vermivora crissalis*	Mexico, USA	010	FS	nt	—
Flame-throated Warbler *Parula gutturalis*	Costa Rica, Panama	020	F	lc	—
Golden-cheeked Warbler *Dendroica chrysoparia*	USA	(s004)	FS	EN	17
Adelaide's Warbler *Dendroica adelaidae*	Antigua and Barbuda, Puerto Rico (to USA), St Lucia	029,030	FS	lc	—
Olive-capped Warbler *Dendroica pityophila*	Bahamas, Cuba	025,026	F	lc	—
Kirtland's Warbler *Dendroica kirtlandii*	USA	(s003)	S	VU	8
Vitelline Warbler *Dendroica vitellina*	Cayman Islands (to UK), Honduras	(s009,s014)	S	nt	—
Plumbeous Warbler *Dendroica plumbea*	Dominica, Guadeloupe (to France)	030	F	lc	—
Arrowhead Warbler *Dendroica pharetra*	Jamaica	027	F	lc	—
Elfin-woods Warbler *Dendroica angelae*	Puerto Rico (to USA)	029	F	nt	—
Whistling Warbler *Catharopeza bishopi*	St Vincent	030	F	VU	8
Belding's Yellowthroat *Geothlypis beldingi*	Mexico	002	W	VU	17
Altamira Yellowthroat *Geothlypis flavovelata*	Mexico	011	W	nt	—
Bahama Yellowthroat *Geothlypis rostrata*	Bahamas	026	S	lc	—
Black-polled Yellowthroat *Geothlypis speciosa*	Mexico	007	W	VU	1
Green-tailed Warbler *Microligea palustris*	Dominican Republic, Haiti	028	F	lc	—
Yellow-headed Warbler *Teretistris fernandinae*	Cuba	025	FS	lc	—
Oriente Warbler *Teretistris fornsi*	Cuba	025	FS	lc	—
Semper's Warbler *Leucopeza semperi*	St Lucia	030	F	CR	8
Pink-headed Warbler *Ergaticus versicolor*	Guatemala, Mexico	018	F	nt	—
Tepui Whitestart *Myioborus castaneocapillus*	Brazil, Guyana, Venezuela	064	FS	lc	—
Paria Whitestart *Myioborus pariae*	Venezuela	032	F	CR	18
White-faced Whitestart *Myioborus albifacies*	Venezuela	064	F	nt	—
Guaiquinima Whitestart *Myioborus cardonai*	Venezuela	064	F	VU	8
Collared Whitestart *Myioborus torquatus*	Costa Rica, Panama	020	F	lc	—
White-fronted Whitestart *Myioborus albifrons*	Venezuela	034	F	lc	—
Yellow-crowned Whitestart *Myioborus flavivertex*	Colombia	036	F	lc	—
Grey-and-gold Warbler *Basileuterus fraseri*	Ecuador, Peru	045	FS	lc	—
Grey-headed Warbler *Basileuterus griseiceps*	Venezuela	032	F	CR	18
Santa Marta Warbler *Basileuterus basilicus*	Colombia	036	F	nt	—
Grey-throated Warbler *Basileuterus cinereicollis*	Colombia, Venezuela	034,038	F	nt	—
White-lored Warbler *Basileuterus conspicillatus*	Colombia	036	F	nt	—
Three-banded Warbler *Basileuterus trifasciatus*	Ecuador, Peru	045	F	lc	—
Black-cheeked Warbler *Basileuterus melanogenys*	Costa Rica, Panama	020	FS	lc	—

	Breeding range	EBAs (and SAs)	Habitat codes	Status	Threat codes
Pirre Warbler *Basileuterus ignotus*	Colombia, Panama	024	F	nt	—
Wrenthrush *Zeledonia coronata*	Costa Rica, Panama	020	F	lc	—
White-winged Warbler *Xenoligea montana*	Dominican Republic, Haiti	028	F	VU	1
Tamarugo Conebill *Conirostrum tamarugense*	Chile, Peru	052	FS	VU	01
Rufous-browed Conebill *Conirostrum rufum*	Colombia, Venezuela	036,038	FS	lc	—
Pardusco *Nephelornis oneillei*	Peru	049	FS	lc	—

Family DREPANIDIDAE: Hawaiian-honeycreepers

	Breeding range	EBAs (and SAs)	Habitat codes	Status	Threat codes
Nihoa Finch *Telespiza ultima*	USA	(s138)	SR	VU	8
Laysan Finch *Telespiza cantans*	USA	216	SG	VU	58
'O'u *Psittirostra psittacea*	USA	217,218	F	CR	1578
Lana'i Hookbill *Dysmorodrepanis munroi*	USA[X]	217[X]	F	EX	—
Palila *Loxioides bailleui*	USA	218	F	EN	157
Lesser Koa-finch *Rhodacanthis flaviceps*	USA[X]	218[X]	F	EX	—
Greater Koa-finch *Rhodacanthis palmeri*	USA[X]	218[X]	F	EX	—
Grosbeak Finch *Chloridops kona*	USA[X]	218[X]	F	EX	—
Maui Parrotbill *Pseudonestor xanthophrys*	USA	217	F	VU	158
Kaua'i 'Amakihi *Viridonia stejnegeri*	USA	217	F	VU	178
Common 'Amakihi *Viridonia virens*	USA	217,218	FSX	lc	—
'Anianiau *Viridonia parva*	USA	217	FX	VU	178
Greater 'Amakihi *Viridonia sagittirostris*	USA[X]	218[X]	F	EX	—
'Akialoa *Hemignathus obscurus*	USA[X]	217[X],218[X]	F	EX	—
Nukupu'u *Hemignathus lucidus*	USA	217,218[X]	F	CR	158
'Akiapola'au *Hemignathus wilsoni*	USA	218	F	EN	1
'Akikiki *Oreomystis bairdi*	USA	217	F	EN	1578
Hawai'i Creeper *Oreomystis mana*	USA	218	F	EN	5
Maui 'Alauahio *Paroreomyza montana*	USA	217	FSVX	nt	—
Kakawahie *Paroreomyza flammea*	USA[X]	217[X]	F	EX	—
O'ahu 'Alauahio *Paroreomyza maculata*	USA	217	F	CR	18
'Akeke'e *Loxops caeruleirostris*	USA	217	F	EN	1578
'Akepa *Loxops coccineus*	USA	217,218	F	EN	15
'Ula-'ai-hawane *Ciridops anna*	USA[X]	218[X]	F	EX	—
'I'iwi *Vestiaria coccinea*	USA	217,218	FX	lc	—
Hawai'i Mamo *Drepanis pacifica*	USA[X]	218[X]	F	EX	—
Black Mamo *Drepanis funerea*	USA[X]	217[X]	F	EX	—
'Akohekohe *Palmeria dolei*	USA	217	F	VU	8
'Apapane *Himatione sanguinea*	USA	216[X],217,218	FSX	lc	—
Po'o-uli *Melamprosops phaeosoma*	USA	217	F	CR	1578

Family VIREONIDAE: Vireos

	Breeding range	EBAs (and SAs)	Habitat codes	Status	Threat codes
Chocó Vireo *Vireo masteri* *	Colombia	041	F	VU	18
Yellow-winged Vireo *Vireo carmioli*	Costa Rica, Panama	020	F	lc	—
Cozumel Vireo *Vireo bairdi*	Mexico	016	F	lc	—
Thick-billed Vireo *Vireo crassirostris*	Bahamas, Cayman Islands (to UK), Colombia, Cuba, Haiti	025,026,028 (s012,s014)	FS	lc	—
San Andrés Vireo *Vireo caribaeus*	Colombia	(s013)	FS	CR	18
Jamaican Vireo *Vireo modestus*	Jamaica	027	FS	lc	—
Flat-billed Vireo *Vireo nanus*	Dominican Republic, Haiti	028	FS	lc	—
Puerto Rican Vireo *Vireo latimeri*	Puerto Rico (to USA)	029	FSX	lc	—
Blue Mountain Vireo *Vireo osburni*	Jamaica	027	F	nt	—
Noronha Vireo *Vireo gracilirostris*	Brazil	069	FS	VU	8
Yucatán Vireo *Vireo magister*	Belize, Cayman Islands (to UK), Honduras, Mexico	016 (s007,s014)	F	lc	—
Tepui Greenlet *Hylophilus sclateri*	Brazil, Guyana, Venezuela	064	FS	lc	—

Family ICTERIDAE: New world orioles

	Breeding range	EBAs (and SAs)	Habitat codes	Status	Threat codes
Baudó Oropendola *Psarocolius cassini*	Colombia	023	F	EN	1
Black Oropendola *Gymnostinops guatimozinus*	Colombia, Panama	023,037	F	lc	—
Selva Cacique *Cacicus koepckeae*	Peru	068	F	VU	1
Ecuadorian Cacique *Cacicus sclateri*	Ecuador, Peru	066	F	lc	—
Jamaican Oriole *Icterus leucopteryx*	Cayman Islands (to UK), Colombia, Jamaica	027 (s013,s014)	FAX	lc	—
White-edged Oriole *Icterus graceannae*	Ecuador, Peru	045	FS	lc	—
Montserrat Oriole *Icterus oberi*	Montserrat (to UK)	030	F	nt	—
Martinique Oriole *Icterus bonana*	Martinique (to France)	030	FX	EN	78
St Lucia Oriole *Icterus laudabilis*	St Lucia	030	FX	nt	—
Bar-winged Oriole *Icterus maculialatus*	El Salvador, Guatemala, Mexico	018	FS	lc	—
Jamaican Blackbird *Nesopsar nigerrimus*	Jamaica	027	F	nt	—
Tricoloured Blackbird *Agelaius tricolor*	Mexico, USA	001	WA	lc	—

	Breeding range	EBAs (and SAs)	Habitat codes	Status	Threat codes
Yellow-shouldered Blackbird *Agelaius xanthomus*	Puerto Rico (to USA)	029	FSRAX	EN	1578
Red-bellied Grackle *Hypopyrrhus pyrohypogaster*	Colombia	040,041	FS	EN	18
Forbes's Blackbird *Curaeus forbesi*	Brazil	071	FW	CR	1678
Bolivian Blackbird *Oreopsar bolivianus*	Bolivia	056	SRA	lc	—
Golden-tufted Grackle *Macroagelaius imthurni*	Brazil, Guyana, Venezuela	064	F	lc	—
Mountain Grackle *Macroagelaius subalaris*	Colombia	038	F	nt	—
Slender-billed Grackle *Quiscalus palustris*	Mexico[X]	007[X]	W	EX	—
Nicaraguan Grackle *Quiscalus nicaraguensis*	Costa Rica, Nicaragua	(s011)	GWA	nt	—

Family FRINGILLIDAE: Finches

	Breeding range	EBAs (and SAs)	Habitat codes	Status	Threat codes
Blue Chaffinch *Fringilla teydea*	Spain	120	F	cd	—
Syrian Serin *Serinus syriacus*	Israel, Jordan, Lebanon, Syria	(s067)	F	lc	—
Island Canary *Serinus canaria*	Portugal, Spain	120 (s069)	FSA	lc	—
Forest Canary *Serinus scotops*	South Africa, Swaziland	089	FSX	lc	—
Yellow-throated Serin *Serinus flavigula*	Ethiopia	115	SRA	EN	8
Lemon-breasted Seedeater *Serinus citrinipectus*	Malawi, Mozambique, South Africa, Zimbabwe	092	SVG	lc	—
Yemen Serin *Serinus menachensis*	Sauda Arabia, Yemen	118	SR	lc	—
Ankober Serin *Serinus ankoberensis*	Ethiopia	115	GR	EN	1
Yellow-browed Seedeater *Serinus whytii*	Malawi, Tanzania, Zambia	105	FSA	lc	—
Príncipe Seedeater *Serinus rufobrunneus*	São Tomé e Príncipe	082,083	FX	lc	—
Kipengere Seedeater *Serinus melanochrous*	Tanzania	105	F	nt	—
Protea Canary *Serinus leucopterus*	South Africa	088	S	nt	—
Cape Siskin *Serinus totta*	South Africa	088	SR	nt	—
Drakensberg Siskin *Serinus symonsi*	Lesotho, South Africa	090	SGR	nt	—
Mountain Serin *Serinus estherae*	Indonesia, Philippines	154,158,160,166	FS	lc	—
São Tomé Grosbeak *Neospiza concolor*	São Tomé e Príncipe	082	F	CR	18
Vietnam Greenfinch *Carduelis monguilloti*	Vietnam	145	FA	nt	—
Black-capped Siskin *Carduelis atriceps*	Guatemala, Mexico	018	FSA	nt	—
Saffron Siskin *Carduelis siemiradzkii*	Ecuador, Peru	045	FS	VU	1
Lawrence's Goldfinch *Carduelis lawrencei*	Mexico, USA	001	FS	lc	—
Antillean Siskin *Carduelis dominicensis*	Dominican Republic, Haiti	028	FA	lc	—
Yemen Linnet *Carduelis yemenensis*	Sauda Arabia, Yemen	118	FSA	lc	—
Warsangli Linnet *Carduelis johannis*	Somalia	116	FSGR	EN	18
Sillem's Mountain-finch *Leucosticte sillemi* *	China	(s076)	Z	DD	—
Spectacled Finch *Callacanthis burtoni*	India, Nepal, Pakistan	128	F	lc	—
Tibetan Rosefinch *Carpodacus roborowskii*	China	(s078)	GR	DD	—
Bonin Grosbeak *Chaunoproctus ferreorostris*	Japan[X]	147[X]	F	EX	—
Scottish Crossbill *Loxia scotica*	United Kingdom	(s070)	F	DD	—
White-cheeked Bullfinch *Pyrrhula leucogenis*	Philippines	151,154	F	nt	—
Orange Bullfinch *Pyrrhula aurantiaca*	India, Pakistan	128	F	nt	—

Family ESTRILDIDAE: Waxbills

	Breeding range	EBAs (and SAs)	Habitat codes	Status	Threat codes
Fernando Po Oliveback *Nesocharis shelleyi*	Cameroon, Equatorial Guinea, Nigeria	086	F	lc	—
Dusky Crimson-wing *Cryptospiza jacksoni*	Burundi, Rwanda, Uganda, Zaïre	106	F	lc	—
Shelley's Crimson-wing *Cryptospiza shelleyi*	Burundi, Rwanda, Uganda, Zaïre	106	F	VU	0
Pink-throated Twinspot *Hypargos margaritatus*	Mozambique, South Africa, Swaziland	092	FS	lc	—
Mali Firefinch *Lagonosticta virata*	Mali, Senegal	(s040)	SG	nt	—
Cinderella Waxbill *Estrilda thomensis*	Angola, Namibia	087	SV	nt	—
Anambra Waxbill *Estrilda poliopareia*	Nigeria	(s042)	GW	VU	18
Arabian Waxbill *Estrilda rufibarba*	Sauda Arabia, Yemen	118	FSRA	lc	—
Black-lored Waxbill *Estrilda nigriloris*	Zaïre	(s054)	G	VU	1
Red-eared Firetail *Stagonopleura oculata*	Australia	186	FS	nt	—
Mountain Firetail *Oreostruthus fuliginosus*	Indonesia, Papua New Guinea	178	FG	lc	—
Green-faced Parrotfinch *Erythrura viridifacies*	Philippines	151,152	FG	EN	1
Tricoloured Parrotfinch *Erythrura tricolor*	Indonesia	164,165	FSA	lc	—
Red-eared Parrotfinch *Erythrura coloria*	Philippines	154	FG	VU	1
Red-throated Parrotfinch *Erythrura psittacea*	New Caledonia (to France)	201	FSVG	lc	—
Fiji Parrotfinch *Erythrura pealii*	Fiji	202	FGA	lc	—
Red-headed Parrotfinch *Erythrura cyaneovirens*	Western Samoa	203	F	lc	—
Royal Parrotfinch *Erythrura regia*	Vanuatu	200	FVX	VU	1
Pink-billed Parrotfinch *Erythrura kleinschmidti*	Fiji	202	FS	EN	08
Cream-bellied Munia *Lonchura pallidiventer* *	Indonesia	See p. 724	Z	NE	—
Grey-banded Munia *Lonchura vana*	Indonesia	173	G	VU	1
Grey-crowned Munia *Lonchura nevermanni*	Indonesia, Papua New Guinea	180	VGW	nt	—
Mottled Munia *Lonchura hunsteini*	Papua New Guinea	195	GA	lc	—

	Breeding range	EBAs (and SAs)	Habitat codes	Status	Threat codes
New Ireland Munia *Lonchura forbesi*	Papua New Guinea	195	G	lc	—
New Hanover Munia *Lonchura nigerrima*	Papua New Guinea	195	FS	lc	—
Yellow-rumped Munia *Lonchura flaviprymna*	Australia	187	VWA	nt	—
Black Munia *Lonchura stygia*	Indonesia, Papua New Guinea	180	VGW	nt	—
Black-breasted Munia *Lonchura teerinki*	Indonesia	178	GA	lc	—
Snow Mountain Munia *Lonchura montana*	Indonesia, Papua New Guinea	178	SGA	lc	—
Alpine Munia *Lonchura monticola*	Papua New Guinea	178	GR	lc	—
Bismarck Munia *Lonchura melaena*	Papua New Guinea	195,198	FSG	lc	—
Timor Sparrow *Padda fuscata*	Indonesia	164	SVA	nt	—

Subfamily PASSERINAE: Old world sparrows

Sind Sparrow *Passer pyrrhonotus*	India, Iran, Pakistan	(s074)	SW	lc	—
Iago Sparrow *Passer iagoensis*	Cape Verde	078	RA	lc	—
Socotra Sparrow *Passer insularis*	Yemen	117	SGD	lc	—
Afghan Snowfinch *Montifringilla theresae*	Afghanistan	(s073)	RA	lc	—

Subfamily PLOCEINAE: Weavers

Rufous-tailed Weaver *Histurgops ruficauda*	Tanzania	108	FGA	lc	—
Bannerman's Weaver *Ploceus bannermani*	Cameroon, Nigeria	086	FS	VU	1
Bates's Weaver *Ploceus batesi*	Cameroon	085	F	VU	1
Loango Weaver *Ploceus subpersonatus*	Angola, Gabon, Zaïre	(s043)	FSV	VU	1
Strange Weaver *Ploceus alienus*	Burundi, Rwanda, Uganda, Zaïre	106	F	lc	—
Príncipe Golden-weaver *Ploceus princeps*	São Tomé e Príncipe	083	FX	lc	—
Kilombero Weaver *Ploceus burnieri*	Tanzania	(s056)	W	VU	18
Lake Lufira Weaver *Ploceus ruweti*	Zaïre	(s053)	F	VU	8
Tanzania Masked-weaver *Ploceus reichardi*	Tanzania, Zambia	(s055)	W	lc	—
Giant Weaver *Ploceus grandis*	São Tomé e Príncipe	082	FVX	lc	—
Fox's Weaver *Ploceus spekeoides*	Uganda	(s059)	SGW	nt	—
Clarke's Weaver *Ploceus golandi*	Kenya	111	F	VU	18
Salvadori's Weaver *Ploceus dicrocephalus*	Ethiopia, Kenya, Somalia	113	GW	lc	—
Golden-naped Weaver *Ploceus aureonucha*	Zaïre	107	FA	VU	18
Tanzanian Mountain Weaver *Ploceus nicolli*	Tanzania	105	F	VU	18
São Tomé Weaver *Ploceus sanctithomae*	São Tomé e Príncipe	082	FVX	lc	—
Yellow-legged Weaver *Ploceus flavipes*	Zaïre	107	F	VU	18
Gola Malimbe *Malimbus ballmanni*	Ivory Coast, Liberia, Sierra Leone	084	F	EN	1
Rachel's Malimbe *Malimbus racheliae*	Cameroon, Gabon, Equatorial Guinea, Nigeria	085	F	lc	—
Ibadan Malimbe *Malimbus ibadanensis*	Nigeria	(s041)	F	CR	18
Red-headed Fody *Foudia eminentissima*	Comoros, Mayotte (to France), Seychelles	098,099	FSX	lc	—
Mauritius Fody *Foudia rubra*	Mauritius	102	FX	CR	158
Seychelles Fody *Foudia sechellarum*	Seychelles	100	FX	VU	58
Rodrigues Fody *Foudia flavicans*	Mauritius	103	F	VU	1578
Golden-backed Bishop *Euplectes aureus*	Angola	087	S	nt	—
Buff-shouldered Widowbird *Euplectes psammocromius*	Malawi, Tanzania, Zambia	105	GW	lc	—
Jackson's Widowbird *Euplectes jacksoni*	Kenya, Tanzania	109	GA	nt	—

Family STURNIDAE: Starlings

Rusty-winged Starling *Aplonis zelandica*	Solomon Islands, Vanuatu	200	FS	nt	—
Santo Mountain Starling *Aplonis santovestris*	Vanuatu	200	F	VU	28
Pohnpei Mountain Starling *Aplonis pelzelni*	Micronesia	192	F	CR	58
Samoan Starling *Aplonis atrifusca*	American Samoa (to USA), Western Samoa	203	FSX	lc	—
Kosrae Starling *Aplonis corvina*	Micronesia[X]	192[X]	F	EX	—
Mysterious Starling *Aplonis mavornata*	Cook Islands (to New Zealand)[X]	210[X]	F	EX	—
Rarotonga Starling *Aplonis cinerascens*	Cook Islands (to New Zealand)	210	F	VU	08
Polynesian Starling *Aplonis tabuensis*	American Samoa (to USA), Fiji, Niue (to New Zealand), Solomon Is., Tonga, Wallis and Futuna Is. (to France), Western Samoa	200,202,203 (s127, s128,s129,s130, s131)	FSX	lc	—
Striated Starling *Aplonis striata*	New Caledonia (to France)	201	FV	lc	—
Norfolk Island Starling *Aplonis fusca*	Australia[X], Norfolk Island[X]	204[X],205[X]	F	EX	—
Micronesian Starling *Aplonis opaca*	Guam (to USA), Micronesia, N Mariana Is. (to USA), Palau	189,190,191,192	FAX	lc	—
Tanimbar Starling *Aplonis crassa*	Indonesia	165	F	nt	—
Atoll Starling *Aplonis feadensis*	Papua New Guinea, Solomon Is.	195 (s126)	FX	lc	—
Rennell Starling *Aplonis insularis*	Solomon Islands	199	F	nt	—
Brown-winged Starling *Aplonis grandis*	Papua New Guinea, Solomon Is.	198	F	lc	—
Makira Starling *Aplonis dichroa*	Solomon Islands	198	F	lc	—

	Breeding range	EBAs (and SAs)	Habitat codes	Status	Threat codes
Long-tailed Starling *Aplonis magna*	Indonesia	174	FS	lc	—
White-eyed Starling *Aplonis brunneicapilla*	Papua New Guinea, Solomon Is.	198	F	EN	127
Kenrick's Starling *Poeoptera kenricki*	Kenya, Tanzania	105,109	F	lc	—
Socotra Starling *Onychognathus frater*	Yemen	117	SGW	VU	78
Copper-tailed Glossy-starling *Lamprotornis cupreocauda*	Ghana, Guinea, Ivory Coast, Liberia, Sierra Leone	084	F	nt	—
Príncipe Glossy-starling *Lamprotornis ornatus*	São Tomé e Príncipe	083	FX	lc	—
Abbott's Starling *Cinnyricinclus femoralis*	Kenya, Tanzania	109	F	VU	1
Rodrigues Starling *Necropsar rodericanus*	Mauritius[X]	103[X]	F	EX	—
Réunion Starling *Fregilupus varius*	Réunion (to France)[X]	101[X]	Z	EX	—
White-faced Starling *Sturnus senex*	Sri Lanka	124	F	nt	—
White-headed Starling *Sturnus erythropygius*	India	125,126	FGA	nt	—
Bali Starling *Leucopsar rothschildi*	Indonesia	160	F	CR	68
Sulawesi Myna *Basilornis celebensis*	Indonesia	166	F	lc	—
Helmeted Myna *Basilornis galeatus*	Indonesia	168	F	nt	—
Long-crested Myna *Basilornis corythaix*	Indonesia	170	FA	lc	—
Apo Myna *Basilornis miranda*	Philippines	154	F	nt	—
Bare-eyed Myna *Streptocitta albertinae*	Indonesia	168	FA	nt	—
Sri Lanka Myna *Gracula ptilogenys*	Sri Lanka	124	F	lc	—
Fiery-browed Myna *Enodes erythrophris*	Indonesia	166	F	lc	—

Family ORIOLIDAE: Orioles

Olive-brown Oriole *Oriolus melanotis*	Indonesia	164	F	lc	—
Black-eared Oriole *Oriolus bouroensis*	Indonesia	165,169	F	lc	—
Grey-collared Oriole *Oriolus forsteni*	Indonesia	170	F	lc	—
Dusky-brown Oriole *Oriolus phaeochromus*	Indonesia	171	FA	lc	—
White-lored Oriole *Oriolus albiloris*	Philippines	151	F	lc	—
Isabela Oriole *Oriolus isabellae*	Philippines	151	F	CR	18
São Tomé Oriole *Oriolus crassirostris*	São Tomé e Príncipe	082	FV	VU	14
Black Oriole *Oriolus hosii*	Malaysia	157	F	nt	—
Silver Oriole *Oriolus mellianus*	China	140	F	VU	1
Wetar Figbird *Sphecotheres hypoleucus*	Indonesia	164	FS	DD	—
Timor Figbird *Sphecotheres viridis* *	Indonesia	164	F	lc	—

Family DICRURIDAE: Drongos

Aldabra Drongo *Dicrurus aldabranus*	Seychelles	099	FS	nt	—
Grand Comoro Drongo *Dicrurus fuscipennis*	Comoros	098	FX	CR	18
Mayotte Drongo *Dicrurus waldenii*	Mayotte (to France)	098	FX	CR	18
Sumatran Drongo *Dicrurus sumatranus*	Indonesia	158	F	nt	—
Sulawesi Drongo *Dicrurus montanus*	Indonesia	166	F	lc	—
Ribbon-tailed Drongo *Dicrurus megarhynchus*	Papua New Guinea	195	F	lc	—
Andaman Drongo *Dicrurus andamanensis*	India, Myanmar	125	F	nt	—

Family CALLAEIDAE: New Zealand wattlebirds

Huia *Heteralocha acutirostris*	New Zealand[X]	206[X]	F	EX	—

Family ARTIMIDAE: Wood swallows

Bismarck Woodswallow *Artamus insignis*	Papua New Guinea	195	F	lc	—
Fiji Woodswallow *Artamus mentalis*	Fiji	202	F	lc	—

Family CRACTICIDAE: Bell magpies

Tagula Butcherbird *Cracticus louisiadensis*	Papua New Guinea	197	F	DD	—
Black Currawong *Strepera fuliginosa*	Australia	185	FSWA	lc	—

Family PTILONORHYNCHIDAE: Bowerbirds

Green Catbird *Ailuroedus crassirostris*	Australia	183	F	lc	—
Tooth-billed Catbird *Ailuroedus dentirostris*	Australia	182	F	nt	—
Archbold's Bowerbird *Archboldia papuensis*	Indonesia	178	F	VU	1
Vogelkop Bowerbird *Amblyornis inornatus*	Indonesia	173	F	lc	—
Streaked Bowerbird *Amblyornis subalaris*	Papua New Guinea	178	F	lc	—
Golden-fronted Bowerbird *Amblyornis flavifrons*	Indonesia	175	F	nt	—
Golden Bowerbird *Prionodura newtoniana*	Australia	182	F	cd	—
Fire-maned Bowerbird *Sericulus bakeri*	Papua New Guinea	177	F	VU	12
Regent Bowerbird *Sericulus chrysocephalus*	Australia	183	F	lc	—

Family PARADISAEIDAE: Birds-of-paradise

Yellow-breasted Bird-of-paradise *Loboparadisea sericea*	Indonesia, Papua New Guinea	178	F	DD	—
Crested Bird-of-paradise *Cnemophilus macgregorii*	Indonesia, Papua New Guinea	178	FS	lc	—
Loria's Bird-of-paradise *Cnemophilus loriae*	Indonesia, Papua New Guinea	178	FS	lc	—
Macgregor's Bird-of-paradise *Macgregoria pulchra*	Indonesia, Papua New Guinea	178	F	VU	2
Paradise-crow *Lycocorax pyrrhopterus*	Indonesia	171	FAX	lc	—

Appendix 1: Restricted-range Bird Species Listed by Family

	Breeding range	EBAs (and SAs)	Habitat codes	Status	Threat codes
Curl-crested Manucode *Manucodia comrii*	Papua New Guinea	196	F	lc	—
Standardwing *Semioptera wallacii*	Indonesia	171	F	nt	—
Long-tailed Paradigalla *Paradigalla carunculata*	Indonesia	173,178	F	nt	—
Short-tailed Paradigalla *Paradigalla brevicauda*	Indonesia, Papua New Guinea	178	F	lc	—
Brown Sicklebill *Epimachus meyeri*	Indonesia, Papua New Guinea	178	F	lc	—
Pale-billed Sicklebill *Epimachus bruijnii*	Indonesia, Papua New Guinea	176	F	nt	—
Western Parotia *Parotia sefilata*	Indonesia	173	F	lc	—
Lawes's Parotia *Parotia lawesii*	Papua New Guinea	178	F	lc	—
Eastern Parotia *Parotia helenae*	Papua New Guinea	178	F	lc	—
Wahnes's Parotia *Parotia wahnesi*	Papua New Guinea	177	F	VU	1
Victoria's Riflebird *Ptiloris victoriae*	Australia	182	F	lc	—
Paradise Riflebird *Ptiloris paradiseus*	Australia	183	F	nt	—
Wilson's Bird-of-paradise *Cicinnurus respublica*	Indonesia	172	F	nt	—
Arfak Astrapia *Astrapia nigra*	Indonesia	173	F	nt	—
Splendid Astrapia *Astrapia splendidissima*	Indonesia, Papua New Guinea	178	F	lc	—
Ribbon-tailed Astrapia *Astrapia mayeri*	Papua New Guinea	178	F	VU	12
Stephanie's Astrapia *Astrapia stephaniae*	Papua New Guinea	178	F	lc	—
Huon Astrapia *Astrapia rothschildi*	Papua New Guinea	177	F	lc	—
King-of-Saxony Bird-of-paradise *Pteridophora alberti*	Indonesia, Papua New Guinea	178	F	lc	—
Red Bird-of-paradise *Paradisaea rubra*	Indonesia	172	F	nt	—
Greater Bird-of-paradise *Paradisaea apoda*	Indonesia, Papua New Guinea	179	F	lc	—
Goldie's Bird-of-paradise *Paradisaea decora*	Papua New Guinea	196	F	VU	1
Emperor Bird-of-paradise *Paradisaea guilielmi*	Papua New Guinea	177	F	nt	—
Blue Bird-of-paradise *Paradisaea rudolphi*	Papua New Guinea	178	F	VU	1237

Family CORVIDAE: Crows

	Breeding range	EBAs (and SAs)	Habitat codes	Status	Threat codes
Beautiful Jay *Cyanolyca pulchra*	Colombia, Ecuador	041	F	nt	—
Dwarf Jay *Cyanolyca nana*	Mexico	012	F	EN	1
White-throated Jay *Cyanolyca mirabilis*	Mexico	009	F	EN	1
Silvery-throated Jay *Cyanolyca argentigula*	Costa Rica, Panama	020	F	lc	—
Bushy-crested Jay *Cyanocorax melanocyaneus*	El Salvador, Guatemala, Honduras, Nicaragua	018	FX	lc	—
San Blas Jay *Cyanocorax sanblasianus*	Mexico	005,008	FS	lc	—
Purplish-backed Jay *Cyanocorax beecheii*	Mexico	005	FS	lc	—
Azure-naped Jay *Cyanocorax heilprini*	Brazil, Colombia, Venezuela	065	F	lc	—
Tufted Jay *Cyanocorax dickeyi*	Mexico	006	F	nt	—
White-tailed Jay *Cyanocorax mystacalis*	Ecuador, Peru	045	FS	lc	—
Lidth's Jay *Garrulus lidthi*	Japan	148	F	VU	1
Sichuan Jay *Perisoreus internigrans*	China	138	F	VU	1
Sri Lanka Magpie *Urocissa ornata*	Sri Lanka	124	F	VU	17
Formosan Magpie *Urocissa caerulea*	Taiwan	149	F	lc	—
White-bellied Treepie *Dendrocitta leucogastra*	India	123	F	nt	—
Andaman Treepie *Dendrocitta bayleyi*	India	125	F	nt	—
Hooded Treepie *Crypsirina cucullata*	Myanmar	132	FSA	VU	1
Yellow-billed Magpie *Pica nuttalli*	USA	001	FS	lc	—
Ethiopian Bush-crow *Zavattariornis stresemanni*	Ethiopia	114	SV	VU	1
Xinjiang Ground-jay *Podoces biddulphi*	China	127	SD	VU	1
New Caledonian Crow *Corvus moneduloides*	New Caledonia (to France)	201	FVG	lc	—
Banggai Crow *Corvus unicolor*	Indonesia	168	Z	VU	8
Flores Crow *Corvus florensis*	Indonesia	162	F	VU	1
Mariana Crow *Corvus kubaryi*	Guam (to USA), Northern Mariana Islands (to USA)	189	F	CR	158
Long-billed Crow *Corvus validus*	Indonesia	171	FGAX	lc	—
Bougainville Crow *Corvus meeki*	Papua New Guinea, Solomon Is.	198	FX	nt	—
White-billed Crow *Corvus woodfordi*	Solomon Islands	198	FX	nt	—
Brown-headed Crow *Corvus fuscicapillus*	Indonesia	172,176 (s112)	F	nt	—
Tamaulipas Crow *Corvus imparatus*	Mexico	011	FA	lc	—
Sinaloa Crow *Corvus sinaloae*	Mexico	005	FA	lc	—
Palm Crow *Corvus palmarum*	Cuba, Dominican Republic, Haiti	025,028	FSW	nt	—
Jamaican Crow *Corvus jamaicensis*	Jamaica	027	FX	lc	—
White-necked Crow *Corvus leucognaphalus*	Dominican Republic, Haiti, Puerto Rico (to USA)[X]	028,029[X]	FAX	VU	12
Hawaiian Crow *Corvus hawaiiensis*	USA	218	F	CR	128

Species of unknown provenance

The following nine species are of unknown provenance but are presumed to have restricted breeding ranges.

Crested Shelduck *Tadorna cristata* (p. 680) is known only by (presumed) non-breeding records from Russia, North Korea, South Korea, Japan and possibly China. It is speculated that it may breed in the mountains on the border between China and North Korea.

Coppery Thorntail *Popelairia letitiae* (p. 691) is known just from three nineteenth century specimens labelled simply Bolivia.

Bogotá Sunangel *Heliangelus zusii* (p. 692) is known from a single specimen purchased in 1909, but only recently described (Graves 1993). It is speculated to have been collected on the East Andes or possibly the Central Andes of Colombia.

White-eyed River-martin *Pseudochelidon sirintarae* (p. 700) is known only by non-breeding records from Bung (Lake) Boraphet in central Thailand, and could breed anywhere in south-eastern Asia, probably along one of the major rivers.

Long-tailed Pipit *Anthus longicaudatus* (p. 700) is recently described from the Kimberley area of South Africa, where it is locally well known but presumed to be a migrant and to breed somewhere north of this region (Liversidge 1996).

Streaked Reed-warbler *Acrocephalus sorghophilus* (p. 707) is recorded from eastern China on passage, and winters in the Philippines. The precise breeding area is unknown, but is speculated to be in wetlands in Liaoning and Hebei provinces in north-east China, which could constitute a new Secondary Area.

Hooded Seedeater *Sporophila melanops* (p. 716) is described from a single specimen probably taken near Registro do Araguaia in west-central Goiás in October 1823.

Cone-billed Tanager *Conothraupis mesoleuca* (p. 717) is known from just one specimen collected in 1938, apparently from dry forest in Mato Grosso state, Brazil.

Cream-bellied Munia *Lonchura pallidiventer* (p. 720) is recently described and known in trade only, but is likely to come from somewhere in the hinterland of Banjarmarsin in south-east Kalimantan, Indonesia (Restall 1996).

APPENDIX 2:   EBAs and restricted-range bird species listed by country

A S most conservation action is nationally based, this appendix presents data by geopolitical unit. For each country there is provided here: a list of Endemic Bird Areas (with their priority rankings; see pp. 42–43) and Secondary Areas part or all of which lie within its borders; a table summarizing the numbers of extant restricted-range species which occur in the country; and a taxonomic list of these species, indicating which are threatened, the number of countries in which they breed, and the EBAs and Secondary Areas where they occur in the country. Some restricted-range species are of unknown provenance (see p. 724), though it has been possible to assign all but one—Crested Shelduck *Tadorna cristata*—to a country.

Key

EX Extinct
EW Extinct in the Wild
EL Extinct locally (i.e. in the country concerned)

X Extinct in that EBA or Secondary Area

The IUCN Red List categories 'Extinct' (EX) and 'Extinct in the Wild' (EW) are defined on p. 679.

AFGHANISTAN

EBAs	Priority
128 Western Himalayas	CRITICAL

Secondary Areas
s073 Afghanistan mountains

Restricted-range species	Threatened	Total
Confined to this country	0	1
Present also in other countries	0	4
Total	0	5

Species (threatened species in **bold**)	No. of countries	EBAs (and SAs)
Brooks's Leaf-warbler *Phylloscopus subviridis*	3	128
Tytler's Leaf-warbler *Phylloscopus tytleri*	4	128
White-cheeked Tit *Aegithalos leucogenys*	3	128
Kashmir Nuthatch *Sitta cashmirensis*	4	128
Afghan Snowfinch *Montifringilla theresae*	1	(s073)

ALGERIA

EBAs none

Secondary Areas
s039 North Algerian mountains

Restricted-range species	Threatened	Total
Confined to this country	1	1
Present also in other countries	0	0
Total	1	1

Species (threatened species in **bold**)	No. of countries	EBAs (and SAs)
Algerian Nuthatch *Sitta ledanti*	1	(s039)

AMERICAN SAMOA (TO USA)

EBAs	Priority
203 Samoan Islands	URGENT

Secondary Areas none

Restricted-range species	Threatened	Total
Confined to this country	0	0
Present also in other countries	0	9
Total	0	9

Species (threatened species in **bold**)	No. of countries	EBAs (and SAs)
Shy Ground-dove *Gallicolumba stairi*	5	203
Many-coloured Fruit-dove *Ptilinopus perousii*	4	203
Purple-capped Fruit-dove *Ptilinopus porphyraceus*	7	203
Blue-crowned Lorikeet *Vini australis*	6	203
Fiji Shrikebill *Clytorhynchus vitiensis*	4	203
Cardinal Myzomela *Myzomela cardinalis*	5	203
Wattled Honeyeater *Foulehaio carunculata*	5	203
EL **Mao** *Gymnomyza samoensis*	1	203
Samoan Starling *Aplonis atrifusca*	2	203
Polynesian Starling *Aplonis tabuensis*	7	203

ANGOLA

EBAs	Priority
087 Western Angola	CRITICAL

Secondary Areas
s043 Gabon–Cabinda coast
s044 West Zaïre and north Angola forests
s045 Namibian escarpment

Restricted-range species	Threatened	Total
Confined to this country	7	12
Present also in other countries	3	5
Total	10	17

Species (threatened species in **bold**)	No. of countries	EBAs (and SAs)
Grey-striped Francolin *Francolinus griseostriatus*	1	087
Swierstra's Francolin *Francolinus swierstrai*	1	087
Orange-breasted Bush-shrike *Laniarius brauni*	1	087

cont.

Angola (cont.)

Gabela Bush-shrike *Laniarius amboimensis*	1	087
Monteiro's Bush-shrike *Malaconotus monteiri*	2	087
Gabela Helmet-shrike *Prionops gabela*	1	087
Gabela Akalat *Sheppardia gabela*	1	087
White-headed Robin-chat *Cossypha heinrichi*	2	(s044)
Angola Cave-chat *Xenocopsychus ansorgei*	1	087
Herero Chat *Namibornis herero*	2	(s045)
Pulitzer's Longbill *Macrosphenus pulitzeri*	1	087
Angola Slaty-flycatcher *Dioptrornis brunneus*	1	087
White-fronted Wattle-eye *Platysteira albifrons*	1	087
Montane Double-collared Sunbird *Nectarinia ludovicensis*	1	087
Cinderella Waxbill *Estrilda thomensis*	2	087
Loango Weaver *Ploceus subpersonatus*	3	(s043)
Golden-backed Bishop *Euplectes aureus*	1	087

ANGUILLA (TO UK)

EBAs	Priority
030 Lesser Antilles	CRITICAL

Secondary Areas none

Restricted-range species	Threatened	Total
Confined to this country	0	0
Present also in other countries	0	4
Total	0	4

Species (threatened species in **bold**)	No. of countries	EBAs (and SAs)
Green-throated Carib *Eulampis holosericeus*	15	030
Antillean Crested Hummingbird *Orthorhyncus cristatus*	15	030
Pearly-eyed Thrasher *Margarops fuscatus*	14	030
Lesser Antillean Bullfinch *Loxigilla noctis*	13	030

ANTIGUA AND BARBUDA

EBAs	Priority
030 Lesser Antilles	CRITICAL

Secondary Areas none

Restricted-range species	Threatened	Total
Confined to this country	0	0
Present also in other countries	0	10
Total	0	10

Species (threatened species in **bold**)	No. of countries	EBAs (and SAs)
Bridled Quail-dove *Geotrygon mystacea*	10	030
Purple-throated Carib *Eulampis jugularis*	9	030
Green-throated Carib *Eulampis holosericeus*	15	030
Antillean Crested Hummingbird *Orthorhyncus cristatus*	15	030
Lesser Antillean Flycatcher *Myiarchus oberi*	7	030
Scaly-breasted Thrasher *Margarops fuscus*	9	030
Pearly-eyed Thrasher *Margarops fuscatus*	14	030
Lesser Antillean Bullfinch *Loxigilla noctis*	13	030
Antillean Euphonia *Euphonia musica*	12	030
Adelaide's Warbler *Dendroica adelaidae*	3	030

ARGENTINA

EBAs	Priority
056 High Andes of Bolivia and Argentina	CRITICAL
057 Argentine and south Bolivian yungas	URGENT
058 Sierras Centrales of Argentina	HIGH
061 Chilean temperate forests	HIGH
062 Southern Patagonia	URGENT
075 Atlantic forest lowlands	CRITICAL
076 Atlantic forest mountains	URGENT
077 Argentine Mesopotamian grasslands	CRITICAL

Secondary Areas
s035 Coastal Uruguay marshes
s036 Salinas Grandes and Ambargasta

Restricted-range species	Threatened	Total
Confined to this country	3	9
Present also in other countries	8	40
Total	11	49

Species (threatened species in **bold**)	No. of countries	EBAs (and SAs)
Hooded Grebe *Podiceps gallardoi*	1	062
Ruddy-headed Goose *Chloephaga rubidiceps*	3	062
Striated Caracara *Phalcoboenus australis*	3	062
Red-faced Guan *Penelope dabbenei*	2	057
Magellanic Plover *Pluvianellus socialis*	2	062
Chilean Pigeon *Columba araucana*	2	061
Bare-eyed Ground-dove *Metriopelia morenoi*	1	056
Tucuman Amazon *Amazona tucumana*	2	057
Red-spectacled Amazon *Amazona pretrei*	2	076
Tawny-browed Owl *Pulsatrix koeniswaldiana*	3	075
Rothschild's Swift *Cypseloides rothschildi*	2	057
Blue-capped Puffleg *Eriocnemis glaucopoides*	2	057
Short-billed Miner *Geositta antarctica*	2	062
Córdoba Cinclodes *Cinclodes comechingonus*	1	058
Olrog's Cinclodes *Cinclodes olrogi*	1	058
Blackish Cinclodes *Cinclodes antarcticus*	2	062
Araucaria Tit-spinetail *Leptasthenura setaria*	2	076
Chestnut Canastero *Asthenes steinbachi*	1	056
Scribble-tailed Canastero *Asthenes maculicauda*	3	056
Canebrake Groundcreeper *Clibanornis dendrocolaptoides*	3	075
Straight-billed Reedhaunter *Limnornis rectirostris*	3	(s035)
White-browed Foliage-gleaner *Philydor amaurotis*	3	075
White-bearded Antshrike *Biatas nigropectus*	2	075
Spot-breasted Antvireo *Dysithamnus stictothorax*	2	075
Bertoni's Antbird *Drymophila rubricollis*	3	075
White-throated Antpitta *Grallaria albigula*	3	057
Black-throated Huet-huet *Pteroptochos tarnii*	2	061
Chucao Tapaculo *Scelorchilus rubecula*	2	061
Spotted Bamboowren *Psilorhamphus guttatus*	2	075
Ochre-flanked Tapaculo *Eugralla paradoxa*	2	061
White-browed Tapaculo *Scytalopus superciliaris*	2	057
Black-capped Manakin *Piprites pileatus*	2	076
Slaty Elaenia *Elaenia strepera*	2	057
Salinas Monjita *Xolmis salinarum*	1	(s036)
Chocolate-vented Tyrant *Neoxolmis rufiventris*	2	062
Rufous-throated Dipper *Cinclus schulzi*	2	057
Yellow-striped Brush-finch *Atlapetes citrinellus*	1	057
Canary-winged Finch *Melanodera melanodera*	3	062
Grey-crested Finch *Lophospingus griseocristatus*	2	056
Short-tailed Finch *Idiopsar brachyurus*	3	056
Tucumán Mountain-finch *Poospiza baeri*	1	056
Citron-headed Yellow-finch *Sicalis luteocephala*	2	056
Buffy-fronted Seedeater *Sporophila frontalis*	3	075
Temminck's Seedeater *Sporophila falcirostris*	3	075

cont.

Argentina (cont.)

Marsh Seedeater *Sporophila palustris*	3	077
Chestnut Seedeater *Sporophila cinnamomea*	3	077
Entre Ríos Seedeater *Sporophila zelichi*	1	077
Rufous-bellied Saltator *Saltator rufiventris*	2	056
Grey-bellied Flower-piercer *Diglossa carbonaria*	2	056

ARMENIA

EBAs	Priority
122 Caucasus	HIGH

Secondary Areas none

Restricted-range species	Threatened	Total
Confined to this country	0	0
Present also in other countries	0	2
Total	0	2

Species (threatened species in **bold**)	No. of countries	EBAs (and SAs)
Caucasian Grouse *Tetrao mlokosiewiczi*	6	122
Caucasian Chiffchaff *Phylloscopus lorenzii*	6	122

ARUBA (TO NETHERLANDS)

EBAs none

Secondary Areas
s015 Netherlands Antilles

Restricted-range species	Threatened	Total
Confined to this country	0	0
Present also in other countries	0	0
Total	0	0

Species (threatened species in **bold**)	No. of countries	EBAs (and SAs)
EL **Yellow-shouldered Amazon** *Amazona barbadensis*	2	(s015)

AUSTRALIA

See also Christmas Island (p. 733), Norfolk Island (p. 758).

EBAs	Priority
181 Cape York	CRITICAL
182 Queensland wet tropics	URGENT
183 Eastern Australia	CRITICAL
184 South-east Australia	CRITICAL
185 Tasmania	URGENT
186 South-west Australia	CRITICAL
187 North-west Australia	URGENT
204 Lord Howe Island	CRITICAL

Secondary Areas
s115 Clarke range
s116 East Australian mangroves
s117 Bulloo and Diamentina rivers
s118 Simpson and Strzelecki deserts
s119 South Australian desert
s120 West Australian mangroves
s121 Gulf of Carpentaria

Australia (cont.)

Restricted-range species	Threatened	Total
Confined to this country	20	78
Present also in other countries	0	0
Total	20	78

Species (threatened species in **bold**)	No. of countries	EBAs (and SAs)
EX Kangaroo Island Emu *Dromaius baudinianus*	0	184ˣ
EX King Island Emu *Dromaius ater*	0	185ˣ
Black-breasted Buttonquail *Turnix melanogaster*	1	183
Chestnut-backed Buttonquail *Turnix castanota*	1	187
Buff-breasted Buttonquail *Turnix olivii*	1	181
Lord Howe Island Rail *Gallirallus sylvestris*	1	204
Chestnut Rail *Eulabeornis castaneoventris*	1	187
EX Lord Howe Island Swamphen *Porphyrio albus*	0	204ˣ
Tasmanian Native-hen *Gallinula mortierii*	1	185
Partridge Pigeon *Geophaps smithii*	1	187
White-quilled Rock-pigeon *Petrophassa albipennis*	1	187
Chestnut-quilled Rock-pigeon *P. rufipennis*	1	187
Black-banded Fruit-dove *Ptilinopus alligator*	1	187
White-tailed Black-cockatoo *Calyptorhynchus baudinii*	1	186
Western Corella *Cacatua pastinator*	1	186
Long-billed Corella *Cacatua tenuirostris*	1	184
Superb Parrot *Polytelis swainsonii*	1	184
Green Rosella *Platycercus caledonicus*	1	185
Hooded Parrot *Psephotus dissimilis*	1	187
Golden-shouldered Parrot *P. chrysopterygius*	1	181
Orange-bellied Parrot *Neophema chrysogaster*	1	185
Swift Parrot *Lathamus discolor*	1	185
Lesser Sooty-owl *Tyto multipunctata*	1	182
Rainbow Pitta *Pitta iris*	1	187
Albert's Lyrebird *Menura alberti*	1	183
Rufous Scrub-bird *Atrichornis rufescens*	1	183
Noisy Scrub-bird *Atrichornis clamosus*	1	186
Chowchilla *Orthonyx spaldingii*	1	182
Western Whipbird *Psophodes nigrogularis*	1	184,186
Lovely Fairywren *Malurus amabilis*	1	181,182
Red-winged Fairywren *Malurus elegans*	1	186
Mallee Emuwren *Stipiturus mallee*	1	184
Grey Grasswren *Amytornis barbatus*	1	(s117)
White-throated Grasswren *Amytornis woodwardi*	1	187
Carpentarian Grasswren *Amytornis dorotheae*	1	(s121)
Eyrean Grasswren *Amytornis goyderi*	1	(s118)
Black Grasswren *Amytornis housei*	1	187
Western Bristlebird *Dasyornis longirostris*	1	186
Eastern Bristlebird *Dasyornis brachypterus*	1	183
Rufous Bristlebird *Dasyornis broadbenti*	1	184,186ˣ
Pilotbird *Pycnoptilus floccosus*	1	183
Origma *Origma solitaria*	1	183
Fernwren *Oreoscopus gutturalis*	1	182
Brown Scrubwren *Sericornis humilis*	1	185
Atherton Scrubwren *Sericornis keri*	1	182
Scrubtit *Acanthornis magnus*	1	185
Mountain Thornbill *Acanthiza katherina*	1	182
Tasmanian Thornbill *Acanthiza ewingii*	1	185
Dusky Gerygone *Gerygone tenebrosa*	1	(s120)
EX Lord Howe Island Gerygone *Gerygone insularis*	0	204ˣ
Chestnut-breasted Whiteface *Aphelocephala pectoralis*	1	(s119)
Dusky Robin *Melanodryas vittata*	1	185
Pale-yellow Robin *Tregellasia capito*	1	182,183
White-breasted Robin *Eopsaltria georgiana*	1	186
Grey-headed Robin *Heteromyias cinereifrons*	1	182
Pied Monarch *Arses kaupi*	1	182
Red-lored Whistler *Pachycephala rufogularis*	1	184
Brown Whistler *Pachycephala simplex*	1	187

cont.

cont.

Australia (cont.)

Bower's Shrike-thrush *Colluricincla boweri*	1	182
Forty-spotted Pardalote *Pardalotus quadragintus*	1	185
Lord Howe Island White-eye	1	204
Zosterops tephropleurus		
EX Robust White-eye *Zosterops strenuus*	0	204X
White-streaked Honeyeater *Trichodere cockerelli*	1	181
Yellow-spotted Honeyeater *Meliphaga notata*	1	181,182
White-lined Honeyeater *Meliphaga albilineata*	1	187
Bridled Honeyeater *Lichenostomus frenatus*	1	182
Eungella Honeyeater *Lichenostomus hindwoodi*	1	(s115)
Mangrove Honeyeater *Lichenostomus fasciogularis*	1	(s116)
Yellow-throated Honeyeater *L. flavicollis*	1	185
Macleay Honeyeater *Xanthotis macleayana*	1	182
Black-headed Honeyeater *Melithreptus affinis*	1	185
Strong-billed Honeyeater *Melithreptus validirostris*	1	185
Black-eared Miner *Manorina melanotis*	1	184
Yellow Wattlebird *Anthochaera paradoxa*	1	185
Red-eared Firetail *Stagonopleura oculata*	1	186
Yellow-rumped Munia *Lonchura flaviprymna*	1	187
EX Norfolk Island Starling *Aplonis fusca*	0	204X
Black Currawong *Strepera fuliginosa*	1	185
Green Catbird *Ailuroedus crassirostris*	1	183
Tooth-billed Catbird *Ailuroedus dentirostris*	1	182
Golden Bowerbird *Prionodura newtoniana*	1	182
Regent Bowerbird *Sericulus chrysocephalus*	1	183
Victoria's Riflebird *Ptiloris victoriae*	1	182
Paradise Riflebird *Ptiloris paradiseus*	1	183

AZERBAIJAN

EBAs	Priority
122 Caucasus	HIGH

Secondary Areas none

Restricted-range species	Threatened	Total
Confined to this country	0	0
Present also in other countries	0	3
Total	0	3

Species (threatened species in **bold**)	No. of countries	EBAs (and SAs)
Caucasian Grouse *Tetrao mlokosiewiczi*	6	122
Caucasian Snowcock *Tetraogallus caucasicus*	3	122
Caucasian Chiffchaff *Phylloscopus lorenzii*	6	122

BAHAMAS

EBAs	Priority
026 Bahamas	HIGH

Secondary Areas none

Restricted-range species	Threatened	Total
Confined to this country	0	2
Present also in other countries	0	5
Total	0	7

Species (threatened species in **bold**)	No. of countries	EBAs (and SAs)
EX Brace's Emerald *Chlorostilbon bracei*	0	026X
Bahama Woodstar *Calliphlox evelynae*	2	026
Bahama Swallow *Tachycineta cyaneoviridis*	1	026
Bahama Mockingbird *Mimus gundlachii*	4	026
Pearly-eyed Thrasher *Margarops fuscatus*	14	026

Bahamas (cont.)

Olive-capped Warbler *Dendroica pityophila*	2	026
Bahama Yellowthroat *Geothlypis rostrata*	1	026
Thick-billed Vireo *Vireo crassirostris*	5	026

BANGLADESH

EBAs	Priority
130 Eastern Himalayas	URGENT
131 Assam plains	URGENT

Secondary Areas none

Restricted-range species	Threatened	Total
Confined to this country	0	0
Present also in other countries	3	4
Total	3	4

Species (threatened species in **bold**)	No. of countries	EBAs (and SAs)
Manipur Bush-quail *Perdicula manipurensis*	2	131
Marsh Babbler *Pellorneum palustre*	2	131
White-naped Yuhina *Yuhina bakeri*	6	130
Black-breasted Parrotbill	2	131
Paradoxornis flavirostris		

BARBADOS

EBAs	Priority
030 Lesser Antilles	CRITICAL

Secondary Areas none

Restricted-range species	Threatened	Total
Confined to this country	0	0
Present also in other countries	0	4
Total	0	4

Species (threatened species in **bold**)	No. of countries	EBAs (and SAs)
Green-throated Carib *Eulampis holosericeus*	15	030
Antillean Crested Hummingbird	15	030
Orthorhyncus cristatus		
Scaly-breasted Thrasher *Margarops fuscus*	9	030
Lesser Antillean Bullfinch *Loxigilla noctis*	13	030

BELIZE

EBAs none

Secondary Areas
s007 Eastern Yucatán

Restricted-range species	Threatened	Total
Confined to this country	0	0
Present also in other countries	0	1
Total	0	1

Species (threatened species in **bold**)	No. of countries	EBAs (and SAs)
Yucatán Vireo *Vireo magister*	4	(s007)

cont.

BHUTAN

EBAs	Priority
130 Eastern Himalayas	URGENT

Secondary Areas none

Restricted-range species	Threatened	Total
Confined to this country	0	0
Present also in other countries	5	9
Total	5	9

Species (threatened species in **bold**)	No. of countries	EBAs (and SAs)
Chestnut-breasted Partridge *Arborophila mandellii*	3	130
Blyth's Tragopan *Tragopan blythii*	4	130
Dark-rumped Swift *Apus acuticauda*	2	130
Ward's Trogon *Harpactes wardi*	5	130
Rufous-throated Wren-babbler *Spelaeornis caudatus*	3	130
Hoary-throated Barwing *Actinodura nipalensis*	4	130
Ludlow's Fulvetta *Alcippe ludlowi*	3	130
White-naped Yuhina *Yuhina bakeri*	6	130
Yellow-vented Warbler *Phylloscopus cantator*	3	130

BOLIVIA

EBAs	Priority
054 Bolivian and Peruvian lower yungas	URGENT
055 Bolivian and Peruvian upper yungas	URGENT
056 High Andes of Bolivia and Argentina	CRITICAL
057 Argentine and south Bolivian yungas	URGENT
068 South-east Peruvian lowlands	URGENT

Secondary Areas
s024 Lake Titicaca
s026 Rio Guaporé
s027 Beni lowlands
s028 East Bolivian cerrado

Restricted-range species	Threatened	Total
Confined to this country	8	17
Present also in other countries	6	44
Total	14	61

Species (threatened species in **bold**)	No. of countries	EBAs (and SAs)
Titicaca Flightless Grebe *Rollandia microptera*	2	(s024)
Red-faced Guan *Penelope dabbenei*	2	057
Southern Helmeted Curassow *Pauxi unicornis*	2	054
Stripe-faced Wood-quail *Odontophorus balliviani*	2	055
Blue-throated Macaw *Ara glaucogularis*	1	(s027)
Red-fronted Macaw *Ara rubrogenys*	1	056
Black-winged Parrot *Hapalopsittaca melanotis*	2	055
Tucumán Amazon *Amazona tucumana*	2	057
Rothschild's Swift *Cypseloides rothschildi*	2	057
Coppery Thorntail *Popelairia letitiae*	1	? (see p. 724)
Wedge-tailed Hillstar *Oreotrochilus adela*	1	056
Black-hooded Sunbeam *Aglaeactis pamela*	1	055
Blue-capped Puffleg *Eriocnemis glaucopoides*	2	057
Scaled Metaltail *Metallura aeneocauda*	2	055
Olivaceous Thornbill *Chalcostigma olivaceum*	2	056
Semicollared Puffbird *Malacoptila semicincta*	3	068
Scarlet-hooded Barbet *Eubucco tucinkae*	2	068
Hooded Mountain-toucan *Andigena cucullata*	2	055

cont.

Bolivia (cont.)

Rusty-necked Piculet *Picumnus fuscus*	2	(s026)
Bolivian Earthcreeper *Upucerthia harterti*	1	056
Royal Cinclodes *Cinclodes aricomae*	2	056
Black-throated Thistletail *Schizoeaca harterti*	1	055
Light-crowned Spinetail *Cranioleuca albiceps*	2	055
Maquis Canastero *Asthenes heterura*	1	056
Berlepsch's Canastero *Asthenes berlepschi*	1	056
Line-fronted Canastero *Asthenes urubambensis*	2	056
Scribble-tailed Canastero *Asthenes maculicauda*	3	056
Bolivian Recurvebill *Simoxenops striatus*	1	054
Upland Antshrike *Thamnophilus aroyae*	2	054
Ashy Antwren *Myrmotherula grisea*	1	054
Yellow-rumped Antwren *Terenura sharpei*	2	054
White-lined Antbird *Percnostola lophotes*	2	068
Goeldi's Antbird *Myrmeciza goeldii*	3	068
White-throated Antpitta *Grallaria albigula*	3	054,057
Rufous-faced Antpitta *Grallaria erythrotis*	1	055
Diademed Tapaculo *Scytalopus schulenbergi*	2	055
White-browed Tapaculo *Scytalopus superciliaris*	2	057
Scimitar-winged Piha *Lipaugus uropygialis*	2	055
Yungas Manakin *Chiroxiphia boliviana*	2	054
Hazel-fronted Pygmy-tyrant *Pseudotriccus simplex*	2	054
Yungas Tody-tyrant *Hemitriccus spodiops*	1	054
Bolivian Tyrannulet *Zimmerius bolivianus*	2	054
Slaty Elaenia *Elaenia strepera*	2	057
Ash-breasted Tit-tyrant *Anairetes alpinus*	2	056
Long-crested Pygmy-tyrant *Lophotriccus eulophotes*	3	068
Unadorned Flycatcher *Myiophobus inornatus*	2	054
Rufous-bellied Bush-tyrant *Myiotheretes fuscorufus*	2	055
Rufous-throated Dipper *Cinclus schulzi*	2	057
Grey-crested Finch *Lophospingus griseocristatus*	2	056
Short-tailed Finch *Idiopsar brachyurus*	3	056
Bolivian Warbling-finch *Poospiza boliviana*	1	056
Cochabamba Mountain-finch *Poospiza garleppi*	1	056
Citron-headed Yellow-finch *Sicalis luteocephala*	2	056
Black-and-tawny Seedeater *Sporophila nigrorufa*	1	(s028)
Rufous-bellied Saltator *Saltator rufiventris*	2	056
Orange-browed Hemispingus *Hemispingus calophrys*	2	055
Slaty Tanager *Creurgops dentata*	2	054
Golden-collared Tanager *Iridosornis jelskii*	2	055
Straw-backed Tanager *Tangara argyrofenges*	2	054
Grey-bellied Flower-piercer *Diglossa carbonaria*	2	055,056
Bolivian Blackbird *Oreopsar bolivianus*	1	056

BRAZIL

EBAs	Priority
063 Rio Branco gallery forests	URGENT
064 Tepuis	URGENT
065 Orinoco–Negro white-sand forests	HIGH
066 Upper Amazon–Napo lowlands	HIGH
067 Amazon flooded forests	HIGH
068 South-east Peruvian lowlands	URGENT
069 Fernando de Noronha	HIGH
070 North-east Brazilian caatinga	CRITICAL
071 Atlantic slope of Alagoas and Pernambuco	CRITICAL
072 Deciduous forests of Bahia	CRITICAL
073 Central Brazilian hills and tablelands	URGENT
074 Deciduous forests of Minas Gerais and Goiás	CRITICAL
075 Atlantic forest lowlands	CRITICAL
076 Atlantic forest mountains	URGENT
077 Argentine Mesopotamian grasslands	CRITICAL

cont.

Brazil (cont.)

Secondary Areas
s025 Rio Ji-paraná
s026 Rio Guaporé
s029 Borba
s030 Upper Rio Cururu
s031 Rio Araguaia
s032 Interior southern Brazil
s033 Ceará caatinga and serras
s034 Coastal Paraná marshes
s035 Coastal Uruguay marshes

Restricted-range species	Threatened	Total
Confined to this country	51	104
Present also in other countries	8	60
Total	59	164

Species (threatened species in **bold**)	No. of countries	EBAs (and SAs)
Grey-legged Tinamou *Crypturellus duidae*	3	065
Barred Tinamou *Crypturellus casiquiare*	3	065
[EW] Alagoas Curassow *Mitu mitu*	0	071[X]
Red-billed Curassow *Crax blumenbachii*	1	075
Lear's Macaw *Anodorhynchus leari*	1	070
Spix's Macaw *Cyanopsitta spixii*	1	070
Fiery-shouldered Parakeet *Pyrrhura egregia*	3	064
Tepui Parrotlet *Nannopsittaca panychlora*	3	064
Brown-backed Parrotlet *Touit melanonota*	1	075
Red-spectacled Amazon *Amazona pretrei*	2	076
Red-tailed Amazon *Amazona brasiliensis*	1	075
Blue-bellied Parrot *Triclaria malachitacea*	1	075
Tawny-browed Owl *Pulsatrix koeniswaldiana*	3	075
Caatinga Nighthawk *Chordeiles vielliardi*	1	070
Pygmy Nightjar *Caprimulgus hirundinaceus*	1	070
Tepui Swift *Cypseloides phelpsi*	3	064
Minute Hermit *Phaethornis idaliae*	1	075
Saw-billed Hermit *Ramphodon naevius*	1	075
Hook-billed Hermit *Glaucis dohrnii*	1	075
Rufous-breasted Sabrewing *Campylopterus hyperythrus*	2	064
Buff-breasted Sabrewing *Campylopterus duidae*	2	064
Peacock Coquette *Lophornis pavoninus*	3	064
Olive-spotted Hummingbird *Leucippus chlorocercus*	4	066
Velvet-browed Brilliant *Heliodoxa xanthogonys*	3	064
Hooded Visorbearer *Augastes lumachellus*	1	073
Hyacinth Visorbearer *Augastes scutatus*	1	073
Three-toed Jacamar *Jacamaralcyon tridactyla*	1	075
Semicollared Puffbird *Malacoptila semicincta*	3	068
Chestnut-headed Nunlet *Nonnula amaurocephala*	1	067
Orinoco Piculet *Picumnus pumilus*	3	065
Rusty-necked Piculet *Picumnus fuscus*	2	(s026)
Várzea Piculet *Picumnus varzeae*	1	067
Tawny Piculet *Picumnus fulvescens*	1	070,071
Ochraceous Piculet *Picumnus limae*	1	(s033)
Yellow-eared Woodpecker *Veniliornis maculifrons*	1	075
Long-tailed Cinclodes *Cinclodes pabsti*	1	076
Striolated Tit-spinetail *Leptasthenura striolata*	1	076
Araucaria Tit-spinetail *Leptasthenura setaria*	2	076
Itatiaia Thistletail *Schizoeaca moreirae*	1	076
Bahia Spinetail *Synallaxis whitneyi*	1	076
Plain Spinetail *Synallaxis infuscata*	1	071
Red-shouldered Spinetail *Gyalophylax hellmayri*	1	070
Hoary-throated Spinetail *Synallaxis kollari*	2	063
Pink-legged Graveteiro *Acrobatornis fonsecai*	1	075
Tepui Spinetail *Cranioleuca demissa*	3	064
Scaled Spinetail *Cranioleuca muelleri*	1	067
Cipó Canastero *Asthenes luizae*	1	073

cont.

Brazil (cont.)

Striated Softtail *Thripophaga macroura*	1	075
Red-eyed Thornbird *Phacellodomus erythrophthalmus*	1	075
Canebrake Groundcreeper *Clibanornis dendrocolaptoides*	3	075
Straight-billed Reedhaunter *Limnornis rectirostris*	3	(s035)
Roraiman Barbtail *Roraimia adusta*	3	064
Pale-browed Treehunter *Cichlocolaptes leucophrus*	1	075
White-browed Foliage-gleaner *Philydor amaurotis*	3	075
Alagoas Foliage-gleaner *Philydor novaesi*	1	071
White-throated Foliage-gleaner *Automolus roraimae*	2	064
White-bearded Antshrike *Biatas nigropectus*	2	075
Streak-backed Antshrike *Thamnophilus insignis*	2	064
Rondônia Bushbird *Clytoctantes atrogularis*	1	(s025)
Spot-breasted Antvireo *Dysithamnus stictothorax*	2	075
Rufous-backed Antvireo *D. xanthopterus*	1	076
Plumbeous Antvireo *Dysithamnus plumbeus*	1	075
Klages's Antwren *Myrmotherula klagesi*	1	067
Yellow-throated Antwren *Myrmotherula ambigua*	3	065
Alagoas Antwren *Myrmotherula snowi*	1	071
Star-throated Antwren *Myrmotherula gularis*	1	075
Rio de Janeiro Antwren *Myrmotherula fluminensis*	1	075
Salvadori's Antwren *Myrmotherula minor*	1	075
Unicoloured Antwren *Myrmotherula unicolor*	1	075
Band-tailed Antwren *Myrmotherula urosticta*	1	075
Spot-backed Antwren *Herpsilochmus dorsimaculatus*	3	065
Roraiman Antwren *Herpsilochmus roraimae*	3	064
Long-billed Antwren *Stymphalornis acutirostris*	1	(s034)
Narrow-billed Antwren *Formicivora iheringi*	1	072
Serra Antwren *Formicivora serrana*	1	075
Black-hooded Antwren *Formicivora erythronotos*	1	075
Restinga Antwren *Formicivora littoralis*	1	075
Bertoni's Antbird *Drymophila rubricollis*	3	075
Rufous-tailed Antbird *Drymophila genei*	1	076
Ochre-rumped Antbird *Drymophila ochropyga*	1	076
Orange-bellied Antwren *Terenura sicki*	1	071
Rio de Janeiro Antbird *Cercomacra brasiliana*	1	075
Bananal Antbird *Cercomacra ferdinandi*	1	(s031)
Rio Branco Antbird *Cercomacra carbonaria*	2	063
Fringe-backed Fire-eye *Pyriglena atra*	1	075
Slender Antbird *Rhopornis ardesiaca*	1	072
Caura Antbird *Percnostola caurensis*	2	064
Scalloped Antbird *Myrmeciza ruficauda*	1	071,075
White-bibbed Antbird *Myrmeciza loricata*	1	075
Squamate Antbird *Myrmeciza squamosa*	1	075
Grey-bellied Antbird *Myrmeciza pelzelni*	3	065
Goeldi's Antbird *Myrmeciza goeldii*	3	068
Chestnut-crested Antbird *Rhegmatorhina cristata*	2	065
Such's Antthrush *Chamaeza meruloides*	1	075
Rufous-tailed Antthrush *Chamaeza ruficauda*	1	076
Brown-breasted Antpitta *Myrmothera simplex*	2	064
Spotted Bamboowren *Psilorhamphus guttatus*	2	075
Slaty Bristlefront *Merulaxis ater*	1	075
Stresemann's Bristlefront *Merulaxis stresemanni*	1	075
Brasília Tapaculo *Scytalopus novacapitalis*	1	073(s032)
Bahia Tapaculo *Scytalopus psychopompus*	1	075
Black-and-gold Cotinga *Tijuca atra*	1	076
Grey-winged Cotinga *Tijuca condita*	1	076
Hooded Berryeater *Carpornis cucullatus*	1	075
Buff-throated Purpletuft *Iodopleura pipra*	1	071,075
Kinglet Calyptura *Calyptura cristata*	1	075
Rose-collared Piha *Lipaugus streptophorus*	3	064
Banded Cotinga *Cotinga maculata*	1	075
White-winged Cotinga *Xipholena atropurpurea*	1	071,075

cont.

Brazil (cont.)

Scarlet-horned Manakin *Pipra cornuta*	3	064
Golden-crowned Manakin *Pipra vilasboasi*	1	(s030)
Orange-bellied Manakin *Lepidothrix suavissima*	3	064
Olive Manakin *Chloropipo uniformis*	3	064
Serra do Mar Tyrant-manakin *Neopelma chrysolophum*	1	073,076
Black-capped Manakin *Piprites pileatus*	2	076
Brown-breasted Bamboo-tyrant *Hemitriccus obsoletus*	1	076
Pelzeln's Tody-tyrant *Hemitriccus inornatus*	1	065
Buff-breasted Tody-tyrant *Hemitriccus mirandae*	1	071(s033)
Kaempfer's Tody-tyrant *Hemitriccus kaempferi*	1	075
Fork-tailed Pygmy-tyrant *Hemitriccus furcatus*	1	075
Buff-cheeked Tody-flycatcher *Todirostrum senex*	1	(s029)
Ruddy Tody-flycatcher *Todirostrum russatum*	2	064
Grey-capped Tyrannulet *Phyllomyias griseocapilla*	1	076
Noronha Elaenia *Elaenia ridleyana*	1	069
Grey-backed Tachuri *Polystictus superciliaris*	1	073,076
Chapman's Tyrannulet *Phylloscartes chapmani*	2	064
Minas Gerais Tyrannulet *Phylloscartes roquettei*	1	074
Oustalet's Tyrannulet *Phylloscartes oustaleti*	1	075
Serra do Mar Tyrannulet *Phylloscartes difficilis*	1	076
Alagoas Tyrannulet *Phylloscartes ceciliae*	1	071
Bahia Tyrannulet *Phylloscartes beckeri*	1	076
Restinga Tyrannulet *Phylloscartes kronei*	1	075
Long-crested Pygmy-tyrant *Lophotriccus eulophotes*	3	068
Brazilian Black-tyrant *Knipolegus franciscanus*	1	074
Tepui Wren *Troglodytes rufulus*	2	064
Flutist Wren *Microcerculus ustulatus*	3	064
Tepui Brush-finch *Atlapetes personatus*	2	064
Bay-chested Warbling-finch *Poospiza thoracica*	1	076
Pale-throated Pampa-finch *Embernagra longicauda*	1	073
Buffy-fronted Seedeater *Sporophila frontalis*	3	075
Temminck's Seedeater *Sporophila falcirostris*	3	075
Dubois's Seedeater *Sporophila ardesiaca*	1	075
Hooded Seedeater *Sporophila melanops*	1	? (see p. 724)
Marsh Seedeater *Sporophila palustris*	3	077
Chestnut Seedeater *Sporophila cinnamomea*	3	077
Black-bellied Seedeater *Sporophila melanogaster*	1	076
White-naped Seedeater *Dolospingus fringilloides*	3	065
Cone-billed Tanager *Conothraupis mesoleuca*	1	? (see p. 724)
Cherry-throated Tanager *Nemosia rourei*	1	075
Olive-backed Tanager *Mitrospingus oleagineus*	3	064
Olive-green Tanager *Orthogonys chloricterus*	1	076
Azure-shouldered Tanager *Thraupis cyanoptera*	1	075
Seven-coloured Tanager *Tangara fastuosa*	1	071
Brassy-breasted Tanager *Tangara desmaresti*	1	076
Gilt-edged Tanager *Tangara cyanoventris*	1	075
Black-backed Tanager *Tangara peruviana*	1	075
Black-legged Dacnis *Dacnis nigripes*	1	075
Scaled Flower-piercer *Diglossa duidae*	2	064
Greater Flower-piercer *Diglossa major*	2	064
Tepui Whitestart *Myioborus castaneocapillus*	3	064
Noronha Vireo *Vireo gracilirostris*	1	069
Tepui Greenlet *Hylophilus sclateri*	3	064
Forbes's Blackbird *Curaeus forbesi*	1	071
Golden-tufted Grackle *Macroagelaius imthurni*	3	064
Azure-naped Jay *Cyanocorax heilprini*	3	065

BRUNEI

EBAs	Priority
157 Bornean mountains	URGENT

Secondary Areas none

Restricted-range species	Threatened	Total
Confined to this country	0	0
Present also in other countries	0	3
Total	0	3

Species (threatened species in **bold**)	No. of countries	EBAs (and SAs)
Mountain Serpent-eagle *Spilornis kinabaluensis*	2	157
Blue-wattled Bulbul *Pycnonotus nieuwenhuisii*	2	157
Sunda Laughingthrush *Garrulax palliatus*	3	157

BURUNDI

EBAs	Priority
106 Albertine Rift mountains	URGENT

Secondary Areas none

Restricted-range species	Threatened	Total
Confined to this country	0	0
Present also in other countries	3	23
Total	3	23

Species (threatened species in **bold**)	No. of countries	EBAs (and SAs)
Handsome Francolin *Francolinus nobilis*	4	106
Ruwenzori Turaco *Musophaga johnstoni*	4	106
Ruwenzori Nightjar *Caprimulgus ruwenzorii*	4	106
Kivu Ground-thrush *Zoothera tanganjicae*	4	106
Red-throated Alethe *Alethe poliophrys*	4	106
Archer's Robin-chat *Cossypha archeri*	4	106
Red-collared Mountain-babbler *Kupeornis rufocinctus*	3	106
Collared Apalis *Apalis ruwenzorii*	4	106
Black-faced Apalis *Apalis personata*	4	106
Kungwe Apalis *Apalis argentea*	4	106
Grauer's Swamp-warbler *Bradypterus graueri*	4	106
Grauer's Warbler *Graueria vittata*	4	106
Neumann's Warbler *Hemitesia neumanni*	4	106
Red-faced Woodland-warbler *Phylloscopus laetus*	4	106
Yellow-eyed Black-flycatcher *Melaenornis ardesiacus*	4	106
Ruwenzori Batis *Batis diops*	4	106
Stripe-breasted Tit *Parus fasciiventer*	4	106
Blue-headed Sunbird *Nectarinia alinae*	4	106
Regal Sunbird *Nectarinia regia*	5	106
Purple-breasted Sunbird *Nectarinia purpureiventris*	4	106
Dusky Crimson-wing *Cryptospiza jacksoni*	4	106
Shelley's Crimson-wing *Cryptospiza shelleyi*	4	106
Strange Weaver *Ploceus alienus*	4	106

CAMBODIA

EBAs none

Secondary Areas
s085 Thailand–Cambodia mountains

Restricted-range species	Threatened	Total
Confined to this country	0	0
Present also in other countries	1	1
Total	1	1

Species (threatened species in **bold**)	No. of countries	EBAs (and SAs)
Chestnut-headed Partridge	2	(s085)
Arborophila cambodiana		

CAMEROON

EBAs	Priority
085 Cameroon and Gabon lowlands	HIGH
086 Cameroon mountains	CRITICAL

Secondary Areas none

Restricted-range species	Threatened	Total
Confined to this country	7	7
Present also in other countries	5	25
Total	12	32

Species (threatened species in **bold**)	No. of countries	EBAs (and SAs)
Mount Cameroon Francolin	1	086
Francolinus camerunensis		
Cameroon Olive-pigeon *Columba sjostedti*	3	086
Bannerman's Turaco *Tauraco bannermani*	1	086
Forest Swallow *Hirundo fuliginosa*	3	085
Mountain Sawwing *Psalidoprocne fuliginosa*	3	086
Cameroon Greenbul *Andropadus montanus*	2	086
Grey-throated Greenbul *Andropadus tephrolaemus*	3	086
Cameroon Olive Greenbul *Phyllastrephus poensis*	3	086
Grey-headed Greenbul	2	086
Phyllastrephus poliocephalus		
Yellow-breasted Boubou *Laniarius atroflavus*	2	086
Mount Kupe Bush-shrike *Telophorus kupeensis*	1	086
Green-breasted Bush-shrike	2	086
Malaconotus gladiator		
Monteiro's Bush-shrike *Malaconotus monteiri*	2	086
Mountain Robin-chat *Cossypha isabellae*	2	086
White-throated Mountain-babbler	2	086
Kupeornis gilberti		
Grey-necked Rockfowl *Picathartes oreas*	4	085,086
Brown-backed Cisticola *Cisticola discolor*	2	086
Green Longtail *Urolais epichlora*	3	086
Bamenda Apalis *Apalis bamendae*	1	086
Dja River Warbler *Bradypterus grandis*	2	085
Bangwa Forest Warbler *Bradypterus bangwaensis*	2	086
White-tailed Warbler *Poliolais lopezi*	3	086
Black-capped Woodland-warbler	3	086
Phylloscopus herberti		
Gabon Batis *Batis minima*	2	085
Banded Wattle-eye *Platysteira laticincta*	1	086
Cameroon Sunbird *Nectarinia oritis*	3	086
Ursula's Sunbird *Nectarinia ursulae*	2	086
Mount Cameroon Speirops	1	086
Speirops melanocephalus		
Fernando Po Oliveback *Nesocharis shelleyi*	3	086

cont.

Cameroon (cont.)

Bannerman's Weaver *Ploceus bannermani*	2	086
Bates's Weaver *Ploceus batesi*	1	085
Rachel's Malimbe *Malimbus racheliae*	4	085

CAPE VERDE

EBAs	Priority
078 Cape Verde Islands	URGENT

Secondary Areas none

Restricted-range species	Threatened	Total
Confined to this country	2	4
Present also in other countries	0	0
Total	2	4

Species (threatened species in **bold**)	No. of countries	EBAs (and SAs)
Cape Verde Swift *Apus alexandri*	1	078
Raso Lark *Alauda razae*	1	078
Cape Verde Warbler *Acrocephalus brevipennis*	1	078
Iago Sparrow *Passer iagoensis*	1	078

CAYMAN ISLANDS (TO UK)

EBAs none

Secondary Areas
s014 Cayman Islands

Restricted-range species	Threatened	Total
Confined to this country	0	0
Present also in other countries	0	4
Total	0	4

Species (threatened species in **bold**)	No. of countries	EBAs (and SAs)
EX Grand Cayman Thrush *Turdus ravidus*	0	(s014X)
Vitelline Warbler *Dendroica vitellina*	2	(s014)
Thick-billed Vireo *Vireo crassirostris*	5	(s014)
Yucatán Vireo *Vireo magister*	4	(s014)
Jamaican Oriole *Icterus leucopteryx*	3	(s014)

CHILE

EBAs	Priority
052 Peru–Chile Pacific slope	HIGH
059 Juan Fernández Islands	CRITICAL
060 Central Chile	URGENT
061 Chilean temperate forests	HIGH
062 Southern Patagonia	URGENT

Secondary Areas none

Restricted-range species	Threatened	Total
Confined to this country	2	11
Present also in other countries	3	15
Total	5	26

Species (threatened species in **bold**)	No. of countries	EBAs (and SAs)
Chilean Tinamou *Nothoprocta perdicaria*	1	060
Ruddy-headed Goose *Chloephaga rubidiceps*	3	062

cont.

Chile (cont.)

Striated Caracara *Phalcoboenus australis*	3	062
Magellanic Plover *Pluvianellus socialis*	2	062
Chilean Pigeon *Columba araucana*	2	061
Slender-billed Parakeet	1	061
Enicognathus leptorhynchus		
Juan Fernández Firecrown	1	059
Sephanoides fernandensis		
Chilean Woodstar *Eulidia yarrellii*	2	052
Short-billed Miner *Geositta antarctica*	2	062
White-throated Earthcreeper *Upucerthia albigula*	2	052
Blackish Cinclodes *Cinclodes antarcticus*	2	062
Crag Chilia *Chilia melanura*	1	060
Masafuera Rayadito *Aphrastura masafuerae*	1	059
Dusky-tailed Canastero *Asthenes humicola*	1	060
Chestnut-throated Huet-huet	1	060
Pteroptochos castaneus		
Black-throated Huet-huet *Pteroptochos tarnii*	2	061
Moustached Turca *Pteroptochos megapodius*	1	060
White-throated Tapaculo *Scelorchilus albicollis*	1	060
Chucao Tapaculo *Scelorchilus rubecula*	2	061
Ochre-flanked Tapaculo *Eugralla paradoxa*	2	060,061
Juan Fernández Tit-tyrant	1	059
Anairetes fernandezianus		
Chocolate-vented Tyrant *Neoxolmis rufiventris*	2	062
Chilean Mockingbird *Mimus thenca*	1	060
Canary-winged Finch *Melanodera melanodera*	3	062
Slender-billed Finch *Xenospingus concolor*	2	052
Tamarugo Conebill *Conirostrum tamarugense*	2	052

CHINA

EBAs	Priority
127 Taklimakan Desert	URGENT
130 Eastern Himalayas	URGENT
133 Southern Tibet	HIGH
134 Eastern Tibet	HIGH
135 Qinghai mountains	HIGH
136 Shanxi mountains	URGENT
137 Central Sichuan mountains	HIGH
138 West Sichuan mountains	URGENT
139 Yunnan mountains	URGENT
140 Chinese subtropical forests	CRITICAL
141 South-east Chinese mountains	CRITICAL
142 Hainan	CRITICAL

Secondary Areas
s076 Southern Xinjiang mountains
s078 Northern Qinghai-Tibetan plateau

Restricted-range species	Threatened	Total
Confined to this country	27	39
Present also in other countries	6	17
Total	33	56

Species (threatened species in **bold**)	No. of countries	EBAs (and SAs)
White-eared Night-heron *Gorsachius magnificus*	1	141,142
Rusty-necklaced Partridge *Alectoris magna*	1	135
Chestnut-breasted Partridge	3	130
Arborophila mandellii		
Sichuan Partridge *Arborophila rufipectus*	1	140
White-necklaced Partridge *Arborophila gingica*	1	141
Hainan Partridge *Arborophila ardens*	1	142
Blyth's Tragopan *Tragopan blythii*	4	130
Cabot's Tragopan *Tragopan caboti*	1	141
Sclater's Monal *Lophophorus sclateri*	3	130

cont.

China (cont.)

Chinese Monal *Lophophorus lhuysii*	1	138
Tibetan Eared-pheasant *Crossoptilon harmani*	1	133
Brown Eared-pheasant *C. mantchuricum*	1	136
Elliot's Pheasant *Syrmaticus ellioti*	1	141
Sichuan Wood-owl *Strix davidi*	1	138
Vaurie's Nightjar *Caprimulgus centralasicus*	1	127
Ward's Trogon *Harpactes wardi*	5	130
Grey-sided Thrush *Turdus feae*	1	136
Rusty-bellied Shortwing *Brachypteryx hyperythra*	2	130
Rufous-headed Robin *Luscinia ruficeps*	1	137
Black-throated Blue Robin *Luscinia obscura*	1	137
Ala Shan Redstart *Phoenicurus alaschanicus*	1	135
Snowy-cheeked Laughingthrush	1	137
Garrulax sukatschewi		
Barred Laughingthrush *Garrulax lunulatus*	1	137
White-speckled Laughingthrush *Garrulax bieti*	1	139
Red-winged Laughingthrush *Garrulax formosus*	2	137
Omei Shan Liocichla *Liocichla omeiensis*	1	140
Wedge-billed Wren-babbler *Sphenocichla humei*	3	130
Giant Babax *Babax waddelli*	2	133
Tibetan Babax *Babax koslowi*	1	134
Hoary-throated Barwing *Actinodura nipalensis*	4	130
Streak-throated Barwing *Actinodura waldeni*	3	130
Gold-fronted Fulvetta *Alcippe variegaticeps*	1	140
Ludlow's Fulvetta *Alcippe ludlowi*	3	130
Grey Sibia *Heterophasia gracilis*	3	130
Beautiful Sibia *Heterophasia pulchella*	3	130
White-naped Yuhina *Yuhina bakeri*	6	130
Three-toed Parrotbill *Paradoxornis paradoxus*	1	137
Brown-winged Parrotbill *Paradoxornis brunneus*	2	139
Grey-hooded Parrotbill *Paradoxornis zappeyi*	1	137
Rusty-throated Parrotbill *P. przewalskii*	1	137
Streaked Reed-warbler	1	? (see
Acrocephalus sorghophilus		p. 724)
Emei Leaf-warbler *Phylloscopus emeiensis*	1	140
Hainan Leaf-warbler *Phylloscopus hainanus*	1	142
Broad-billed Warbler *Tickellia hodgsoni*	6	130
Brown-chested Jungle-flycatcher	1	141
Rhinomyias brunneata		
White-necklaced Tit *Aegithalos fuliginosus*	1	137
Rusty-breasted Tit *Parus davidi*	1	137
Yunnan Nuthatch *Sitta yunnanensis*	1	139
Yellow-billed Nuthatch *Sitta solangiae*	2	142
Slaty Bunting *Latoucheornis siemsseni*	1	137
Tibetan Bunting *Emberiza koslowi*	1	134
Sillem's Mountain-finch *Leucosticte sillemi*	1	(s076)
Tibetan Rosefinch *Carpodacus roborowskii*	1	(s078)
Silver Oriole *Oriolus mellianus*	1	140
Sichuan Jay *Perisoreus internigrans*	1	138
Xinjiang Ground-jay *Podoces biddulphi*	1	127

CHRISTMAS ISLAND (TO AUSTRALIA)

EBAs	Priority
188 Christmas Island	HIGH

Secondary Areas none

Restricted-range species	Threatened	Total
Confined to this country	1	2
Present also in other countries	0	0
Total	1	2

Species (threatened species in **bold**)	No. of countries	EBAs (and SAs)
Christmas Island Imperial-pigeon	1	188
Ducula whartoni		
Christmas Island White-eye *Zosterops natalis*	1	188

COLOMBIA

EBAs	Priority
023 Darién lowlands	CRITICAL
024 Darién highlands	HIGH
035 Caribbean Colombia and Venezuela	URGENT
036 Santa Marta mountains	URGENT
037 Nechí lowlands	CRITICAL
038 Colombian East Andes	CRITICAL
039 Colombian inter-Andean valleys	HIGH
040 Colombian inter-Andean slopes	CRITICAL
041 Chocó	URGENT
042 Northern Central Andes	CRITICAL
043 Central Andean páramo	URGENT
044 Ecuador-Peru East Andes	HIGH
065 Orinoco–Negro white-sand forests	HIGH
066 Upper Amazon–Napo lowlands	HIGH

Secondary Areas
s012 Providence Island
s013 San Andrés Island
s018 Lower Río Magdelana
s019 Macarena mountains
s020 Sierra de Chiribiquete
s021 Tumaco and Bocagrande Islands

Restricted-range species	Threatened	Total
Confined to this country	36	63
Present also in other countries	18	129
Total	54	192

Species (threatened species in **bold**)	No. of countries	EBAs (and SAs)
Black Tinamou *Tinamus osgoodi*	2	040
Berlepsch's Tinamou *Crypturellus berlepschi*	2	041
Chocó Tinamou *Crypturellus kerriae*	2	023
Magdalena Tinamou *Crypturellus saltuarius*	1	(s018)
Grey-legged Tinamou *Crypturellus duidae*	3	065(s019)
Barred Tinamou *Crypturellus casiquiare*	3	065
EX Colombian Grebe *Podiceps andinus*	0	038ˣ
Carunculated Caracara *Phalcoboenus carunculatus*	2	043
Plumbeous Forest-falcon *Micrastur plumbeus*	2	041
Baudó Guan *Penelope ortoni*	2	041
Cauca Guan *Penelope perspicax*	1	040
Northern Helmeted Curassow *Pauxi pauxi*	2	038
Blue-billed Curassow *Crax alberti*	1	036,037
Black-fronted Wood-quail *Odontophorus atrifrons*	2	036,038
Chestnut Wood-quail *Odontophorus hyperythrus*	1	040,042
Dark-backed Wood-quail *O. melanonotus*	2	041
Tacarcuna Wood-quail *Odontophorus dialeucos*	2	024
Gorgeted Wood-quail *Odontophorus strophium*	1	038
Bogotá Rail *Rallus semiplumbeus*	1	038
Dusky Pigeon *Columba goodsoni*	2	041
Tolima Dove *Leptotila conoveri*	1	040
Russet-crowned Quail-dove *Geotrygon goldmani*	2	024
Santa Marta Parakeet *Pyrrhura viridicata*	1	036
Flame-winged Parakeet *Pyrrhura calliptera*	1	038
Rufous-fronted Parakeet *Bolborhynchus ferrugineifrons*	1	043
Rose-faced Parrot *Pionopsitta pulchra*	2	041
Rusty-faced Parrot *Hapalopsittaca amazonina*	3	038,042
Fuertes's Parrot *Hapalopsittaca fuertesi*	1	042
Banded Ground-cuckoo *Neomorphus radiolosus*	2	041
Bare-shanked Screech-owl *Otus clarkii*	3	024
Colombian Screech-owl *Otus colombianus*	2	041
Chocó Poorwill *Nyctiphrynus rosenbergi*	2	041
White-chested Swift *Cypseloides lemosi*	1	039
Pygmy Swift *Tachornis furcata*	2	035

Colombia (cont.)

Santa Marta Sabrewing *Campylopterus phainopeplus*	1	036
Chiribiquete Emerald *Chlorostilbon olivaresi*	1	(s020)
Coppery Emerald *Chlorostilbon russatus*	2	036,038
Narrow-tailed Emerald *Chlorostilbon stenura*	2	038
Short-tailed Emerald *Chlorostilbon poortmani*	2	038
Sapphire-bellied Hummingbird *Lepidopyga lilliae*	1	035
Violet-capped Hummingbird *Goldmania violiceps*	2	024
Rufous-cheeked Hummingbird *Goethalsia bella*	2	024
Buffy Hummingbird *Leucippus fallax*	2	035
Olive-spotted Hummingbird *Leucippus chlorocercus*	4	066
Purple-chested Hummingbird *Amazilia rosenbergi*	2	041
Chestnut-bellied Hummingbird *Amazilia castaneiventris*	1	037,038
Blossomcrown *Anthocephala floriceps*	1	036,040
Ecuadorian Piedtail *Phlogophilus hemileucurus*	3	044
Empress Brilliant *Heliodoxa imperatrix*	2	041
Pink-throated Brilliant *Heliodoxa gularis*	3	044
Brown Inca *Coeligena wilsoni*	2	041
Black Inca *Coeligena prunellei*	1	038
White-tailed Starfrontlet *Coeligena phalerata*	1	036
Golden-bellied Starfrontlet *Coeligena bonapartei*	2	038
Blue-throated Starfrontlet *Coeligena helianthea*	2	038
Velvet-purple Coronet *Boissonneaua jardini*	2	041
Orange-throated Sunangel *Heliangelus mavors*	2	038
Gorgeted Sunangel *Heliangelus strophianus*	2	041
Bogotá Sunangel *Heliangelus zusii*	1	? (see p. 724)
Coppery-bellied Puffleg *Eriocnemis cupreoventris*	2	038
Colourful Puffleg *Eriocnemis mirabilis*	1	041
Black-thighed Puffleg *Eriocnemis derbyi*	2	042
Hoary Puffleg *Haplophaedia lugens*	2	041
Purple-bibbed Whitetip *Urosticte benjamini*	2	041
Rufous-vented Whitetip *Urosticte ruficrissa*	3	040,044
Black-backed Thornbill *Ramphomicron dorsale*	1	036
Perijá Metaltail *Metallura iracunda*	2	038
Bronze-tailed Thornbill *Chalcostigma heteropogon*	2	038
Bearded Helmetcrest *Oxypogon guerinii*	2	036,038, 043
Violet-tailed Sylph *Aglaiocercus coelestis*	2	041
Santa Marta Woodstar *Acestrura astreans*	1	036
White-tipped Quetzal *Pharomachrus fulgidus*	2	036
White-eyed Trogon *Trogon comptus*	2	037,041
Dusky-backed Jacamar *Brachygalba salmoni*	2	023,037
Coppery-chested Jacamar *Galbula pastazae*	3	044
Sooty-capped Puffbird *Bucco noanamae*	1	023,041
Brown Nunlet *Nonnula brunnea*	3	066
Orange-fronted Barbet *Capito squamatus*	2	041
White-mantled Barbet *Capito hypoleucus*	1	037
Five-coloured Barbet *Capito quinticolor*	1	041
Toucan Barbet *Semnornis ramphastinus*	2	041
Plate-billed Mountain-toucan *Andigena laminirostris*	2	041
Chocó Toucan *Ramphastos brevis*	2	041
Orinoco Piculet *Picumnus pumilus*	3	065
Greyish Piculet *Picumnus granadensis*	1	039
Chestnut Piculet *Picumnus cinnamomeus*	2	035
Golden-naped Woodpecker *Melanerpes chrysauchen*	3	037
Chocó Woodpecker *Veniliornis chocoensis*	1	041
Lita Woodpecker *Piculus litae*	2	041
Stout-billed Cinclodes *Cinclodes excelsior*	2	043
Perijá Thistletail *Schizoeaca perijana*	2	038
Silvery-throated Spinetail *Synallaxis subpudica*	1	038
Rusty-headed Spinetail *Synallaxis fuscorufa*	1	036

cont.

cont.

Colombia (cont.)

White-whiskered Spinetail *Synallaxis candei*	2	035
Streak-capped Spinetail *Cranioleuca hellmayri*	1	036
Fulvous-dotted Treerunner *Margarornis stellatus*	2	041
Uniform Treehunter *Thripadectes ignobilis*	2	041
Black-backed Antshrike *Sakesphorus melanonotus*	2	035
Recurve-billed Bushbird *Clytoctantes alixii*	2	037,038
Speckled Antshrike *Xenornis setifrons*	2	023
Bicoloured Antvireo *Dysithamnus occidentalis*	2	041,044
Yellow-throated Antwren *Myrmotherula ambigua*	3	065
Spot-backed Antwren *Herpsilochmus dorsimaculatus*	3	065
Stub-tailed Antbird *Myrmeciza berlepschi*	2	041
Yapacana Antbird *Myrmeciza disjuncta*	2	065
Grey-bellied Antbird *Myrmeciza pelzelni*	3	065
Chestnut-crested Antbird *Rhegmatorhina cristata*	2	065
Schwartz's Antthrush *Chamaeza turdina*	2	040
Black-crowned Antpitta *Pittasoma michleri*	3	023
Rufous-crowned Antpitta *Pittasoma rufopileatum*	2	041
Giant Antpitta *Grallaria gigantea*	2	042
Moustached Antpitta *Grallaria alleni*	1	040
Ochre-striped Antpitta *Grallaria dignissima*	3	066
Cundinamarca Antpitta *Grallaria kaestneri*	1	038
Santa Marta Antpitta *Grallaria bangsi*	1	036
Bicoloured Antpitta *Grallaria rufocinerea*	1	042
Yellow-breasted Antpitta *Grallaria flavotincta*	2	041
Brown-banded Antpitta *Grallaria milleri*	1	042
Crescent-faced Antpitta *Grallaricula lineifrons*	2	042
Hooded Antpitta *Grallaricula cucullata*	2	038,040
Tacarcuna Tapaculo *Scytalopus panamensis*	2	024
Nariño Tapaculo *Scytalopus vicinior*	3	024,041
Chestnut-bellied Cotinga *Doliornis remseni*	3	043
Orange-breasted Fruiteater *Pipreola jucunda*	2	041
Black-chested Fruiteater *Pipreola lubomirskii*	3	040,044
Long-wattled Umbrellabird *Cephalopterus penduliger*	2	041
Club-winged Manakin *Machaeropterus deliciosus*	2	041
Yellow-headed Manakin *Chloropipo flavicapilla*	2	040,041,044
Golden-winged Tody-flycatcher *Todirostrum calopterum*	3	066
Slender-billed Tyrannulet *Inezia tenuirostris*	2	035
Antioquia Bristle-tyrant *Phylloscartes lanyoni*	1	037
Black-billed Flycatcher *Aphanotriccus audax*	2	023,037
Santa Marta Bush-tyrant *Myiotheretes pernix*	1	036
Apical Flycatcher *Myiarchus apicalis*	1	039
Apolinar's Wren *Cistothorus apolinari*	1	038
Niceforo's Wren *Thryothorus nicefori*	1	038
Santa Marta Wren *Troglodytes monticola*	1	036
Varied Solitaire *Myadestes coloratus*	2	024
Black Solitaire *Entomodestes coracinus*	2	041
Tocuyo Sparrow *Arremonops tocuyensis*	2	035
White-rimmed Brush-finch *Atlapetes leucopis*	2	042
Santa Marta Brush-finch *Atlapetes melanocephalus*	1	036
Yellow-headed Brush-finch *Atlapetes flaviceps*	1	040
Dusky-headed Brush-finch *A. fuscoolivaceus*	1	040
Moustached Brush-finch *Atlapetes albofrenatus*	2	038
Sooty-faced Finch *Lysurus crassirostris*	3	024
Tanager-finch *Oreothraupis arremonops*	2	041
Black-backed Bush-tanager *Urothraupis stolzmanni*	2	043
Tumaco Seedeater *Sporophila insulata*	1	(s021)
White-naped Seedeater *Dolospingus fringilloides*	3	065
Vermilion Cardinal *Cardinalis phoeniceus*	2	035
Tacarcuna Bush-tanager *Chlorospingus tacarcunae*	2	024
Dusky Bush-tanager *Chlorospingus semifuscus*	2	041
Yellow-green Bush-tanager *C. flavovirens*	2	041
Fulvous-headed Tanager *Thlypopsis fulviceps*	2	038
Scarlet-and-white Tanager *Chrysothlypis salmoni*	2	037,041

cont.

Colombia (cont.)

Sooty Ant-tanager *Habia gutturalis*	1	037
Crested Ant-tanager *Habia cristata*	1	041
Black-and-gold Tanager *Bangsia melanochlamys*	1	040,041
Golden-chested Tanager *Bangsia rothschildi*	2	041
Moss-backed Tanager *Bangsia edwardsi*	2	041
Gold-ringed Tanager *Bangsia aureocincta*	1	041
Masked Mountain-tanager *Buthraupis wetmorei*	3	043
Santa Marta Mountain-tanager *Anisognathus melanogenys*	1	036
Black-chinned Mountain-tanager *A. notabilis*	2	041
Purplish-mantled Tanager *Iridosornis porphyrocephala*	2	041
Velvet-fronted Euphonia *Euphonia concinna*	1	039
Yellow-collared Chlorophonia *Chlorophonia flavirostris*	3	024,041
Glistening-green Tanager *Chlorochrysa phoenicotis*	2	041
Multicoloured Tanager *Chlorochrysa nitidissima*	1	040,041
Blue-whiskered Tanager *Tangara johannae*	2	041
Green-naped Tanager *Tangara fucosa*	2	024
Turquoise Dacnis *Dacnis hartlaubi*	1	038,040,041
Viridian Dacnis *Dacnis viguieri*	2	023
Scarlet-breasted Dacnis *Dacnis berlepschi*	2	041
Chestnut-bellied Flower-piercer *Diglossa gloriosissima*	1	041
Indigo Flower-piercer *Diglossopis indigotica*	2	041
Yellow-crowned Whitestart *Myioborus flavivertex*	1	036
Santa Marta Warbler *Basileuterus basilicus*	1	036
Grey-throated Warbler *Basileuterus cinereicollis*	2	038
White-lored Warbler *Basileuterus conspicillatus*	1	036
Pirre Warbler *Basileuterus ignotus*	2	024
Rufous-browed Conebill *Conirostrum rufum*	2	036,038
Chocó Vireo *Vireo masteri*	1	041
Thick-billed Vireo *Vireo crassirostris*	5	(s012)
San Andrés Vireo *Vireo caribaeus*	1	(s013)
Baudó Oropendola *Psarocolius cassini*	1	023
Black Oropendola *Gymnostinops guatimozinus*	2	023,037
Jamaican Oriole *Icterus leucopteryx*	3	(s013)
Red-bellied Grackle *Hypopyrrhus pyrohypogaster*	1	040,041
Mountain Grackle *Macroagelaius subalaris*	1	038
Beautiful Jay *Cyanolyca pulchra*	2	041
Azure-naped Jay *Cyanocorax heilprini*	3	065

COMOROS

EBAs	Priority
098 Comoro Islands	CRITICAL

Secondary Areas none

Restricted-range species	Threatened	Total
Confined to this country	5	12
Present also in other countries	0	3
Total	5	15

Species (threatened species in **bold**)	No. of countries	EBAs (and SAs)
Comoro Olive-pigeon *Columba pollenii*	2	098
Comoro Blue-pigeon *Alectroenas sganzini*	3	098
Anjouan Scops-owl *Otus capnodes*	1	098
Grand Comoro Scops-owl *Otus pauliani*	1	098
Comoro Bulbul *Hypsipetes parvirostris*	1	098
Comoro Thrush *Turdus bewsheri*	1	098
Anjouan Brush-warbler *Nesillas longicaudata*	1	098
Grand Comoro Brush-warbler *Nesillas brevicaudata*	1	098

cont.

Comoros (cont.)

Moheli Brush-warbler *Nesillas mariae*	1	098
Grand Comoro Flycatcher *Humblotia flavirostris*	1	098
Humblot's Sunbird *Nectarinia humbloti*	1	098
Anjouan Sunbird *Nectarinia comorensis*	1	098
Mount Karthala White-eye *Zosterops mouroniensis*	1	098
Red-headed Fody *Foudia eminentissima*	3	098
Grand Comoro Drongo *Dicrurus fuscipennis*	1	098

COOK ISLANDS (TO NEW ZEALAND)

EBAs	Priority
210 Southern Cook Islands	URGENT

Secondary Areas
s135 Aitutaki

Restricted-range species	Threatened	Total
Confined to this country	4	6
Present also in other countries	1	2
Total	5	8

Species (threatened species in **bold**)	No. of countries	EBAs (and SAs)
Cook Islands Fruit-dove *Ptilinopus rarotongensis*	1	210
Blue Lorikeet *Vini peruviana*	2	(s135)
Atiu Swiftlet *Collocalia sawtelli*	1	210
Mangaia Kingfisher *Todirhamphus ruficollaris*	1	210
Chattering Kingfisher *Todirhamphus tuta*	2	210
Cook Islands Reed-warbler *Acrocephalus kerearako*	1	210
EX **Rarotonga Monarch** *Pomarea dimidiata*	1	210
EX Mysterious Starling *Aplonis mavornata*	0	210[X]
Rarotonga Starling *Aplonis cinerascens*	1	210

COSTA RICA

EBAs	Priority
019 Central American Caribbean slope	HIGH
020 Costa Rica and Panama highlands	URGENT
021 South Central American Pacific slope	HIGH
022 Cocos Island	URGENT

Secondary Areas
s011 Lake Nicaragua marshes

Restricted-range species	Threatened	Total
Confined to this country	5	6
Present also in other countries	3	71
Total	8	77

Species (threatened species in **bold**)	No. of countries	EBAs (and SAs)
Black Guan *Chamaepetes unicolor*	2	020
Black-breasted Wood-quail *Odontophorus leucolaemus*	2	020
Purplish-backed Quail-dove *Geotrygon lawrencii*	2	019,021
Buff-fronted Quail-dove *Geotrygon costaricensis*	2	020
Rufous-breasted Quail-dove *G. chiriquensis*	2	020
Sulphur-winged Parakeet *Pyrrhura hoffmanni*	2	020
Red-fronted Parrotlet *Touit costaricensis*	2	020
Cocos Cuckoo *Coccyzus ferrugineus*	1	022
Bare-shanked Screech-owl *Otus clarkii*	3	020
Dusky Nightjar *Caprimulgus saturatus*	2	020
White-crested Coquette *Lophornis adorabilis*	2	021

Costa Rica (cont.)

Fiery-throated Hummingbird *Panterpe insignis*	2	020
Charming Hummingbird *Amazilia decora*	2	021
Mangrove Hummingbird *Amazilia boucardi*	1	021
Black-bellied Hummingbird *Eupherusa nigriventris*	2	020
White-tailed Emerald *Elvira chionura*	2	020
Coppery-headed Emerald *Elvira cupreiceps*	1	020
White-bellied Mountain-gem *Lampornis hemileucus*	2	020
Magenta-throated Woodstar *Philodice bryantae*	2	020
Volcano Hummingbird *Selasphorus flammula*	2	020
Scintillant Hummingbird *Selasphorus scintilla*	2	020
Lattice-tailed Trogon *Trogon clathratus*	2	019
Baird's Trogon *Trogon bairdii*	2	021
Orange-bellied Trogon *Trogon aurantiiventris*	2	020
Prong-billed Barbet *Semnornis frantzii*	2	020
Fiery-billed Aracari *Pteroglossus frantzii*	2	021
Golden-naped Woodpecker *Melanerpes chrysauchen*	3	021
Ruddy Treerunner *Margarornis rubiginosus*	2	020
Streak-breasted Treehunter *Thripadectes rufobrunneus*	2	020
Black-hooded Antshrike *Thamnophilus bridgesi*	2	021
Streak-crowned Antvireo *Dysithamnus striaticeps*	3	019
Black-crowned Antpitta *Pittasoma michleri*	3	019
Silvery-fronted Tapaculo *Scytalopus argentifrons*	2	020
Turquoise Cotinga *Cotinga ridgwayi*	2	021
Snowy Cotinga *Carpodectes nitidus*	4	019
Yellow-billed Cotinga *Carpodectes antoniae*	2	021
Bare-necked Umbrellabird *Cephalopterus glabricollis*	2	020
Grey-headed Piprites *Piprites griseiceps*	4	019
Cocos Flycatcher *Nesotriccus ridgwayi*	1	022
Tawny-chested Flycatcher *Aphanotriccus capitalis*	2	019
Dark Pewee *Contopus lugubris*	2	020
Ochraceous Pewee *Contopus ochraceus*	2	020
Black-capped Flycatcher *Empidonax atriceps*	2	020
Golden-bellied Flycatcher *Myiodynastes hemichrysus*	2	020
Long-tailed Silky-flycatcher *Ptilogonys caudatus*	2	020
Black-and-yellow Silky-flycatcher *Myiodynastes melanoxantha*	2	020
Black-throated Wren *Thryothorus atrogularis*	3	019
Riverside Wren *Thryothorus semibadius*	2	021
Ochraceous Wren *Troglodytes ochraceus*	2	020
Timberline Wren *Thryorchilus browni*	2	020
Black-faced Solitaire *Myadestes melanops*	2	020
Black-billed Nightingale-thrush *Myiodynastes gracilirostris*	2	020
Sooty Thrush *Turdus nigrescens*	2	020
Volcano Junco *Junco vulcani*	2	020
Large-footed Finch *Pezopetes capitalis*	2	020
Yellow-thighed Finch *Pselliophorus tibialis*	2	020
Sooty-faced Finch *Lysurus crassirostris*	3	020
Peg-billed Finch *Acanthidops bairdii*	2	020
Nicaraguan Seed-finch *Oryzoborus nuttingi*	3	019
Cocos Finch *Pinaroloxias inornata*	1	022
Black-thighed Grosbeak *Pheucticus tibialis*	2	020
Sooty-capped Bush-tanager *Chlorospingus pileatus*	2	020
Black-and-yellow Tanager *Chrysothlypis chrysomelas*	2	019
Sulphur-rumped Tanager *Heterospingus rubrifrons*	2	019
Black-cheeked Ant-tanager *Habia atrimaxillaris*	1	021
Blue-and-gold Tanager *Bangsia arcaei*	2	020
Spot-crowned Euphonia *Euphonia imitans*	2	021
Golden-browed Chlorophonia *Chlorophonia callophrys*	2	020

cont.

cont.

Costa Rica (cont.)

Species	No. of countries	EBAs (and SAs)
Spangle-cheeked Tanager *Tangara dowii*	2	020
Slaty Flower-piercer *Diglossa plumbea*	2	020
Flame-throated Warbler *Parula gutturalis*	2	020
Collared Whitestart *Myioborus torquatus*	2	020
Black-cheeked Warbler *Basileuterus melanogenys*	2	020
Wrenthrush *Zeledonia coronata*	2	020
Yellow-winged Vireo *Vireo carmioli*	2	020
Nicaraguan Grackle *Quiscalus nicaraguensis*	2	(s011)
Silvery-throated Jay *Cyanolyca argentigula*	2	020

CUBA

EBAs	Priority
025 Cuba	CRITICAL

Secondary Areas none

Restricted-range species	Threatened	Total
Confined to this country	3	6
Present also in other countries	0	4
Total	3	10

Species (threatened species in **bold**)	No. of countries	EBAs (and SAs)
Zapata Rail *Cyanolimnas cerverai*	1	025
EX Cuban Macaw *Ara tricolor*	0	025X
Zapata Wren *Ferminia cerverai*	1	025
Bahama Mockingbird *Mimus gundlachii*	4	025
Cuban Gnatcatcher *Polioptila lembeyei*	1	025
Cuban Sparrow *Torreornis inexpectata*	1	025
Olive-capped Warbler *Dendroica pityophila*	2	025
Yellow-headed Warbler *Teretistris fernandinae*	1	025
Oriente Warbler *Teretistris fornsi*	1	025
Thick-billed Vireo *Vireo crassirostris*	5	025
Palm Crow *Corvus palmarum*	3	025

CYPRUS

EBAs	Priority
121 Cyprus	HIGH

Secondary Areas none

Restricted-range species	Threatened	Total
Confined to this country	0	2
Present also in other countries	0	0
Total	0	2

Species (threatened species in **bold**)	No. of countries	EBAs (and SAs)
Cyprus Wheatear *Oenanthe cypriaca*	1	121
Cyprus Warbler *Sylvia melanothorax*	1	121

DJIBOUTI

EBAs none

Secondary Areas
s065 Djibouti juniper forests

Restricted-range species	Threatened	Total
Confined to this country	1	1
Present also in other countries	0	0
Total	1	1

Djibouti (cont.)

Species (threatened species in **bold**)	No. of countries	EBAs (and SAs)
Djibouti Francolin *Francolinus ochropectus*	1	(s065)

DOMINICA

EBAs	Priority
030 Lesser Antilles	CRITICAL

Secondary Areas none

Restricted-range species	Threatened	Total
Confined to this country	2	2
Present also in other countries	0	16
Total	2	18

Species (threatened species in **bold**)	No. of countries	EBAs (and SAs)
Bridled Quail-dove *Geotrygon mystacea*	10	030
Red-necked Amazon *Amazona arausiaca*	1	030
Imperial Amazon *Amazona imperialis*	1	030
Lesser Antillean Swift *Chaetura martinica*	5	030
Purple-throated Carib *Eulampis jugularis*	9	030
Green-throated Carib *Eulampis holosericeus*	15	030
Antillean Crested Hummingbird *Orthorhyncus cristatus*	15	030
Blue-headed Hummingbird *Cyanophaia bicolor*	2	030
Lesser Antillean Pewee *Contopus latirostris*	5	030
Lesser Antillean Flycatcher *Myiarchus oberi*	7	030
Brown Trembler *Cinclocerthia ruficauda*	6	030
Scaly-breasted Thrasher *Margarops fuscus*	9	030
Pearly-eyed Thrasher *Margarops fuscatus*	14	030
Forest Thrush *Cichlherminia lherminieri*	4	030
Rufous-throated Solitaire *Myadestes genibarbis*	7	030
Lesser Antillean Bullfinch *Loxigilla noctis*	13	030
Antillean Euphonia *Euphonia musica*	12	030
Plumbeous Warbler *Dendroica plumbea*	2	030

DOMINICAN REPUBLIC

EBAs	Priority
028 Hispaniola	URGENT

Secondary Areas none

Restricted-range species	Threatened	Total
Confined to this country	0	0
Present also in other countries	7	32
Total	7	32

Species (threatened species in **bold**)	No. of countries	EBAs (and SAs)
Hispaniolan Hawk *Buteo ridgwayi*	2	028
Hispaniolan Parakeet *Aratinga chloroptera*	3	028
Hispaniolan Amazon *Amazona ventralis*	2	028
Rufous-breasted Cuckoo *Hyetornis rufigularis*	2	028
Hispaniolan Lizard-cuckoo *Saurothera longirostris*	2	028
Ashy-faced Owl *Tyto glaucops*	2	028
Least Poorwill *Siphonorhis brewsteri*	2	028
Antillean Mango *Anthracothorax dominicus*	4	028
Hispaniolan Emerald *Chlorostilbon swainsonii*	2	028
Vervain Hummingbird *Mellisuga minima*	3	028
Hispaniolan Trogon *Priotelus roseigaster*	2	028
Narrow-billed Tody *Todus angustirostris*	2	028

cont.

cont.

Dominican Republic (cont.)

Broad-billed Tody *Todus subulatus*	2	028
Antillean Piculet *Nesoctites micromegas*	2	028
Hispaniolan Woodpecker *Melanerpes striatus*	2	028
Greater Antillean Elaenia *Elaenia fallax*	3	028
Hispaniolan Pewee *Contopus hispaniolensis*	2	028
Stolid Flycatcher *Myiarchus stolidus*	3	028
Golden Swallow *Tachycineta euchrysea*	3	028
Palmchat *Dulus dominicus*	2	028
Pearly-eyed Thrasher *Margarops fuscatus*	14	028
Rufous-throated Solitaire *Myadestes genibarbis*	7	028
La Selle Thrush *Turdus swalesi*	2	028
Black-crowned Palm-tanager *Phaenicophilus palmarum*	2	028
Chat-tanager *Calyptophilus frugivorus*	2	028
Antillean Euphonia *Euphonia musica*	12	028
Green-tailed Warbler *Microligea palustris*	2	028
White-winged Warbler *Xenoligea montana*	2	028
Flat-billed Vireo *Vireo nanus*	2	028
Antillean Siskin *Carduelis dominicensis*	2	028
Palm Crow *Corvus palmarum*	3	028
White-necked Crow *Corvus leucognaphalus*	2	028

ECUADOR

EBAs	Priority
031 Galápagos Islands	URGENT
041 Chocó	URGENT
042 Northern Central Andes	CRITICAL
043 Central Andean páramo	URGENT
044 Ecuador–Peru East Andes	HIGH
045 Tumbesian region	CRITICAL
046 Southern Central Andes	URGENT
047 Andean ridge-top forests	URGENT
066 Upper Amazon–Napo lowlands	HIGH

Secondary Areas none

Restricted-range species	Threatened	Total
Confined to this country	10	30
Present also in other countries	26	130
Total	36	160

Species (threatened species in **bold**)	No. of countries	EBAs (and SAs)
Berlepsch's Tinamou *Crypturellus berlepschi*	2	041
Pale-browed Tinamou *C. transfasciatus*	2	045
Galápagos Heron *Butorides sundevalli*	1	031
Grey-backed Hawk *Leucopternis occidentalis*	2	045
Galápagos Hawk *Buteo galapagoensis*	1	031
Carunculated Caracara *Phalcoboenus carunculatus*	2	043
Plumbeous Forest-falcon *Micrastur plumbeus*	2	041
Rufous-headed Chachalaca *Ortalis erythroptera*	2	045
Bearded Guan *Penelope barbata*	2	046
Baudó Guan *Penelope ortoni*	2	041
Dark-backed Wood-quail *Odontophorus melanonotus*	2	041
Galápagos Rail *Laterallus spilonotus*	1	031
Dusky Pigeon *Columba goodsoni*	2	041
Galápagos Dove *Zenaida galapagoensis*	1	031
Ecuadorian Ground-dove *Columbina buckleyi*	2	045
Ochre-bellied Dove *Leptotila ochraceiventris*	2	045
Red-masked Parakeet *Aratinga erythrogenys*	2	045
El Oro Parakeet *Pyrrhura orcesi*	1	045
White-necked Parakeet *Pyrrhura albipectus*	1	044
Pacific Parrotlet *Forpus coelestis*	2	045
Grey-cheeked Parakeet *Brotogeris pyrrhopterus*	2	045

Ecuador (cont.)

Rose-faced Parrot *Pionopsitta pulchra*	2	041
Rusty-faced Parrot *Hapalopsittaca amazonica*	3	042
Red-faced Parrot *Hapalopsittaca pyrrhops*	2	046
Banded Ground-cuckoo *Neomorphus radiolosus*	2	041
Colombian Screech-owl *Otus colombianus*	2	041
Cinnamon Screech-owl *Otus petersoni*	2	044
Chocó Poorwill *Nyctiphrynus rosenbergi*	2	041
Scrub Nightjar *Caprimulgus anthonyi*	2	045
Napo Sabrewing *Campylopterus villaviscensio*	2	044
Olive-spotted Hummingbird *Leucippus chlorocercus*	4	066
Purple-chested Hummingbird *Amazilia rosenbergi*	2	041
Ecuadorian Piedtail *Phlogophilus hemileucurus*	3	044
Empress Brilliant *Heliodoxa imperatrix*	2	041
Pink-throated Brilliant *Heliodoxa gularis*	3	044
Brown Inca *Coeligena wilsoni*	2	041
Rainbow Starfrontlet *Coeligena iris*	2	046
Velvet-purple Coronet *Boissonneaua jardini*	2	041
Gorgeted Sunangel *Heliangelus strophianus*	2	041
Purple-throated Sunangel *Heliangelus viola*	2	046
Black-breasted Puffleg *Eriocnemis nigrivestis*	1	043
Turquoise-throated Puffleg *Eriocnemis godini*	1	041
Black-thighed Puffleg *Eriocnemis derbyi*	2	042
Hoary Puffleg *Haplophaedia lugens*	2	041
Purple-bibbed Whitetip *Urosticte benjamini*	2	041
Rufous-vented Whitetip *Urosticte ruficrissa*	3	044
Violet-throated Metaltail *Metallura baroni*	1	043
Neblina Metaltail *Metallura odomae*	2	043
Violet-tailed Sylph *Aglaiocercus coelestis*	2	041
Short-tailed Woodstar *Myrmia micrura*	2	045
Esmeraldas Woodstar *Acestrura berlepschi*	1	045
White-eyed Trogon *Trogon comptus*	2	041
Coppery-chested Jacamar *Galbula pastazae*	3	044
Brown Nunlet *Nonnula brunnea*	3	066
Orange-fronted Barbet *Capito squamatus*	2	041
Toucan Barbet *Semnornis ramphastinus*	2	041
Plate-billed Mountain-toucan *Andigena laminirostris*	2	041
Chocó Toucan *Ramphastos brevis*	2	041
Ecuadorian Piculet *Picumnus sclateri*	2	045
Lita Woodpecker *Piculus litae*	2	041
Stout-billed Cinclodes *Cinclodes excelsior*	2	043
Mouse-coloured Thistletail *Schizoeaca griseomurina*	2	043
Blackish-headed Spinetail *Synallaxis tithys*	2	045
Necklaced Spinetail *Synallaxis stictothorax*	2	045
Equatorial Greytail *Xenerpestes singularis*	2	044
Fulvous-dotted Treerunner *Margarornis stellatus*	2	041
Rufous-necked Foliage-gleaner *Syndactyla ruficollis*	2	045
Uniform Treehunter *Thripadectes ignobilis*	2	041
Henna-hooded Foliage-gleaner *Hylocryptus erythrocephalus*	2	045
Collared Antshrike *Sakesphorus bernardi*	2	045
Chapman's Antshrike *Thamnophilus zarumae*	2	045
Cocha Antshrike *Thamnophilus praecox*	1	066
Bicoloured Antvireo *Dysithamnus occidentalis*	2	041,044
Stub-tailed Antbird *Myrmeciza berlepschi*	2	041
Grey-headed Antbird *Myrmeciza griseiceps*	2	045
Rufous-crowned Antpitta *Pittasoma rufopileatum*	2	041
Giant Antpitta *Grallaria gigantea*	2	042,046
Ochre-striped Antpitta *Grallaria dignissima*	3	066
Scrub Antpitta *Grallaria watkinsi*	2	045
Yellow-breasted Antpitta *Grallaria flavotincta*	2	041
Peruvian Antpitta *Grallaricula peruviana*	2	044
Crescent-faced Antpitta *Grallaricula lineifrons*	2	042,046
Elegant Crescent-chest *Melanopareia elegans*	2	045

cont.

cont.

Ecuador (cont.)

Nariño Tapaculo *Scytalopus vicinior*	3	041
Slaty Becard *Pachyramphus spodiurus*	2	045
Chestnut-bellied Cotinga *Doliornis remseni*	3	043
Orange-breasted Fruiteater *Pipreola jucunda*	2	041
Black-chested Fruiteater *Pipreola lubomirskii*	3	044
Long-wattled Umbrellabird	2	041
Cephalopterus penduliger		
Club-winged Manakin *Machaeropterus deliciosus*	2	041
Yellow-headed Manakin *Chloropipo flavicapilla*	2	041,044
Orange-crested Manakin	2	066
Heterocercus aurantiivertex		
Cinnamon-breasted Tody-tyrant	2	047
Hemitriccus cinnamomeipectus		
Golden-winged Tody-flycatcher	3	066
Todirostrum calopterum		
Red-billed Tyrannulet *Zimmerius cinereicapillus*	2	044
Pacific Elaenia *Myiopagis subplacens*	2	045
Grey-and-white Tyrannulet	2	045
Pseudelaenia leucospodia		
Ecuadorian Tyrannulet *Phylloscartes gualaquizae*	2	044
Pacific Royal Flycatcher	2	045
Onychorhynchus occidentalis		
Orange-banded Flycatcher *Myiophobus lintoni*	2	046
Olive-chested Flycatcher *M. cryptoxanthus*	2	066
Grey-breasted Flycatcher	2	045
Lathrotriccus griseipectus		
Sooty-crowned Flycatcher	2	045
Myiarchus phaeocephalus		
Large-billed Flycatcher *Myiarchus magnirostris*	1	031
Baird's Flycatcher *Myiodynastes bairdii*	2	045
Superciliated Wren *Thryothorus superciliaris*	2	045
Bar-winged Wood-wren *Henicorhina leucoptera*	2	047
Galápagos Mockingbird *Nesomimus parvulus*	1	031
Floreana Mockingbird *Nesomimus trifasciatus*	1	031
Hood Mockingbird *Nesomimus macdonaldi*	1	031
San Cristóbal Mockingbird *Nesomimus melanotis*	1	031
Black Solitaire *Entomodestes coracinus*	2	041
Plumbeous-backed Thrush *Turdus reevei*	2	045
Ecuadorian Thrush *Turdus maculirostris*	2	045
Tumbes Sparrow *Aimophila stolzmanni*	2	045
Black-capped Sparrow *Arremon abeillei*	2	045
White-rimmed Brush-finch *Atlapetes leucopis*	2	042,046
Bay-crowned Brush-finch *Atlapetes seebohmi*	2	045
White-headed Brush-finch *Atlapetes albiceps*	2	045
Pale-headed Brush-finch *Atlapetes pallidiceps*	1	045
Tanager-finch *Oreothraupis arremonops*	2	041
Black-backed Bush-tanager	2	043
Urothraupis stolzmanni		
Crimson Finch-tanager *Rhodospingus cruentus*	2	045
Sulphur-throated Finch *Sicalis taczanowskii*	2	045
Drab Seedeater *Sporophila simplex*	2	045
Large Ground-finch *Geospiza magnirostris*	1	031
Medium Ground-finch *Geospiza fortis*	1	031
Small Ground-finch *Geospiza fuliginosa*	1	031
Sharp-beaked Ground-finch *Geospiza difficilis*	1	031
Common Cactus-finch *Geospiza scandens*	1	031
Large Cactus-finch *Geospiza conirostris*	1	031
Vegetarian Finch *Camarhynchus crassirostris*	1	031
Large Tree-finch *Camarhynchus psittacula*	1	031
Medium Tree-finch *Camarhynchus pauper*	1	031
Small Tree-finch *Camarhynchus parvulus*	1	031
Woodpecker Finch *Camarhynchus pallidus*	1	031
Mangrove Finch *Camarhynchus heliobates*	1	031
Warbler Finch *Certhidea olivacea*	1	031
Black-cowled Saltator *Saltator nigriceps*	2	045
Dusky Bush-tanager *Chlorospingus semifuscus*	2	041
Yellow-green Bush-tanager *C. flavivirens*	2	041

Ecuador (cont.)

Scarlet-and-white Tanager *Chrysothlypis salmoni*	2	041
Golden-chested Tanager *Bangsia rothschildi*	2	041
Moss-backed Tanager *Bangsia edwardsi*	2	041
Masked Mountain-tanager *Buthraupis wetmorei*	3	043
Orange-throated Tanager	2	047
Wetmorethraupis sterrhopteron		
Black-chinned Mountain-tanager	2	041
Anisognathus notabilis		
Purplish-mantled Tanager	2	041
Iridosornis porphyrocephala		
Yellow-collared Chlorophonia	3	041
Chlorophonia flavirostris		
Glistening-green Tanager	2	041
Chlorochrysa phoenicotis		
Blue-whiskered Tanager *Tangara johannae*	2	041
Scarlet-breasted Dacnis *Dacnis berlepschi*	2	041
Indigo Flower-piercer *Diglossopis indigotica*	2	041
Grey-and-gold Warbler *Basileuterus fraseri*	2	045
Three-banded Warbler *Basileuterus trifasciatus*	2	045
Ecuadorian Cacique *Cacicus sclateri*	2	066
White-edged Oriole *Icterus graceannae*	2	045
Saffron Siskin *Carduelis siemiradzkii*	2	045
Beautiful Jay *Cyanolyca pulchra*	2	041
White-tailed Jay *Cyanocorax mystacalis*	2	045

EL SALVADOR

EBAs		Priority
017 North Central American Pacific slope		HIGH
018 North Central American highlands		URGENT

Secondary Areas none

Restricted-range species	Threatened	Total
Confined to this country	0	0
Present also in other countries	0	17
Total	0	17

Species (threatened species in **bold**)	No. of countries	EBAs (and SAs)
White-bellied Chachalaca *Ortalis leucogastra*	5	017
Ocellated Quail *Cyrtonyx ocellatus*	5	018
Pacific Parakeet *Aratinga strenua*	5	017
Fulvous Owl *Strix fulvescens*	4	018
Rufous Sabrewing *Campylopterus rufus*	3	018
Blue-tailed Hummingbird *Amazilia cyanura*	5	017
Green-throated Mountain-gem	5	018
Lampornis viridipallens		
Slender Sheartail *Doricha enicura*	4	018
Wine-throated Hummingbird *Atthis ellioti*	4	018
Blue-throated Motmot *Aspatha gularis*	4	018
Belted Flycatcher *Xenotriccus callizonus*	3	018
Black-capped Swallow *Notiochelidon pileata*	3	018
Rufous-browed Wren *Troglodytes rufociliatus*	4	018
Blue-and-white Mockingbird *Melanotis hypoleucus*	4	018
Rufous-collared Robin *Turdus rufitorques*	4	018
Bar-winged Oriole *Icterus maculialatus*	3	018
Bushy-crested Jay *Cyanocorax melanocyaneus*	4	018

cont.

EQUATORIAL GUINEA

EBAs	Priority
081 Annobón	URGENT
085 Cameroon and Gabon lowlands	HIGH
086 Cameroon mountains	CRITICAL

Secondary Areas none

Restricted-range species	Threatened	Total
Confined to this country	3	4
Present also in other countries	1	13
Total	4	17

Species (threatened species in **bold**)	No. of countries	EBAs (and SAs)
Cameroon Olive-pigeon *Columba sjostedti*	3	086
São Tomé Bronze-naped Pigeon *C. malherbii*	2	081
Mountain Sawwing *Psalidoprocne fuliginosa*	3	086
Grey-throated Greenbul *Andropadus tephrolaemus*	3	086
Cameroon Olive Greenbul *Phyllastrephus poensis*	3	086
Grey-necked Rockfowl *Picathartes oreas*	4	085,086
Green Longtail *Urolais epichlora*	3	086
White-tailed Warbler *Poliolais lopezi*	3	086
Black-capped Woodland-warbler *Phylloscopus herberti*	3	086
Fernando Po Batis *Batis poensis*	1	086
Annobón Paradise-flycatcher *Terpsiphone smithii*	1	081
Cameroon Sunbird *Nectarinia oritis*	3	086
Ursula's Sunbird *Nectarinia ursulae*	2	086
Fernando Po Speirops *Speirops brunneus*	1	086
Annobón White-eye *Zosterops griseovirescens*	1	081
Fernando Po Oliveback *Nesocharis shelleyi*	3	086
Rachel's Malimbe *Malimbus racheliae*	4	085

ERITREA

EBAs	Priority
115 Central Ethiopian highlands	CRITICAL

Secondary Areas none

Restricted-range species	Threatened	Total
Confined to this country	0	0
Present also in other countries	0	1
Total	0	1

Species (threatened species in **bold**)	No. of countries	EBAs (and SAs)
Rüppell's Chat *Myrmecocichla melaena*	2	115

ETHIOPIA

EBAs	Priority
113 Jubba and Shabeelle valleys	CRITICAL
114 South Ethiopian highlands	CRITICAL
115 Central Ethiopian highlands	CRITICAL

Secondary Areas
s063 Northern Ethiopia

Restricted-range species	Threatened	Total
Confined to this country	8	9
Present also in other countries	0	4
Total	8	13

Ethiopia (cont.)

Species (threatened species in **bold**)	No. of countries	EBAs (and SAs)
Harwood's Francolin *Francolinus harwoodi*	1	115
White-winged Collared-dove *Streptopelia reichenowi*	3	113
Prince Ruspoli's Turaco *Tauraco ruspolii*	1	114
Nechisar Nightjar *Caprimulgus solala*	1	114
Degodi Lark *Mirafra degodiensis*	1	113
Sidamo Lark *Heteromirafra sidamoensis*	1	114
White-tailed Swallow *Hirundo megaensis*	1	114
Sombre Chat *Cercomela dubia*	2	(s063)
Rüppell's Chat *Myrmecocichla melaena*	2	115
Yellow-throated Serin *Serinus flavigula*	1	115
Ankober Serin *Serinus ankoberensis*	1	115
Salvadori's Weaver *Ploceus dicrocephalus*	3	113
Ethiopian Bush-crow *Zavattariornis stresemanni*	1	114

FALKLAND ISLANDS (TO UK)

EBAs	Priority
062 Southern Patagonia	URGENT

Secondary Areas none

Restricted-range species	Threatened	Total
Confined to this country	1	2
Present also in other countries	0	3
Total	1	5

Species (threatened species in **bold**)	No. of countries	EBAs (and SAs)
Ruddy-headed Goose *Chloephaga rubidiceps*	3	062
Falkland Steamerduck *Tachyeres brachypterus*	1	062
Striated Caracara *Phalcoboenus australis*	3	062
Cobb's Wren *Troglodytes cobbi*	1	062
Canary-winged Finch *Melanodera melanodera*	3	062

FIJI

EBAs	Priority
202 Fiji	HIGH

Secondary Areas
s127 Rotuma

Restricted-range species	Threatened	Total
Confined to this country	6	25
Present also in other countries	0	11
Total	6	36

Species (threatened species in **bold**)	No. of countries	EBAs (and SAs)
Fiji Goshawk *Accipiter rufitorques*	1	202
EX Bar-winged Rail *Nesoclopeus poecilopterus*	0	202[X]
Shy Ground-dove *Gallicolumba stairi*	5	202
Many-coloured Fruit-dove *Ptilinopus perousii*	4	202
Purple-capped Fruit-dove *P. porphyraceus*	7	202(s127)
Orange Dove *Ptilinopus victor*	1	202
Golden Dove *Ptilinopus luteovirens*	1	202
Whistling Dove *Ptilinopus layardi*	1	202
Peale's Imperial-pigeon *Ducula latrans*	1	202
Collared Lory *Phigys solitarius*	1	202
Blue-crowned Lorikeet *Vini australis*	6	202
Red-throated Lorikeet *Charmosyna amabilis*	1	202

cont.

cont.

Fiji (cont.)

Crimson Shining-parrot *Prosopeia splendens*	1	202
Masked Shining-parrot *Prosopeia personata*	1	202
Red Shining-parrot *Prosopeia tabuensis*	1	202
Polynesian Triller *Lalage maculosa*	7	202(s127)
Fiji Bush-warbler *Cettia ruficapilla*	1	202
Long-legged Thicketbird *Trichocichla rufa*	1	202
Silktail *Lamprolia victoriae*	1	202
Ogea Monarch *Mayrornis versicolor*	1	202
Slaty Monarch *Mayrornis lessoni*	1	202
Fiji Shrikebill *Clytorhynchus vitiensis*	4	202(s127)
Black-throated Shrikebill *C. nigrogularis*	2	202
Vanikoro Flycatcher *Myiagra vanikorensis*	2	202
Blue-crested Flycatcher *Myiagra azureocapilla*	1	202
Streaked Fantail *Rhipidura spilodera*	3	202
Kadavu Fantail *Rhipidura personata*	1	202
Layard's White-eye *Zosterops explorator*	1	202
Rotuma Myzomela *Myzomela chermesina*	1	(s127)
Orange-breasted Myzomela *Myzomela jugularis*	1	202
Wattled Honeyeater *Foulehaio carunculata*	5	202
Kadavu Honeyeater *Xanthotis provocator*	1	202
Giant Honeyeater *Gymnomyza viridis*	1	202
Fiji Parrotfinch *Erythrura pealii*	1	202
Pink-billed Parrotfinch *Erythrura kleinschmidti*	1	202
Polynesian Starling *Aplonis tabuensis*	7	202(s127)
Fiji Woodswallow *Artamus mentalis*	1	202

FRANCE

See also French Polynesia (p. 741), French Southern Territories (p. 741), Guadeloupe (p. 742), Martinique (p. 753), Mayotte (p. 754), New Caledonia (p. 757), Réunion (p. 766), Wallis and Futuna (p. 777).

EBAs none

Secondary Areas
s068 Corsican mountains

Restricted-range species	Threatened	Total
Confined to this country	0	1
Present also in other countries	0	0
Total	0	1

Species (threatened species in **bold**)	No. of countries	EBAs (and SAs)
Corsican Nuthatch *Sitta whiteheadi*	1	(s068)

FRENCH POLYNESIA (TO FRANCE)

EBAs	Priority
211 Rimatara	CRITICAL
212 Marquesas Islands	CRITICAL
213 Society Islands	URGENT
214 Tuamotu archipelago	CRITICAL

Secondary Areas
s136 Rapa

Restricted-range species	Threatened	Total
Confined to this country	17	25
Present also in other countries	1	2
Total	18	27

cont.

French Polynesia (cont.)

Species (threatened species in **bold**)	No. of countries	EBAs (and SAs)
Tuamotu Sandpiper *Prosobonia cancellata*	1	214
Polynesian Ground-dove	1	213[X],214
Gallicolumba erythroptera		
Marquesan Ground-dove *G. rubescens*	1	212
Rapa Fruit-dove *Ptilinopus huttoni*	1	(s136)
Grey-green Fruit-dove *Ptilinopus purpuratus*	1	213
Atoll Fruit-dove *Ptilinopus coralensis*	1	214
Makatea Fruit-dove *Ptilinopus chalcurus*	1	214
[EX] Red-moustached Fruit-dove *Ptilinopus mercierii*	0	212[X]
White-capped Fruit-dove *P. dupetithouarsii*	1	212
Polynesian Imperial-pigeon *Ducula aurorae*	1	213,214
Marquesan Imperial-pigeon *Ducula galeata*	1	212
Kuhl's Lorikeet *Vini kuhlii*	1	211
Blue Lorikeet *Vini peruviana*	2	213,214
Ultramarine Lorikeet *Vini ultramarina*	1	212
[EX] Black-fronted Parakeet	0	213[X]
Cyanoramphus zealandicus		
Tahiti Swiftlet *Collocalia leucophaeus*	1	213
Marquesan Swiftlet *Collocalia ocista*	1	212
Tahiti Kingfisher *Todirhamphus veneratus*	1	213
Chattering Kingfisher *Todirhamphus tuta*	2	213
Marquesan Kingfisher *T. godeffroyi*	1	212
Tuamotu Kingfisher *Todirhamphus gambieri*	1	214
Tahiti Reed-warbler *Acrocephalus caffer*	1	213
Marquesan Reed-warbler *A. mendanae*	1	212
Tuamotu Reed-warbler *Acrocephalus atyphus*	1	214
Rimatara Reed-warbler *Acrocephalus rimatarae*	1	211
Tahiti Monarch *Pomarea nigra*	1	213
[EX] Maupiti Monarch *Pomarea pomarea*	0	213[X]
Iphis Monarch *Pomarea iphis*	1	212
Marquesan Monarch *Pomarea mendozae*	1	212
Fatuhiva Monarch *Pomarea whitneyi*	1	212

FRENCH SOUTHERN TERRITORIES (TO FRANCE)

EBAs none

Secondary Areas
s048 Kerguelen and Crozet Islands

Restricted-range species	Threatened	Total
Confined to this country	0	1
Present also in other countries	0	0
Total	0	1

Species (threatened species in **bold**)	No. of countries	EBAs (and SAs)
Eaton's Pintail *Anas eatoni*	1	(s048)

GABON

EBAs	Priority
085 Cameroon and Gabon lowlands	HIGH

Secondary Areas
s043 Gabon–Cabinda coast

Restricted-range species	Threatened	Total
Confined to this country	0	0
Present also in other countries	2	6
Total	2	6

cont.

Gabon (cont.)

Species (threatened species in **bold**)	No. of countries	EBAs (and SAs)
Forest Swallow *Hirundo fuliginosa*	3	085
Grey-necked Rockfowl *Picathartes oreas*	4	085
Dja River Warbler *Bradypterus grandis*	2	085
Gabon Batis *Batis minima*	2	085
Loango Weaver *Ploceus subpersonatus*	3	(s043)
Rachel's Malimbe *Malimbus racheliae*	4	085

GEORGIA

EBAs	Priority
122 Caucasus	HIGH

Secondary Areas none

Restricted-range species	Threatened	Total
Confined to this country	0	0
Present also in other countries	0	3
Total	0	3

Species (threatened species in **bold**)	No. of countries	EBAs (and SAs)
Caucasian Grouse *Tetrao mlokosiewiczi*	6	122
Caucasian Snowcock *Tetraogallus caucasicus*	3	122
Caucasian Chiffchaff *Phylloscopus lorenzii*	6	122

GHANA

EBAs	Priority
084 Upper Guinea forests	CRITICAL

Secondary Areas none

Restricted-range species	Threatened	Total
Confined to this country	0	0
Present also in other countries	7	11
Total	7	11

Species (threatened species in **bold**)	No. of countries	EBAs (and SAs)
White-breasted Guineafowl *Agelastes meleagrides*	4	084
Rufous Fishing-owl *Scotopelia ussheri*	5	084
Brown-cheeked Hornbill *Ceratogymna cylindricus*	5	084
Western Wattled Cuckoo-shrike *Campephaga lobata*	5	084
Green-tailed Bristlebill *Bleda eximia*	5	084
Yellow-throated Olive Greenbul *Criniger olivaceus*	5	084
Rufous-winged Illadopsis *Illadopsis rufescens*	5	084
White-necked Rockfowl *Picathartes gymnocephalus*	5	084
Sharpe's Apalis *Apalis sharpei*	5	084
Black-capped Rufous Warbler *Bathmocercus cerviniventris*	5	084
Copper-tailed Glossy-starling *Lamprotornis cupreocauda*	5	084

GRENADA

EBAs	Priority
030 Lesser Antilles	CRITICAL

Secondary Areas none

Restricted-range species	Threatened	Total
Confined to this country	1	1
Present also in other countries	0	7
Total	1	8

Species (threatened species in **bold**)	No. of countries	EBAs (and SAs)
Grenada Dove *Leptotila wellsi*	1	030
Green-throated Carib *Eulampis holosericeus*	15	030
Antillean Crested Hummingbird *Orthorhyncus cristatus*	15	030
Grenada Flycatcher *Myiarchus nugator*	2	030
Scaly-breasted Thrasher *Margarops fuscus*	9	030
Lesser Antillean Bullfinch *Loxigilla noctis*	13	030
Antillean Euphonia *Euphonia musica*	12	030
Lesser Antillean Tanager *Tangara cucullata*	2	030

GUADELOUPE (TO FRANCE)

EBAs	Priority
030 Lesser Antilles	CRITICAL

Secondary Areas .none

Restricted-range species	Threatened	Total
Confined to this country	0	1
Present also in other countries	0	14
Total	0	15

Species (threatened species in **bold**)	No. of countries	EBAs (and SAs)
Bridled Quail-dove *Geotrygon mystacea*	10	030
Lesser Antillean Swift *Chaetura martinica*	5	030
Purple-throated Carib *Eulampis jugularis*	9	030
Green-throated Carib *Eulampis holosericeus*	15	030
Antillean Crested Hummingbird *Orthorhyncus cristatus*	15	030
Guadeloupe Woodpecker *Melanerpes herminieri*	1	030
Lesser Antillean Pewee *Contopus latirostris*	5	030
Lesser Antillean Flycatcher *Myiarchus oberi*	7	030
Brown Trembler *Cinclocerthia ruficauda*	6	030
Scaly-breasted Thrasher *Margarops fuscus*	9	030
Pearly-eyed Thrasher *Margarops fuscatus*	14	030
Forest Thrush *Cichlherminia lherminieri*	4	030
Lesser Antillean Bullfinch *Loxigilla noctis*	13	030
Antillean Euphonia *Euphonia musica*	12	030
Plumbeous Warbler *Dendroica plumbea*	2	030

GUAM (TO USA)

EBAs	Priority
189 Mariana Islands	URGENT

Secondary Areas none

Restricted-range species	Threatened	Total
Confined to this country	0	0
Present also in other countries	1	3
Total	1	3

cont.

Guam (cont.)

Species (threatened species in **bold**)	No. of countries	EBAs (and SAs)
EL **Micronesian Scrubfowl** *Megapodius laperouse*	2	189
EW Guam Rail *Gallirallus owstoni*	0	189ˣ
EL White-throated Ground-dove *Gallicolumba xanthonura*	2	189
EL Mariana Fruit-dove *Ptilinopus roseicapilla*	1	189
Micronesian Swiftlet *Collocalia inquieta*	3	189
EL Micronesian Kingfisher *Todirhamphus cinnamominus*	2	189ˣ
EL **Nightingale Reed-warbler** *Acrocephalus luscinia*	1	189
EX Guam Flycatcher *Myiagra freycineti*	0	189ˣ
EX Guam Bridled White-eye *Zosterops conspicillatus*	0	189ˣ
EL Micronesian Myzomela *Myzomela rubratra*	3	189
Micronesian Starling *Aplonis opaca*	4	189
Mariana Crow *Corvus kubaryi*	2	189

GUATEMALA

EBAs	Priority
017 North Central American Pacific slope	HIGH
018 North Central American highlands	URGENT
019 Central American Caribbean slope	HIGH

Secondary Areas none

Restricted-range species	Threatened	Total
Confined to this country	0	0
Present also in other countries	2	23
Total	2	23

Species (threatened species in **bold**)	No. of countries	EBAs (and SAs)
EX Atitlán Grebe *Podilymbus gigas*	0	018ˣ
White-bellied Chachalaca *Ortalis leucogastra*	5	017
Horned Guan *Oreophasis derbianus*	2	018
Ocellated Quail *Cyrtonyx ocellatus*	5	018
Pacific Parakeet *Aratinga strenua*	5	017
Santa Barbara Screech-owl *Otus barbarus*	2	018
Fulvous Owl *Strix fulvescens*	4	018
Rufous Sabrewing *Campylopterus rufus*	3	018
Blue-tailed Hummingbird *Amazilia cyanura*	5	017
Green-throated Mountain-gem *Lampornis viridipallens*	5	018
Slender Sheartail *Doricha enicura*	4	018
Wine-throated Hummingbird *Atthis ellioti*	4	018
Blue-throated Motmot *Aspatha gularis*	4	018
Grey-headed Piprites *Piprites griseiceps*	4	019
Belted Flycatcher *Xenotriccus callizonus*	3	018
Black-capped Swallow *Notiochelidon pileata*	3	018
Rufous-browed Wren *Troglodytes rufociliatus*	4	018
Blue-and-white Mockingbird *Melanotis hypoleucus*	4	018
Rufous-collared Robin *Turdus rufitorques*	4	018
Azure-rumped Tanager *Tangara cabanisi*	2	018
Pink-headed Warbler *Ergaticus versicolor*	2	018
Bar-winged Oriole *Icterus maculialatus*	3	018
Black-capped Siskin *Carduelis atriceps*	2	018
Bushy-crested Jay *Cyanocorax melanocyaneus*	4	018

GUINEA

EBAs	Priority
084 Upper Guinea forests	CRITICAL

Secondary Areas none

Restricted-range species	Threatened	Total
Confined to this country	0	0
Present also in other countries	8	12
Total	8	12

Species (threatened species in **bold**)	No. of countries	EBAs (and SAs)
Rufous Fishing-owl *Scotopelia ussheri*	5	084
Brown-cheeked Hornbill *Ceratogymna cylindricus*	5	084
Western Wattled Cuckoo-shrike *Campephaga lobata*	5	084
Green-tailed Bristlebill *Bleda eximia*	5	084
Yellow-throated Olive Greenbul *Criniger olivaceus*	5	084
Rufous-winged Illadopsis *Illadopsis rufescens*	5	084
White-necked Rockfowl *Picathartes gymnocephalus*	5	084
White-eyed Prinia *Prinia leontica*	4	084
Sharpe's Apalis *Apalis sharpei*	5	084
Black-capped Rufous Warbler *Bathmocercus cerviniventris*	5	084
Nimba Flycatcher *Melaenornis annamarulae*	4	084
Copper-tailed Glossy-starling *Lamprotornis cupreocauda*	5	084

GUYANA

EBAs	Priority
063 Rio Branco gallery forests	URGENT
064 Tepuis	URGENT

Secondary Areas none

Restricted-range species	Threatened	Total
Confined to this country	0	0
Present also in other countries	2	20
Total	2	20

Species (threatened species in **bold**)	No. of countries	EBAs (and SAs)
Fiery-shouldered Parakeet *Pyrrhura egregia*	3	064
Tepui Parrotlet *Nannopsittaca panychlora*	3	064
Tepui Swift *Cypseloides phelpsi*	3	064
Peacock Coquette *Lophornis pavoninus*	3	064
Velvet-browed Brilliant *Heliodoxa xanthogonys*	3	064
Hoary-throated Spinetail *Synallaxis kollari*	2	063
Tepui Spinetail *Cranioleuca demissa*	3	064
Roraiman Barbtail *Roraimia adusta*	3	064
Roraiman Antwren *Herpsilochmus roraimae*	3	064
Rio Branco Antbird *Cercomacra carbonaria*	2	063
Red-banded Fruiteater *Pipreola whitelyi*	2	064
Rose-collared Piha *Lipaugus streptophorus*	3	064
Scarlet-horned Manakin *Pipra cornuta*	3	064
Orange-bellied Manakin *Lepidothrix suavissima*	3	064
Olive Manakin *Chloropipo uniformis*	3	064
Flutist Wren *Microcerculus ustulatus*	3	064
Olive-backed Tanager *Mitrospingus oleagineus*	3	064
Tepui Whitestart *Myioborus castaneocapillus*	3	064
Tepui Greenlet *Hylophilus sclateri*	3	064
Golden-tufted Grackle *Macroagelaius imthurni*	3	064

HAITI

EBAs	Priority
028 Hispaniola	URGENT

Secondary Areas none

Restricted-range species	Threatened	Total
Confined to this country	0	1
Present also in other countries	7	32
Total	7	33

Species (threatened species in **bold**)	No. of countries	EBAs (and SAs)
Hispaniolan Hawk *Buteo ridgwayi*	2	028
Hispaniolan Parakeet *Aratinga chloroptera*	3	028
Hispaniolan Amazon *Amazona ventralis*	2	028
Rufous-breasted Cuckoo *Hyetornis rufigularis*	2	028
Hispaniolan Lizard-cuckoo *Saurothera longirostris*	2	028
Ashy-faced Owl *Tyto glaucops*	2	028
Least Poorwill *Siphonorhis brewsteri*	2	028
Antillean Mango *Anthracothorax dominicus*	4	028
Hispaniolan Emerald *Chlorostilbon swainsonii*	2	028
Vervain Hummingbird *Mellisuga minima*	3	028
Hispaniolan Trogon *Priotelus roseigaster*	2	028
Narrow-billed Tody *Todus angustirostris*	2	028
Broad-billed Tody *Todus subulatus*	2	028
Antillean Piculet *Nesoctites micromegas*	2	028
Hispaniolan Woodpecker *Melanerpes striatus*	2	028
Greater Antillean Elaenia *Elaenia fallax*	3	028
Hispaniolan Pewee *Contopus hispaniolensis*	2	028
Stolid Flycatcher *Myiarchus stolidus*	3	028
Golden Swallow *Tachycineta euchrysea*	3	028
Palmchat *Dulus dominicus*	2	028
Rufous-throated Solitaire *Myadestes genibarbis*	7	028
La Selle Thrush *Turdus swalesi*	2	028
Black-crowned Palm-tanager *Phaenicophilus palmarum*	2	028
Grey-crowned Palm-tanager *P. poliocephalus*	1	028
Chat-tanager *Calyptophilus frugivorus*	2	028
Antillean Euphonia *Euphonia musica*	12	028
Green-tailed Warbler *Microligea palustris*	2	028
White-winged Warbler *Xenoligea montana*	2	028
Thick-billed Vireo *Vireo crassirostris*	5	028
Flat-billed Vireo *Vireo nanus*	2	028
Antillean Siskin *Carduelis dominicensis*	2	028
Palm Crow *Corvus palmarum*	3	028
White-necked Crow *Corvus leucognaphalus*	2	028

HONDURAS

EBAs	Priority
017 North Central American Pacific slope	HIGH
018 North Central American highlands	URGENT
019 Central American Caribbean slope	HIGH

Secondary Areas
s007 Eastern Yucatán
s009 Swan Islands
s010 North Honduran thorn forests

Restricted-range species	Threatened	Total
Confined to this country	1	1
Present also in other countries	0	19
Total	1	20

cont.

Honduras (cont.)

Species (threatened species in **bold**)	No. of countries	EBAs (and SAs)
White-bellied Chachalaca *Ortalis leucogastra*	5	017
Ocellated Quail *Cyrtonyx ocellatus*	5	018
Pacific Parakeet *Aratinga strenua*	5	017
Fulvous Owl *Strix fulvescens*	4	018
Honduran Emerald *Amazilia luciae*	1	(s010)
Blue-tailed Hummingbird *Amazilia cyanura*	5	017
Green-throated Mountain-gem *Lampornis viridipallens*	5	018
Green-breasted Mountain-gem *L. sybillae*	2	018
Slender Sheartail *Doricha enicura*	4	018
Wine-throated Hummingbird *Atthis ellioti*	4	018
Blue-throated Motmot *Aspatha gularis*	4	018
Streak-crowned Antvireo *Dysithamnus striaticeps*	3	019
Snowy Cotinga *Carpodectes nitidus*	4	019
Grey-headed Piprites *Piprites griseiceps*	4	019
Rufous-browed Wren *Troglodytes rufociliatus*	4	018
Blue-and-white Mockingbird *Melanotis hypoleucus*	4	018
Rufous-collared Robin *Turdus rufitorques*	4	018
Vitelline Warbler *Dendroica vitellina*	2	(s009)
Yucatán Vireo *Vireo magister*	4	(s007)
Bushy-crested Jay *Cyanocorax melanocyaneus*	4	018

INDIA

EBAs	Priority
123 Western Ghats	HIGH
125 Andaman Islands	HIGH
126 Nicobar Islands	HIGH
128 Western Himalayas	CRITICAL
130 Eastern Himalayas	URGENT
131 Assam plains	URGENT
133 Southern Tibet	HIGH

Secondary Areas
s071 Eastern Andhra Pradesh
s072 Southern Deccan plateau
s074 Indus plains
s075 Central Indian forests
s079 North Myanmar lowlands

Restricted-range species	Threatened	Total
Confined to this country	10	38
Present also in other countries	13	36
Total	23	74

Species (threatened species in **bold**)	No. of countries	EBAs (and SAs)
Nicobar Serpent-eagle *Spilornis minimus*	1	126
Andaman Serpent-eagle *Spilornis elgini*	1	125
Nicobar Sparrowhawk *Accipiter butleri*	1	126
Nicobar Scrubfowl *Megapodius nicobariensis*	1	125[X],126
Manipur Bush-quail *Perdicula manipurensis*	2	131
Chestnut-breasted Partridge *Arborophila mandellii*	3	130
Himalayan Quail *Ophrysia superciliosa*	1	128
Western Tragopan *Tragopan melanocephalus*	2	128
Blyth's Tragopan *Tragopan blythii*	4	130
Sclater's Monal *Lophophorus sclateri*	3	130
Cheer Pheasant *Catreus wallichi*	3	128
Andaman Crake *Rallina canningi*	1	125
Jerdon's Courser *Rhinoptilus bitorquatus*	1	(s071)
Nilgiri Wood-pigeon *Columba elphinstonii*	1	123

cont.

India (cont.)

Andaman Wood-pigeon *Columba palumboides*	1	125,126
Andaman Cuckoo-dove *Macropygia rufipennis*	1	125,126
Malabar Parakeet *Psittacula columboides*	1	123
Nicobar Parakeet *Psittacula caniceps*	1	126
Brown Coucal *Centropus andamanensis*	2	125
Andaman Scops-owl *Otus balli*	1	125
Forest Owlet *Athene blewitti*	1	(s075)
Andaman Hawk-owl *Ninox affinis*	1	125,126
Dark-rumped Swift *Apus acuticauda*	2	130
Ward's Trogon *Harpactes wardi*	5	130
Malabar Grey-hornbill *Ocyceros griseus*	1	123
Narcondam Hornbill *Aceros narcondami*	1	125
Andaman Woodpecker *Dryocopus hodgei*	1	125
Nilgiri Pipit *Anthus nilghiriensis*	1	123
Grey-headed Bulbul *Pycnonotus priocephalus*	1	123
Yellow-throated Bulbul *Pycnonotus xantholaemus*	1	(s072)
Nicobar Bulbul *Hypsipetes nicobariensis*	1	126
Rusty-bellied Shortwing *Brachypteryx hyperythra*	2	130
White-bellied Shortwing *Brachypteryx major*	1	123
Chestnut-backed Laughingthrush *Garrulax nuchalis*	2	(s079)
Wynaad Laughingthrush *Garrulax delesserti*	1	123
Rufous-breasted Laughingthrush *G. cachinnans*	1	123
Grey-breasted Laughingthrush *Garrulax jerdoni*	1	123
Striped Laughingthrush *Garrulax virgatus*	2	130
Brown-capped Laughingthrush *G. austeni*	2	130
Marsh Babbler *Pellorneum palustre*	2	131
Rufous-throated Wren-babbler *Spelaeornis caudatus*	3	130
Rusty-throated Wren-babbler *S. badeigularis*	1	130
Tawny-breasted Wren-babbler *S. longicaudatus*	1	130
Wedge-billed Wren-babbler *Sphenocichla humei*	3	130
Snowy-throated Babbler *Stachyris oglei*	1	130
Rufous Babbler *Turdoides subrufus*	1	123
Giant Babax *Babax waddelli*	2	133
Hoary-throated Barwing *Actinodura nipalensis*	4	130
Streak-throated Barwing *Actinodura waldeni*	3	130
Ludlow's Fulvetta *Alcippe ludlowi*	3	130
Grey Sibia *Heterophasia gracilis*	3	130
Beautiful Sibia *Heterophasia pulchella*	3	130
White-naped Yuhina *Yuhina bakeri*	6	130
Black-breasted Parrotbill *Paradoxornis flavirostris*	2	131
Brooks's Leaf-warbler *Phylloscopus subviridis*	3	128
Tytler's Leaf-warbler *Phylloscopus tytleri*	4	128
Yellow-vented Warbler *Phylloscopus cantator*	3	130
Broad-billed Warbler *Tickellia hodgsoni*	6	130
Broad-tailed Grassbird *Schoenicola platyura*	1	123
Kashmir Flycatcher *Ficedula subrubra*	2	128
Black-and-rufous Flycatcher *F. nigrorufa*	1	123
Nilgiri Flycatcher *Eumyias albicaudata*	1	123
White-bellied Blue-flycatcher *Cyornis pallipes*	1	123
White-cheeked Tit *Aegithalos leucogenys*	3	128
White-throated Tit *Aegithalos niveogularis*	3	128
Kashmir Nuthatch *Sitta cashmirensis*	4	128
Crimson-backed Sunbird *Nectarinia minima*	1	123
Spectacled Finch *Callacanthis burtoni*	3	128
Orange Bullfinch *Pyrrhula aurantiaca*	2	128
Sind Sparrow *Passer pyrrhonotus*	3	(s074)
White-headed Starling *Sturnus erythropygius*	1	125,126
Andaman Drongo *Dicrurus andamanensis*	2	125
White-bellied Treepie *Dendrocitta leucogastra*	1	123
Andaman Treepie *Dendrocitta bayleyi*	1	125

INDONESIA

EBAs	Priority
157 Bornean mountains	URGENT
158 Sumatra and Peninsular Malaysia	URGENT
159 Enggano	HIGH
160 Java and Bali forests	CRITICAL
161 Javan coastal zone	HIGH
162 Northern Nusa Tenggara	HIGH
163 Sumba	HIGH
164 Timor and Wetar	HIGH
165 Banda Sea Islands	HIGH
166 Sulawesi	HIGH
167 Sangihe and Talaud	CRITICAL
168 Banggai and Sula Islands	HIGH
169 Buru	HIGH
170 Seram	HIGH
171 Northern Maluku	HIGH
172 West Papuan lowlands	HIGH
173 West Papuan highlands	HIGH
174 Geelvink Islands	HIGH
175 North Papuan mountains	HIGH
176 North Papuan lowlands	HIGH
178 Central Papuan mountains	URGENT
179 South Papuan lowlands	HIGH
180 Trans-Fly	HIGH

Secondary Areas

s097 North-east Bornean islands
s099 Kalimantan lowlands
s100 Bornean coastal zone
s101 Natuna Islands
s103 Riau and Lingga islands
s104 North Sumatran lowlands
s105 Simeulue
s106 Mentawai Islands
s107 Seribu Islands
s108 Masalembu
s109 Kangean
s110 Salayar and Bonerate Islands
s111 Tukangbesi Islands
s112 Aru
s113 Yapen

Restricted-range species	Threatened	Total
Confined to this country	63	319
Present also in other countries	3	84
Total	66	403

Species (threatened species in **bold**)	No. of countries	EBAs (and SAs)
Moluccan Goshawk *Accipiter henicogrammus*	1	171
Small Sparrowhawk *Accipiter nanus*	1	166
Rufous-necked Sparrowhawk *A. erythrauchen*	1	169,170, 171
Javan Hawk-eagle *Spizaetus bartelsi*	1	160
Bruijn's Brush-turkey *Aepypodius bruijnii*	1	172
Red-billed Brush-turkey *Talegalla cuvieri*	1	172
Maleo *Macrocephalon maleo*	1	166
Sula Scrubfowl *Megapodius bernsteinii*	1	168
Dusky Scrubfowl *Megapodius freycinet*	1	171,172, 174
Moluccan Scrubfowl *Megapodius wallacei*	1	169,170, 171
Snow Mountain Quail *Anurophasis monorthonyx*	1	178
Chestnut-bellied Partridge *Arborophila javanica*	1	160
Red-breasted Partridge *Arborophila hyperythra*	2	157
Red-billed Partridge *Arborophila rubrirostris*	1	158

cont.

Indonesia (cont.)

Crimson-headed Partridge	2	157
Haematortyx sanguiniceps		
Sumatran Pheasant Lophura hoogerwerfi	1	158
Salvadori's Pheasant Lophura inornata	1	158
Bronze-tailed Peacock-pheasant	1	158
Polyplectron chalcurum		
Sumba Buttonquail Turnix everetti	1	163
Chestnut Forest-rail Rallina rubra	2	173,178
White-striped Forest-rail Rallina leucospila	1	173
Mayr's Forest-rail Rallina mayri	2	175
Snoring Rail Aramidopsis plateni	1	166
Bald-faced Rail Gymnocrex rosenbergii	1	166,168
Isabelline Waterhen Amaurornis isabellinus	1	166
Invisible Rail Habroptila wallacii	1	171
Javan Plover Charadrius javanicus	1	161(s109)
EX Javanese Lapwing Vanellus macropterus	0	161X
Sulawesi Woodcock Scolopax celebensis	1	166
Moluccan Woodcock Scolopax rochussenii	1	171
Silvery Wood-pigeon Columba argentina	2	(s101, s103,s105, s106)
Dusky Cuckoo-dove Macropygia magna	1	162,164, 165(s110)
Black Cuckoo-dove Turacoena modesta	1	164
Sulawesi Ground-dove Gallicolumba tristigmata	1	166
Wetar Ground-dove Gallicolumba hoedtii	1	164
Flores Green-pigeon Treron floris	1	162
Sumba Green-pigeon Treron teysmannii	1	163
Timor Green-pigeon Treron psittacea	1	164
Sumatran Green-pigeon Treron oxyura	1	158,160
Pink-headed Fruit-dove Ptilinopus porphyreus	1	158,160
Red-naped Fruit-dove Ptilinopus dohertyi	1	163
Red-eared Fruit-dove Ptilinopus fischeri	1	166
Maroon-chinned Fruit-dove P. subgularis	1	166,168
Scarlet-breasted Fruit-dove P. bernsteinii	1	171
Wallace's Fruit-dove Ptilinopus wallacii	1	165,179 (s112)
Blue-capped Fruit-dove Ptilinopus monacha	1	171
Yellow-bibbed Fruit-dove P. solomonensis	3	174
Grey-headed Fruit-dove Ptilinopus hyogastra	1	171
Carunculated Fruit-dove P. granulifrons	1	171
White-bellied Imperial-pigeon Ducula forsteni	1	166
Grey-headed Imperial-pigeon Ducula radiata	1	166
White-eyed Imperial-pigeon D. perspicillata	1	169,170, 171
Elegant Imperial-pigeon Ducula concinna	1	165,166, 167,169, 170,172 (s110, s111,s112)
Spice Imperial-pigeon Ducula myristicivora	1	171,172, 174(s113)
Pink-headed Imperial-pigeon Ducula rosacea	1	162,164, 165,171 (s107, s108,s109, s110,s111)
Grey Imperial-pigeon Ducula pickeringii	3	167 (s097)
Cinnamon-bellied Imperial-pigeon D. basilica	1	171
Dark-backed Imperial-pigeon D. lacernulata	1	160,162
Timor Imperial-pigeon Ducula cineracea	1	164
White Imperial-pigeon Ducula luctuosa	1	166,168
Sombre Pigeon Cryptophaps poecilorrhoa	1	166
Long-tailed Mountain-pigeon Gymnophaps mada	1	169,170
Western Crowned-pigeon Goura cristata	1	172
Black Lory Chalcopsitta atra	1	172

Indonesia (cont.)

Brown Lory Chalcopsitta duivenbodei	2	176
Red-and-blue Lory Eos histrio	1	167
Violet-necked Lory Eos squamata	1	171,172
Red Lory Eos bornea	1	165,169, 170
Blue-streaked Lory Eos reticulata	1	165
Black-winged Lory Eos cyanogenia	1	174
Blue-eared Lory Eos semilarvata	1	170
Olive-headed Lorikeet Trichoglossus euteles	1	162,164, 165
Yellow-and-green Lorikeet T. flavoviridis	1	166,168
Iris Lorikeet Psitteuteles iris	1	164
Chattering Lory Lorius garrulus	1	171
Purple-naped Lory Lorius domicella	1	170
Blue-fronted Lorikeet Charmosyna toxopei	1	169
Striated Lorikeet Charmosyna multistriata	2	179
Salmon-crested Cockatoo Cacatua moluccensis	1	170
White Cockatoo Cacatua alba	1	171
Tanimbar Cockatoo Cacatua goffini	1	165
Geelvink Pygmy-parrot Micropsitta geelvinkiana	1	174
Edwards's Fig-parrot Psittaculirostris edwardsii	2	176
Salvadori's Fig-parrot P. salvadorii	1	176
Painted Tiger-parrot Psittacella picta	2	178
Modest Tiger-parrot Psittacella modesta	2	173,178
Yellowish-breasted Racquet-tail	1	166
Prioniturus flavicans		
Buru Racquet-tail Prioniturus mada	1	169
Black-lored Parrot Tanygnathus gramineus	1	169
Olive-shouldered Parrot Aprosmictus jonquillaceus	1	164
Moluccan Hanging-parrot Loriculus amabilis	1	168,171
Sangihe Hanging-parrot Loriculus catamene	1	167
Red-billed Hanging-parrot Loriculus exilis	1	166
Wallace's Hanging-parrot Loriculus flosculus	1	162
Sulawesi Hawk-cuckoo Cuculus crassirostris	1	166
Moluccan Cuckoo Cacomantis heinrichi	1	171
Green-cheeked Bronze-cuckoo	1	165
Chrysococcyx rufomerus		
Pied Bronze-cuckoo Chrysococcyx crassirostris	1	165
Sumatran Ground-cuckoo Carpococcyx viridis	1	158
Goliath Coucal Centropus goliath	1	171
Kai Coucal Centropus spilopterus	1	165
Biak Coucal Centropus chalybeus	1	174
Sunda Coucal Centropus nigrorufus	1	161
Minahassa Masked-owl Tyto inexspectata	1	166
Taliabu Masked-owl Tyto nigrobrunnea	1	168
Lesser Masked-owl Tyto sororcula	1	165,169
Simeulue Scops-owl Otus umbra	1	(s105)
Javan Scops-owl Otus angelinae	1	160
Flores Scops-owl Otus alfredi	1	162
Enggano Scops-owl Otus enganensis	1	159
Rajah Scops-owl Otus brookii	2	157,158
Mentawai Scops-owl Otus mentawi	1	(s106)
Wallace's Scops-owl Otus silvicola	1	162
Sumba Boobook Ninox rudolfi	1	163
Ochre-bellied Hawk-owl Ninox ochracea	1	166
Moluccan Hawk-owl Ninox squamipila	1	165,169, 170,171
Dulit Frogmouth Batrachostomus harterti	2	157
Short-tailed Frogmouth B. poliolophus	2	157,158
Long-whiskered Owlet-nightjar	1	171
Aegotheles crinifrons		
Archbold's Owlet-nightjar A. archboldi	2	178
Satanic Eared-nightjar Eurostopodus diabolicus	1	166
Mountain Eared-nightjar Eurostopodus archboldi	2	173,178
Salvadori's Nightjar Caprimulgus pulchellus	1	158,160
Waterfall Swift Hydrochrous gigas	2	158,160
Volcano Swiftlet Collocalia vulcanorum	1	160

cont.

cont.

Indonesia (cont.)

Bare-legged Swiftlet *Collocalia nuditarsus*	2	178
Blue-tailed Trogon *Harpactes reinwardtii*	1	158,160
Whitehead's Trogon *Harpactes whiteheadi*	2	157
Sulawesi Kingfisher *Ceyx fallax*	1	166,167
Spangled Kookaburra *Dacelo tyro*	2	180(s112)
Lilac-cheeked Kingfisher *Cittura cyanotis*	1	167,166
Blue-and-white Kingfisher *Todirhamphus diops*	1	171
Lazuli Kingfisher *Todirhamphus lazuli*	1	170
Sombre Kingfisher *Todirhamphus funebris*	1	171
Talaud Kingfisher *Todirhamphus enigma*	1	167
Cinnamon-banded Kingfisher *T. australasia*	1	162,163, 164,165
White-rumped Kingfisher *Caridonax fulgidus*	1	162
Green-backed Kingfisher *Actenoides monachus*	1	166
Scaly Kingfisher *Actenoides princeps*	1	166
Little Paradise-kingfisher *Tanysiptera hydrocharis*	2	180(s112)
Kofiau Paradise-kingfisher *Tanysiptera ellioti*	1	172
Biak Paradise-kingfisher *Tanysiptera riedelii*	1	174
Numfor Paradise-kingfisher *T. carolinae*	1	174
Red-breasted Paradise-kingfisher *T. nympha*	2	172,176
Purple-bearded Bee-eater *Meropogon forsteni*	1	166
Purple Roller *Eurystomus azureus*	1	171
Sumba Hornbill *Aceros everetti*	1	163
Fire-tufted Barbet *Psilopogon pyrolophus*	2	158
Brown-throated Barbet *Megalaima corvina*	1	160
Mountain Barbet *Megalaima monticola*	2	157
Flame-fronted Barbet *Megalaima armillaris*	1	160
Golden-naped Barbet *Megalaima pulcherrima*	2	157
Bornean Barbet *Megalaima eximia*	2	157
Hose's Broadbill *Calyptomena hosii*	2	157
Whitehead's Broadbill *Calyptomena whiteheadi*	2	157
Schneider's Pitta *Pitta schneideri*	1	158
Ivory-breasted Pitta *Pitta maxima*	1	171
Black-crowned Pitta *Pitta venusta*	1	158
Alpine Pipit *Anthus gutturalis*	2	178
Slaty Cuckoo-shrike *Coracina schistacea*	1	168
Moluccan Cuckoo-shrike *Coracina atriceps*	1	170,171
Buru Cuckoo-shrike *Coracina fortis*	1	169
Cerulean Cuckoo-shrike *Coracina temminckii*	1	166
Pied Cuckoo-shrike *Coracina bicolor*	1	166,167
Halmahera Cuckoo-shrike *Coracina parvula*	1	171
Pygmy Cuckoo-shrike *Coracina abbotti*	1	166
Sumba Cicadabird *Coracina dohertyi*	1	162,163
Sula Cicadabird *Coracina sula*	1	168
Kai Cicadabird *Coracina dispar*	1	165
Pale Cicadabird *Coracina ceramensis*	1	169,170, 171
Rufous-bellied Triller *Lalage aurea*	1	171
Flores Minivet *Pericrocotus lansbergei*	1	162
Sunda Minivet *Pericrocotus miniatus*	1	158,160
Black-breasted Fruit-hunter *Chlamydochaera jefferyi*	2	157
Cream-striped Bulbul *Pycnonotus leucogrammicus*	1	158
Spot-necked Bulbul *Pycnonotus tympanistrigus*	1	158
Blue-wattled Bulbul *Pycnonotus nieuwenhuisii*	2	157,158
Orange-spotted Bulbul *Pycnonotus bimaculatus*	1	158,160
Green-winged Bulbul *Hypsipetes virescens*	1	158,160
Blue-masked Leafbird *Chloropsis venusta*	1	158
Greater Ground-robin *Amalocichla sclateriana*	2	178
Shiny Whistling-thrush *Myiophonus melanurus*	1	158
Geomalia *Geomalia heinrichi*	1	166
Slaty-backed Thrush *Zoothera schistacea*	1	165
Moluccan Thrush *Zoothera dumasi*	1	169,170
Red-backed Thrush *Zoothera erythronota*	1	166,168
Chestnut-backed Thrush *Zoothera dohertyi*	1	162,163, 164
Orange-banded Thrush *Zoothera peronii*	1	164,165

Indonesia (cont.)

Fawn-breasted Thrush *Zoothera machiki*	1	165
Sulawesi Thrush *Cataponera turdoides*	1	166
Great Shortwing *Heinrichia calligyna*	1	166
Sunda Robin *Cinclidium diana*	1	158,160
Sunda Forktail *Enicurus velatus*	1	158,160
Sumatran Cochoa *Cochoa beccarii*	1	158
Javan Cochoa *Cochoa azurea*	1	160
White-bellied Bushchat *Saxicola gutturalis*	1	164
Papuan Whipbird *Androphobus viridis*	2	178
Painted Quail-thrush *Cinclosoma ajax*	2	172,179, 180
Greater Melampitta *Melampitta gigantea*	2	173,175, 178
Malia *Malia grata*	1	166
Sunda Laughingthrush *Garrulax palliatus*	3	157,158
Rufous-fronted Laughingthrush *Garrulax rufifrons*	1	160
Black Laughingthrush *Garrulax lugubris*	2	158
Black-browed Babbler *Malacocincla perspicillata*	1	(s099)
Rusty-breasted Wren-babbler *Napothera rufipectus*	1	158
Marbled Wren-babbler *Napothera marmorata*	2	158
Mountain Wren-babbler *Napothera crassa*	2	157
White-breasted Babbler *Stachyris grammiceps*	1	160
White-bibbed Babbler *Stachyris thoracica*	1	160
Crescent-chested Babbler *Stachyris melanothorax*	1	160
Grey-cheeked Tit-babbler *Macronous flavicollis*	1	160(s109)
Javan Fulvetta *Alcippe pyrrhoptera*	1	160
Spotted Crocias *Crocias albonotatus*	1	160
Chestnut-crested Yuhina *Yuhina everetti*	2	157
Javan Tesia *Tesia superciliaris*	1	160
Russet-capped Tesia *Tesia everetti*	1	162
Timor Stubtail *Urosphena subulata*	1	164,165
Bornean Stubtail *Urosphena whiteheadi*	2	157
Tanimbar Bush-warbler *Cettia carolinae*	1	165
Chestnut-backed Bush-warbler *Bradypterus castaneus*	1	166,169, 170
Sulawesi Leaf-warbler *Phylloscopus sarasinorum*	1	166
Timor Leaf-warbler *Phylloscopus presbytes*	1	162,164
Sunda Warbler *Seicercus grammiceps*	1	158,160
Buff-banded Grassbird *Buettikoferella bivittata*	1	164
Vogelkop Scrubwren *Sericornis rufescens*	1	173
Papuan Thornbill *Acanthiza murina*	2	178
Biak Gerygone *Gerygone hypoxantha*	1	174
Plain Gerygone *Gerygone inornata*	1	164
Rufous-sided Gerygone *Gerygone dorsalis*	1	165(s110)
Golden-bellied Flyrobin *Microeca hemixantha*	1	165
Alpine Robin *Petroica bivittata*	2	178
Snow Mountain Robin *Petroica archboldi*	1	178
Olive-yellow Robin *Poecilodryas placens*	2	172,176, 179
Smoky Robin *Peneothello cryptoleucus*	1	173,175, 178
Green-backed Robin *Pachycephalopsis hattamensis*	2	173,175, 178(s113)
Streaky-breasted Jungle-flycatcher *Rhinomyias addita*	1	169
Russet-backed Jungle-flycatcher *R. oscillans*	1	162,163
Henna-tailed Jungle-flycatcher *R. colonus*	1	168
Eyebrowed Jungle-flycatcher *R. gularis*	2	157
Rufous-throated Flycatcher *Ficedula rufigula*	1	166
Cinnamon-chested Flycatcher *F. buruensis*	1	165,169, 170
Damar Flycatcher *Ficedula henrici*	1	165
Sumba Flycatcher *Ficedula harterti*	1	163
Lompobattang Flycatcher *Ficedula bonthaina*	1	166
Black-banded Flycatcher *Ficedula timorensis*	1	164

cont.

cont.

Indonesia (cont.)

Rufous-vented Niltava *Niltava sumatrana*	2	158
Matinan Flycatcher *Cyornis sanfordi*	1	166
Blue-fronted Flycatcher *Cyornis hoevelli*	1	166
Timor Blue-flycatcher *Cyornis hyacinthinus*	1	164
Rueck's Blue-flycatcher *Cyornis ruckii*	1	(s104)
Cerulean Paradise-flycatcher	1	167
Eutrichomyias rowleyi		
White-naped Monarch *Monarcha pileatus*	1	165,169, 171
Black-bibbed Monarch *Monarcha mundus*	1	165
Flores Monarch *Monarcha sacerdotum*	1	162
White-tipped Monarch *Monarcha everetti*	1	(s110)
Black-tipped Monarch *Monarcha loricatus*	1	169
Black-chinned Monarch *Monarcha boanensis*	1	170
White-tailed Monarch *Monarcha leucurus*	1	165
Black-backed Monarch *Monarcha julianae*	1	172
Biak Monarch *Monarcha brehmii*	1	174
Biak Flycatcher *Myiagra atra*	1	174
Dark-grey Flycatcher *Myiagra galeata*	1	165,169, 170,171
Rufous-tailed Fantail *Rhipidura phoenicura*	1	160
White-bellied Fantail *Rhipidura euryura*	1	160
Brown-capped Fantail *Rhipidura diluta*	1	162
Cinnamon-tailed Fantail *Rhipidura fuscorufa*	1	165
Rusty-bellied Fantail *Rhipidura teysmanni*	1	166,168
Tawny-backed Fantail *Rhipidura superflua*	1	169
Streaky-breasted Fantail *Rhipidura dedemi*	1	170
Long-tailed Fantail *Rhipidura opistherythra*	1	165
Olive-flanked Whistler *Hylocitrea bonensis*	1	166
Maroon-backed Whistler *Coracornis raveni*	1	166
Island Whistler *Pachycephala phaionotus*	1	165,171, 172,174 (s112)
Bornean Whistler *Pachycephala hypoxantha*	2	157
Sulphur-bellied Whistler *P. sulfuriventer*	1	166
Vogelkop Whistler *Pachycephala meyeri*	1	173
Fawn-breasted Whistler *Pachycephala orpheus*	1	164
Lorentz's Whistler *Pachycephala lorentzi*	2	178
Bare-throated Whistler *Pachycephala nudigula*	1	162
Drab Whistler *Pachycephala griseonota*	1	165,168, 169,170, 171
Sooty Shrike-thrush *Colluricincla umbrina*	2	178
White-bellied Pitohui *Pitohui incertus*	2	179
Wattled Ploughbill *Eulacestoma nigropectus*	2	178
Pygmy Tit *Psaltria exilis*	1	160
Black Sittella *Daphoenositta miranda*	2	178
Golden-rumped Flowerpecker *Dicaeum annae*	1	162
Crimson-crowned Flowerpecker *D. nehrkorni*	1	166
Flame-breasted Flowerpecker *D. erythrothorax*	1	169,171
Ashy Flowerpecker *Dicaeum vulneratum*	1	165,170
Olive-crowned Flowerpecker *D. pectorale*	1	172
Black-fronted Flowerpecker *Dicaeum igniferum*	1	162
Red-chested Flowerpecker *Dicaeum maugei*	1	162,164, 165(s110)
Black-sided Flowerpecker *Dicaeum monticolum*	2	157
Obscure Berrypecker *Melanocharis arfakiana*	2	173,178
Apricot-breasted Sunbird *Nectarinia buettikoferi*	1	163
Flame-breasted Sunbird *Nectarinia solaris*	1	162,164
Elegant Sunbird *Aethopyga duyvenbodei*	1	167
White-flanked Sunbird *Aethopyga eximia*	1	160
Whitehead's Spiderhunter *Arachnothera juliae*	2	157
Enggano White-eye *Zosterops salvadorii*	1	159
Black-capped White-eye *Zosterops atricapillus*	2	157,158
Javan White-eye *Zosterops flavus*	2	161(s100)
Pearl-bellied White-eye *Zosterops grayi*	1	165
Golden-bellied White-eye *Z. uropygialis*	1	165

Indonesia (cont.)

Pale-bellied White-eye *Z. consobrinorum*	1	166
Lemon-throated White-eye *Zosterops anomalus*	1	166
Yellow-spectacled White-eye *Z. wallacei*	1	162,163
Creamy-throated White-eye *Zosterops atriceps*	1	171
Biak White-eye *Zosterops mysorensis*	1	174
Buru Yellow White-eye *Zosterops buruensis*	1	169
Ambon Yellow White-eye *Zosterops kuehni*	1	170
Bicoloured White-eye *Tephrozosterops stalkeri*	1	170
Rufous-throated White-eye *Madanga ruficollis*	1	169
Javan Grey-throated White-eye	1	160
Lophozosterops javanicus		
Streaky-headed White-eye *L. squamiceps*	1	166
Yellow-browed White-eye *L. superciliaris*	1	162
Grey-hooded White-eye *L. pinaiae*	1	170
Crested White-eye *Lophozosterops dohertyi*	1	162
Pygmy White-eye *Oculocincta squamifrons*	2	157
Thick-billed White-eye *Heleia crassirostris*	1	162
Spot-breasted White-eye *Heleia muelleri*	1	164
Mountain Blackeye *Chlorocharis emiliae*	2	157
Drab Myzomela *Myzomela blasii*	1	170
Crimson-hooded Myzomela *Myzomela kuehni*	1	164
Red-rumped Myzomela *Myzomela vulnerata*	1	164
Scaly-crowned Honeyeater *Lichmera lombokia*	1	162
Olive Honeyeater *Lichmera argentauris*	1	170,171, 172
White-tufted Honeyeater *Lichmera squamata*	1	164,165
Buru Honeyeater *Lichmera deningeri*	1	169
Seram Honeyeater *Lichmera monticola*	1	170
Yellow-eared Honeyeater *Lichmera flavicans*	1	164
Black-chested Honeyeater *Lichmera notabilis*	1	164
Streaky-breasted Honeyeater *Meliphaga reticulata*	1	164
Orange-cheeked Honeyeater *Oreornis chrysogenys*	1	178
White-streaked Friarbird *Melitograis gilolensis*	1	171
Plain Friarbird *Philemon inornatus*	1	164
Brass's Friarbird *Philemon brassi*	1	176
Dusky Friarbird *Philemon fuscicapillus*	1	171
Black-faced Friarbird *Philemon moluccensis*	1	165,169
Grey-necked Friarbird *P. subcorniculatus*	1	170
Leaden Honeyeater *Ptiloprora plumbea*	2	178
Olive-streaked Honeyeater *Ptiloprora meekiana*	2	178
Rufous-sided Honeyeater *P. erythropleura*	1	173,178
Mayr's Honeyeater *Ptiloprora mayri*	2	175
Black-backed Honeyeater *Ptiloprora perstriata*	2	173,178
Sooty Melidectes *Melidectes fuscus*	2	178
Short-bearded Melidectes *Melidectes nouhuysi*	1	178
Cinnamon-browed Melidectes *M. ochromelas*	2	173,178
Vogelkop Melidectes *Melidectes leucostephes*	1	173
Belford's Melidectes *Melidectes belfordi*	2	178
Yellow-browed Melidectes *M. rufocrissalis*	2	178
Arfak Honeyeater *Melipotes gymnops*	1	173
Dark-eared Myza *Myza celebensis*	1	166
White-eared Myza *Myza sarasinorum*	1	166
Mountain Serin *Serinus estherae*	2	158,160, 166
Mountain Firetail *Oreostruthus fuliginosus*	2	178
Tricoloured Parrotfinch *Erythrura tricolor*	1	164,165
Cream-bellied Munia *Lonchura pallidiventer*	1	? (see p. 724)
Grey-banded Munia *Lonchura vana*	1	173
Grey-crowned Munia *Lonchura nevermanni*	2	180
Black Munia *Lonchura stygia*	2	180
Black-breasted Munia *Lonchura teerinki*	1	178
Snow Mountain Munia *Lonchura montana*	2	178
Timor Sparrow *Padda fuscata*	1	164
Tanimbar Starling *Aplonis crassa*	1	165
Long-tailed Starling *Aplonis magna*	1	174
Bali Starling *Leucopsar rothschildi*	1	160

cont.　　　　　　　　　　　　　　　　　　　cont.

Indonesia (cont.)

Sulawesi Myna *Basilornis celebensis*	1	166
Helmeted Myna *Basilornis galeatus*	1	168
Long-crested Myna *Basilornis corythaix*	1	170
Bare-eyed Myna *Streptocitta albertinae*	1	168
Fiery-browed Myna *Enodes erythrophris*	1	166
Olive-brown Oriole *Oriolus melanotis*	1	164
Black-eared Oriole *Oriolus bouroensis*	1	165,169
Grey-collared Oriole *Oriolus forsteni*	1	170
Dusky-brown Oriole *Oriolus phaeochromus*	1	171
Wetar Figbird *Sphecotheres hypoleucus*	1	164
Timor Figbird *Sphecotheres viridis*	1	164
Sumatran Drongo *Dicrurus sumatranus*	1	158
Sulawesi Drongo *Dicrurus montanus*	1	166
Archbold's Bowerbird *Archboldia papuensis*	1	178
Vogelkop Bowerbird *Amblyornis inornatus*	1	173
Golden-fronted Bowerbird *Amblyornis flavifrons*	1	175
Yellow-breasted Bird-of-paradise	2	178
Loboparadisea sericea		
Crested Bird-of-paradise *Cnemophilus macgregorii*	2	178
Loria's Bird-of-paradise *Cnemophilus loriae*	2	178
Macgregor's Bird-of-paradise	2	178
Macgregoria pulchra		
Paradise-crow *Lycocorax pyrrhopterus*	1	171
Standardwing *Semioptera wallacii*	1	171
Long-tailed Paradigalla *Paradigalla carunculata*	1	173,178
Short-tailed Paradigalla *Paradigalla brevicauda*	2	178
Brown Sicklebill *Epimachus meyeri*	2	178
Pale-billed Sicklebill *Epimachus bruijnii*	2	176
Western Parotia *Parotia sefilata*	1	173
Wilson's Bird-of-paradise *Cicinnurus respublica*	1	172
Arfak Astrapia *Astrapia nigra*	1	173
Splendid Astrapia *Astrapia splendidissima*	2	178
King-of-Saxony Bird-of-paradise	2	178
Pteridophora alberti		
Red Bird-of-paradise *Paradisaea rubra*	1	172
Greater Bird-of-paradise *Paradisaea apoda*	2	179
Banggai Crow *Corvus unicolor*	1	168
Flores Crow *Corvus florensis*	1	162
Long-billed Crow *Corvus validus*	1	171
Brown-headed Crow *Corvus fuscicapillus*	1	172,176
		(s112)

IRAN

EBAs	Priority
119 Mesopotamian marshes	HIGH
122 Caucasus	HIGH

Secondary Areas
s074 Indus plains

Restricted-range species	Threatened	Total
Confined to this country	0	0
Present also in other countries	0	4
Total	0	4

Species (threatened species in **bold**)	No. of countries	EBAs (and SAs)
Caucasian Grouse *Tetrao mlokosiewiczi*	6	122
Iraq Babbler *Turdoides altirostris*	2	119
Caucasian Chiffchaff *Phylloscopus lorenzii*	6	122
Sind Sparrow *Passer pyrrhonotus*	3	(s074)

IRAQ

EBAs	Priority
119 Mesopotamian marshes	HIGH

Secondary Areas none

Restricted-range species	Threatened	Total
Confined to this country	0	1
Present also in other countries	0	1
Total	0	2

Species (threatened species in **bold**)	No. of countries	EBAs (and SAs)
Iraq Babbler *Turdoides altirostris*	2	119
Basra Reed-warbler *Acrocephalus griseldis*	1	119

ISRAEL

EBAs none

Secondary Areas
s067 Levantine mountains

Restricted-range species	Threatened	Total
Confined to this country	0	0
Present also in other countries	0	1
Total	0	1

Species (threatened species in **bold**)	No. of countries	EBAs (and SAs)
Syrian Serin *Serinus syriacus*	4	(s067)

IVORY COAST

EBAs	Priority
084 Upper Guinea forests	CRITICAL

Secondary Areas none

Restricted-range species	Threatened	Total
Confined to this country	0	0
Present also in other countries	10	14
Total	10	14

Species (threatened species in **bold**)	No. of countries	EBAs (and SAs)
White-breasted Guineafowl	4	084
Agelastes meleagrides		
Rufous Fishing-owl *Scotopelia ussheri*	5	084
Brown-cheeked Hornbill *Ceratogymna cylindricus*	5	084
Western Wattled Cuckoo-shrike	5	084
Campephaga lobata		
Green-tailed Bristlebill *Bleda eximia*	5	084
Yellow-throated Olive Greenbul	5	084
Criniger olivaceus		
Rufous-winged Illadopsis *Illadopsis rufescens*	5	084
White-necked Rockfowl	5	084
Picathartes gymnocephalus		
White-eyed Prinia *Prinia leontica*	4	084
Sharpe's Apalis *Apalis sharpei*	5	084
Black-capped Rufous Warbler	5	084
Bathmocercus cerviniventris		
Nimba Flycatcher *Melaenornis annamarulae*	4	084
Gola Malimbe *Malimbus ballmanni*	3	084
Copper-tailed Glossy-starling	5	084
Lamprotornis cupreocauda		

JAMAICA

EBAs	Priority
027 Jamaica	CRITICAL

Secondary Areas none

Restricted-range species	Threatened	Total
Confined to this country	3	28
Present also in other countries	0	7
Total	3	35

Species (threatened species in **bold**)	No. of countries	EBAs (and SAs)
Ring-tailed Pigeon *Columba caribaea*	1	027
Crested Quail-dove *Geotrygon versicolor*	1	027
Yellow-billed Amazon *Amazona collaria*	1	027
Black-billed Amazon *Amazona agilis*	1	027
Chestnut-bellied Cuckoo *Hyetornis pluvialis*	1	027
Jamaican Lizard-cuckoo *Saurothera vetula*	1	027
Jamaican Owl *Pseudoscops grammicus*	1	027
Jamaican Pauraque *Siphonorhis americanus*	1	027
Jamaican Mango *Anthracothorax mango*	1	027
Red-billed Streamertail *Trochilus polytmus*	1	027
Black-billed Streamertail *Trochilus scitulus*	1	027
Vervain Hummingbird *Mellisuga minima*	3	027
Jamaican Tody *Todus todus*	1	027
Jamaican Woodpecker *Melanerpes radiolatus*	1	027
Jamaican Becard *Pachyramphus niger*	1	027
Jamaican Elaenia *Myiopagis cotta*	1	027
Greater Antillean Elaenia *Elaenia fallax*	3	027
Jamaican Pewee *Contopus pallidus*	1	027
Sad Flycatcher *Myiarchus barbirostris*	1	027
Rufous-tailed Flycatcher *Myiarchus validus*	1	027
Stolid Flycatcher *Myiarchus stolidus*	3	027
Golden Swallow *Tachycineta euchrysea*	3	027
Bahama Mockingbird *Mimus gundlachii*	4	027
Rufous-throated Solitaire *Myadestes genibarbis*	7	027
White-chinned Thrush *Turdus aurantius*	1	027
White-eyed Thrush *Turdus jamaicensis*	1	027
Yellow-shouldered Grassquit *Loxipasser anoxanthus*	1	027
Jamaican Euphonia *Euphonia jamaica*	1	027
Orangequit *Euneornis campestris*	1	027
Arrowhead Warbler *Dendroica pharetra*	1	027
Jamaican Vireo *Vireo modestus*	1	027
Blue Mountain Vireo *Vireo osburni*	1	027
Jamaican Oriole *Icterus leucopteryx*	3	027
Jamaican Blackbird *Nesopsar nigerrimus*	1	027
Jamaican Crow *Corvus jamaicensis*	1	027

JAPAN

EBAs	Priority
146 Izu Islands	URGENT
147 Ogasawara Islands	CRITICAL
148 Nansei Shoto	CRITICAL

Secondary Areas
s089 Central Honshu lowland forests
s090 Central Honshu montane forests
s091 Iwo Islands
s092 Japanese and Korean offshore islands

Restricted-range species	Threatened	Total
Confined to this country	10	12
Present also in other countries	0	3
Total	10	15

Japan (cont.)

Species (threatened species in **bold**)	No. of countries	EBAs (and SAs)
Japanese Night-heron *Gorsachius goisagi*	1	146[X] (s089)
Okinawa Rail *Gallirallus okinawae*	1	148
Amami Woodcock *Scolopax mira*	1	148
Japanese Wood-pigeon *Columba janthina*	2	148,147[X], 146(s092, s091[X])
[EX] Bonin Wood-pigeon *Columba versicolor*	0	147[X]
[EX] Ryukyu Pigeon *Columba jouyi*	0	148[X]
Whistling Green-pigeon *Treron formosae*	3	148
Elegant Scops-owl *Otus elegans*	3	148
[EL] Micronesian Kingfisher *Todirhamphus cinnamominus*	2	148[X]
Okinawa Woodpecker *Sapheopipo noguchii*	1	148
Ryukyu Minivet *Pericrocotus tegimae*	1	148
Amami Thrush *Zoothera major*	1	148
[EX] Bonin Thrush *Zoothera terrestris*	0	147[X]
Izu Thrush *Turdus celaenops*	1	146
Ryukyu Robin *Erithacus komadori*	1	148
Ijima's Leaf-warbler *Phylloscopus ijimae*	1	146
Bonin Honeyeater *Apalopteron familiare*	1	147
Yellow Bunting *Emberiza sulphurata*	1	(s090)
[EX] Bonin Grosbeak *Chaunoproctus ferreorostris*	0	147[X]
Lidth's Jay *Garrulus lidthi*	1	148

JORDAN

EBAs none

Secondary Areas
s067 Levantine mountains

Restricted-range species	Threatened	Total
Confined to this country	0	0
Present also in other countries	0	1
Total	0	1

Species (threatened species in **bold**)	No. of countries	EBAs (and SAs)
Syrian Serin *Serinus syriacus*	4	(s067)

KENYA

EBAs	Priority
105 Tanzania–Malawi mountains	CRITICAL
108 Serengeti plains	HIGH
109 Kenyan mountains	URGENT
111 East African coastal forests	URGENT
113 Jubba and Shabeelle valleys	CRITICAL

Secondary Areas
s058 Kakamega and Nandi forests
s061 North Kenyan short-grass plains
s062 Mount Kulal

Restricted-range species	Threatened	Total
Confined to this country	6	10
Present also in other countries	7	15
Total	13	25

cont.

cont.

Kenya (cont.)

Species (threatened species in **bold**)	No. of countries	EBAs (and SAs)
Jackson's Francolin *Francolinus jacksoni*	2	109
White-winged Collared-dove *Streptopelia reichenowi*	3	113
Fischer's Turaco *Tauraco fischeri*	3	111,105
Sokoke Scops-owl *Otus ireneae*	2	111,105
Usambiro Barbet *Trachyphonus usambiro*	2	108
Williams's Lark *Mirafra williamsi*	1	(s061)
Sharpe's Longclaw *Macronyx sharpei*	1	109
Sokoke Pipit *Anthus sokokensis*	2	111
Grey-crested Helmet-shrike *Prionops poliolophus*	2	108
Taita Thrush *Turdus helleri*	1	105
Hinde's Pied-babbler *Turdoides hindei*	1	109
Hunter's Cisticola *Cisticola hunteri*	3	109
Tana River Cisticola *Cisticola restrictus*	1	111
Aberdare Cisticola *Cisticola aberdare*	1	109
Taita Apalis *Apalis fuscigularis*	1	105
White-winged Apalis *Apalis chariessa*	4	111,105
Chapin's Flycatcher *Muscicapa lendu*	3	(s058)
Amani Sunbird *Anthreptes pallidigaster*	2	111,105
Kulal White-eye *Zosterops kulalensis*	1	(s062)
Taita White-eye *Zosterops silvanus*	1	105
Clarke's Weaver *Ploceus golandi*	1	111
Salvadori's Weaver *Ploceus dicrocephalus*	3	113
Jackson's Widowbird *Euplectes jacksoni*	2	109
Kenrick's Starling *Poeoptera kenricki*	2	105,109
Abbott's Starling *Cinnyricinclus femoralis*	2	109

KIRIBATI

EBAs none

Secondary Areas
s125 Gilbert Islands
s134 Northern Line Islands

Restricted-range species	Threatened	Total
Confined to this country	0	1
Present also in other countries	0	0
Total	0	1

Species (threatened species in **bold**)	No. of countries	EBAs (and SAs)
EL **Tuamotu Sandpiper** *Prosobonia cancellata*	1	(s134X)
EL Micronesian Imperial-pigeon *Ducula oceanica*	3	(s125X)
Bokikokiko *Acrocephalus aequinoctialis*	1	(s134)

LAOS

EBAs	Priority
143 Annamese lowlands	CRITICAL

Secondary Areas
s082 Fan-Si-Pan and northern Laos
s083 Southern Laos

Restricted-range species	Threatened	Total
Confined to this country	0	0
Present also in other countries	3	6
Total	3	6

Laos (cont.)

Species (threatened species in **bold**)	No. of countries	EBAs (and SAs)
Crested Argus *Rheinardia ocellata*	3	143
White-cheeked Laughingthrush *Garrulax vassali*	2	143(s083)
Short-tailed Scimitar-babbler *Jabouilleia danjoui*	2	143
Sooty Babbler *Stachyris herberti*	2	143
Grey-faced Tit-babbler *Macronous kelleyi*	2	143(s083)
Broad-billed Warbler *Tickellia hodgsoni*	6	(s082)

LEBANON

EBAs none

Secondary Areas
s067 Levantine mountains

Restricted-range species	Threatened	Total
Confined to this country	0	0
Present also in other countries	0	1
Total	0	1

Species (threatened species in **bold**)	No. of countries	EBAs (and SAs)
Syrian Serin *Serinus syriacus*	4	(s067)

LESOTHO

EBAs	Priority
090 Lesotho highlands	HIGH
091 Southern African grasslands	CRITICAL

Secondary Areas none

Restricted-range species	Threatened	Total
Confined to this country	0	0
Present also in other countries	1	4
Total	1	4

Species (threatened species in **bold**)	No. of countries	EBAs (and SAs)
Yellow-breasted Pipit *Anthus chloris*	2	091
Mountain Pipit *Anthus hoeschi*	2	090
Orange-breasted Rockjumper *Chaetops aurantius*	2	090
Drakensberg Siskin *Serinus symonsi*	2	090

LIBERIA

EBAs	Priority
084 Upper Guinea forests	CRITICAL

Secondary Areas none

Restricted-range species	Threatened	Total
Confined to this country	1	1
Present also in other countries	10	14
Total	11	15

Species (threatened species in **bold**)	No. of countries	EBAs (and SAs)
White-breasted Guineafowl *Agelastes meleagrides*	4	084
Rufous Fishing-owl *Scotopelia ussheri*	5	084

cont.

cont.

Liberia (cont.)

Brown-cheeked Hornbill *Ceratogymna cylindricus*	5	084
Western Wattled Cuckoo-shrike	5	084
Campephaga lobata		
Liberian Greenbul *Phyllastrephus leucolepis*	1	084
Green-tailed Bristlebill *Bleda eximia*	5	084
Yellow-throated Olive Greenbul	5	084
Criniger olivaceus		
Rufous-winged Illadopsis *Illadopsis rufescens*	5	084
White-necked Rockfowl	5	084
Picathartes gymnocephalus		
White-eyed Prinia *Prinia leontica*	4	084
Sharpe's Apalis *Apalis sharpei*	5	084
Black-capped Rufous Warbler	5	084
Bathmocercus cerviniventris		
Nimba Flycatcher *Melaenornis annamarulae*	4	084
Gola Malimbe *Malimbus ballmanni*	3	084
Copper-tailed Glossy-starling	5	084
Lamprotornis cupreocauda		

MADAGASCAR

EBAs	Priority
093 West Malagasy dry forests	HIGH
094 East Malagasy wet forests	CRITICAL
095 East Malagasy wetlands	CRITICAL
096 West Malagasy wetlands	CRITICAL
097 South Malagasy spiny forests	URGENT

Secondary Areas
s049 Isalo Massif
s050 Ile de Sainte-Marie

Restricted-range species	Threatened	Total
Confined to this country	27	49
Present also in other countries	0	0
Total	27	49

Species (threatened species in **bold**)	No. of countries	EBAs (and SAs)
Alaotra Grebe *Tachybaptus rufolavatus*	1	095
Madagascar Heron *Ardea humbloti*	1	096
Meller's Duck *Anas melleri*	1	095,096
Madagascar Teal *Anas bernieri*	1	096
Madagascar Pochard *Aythya innotata*	1	095
Madagascar Fish-eagle *Haliaeetus vociferoides*	1	095ˣ,096
Madagascar Serpent-eagle *Eutriorchis astur*	1	094
White-breasted Mesite *Mesitornis variegata*	1	093
Brown Mesite *Mesitornis unicolor*	1	094
Subdesert Mesite *Monias benschi*	1	097
Slender-billed Flufftail *Sarothrura watersi*	1	095
Madagascar Rail *Rallus madagascariensis*	1	095
Sakalava Rail *Amaurornis olivieri*	1	096
Madagascar Jacana *Actophilornis albinucha*	1	095,096
Madagascar Plover *Charadrius thoracicus*	1	096
Madagascar Snipe *Gallinago macrodactyla*	1	095
ᴱˣ Snail-eating Coua *Coua delalandei*	0	(s050ˣ)
Coquerel's Coua *Coua coquereli*	1	093,094
Red-breasted Coua *Coua serriana*	1	094
Running Coua *Coua cursor*	1	097
Verreaux's Coua *Coua verreauxi*	1	097
Madagascar Red Owl *Tyto soumagnei*	1	094
Short-legged Ground-roller	1	094
Brachypteracias leptosomus		
Scaly Ground-roller *B. squamigera*	1	094
Rufous-headed Ground-roller *Atelornis crossleyi*	1	094
Long-tailed Ground-roller *Uratelornis chimaera*	1	097

Madagascar (cont.)

Schlegel's Asity *Philepitta schlegeli*	1	093,094
Yellow-bellied Asity *Neodrepanis hypoxanthus*	1	094
Appert's Greenbul *Phyllastrephus apperti*	1	093
Dusky Greenbul *Phyllastrephus tenebrosus*	1	094
Grey-crowned Greenbul *P. cinereiceps*	1	094
Red-shouldered Vanga *Calicalicus rufocarpalis*	1	097
Lafresnaye's Vanga *Xenopirostris xenopirostris*	1	097
Van Dam's Vanga *Xenopirostris damii*	1	093
Pollen's Vanga *Xenopirostris polleni*	1	094
Bernier's Vanga *Oriolia bernieri*	1	094
Helmet Vanga *Euryceros prevostii*	1	094
Nuthatch Vanga *Hypositta corallirostris*	1	094
Forest Rock-thrush *Monticola sharpei*	1	094
Benson's Rock-thrush *Monticola bensoni*	1	093,094 (s049)
Littoral Rock-thrush *Monticola imerinus*	1	097
Wedge-tailed Jery *Hartertula flavoviridis*	1	094
Madagascar Yellowbrow *Crossleyia xanthophrys*	1	094
Brown Emu-tail *Dromaeocercus brunneus*	1	094
Lantz's Brush-warbler *Nesillas lantzii*	1	097
Thamnornis Warbler *Thamnornis chloropetoides*	1	093,097
Grey Emu-tail *Amphilais seebohmi*	1	095
Cryptic Warbler *Cryptosylvicola randrianasoloi*	1	094
Archbold's Newtonia *Newtonia archboldi*	1	093,097
Red-tailed Newtonia *Newtonia fanovanae*	1	094

MALAWI

EBAs	Priority
092 South-east African coast	HIGH
105 Tanzania–Malawi mountains	CRITICAL

Secondary Areas none

Restricted-range species	Threatened	Total
Confined to this country	0	0
Present also in other countries	2	13
Total	2	13

Species (threatened species in **bold**)	No. of countries	EBAs (and SAs)
Sharpe's Greenbul *Phyllastrephus alfredi*	3	105
Fuelleborn's Boubou *Laniarius fuelleborni*	3	105
Thyolo Alethe *Alethe choloensis*	2	105
Sharpe's Akalat *Sheppardia sharpei*	3	105
Spot-throat *Modulatrix stictigula*	2	105
Black-lored Cisticola *Cisticola nigriloris*	3	105
Churring Cisticola *Cisticola njombe*	3	105
White-winged Apalis *Apalis chariessa*	4	105
Rudd's Apalis *Apalis ruddi*	4	092
Chapin's Apalis *Apalis chapini*	3	105
Lemon-breasted Seedeater *Serinus citrinipectus*	4	092
Yellow-browed Seedeater *Serinus whytii*	3	105
Buff-shouldered Widowbird	3	105
Euplectes psammocromius		

cont.

MALAYSIA

EBAs	Priority
157 Bornean mountains	URGENT
158 Sumatra and Peninsular Malaysia	URGENT

Secondary Areas
s097 North-east Bornean islands
s098 Sabah lowlands
s100 Bornean coastal zone
s101 Natuna Islands
s102 Malayan peninsula lowlands

Restricted-range species	Threatened	Total
Confined to this country	1	7
Present also in other countries	4	35
Total	5	42

Species (threatened species in **bold**)	No. of countries	EBAs (and SAs)
Mountain Serpent-eagle *Spilornis kinabaluensis*	2	157
White-fronted Falconet *Microhierax latifrons*	1	(s098)
Red-breasted Partridge *Arborophila hyperythra*	2	157
Crimson-headed Partridge *Haematortyx sanguiniceps*	2	157
Mountain Peacock-pheasant *Polyplectron inopinatum*	1	158
Malayan Peacock-pheasant *P. malacense*	2	(s102)
Crested Argus *Rheinardia ocellata*	3	158
Silvery Wood-pigeon *Columba argentina*	2	(s101)
Grey Imperial-pigeon *Ducula pickeringii*	3	(s097)
Mantanani Scops-owl *Otus mantananensis*	2	(s097)
Rajah Scops-owl *Otus brookii*	2	157,158
Dulit Frogmouth *Batrachostomus harterti*	2	157
Short-tailed Frogmouth *B. poliolophus*	2	157,158
Waterfall Swift *Hydrochrous gigas*	2	158
Whitehead's Trogon *Harpactes whiteheadi*	2	157
Fire-tufted Barbet *Psilopogon pyrolophus*	2	158
Mountain Barbet *Megalaima monticola*	2	157
Golden-naped Barbet *Megalaima pulcherrima*	2	157
Bornean Barbet *Megalaima eximia*	2	157
Hose's Broadbill *Calyptomena hosii*	2	157
Whitehead's Broadbill *Calyptomena whiteheadi*	2	157
Black-breasted Fruit-hunter *Chlamydochaera jefferyi*	2	157
Malayan Whistling-thrush *Myiophonus robinsoni*	1	158
Everett's Thrush *Zoothera everetti*	1	157
Sunda Laughingthrush *Garrulax palliatus*	3	157,158
Black Laughingthrush *Garrulax lugubris*	2	158
Bare-headed Laughingthrush *Garrulax calvus*	1	157
Marbled Wren-babbler *Napothera marmorata*	2	158
Mountain Wren-babbler *Napothera crassa*	2	157
Chestnut-crested Yuhina *Yuhina everetti*	2	157
Bornean Stubtail *Urosphena whiteheadi*	2	157
Friendly Bush-warbler *Bradypterus accentor*	1	157
Eyebrowed Jungle-flycatcher *Rhinomyias gularis*	2	157
Rufous-vented Niltava *Niltava sumatrana*	2	158
Bornean Whistler *Pachycephala hypoxantha*	2	157
Black-sided Flowerpecker *Dicaeum monticolum*	2	157
Whitehead's Spiderhunter *Arachnothera juliae*	2	157
Black-capped White-eye *Zosterops atricapillus*	2	157,158
Javan White-eye *Zosterops flavus*	2	(s100)
Pygmy White-eye *Oculocincta squamifrons*	2	157
Mountain Blackeye *Chlorocharis emiliae*	2	157
Black Oriole *Oriolus hosii*	1	157

MALI

EBAs none

Secondary Areas
s040 Upper Niger valley

Restricted-range species	Threatened	Total
Confined to this country	0	0
Present also in other countries	0	1
Total	0	1

Species (threatened species in **bold**)	No. of countries	EBAs (and SAs)
Mali Firefinch *Lagonosticta virata*	2	(s040)

MARSHALL ISLANDS

EBAs none

Secondary Areas
s123 Marshall Islands

Restricted-range species	Threatened	Total
Confined to this country	0	0
Present also in other countries	0	1
Total	0	1

Species (threatened species in **bold**)	No. of countries	EBAs (and SAs)
EL. Purple-capped Fruit-dove *Ptilinopus porphyraceus*	7	(s123X)
Micronesian Imperial-pigeon *Ducula oceanica*	3	(s123)

MARTINIQUE (TO FRANCE)

EBAs	Priority
030 Lesser Antilles	CRITICAL

Secondary Areas none

Restricted-range species	Threatened	Total
Confined to this country	1	1
Present also in other countries	1	15
Total	2	16

Species (threatened species in **bold**)	No. of countries	EBAs (and SAs)
Bridled Quail-dove *Geotrygon mystacea*	10	030
Lesser Antillean Swift *Chaetura martinica*	5	030
Purple-throated Carib *Eulampis jugularis*	9	030
Green-throated Carib *Eulampis holosericeus*	15	030
Antillean Crested Hummingbird *Orthorhyncus cristatus*	15	030
Blue-headed Hummingbird *Cyanophaia bicolor*	2	030
Lesser Antillean Pewee *Contopus latirostris*	5	030
Lesser Antillean Flycatcher *Myiarchus oberi*	7	030
Grey Trembler *Cinclocerthia gutturalis*	2	030
White-breasted Thrasher *Ramphocinclus brachyurus*	2	030
Scaly-breasted Thrasher *Margarops fuscus*	9	030
Pearly-eyed Thrasher *Margarops fuscatus*	14	030
Rufous-throated Solitaire *Myadestes genibarbis*	7	030
Lesser Antillean Bullfinch *Loxigilla noctis*	13	030
Antillean Euphonia *Euphonia musica*	12	030
Martinique Oriole *Icterus bonana*	1	030

MAURITIUS

EBAs	Priority
102 Mauritius	CRITICAL
103 Rodrigues	CRITICAL

Secondary Areas none

Restricted-range species	Threatened	Total
Confined to this country	9	9
Present also in other countries	0	3
Total	9	12

Species (threatened species in **bold**)	No. of countries	EBAs (and SAs)
Mauritius Kestrel *Falco punctatus*	1	102
Pink Pigeon *Columba mayeri*	1	102
EX Mauritius Blue-pigeon *Alectroenas nitidissima*	0	102X
Mauritius Parakeet *Psittacula eques*	1	102
EX Rodrigues Parakeet *Psittacula exsul*	0	103X
Mascarene Swiftlet *Collocalia francica*	2	102
Mauritius Cuckoo-shrike *Coracina typica*	1	102
Mauritius Bulbul *Hypsipetes olivaceus*	1	102
Rodrigues Warbler *Acrocephalus rodericanus*	1	103
Mascarene Paradise-flycatcher *Terpsiphone bourbonnensis*	2	102
Mauritius Olive White-eye *Zosterops chloronothos*	1	102
Mauritius Fody *Foudia rubra*	1	102
Rodrigues Fody *Foudia flavicans*	1	103
EX Rodrigues Starling *Necropsar rodericanus*	0	103X

MAYOTTE (TO FRANCE)

EBAs	Priority
098 Comoro Islands	CRITICAL

Secondary Areas none

Restricted-range species	Threatened	Total
Confined to this country	1	3
Present also in other countries	0	3
Total	1	6

Species (threatened species in **bold**)	No. of countries	EBAs (and SAs)
Comoro Olive-pigeon *Columba pollenii*	2	098
Comoro Blue-pigeon *Alectroenas sganzini*	3	098
Mayotte Sunbird *Nectarinia coquerellii*	1	098
Chestnut-sided White-eye *Zosterops mayottensis*	1	098
Red-headed Fody *Foudia eminentissima*	3	098
Mayotte Drongo *Dicrurus waldenii*	1	098

MEXICO

EBAs	Priority
001 California	HIGH
002 Baja California	HIGH
003 Guadalupe Island	CRITICAL
004 Socorro Island	CRITICAL
005 North-west Mexican Pacific slope	HIGH
006 Sierra Madre Occidental and trans-Mexican range	CRITICAL
007 Central Mexican marshes	URGENT
008 Balsas region and interior Oaxaca	HIGH
009 Sierra Madre del Sur	CRITICAL

cont

Mexico (cont.)

EBAs	Priority
010 Northern Sierra Madre Oriental	HIGH
011 North-east Mexican Gulf slope	URGENT
012 Southern Sierra Madre Oriental	CRITICAL
013 Los Tuxtlas and Uxpanapa	CRITICAL
014 Isthmus of Tehuantepec	HIGH
015 Yucatán peninsula coastal scrub	HIGH
016 Cozumel Island	URGENT
017 North Central American Pacific slope	HIGH
018 North Central American highlands	URGENT

Secondary Areas
s005 South Veracruz coastal scrub
s006 South Mexican karst forests
s007 Eastern Yucatán
s008 Clarión Island

Restricted-range species	Threatened	Total
Confined to this country	21	55
Present also in other countries	2	28
Total	23	83

Species (threatened species in **bold**)	No. of countries	EBAs (and SAs)
EX Guadalupe Caracara *Polyborus lutosus*	0	003X
Rufous-bellied Chachalaca *Ortalis wagleri*	1	005
White-bellied Chachalaca *Ortalis leucogastra*	5	017
Horned Guan *Oreophasis derbianus*	2	018
Bearded Wood-partridge *Dendrortyx barbatus*	1	012
Banded Quail *Philortyx fasciatus*	1	008
Ocellated Quail *Cyrtonyx ocellatus*	5	018
EW Socorro Dove *Zenaida graysoni*	0	004X
Veracruz Quail-dove *Geotrygon carrikeri*	1	013
Socorro Parakeet *Aratinga brevipes*	1	004
Pacific Parakeet *Aratinga strenua*	5	014,017
Thick-billed Parrot *Rhynchopsitta pachyrhyncha*	1	006
Maroon-fronted Parrot *Rhynchopsitta terrisi*	1	010
Mexican Parrotlet *Forpus cyanopygius*	1	005
Green-cheeked Amazon *Amazona viridigenalis*	1	011
Santa Barbara Screech-owl *Otus barbarus*	2	018
Fulvous Owl *Strix fulvescens*	4	018
Tamaulipas Pygmy-owl *Glaucidium sanchezi*	1	012
White-fronted Swift *Cypseloides storeri*	1	006,009
Long-tailed Sabrewing *Campylopterus excellens*	1	013
Rufous Sabrewing *Campylopterus rufus*	3	018
Short-crested Coquette *Lophornis brachylopha*	1	009
Cozumel Emerald *Chlorostilbon forficatus*	1	016
Dusky Hummingbird *Cynanthus sordidus*	1	008
Mexican Woodnymph *Thalurania ridgwayi*	1	005
Xantus's Hummingbird *Hylocharis xantusii*	1	002
Blue-tailed Hummingbird *Amazilia cyanura*	5	017
White-tailed Hummingbird *Eupherusa poliocerca*	1	009
Oaxaca Hummingbird *Eupherusa cyanophrys*	1	009
Green-throated Mountain-gem *Lampornis viridipallens*	5	018
Slender Sheartail *Doricha enicura*	4	018
Mexican Sheartail *Doricha eliza*	1	015(s005)
Beautiful Hummingbird *Calothorax pulcher*	1	008
Wine-throated Hummingbird *Atthis ellioti*	4	018
Allen's Hummingbird *Selasphorus sasin*	2	001
Blue-throated Motmot *Aspatha gularis*	4	018
Grey-breasted Woodpecker *Melanerpes hypopolius*	1	008
Nuttall's Woodpecker *Picoides nuttallii*	2	001
Imperial Woodpecker *Campephilus imperialis*	1	006
Belted Flycatcher *Xenotriccus callizonus*	3	018
Pileated Flycatcher *Xenotriccus mexicanus*	1	008
Black-capped Swallow *Notiochelidon pileata*	3	018

cont.

Mexico (cont.)

Yucatán Wren *Campylorhynchus yucatanicus*	1	015
Giant Wren *Campylorhynchus chiapensis*	1	017
Grey-barred Wren *C. megalopterus*	1	012,006
Sumichrast's Wren *Hylorchilus sumichrasti*	1	(s006)
Nava's Wren *Hylorchilus navai*	1	013
Socorro Wren *Thryomanes sissonii*	1	004
Clarión Wren *Troglodytes tanneri*	1	(s008)
Rufous-browed Wren *Troglodytes rufociliatus*	4	018
Blue-and-white Mockingbird *Melanotis hypoleucus*	4	018
Socorro Mockingbird *Mimodes graysoni*	1	004
Cozumel Thrasher *Toxostoma guttatum*	1	016
California Thrasher *Toxostoma redivivum*	2	001
Grayson's Thrush *Turdus graysoni*	1	005
Rufous-collared Robin *Turdus rufitorques*	4	018
Guadalupe Junco *Junco insularis*	1	003
Sierra Madre Sparrow *Xenospiza baileyi*	1	006
Bridled Sparrow *Aimophila mystacalis*	1	008
Black-chested Sparrow *Aimophila humeralis*	1	008
Cinnamon-tailed Sparrow *Aimophila sumichrasti*	1	014
Oaxaca Sparrow *Aimophila notosticta*	1	008
White-throated Towhee *Pipilo albicollis*	1	008
Green-striped Brush-finch *Atlapetes virenticeps*	1	006
Crimson-collared Grosbeak *Rhodothraupis celaeno*	1	011
Rose-bellied Bunting *Passerina rositae*	1	014
Azure-rumped Tanager *Tangara cabanisi*	2	018
Colima Warbler *Vermivora crissalis*	2	010
Belding's Yellowthroat *Geothlypis beldingi*	1	002
Altamira Yellowthroat *Geothlypis flavovelata*	1	011
Black-polled Yellowthroat *Geothlypis speciosa*	1	007
Pink-headed Warbler *Ergaticus versicolor*	2	018
Cozumel Vireo *Vireo bairdi*	1	016
Yucatán Vireo *Vireo magister*	4	016(s007)
Bar-winged Oriole *Icterus maculialatus*	3	018
Tricoloured Blackbird *Agelaius tricolor*	2	001
EX Slender-billed Grackle *Quiscalus palustris*	0	007X
Black-capped Siskin *Carduelis atriceps*	2	018
Lawrence's Goldfinch *Carduelis lawrencei*	2	001
Dwarf Jay *Cyanolyca nana*	1	012
White-throated Jay *Cyanolyca mirabilis*	1	009
San Blas Jay *Cyanocorax sanblasianus*	1	005,008
Purplish-backed Jay *Cyanocorax beecheii*	1	005
Tufted Jay *Cyanocorax dickeyi*	1	006
Tamaulipas Crow *Corvus imparatus*	1	011
Sinaloa Crow *Corvus sinaloae*	1	005

MICRONESIA

EBAs		Priority
191 Yap Islands		HIGH
192 East Caroline Islands		CRITICAL

Secondary Areas none

Restricted-range species	Threatened	Total
Confined to this country	5	14
Present also in other countries	0	8
Total	5	22

Species (threatened species in **bold**)	No. of countries	EBAs (and SAs)
EX Kosrae Crake *Porzana monasa*	0	192X
Caroline Islands Ground-dove *Gallicolumba kubaryi*	1	192
White-throated Ground-dove *G. xanthonura*	2	191
Purple-capped Fruit-dove *Ptilinopus porphyraceus*	7	192
Micronesian Imperial-pigeon *Ducula oceanica*	3	191,192

Micronesia (cont.)

Pohnpei Lorikeet *Trichoglossus rubiginosus*	1	192
Micronesian Swiftlet *Collocalia inquieta*	3	192
Micronesian Kingfisher *Todirhamphus cinnamominus*	2	192
Caroline Islands Reed-warbler *Acrocephalus syrinx*	1	192
Truk Monarch *Metabolus rugensis*	1	192
Yap Monarch *Monarcha godeffroyi*	1	191
Oceanic Flycatcher *Myiagra oceanica*	1	192
Pohnpei Flycatcher *Myiagra pluto*	1	192
Pohnpei Fantail *Rhipidura kubaryi*	1	192
Plain White-eye *Zosterops hypolais*	1	191
Caroline Islands White-eye *Zosterops semperi*	2	192
Grey-brown White-eye *Zosterops cinereus*	1	192
Yap Olive White-eye *Zosterops oleagineus*	1	191
Long-billed White-eye *Rukia longirostra*	1	192
Faichuk White-eye *Rukia ruki*	1	192
Micronesian Myzomela *Myzomela rubratra*	3	191,192
Pohnpei Mountain Starling *Aplonis pelzelni*	1	192
EX Kosrae Starling *Aplonis corvina*	0	192X
Micronesian Starling *Aplonis opaca*	4	191,192

MONGOLIA

EBAs none

Secondary Areas
s077 Mongolian mountains

Restricted-range species	Threatened	Total
Confined to this country	0	1
Present also in other countries	0	0
Total	0	1

Species (threatened species in **bold**)	No. of countries	EBAs (and SAs)
Mongolian Accentor *Prunella koslowi*	1	(s077)

MONTSERRAT (TO UK)

EBAs	Priority
030 Lesser Antilles	CRITICAL

Secondary Areas none

Restricted-range species	Threatened	Total
Confined to this country	0	1
Present also in other countries	0	11
Total	0	12

Species (threatened species in **bold**)	No. of countries	EBAs (and SAs)
Bridled Quail-dove *Geotrygon mystacea*	10	030
Purple-throated Carib *Eulampis jugularis*	9	030
Green-throated Carib *Eulampis holosericeus*	15	030
Antillean Crested Hummingbird *Orthorhyncus cristatus*	15	030
Lesser Antillean Flycatcher *Myiarchus oberi*	7	030
Brown Trembler *Cinclocerthia ruficauda*	6	030
Scaly-breasted Thrasher *Margarops fuscus*	9	030
Pearly-eyed Thrasher *Margarops fuscatus*	14	030
Forest Thrush *Cichlherminia lherminieri*	4	030
Lesser Antillean Bullfinch *Loxigilla noctis*	13	030
Antillean Euphonia *Euphonia musica*	12	030
Montserrat Oriole *Icterus oberi*	1	030

cont.

MOZAMBIQUE

EBAs	Priority
089 South African forests	HIGH
092 South-east African coast	HIGH
104 Eastern Zimbabwe mountains	HIGH
105 Tanzania–Malawi mountains	CRITICAL

Secondary Areas none

Restricted-range species	Threatened	Total
Confined to this country	1	1
Present also in other countries	5	13
Total	6	14

Species (threatened species in **bold**)	No. of countries	EBAs (and SAs)
Thyolo Alethe Alethe choloensis	2	105
Swynnerton's Robin Swynnertonia swynnertoni	3	104,105
Brown Scrub-robin Cercotrichas signata	2	089
Dappled Mountain-robin Modulatrix orostruthus	2	105
Briar Warbler Prinia robertsi	2	104
Namuli Apalis Apalis lynesi	1	105
White-winged Apalis Apalis chariessa	4	105
Rudd's Apalis Apalis ruddi	4	092
Chirinda Apalis Apalis chirindensis	2	104
African Tailorbird Orthotomus metopias	2	105
Long-billed Tailorbird Orthotomus moreaui	2	105
Neergaard's Sunbird Nectarinia neergaardi	2	092
Lemon-breasted Seedeater Serinus citrinipectus	4	092
Pink-throated Twinspot Hypargos margaritatus	3	092

MYANMAR

EBAs	Priority
125 Andaman Islands	HIGH
130 Eastern Himalayas	URGENT
132 Irrawaddy plains	HIGH
139 Yunnan mountains	URGENT

Secondary Areas
s079 North Myanmar lowlands
s080 Myanmar-Thailand mountains
s086 Peninsular Thailand lowland forests

Restricted-range species	Threatened	Total
Confined to this country	2	3
Present also in other countries	4	17
Total	6	20

Species (threatened species in **bold**)	No. of countries	EBAs (and SAs)
[EL] **Nicobar Scrubfowl** Megapodius nicobariensis	1	125[X]
Blyth's Tragopan Tragopan blythii	4	130
Sclater's Monal Lophophorus sclateri	3	130
Brown Coucal Centropus andamanensis	2	125
Ward's Trogon Harpactes wardi	5	130
Gurney's Pitta Pitta gurneyi	2	(s086)
Chestnut-backed Laughingthrush Garrulax nuchalis	2	(s079)
Striped Laughingthrush Garrulax virgatus	2	130
Brown-capped Laughingthrush G. austeni	2	130
Wedge-billed Wren-babbler Sphenocichla humei	3	130
White-throated Babbler Turdoides gularis	1	132
Streak-throated Barwing Actinodura waldeni	3	130
Grey Sibia Heterophasia gracilis	3	130
Beautiful Sibia Heterophasia pulchella	3	130

Myanmar (cont.)

White-naped Yuhina Yuhina bakeri	6	130
Burmese Yuhina Yuhina humilis	2	(s080)
Brown-winged Parrotbill Paradoxornis brunneus	2	139
Broad-billed Warbler Tickellia hodgsoni	6	130
White-browed Nuthatch Sitta victoriae	1	130
Andaman Drongo Dicrurus andamanensis	2	125
Hooded Treepie Crypsirina cucullata	1	132

NAMIBIA

EBAs	Priority
087 Western Angola	CRITICAL

Secondary Areas
s045 Namibian escarpment
s046 Namib desert
s047 Karoo

Restricted-range species	Threatened	Total
Confined to this country	0	1
Present also in other countries	1	3
Total	1	4

Species (threatened species in **bold**)	No. of countries	EBAs (and SAs)
Dune Lark Certhilauda erythrochlamys	1	(s046)
Red Lark Certhilauda burra	2	(s047)
Herero Chat Namibornis herero	2	(s045)
Cinderella Waxbill Estrilda thomensis	2	087

NAURU

EBAs none

Secondary Areas
s124 Nauru

Restricted-range species	Threatened	Total
Confined to this country	1	1
Present also in other countries	0	0
Total	1	1

Species (threatened species in **bold**)	No. of countries	EBAs (and SAs)
Nauru Reed-warbler Acrocephalus rehsei	1	(s124)

NEPAL

EBAs	Priority
128 Western Himalayas	CRITICAL
129 Central Himalayas	HIGH
130 Eastern Himalayas	URGENT
131 Assam plains	URGENT

Secondary Areas none

Restricted-range species	Threatened	Total
Confined to this country	0	2
Present also in other countries	2	10
Total	2	12

cont.

cont.

Nepal (cont.)

Species (threatened species in **bold**)	No. of countries	EBAs (and SAs)
Cheer Pheasant *Catreus wallichi*	3	128
Nepal Wren-babbler *Pnoepyga immaculata*	1	129
Rufous-throated Wren-babbler	3	130
Spelaeornis caudatus		
Spiny Babbler *Turdoides nipalensis*	1	129
Hoary-throated Barwing *Actinodura nipalensis*	4	129,130
White-naped Yuhina *Yuhina bakeri*	6	130
EL **Black-breasted Parrotbill**	2	131
Paradoxornis flavirostris		
Tytler's Leaf-warbler *Phylloscopus tytleri*	4	128
Yellow-vented Warbler *Phylloscopus cantator*	3	130
Broad-billed Warbler *Tickellia hodgsoni*	6	130
White-throated Tit *Aegithalos niveogularis*	3	128
Kashmir Nuthatch *Sitta cashmirensis*	4	128
Spectacled Finch *Callacanthis burtoni*	3	128

NETHERLANDS ANTILLES (TO NETHERLANDS)

EBAs	Priority
030 Lesser Antilles	CRITICAL

Secondary Areas
s015 Netherlands Antilles

Restricted-range species	Threatened	Total
Confined to this country	0	0
Present also in other countries	1	10
Total	1	10

Species (threatened species in **bold**)	No. of countries	EBAs (and SAs)
Bridled Quail-dove *Geotrygon mystacea*	10	030
Yellow-shouldered Amazon	2	(s015)
Amazona barbadensis		
Purple-throated Carib *Eulampis jugularis*	9	030
Green-throated Carib *Eulampis holosericeus*	15	030
Antillean Crested Hummingbird	15	030
Orthorhyncus cristatus		
Brown Trembler *Cinclocerthia ruficauda*	6	030
Scaly-breasted Thrasher *Margarops fuscus*	9	030
Pearly-eyed Thrasher *Margarops fuscatus*	14	030(s015)
Lesser Antillean Bullfinch *Loxigilla noctis*	13	030
Antillean Euphonia *Euphonia musica*	12	030

NEW CALEDONIA (TO FRANCE)

EBAs	Priority
201 New Caledonia	URGENT

Secondary Areas none

Restricted-range species	Threatened	Total
Confined to this country	8	22
Present also in other countries	0	9
Total	8	31

cont.

New Caledonia (cont.)

Species (threatened species in **bold**)	No. of countries	EBAs (and SAs)
White-bellied Goshawk *Accipiter haplochrous*	1	201
New Caledonian Rail *Gallirallus lafresnayanus*	1	201
Kagu *Rhynochetos jubatus*	1	201
Red-bellied Fruit-dove *Ptilinopus greyii*	3	201
Cloven-feathered Dove *Drepanoptila holosericea*	1	201
New Caledonian Imperial-pigeon *Ducula goliath*	1	201
New Caledonian Lorikeet *Charmosyna diadema*	1	201
Horned Parakeet *Eunymphicus cornutus*	1	201
New Caledonian Owlet-nightjar	1	201
Aegotheles savesi		
Melanesian Cuckoo-shrike *Coracina caledonica*	4	201
New Caledonian Cuckoo-shrike *Coracina analis*	1	201
Long-tailed Triller *Lalage leucopyga*	3	201
New Caledonian Grassbird *Megalurulus mariei*	1	201
Fan-tailed Gerygone *Gerygone flavolateralis*	3	201
Yellow-bellied Robin *Eopsaltria flaviventris*	1	201
Southern Shrikebill	2	201
Clytorhynchus pachycephaloides		
Melanesian Flycatcher *Myiagra caledonica*	3	201
Streaked Fantail *Rhipidura spilodera*	3	201
New Caledonian Whistler	1	201
Pachycephala caledonica		
Large Lifou White-eye *Zosterops inornatus*	1	201
Green-backed White-eye *Z. xanthochrous*	1	201
Small Lifou White-eye *Zosterops minutus*	1	201
New Caledonian Myzomela *Myzomela caledonica*	1	201
Cardinal Myzomela *Myzomela cardinalis*	5	201
Dark-brown Honeyeater *Lichmera incana*	2	201
New Caledonian Friarbird *Philemon diemenensis*	1	201
Crow Honeyeater *Gymnomyza aubryana*	1	201
Barred Honeyeater *Phylidonyris undulata*	1	201
Red-throated Parrotfinch *Erythrura psittacea*	1	201
Striated Starling *Aplonis striata*	1	201
New Caledonian Crow *Corvus moneduloides*	1	201

NEW ZEALAND

See also Cook Islands (p. 736), Niue (p. 758).

EBAs	Priority
206 North Island of New Zealand	CRITICAL
207 South Island of New Zealand	URGENT
208 Auckland Islands	HIGH
209 Chatham Islands	CRITICAL

Secondary Areas
s132 Snares and Stewart Islands
s133 Antipodes Islands

Restricted-range species	Threatened	Total
Confined to this country	12	17
Present also in other countries	0	0
Total	12	17

Species (threatened species in **bold**)	No. of countries	EBAs (and SAs)
Great Spotted Kiwi *Apteryx haastii*	1	207
New Zealand Dabchick *Poliocephalus rufopectus*	1	206
EX Auckland Islands Merganser *Mergus australis*	0	208ˣ
EX Dieffenbach's Rail *Gallirallus dieffenbachii*	0	209ˣ
EX Chatham Islands Rail *Gallirallus modestus*	0	209ˣ
Auckland Islands Rail *Lewinia muelleri*	1	208
Takahe *Porphyrio mantelli*	1	207

cont.

New Zealand (cont.)

Chatham Islands Oystercatcher	1	209
Haematopus chathamensis		
Shore Plover *Thinornis novaeseelandiae*	1	209
Wrybill *Anarhynchus frontalis*	1	207
Chatham Islands Snipe *Coenocorypha pusilla*	1	209
New Zealand Snipe *Coenocorypha aucklandica*	1	206ˣ,208
		(s132, s133)
Kea *Nestor notabilis*	1	207
Antipodes Parakeet *Cyanoramphus unicolor*	1	(s133)
South Island Rock Wren *Xenicus gilviventris*	1	207
ᴱˣ Stephens Island Wren *Xenicus lyalli*	0	207ˣ
ᴱˣ Chatham Islands Fernbird *Megalurus rufescens*	0	209ˣ
Chatham Islands Warbler *Gerygone albofrontata*	1	209
Whitehead *Mohoua albicilla*	1	206
Yellowhead *Mohoua ochrocephala*	1	207
Chatham Islands Robin *Petroica traversi*	1	209
Stitchbird *Notiomystis cincta*	1	206
ᴱˣ Huia *Heteralocha acutirostris*	0	206ˣ

NICARAGUA

EBAs	Priority
017 North Central American Pacific slope	HIGH
018 North Central American highlands	URGENT
019 Central American Caribbean slope	HIGH

Secondary Areas
s011 Lake Nicaragua marshes

Restricted-range species	Threatened	Total
Confined to this country	0	0
Present also in other countries	0	14
Total	0	14

Species (threatened species in **bold**)	No. of countries	EBAs (and SAs)
White-bellied Chachalaca *Ortalis leucogastra*	5	017
Ocellated Quail *Cyrtonyx ocellatus*	5	018
Pacific Parakeet *Aratinga strenua*	5	017
Blue-tailed Hummingbird *Amazilia cyanura*	5	017
Green-throated Mountain-gem	5	018
Lampornis viridipallens		
Green-breasted Mountain-gem *L. sybillae*	2	018
Streak-crowned Antvireo *Dysithamnus striaticeps*	3	019
Snowy Cotinga *Carpodectes nitidus*	4	019
Grey-headed Piprites *Piprites griseiceps*	4	019
Tawny-chested Flycatcher *Aphanotriccus capitalis*	2	019
Black-throated Wren *Thryothorus atrogularis*	3	019
Nicaraguan Seed-finch *Oryzoborus nuttingi*	3	019
Nicaraguan Grackle *Quiscalus nicaraguensis*	2	(s011)
Bushy-crested Jay *Cyanocorax melanocyaneus*	4	018

NIGERIA

EBAs	Priority
085 Cameroon and Gabon lowlands	HIGH
086 Cameroon mountains	CRITICAL

Secondary Areas
s041 South-west Nigeria
s042 Lower Niger valley

cont.

Nigeria (cont.)

Restricted-range species	Threatened	Total
Confined to this country	2	2
Present also in other countries	4	21
Total	6	23

Species (threatened species in **bold**)	No. of countries	EBAs (and SAs)
Cameroon Olive-pigeon *Columba sjostedti*	3	086
Forest Swallow *Hirundo fuliginosa*	3	085
Mountain Sawwing *Psalidoprocne fuliginosa*	3	086
Cameroon Greenbul *Andropadus montanus*	2	086
Grey-throated Greenbul *A. tephrolaemus*	3	086
Cameroon Olive Greenbul *Phyllastrephus poensis*	3	086
Grey-headed Greenbul *P. poliocephalus*	2	086
Yellow-breasted Boubou *Laniarius atroflavus*	2	086
Green-breasted Bush-shrike	2	086
Malaconotus gladiator		
Mountain Robin-chat *Cossypha isabellae*	2	086
White-throated Mountain-babbler	2	086
Kupeornis gilberti		
Grey-necked Rockfowl *Picathartes oreas*	4	085,086
Brown-backed Cisticola *Cisticola discolor*	2	086
Green Longtail *Urolais epichlora*	3	086
Bangwa Forest Warbler *Bradypterus bangwaensis*	2	086
White-tailed Warbler *Poliolais lopezi*	3	086
Black-capped Woodland-warbler	3	086
Phylloscopus herberti		
Cameroon Sunbird *Nectarinia oritis*	3	086
Fernando Po Oliveback *Nesocharis shelleyi*	3	086
Anambra Waxbill *Estrilda poliopareia*	1	(s042)
Bannerman's Weaver *Ploceus bannermani*	2	086
Rachel's Malimbe *Malimbus racheliae*	4	085
Ibadan Malimbe *Malimbus ibadanensis*	1	(s041)

NIUE (TO NEW ZEALAND)

EBAs none

Secondary Areas
s131 Niue

Restricted-range species	Threatened	Total
Confined to this country	0	0
Present also in other countries	0	4
Total	0	4

Species (threatened species in **bold**)	No. of countries	EBAs (and SAs)
Purple-capped Fruit-dove *Ptilinopus porphyraceus*	7	(s131)
Blue-crowned Lorikeet *Vini australis*	6	(s131)
Polynesian Triller *Lalage maculosa*	7	(s131)
Polynesian Starling *Aplonis tabuensis*	7	(s131)

NORFOLK ISLAND (TO AUSTRALIA)

EBAs	Priority
205 Norfolk Island	CRITICAL

Secondary Areas none

Restricted-range species	Threatened	Total
Confined to this country	3	3
Present also in other countries	0	0
Total	3	3

cont.

Norfolk Island (cont.)

Species (threatened species in **bold**)	No. of countries	EBAs (and SAs)
EX Norfolk Island Kaka *Nestor productus*	0	205ˣ
EL Long-tailed Triller *Lalage leucopyga*	3	205ˣ
Norfolk Island Gerygone *Gerygone modesta*	1	205
Slender-billed White-eye *Zosterops tenuirostris*	1	205
White-chested White-eye *Z. albogularis*	1	205
EX Norfolk Island Starling *Aplonis fusca*	0	205ˣ

NORTHERN MARIANA ISLANDS (TO USA)

EBAs	Priority
189 Mariana Islands	URGENT

Secondary Areas none

Restricted-range species	Threatened	Total
Confined to this country	4	6
Present also in other countries	2	6
Total	6	12

Species (threatened species in **bold**)	No. of countries	EBAs (and SAs)
Micronesian Scrubfowl *Megapodius laperouse*	2	189
White-throated Ground-dove *Gallicolumba xanthonura*	2	189
Mariana Fruit-dove *Ptilinopus roseicapilla*	1	189
Micronesian Swiftlet *Collocalia inquieta*	3	189
Nightingale Reed-warbler *Acrocephalus luscinia*	1	189
Tinian Monarch *Monarcha takatsukasae*	1	189
Saipan Bridled White-eye *Zosterops saypani*	1	189
Rota Bridled White-eye *Zosterops rotensis*	1	189
Golden White-eye *Cleptornis marchei*	1	189
Micronesian Myzomela *Myzomela rubratra*	3	189
Micronesian Starling *Aplonis opaca*	4	189
Mariana Crow *Corvus kubaryi*	2	189

PAKISTAN

EBAs	Priority
128 Western Himalayas	CRITICAL

Secondary Areas
s074 Indus plains

Restricted-range species	Threatened	Total
Confined to this country	0	0
Present also in other countries	3	11
Total	3	11

Species (threatened species in **bold**)	No. of countries	EBAs (and SAs)
Western Tragopan *Tragopan melanocephalus*	2	128
Cheer Pheasant *Catreus wallichi*	3	128
Brooks's Leaf-warbler *Phylloscopus subviridis*	3	128
Tytler's Leaf-warbler *Phylloscopus tytleri*	4	128
Kashmir Flycatcher *Ficedula subrubra*	2	128
White-cheeked Tit *Aegithalos leucogenys*	3	128
White-throated Tit *Aegithalos niveogularis*	3	128
Kashmir Nuthatch *Sitta cashmirensis*	4	128
Spectacled Finch *Callacanthis burtoni*	3	128
Orange Bullfinch *Pyrrhula aurantiaca*	2	128
Sind Sparrow *Passer pyrrhonotus*	3	(s074)

PALAU

EBAs	Priority
190 Palau	HIGH

Secondary Areas none

Restricted-range species	Threatened	Total
Confined to this country	0	10
Present also in other countries	1	6
Total	1	16

Species (threatened species in **bold**)	No. of countries	EBAs (and SAs)
Micronesian Scrubfowl *Megapodius laperouse*	2	190
Palau Ground-dove *Gallicolumba canifrons*	1	190
Palau Fruit-dove *Ptilinopus pelewensis*	1	190
Micronesian Imperial-pigeon *Ducula oceanica*	3	190
Palau Owl *Otus podarginus*	1	190
Palau Swiftlet *Collocalia pelewensis*	1	190
Micronesian Kingfisher *Todirhamphus cinnamominus*	2	190
Palau Bush-warbler *Cettia annae*	1	190
Mangrove Flycatcher *Myiagra erythrops*	1	190
Palau Fantail *Rhipidura lepida*	1	190
Morningbird *Colluricincla tenebrosa*	1	190
Caroline Islands White-eye *Zosterops semperi*	2	190
Dusky White-eye *Zosterops finschii*	1	190
Giant White-eye *Megazosterops palauensis*	1	190
Micronesian Myzomela *Myzomela rubratra*	3	190
Micronesian Starling *Aplonis opaca*	4	190

PANAMA

EBAs	Priority
019 Central American Caribbean slope	HIGH
020 Costa Rica and Panama highlands	URGENT
021 South Central American Pacific slope	HIGH
023 Darién lowlands	CRITICAL
024 Darién highlands	HIGH

Secondary Areas none

Restricted-range species	Threatened	Total
Confined to this country	2	7
Present also in other countries	5	84
Total	7	91

Species (threatened species in **bold**)	No. of countries	EBAs (and SAs)
Chocó Tinamou *Crypturellus kerriae*	2	023
Black Guan *Chamaepetes unicolor*	2	020
Tacarcuna Wood-quail *Odontophorus dialeucos*	2	024
Black-breasted Wood-quail *O. leucolaemus*	2	020
Brown-backed Dove *Leptotila battyi*	1	021
Purplish-backed Quail-dove *Geotrygon lawrencii*	2	019,021, 023
Buff-fronted Quail-dove *Geotrygon costaricensis*	2	020
Rufous-breasted Quail-dove *G. chiriquensis*	2	020
Russet-crowned Quail-dove *G. goldmani*	2	024
Sulphur-winged Parakeet *Pyrrhura hoffmanni*	2	020
Red-fronted Parrotlet *Touit costaricensis*	2	020
Bare-shanked Screech-owl *Otus clarkii*	3	020,024
Dusky Nightjar *Caprimulgus saturatus*	2	020
White-crested Coquette *Lophornis adorabilis*	2	021
Fiery-throated Hummingbird *Panterpe insignis*	2	020
Violet-capped Hummingbird *Goldmania violiceps*	2	024

cont.

Panama (cont.)

Rufous-cheeked Hummingbird *Goethalsia bella*	2	024
Charming Hummingbird *Amazilia decora*	2	021
Black-bellied Hummingbird *Eupherusa nigriventris*	2	020
White-tailed Emerald *Elvira chionura*	2	020
White-bellied Mountain-gem *Lampornis hemileucus*	2	020
Magenta-throated Woodstar *Philodice bryantae*	2	020
Volcano Hummingbird *Selasphorus flammula*	2	020
Scintillant Hummingbird *Selasphorus scintilla*	2	020
Glow-throated Hummingbird *S. ardens*	1	020
Lattice-tailed Trogon *Trogon clathratus*	2	019
Baird's Trogon *Trogon bairdii*	2	021
Orange-bellied Trogon *Trogon aurantiiventris*	2	020
Dusky-backed Jacamar *Brachygalba salmoni*	2	023
Prong-billed Barbet *Semnornis frantzii*	2	020
Fiery-billed Aracari *Pteroglossus frantzii*	2	021
Golden-naped Woodpecker *Melanerpes chrysauchen*	3	021
Stripe-cheeked Woodpecker *Piculus callopterus*	1	019,023
Coiba Spinetail *Cranioleuca dissita*	1	021
Ruddy Treerunner *Margarornis rubiginosus*	2	020
Beautiful Treerunner *Margarornis bellulus*	1	024
Streak-breasted Treehunter *Thripadectes rufobrunneus*	2	020
Black-hooded Antshrike *Thamnophilus bridgesi*	2	021
Speckled Antshrike *Xenornis setifrons*	2	023
Black-crowned Antpitta *Pittasoma michleri*	3	019,023
Tacarcuna Tapaculo *Scytalopus panamensis*	2	024
Nariño Tapaculo *Scytalopus vicinior*	3	024
Silvery-fronted Tapaculo *S. argentifrons*	2	020
Turquoise Cotinga *Cotinga ridgwayi*	2	021
Snowy Cotinga *Carpodectes nitidus*	4	019
Yellow-billed Cotinga *Carpodectes antoniae*	2	021
Bare-necked Umbrellabird *Cephalopterus glabricollis*	2	020
Black-billed Flycatcher *Aphanotriccus audax*	2	023
Dark Pewee *Contopus lugubris*	2	020
Ochraceous Pewee *Contopus ochraceus*	2	020
Black-capped Flycatcher *Empidonax atriceps*	2	020
Golden-bellied Flycatcher *Myiodynastes hemichrysus*	2	020
Long-tailed Silky-flycatcher *Ptilogonys caudatus*	2	020
Black-and-yellow Silky-flycatcher *Phainoptila melanoxantha*	2	020
Black-throated Wren *Thryothorus atrogularis*	3	019
Riverside Wren *Thryothorus semibadius*	2	021
Ochraceous Wren *Troglodytes ochraceus*	2	020
Timberline Wren *Thryorchilus browni*	2	020
Black-faced Solitaire *Myadestes melanops*	2	020
Varied Solitaire *Myadestes coloratus*	2	024
Black-billed Nightingale-thrush *Catharus gracilirostris*	2	020
Sooty Thrush *Turdus nigrescens*	2	020
Volcano Junco *Junco vulcani*	2	020
Large-footed Finch *Pezopetes capitalis*	2	020
Yellow-thighed Finch *Pselliophorus tibialis*	2	020
Yellow-green Finch *Pselliophorus luteoviridis*	1	020
Sooty-faced Finch *Lysurus crassirostris*	3	020,024
Peg-billed Finch *Acanthidops bairdii*	2	020
Nicaraguan Seed-finch *Oryzoborus nuttingi*	3	019
Black-thighed Grosbeak *Pheucticus tibialis*	2	020
Tacarcuna Bush-tanager *Chlorospingus tacarcunae*	2	024
Pirre Bush-tanager *Chlorospingus inornatus*	1	024
Sooty-capped Bush-tanager *C. pileatus*	2	020
Black-and-yellow Tanager *Chrysothlypis chrysomelas*	2	019,023
Sulphur-rumped Tanager *Heterospingus rubrifrons*	2	019,023

Panama (cont.)

Blue-and-gold Tanager *Bangsia arcaei*	2	020,024
Spot-crowned Euphonia *Euphonia imitans*	2	021
Yellow-collared Chlorophonia *Chlorophonia flavirostris*	3	024
Golden-browed Chlorophonia *C. callophrys*	2	020
Spangle-cheeked Tanager *Tangara dowii*	2	020
Green-naped Tanager *Tangara fucosa*	2	024
Viridian Dacnis *Dacnis viguieri*	2	023
Slaty Flower-piercer *Diglossa plumbea*	2	020
Flame-throated Warbler *Parula gutturalis*	2	020
Collared Whitestart *Myioborus torquatus*	2	020
Black-cheeked Warbler *Basileuterus melanogenys*	2	020
Pirre Warbler *Basileuterus ignotus*	2	024
Wrenthrush *Zeledonia coronata*	2	020
Yellow-winged Vireo *Vireo carmioli*	2	020
Black Oropendola *Gymnostinops guatimozinus*	2	023
Silvery-throated Jay *Cyanolyca argentigula*	2	020

PAPUA NEW GUINEA

EBAs	Priority
175 North Papuan mountains	HIGH
176 North Papuan lowlands	HIGH
177 Adelbert and Huon ranges	HIGH
178 Central Papuan mountains	URGENT
179 South Papuan lowlands	HIGH
180 Trans-Fly	HIGH
193 Admiralty Islands	HIGH
194 St Matthias Islands	HIGH
195 New Britain and New Ireland	HIGH
196 D'Entrecasteaux and Trobriand Islands	HIGH
197 Louisiade archipelago	URGENT
198 Solomon group	CRITICAL

Secondary Areas
s114 South-east Papuan lowlands

Restricted-range species	Threatened	Total
Confined to this country	12	81
Present also in other countries	9	86
Total	21	167

Species (threatened species in **bold**)	No. of countries	EBAs (and SAs)
Black Honey-buzzard *Henicopernis infuscatus*	1	195
Sanford's Fish-eagle *Haliaeetus sanfordi*	2	198
Pied Goshawk *Accipiter albogularis*	2	195,198
Slaty-mantled Sparrowhawk *A. luteoschistaceus*	1	195
Imitator Sparrowhawk *Accipiter imitator*	2	198
New Britain Goshawk *Accipiter princeps*	1	195
New Britain Sparrowhawk *A. brachyurus*	1	195
Melanesian Scrubfowl *Megapodius eremita*	2	193,194, 195,198
Chestnut Forest-rail *Rallina rubra*	2	178
Mayr's Forest-rail *Rallina mayri*	2	175
Woodford's Rail *Nesoclopeus woodfordi*	2	198
New Britain Rail *Gallirallus insignis*	1	195
Yellow-legged Pigeon *Columba pallidiceps*	2	195,198
Pied Cuckoo-dove *Reinwardtoena browni*	1	193,195
Crested Cuckoo-dove *R. crassirostris*	2	198
New Britain Bronzewing *Henicophaps foersteri*	1	195
Yellow-bibbed Fruit-dove *Ptilinopus solomonensis*	3	193,194, 195,198
Knob-billed Fruit-dove *Ptilinopus insolitus*	1	194,195
Red-knobbed Imperial-pigeon *Ducula rubricera*	2	195,198
Finsch's Imperial-pigeon *Ducula finschii*	1	195

cont.

cont.

Papua New Guinea (cont.)

Bismarck Imperial-pigeon *Ducula melanochroa*	1	195
Yellow-tinted Imperial-Pigeon *D. subflavescens*	1	193,195
Pale Mountain-pigeon *Gymnophaps solomonensis*	2	198
Brown Lory *Chalcopsitta duivenbodei*	2	176
Cardinal Lory *Chalcopsitta cardinalis*	2	195,198
White-naped Lory *Lorius albidinuchus*	1	195
Red-chinned Lorikeet *Charmosyna rubrigularis*	1	195
Meek's Lorikeet *Charmosyna meeki*	2	198
Striated Lorikeet *Charmosyna multistriata*	2	179
Duchess Lorikeet *Charmosyna margarethae*	2	198
Blue-eyed Cockatoo *Cacatua ophthalmica*	1	195
Ducorps's Cockatoo *Cacatua ducorpsii*	2	198
Meek's Pygmy-parrot *Micropsitta meeki*	1	193,194
Finsch's Pygmy-parrot *Micropsitta finschii*	2	195,198
Edwards's Fig-parrot *Psittaculirostris edwardsii*	2	176
Painted Tiger-parrot *Psittacella picta*	2	178
Modest Tiger-parrot *Psittacella modesta*	2	178
Singing Parrot *Geoffroyus heteroclitus*	2	195,198
Green-fronted Hanging-parrot *Loriculus tener*	1	195
Violaceous Coucal *Centropus violaceus*	1	195
Pied Coucal *Centropus ateralbus*	1	195
Manus Masked-owl *Tyto manusi*	1	193
Bismarck Masked-owl *Tyto aurantia*	1	195
Manus Hawk-owl *Ninox meeki*	1	193
Bismarck Hawk-owl *Ninox variegata*	1	195
Russet Hawk-owl *Ninox odiosa*	1	195
Solomon Islands Hawk-owl *Ninox jacquinoti*	2	198
Fearful Owl *Nesasio solomonensis*	2	198
Archbold's Owlet-nightjar *Aegotheles archboldi*	2	178
Mountain Eared-nightjar *Eurostopodus archboldi*	2	177,178
Bare-legged Swiftlet *Collocalia nuditarsus*	2	178
Mayr's Swiftlet *Collocalia orientalis*	2	195,198
Bismarck Kingfisher *Alcedo websteri*	1	195
Spangled Kookaburra *Dacelo tyro*	2	180
New Britain Kingfisher *Todirhamphus albonotatus*	1	195
Ultramarine Kingfisher *T. leucopygius*	2	198
Moustached Kingfisher *Actenoides bougainvillei*	2	198
Little Paradise-kingfisher *Tanysiptera hydrocharis*	2	180
Red-breasted Paradise-kingfisher *T. nympha*	2	176
Brown-headed Paradise-kingfisher *T. danae*	1	(s114)
Superb Pitta *Pitta superba*	1	193
Black-faced Pitta *Pitta anerythra*	2	198
Alpine Pipit *Anthus gutturalis*	2	177,178
Melanesian Cuckoo-shrike *Coracina caledonica*	4	198
Solomon Islands Cuckoo-shrike *C. holopolia*	2	198
Greater Ground-robin *Amalocichla sclateriana*	2	178
New Britain Thrush *Zoothera talaseae*	1	195,198
Papuan Whipbird *Androphobus viridis*	2	178
Painted Quail-thrush *Cinclosoma ajax*	2	179,180 (s114)
Greater Melampitta *Melampitta gigantea*	2	175,178
Fly River Grassbird *Megalurus albolimbatus*	1	180
Bismarck Thicketbird *Megalurulus grosvenori*	1	195
Bougainville Thicketbird *Megalurulus llaneae*	1	198
Rusty Thicketbird *Ortygocichla rubiginosa*	1	195
Papuan Thornbill *Acanthiza murina*	2	178
Alpine Robin *Petroica bivittata*	2	178
Olive-yellow Robin *Poecilodryas placens*	2	176,179 (s114)
Green-backed Robin *Pachycephalopsis hattamensis*	2	175,178
Bougainville Monarch *Monarcha erythrostictus*	1	198
Manus Monarch *Monarcha infelix*	1	193
White-breasted Monarch *Monarcha menckei*	1	194
Black-tailed Monarch *Monarcha verticalis*	1	195
Black-and-white Monarch *Monarcha barbatus*	2	198
Steel-blue Flycatcher *Myiagra ferrocyanea*	2	198

cont.

Papua New Guinea (cont.)

Dull Flycatcher *Myiagra hebetior*	1	194,195
White-winged Fantail *Rhipidura cockerelli*	2	198
Brown Fantail *Rhipidura drownei*	2	198
Bismarck Fantail *Rhipidura dahli*	1	195
Matthias Fantail *Rhipidura matthiae*	1	194
Manus Fantail *Rhipidura semirubra*	1	193
Lorentz's Whistler *Pachycephala lorentzi*	2	178
Hooded Whistler *Pachycephala implicata*	2	198
White-bellied Whistler *P. leucogastra*	1	176,197 (s114)
Sooty Shrike-thrush *Colluricincla umbrina*	2	178
White-bellied Pitohui *Pitohui incertus*	2	179
Wattled Ploughbill *Eulacestoma nigropectus*	2	178
Black Sittella *Daphoenositta miranda*	2	178
Louisiade Flowerpecker *Dicaeum nitidum*	1	197
Red-banded Flowerpecker *Dicaeum eximium*	1	195
Midget Flowerpecker *Dicaeum aeneum*	2	198
Obscure Berrypecker *Melanocharis arfakiana*	2	178
White-throated White-eye *Zosterops meeki*	1	197
Black-headed White-eye *Z. hypoxanthus*	1	193,195
Louisiade White-eye *Zosterops griseotinctus*	1	195,197
Yellow-throated White-eye *Zosterops metcalfii*	2	198
White-chinned Myzomela *Myzomela albigula*	1	197
Olive-yellow Myzomela *Myzomela pulchella*	1	195
Scarlet-bibbed Myzomela *Myzomela sclateri*	1	195
Ebony Myzomela *Myzomela pammelaena*	1	193,194, 195
Scarlet-naped Myzomela *Myzomela lafargei*	2	198
Black-bellied Myzomela *M. erythromelas*	1	195
Bougainville Honeyeater *Stresemannia bougainvillei*	1	198
Tagula Honeyeater *Meliphaga vicina*	1	197
White-naped Friarbird *Philemon albitorques*	1	193
New Britain Friarbird *Philemon cockerelli*	1	195
New Ireland Friarbird *Philemon eichhorni*	1	195
Leaden Honeyeater *Ptiloprora plumbea*	2	178
Olive-streaked Honeyeater *Ptiloprora meekiana*	2	177,178
Mayr's Honeyeater *Ptiloprora mayri*	2	175
Rufous-backed Honeyeater *Ptiloprora guisei*	1	177,178
Black-backed Honeyeater *Ptiloprora perstriata*	2	178
Sooty Melidectes *Melidectes fuscus*	2	178
Bismarck Melidectes *Melidectes whitemanensis*	1	195
Long-bearded Melidectes *Melidectes princeps*	1	178
Cinnamon-browed Melidectes *M. ochromelas*	2	177,178
Belford's Melidectes *Melidectes belfordi*	2	178
Yellow-browed Melidectes *M. rufocrissalis*	2	178
Huon Melidectes *Melidectes foersteri*	1	177
Spangled Honeyeater *Melipotes ater*	1	177
Mountain Firetail *Oreostruthus fuliginosus*	2	178
Grey-crowned Munia *Lonchura nevermanni*	2	180
Mottled Munia *Lonchura hunsteini*	1	195
New Ireland Munia *Lonchura forbesi*	1	195
New Hanover Munia *Lonchura nigerrima*	1	195
Black Munia *Lonchura stygia*	2	180
Snow Mountain Munia *Lonchura montana*	2	178
Alpine Munia *Lonchura monticola*	1	178
Bismarck Munia *Lonchura melaena*	1	195,198
Atoll Starling *Aplonis feadensis*	2	195
Brown-winged Starling *Aplonis grandis*	2	198
White-eyed Starling *Aplonis brunneicapilla*	2	198
Ribbon-tailed Drongo *Dicrurus megarhynchus*	1	195
Bismarck Woodswallow *Artamus insignis*	1	195
Tagula Butcherbird *Cracticus louisiadensis*	1	197
Streaked Bowerbird *Amblyornis subalaris*	1	178
Fire-maned Bowerbird *Sericulus bakeri*	1	177

cont.

Papua New Guinea (cont.)

Yellow-breasted Bird-of-paradise	2	178
Loboparadisea sericea		
Crested Bird-of-paradise *Cnemophilus macgregorii*	2	178
Loria's Bird-of-paradise *Cnemophilus loriae*	2	178
Macgregor's Bird-of-paradise	2	178
Macgregoria pulchra		
Curl-crested Manucode *Manucodia comrii*	1	196
Short-tailed Paradigalla *Paradigalla brevicauda*	2	178
Brown Sicklebill *Epimachus meyeri*	2	178
Pale-billed Sicklebill *Epimachus bruijnii*	2	176
Lawes's Parotia *Parotia lawesii*	1	178
Eastern Parotia *Parotia helenae*	1	178
Wahnes's Parotia *Parotia wahnesi*	1	177
Splendid Astrapia *Astrapia splendidissima*	2	178
Ribbon-tailed Astrapia *Astrapia mayeri*	1	178
Stephanie's Astrapia *Astrapia stephaniae*	1	178
Huon Astrapia *Astrapia rothschildi*	1	177
King-of-Saxony Bird-of-paradise	2	178
Pteridophora alberti		
Greater Bird-of-paradise *Paradisaea apoda*	2	179
Goldie's Bird-of-paradise *Paradisaea decora*	1	196
Emperor Bird-of-paradise *Paradisaea guilielmi*	1	177
Blue Bird-of-paradise *Paradisaea rudolphi*	1	178
Bougainville Crow *Corvus meeki*	2	198

PARAGUAY

EBAs	Priority
075 Atlantic forest lowlands	CRITICAL

Secondary Areas none

Restricted-range species	Threatened	Total
Confined to this country	0	0
Present also in other countries	2	6
Total	2	6

Species (threatened species in **bold**)	No. of countries	EBAs (and SAs)
Tawny-browed Owl *Pulsatrix koeniswaldiana*	3	075
Canebrake Groundcreeper	3	075
Clibanornis dendrocolaptoides		
White-browed Foliage-gleaner *Philydor amaurotis*	3	075
Bertoni's Antbird *Drymophila rubricollis*	3	075
Buffy-fronted Seedeater *Sporophila frontalis*	3	075
Temminck's Seedeater *Sporophila falcirostris*	3	075

PERU

EBAs	Priority
043 Central Andean páramo	URGENT
044 Ecuador–Peru East Andes	HIGH
045 Tumbesian region	CRITICAL
046 Southern Central Andes	URGENT
047 Andean ridge-top forests	URGENT
048 Marañón valley	URGENT
049 North-east Peruvian cordilleras	URGENT
050 Junín puna	CRITICAL
051 Peruvian high Andes	CRITICAL
052 Peru–Chile Pacific slope	HIGH
053 Peruvian East Andean foothills	HIGH
054 Bolivian and Peruvian lower yungas	URGENT
055 Bolivian and Peruvian upper yungas	URGENT
056 High Andes of Bolivia and Argentina	CRITICAL
066 Upper Amazon–Napo lowlands	HIGH
068 South-east Peruvian lowlands	URGENT

Secondary Areas
s022 Huallaga valley
s023 Upper Inambari valley
s024 Lake Titicaca

Restricted-range species	Threatened	Total
Confined to this country	25	101
Present also in other countries	23	110
Total	48	211

Species (threatened species in **bold**)	No. of countries	EBAs (and SAs)
Black Tinamou *Tinamus osgoodi*	2	053,054
Pale-browed Tinamou *Crypturellus transfasciatus*	2	045
Taczanowski's Tinamou	1	051
Nothoprocta taczanowskii		
Kalinowski's Tinamou *N. kalinowskii*	1	051
Titicaca Flightless Grebe *Rollandia microptera*	2	(s024)
Junín Grebe *Podiceps taczanowskii*	1	050
Grey-backed Hawk *Leucopternis occidentalis*	2	045
Rufous-headed Chachalaca *Ortalis erythroptera*	2	045
Bearded Guan *Penelope barbata*	2	046
White-winged Guan *Penelope albipennis*	1	045
Southern Helmeted Curassow *Pauxi unicornis*	2	053,054
Stripe-faced Wood-quail *Odontophorus balliviani*	2	055
Junín Rail *Laterallus tuerosi*	1	050
Peruvian Pigeon *Columba oenops*	1	048
Ecuadorian Ground-dove *Columbina buckleyi*	2	045
Ochre-bellied Dove *Leptotila ochraceiventris*	2	045
Red-masked Parakeet *Aratinga erythrogenys*	2	045
Pacific Parrotlet *Forpus coelestis*	2	045
Yellow-faced Parrotlet *Forpus xanthops*	1	048
Grey-cheeked Parakeet *Brotogeris pyrrhopterus*	2	045
Black-winged Parrot *Hapalopsittaca melanotis*	2	049,055
Red-faced Parrot *Hapalopsittaca pyrrhops*	2	046
Cinnamon Screech-owl *Otus petersoni*	2	044
Cloud-forest Screech-owl *Otus marshalli*	1	053
Long-whiskered Owlet *Xenoglaux loweryi*	1	047
Scrub Nightjar *Caprimulgus anthonyi*	2	045,048
Napo Sabrewing *Campylopterus villaviscensio*	2	044
Tumbes Hummingbird *Leucippus baeri*	1	045
Spot-throated Hummingbird *L. taczanowskii*	1	048,051
Olive-spotted Hummingbird *L. chlorocercus*	4	066
Green-and-white Hummingbird	1	053
Amazilia viridicauda		
Ecuadorian Piedtail *Phlogophilus hemileucurus*	3	044
Peruvian Piedtail *Phlogophilus harterti*	1	053,054
Pink-throated Brilliant *Heliodoxa gularis*	3	044
Rufous-webbed Brilliant *Heliodoxa branickii*	1	053

cont.

Peru (cont.)

Black-breasted Hillstar *Oreotrochilus melanogaster*	1	050
White-tufted Sunbeam *Aglaeactis castelnaudii*	1	051
Purple-backed Sunbeam *Aglaeactis aliciae*	1	048
Rainbow Starfrontlet *Coeligena iris*	2	046
Purple-throated Sunangel *Heliangelus viola*	2	046
Royal Sunangel *Heliangelus regalis*	1	047
Rufous-vented Whitetip *Urosticte ruficrissa*	3	044
Neblina Metaltail *Metallura odomae*	2	043
Coppery Metaltail *Metallura theresiae*	1	049
Fire-throated Metaltail *Metallura eupogon*	1	049
Scaled Metaltail *Metallura aeneocauda*	2	055
Olivaceous Thornbill *Chalcostigma olivaceum*	2	051,056
Grey-bellied Comet *Taphrolesbia griseiventris*	1	048,051
Bearded Mountaineer *Oreonympha nobilis*	1	051
Marvellous Spatuletail *Loddigesia mirabilis*	1	049
Chilean Woodstar *Eulidia yarrellii*	2	052
Short-tailed Woodstar *Myrmia micrura*	2	045
Coppery-chested Jacamar *Galbula pastazae*	3	044
Semicollared Puffbird *Malacoptila semicincta*	3	068
Brown Nunlet *Nonnula brunnea*	3	066
Scarlet-hooded Barbet *Eubucco tucinkae*	2	068
Yellow-browed Toucanet	1	049
Aulacorhynchus huallagae		
Hooded Mountain-toucan *Andigena cucullata*	2	055
Ecuadorian Piculet *Picumnus sclateri*	2	045
Speckle-chested Piculet *Picumnus steindachneri*	1	044
Fine-barred Piculet *Picumnus subtilis*	1	068
Coastal Miner *Geositta peruviana*	1	045,052
Dark-winged Miner *Geositta saxicolina*	1	050
Thick-billed Miner *Geositta crassirostris*	1	052
Striated Earthcreeper *Upucerthia serrana*	1	051
White-throated Earthcreeper *U. albigula*	2	052
Royal Cinclodes *Cinclodes aricomae*	2	051,056
Surf Cinclodes *Cinclodes taczanowskii*	1	045,052
White-bellied Cinclodes *Cinclodes palliatus*	1	050
Rusty-crowned Tit-spinetail *Leptasthenura pileata*	1	051
White-browed Tit-spinetail *L. xenothorax*	1	051
Mouse-coloured Thistletail	2	043
Schizoeaca griseomurina		
Eye-ringed Thistletail *Schizoeaca palpebralis*	1	049
Vilcabamba Thistletail *Schizoeaca vilcabambae*	1	049
Puna Thistletail *Schizoeaca helleri*	1	055
Apurímac Spinetail *Synallaxis coursoni*	1	051
Blackish-headed Spinetail *Synallaxis tithys*	2	045
Marañón Spinetail *Synallaxis maranonica*	1	048
Russet-bellied Spinetail *Synallaxis zimmeri*	1	051
Necklaced Spinetail *Synallaxis stictothorax*	2	045,048
Marcapata Spinetail *Cranioleuca marcapatae*	1	055
Light-crowned Spinetail *Cranioleuca albiceps*	2	055
Creamy-crested Spinetail *C. albicapilla*	1	051
Canyon Canastero *Asthenes pudibunda*	1	051
Rusty-fronted Canastero *Asthenes ottonis*	1	051
Cactus Canastero *Asthenes cactorum*	1	052
Line-fronted Canastero *Asthenes urubambensis*	2	051,056
Junín Canastero *Asthenes virgata*	1	050,051
Scribble-tailed Canastero *A. maculicauda*	3	056
Russet-mantled Softtail *Thripophaga berlepschi*	1	049
Great Spinetail *Siptornopsis hypochondriacus*	1	048
Chestnut-backed Thornbird	1	048
Phacellodomus dorsalis		
Equatorial Greytail *Xenerpestes singularis*	2	044
Rufous-necked Foliage-gleaner	2	045
Syndactyla ruficollis		
Henna-hooded Foliage-gleaner	2	045
Hylocryptus erythrocephalus		
Collared Antshrike *Sakesphorus bernardi*	2	045,048
Chapman's Antshrike *Thamnophilus zarumae*	2	045

Peru (cont.)

Upland Antshrike *Thamnophilus aroyae*	2	054
Ash-throated Antwren *Herpsilochmus parkeri*	1	047
Creamy-bellied Antwren *H. motacilloides*	1	053
Yellow-rumped Antwren *Terenura sharpei*	2	054
Black-tailed Antbird *Myrmoborus melanurus*	1	066
White-lined Antbird *Percnostola lophotes*	2	068
Goeldi's Antbird *Myrmeciza goeldii*	3	068
Grey-headed Antbird *Myrmeciza griseiceps*	2	045
White-masked Antbird *Pithys castanea*	1	066
Rufous-fronted Antthrush *Formicarius rufifrons*	1	068
Ochre-striped Antpitta *Grallaria dignissima*	3	066
Elusive Antpitta *Grallaria eludens*	1	068
Scrub Antpitta *Grallaria watkinsi*	2	045
Pale-billed Antpitta *Grallaria carrikeri*	1	049
White-throated Antpitta *Grallaria albigula*	3	054
Rusty-tinged Antpitta *Grallaria przewalskii*	1	049
Bay Antpitta *Grallaria capitalis*	1	049
Red-and-white Antpitta *Grallaria erythroleuca*	1	055
Chestnut Antpitta *Grallaria blakei*	1	049
Peruvian Antpitta *Grallaricula peruviana*	2	044
Ochre-fronted Antpitta *G. ochraceifrons*	1	047
Elegant Crescent-chest *Melanopareia elegans*	2	045
Marañón Crescent-chest *M. maranonica*	1	048
Large-footed Tapaculo *Scytalopus macropus*	1	049
Diademed Tapaculo *Scytalopus schulenbergi*	2	055
Slaty Becard *Pachyramphus spodiurus*	2	045,048
Bay-vented Cotinga *Doliornis sclateri*	1	049
Chestnut-bellied Cotinga *Doliornis remseni*	3	043
White-cheeked Cotinga *Zaratornis stresemanni*	1	051
Black-chested Fruiteater *Pipreola lubomirskii*	3	044
Masked Fruiteater *Pipreola pulchra*	1	044
Scimitar-winged Piha *Lipaugus uropygialis*	2	055
Black-faced Cotinga *Conioptilon mcilhennyi*	1	068
Cerulean-capped Manakin *Pipra coeruleocapilla*	1	053
Yungas Manakin *Chiroxiphia boliviana*	2	053,054
Orange-crested Manakin	2	066
Heterocercus aurantiivertex		
Inca Flycatcher *Leptopogon taczanowskii*	1	049
Hazel-fronted Pygmy-tyrant	2	054
Pseudotriccus simplex		
White-cheeked Tody-tyrant	1	068
Poecilotriccus albifacies		
Cinnamon-breasted Tody-tyrant	2	047
Hemitriccus cinnamomeipectus		
Golden-winged Tody-flycatcher	3	066
Todirostrum calopterum		
Black-backed Tody-flycatcher *T. pulchellum*	1	068
Bolivian Tyrannulet *Zimmerius bolivianus*	2	053,054
Red-billed Tyrannulet *Z. cinereicapillus*	2	044,053
Peruvian Tyrannulet *Zimmerius viridiflavus*	1	049
Pacific Elaenia *Myiopagis subplacens*	2	045
Grey-and-white Tyrannulet	2	045
Pseudelaenia leucospodia		
Unstreaked Tit-tyrant *Uromyias agraphia*	1	049
Ash-breasted Tit-tyrant *Anairetes alpinus*	2	051,056
Ecuadorian Tyrannulet *Phylloscartes gualaquizae*	2	044
Long-crested Pygmy-tyrant	3	068
Lophotriccus eulophotes		
Pacific Royal Flycatcher	2	045
Onychorhynchus occidentalis		
Unadorned Flycatcher *Myiophobus inornatus*	2	054
Orange-banded Flycatcher *Myiophobus lintoni*	2	046
Olive-chested Flycatcher *M. cryptoxanthus*	2	066
Grey-breasted Flycatcher	2	045,048
Lathrotriccus griseipectus		
Piura Chat-tyrant *Ochthoeca piurae*	1	045
Tumbes Tyrant *Ochthoeca salvini*	1	045

cont.

cont.

Peru (cont.)

Rufous-bellied Bush-tyrant	2	049,055
Myiotheretes fuscorufus		
Rufous Flycatcher *Myiarchus semirufus*	1	045
Sooty-crowned Flycatcher *M. phaeocephalus*	2	045,048
Baird's Flycatcher *Myiodynastes bairdii*	2	045
Peruvian Plantcutter *Phytotoma raimondii*	1	045
Inca Wren *Thryothorus eisenmanni*	1	055
Superciliated Wren *Thryothorus superciliaris*	2	045
Bar-winged Wood-wren *Henicorhina leucoptera*	2	047,049
Plumbeous-backed Thrush *Turdus reevei*	2	045
Marañón Thrush *Turdus maranonicus*	1	048
Ecuadorian Thrush *Turdus maculirostris*	2	045
Tumbes Sparrow *Aimophila stolzmanni*	2	045
Black-capped Sparrow *Arremon abeillei*	2	045,048
Bay-crowned Brush-finch *Atlapetes seebohmi*	2	045
Rusty-bellied Brush-finch *Atlapetes nationi*	1	051
White-headed Brush-finch *Atlapetes albiceps*	2	045
Rufous-eared Brush-finch *Atlapetes rufigenis*	1	051
Crimson Finch-tanager *Rhodospingus cruentus*	2	045
Short-tailed Finch *Idiopsar brachyurus*	3	056
Cinereous Finch *Piezorhina cinerea*	1	045
Slender-billed Finch *Xenospingus concolor*	2	052
Great Inca-finch *Incaspiza pulchra*	1	051
Rufous-backed Inca-finch *Incaspiza personata*	1	048,051
Grey-winged Inca-finch *Incaspiza ortizi*	1	048,051
Buff-bridled Inca-finch *Incaspiza laeta*	1	048
Little Inca-finch *Incaspiza watkinsi*	1	048
Plain-tailed Warbling-finch *Poospiza alticola*	1	051
Rufous-breasted Warbling-finch *P. rubecula*	1	051
Chestnut-breasted Mountain-finch *P. caesar*	1	051
Sulphur-throated Finch *Sicalis taczanowskii*	2	045
Drab Seedeater *Sporophila simplex*	2	045,052
Black-cowled Saltator *Saltator nigriceps*	2	045
Orange-browed Hemispingus	2	055
Hemispingus calophrys		
Parodi's Hemispingus *Hemispingus parodii*	1	055
Rufous-browed Hemispingus *H. rufosuperciliaris*	1	049
Brown-flanked Tanager *Thlypopsis pectoralis*	1	051
Buff-bellied Tanager *Thlypopsis inornata*	1	048
Slaty Tanager *Creurgops dentata*	2	053,054
Huallaga Tanager *Ramphocelus melanogaster*	1	(s022)
Golden-backed Mountain-tanager	1	049
Buthraupis aureodorsalis		
Masked Mountain-tanager *B. wetmorei*	3	043
Orange-throated Tanager	2	047
Wetmorethraupis sterrhopteron		
Golden-collared Tanager *Iridosornis jelskii*	2	049,055
Yellow-scarfed Tanager *Iridosornis reinhardti*	1	049,055
Green-capped Tanager	1	(s023)
Tangara meyerdeschauenseei		
Sira Tanager *Tangara phillipsi*	1	053
Straw-backed Tanager *Tangara argyrofenges*	2	044,053, 054
Grey-and-gold Warbler *Basileuterus fraseri*	2	045
Three-banded Warbler *Basileuterus trifasciatus*	2	045
Tamarugo Conebill *Conirostrum tamarugense*	2	052
Pardusco *Nephelornis oneillei*	1	049
Selva Cacique *Cacicus koepckeae*	1	068
Ecuadorian Cacique *Cacicus sclateri*	2	066
White-edged Oriole *Icterus graceannae*	2	045
Saffron Siskin *Carduelis siemiradzkii*	2	045
White-tailed Jay *Cyanocorax mystacalis*	2	045

PHILIPPINES

EBAs	Priority
150 Mindoro	CRITICAL
151 Luzon	CRITICAL
152 Negros and Panay	CRITICAL
153 Cebu	CRITICAL
154 Mindanao and the Eastern Visayas	CRITICAL
155 Sulu archipelago	CRITICAL
156 Palawan	URGENT

Secondary Areas
s094 Batanes and Babuyan Islands
s095 Tablas, Romblon and Sibuyan
s096 Siquijor

Restricted-range species	Threatened	Total
Confined to this country	66	121
Present also in other countries	1	5
Total	67	126

Species (threatened species in **bold**)	No. of countries	EBAs (and SAs)
Palawan Peacock-pheasant	1	156
Polyplectron emphanum		
Spotted Buttonquail *Turnix ocellata*	1	151,152
Worcester's Buttonquail *Turnix worcesteri*	1	151
Brown-banded Rail *Lewinia mirificus*	1	151,154
Luzon Bleeding-heart *Gallicolumba luzonica*	1	151
Mindoro Bleeding-heart *Gallicolumba platenae*	1	150
Negros Bleeding-heart *Gallicolumba keayi*	1	152
Mindanao Bleeding-heart *G. criniger*	1	154
Sulu Bleeding-heart *Gallicolumba menagei*	1	155
Mindanao Brown-dove *Phapitreron brunneiceps*	1	154
Tawitawi Brown-dove *Phapitreron cinereiceps*	1	155
Whistling Green-pigeon *Treron formosae*	3	(s094)
Flame-breasted Fruit-dove *Ptilinopus marchei*	1	151
Cream-bellied Fruit-dove *Ptilinopus merrilli*	1	151
Negros Fruit-dove *Ptilinopus arcanus*	1	152
Mindoro Imperial-pigeon *Ducula mindorensis*	1	150
Grey Imperial-pigeon *Ducula pickeringii*	3	156,155
Mindanao Lorikeet *Trichoglossus johnstoniae*	1	154
Luzon Racquet-tail *Prioniturus montanus*	1	151
Mindanao Racquet-tail *P. waterstradti*	1	154
Blue-headed Racquet-tail *P. platenae*	1	156
Green Racquet-tail *Prioniturus luconensis*	1	151
Blue-winged Racquet-tail *P. verticalis*	1	155
Red-crested Malkoha	1	151
Phaenicophaeus superciliosus		
Scale-feathered Malkoha *P. cumingi*	1	151
Black-hooded Coucal *Centropus steerii*	1	150
Rufous Coucal *Centropus unirufus*	1	151
Luzon Scops-owl *Otus longicornis*	1	151
Mindoro Scops-owl *Otus mindorensis*	1	150
Mindanao Scops-owl *Otus mirus*	1	154
Elegant Scops-owl *Otus elegans*	3	(s094)
Mantanani Scops-owl *Otus mantananensis*	2	155,156 (s095)
Palawan Scops-owl *Otus fuliginosus*	1	156
Lesser Eagle-owl *Mimizuku gurneyi*	1	154
Whitehead's Swiftlet *Collocalia whiteheadi*	1	151,154
Palawan Swiftlet *Collocalia palawanensis*	1	156
Philippine Needletail *Mearnsia picina*	1	152,153X, 154,155
Silvery Kingfisher *Alcedo argentata*	1	154
Blue-capped Kingfisher *Actenoides hombroni*	1	154
Palawan Hornbill *Anthracoceros marchei*	1	156
Sulu Hornbill *Anthracoceros montani*	1	155

cont.

Philippines (cont.)

Luzon Hornbill *Penelopides manillae*	1	151
Mindoro Hornbill *Penelopides mindorensis*	1	150
Visayan Hornbill *Penelopides panini*	1	152
Samar Hornbill *Penelopides samarensis*	1	154
Mindanao Hornbill *Penelopides affinis*	1	154
Writhed-billed Hornbill *Aceros waldeni*	1	152
Writhed Hornbill *Aceros leucocephalus*	1	154
Wattled Broadbill *Eurylaimus steerii*	1	154
Visayan Broadbill *Eurylaimus samarensis*	1	154
Azure-breasted Pitta *Pitta steerii*	1	154
Whiskered Pitta *Pitta kochi*	1	151
Blackish Cuckoo-shrike *Coracina coerulescens*	1	151,153[X]
McGregor's Cuckoo-shrike *C. mcgregori*	1	154
White-winged Cuckoo-shrike *C. ostenta*	1	152
Sulphur-bellied Bulbul *Ixos palawanensis*	1	156
Zamboanga Bulbul *Ixos rufigularis*	1	154
Streak-breasted Bulbul *Ixos siquijorensis*	1	153[X](s095, s096)
Yellowish Bulbul *Ixos everetti*	1	154,155
Philippine Leafbird *Chloropsis flavipennis*	1	153[X],154
Yellow-throated Leafbird *C. palawanensis*	1	156
Mountain Shrike *Lanius validirostris*	1	151,150, 152,154
Ashy Thrush *Zoothera cinerea*	1	150,151
White-vented Shama *Copsychus niger*	1	156
Black Shama *Copsychus cebuensis*	1	153
Luzon Water-redstart *Rhyacornis bicolor*	1	150,151
Bagobo Babbler *Trichastoma woodi*	1	154
Ashy-headed Babbler *Malacocincla cinereiceps*	1	156
Melodious Babbler *Malacopteron palawanense*	1	156
Striated Wren-babbler *Ptilocichla mindanensis*	1	154
Falcated Wren-babbler *Ptilocichla falcata*	1	156
Rabor's Wren-babbler *Napothera rabori*	1	151
Pygmy Babbler *Stachyris plateni*	1	154
Golden-crowned Babbler *Stachyris dennistouni*	1	151
Rusty-crowned Babbler *Stachyris capitalis*	1	154
Flame-templed Babbler *Stachyris speciosa*	1	152
Chestnut-faced Babbler *Stachyris whiteheadi*	1	151
Luzon Striped-babbler *Stachyris striata*	1	151
Panay Striped-babbler *Stachyris latistriata*	1	152
Negros Striped-babbler *Stachyris nigrorum*	1	152
Palawan Striped-babbler *S. hypogrammica*	1	156
Miniature Tit-babbler *Micromacronus leytensis*	1	154
Philippine Bush-warbler *Cettia seebohmi*	1	151
Long-tailed Bush-warbler *Bradypterus caudatus*	1	151,154
Rufous-headed Tailorbird *Orthotomus heterolaemus*	1	154
Grey-backed Tailorbird *Orthotomus derbianus*	1	151,156
Yellow-breasted Tailorbird *O. samarensis*	1	154
Black-headed Tailorbird *Orthotomus nigriceps*	1	154
White-eared Tailorbird *Orthotomus cinereiceps*	1	154
White-browed Jungle-flycatcher *Rhinomyias insignis*	1	151
White-throated Jungle-flycatcher *R. albigularis*	1	152
Slaty-backed Jungle-flycatcher *R. goodfellowi*	1	154
Ashy-breasted Flycatcher *Muscicapa randi*	1	151,152
Little Slaty Flycatcher *Ficedula basilanica*	1	154
Palawan Flycatcher *Ficedula platenae*	1	156
Cryptic Flycatcher *Ficedula crypta*	1	154
Furtive Flycatcher *Ficedula disposita*	1	151
Blue-breasted Flycatcher *Cyornis herioti*	1	151
Palawan Blue-flycatcher *Cyornis lemprieri*	1	156
Short-crested Monarch *Hypothymis helenae*	1	151,154
Celestial Monarch *Hypothymis coelestis*	1	151,152, 154,155 (s095)
Blue Paradise-flycatcher *Terpsiphone cyanescens*	1	156

cont.

Philippines (cont.)

Black-and-cinnamon Fantail *Rhipidura nigrocinnamomea*	1	154
Green-backed Whistler *Pachycephala albiventris*	1	150,151
Palawan Tit *Parus amabilis*	1	156
White-fronted Tit *Parus semilarvatus*	1	151,154
Long-billed Rhabdornis *Rhabdornis grandis*	1	151
Palawan Flowerpecker *Prionochilus plateni*	1	156
Whiskered Flowerpecker *Dicaeum proprium*	1	154
Olive-capped Flowerpecker *Dicaeum nigrilore*	1	154
Flame-crowned Flowerpecker *D. anthonyi*	1	151,154
Cebu Flowerpecker *Dicaeum quadricolor*	1	153
Visayan Flowerpecker *D. haematostictum*	1	152
Scarlet-collared Flowerpecker *D. retrocinctum*	1	150,152
Grey-hooded Sunbird *Aethopyga primigenius*	1	154
Apo Sunbird *Aethopyga boltoni*	1	154
Lina's Sunbird *Aethopyga linaraborae*	1	154
Black-masked White-eye *Lophozosterops goodfellowi*	1	154
Cinnamon Ibon *Hypocryptadius cinnamomeus*	1	154
Mountain Serin *Serinus estherae*	2	154
White-cheeked Bullfinch *Pyrrhula leucogenis*	1	151,154
Green-faced Parrotfinch *Erythrura viridifacies*	1	151,152
Red-eared Parrotfinch *Erythrura coloria*	1	154
Apo Myna *Basilornis miranda*	1	154
White-lored Oriole *Oriolus albiloris*	1	151
Isabela Oriole *Oriolus isabellae*	1	151

PITCAIRN ISLANDS (TO UK)

EBAs	Priority
215 Henderson Island	URGENT

Secondary Areas
s137 Pitcairn

Restricted-range species	Threatened	Total
Confined to this country	3	5
Present also in other countries	0	0
Total	3	5

Species (threatened species in **bold**)	No. of countries	EBAs (and SAs)
Henderson Crake *Porzana atra*	1	215
Henderson Fruit-dove *Ptilinopus insularis*	1	215
Henderson Lorikeet *Vini stepheni*	1	215
Pitcairn Reed-warbler *Acrocephalus vaughani*	1	(s137)
Henderson Reed-warbler *Acrocephalus taiti*	1	215

PORTUGAL

EBAs	Priority
120 Madeira and the Canary Islands	HIGH

Secondary Areas
s069 Azores

Restricted-range species	Threatened	Total
Confined to this country	0	1
Present also in other countries	0	3
Total	0	4

Species (threatened species in **bold**)	No. of countries	EBAs (and SAs)
Madeira Laurel Pigeon *Columba trocaz*	1	120
Plain Swift *Apus unicolor*	2	120
Berthelot's Pipit *Anthus berthelotii*	2	120
Island Canary *Serinus canaria*	2	120(s069)

PUERTO RICO (TO USA)

EBAs	Priority
029 Puerto Rico and the Virgin Islands	URGENT

Secondary Areas none

Restricted-range species	Threatened	Total
Confined to this country	3	11
Present also in other countries	1	12
Total	4	23

Species (threatened species in **bold**)	No. of countries	EBAs (and SAs)
Bridled Quail-dove *Geotrygon mystacea*	10	029
Hispaniolan Parakeet *Aratinga chloroptera*	3	029
Puerto Rican Amazon *Amazona vittata*	1	029
Puerto Rican Lizard-cuckoo *Saurothera vieilloti*	1	029
Puerto Rican Screech-owl *Otus nudipes*	3	029
Puerto Rican Nightjar *Caprimulgus noctitherus*	1	029
Antillean Mango *Anthracothorax dominicus*	4	029
Green Mango *Anthracothorax viridis*	1	029
Green-throated Carib *Eulampis holosericeus*	15	029
Antillean Crested Hummingbird *Orthorhyncus cristatus*	15	029
Puerto Rican Emerald *Chlorostilbon maugaeus*	1	029
Puerto Rican Tody *Todus mexicanus*	1	029
Puerto Rican Woodpecker *Melanerpes portoricensis*	2	029
Lesser Antillean Pewee *Contopus latirostris*	5	029
Puerto Rican Flycatcher *Myiarchus antillarum*	3	029
Pearly-eyed Thrasher *Margarops fuscatus*	14	029
Puerto Rican Bullfinch *Loxigilla portoricensis*	1	029
Puerto Rican Tanager *Nesospingus speculiferus*	1	029
Antillean Euphonia *Euphonia musica*	12	029
Adelaide's Warbler *Dendroica adelaidae*	3	029
Elfin-woods Warbler *Dendroica angelae*	1	029
Puerto Rican Vireo *Vireo latimeri*	1	029
Yellow-shouldered Blackbird *Agelaius xanthomus*	1	029
EL **White-necked Crow** *Corvus leucognaphalus*	2	029X

RUSSIA

EBAs	Priority
122 Caucasus	HIGH

Secondary Areas
s087 Chukotski peninsula
s088 Sakhalin

Restricted-range species	Threatened	Total
Confined to this country	2	2
Present also in other countries	0	3
Total	2	5

Species (threatened species in **bold**)	No. of countries	EBAs (and SAs)
Caucasian Grouse *Tetrao mlokosiewiczi*	6	122
Caucasian Snowcock *Tetraogallus caucasicus*	3	122
Nordmann's Greenshank *Tringa guttifer*	1	(s088)
Spoon-billed Sandpiper *Eurynorhynchus pygmeus*	1	(s087)
Caucasian Chiffchaff *Phylloscopus lorenzii*	6	122

RWANDA

EBAs	Priority
106 Albertine Rift mountains	URGENT

Secondary Areas
s057 Dry Woodlands west of Lake Victoria

Restricted-range species	Threatened	Total
Confined to this country	0	0
Present also in other countries	4	26
Total	4	26

Species (threatened species in **bold**)	No. of countries	EBAs (and SAs)
Handsome Francolin *Francolinus nobilis*	4	106
Ruwenzori Turaco *Musophaga johnstoni*	4	106
Albertine Owlet *Glaucidium albertinum*	2	106
Ruwenzori Nightjar *Caprimulgus ruwenzorii*	4	106
Red-faced Barbet *Lybius rubrifacies*	3	(s057)
Dwarf Honeyguide *Indicator pumilio*	3	106
Kivu Ground-thrush *Zoothera tanganjicae*	4	106
Red-throated Alethe *Alethe poliophrys*	4	106
Archer's Robin-chat *Cossypha archeri*	4	106
Red-collared Mountain-babbler *Kupeornis rufocinctus*	3	106
Collared Apalis *Apalis ruwenzorii*	4	106
Black-faced Apalis *Apalis personata*	4	106
Kungwe Apalis *Apalis argentea*	4	106
Grauer's Swamp-warbler *Bradypterus graueri*	4	106
Grauer's Warbler *Graueria vittata*	4	106
Neumann's Warbler *Hemitesia neumanni*	4	106
Red-faced Woodland-warbler *Phylloscopus laetus*	4	106
Yellow-eyed Black-flycatcher *Melaenornis ardesiacus*	4	106
Ruwenzori Batis *Batis diops*	4	106
Stripe-breasted Tit *Parus fasciiventer*	4	106
Blue-headed Sunbird *Nectarinia alinae*	4	106
Regal Sunbird *Nectarinia regia*	5	106
Purple-breasted Sunbird *N. purpureiventris*	4	106
Dusky Crimson-wing *Cryptospiza jacksoni*	4	106
Shelley's Crimson-wing *Cryptospiza shelleyi*	4	106
Strange Weaver *Ploceus alienus*	4	106

RÉUNION (TO FRANCE)

EBAs	Priority
101 Réunion	URGENT

Secondary Areas none

Restricted-range species	Threatened	Total
Confined to this country	1	4
Present also in other countries	0	3
Total	1	7

Species (threatened species in **bold**)	No. of countries	EBAs (and SAs)
EX Mascarene Parrot *Mascarinus mascarinus*	0	101X
Mascarene Swiftlet *Collocalia francica*	2	101
Réunion Cuckoo-shrike *Coracina newtoni*	1	101
Olivaceous Bulbul *Hypsipetes borbonicus*	1	101
Réunion Stonechat *Saxicola tectes*	1	101
Mascarene Paradise-flycatcher *Terpsiphone bourbonnensis*	2	101
Mascarene Grey White-eye *Zosterops borbonicus*	2	101
Réunion Olive White-eye *Zosterops olivaceus*	1	101
EX Réunion Starling *Fregilupus varius*	0	101X

SAUDI ARABIA

EBAs	Priority
118 South-west Arabian mountains	HIGH

Secondary Areas none

Restricted-range species	Threatened	Total
Confined to this country	0	0
Present also in other countries	2	7
Total	2	7

Species (threatened species in **bold**)	No. of countries	EBAs (and SAs)
Philby's Partridge *Alectoris philbyi*	2	118
Yemen Accentor *Prunella fagani*	2	118
Yemen Thrush *Turdus menachensis*	2	118
Yemen Warbler *Sylvia buryi*	2	118
Yemen Serin *Serinus menachensis*	2	118
Yemen Linnet *Carduelis yemenensis*	2	118
Arabian Waxbill *Estrilda rufibarba*	2	118

SENEGAL

EBAs none

Secondary Areas
s040 Upper Niger valley

Restricted-range species	Threatened	Total
Confined to this country	0	0
Present also in other countries	0	1
Total	0	1

Species (threatened species in **bold**)	No. of countries	EBAs (and SAs)
Mali Firefinch *Lagonosticta virata*	2	(s040)

SEYCHELLES

EBAs	Priority
099 Aldabra	HIGH
100 Granitic Seychelles	CRITICAL

Secondary Areas none

Restricted-range species	Threatened	Total
Confined to this country	8	12
Present also in other countries	0	2
Total	8	14

Species (threatened species in **bold**)	No. of countries	EBAs (and SAs)
Seychelles Kestrel *Falco araea*	1	100
Comoro Blue-pigeon *Alectroenas sganzini*	3	099
Seychelles Blue-pigeon *A. pulcherrima*	1	100
EX Seychelles Parakeet *Psittacula wardi*	0	100X
Seychelles Scops-owl *Otus insularis*	1	100
Seychelles Swiftlet *Collocalia elaphra*	1	100
Seychelles Bulbul *Hypsipetes crassirostris*	1	100
Seychelles Magpie-robin *Copsychus sechellarum*	1	100
EX Aldabra Warbler *Nesillas aldabrana*	0	099X
Seychelles Warbler *Acrocephalus sechellensis*	1	100
Seychelles Paradise-flycatcher *Terpsiphone corvina*	1	100
Seychelles Sunbird *Nectarinia dussumieri*	1	100

Seychelles (cont.)

EL Chestnut-sided White-eye *Zosterops mayottensis*	1	100X
Seychelles White-eye *Zosterops modestus*	1	100
Red-headed Fody *Foudia eminentissima*	3	099
Seychelles Fody *Foudia sechellarum*	1	100
Aldabra Drongo *Dicrurus aldabranus*	1	099

SIERRA LEONE

EBAs	Priority
084 Upper Guinea forests	CRITICAL

Secondary Areas none

Restricted-range species	Threatened	Total
Confined to this country	0	0
Present also in other countries	10	14
Total	10	14

Species (threatened species in **bold**)	No. of countries	EBAs (and SAs)
White-breasted Guineafowl *Agelastes meleagrides*	4	084
Rufous Fishing-owl *Scotopelia ussheri*	5	084
Brown-cheeked Hornbill *Ceratogymna cylindricus*	5	084
Western Wattled Cuckoo-shrike *Campephaga lobata*	5	084
Green-tailed Bristlebill *Bleda eximia*	5	084
Yellow-throated Olive Greenbul *Criniger olivaceus*	5	084
Rufous-winged Illadopsis *Illadopsis rufescens*	5	084
White-necked Rockfowl *Picathartes gymnocephalus*	5	084
White-eyed Prinia *Prinia leontica*	4	084
Sharpe's Apalis *Apalis sharpei*	5	084
Black-capped Rufous Warbler *Bathmocercus cerviniventris*	5	084
Nimba Flycatcher *Melaenornis annamarulae*	4	084
Gola Malimbe *Malimbus ballmanni*	3	084
Copper-tailed Glossy-starling *Lamprotornis cupreocauda*	5	084

SOLOMON ISLANDS

EBAs	Priority
198 Solomon group	CRITICAL
199 Rennell and Bellona	HIGH
200 Vanuatu and Temotu	HIGH

Secondary Areas
s126 Ontong Java atoll

Restricted-range species	Threatened	Total
Confined to this country	6	43
Present also in other countries	9	49
Total	15	92

Species (threatened species in **bold**)	No. of countries	EBAs (and SAs)
Sanford's Fish-eagle *Haliaeetus sanfordi*	2	198
Pied Goshawk *Accipiter albogularis*	2	198,200
Imitator Sparrowhawk *Accipiter imitator*	2	198
Melanesian Scrubfowl *Megapodius eremita*	2	198
Woodford's Rail *Nesoclopeus woodfordi*	2	198
Roviana Rail *Gallirallus rovianae*	1	198
Makira Moorhen *Gallinula silvestris*	1	198

cont.

cont.

Solomon Islands (cont.)

Yellow-legged Pigeon *Columba pallidiceps*	2	198
Crested Cuckoo-dove *Reinwardtoena crassirostris*	2	198
Santa Cruz Ground-dove	2	200
Gallicolumba sanctaecrucis		
Thick-billed Ground-dove G. *salamonis*	1	198
[EX] Choiseul Pigeon *Microgoura meeki*	0	198[X]
Red-bellied Fruit-dove *Ptilinopus greyii*	3	200
Silver-capped Fruit-dove *Ptilinopus richardsii*	1	198,199
Yellow-bibbed Fruit-dove *P. solomonensis*	3	198
White-headed Fruit-dove *Ptilinopus eugeniae*	1	198
Red-knobbed Imperial-pigeon *Ducula rubricera*	2	198
Chestnut-bellied Imperial-pigeon D. *brenchleyi*	1	198
Pale Mountain-pigeon *Gymnophaps solomonensis*	2	198
Cardinal Lory *Chalcopsitta cardinalis*	2	198
Yellow-bibbed Lory *Lorius chlorocercus*	1	198,199
Palm Lorikeet *Charmosyna palmarum*	2	200
Meek's Lorikeet *Charmosyna meeki*	2	198
Duchess Lorikeet *Charmosyna margarethae*	2	198
Ducorps's Cockatoo *Cacatua ducorpsii*	2	198
Finsch's Pygmy-parrot *Micropsitta finschii*	2	198,199
Singing Parrot *Geoffroyus heteroclitus*	2	198,199
Buff-headed Coucal *Centropus milo*	1	198
Solomon Islands Hawk-owl *Ninox jacquinoti*	2	198
Fearful Owl *Nesasio solomonensis*	2	198
Mayr's Swiftlet *Collocalia orientalis*	2	198
Ultramarine Kingfisher *Todirhamphus leucopygius*	2	198
Moustached Kingfisher *Actenoides bougainvillei*	2	198
Black-faced Pitta *Pitta anerythra*	2	198
Melanesian Cuckoo-shrike *Coracina caledonica*	4	198,200
Solomon Islands Cuckoo-shrike *C. holopolia*	2	198
Polynesian Triller *Lalage maculosa*	7	200
Long-tailed Triller *Lalage leucopyga*	3	198,200
Makira Thrush *Zoothera margaretae*	1	198
Shade Warbler *Cettia parens*	1	198
Makira Leaf-warbler *Phylloscopus makirensis*	1	198
Sombre Leaf-warbler *Phylloscopus amoenus*	1	198
Guadalcanal Thicketbird *Megalurulus whitneyi*	2	198,200
Fan-tailed Gerygone *Gerygone flavolateralis*	3	199,200
Vanikoro Monarch *Mayrornis schistaceus*	1	200
Black-throated Shrikebill	2	200
Clytorhynchus nigrogularis		
Rennell Shrikebill *Clytorhynchus hamlini*	1	199
Chestnut-bellied Monarch	1	198
Monarcha castaneiventris		
White-capped Monarch *Monarcha richardsii*	1	198
Black-and-white Monarch *Monarcha barbatus*	2	198
Kolombangara Monarch *Monarcha browni*	1	198
White-collared Monarch *Monarcha viduus*	1	198
Steel-blue Flycatcher *Myiagra ferrocyanea*	2	198
Ochre-tailed Flycatcher *Myiagra cervinicauda*	1	198
Melanesian Flycatcher *Myiagra caledonica*	3	199,200
Vanikoro Flycatcher *Myiagra vanikorensis*	2	200
White-winged Fantail *Rhipidura cockerelli*	2	198
Brown Fantail *Rhipidura drownei*	2	198
Dusky Fantail *Rhipidura tenebrosa*	1	198
Rennell Fantail *Rhipidura rennelliana*	1	199
Malaita Fantail *Rhipidura malaitae*	1	198
Hooded Whistler *Pachycephala implicata*	2	198
Midget Flowerpecker *Dicaeum aeneum*	2	198
Mottled Flowerpecker *Dicaeum tristrami*	1	198
Rennell White-eye *Zosterops rennellianus*	1	199
Banded White-eye *Zosterops vellalavella*	1	198
Ranongga White-eye *Zosterops splendidus*	1	198
Ghizo White-eye *Zosterops luteirostris*	1	198
Solomon Islands White-eye *Z. kulambangrae*	1	198
Hermit White-eye *Zosterops murphyi*	1	198
Yellow-throated White-eye *Zosterops metcalfii*	2	198

Solomon Islands (cont.)

Grey-throated White-eye *Zosterops rendovae*	1	198
Malaita White-eye *Zosterops stresemanni*	1	198
Nendo White-eye *Zosterops sanctaecrucis*	1	200
Bare-eyed White-eye *Woodfordia superciliosa*	1	199
Sanford's White-eye *Woodfordia lacertosa*	1	200
Cardinal Myzomela *Myzomela cardinalis*	5	198,199, 200
Scarlet-naped Myzomela *Myzomela lafargei*	2	198
Yellow-vented Myzomela *Myzomela eichhorni*	1	198
Black-headed Myzomela *M. melanocephala*	1	198
Red-bellied Myzomela *Myzomela malaitae*	1	198
Sooty Myzomela *Myzomela tristrami*	1	198
Guadalcanal Honeyeater	1	198
Guadalcanaria inexpectata		
Makira Melidectes *Melidectes sclateri*	1	198
Rusty-winged Starling *Aplonis zelandica*	2	200
Polynesian Starling *Aplonis tabuensis*	7	200
Atoll Starling *Aplonis feadensis*	2	(s126)
Rennell Starling *Aplonis insularis*	1	199
Brown-winged Starling *Aplonis grandis*	2	198
Makira Starling *Aplonis dichroa*	1	198
White-eyed Starling *Aplonis brunneicapilla*	2	198
Bougainville Crow *Corvus meeki*	2	198
White-billed Crow *Corvus woodfordi*	1	198

SOMALIA

EBAs	Priority
111 East African coastal forests	URGENT
112 Central Somali coast	CRITICAL
113 Jubba and Shabeelle valleys	CRITICAL
116 North Somali mountains	CRITICAL

Secondary Areas
s063 Northern Ethiopia
s064 North-west Somalia

Restricted-range species	Threatened	Total
Confined to this country	6	7
Present also in other countries	0	4
Total	6	11

Species (threatened species in **bold**)	No. of countries	EBAs (and SAs)
Somali Pigeon *Columba oliviae*	1	116
White-winged Collared-dove	3	113
Streptopelia reichenowi		
Fischer's Turaco *Tauraco fischeri*	3	111
Ash's Lark *Mirafra ashi*	1	112
Archer's Lark *Heteromirafra archeri*	1	(s064)
Obbia Lark *Spizocorys obbiensis*	1	112
Bulo Burti Bush-shrike *Laniarius liberatus*	1	113
Somali Thrush *Turdus ludoviciae*	1	116
Sombre Chat *Cercomela dubia*	2	(s063)
Warsangli Linnet *Carduelis johannis*	1	116
Salvadori's Weaver *Ploceus dicrocephalus*	3	113

cont.

SOUTH AFRICA

EBAs	Priority
088 Cape fynbos	HIGH
089 South African forests	HIGH
090 Lesotho highlands	HIGH
091 Southern African grasslands	CRITICAL
092 South-east African coast	HIGH

Secondary Areas
s047 Karoo

Restricted-range species	Threatened	Total
Confined to this country	2	13
Present also in other countries	2	12
Total	4	25

Species (threatened species in **bold**)	No. of countries	EBAs (and SAs)
Knysna Turaco *Tauraco corythaix*	1	089
Knysna Woodpecker *Campethera notata*	1	089
Rudd's Lark *Heteromirafra ruddi*	1	091
Red Lark *Certhilauda burra*	2	(s047)
Botha's Lark *Spizocorys fringillaris*	1	091
Yellow-breasted Pipit *Anthus chloris*	2	091
Mountain Pipit *Anthus hoeschi*	2	090
Long-tailed Pipit *Anthus longicaudatus*	1	? (see p. 724)
Rufous Rockjumper *Chaetops frenatus*	1	088
Orange-breasted Rockjumper *C. aurantius*	2	090
Chorister Robin-chat *Cossypha dichroa*	2	089
Brown Scrub-robin *Cercotrichas signata*	2	089
Bush Blackcap *Lioptilus nigricapillus*	1	089
Rudd's Apalis *Apalis ruddi*	4	092
Knysna Scrub-warbler *Bradypterus sylvaticus*	1	089
Victorin's Scrub-warbler *Bradypterus victorini*	1	088
Orange-breasted Sunbird *Nectarinia violacea*	1	088
Neergaard's Sunbird *Nectarinia neergaardi*	2	092
Cape Sugarbird *Promerops cafer*	1	088
Forest Canary *Serinus scotops*	2	089
Lemon-breasted Seedeater *Serinus citrinipectus*	4	092
Protea Canary *Serinus leucopterus*	1	088
Cape Siskin *Serinus totta*	1	088
Drakensberg Siskin *Serinus symonsi*	2	090
Pink-throated Twinspot *Hypargos margaritatus*	3	092

SOUTH GEORGIA (TO UK)

EBAs none

Secondary Areas
s037 South Georgia

Restricted-range species	Threatened	Total
Confined to this country	0	1
Present also in other countries	0	0
Total	0	1

Species (threatened species in **bold**)	No. of countries	EBAs (and SAs)
South Georgia Pipit *Anthus antarcticus*	1	(s037)

SOUTH KOREA

EBAs none

Secondary Areas
s092 Japanese and Korean offshore islands

Restricted-range species	Threatened	Total
Confined to this country	0	0
Present also in other countries	0	1
Total	0	1

Species (threatened species in **bold**)	No. of countries	EBAs (and SAs)
Japanese Wood-pigeon *Columba janthina*	2	(s092)

SPAIN

EBAs	Priority
120 Madeira and the Canary Islands	HIGH

Secondary Areas none

Restricted-range species	Threatened	Total
Confined to this country	2	5
Present also in other countries	0	3
Total	2	8

Species (threatened species in **bold**)	No. of countries	EBAs (and SAs)
[EX] Canary Islands Oystercatcher *Haematopus meadewaldoi*	0	120[X]
Dark-tailed Laurel Pigeon *Columba bollii*	1	120
White-tailed Laurel Pigeon *Columba junoniae*	1	120
Plain Swift *Apus unicolor*	2	120
Berthelot's Pipit *Anthus berthelotii*	2	120
Fuerteventura Chat *Saxicola dacotiae*	1	120
Canary Islands Kinglet *Regulus teneriffae*	1	120
Blue Chaffinch *Fringilla teydea*	1	120
Island Canary *Serinus canaria*	2	120

SRI LANKA

EBAs	Priority
124 Sri Lanka	URGENT

Secondary Areas none

Restricted-range species	Threatened	Total
Confined to this country	6	23
Present also in other countries	0	0
Total	6	23

Species (threatened species in **bold**)	No. of countries	EBAs (and SAs)
Sri Lanka Spurfowl *Galloperdix bicalcarata*	1	124
Sri Lanka Junglefowl *Gallus lafayetii*	1	124
Sri Lanka Wood-pigeon *Columba torringtoni*	1	124
Sri Lanka Hanging-parrot *Loriculus beryllinus*	1	124
Layard's Parakeet *Psittacula calthropae*	1	124
Red-faced Malkoha *Phaenicophaeus pyrrhocephalus*	1	124
Green-billed Coucal *Centropus chlororhynchus*	1	124
Chestnut-backed Owlet *Glaucidium castanonotum*	1	124
Sri Lanka Grey-hornbill *Ocyceros gingalensis*	1	124
Yellow-fronted Barbet *Megalaima flavifrons*	1	124

cont.

Sri Lanka (cont.)

Yellow-eared Bulbul *Pycnonotus penicillatus*	1	124
Sri Lanka Whistling-thrush *Myiophonus blighi*	1	124
Spot-winged Thrush *Zoothera spiloptera*	1	124
Ashy-headed Laughingthrush *Garrulax cinereifrons*	1	124
Brown-capped Babbler *Pellorneum fuscocapillum*	1	124
Orange-billed Babbler *Turdoides rufescens*	1	124
Sri Lanka Bush-warbler *Bradypterus palliseri*	1	124
Dull-blue Flycatcher *Eumyias sordida*	1	124
White-throated Flowerpecker *Dicaeum vincens*	1	124
Sri Lanka White-eye *Zosterops ceylonensis*	1	124
White-faced Starling *Sturnus senex*	1	124
Sri Lanka Myna *Gracula ptilogenys*	1	124
Sri Lanka Magpie *Urocissa ornata*	1	124

ST HELENA (TO UK)

EBAs	Priority
079 Tristan Islands	URGENT
080 Gough Island	URGENT

Secondary Areas
s038 St Helena

Restricted-range species	Threatened	Total
Confined to this country	6	7
Present also in other countries	0	0
Total	6	7

Species (threatened species in **bold**)	No. of countries	EBAs (and SAs)
Inaccessible Rail *Atlantisia rogersi*	1	079
Gough Moorhen *Gallinula comeri*	1	080
EX Tristan Moorhen *Gallinula nesiotis*	0	079X
St Helena Plover *Charadrius sanctaehelenae*	1	(s038)
Tristan Thrush *Nesocichla eremita*	1	079
Gough Bunting *Rowettia goughensis*	1	080
Tristan Bunting *Nesospiza acunhae*	1	079
Grosbeak Bunting *Nesospiza wilkinsi*	1	079

ST KITTS AND NEVIS

EBAs	Priority
030 Lesser Antilles	CRITICAL

Secondary Areas none

Restricted-range species	Threatened	Total
Confined to this country	0	0
Present also in other countries	0	7
Total	0	7

Species (threatened species in **bold**)	No. of countries	EBAs (and SAs)
Purple-throated Carib *Eulampis jugularis*	9	030
Green-throated Carib *Eulampis holosericeus*	15	030
Antillean Crested Hummingbird *Orthorhyncus cristatus*	15	030
Lesser Antillean Flycatcher *Myiarchus oberi*	7	030
Brown Trembler *Cinclocerthia ruficauda*	6	030
Pearly-eyed Thrasher *Margarops fuscatus*	14	030
EL Puerto Rican Bullfinch *Loxigilla portoricensis*	1	030X
Lesser Antillean Bullfinch *Loxigilla noctis*	13	030

ST LUCIA

EBAs	Priority
030 Lesser Antilles	CRITICAL

Secondary Areas none

Restricted-range species	Threatened	Total
Confined to this country	2	4
Present also in other countries	1	16
Total	3	20

Species (threatened species in **bold**)	No. of countries	EBAs (and SAs)
Bridled Quail-dove *Geotrygon mystacea*	10	030
St Lucia Amazon *Amazona versicolor*	1	030
Lesser Antillean Swift *Chaetura martinica*	5	030
Purple-throated Carib *Eulampis jugularis*	9	030
Green-throated Carib *Eulampis holosericeus*	15	030
Antillean Crested Hummingbird *Orthorhyncus cristatus*	15	030
Lesser Antillean Pewee *Contopus latirostris*	5	030
Lesser Antillean Flycatcher *Myiarchus oberi*	7	030
Grey Trembler *Cinclocerthia gutturalis*	2	030
White-breasted Thrasher *Ramphocinclus brachyurus*	2	030
Scaly-breasted Thrasher *Margarops fuscus*	9	030
Pearly-eyed Thrasher *Margarops fuscatus*	14	030
Forest Thrush *Cichlherminia lherminieri*	4	030
Rufous-throated Solitaire *Myadestes genibarbis*	7	030
Lesser Antillean Bullfinch *Loxigilla noctis*	13	030
St Lucia Black Finch *Melanospiza richardsoni*	1	030
Antillean Euphonia *Euphonia musica*	12	030
Adelaide's Warbler *Dendroica adelaidae*	3	030
Semper's Warbler *Leucopeza semperi*	1	030
St Lucia Oriole *Icterus laudabilis*	1	030

ST VINCENT

EBAs	Priority
030 Lesser Antilles	CRITICAL

Secondary Areas none

Restricted-range species	Threatened	Total
Confined to this country	2	2
Present also in other countries	0	10
Total	2	12

Species (threatened species in **bold**)	No. of countries	EBAs (and SAs)
St Vincent Amazon *Amazona guildingii*	1	030
Lesser Antillean Swift *Chaetura martinica*	5	030
Purple-throated Carib *Eulampis jugularis*	9	030
Green-throated Carib *Eulampis holosericeus*	15	030
Antillean Crested Hummingbird *Orthorhyncus cristatus*	15	030
Grenada Flycatcher *Myiarchus nugator*	2	030
Brown Trembler *Cinclocerthia ruficauda*	6	030
Rufous-throated Solitaire *Myadestes genibarbis*	7	030
Lesser Antillean Bullfinch *Loxigilla noctis*	13	030
Antillean Euphonia *Euphonia musica*	12	030
Lesser Antillean Tanager *Tangara cucullata*	2	030
Whistling Warbler *Catharopeza bishopi*	1	030

SUDAN

EBAs none

Secondary Areas
s066 North-east Sudan

Restricted-range species	Threatened	Total
Confined to this country	1	1
Present also in other countries	0	0
Total	1	1

Species (threatened species in **bold**)	No. of countries	EBAs (and SAs)
Red Sea Swallow *Hirundo perdita*	1	(s066)

SWAZILAND

EBAs	Priority
089 South African forests	HIGH
092 South-east African coast	HIGH

Secondary Areas none

Restricted-range species	Threatened	Total
Confined to this country	0	0
Present also in other countries	0	4
Total	0	4

Species (threatened species in **bold**)	No. of countries	EBAs (and SAs)
Chorister Robin-chat *Cossypha dichroa*	2	089
Rudd's Apalis *Apalis ruddi*	4	092
Forest Canary *Serinus scotops*	2	089
Pink-throated Twinspot *Hypargos margaritatus*	3	092

SYRIA

EBAs none

Secondary Areas
s067 Levantine mountains

Restricted-range species	Threatened	Total
Confined to this country	0	0
Present also in other countries	0	1
Total	0	1

Species (threatened species in **bold**)	No. of countries	EBAs (and SAs)
Syrian Serin *Serinus syriacus*	4	(s067)

SÃO TOMÉ E PRÍNCIPE

EBAs	Priority
082 São Tomé	CRITICAL
083 Príncipe	HIGH

Secondary Areas none

Restricted-range species	Threatened	Total
Confined to this country	9	26
Present also in other countries	0	1
Total	9	27

cont.

São Tomé e Príncipe (cont.)

Species (threatened species in **bold**)	No. of countries	EBAs (and SAs)
Dwarf Olive Ibis *Bostrychia bocagei*	1	082
Maroon Pigeon *Columba thomensis*	1	082
São Tomé Bronze-naped Pigeon *C. malherbii*	2	082,083
São Tomé Green-pigeon *Treron sanctithomae*	1	082
São Tomé Scops-owl *Otus hartlaubi*	1	082
São Tomé Spinetail *Zoonavena thomensis*	1	082,083
São Tomé Kingfisher *Alcedo thomensis*	1	082
Príncipe Kingfisher *Alcedo nais*	1	083
São Tomé Fiscal *Lanius newtoni*	1	082
São Tomé Thrush *Turdus olivaceofuscus*	1	082,083
Dohrn's Thrush-babbler *Horizorhinus dohrni*	1	083
São Tomé Prinia *Prinia molleri*	1	082
São Tomé Short-tail *Amaurocichla bocagii*	1	082
São Tomé Paradise-flycatcher *Terpsiphone atrochalybeia*	1	082
Príncipe Sunbird *Nectarinia hartlaubii*	1	083
Newton's Sunbird *Nectarinia newtonii*	1	082
Giant Sunbird *Nectarinia thomensis*	1	082
Black-capped Speirops *Speirops lugubris*	1	082
Príncipe Speirops *Speirops leucophaeus*	1	083
São Tomé White-eye *Zosterops ficedulinus*	1	082,083
Príncipe Seedeater *Serinus rufobrunneus*	1	082,083
São Tomé Grosbeak *Neospiza concolor*	1	082
Príncipe Golden-weaver *Ploceus princeps*	1	083
Giant Weaver *Ploceus grandis*	1	082
São Tomé Weaver *Ploceus sanctithomae*	1	082
Príncipe Glossy-starling *Lamprotornis ornatus*	1	083
São Tomé Oriole *Oriolus crassirostris*	1	082

TAIWAN

EBAs	Priority
149 Taiwan	HIGH

Secondary Areas
s093 Lanyu

Restricted-range species	Threatened	Total
Confined to this country	0	14
Present also in other countries	0	2
Total	0	16

Species (threatened species in **bold**)	No. of countries	EBAs (and SAs)
Taiwan Partridge *Arborophila crudigularis*	1	149
Swinhoe's Pheasant *Lophura swinhoii*	1	149
Mikado Pheasant *Syrmaticus mikado*	1	149
Whistling Green-pigeon *Treron formosae*	3	149(s093)
Elegant Scops-owl *Otus elegans*	3	(s093)
Styan's Bulbul *Pycnonotus taivanus*	1	149
Formosan Whistling-thrush *Myiophonus insularis*	1	149
Collared Bush-robin *Tarsiger johnstoniae*	1	149
White-whiskered Laughingthrush *Garrulax morrisonianus*	1	149
Steere's Liocichla *Liocichla steerii*	1	149
Formosan Barwing *Actinodura morrisoniana*	1	149
White-eared Sibia *Heterophasia auricularis*	1	149
Formosan Yuhina *Yuhina brunneiceps*	1	149
Flamecrest *Regulus goodfellowi*	1	149
Yellow Tit *Parus holsti*	1	149
Formosan Magpie *Urocissa caerulea*	1	149

TANZANIA

EBAs	Priority
105 Tanzania–Malawi mountains	CRITICAL
106 Albertine Rift mountains	URGENT
108 Serengeti plains	HIGH
109 Kenyan mountains	URGENT
110 Pemba	HIGH
111 East African coastal forests	URGENT

Secondary Areas
s055 South-west Tanzanian swamps
s056 Kilombero floodplain
s057 Dry Woodlands west of Lake Victoria

Restricted-range species	Threatened	Total
Confined to this country	11	23
Present also in other countries	11	29
Total	22	52

Species (threatened species in **bold**)	No. of countries	EBAs (and SAs)
Grey-breasted Spurfowl *Francolinus rufopictus*	1	108
Udzungwa Forest-partridge *Xenoperdix udzungwensis*	1	105
Pemba Green-pigeon *Treron pembaensis*	1	110
Fischer's Lovebird *Agapornis fischeri*	1	108
Fischer's Turaco *Tauraco fischeri*	3	105,111
Sokoke Scops-owl *Otus ireneae*	2	105,111
Pemba Scops-owl *Otus pembaensis*	1	110
Usambara Eagle-owl *Bubo vosseleri*	1	105
Red-faced Barbet *Lybius rubrifacies*	3	(s057)
Usambiro Barbet *Trachyphonus usambiro*	2	108
Sokoke Pipit *Anthus sokokensis*	2	111
Green-throated Greenbul *Andropadus chlorigula*	1	105
Sharpe's Greenbul *Phyllastrephus alfredi*	3	105
Uhehe Fiscal *Lanius marwitzi*	1	105
Fuelleborn's Boubou *Laniarius fuelleborni*	3	105
Uluguru Bush-shrike *Malaconotus alius*	1	105
Grey-crested Helmet-shrike *Prionops poliolophus*	2	108
Swynnerton's Robin *Swynnertonia swynnertoni*	3	105
Sharpe's Akalat *Sheppardia sharpei*	3	105
Usambara Akalat *Sheppardia montana*	1	105
Iringa Akalat *Sheppardia lowei*	1	105
Spot-throat *Modulatrix stictigula*	2	105
Dappled Mountain-robin *Modulatrix orostruthus*	2	105
Hunter's Cisticola *Cisticola hunteri*	3	109
Black-lored Cisticola *Cisticola nigriloris*	3	105
Churring Cisticola *Cisticola njombe*	3	105
White-winged Apalis *Apalis chariessa*	4	105,111
Kungwe Apalis *Apalis argentea*	4	106
Chapin's Apalis *Apalis chapini*	3	105
Karamoja Apalis *Apalis karamojae*	2	108
Mrs Moreau's Warbler *Bathmocercus winifredae*	1	105
African Tailorbird *Orthotomus metopias*	2	105
Long-billed Tailorbird *Orthotomus moreaui*	2	105
Amani Sunbird *Anthreptes pallidigaster*	2	105,111
Banded Sunbird *Anthreptes rubritorques*	1	105
Regal Sunbird *Nectarinia regia*	5	106
Loveridge's Sunbird *Nectarinia loveridgei*	1	105
Moreau's Sunbird *Nectarinia moreaui*	1	105
Rufous-winged Sunbird *Nectarinia rufipennis*	1	105
Pemba Sunbird *Nectarinia pembae*	1	110
Pemba White-eye *Zosterops vaughani*	1	110
South Pare White-eye *Zosterops winifredae*	1	109
Yellow-browed Seedeater *Serinus whytii*	3	105
Kipengere Seedeater *Serinus melanochrous*	1	105

cont.

Tanzania (cont.)

Rufous-tailed Weaver *Histurgops ruficauda*	1	108
Kilombero Weaver *Ploceus burnieri*	1	(s056)
Tanzania Masked-weaver *Ploceus reichardi*	2	(s055)
Tanzanian Mountain Weaver *Ploceus nicolli*	1	105
Buff-shouldered Widowbird *Euplectes psammocromius*	3	105
Jackson's Widowbird *Euplectes jacksoni*	2	109
Kenrick's Starling *Poeoptera kenricki*	2	105,109
Abbott's Starling *Cinnyricinclus femoralis*	2	109

THAILAND

EBAs none

Secondary Areas
s080 Myanmar–Thailand mountains
s081 Doi Chiang Dao
s085 Thailand–Cambodia mountains
s086 Peninsular Thailand lowland forests
s102 Malayan peninsula lowlands

Restricted-range species	Threatened	Total
Confined to this country	2	2
Present also in other countries	3	4
Total	5	6

Species (threatened species in **bold**)	No. of countries	EBAs (and SAs)
Chestnut-headed Partridge *Arborophila cambodiana*	2	(s085)
Malayan Peacock-pheasant *Polyplectron malacense*	2	(s102)
Gurney's Pitta *Pitta gurneyi*	2	(s086)
White-eyed River-martin *Pseudochelidon sirintarae*	1	? (see p. 724)
Deignan's Babbler *Stachyris rodolphei*	1	(s081)
Burmese Yuhina *Yuhina humilis*	2	(s080)

TONGA

EBAs none

Secondary Areas
s129 Niuafo'ou
s130 Tonga

Restricted-range species	Threatened	Total
Confined to this country	1	2
Present also in other countries	0	8
Total	1	10

Species (threatened species in **bold**)	No. of countries	EBAs (and SAs)
Niuafo'ou Scrubfowl *Megapodius pritchardii*	1	(s129)
Shy Ground-dove *Gallicolumba stairi*	5	(s130)
Many-coloured Fruit-dove *Ptilinopus perousii*	4	(s130)
Purple-capped Fruit-dove *P. porphyraceus*	7	(s129, s130)
Blue-crowned Lorikeet *Vini australis*	6	(s129, s130)
Polynesian Triller *Lalage maculosa*	7	(s130)
Fiji Shrikebill *Clytorhynchus vitiensis*	4	(s130)
Tongan Whistler *Pachycephala jacquinoti*	1	(s130)
Wattled Honeyeater *Foulehaio carunculata*	5	(s130)
Polynesian Starling *Aplonis tabuensis*	7	(s129, s130)

TRINIDAD AND TOBAGO

EBAs none

Secondary Areas
s016 Trinidad
s017 Tobago

Restricted-range species	Threatened	Total
Confined to this country	1	1
Present also in other countries	1	1
Total	2	2

Species (threatened species in **bold**)	No. of countries	EBAs (and SAs)
Trinidad Piping-guan *Pipile pipile*	1	(s016)
White-tailed Sabrewing *Campylopterus ensipennis*	2	(s017)

TURKEY

EBAs	Priority
122 Caucasus	HIGH

Secondary Areas none

Restricted-range species	Threatened	Total
Confined to this country	0	0
Present also in other countries	0	2
Total	0	2

Species (threatened species in **bold**)	No. of countries	EBAs (and SAs)
Caucasian Grouse *Tetrao mlokosiewiczi*	6	122
Caucasian Chiffchaff *Phylloscopus lorenzii*	6	122

TURKS AND CAICOS ISLANDS (TO UK)

EBAs	Priority
026 Bahamas	HIGH

Secondary Areas none

Restricted-range species	Threatened	Total
Confined to this country	0	0
Present also in other countries	0	2
Total	0	2

Species (threatened species in **bold**)	No. of countries	EBAs (and SAs)
Bahama Woodstar *Calliphlox evelynae*	2	026
Bahama Mockingbird *Mimus gundlachii*	4	026

UGANDA

EBAs	Priority
106 Albertine Rift mountains	URGENT
107 Eastern Zaïre lowlands	HIGH
109 Kenyan mountains	URGENT

Secondary Areas
s057 Dry Woodlands west of Lake Victoria
s059 North Ugandan swamps
s060 North-east Uganda

Uganda (cont.)

Restricted-range species	Threatened	Total
Confined to this country	0	1
Present also in other countries	5	30
Total	5	31

Species (threatened species in **bold**)	No. of countries	EBAs (and SAs)
Handsome Francolin *Francolinus nobilis*	4	106
Jackson's Francolin *Francolinus jacksoni*	2	109
Ruwenzori Turaco *Musophaga johnstoni*	4	106
Ruwenzori Nightjar *Caprimulgus ruwenzorii*	4	106
Red-faced Barbet *Lybius rubrifacies*	3	(s057)
Dwarf Honeyguide *Indicator pumilio*	3	106
African Green Broadbill *Pseudocalyptomena graueri*	2	106
Sassi's Greenbul *Phyllastrephus lorenzi*	2	107
Kivu Ground-thrush *Zoothera tanganjicae*	4	106
Forest Ground-thrush *Zoothera oberlaenderi*	2	107
Red-throated Alethe *Alethe poliophrys*	4	106
Archer's Robin-chat *Cossypha archeri*	4	106
Hunter's Cisticola *Cisticola hunteri*	3	109
Collared Apalis *Apalis ruwenzorii*	4	106
Black-faced Apalis *Apalis personata*	4	106
Karamoja Apalis *Apalis karamojae*	2	(s060)
Grauer's Swamp-warbler *Bradypterus graueri*	4	106
Grauer's Warbler *Graueria vittata*	4	106
Neumann's Warbler *Hemitesia neumanni*	4	106
Red-faced Woodland-warbler *Phylloscopus laetus*	4	106
Yellow-eyed Black-flycatcher *Melaenornis ardesiacus*	4	106
Chapin's Flycatcher *Muscicapa lendu*	3	106
Ruwenzori Batis *Batis diops*	4	106
Stripe-breasted Tit *Parus fasciiventer*	4	106
Blue-headed Sunbird *Nectarinia alinae*	4	106
Regal Sunbird *Nectarinia regia*	5	106
Purple-breasted Sunbird *N. purpureiventris*	4	106
Dusky Crimson-wing *Cryptospiza jacksoni*	4	106
Shelley's Crimson-wing *Cryptospiza shelleyi*	4	106
Strange Weaver *Ploceus alienus*	4	106
Fox's Weaver *Ploceus spekeoides*	1	(s059)

UNITED KINGDOM

See also Anguilla (p. 726), Cayman Islands (p. 732), Falkland Islands (p. 740), Montserrat (p. 755), Pitcairn Islands (p. 765), South Georgia (p. 769), St Helena (p. 770), Turks and Caicos Islands (p. 773), Virgin Islands (p. 776).

EBAs none

Secondary Areas
s070 Caledonian pine forests

Restricted-range species	Threatened	Total
Confined to this country	0	1
Present also in other countries	0	0
Total	0	1

Species (threatened species in **bold**)	No. of countries	EBAs (and SAs)
Scottish Crossbill *Loxia scotica*	1	(s070)

cont.

UNITED STATES OF AMERICA

See also American Samoa (p. 725), Guam (p. 742), Northern Mariana Islands (p. 759), Puerto Rico (p. 766), United States Minor Outlying Islands (p. 774), Virgin Islands (p. 776).

EBAs	Priority
001 California	HIGH
010 Northern Sierra Madre Oriental	HIGH
216 Laysan Island	CRITICAL
217 Central Hawaiian Islands	CRITICAL
218 Hawai'i	CRITICAL

Secondary Areas
s001 Eastern Bering Sea Islands
s002 Seaward peninsula and Yukon delta
s003 Michigan jack pine savanna
s004 Edwards Plateau
s138 Nihoa

Restricted-range species	Threatened	Total
Confined to this country	30	39
Present also in other countries	0	6
Total	30	45

Species (threatened species in **bold**)	No. of countries	EBAs (and SAs)
Nene Branta sandvicensis	1	218
Hawaiian Duck Anas wyvilliana	1	217,218
Laysan Duck Anas laysanensis	1	216
Hawaiian Hawk Buteo solitarius	1	218
EX Laysan Crake Porzana palmeri	0	216^X
EX Hawaiian Crake Porzana sandwichensis	0	218^X
Hawaiian Coot Fulica alai	1	217,218
Bristle-thighed Curlew Numenius tahitiensis	1	(s002)
Allen's Hummingbird Selasphorus sasin	2	001
Nuttall's Woodpecker Picoides nuttallii	2	001
California Thrasher Toxostoma redivivum	2	001
Kama'o Myadestes myadestinus	1	217
EX 'Amaui Myadestes oahensis	0	217^X
Oloma'o Myadestes lanaiensis	1	217
'Oma'o Myadestes obscurus	1	218
Puaiohi Myadestes palmeri	1	217
Millerbird Acrocephalus familiaris	1	216^X (s138)
'Elepaio Chasiempis sandwichensis	1	217,218
Kaua'i O'o Moho braccatus	1	217
EX O'ahu O'o Moho apicalis	0	217^X
Bishop's O'o Moho bishopi	1	217
EX Hawai'i O'o Moho nobilis	0	218^X
EX Kioea Chaetoptila angustipluma	0	218^X
McKay's Bunting Plectrophenax hyperboreus	1	(s001)
Colima Warbler Vermivora crissalis	2	010
Golden-cheeked Warbler Dendroica chrysoparia	1	(s004)
Kirtland's Warbler Dendroica kirtlandii	1	(s003)
Nihoa Finch Telespiza ultima	1	(s138)
Laysan Finch Telespiza cantans	1	216
'O'u Psittirostra psittacea	1	217,218
EX Lana'i Hookbill Dysmorodrepanis munroi	0	217^X
Palila Loxioides bailleui	1	218
EX Lesser Koa-finch Rhodacanthis flaviceps	0	218^X
EX Greater Koa-finch Rhodacanthis palmeri	0	218^X
EX Grosbeak Finch Chloridops kona	0	218^X
Maui Parrotbill Pseudonestor xanthophrys	1	217
Kaua'i 'Amakihi Viridonia stejnegeri	1	217
Common 'Amakihi Viridonia virens	1	217,218
'Anianiau Viridonia parva	1	217
EX Greater 'Amakihi Viridonia sagittirostris	0	218^X
EX 'Akialoa Hemignathus obscurus	0	217^X,218^X

cont.

United States of America (cont.)

Nukupu'u Hemignathus lucidus	1	217,218^X
'Akiapola'au Hemignathus wilsoni	1	218
'Akikiki Oreomystis bairdi	1	217
Hawai'i Creeper Oreomystis mana	1	218
Maui 'Alauahio Paroreomyza montana	1	217
EX Kakawahie Paroreomyza flammea	0	217^X
O'ahu 'Alauahio Paroreomyza maculata	1	217
'Akeke'e Loxops caeruleirostris	1	217
'Akepa Loxops coccineus	1	217,218
EX 'Ula-'ai-hawane Ciridops anna	0	218^X
'I'iwi Vestiaria coccinea	1	217,218
EX Hawai'i Mamo Drepanis pacifica	0	218^X
EX Black Mamo Drepanis funerea	0	217^X
'Akohekohe Palmeria dolei	1	217
'Apapane Himatione sanguinea	1	216^X, 217,218
Po'o-uli Melamprosops phaeosoma	1	217
Tricoloured Blackbird Agelaius tricolor	2	001
Lawrence's Goldfinch Carduelis lawrencei	2	001
Yellow-billed Magpie Pica nuttalli	1	001
Hawaiian Crow Corvus hawaiiensis	1	218

UNITED STATES MINOR OUTLYING ISLANDS (TO USA)

EBAs none

Secondary Areas
s122 Wake Island

Restricted-range species	Threatened	Total
Confined to this country	0	0
Present also in other countries	0	0
Total	0	0

Species (threatened species in **bold**)	No. of countries	EBAs (and SAs)
EX Wake Island Rail Gallirallus wakensis	0	(s122^X)

URUGUAY

EBAs	Priority
077 Argentine Mesopotamian grasslands	CRITICAL

Secondary Areas
s035 Coastal Uruguay marshes

Restricted-range species	Threatened	Total
Confined to this country	0	0
Present also in other countries	1	3
Total	1	3

Species (threatened species in **bold**)	No. of countries	EBAs (and SAs)
Straight-billed Reedhaunter Limnornis rectirostris	3	(s035)
Marsh Seedeater Sporophila palustris	3	077
Chestnut Seedeater Sporophila cinnamomea	3	077

VANUATU

EBAs	Priority
200 Vanuatu and Temotu	HIGH

Secondary Areas none

Restricted-range species	Threatened	Total
Confined to this country	5	9
Present also in other countries	1	14
Total	6	23

Species (threatened species in **bold**)	No. of countries	EBAs (and SAs)
Vanuatu Scrubfowl *Megapodius layardi*	1	200
Santa Cruz Ground-dove	2	200
Gallicolumba sanctaecrucis		
Tanna Fruit-dove *Ptilinopus tannensis*	1	200
Red-bellied Fruit-dove *Ptilinopus greyii*	3	200
Vanuatu Imperial-pigeon *Ducula bakeri*	1	200
Palm Lorikeet *Charmosyna palmarum*	2	200
Chestnut-bellied Kingfisher	1	200
Todirhamphus farquhari		
Melanesian Cuckoo-shrike *Coracina caledonica*	4	200
Polynesian Triller *Lalage maculosa*	7	200
Long-tailed Triller *Lalage leucopyga*	3	200
Guadalcanal Thicketbird *Megalurulus whitneyi*	2	200
Fan-tailed Gerygone *Gerygone flavolateralis*	3	200
Buff-bellied Monarch *Neolalage banksiana*	1	200
Southern Shrikebill	2	200
Clytorhynchus pachycephaloides		
Melanesian Flycatcher *Myiagra caledonica*	3	200
Streaked Fantail *Rhipidura spilodera*	3	200
Yellow-fronted White-eye *Zosterops flavifrons*	1	200
Cardinal Myzomela *Myzomela cardinalis*	5	200
Dark-brown Honeyeater *Lichmera incana*	2	200
New Hebrides Honeyeater *Phylidonyris notabilis*	1	200
Royal Parrotfinch *Erythrura regia*	1	200
Rusty-winged Starling *Aplonis zelandica*	2	200
Santo Mountain Starling *Aplonis santovestris*	1	200

VENEZUELA

EBAs	Priority
032 Caripe–Paria region	CRITICAL
033 Cordillera de la Costa Central	HIGH
034 Cordillera de Mérida	URGENT
035 Caribbean Colombia and Venezuela	URGENT
038 Colombian East Andes	CRITICAL
064 Tepuis	URGENT
065 Orinoco–Negro white-sand forests	HIGH

Secondary Areas none

Restricted-range species	Threatened	Total
Confined to this country	13	39
Present also in other countries	6	71
Total	19	110

Species (threatened species in **bold**)	No. of countries	EBAs (and SAs)
Tepui Tinamou *Crypturellus ptaritepui*	1	064
Grey-legged Tinamou *Crypturellus duidae*	3	065
Barred Tinamou *Crypturellus casiquiare*	3	065
Northern Helmeted Curassow *Pauxi pauxi*	2	033,034, 038
Black-fronted Wood-quail *Odontophorus atrifrons*	2	038

Venezuela (cont.)

Venezuelan Wood-quail *O. columbianus*	1	033,038
Rusty-flanked Crake *Laterallus levraudi*	1	033
Plain-flanked Rail *Rallus wetmorei*	1	035
Fiery-shouldered Parakeet *Pyrrhura egregia*	3	064
Red-eared Parakeet *Pyrrhura hoematotis*	1	033,034
Rose-headed Parakeet *Pyrrhura rhodocephala*	1	034
Tepui Parrotlet *Nannopsittaca panychlora*	3	032,064
Rusty-faced Parrot *Hapalopsittaca amazonina*	3	034,038
Yellow-shouldered Amazon	2	035
Amazona barbadensis		
Roraiman Nightjar *Caprimulgus whitelyi*	1	064
Tepui Swift *Cypseloides phelpsi*	3	033,064
Pygmy Swift *Tachornis furcata*	2	035
Rufous-breasted Sabrewing	2	064
Campylopterus hyperythrus		
Buff-breasted Sabrewing *Campylopterus duidae*	2	064
White-tailed Sabrewing *C. ensipennis*	2	032
Peacock Coquette *Lophornis pavoninus*	3	064
Coppery Emerald *Chlorostilbon russatus*	2	038
Narrow-tailed Emerald *Chlorostilbon stenura*	2	034,038
Green-tailed Emerald *Chlorostilbon alice*	1	032,033, 034
Short-tailed Emerald *Chlorostilbon poortmani*	2	034,038
Tepui Goldenthroat *Polytmus milleri*	1	064
Buffy Hummingbird *Leucippus fallax*	2	035
Táchira Emerald *Amazilia distans*	1	034
Velvet-browed Brilliant *Heliodoxa xanthogonys*	3	064
Scissor-tailed Hummingbird	1	032
Hylonympha macrocerca		
Violet-chested Hummingbird	1	033,034
Sternoclyta cyanopectus		
Golden-bellied Starfrontlet *Coeligena bonapartei*	2	034,038
Blue-throated Starfrontlet *Coeligena helianthea*	2	038
Orange-throated Sunangel *Heliangelus mavors*	2	034,038
Mérida Sunangel *Heliangelus spencei*	1	034
Coppery-bellied Puffleg *Eriocnemis cupreoventris*	2	034,038
Perijá Metaltail *Metallura iracunda*	2	038
Bronze-tailed Thornbill *Chalcostigma heteropogon*	2	038
Bearded Helmetcrest *Oxypogon guerinii*	2	034,038
White-tipped Quetzal *Pharomachrus fulgidus*	2	032,033
Orinoco Piculet *Picumnus pumilus*	3	065
Chestnut Piculet *Picumnus cinnamomeus*	2	035
Perijá Thistletail *Schizoeaca perijana*	2	038
Ochre-browed Thistletail *Schizoeaca coryi*	1	034
Black-throated Spinetail *Synallaxis castanea*	1	033
White-whiskered Spinetail *Synallaxis candei*	2	035
Tepui Spinetail *Cranioleuca demissa*	3	064
Orinoco Softtail *Thripophaga cherriei*	1	065
Roraiman Barbtail *Roraimia adusta*	3	064
White-throated Barbtail *Premnoplex tatei*	1	032
Guttulated Foliage-gleaner *Syndactyla guttulata*	1	032,033
White-throated Foliage-gleaner	2	064
Automolus roraimae		
Black-backed Antshrike *Sakesphorus melanonotus*	2	035
Streak-backed Antshrike *Thamnophilus insignis*	2	064
Recurve-billed Bushbird *Clytoctantes alixii*	2	038
Yellow-throated Antwren *Myrmotherula ambigua*	3	065
Spot-backed Antwren	3	065
Herpsilochmus dorsimaculatus		
Roraiman Antwren *Herpsilochmus roraimae*	3	064
Caura Antbird *Percnostola caurensis*	2	064
Yapacana Antbird *Myrmeciza disjuncta*	2	065
Grey-bellied Antbird *Myrmeciza pelzelni*	3	065
Schwartz's Antthrush *Chamaeza turdina*	2	033
Great Antpitta *Grallaria excelsa*	1	033,034, 038
Táchira Antpitta *Grallaria chthonia*	1	038

cont.

cont.

Venezuela (cont.)

Species	No.	EBAs
Grey-naped Antpitta *Grallaria griseonucha*	1	034
Brown-breasted Antpitta *Myrmothera simplex*	2	064
Scallop-breasted Antpitta *Grallaricula loricata*	1	033
Hooded Antpitta *Grallaricula cucullata*	2	038
Handsome Fruiteater *Pipreola formosa*	1	032,033
Red-banded Fruiteater *Pipreola whitelyi*	2	064
Rose-collared Piha *Lipaugus streptophorus*	3	064
Scarlet-horned Manakin *Pipra cornuta*	3	064
Orange-bellied Manakin *Lepidothrix suavissima*	3	064
Olive Manakin *Chloropipo uniformis*	3	064
Ruddy Tody-flycatcher *Todirostrum russatum*	2	064
Maracaibo Tody-flycatcher *T. viridanum*	1	035
Great Elaenia *Elaenia dayi*	1	064
Slender-billed Tyrannulet *Inezia tenuirostris*	2	035
Venezuelan Bristle-tyrant *Phylloscartes venezuelanus*	1	033
Black-fronted Tyrannulet *P. nigrifrons*	1	064
Chapman's Tyrannulet *Phylloscartes chapmani*	2	064
Mérida Wren *Cistothorus meridae*	1	034
Tepui Wren *Troglodytes rufulus*	2	064
Flutist Wren *Microcerculus ustulatus*	3	064
Tocuyo Sparrow *Arremonops tocuyensis*	2	035
Moustached Brush-finch *Atlapetes albofrenatus*	2	034,038
Tepui Brush-finch *Atlapetes personatus*	2	064
Duida Grass-finch *Emberizoides duidae*	1	064
White-naped Seedeater *Dolospingus fringilloides*	3	065
Vermilion Cardinal *Cardinalis phoeniceus*	2	035
Grey-capped Hemispingus *Hemispingus reyi*	1	034
Slaty-backed Hemispingus *H. goeringi*	1	034
Fulvous-headed Tanager *Thlypopsis fulviceps*	2	032,033, 034,038
Olive-backed Tanager *Mitrospingus oleagineus*	3	064
Rufous-cheeked Tanager *Tangara rufigenis*	1	033
Venezuelan Flowerpiercer *Diglossa venezuelensis*	1	032
Mérida Flower-piercer *Diglossa gloriosa*	1	034
Scaled Flower-piercer *Diglossa duidae*	2	064
Greater Flower-piercer *Diglossa major*	2	064
Tepui Whitestart *Myioborus castaneocapillus*	3	064
Paria Whitestart *Myioborus pariae*	1	032
White-faced Whitestart *Myioborus albifacies*	1	064
Guaiquinima Whitestart *Myioborus cardonai*	1	064
White-fronted Whitestart *Myioborus albifrons*	1	034
Grey-headed Warbler *Basileuterus griseiceps*	1	032
Grey-throated Warbler *Basileuterus cinereicollis*	2	034,038
Rufous-browed Conebill *Conirostrum rufum*	2	038
Tepui Greenlet *Hylophilus sclateri*	3	064
Golden-tufted Grackle *Macroagelaius imthurni*	3	064
Azure-naped Jay *Cyanocorax heilprini*	3	065

VIETNAM

EBAs	Priority
143 Annamese lowlands	CRITICAL
144 South Vietnamese lowlands	CRITICAL
145 Da Lat plateau	URGENT

Secondary Areas
s082 Fan-Si-Pan and northern Laos
s084 Kontum plateau

Restricted-range species	Threatened	Total
Confined to this country	9	10
Present also in other countries	5	9
Total	14	19

cont.

Vietnam (cont.)

Species (threatened species in **bold**)	No. of countries	EBAs (and SAs)
Orange-necked Partridge *Arborophila davidi*	1	144
Annam Partridge *Arborophila merlini*	1	143
Imperial Pheasant *Lophura imperialis*	1	143
Edwards's Pheasant *Lophura edwardsi*	1	143
Vietnamese Pheasant *Lophura hatinhensis*	1	143
Germain's Peacock-pheasant *Polyplectron germaini*	1	144
Crested Argus *Rheinardia ocellata*	3	143,145 (s084)
Ward's Trogon *Harpactes wardi*	5	(s082)
Black-hooded Laughingthrush *Garrulax milleti*	1	145
White-cheeked Laughingthrush *G. vassali*	2	143,145 (s084)
Collared Laughingthrush *Garrulax yersini*	1	145
Red-winged Laughingthrush *Garrulax formosus*	2	(s082)
Short-tailed Scimitar-babbler *Jabouilleia danjoui*	2	143,145
Sooty Babbler *Stachyris herberti*	2	143
Grey-faced Tit-babbler *Macronous kelleyi*	2	143,144 (s084)
Grey-crowned Crocias *Crocias langbianis*	1	145
Broad-billed Warbler *Tickellia hodgsoni*	6	(s082)
Yellow-billed Nuthatch *Sitta solangiae*	2	145(s082)
Vietnam Greenfinch *Carduelis monguilloti*	1	145

VIRGIN ISLANDS (TO UK)

EBAs	Priority
029 Puerto Rico and the Virgin Islands	URGENT

Secondary Areas none

Restricted-range species	Threatened	Total
Confined to this country	0	0
Present also in other countries	0	6
Total	0	6

Species (threatened species in **bold**)	No. of countries	EBAs (and SAs)
Bridled Quail-dove *Geotrygon mystacea*	10	029
Puerto Rican Screech-owl *Otus nudipes*	3	029
Green-throated Carib *Eulampis holosericeus*	15	029
Antillean Crested Hummingbird *Orthorhyncus cristatus*	15	029
Puerto Rican Flycatcher *Myiarchus antillarum*	3	029
Pearly-eyed Thrasher *Margarops fuscatus*	14	029

VIRGIN ISLANDS (TO USA)

EBAs	Priority
029 Puerto Rico and the Virgin Islands	URGENT

Secondary Areas none

Restricted-range species	Threatened	Total
Confined to this country	0	0
Present also in other countries	0	9
Total	0	9

cont.

Virgin Islands (cont.)

Species (threatened species in **bold**)	No. of countries	EBAs (and SAs)
Bridled Quail-dove *Geotrygon mystacea*	10	029
Puerto Rican Screech-owl *Otus nudipes*	3	029
Antillean Mango *Anthracothorax dominicus*	4	029
Green-throated Carib *Eulampis holosericeus*	15	029
Antillean Crested Hummingbird *Orthorhyncus cristatus*	15	029
Puerto Rican Woodpecker *Melanerpes portoricensis*	2	029
Puerto Rican Flycatcher *Myiarchus antillarum*	3	029
Pearly-eyed Thrasher *Margarops fuscatus*	14	029
Lesser Antillean Bullfinch *Loxigilla noctis*	13	029

WALLIS AND FUTUNA ISLANDS (TO FRANCE)

EBAs none

Secondary Areas
s128 Wallis and Futuna

Restricted-range species	Threatened	Total
Confined to this country	0	0
Present also in other countries	0	7
Total	0	7

Species (threatened species in **bold**)	No. of countries	EBAs (and SAs)
Shy Ground-dove *Gallicolumba stairi*	5	(s128)
Purple-capped Fruit-dove *Ptilinopus porphyraceus*	7	(s128)
Blue-crowned Lorikeet *Vini australis*	6	(s128)
Polynesian Triller *Lalage maculosa*	7	(s128)
Fiji Shrikebill *Clytorhynchus vitiensis*	4	(s128)
Wattled Honeyeater *Foulehaio carunculata*	5	(s128)
Polynesian Starling *Aplonis tabuensis*	7	(s128)

WESTERN SAMOA

EBAs		Priority
203 Samoan Islands		URGENT

Secondary Areas none

Restricted-range species	Threatened	Total
Confined to this country	5	10
Present also in other countries	0	9
Total	5	19

Species (threatened species in **bold**)	No. of countries	EBAs (and SAs)
Samoan Moorhen *Gallinula pacifica*	1	203
Shy Ground-dove *Gallicolumba stairi*	5	203
Many-coloured Fruit-dove *Ptilinopus perousii*	4	203
Purple-capped Fruit-dove *P. porphyraceus*	7	203
Tooth-billed Pigeon *Didunculus strigirostris*	1	203
Blue-crowned Lorikeet *Vini australis*	6	203
Flat-billed Kingfisher *Todirhamphus recurvirostris*	1	203
Polynesian Triller *Lalage maculosa*	7	203
Samoan Triller *Lalage sharpei*	1	203
Samoan Flycatcher *Myiagra albiventris*	1	203
Samoan Fantail *Rhipidura nebulosa*	1	203
Samoan Whistler *Pachycephala flavifrons*	1	203

Western Samoa (cont.)

Species (threatened species in **bold**)	No. of countries	EBAs (and SAs)
Samoan White-eye *Zosterops samoensis*	1	203
Cardinal Myzomela *Myzomela cardinalis*	5	203
Wattled Honeyeater *Foulehaio carunculata*	5	203
Mao *Gymnomyza samoensis*	1	203
Red-headed Parrotfinch *Erythrura cyaneovirens*	1	203
Samoan Starling *Aplonis atrifusca*	2	203
Polynesian Starling *Aplonis tabuensis*	7	203

YEMEN

EBAs	Priority
117 Socotra	HIGH
118 South-west Arabian mountains	HIGH

Secondary Areas none

Restricted-range species	Threatened	Total
Confined to this country	3	6
Present also in other countries	2	7
Total	5	13

Species (threatened species in **bold**)	No. of countries	EBAs (and SAs)
Philby's Partridge *Alectoris philbyi*	2	118
Yemen Accentor *Prunella fagani*	2	118
Yemen Thrush *Turdus menachensis*	2	118
Socotra Cisticola *Cisticola incanus*	1	117
Island Cisticola *Cisticola haesitatus*	1	117
Yemen Warbler *Sylvia buryi*	2	118
Socotra Sunbird *Nectarinia balfouri*	1	117
Socotra Bunting *Emberiza socotrana*	1	117
Yemen Serin *Serinus menachensis*	2	118
Yemen Linnet *Carduelis yemenensis*	2	118
Arabian Waxbill *Estrilda rufibarba*	2	118
Socotra Sparrow *Passer insularis*	1	117
Socotra Starling *Onychognathus frater*	1	117

ZAÏRE

For practical reasons, the name Zaïre (rather than 'Democratic Republic of Congo') has been retained here (see p. 95).

EBAs	Priority
106 Albertine Rift mountains	URGENT
107 Eastern Zaïre lowlands	HIGH

Secondary Areas
s043 Gabon–Cabinda coast
s044 West Zaïre and north Angola forests
s053 Lake Lufira
s054 Upemba plains

Restricted-range species	Threatened	Total
Confined to this country	10	16
Present also in other countries	8	31
Total	18	47

Species (threatened species in **bold**)	No. of countries	EBAs (and SAs)
Handsome Francolin *Francolinus nobilis*	4	106
Ruwenzori Turaco *Musophaga johnstoni*	4	106
Congo Bay-owl *Phodilus prigoginei*	1	106
Albertine Owlet *Glaucidium albertinum*	2	106
Itombwe Nightjar *Caprimulgus prigoginei*	1	106
Ruwenzori Nightjar *Caprimulgus ruwenzorii*	4	106

cont.

Zaïre (cont.)

Schouteden's Swift *Schoutedenapus schoutedeni*	1	107
Dwarf Honeyguide *Indicator pumilio*	3	106
African Green Broadbill	2	106
Pseudocalyptomena graueri		
Grauer's Cuckoo-shrike *Coracina graueri*	1	106
Prigogine's Greenbul *Chlorocichla prigoginei*	1	106
Sassi's Greenbul *Phyllastrephus lorenzi*	2	107
Yellow-crested Helmet-shrike *Prionops alberti*	1	106
Kivu Ground-thrush *Zoothera tanganjicae*	4	106
Forest Ground-thrush *Zoothera oberlaenderi*	2	107
Red-throated Alethe *Alethe poliophrys*	4	106
Archer's Robin-chat *Cossypha archeri*	4	106
White-headed Robin-chat *Cossypha heinrichi*	2	(s044)
Red-collared Mountain-babbler	3	106
Kupeornis rufocinctus		
Chapin's Mountain-babbler *Kupeornis chapini*	1	106
Collared Apalis *Apalis ruwenzorii*	4	106
Black-faced Apalis *Apalis personata*	4	106
Kungwe Apalis *Apalis argentea*	4	106
Kabobo Apalis *Apalis kaboboensis*	1	106
Grauer's Swamp-warbler *Bradypterus graueri*	4	106
Grauer's Warbler *Graueria vittata*	4	106
Chapin's Crombec *Sylvietta chapini*	1	106
Neumann's Warbler *Hemitesia neumanni*	4	106
Red-faced Woodland-warbler *Phylloscopus laetus*	4	106
Yellow-eyed Black-flycatcher	4	106
Melaenornis ardesiacus		
Chapin's Flycatcher *Muscicapa lendu*	3	106
Ruwenzori Batis *Batis diops*	4	106
Bedford's Paradise-flycatcher	1	107
Terpsiphone bedfordi		
Stripe-breasted Tit *Parus fasciiventer*	4	106
Blue-headed Sunbird *Nectarinia alinae*	4	106
Stuhlmann's Double-collared Sunbird	1	106
Nectarinia stuhlmanni		
Regal Sunbird *Nectarinia regia*	5	106
Rockefeller's Sunbird *Nectarinia rockefelleri*	1	106
Purple-breasted Sunbird *N. purpureiventris*	4	106
Dusky Crimson-wing *Cryptospiza jacksoni*	4	106
Shelley's Crimson-wing *Cryptospiza shelleyi*	4	106
Black-lored Waxbill *Estrilda nigriloris*	1	(s054)
Loango Weaver *Ploceus subpersonatus*	3	(s043)
Strange Weaver *Ploceus alienus*	4	106
Lake Lufira Weaver *Ploceus ruweti*	1	(s053)
Golden-naped Weaver *Ploceus aureonucha*	1	107
Yellow-legged Weaver *Ploceus flavipes*	1	107

ZAMBIA

EBAs	Priority
105 Tanzania–Malawi mountains	CRITICAL

Secondary Areas
s051 Southern Zambia
s052 North-west Zambia
s055 South-west Tanzanian swamps

Restricted-range species	Threatened	Total
Confined to this country	2	2
Present also in other countries	0	9
Total	2	11

Species (threatened species in **bold**)	No. of countries	EBAs (and SAs)
Black-cheeked Lovebird *Agapornis nigrigenis*	1	(s051)
White-chested Tinkerbird *Pogoniulus makawai*	1	(s052)
Sharpe's Greenbul *Phyllastrephus alfredi*	3	105
Fuelleborn's Boubou *Laniarius fuelleborni*	3	105
Sharpe's Akalat *Sheppardia sharpei*	3	105
Black-lored Cisticola *Cisticola nigriloris*	3	105
Churring Cisticola *Cisticola njombe*	3	105
Chapin's Apalis *Apalis chapini*	3	105
Yellow-browed Seedeater *Serinus whytii*	3	105
Tanzania Masked-weaver *Ploceus reichardi*	2	(s055)
Buff-shouldered Widowbird	3	105
Euplectes psammocromius		

ZIMBABWE

EBAs	Priority
104 Eastern Zimbabwe mountains	HIGH
092 South-east African coast	HIGH

Secondary Areas none

Restricted-range species	Threatened	Total
Confined to this country	0	0
Present also in other countries	1	4
Total	1	4

Species (threatened species in **bold**)	No. of countries	EBAs (and SAs)
Swynnerton's Robin *Swynnertonia swynnertoni*	3	104
Briar Warbler *Prinia robertsi*	2	104
Chirinda Apalis *Apalis chirindensis*	2	104
Lemon-breasted Seedeater *Serinus citrinipectus*	4	092

Unique EBA codes of the previous analysis

UNIQUE codes were assigned to EBAs during the course of the project, 1988–1997, and first appeared in print in *Putting biodiversity on the map* (ICBP 1992). However, because of changes to the analysis—including the splitting and combining of some EBAs, and the dropping and adding of others—that coding no longer reflects geography. For this book new EBA numbers have therefore been assigned in a geographical sequence. The following list shows the relationship between the unique codes and these new numbers so that comparisons can be made with ICBP (1992) and with material published subsequent to it (some unique codes were assigned after the publication of ICBP 1992: such changes are marked * and are explained fully in Appendix 4, p. 781).

Unique code	New EBA number	New EBA name
A01	001	California
A02	003	Guadalupe Island
A03	002	Baja California
A04	006	Sierra Madre Occidental and trans-Mexican range
A05	005	North-west Mexican Pacific slope
A06	010	Northern Sierra Madre Oriental
A07	011	North-east Mexican Gulf slope
A08	007	Central Mexican marshes
A09*	015	Yucatán peninsula coastal scrub
	016	Cozumel Island
A10	004	Socorro Island
A11*	012	Southern Sierra Madre Oriental
	008	Balsas region and interior Oaxaca
A12	009	Sierra Madre del Sur
A13	014	Isthmus of Tehuantepec
A14	018	North Central American highlands
A15	017	North Central American Pacific slope
A16	019	Central American Caribbean slope
A17	021	South Central American Pacific slope
A18	020	Costa Rica and Panama highlands
A19	023	Darién lowlands
A20	024	Darién highlands
A21	022	Cocos Island
A22*	025	Cuba
	026	Bahamas
A23	027	Jamaica
A24	028	Hispaniola
A25	029	Puerto Rico and the Virgin Islands
A26	030	Lesser Antilles
A27*	008	Balsas region and interior Oaxaca
A28*	026	Bahamas
A29*	016	Cozumel Island
A30*	013	Los Tuxtlas and Uxpanapa
B01*	—	*dropped*
B02	064	Tepuis
B03	032	Caripe–Paria region
B04	033	Cordillera de la Costa Central
B05*	—	*dropped*
B06	034	Cordillera de Mérida
B07	035	Caribbean Colombia and Venezuela
B08	036	Santa Marta mountains
B09	037	Nechí lowlands

Unique code	New EBA number	New EBA name
B10	038	Colombian East Andes
B11	065	Orinoco-Negro white-sand forests
B12	040	Colombian inter-Andean slopes
B13	039	Colombian inter-Andean valleys
B14+B15*	041	Chocó
B16	031	Galápagos Islands
B17*	042	Northern Central Andes
	043	Central Andean páramo
B18	044	Ecuador–Peru East Andes
B19+B23*	066	Upper Amazon–Napo lowlands
B20+B26*	045	Tumbesian region
B21*	046	Southern Central Andes
	043	Central Andean páramo
B22	048	Marañón valley
B23+B19*	066	Upper Amazon–Napo lowlands
B24	047	Andean ridge-top forests
B25	049	North-east Peruvian cordilleras
B26+B20*	045	Tumbesian region
B27+B31*	051	Peruvian high Andes
B28	050	Junín puna
B29	053	Peruvian East Andean foothills
B30	068	South-east Peruvian lowlands
B31+B27*	051	Peruvian high Andes
B32	052	Peru–Chile Pacific slope
B33	055	Bolivian and Peruvian upper yungas
B34*	054	Bolivian and Peruvian lower yungas
	057	Bolivian and Argentine yungas
B35+B37*	056	Bolivian and Argentine high Andes
B36*	—	*dropped*
B37+B35*	056	Bolivian and Argentine high Andes
B38*	—	*dropped*
B39	058	Sierras Centrales of Argentina
B40	059	Juan Fernández Islands
B41*	060	Central Chile
	061	Chilean temperate forests
B42	062	Southern Patagonia
B43	067	Amazon flooded forests
B44*	—	*dropped*
B45	069	Fernando de Noronha
B46	070	North-east Brazilian caatinga
B47	071	Atlantic slope of Alagoas and Pernambuco
B48	072	Deciduous forests of Bahia
B49	074	Deciduous forests of Minas Gerais and Goiás
B50	073	Central Brazilian hills and tablelands
B51+B52*	075	Atlantic forest lowlands
B53+B54*	076	Atlantic forest mountains
B55	077	Argentine Mesopotamian grasslands
B56*	063	Rio Branco gallery forests
B57*	057	Bolivian and Argentine yungas
B58*	061	Chilean temperate forests
B59*	—	*dropped*
B60*	043	Central Andean páramo
C01	120	Madeira and the Canary Islands
C02	078	Cape Verde Islands
C03	084	Upper Guinea forests
C04	086	Cameroon mountains
C05	085	Cameroon and Gabon lowlands
C06	083	Príncipe
C07	082	São Tomé
C08	087	Western Angola
C09*	079	Tristan Islands
	080	Gough Island
C10	122	Caucasus

Unique code	New EBA number	New EBA name
C11	121	Cyprus
C12	119	Mesopotamian marshes
C13	118	South-west Arabian mountains
C14	117	Socotra
C15	116	North Somali mountains
C16	115	Central Ethiopian highlands
C17	114	South Ethiopian highlands
C18	112	Central Somali coast
C19	107	Eastern Zaïre lowlands
C20	106	Albertine Rift mountains
C21	109	Kenyan mountains
C22	108	Serengeti plains
C23	111	East African coastal forests
C24	105	Tanzania–Malawi mountains
C25*	—	*dropped*
C26	104	Eastern Zimbabwe mountains
C27	092	South-east African coast
C28	091	Southern African grasslands
C29	088	Cape fynbos
C30	100	Granitic Seychelles
C31	099	Aldabra
C32+C33*	098	Comoro Islands
C34	093	West Malagasy dry forests
C35	094	East Malagasy wet forests
C36	095	East Malagasy wetlands
C37	096	West Malagasy wetlands
C38	097	South Malagasy spiny forests
C39	101	Réunion
C40	102	Mauritius
C41	103	Rodrigues
C42*	—	*dropped*
C43*	113	Jubba and Shabeelle valleys
C44*	090	Lesotho highlands
C45*	110	Pemba
C46*	089	South African forests
C47*	080	Gough Island
C48*	081	Annobón
D01	127	Taklimakan Desert
D02	128	Western Himalayas
D03*	—	*dropped*
D04	123	Western Ghats
D05	124	Sri Lanka
D06	134	Eastern Tibet
D07	133	Southern Tibet
D08+D10*	130	Eastern Himalayas
D09	131	Assam plains
D10+D08*	130	Eastern Himalayas
D11	135	Qinghai mountains
D12	137	Central Sichuan mountains
D13	138	West Sichuan mountains
D14	140	Chinese subtropical forests
D15	139	Yunnan mountains
D16	132	Irrawaddy plains
D17	125	Andaman Islands
D18	126	Nicobar Islands
D19	143	Annamese lowlands
D20	142	Hainan
D21	145	Da Lat plateau
D22	144	South Vietnamese lowlands
D23	136	Shanxi mountains
D24	141	South-east Chinese mountains
D25	149	Taiwan
D26*	148	Nansei Shoto
D26*	146	Izu Islands
D27	147	Ogasawara Islands
D28*	129	Central Himalayas
D29*	146	Izu Islands
E01+E02*	151	Luzon
E03	150	Mindoro
E04	152	Negros and Panay
E05	153	Cebu
E06	156	Palawan
E07+E08*	154	Mindanao and the Eastern Visayas
E09	155	Sulu archipelago
E10	157	Bornean mountains
E11	158	Sumatra and Peninsular Malaysia
E12	159	Enggano
E13	160	Java and Bali forests
E14	161	Javan coastal zone
E15	162	Northern Nusa Tenggara
E16	163	Sumba
E17	164	Timor and Wetar
E18	165	Banda Sea Islands
E19	167	Sangihe and Talaud
E20+E21*	166	Sulawesi
E22	168	Banggai and Sula Islands
E23	169	Buru
E24	170	Seram
E25	171	Northern Maluku
E26	172	West Papuan lowlands
E27	173	West Papuan highlands
E28	174	Geelvink Islands
E29	175	North Papuan mountains
E30	176	North Papuan lowlands
E31	177	Adelbert and Huon ranges
E32+E33*	178	Central Papuan mountains
E34*	180	Trans-Fly
E34*	179	South Papuan lowlands
E35	188	Christmas Island
E36	187	North-west Australia
E37	181	Cape York
E38	182	Queensland wet tropics
E39	186	South-west Australia
E40	184	South-east Australia
E41	183	Eastern Australia
E42	185	Tasmania
E43*	—	*dropped*
E44*	179	South Papuan lowlands
F01	189	Mariana Islands
F02	191	Yap Islands
F03	190	Palau
F04	192	East Caroline Islands
F05	193	Admiralty Islands
F06	194	St Matthias Islands
F07	195	New Britain and New Ireland
F08	196	D'Entrecasteaux and Trobriand Islands
F09	197	Louisiade archipelago
F10+F11*	198	Solomon group
F12	199	Rennell and Bellona
F13	200	Vanuatu and Temotu
F14	201	New Caledonia
F15	203	Samoan Islands
F16	202	Fiji
F17	205	Norfolk Island
F18	204	Lord Howe Island
F19	206	North Island of New Zealand
F20	207	South Island of New Zealand
F21	208	Auckland Islands
F22	209	Chatham Islands
F23	216	Laysan Island
F24	217	Central Hawaiian Islands
F25	218	Hawai'i
F26	212	Marquesas Islands
F27	213	Society Islands
F28	214	Tuamotu archipelago
F29	210	Southern Cook Islands
F30	215	Henderson Island
F31*	211	Rimatara

SINCE the initial EBA analysis was published in *Putting biodiversity on the map* (ICBP 1992), it has been modified in the light of new information, in particular a better understanding of the ecological requirements of the restricted-range species whose ranges determine the boundaries of EBAs. Some EBAs have been split into two, while pairs of others have been combined into one; in addition, some new EBAs have been recognized while others have been dropped. Overall these changes are small (see below; also Box 2, p. 46), and their extent is summarized as follows (figures are the number of EBAs in the two analyses).

	Nos. of EBAs common to both analyses			Unique to old or to new analysis	Total no. of EBAs
	Unchanged since original analysis	Split since original analysis	Combined since original analysis		
Original analysis, 1992	177	9	28	7	221
	↓	↓	↓	↓	↓
New analysis, 1997	177	18	14	9	218

A full list of the original unique codes and corresponding new EBA numbers is given in Appendix 3 (p. 779). The reasons for incorporating these changes in the present analysis are outlined below (see also Long *et al.* 1996).

Unique code	New EBA no.	New EBA name	Notes
A09	015	Yucatán peninsula coastal scrub	The original Yucatán peninsula EBA has been split into the Yucatán peninsula coastal scrub (retaining the unique code A09) and Cozumel Island (unique code A29, new number 016) because several of the birds have larger ranges than originally thought and so have been dropped, leaving Cozumel, with three endemic species, as a separate EBA.
A11	012	Southern Sierra Madre Oriental	The original Central Mexican highlands EBA has been split into the Southern Sierra Madre (retaining the unique code A11) and the Balsas region and interior Oaxaca (unique code A27, new number 008) as the species in the separate EBAs have different habitat requirements.
A22	025	Cuba	The original Cuba and the Bahamas EBA has been split into Cuba (retaining the unique code A22) and the Bahamas (unique code A28, new number 026) as both are regarded as sufficiently distinct to qualify as EBAs in their own rights.
A27	008	Balsas region and interior Oaxaca	See A11.
A28	026	Bahamas	See A22.
A29	016	Cozumel Island	See A09.
A30	013	Los Tuxtlas and Uxpanapa	This new EBA has been recognized following the elevation to species rank of two taxa endemic to the region.
B01	—	Guianas	These EBAs have been dropped because recent fieldwork and a more detailed analysis of bird distributions in the regions reveal that the species originally treated as having restricted ranges are too widespread to qualify.
B05	—	Venezuelan llanos	
B14+B15	041	Chocó	The original Chocó EBA (B14) and the Western Andes of Colombia and Ecuador EBA (B15) have been combined into a single EBA because it was felt that the original division between the lowland and montane species in the region was not sufficiently clear-cut to warrant separate treatment.
B17	042	Northern Central Andes	The original Central Andes of Colombia and Ecuador EBA has been split into the Northern Central Andes (retaining the unique code B17) and part of the Central Andean páramo (unique code B60, new number 043; see also B21) because the high-altitude-grassland species of this region are distributed throughout, and are therefore best treated in their own EBA separate from the montane forest species which show latitudinal division.
B19+B23	066	Upper Amazon–Napo lowlands	The original Napo lowlands EBA (B19) and the North-east Peruvian riverine forests EBA (B23) have been combined into a single EBA owing to the apparent overlap in the distribution of the restricted-range species, although limited ecological data suggest that some species may only occur in riverine forest and on river islands.

Unique code	New EBA no.	New EBA name	Notes
B20+B26	045	Tumbesian region	The original Ecuadorian dry forests EBA (B20) and the North Peruvian coast EBA (B26) have been combined into a single EBA because it was found that many of the birds overlap both ecologically and geographically.
B21	046	Southern Central Andes	The original South Central Andes EBA has been split into the Southern Central Andes EBA (retaining the unique code B21, EBA number 046) and part of the Central Andean páramo (unique code B60, new number 043; see also B17) because the high-altitude-grassland species of this region are distributed throughout, and are therefore best treated in their own EBA separate from the montane-forest species which show latitudinal division.
B23+B19	066	Upper Amazon–Napo lowlands	See B19.
B26+B20	045	Tumbesian region	See B20.
B27+B31	051	Peruvian High Andes	The original Western Andes of Peru EBA (B27) and South-east Peruvian Andes EBA (B31) have been combined into a single EBA because, although there are species confined to the Andes of south-east Peru, an equal number (or more) occur both there and to the north around Lake Junín and in the north-western cordilleras.
B34	054	Bolivian and Peruvian lower yungas	The original Lower Bolivian yungas EBA has been split into the Bolivian and Peruvian lower yungas (retaining the unique code B34) and the Bolivian and Argentine yungas (unique code B57, new number 057) because the two areas are disjunct, and the addition of newly identified restricted-range species makes the two areas sufficiently distinct to qualify as separate EBAs in their own rights.
B35+B37	056	Bolivian and Argentine high Andes	The original Bolivian Andes EBA (B35) and the North Argentinian Andes EBA (B37) have been combined into a single EBA because recent fieldwork on both sides of the Argentine–Bolivian border has shown that there is considerable overlap in the distribution of the restricted-range species of the two former EBAs.
B36	—	East Bolivian lowlands	This EBA has been dropped because recent fieldwork and a more detailed analysis of bird distributions reveal that the species originally treated as having restricted ranges are too widespread to qualify.
B37+B35	056	Bolivian and Argentine high Andes	See B35.
B38	—	Argentinian grasslands	This EBA has been dropped because recent fieldwork and a more detailed analysis of bird distributions reveal that the species originally treated as having restricted ranges are too widespread to qualify.
B41	060	Central Chile	The original Central Chile EBA has been split into a different Central Chilean EBA (retaining the unique code B41) and the Chilean temperate forests (unique code B58, new number 061) as the species in the two areas have different habitat requirements and distributions.
B44	—	West Amazonian Brazil	This EBA has been dropped because recent fieldwork and a more detailed analysis of bird distributions reveal that the species originally treated as having restricted ranges are too widespread to qualify.
B51+B52	075	Atlantic forest lowlands	The original Bahian and Espírito Santo Atlantic slope EBA (B51) and the South-east Brazilian lowland to foothills EBA (B52) have been combined into a single EBA as there appears to be too much overlap in the ranges of the restricted-range birds to warrant subdivision, although further work is needed on the distribution patterns of all the birds of these forests.
B53+B54	076	Atlantic forest mountains	The original South-east Brazilian mountains EBA (B53) and the South-east Brazilian *Araucaria* forest EBA (B54) have been combined into a single EBA because it was felt that the species which occur in *Araucaria* forests were not as tied to this habitat as originally thought, with several occurring in montane habitats.
B56	063	Rio Branco gallery forests	This new EBA clearly embraces the ranges of two threatened gallery-forest restricted-range species.
B57	057	Bolivian and Argentine yungas	See B34.
B58	061	Chilean temperate forests	See B41.
B59	—	—	This code was temporarily assigned to the region of the Araguaia river in Brazil (post 1992), which is now treated as Secondary Area s031.
B60	043	Central Andean páramo	See B17 and B21.

Appendix 4: Changes in the EBA Analysis, 1992–1997

Unique code	New EBA no.	New EBA name	Notes
C09	079	Tristan Islands	The original Tristan da Cunha islands EBA has been split into the Tristan Islands (retaining the unique code C09) and Gough Island (unique code C47, new number 080) following the recognition of the specific status of two island races.
C25	—	South Zambia	This EBA has been dropped because new range information on one of its two endemic species showed that it clearly exceeds 50,000 km².
C32+C33	098	Comoro Islands	The original Comoros Islands EBA (C32) and Mayotte EBA (C33) have been combined into a single EBA because as many species are shared between them as are endemic to individual islands.
C42	—	—	This code was temporarily assigned (post 1992) to North-west Somalia, which is now treated as Secondary Area s064.
C43	113	Jubba and Shabeelle valleys	This new EBA has been recognized because of the description of a new species, the inclusion of a species which was wrongly excluded from the original analysis, and a species which was formerly allocated to a Secondary Area.
C44	090	Lesotho highlands	These two new EBAs have been recognized because taxa treated as a full species in Sibley and Monroe (1993) coincided in distribution with other restricted-range species.
C45	110	Pemba	
C46	089	South African forests	This new EBA has been recognized because of the description of a new species and the inclusion of several species which were wrongly excluded from the original analysis.
C47	080	Gough Island	See C09.
C48	081	Annobón	This new EBA, with two endemic species, has been recognized following the elevation to species rank of one of its endemic taxa.
D03	—	Indus valley	This EBA has been dropped because one of the two taxa endemic to the region is no longer considered to be a full species (following Sibley and Monroe 1993).
D08+D10	130	Eastern Himalayas	The original Eastern Himalayas EBA (D08) and the Tirap Frontier EBA (D10) have been combined into a single EBA as new information suggests that one of its two species is not sufficiently distinct in distribution and habitat requirements from several of the other Eastern Himalayan restricted-range species to justify separation.
D26	148	Nansei Shoto	The original Nansei Islands EBA has been split into the Nansei Shoto (retaining the unique code D26) and the Izu islands (unique code D29, new number 146). This is despite the fact that two of the Izu islands' restricted-range species have been recorded breeding in the Nansei Shoto EBA, c.1,000 km away, because the numbers of birds involved are very small.
D28	129	Central Himalayas	This new EBA has been recognized following the description of a new species.
D29	146	Izu Islands	See D26.
E01+E02	151	Luzon	Four pairs of original EBAs have been combined into single EBAs: the Luzon mountains EBA (E01) and the Luzon lowlands and foothills EBA (E02); the Samar, Leyte, Bohol and Mindanao lowlands EBA (E07) and the Mindanao mountains EBA (E08); the Sulawesi mountains EBA (E20) and the Sulawesi lowlands EBA (E21); and the Central New Guinean high mountains EBA (E32) and the Central New Guinean mid-mountains EBA (E33). This is because a review of the data on the restricted-range species' habitat requirements and altitudinal ranges has shown that many share similar distributions and, although most species can be divided into different vegetational zones, there is often partial altitudinal overlap between these zones.
E07+E08	154	Mindanao and the Eastern Visayas	
E20+E21	166	Sulawesi	
E32+E33	178	Central Papuan mountains	
E34	180	Trans-Fly	The original Trans-Fly and Upper-Fly EBA has been split into the Trans-Fly (retaining the unique code E34) and the south Papuan lowlands (unique code E44, new number 179) because further analysis revealed that there was little distributional overlap between the restricted-range species of these two regions.
E43	—	—	This code was temporarily assigned to the Sabah lowlands in Malaysia (post 1992), which is now treated as Secondary Area s098.
E44	179	South Papuan lowlands	See E34.
F10+F11	198	Solomon group	The original Solomon Islands EBA (F10) and San Cristobal EBA (F11), part of the same archipelago, have been combined into a single EBA as many species are shared between them, although San Cristobal/Makira is clearly an important area of endemism in its own right.
F31	211	Rimatara	This new EBA has been recognized following the elevation to species rank of one of its taxa.

OVER the course of BirdLife International's Biodiversity Project, which began in 1987, several analyses of the data have been published, notably by ICBP/BirdLife in *Putting biodiversity on the map: priority areas for global conservation* (ICBP 1992) and *Conserving Indonesian biodiversity:* *the Endemic Bird Area approach* (Sujatnika *et al.* 1995). Information on EBAs has also been used widely by other researchers and conservationists in their own priority-setting work. A selection of these publications is listed below.

BALMFORD, A. AND LONG, A. (1994) Avian endemism and forest loss. *Nature* 372: 623–624.

BALMFORD, A. AND LONG, A. (1995) Across-country analyses of biodiversity congruence and current conservation effort in the tropics. *Conserv. Biol.* 9: 1539–1547.

BEEHLER, B. M. (1993) Biodiversity and conservation of the warm-blooded vertebrates of Papua New Guinea. Pp. 77–155 in B. M. Beehler *Papua New Guinea: conservation needs assessment*, 2. Boroko, Papua New Guinea: Department of Environment and Conservation.

BEST, B. AND KESSLER, M. (1995) *Biodiversity and conservation in Tumbesian Ecuador and Peru.* Cambridge, UK: BirdLife International.

BIBBY, C. (1994) Recent past and future extinction in birds. *Phil. Trans. Roy. Soc. Lond.* B344(1307): 35–40.

BIBBY, C. (1995) A global view of priorities for bird conservation: a summary. *Ibis* 137: 247–248.

BROOKS, T. AND BALMFORD, A. (1996) Atlantic forest extinctions. *Nature* 380: 115.

BROOKS, T. M., PIMM, S. L. AND COLLAR, N. J. (1997) Deforestation predicts the number of threatened birds in insular Southeast Asia. *Conserv. Biol.* 11: 382–394.

COLLAR, N. J., CROSBY, M. J. AND STATTERSFIELD, A. J. (1994) *Birds to watch 2: the world list of threatened birds.* Cambridge, UK: BirdLife International (BirdLife Conservation Series no. 4).

COLLAR, N. J., WEGE, D. C. AND LONG, A. J. (1997) Patterns and causes of endangerment in the New World avifauna. Pp. in J. V. Remsem, ed. *Studies in Neotropical ornithology honoring Ted Parker* (Ornithol. Monogr. 48).

CROSBY, M. J. (1996) Threatened birds in the eastern Himalayas. *Oriental Bird Club Bull.* 23: 21–23.

DANIELSEN, F., BALETE, D. S., CHRISTENSEN, T. D., HEEGAARD, M., JAKOBSEN, O. F., JENSEN, A., LUND, T. AND POULSEN, M. K. (1994) *Conservation of biological diversity in the Sierra Madre mountains of Isabela and southern Cagayan province, the Philippines.* Manila and Copenhagen: Department of Environment and Natural Resources, BirdLife International and Danish Ornithological Society.

FORRESTER, B. C. (1993) *Birding Brazil: a check-list and site guide.* Privately published.

JOHNSON, N. (1995) *Biodiversity in the balance: approaches to setting geographic conservation priorities.* Washington, D.C.: Biodiversity Support Program.

LONG, A. J. (1994) The importance of tropical montane cloud forests for endemic and threatened birds. Pp. 79–106 in L. S. Hamilton, J. O. Juvik and F. N. Scatena, eds. *Tropical montane cloud forests.* New York: Springer-Verlag (Ecology).

LONG, A. J. (1996) Establishing conservation priorities in South America using endemic birds. Pp. 35–46 in C. Harcourt and J. Sayer, eds. *The conservation atlas of tropical forests: America.* New York and London: Simon & Schuster.

LONG, A. J., CROSBY, M. J., STATTERSFIELD, A. J. AND WEGE, D. C. (1996) Towards a global map of biodiversity: patterns in the distribution of restricted-range birds. *Global Ecol. and Biogeog. Letters* 5: 281–304.

LOWEN, J. C., BATRINA, L., CLAY, R. P. AND TOBIAS, J. A. (1996) *Biological surveys and conservation priorities in eastern Paraguay.* Cambridge, UK: CSB Conservation Publications.

MACKINNON, J., ed. (in press) *Protected areas system review of the Indo-Malayan realm.* Hong Kong and Canterbury, UK: Asian Bureau for Conservation.

OLSON, D. M. AND DINERSTEIN, E. (1997) *The global 200: conserving the world's distinctive ecoregions.* Washington, DC: World Wildlife Fund-US.

ROCA, R., ADKINS, L., WURSCHY, M. C. AND SKERL, K. L. (1996) *Wings from afar: an ecoregional approach to conservation of neotropical migratory birds in South America.* Arlington: The Nature Conservancy.

SALAMAN, P. G. W., ED. (1994) *Surveys and conservation of biodiversity in the Chocó, south-west Colombia.* Cambridge, UK: BirdLife International (BirdLife Study report 61).

SUJATNIKA, JEPSON, P., SOEHARTONO, T. R., CROSBY, M. J. AND MARDIASTUTI, A. (1995) *Conserving Indonesian biodiversity: the Endemic Bird Area approach.* Bogor: BirdLife International Indonesia Programme.

THIRGOOD, S. J. AND HEATH, M. F. (1994) Global patterns of endemism and the conservation of biodiversity. Pp. 207–227 in P. L. Forey, C. J. Humphries and R. I. Vane-Wright, eds. *Systematics and conservation evaluation.* Oxford: Clarendon Press.

WEGE, D. C. (1996) Threatened birds of the Darién Highland, Panama: a reassessment. *Bird Conserv. Internatn.* 6: 191–195.

WEGE, D. C. (1997) Ecuador's Endemic Bird Areas. Pp. 43–50 in R. S. R. Williams, B. J. Best and T. A. Heijnen *A guide to bird-watching in Ecuador and the Galápagos Islands.* Otley, UK: Biosphere Publications.

WEGE, D. C. AND LONG, A. J. (1995) *Key Areas for threatened birds in the Neotropics.* Cambridge, UK: BirdLife International (BirdLife Conservation Series no. 5).

WWF/IUCN (1994–1997) *Centres of plant diversity: a guide and strategy for their conservation.* 3 volumes. Cambridge, UK: World Wide Fund for Nature and International Union for Conservation of Nature and Natural Resources.

REFERENCES

ACOCKS, J. P. H. (1988) Veld types of South Africa. *Mem. Bot. Surv. South Africa* 57: 1–146.

ALI, S. AND RIPLEY, S. D. (1948) The birds of the Mishmi Hills. *J. Bombay Nat. Hist. Soc.* 48: 1–37.

ALI, S. AND RIPLEY, S. D. (1987) *Compact handbook of the birds of India and Pakistan together with those of Bangladesh, Nepal, Bhutan and Sri Lanka.* Second edition. Delhi: Oxford University Press.

ALI, S., BISWAS, B. AND RIPLEY, S. D. (1996) The birds of Bhutan. *Rec. Zool. Surv. India Occas. Pap. no.* 136: 1–263.

ALLAN, D. AND NUTTALL, R. (1995) South Africa—the rainbow country. *World Birdw.* 17(1): 10–13.

ALLAN, D. G., BATCHELOR, G. R. AND TARBOTON, W. R. (1983) Breeding of Botha's Lark. *Ostrich* 54: 55–57.

ALLEN, P. E. (1996) Breeding biology and natural history of the Bahama Swallow. *Wilson Bull.* 108: 480–495.

ALLPORT, G. (1991) The status and conservation of threatened birds in the Upper Guinea Forest. *Bird Conserv. Internatn.* 1: 53–74.

ALPERT, P. (1993) Conserving biodiversity in Cameroon. *Ambio* 22: 44–49.

AL SAGHEIR, O. AND PORTER, R. F. (1996) The bird biodiversity of Socotra. Paper presented at the First International Scientific Symposium on Socotra Island, present and future.

ALSTRÖM, P. (in prep.) Taxonomy of the *Mirafra assamica* Horsfield complex. [*Bull. Brit. Orn. Club.*]

ALSTRÖM, P. AND OLSSON, U. (1995) A new species of *Phylloscopus* warbler from Sichuan Province, China. *Ibis* 117: 459–468.

ALSTRÖM, P., OLSSON, U. AND COLSTON, P. R. (1997) Re-evaluation of the taxonomic status of *Phylloscopus proregulus kansuensis* Meise. *Bull. Brit. Orn. Club* 117: 177–193.

ALSTRÖM, P., CROSBY, M. J., OLSSON, U. AND HOLT, P. (in prep.) *Ficedula narcissina elisae*—taxonomic position, distribution and status.

ALVAREZ, M. E. AND BLENDINGER, P. G. (1995) Primer registro de distribución del picaflor Andino Castaño *Oreotrochilus adela* para Argentina. *Hornero* 14: 75.

AMADON, D. (1942) Birds collected during the Whitney South Sea expedition. L. Notes on some non-passerine genera, 3. *Amer. Mus. Novit.* 1176: 1–21.

AMERSON, A. B., WHISTLER, W. AND SCHWANER, T. (1982a) *Wildlife and wildlife habitat of American Samoa, 1: environment and ecology.* Washington, DC: US Fish and Wildlife Service.

AMERSON, A. B., WHISTLER, W. AND SCHWANER, T. (1982b) *Wildlife and wildlife habitat of American Samoa, 11: accounts of flora and fauna.* Washington, DC: US Fish and Wildlife Service.

ANDERSEN, C. Y., POULSEN, M. K., JAKOBSEN, O. F. AND HEEGAARD, M. (1992) Observations on the Luzon Water Redstart *Rhyacornis bicolor* in the Mount Pulog National Park, Philippines. *Forktail* 7: 147–150.

ANDERSON, S. J. AND STONE, C. P. (1993) Snaring to control feral pigs *Sus scrofa* in a remote Hawaiian rain forest. *Biol. Conserv.* 63: 195–201.

DE ANDRADE, M. A., DE FREITAS, M. V. AND DE MATTOS, G. T. (1986) A redescoberta de '*Xiphocolaptes franciscanus*' Snethlage 1927 no estado de Minas Gerais, Brasil. *An. Soc. Sul-Riogrand. Orn.* 7: 18–20.

ANDREW, P. (1992) *The birds of Indonesia: a checklist (Peters' sequence).* Jakarta: Indonesian Ornithological Society.

ANDRLE, R. F. (1967) Birds of the Sierr de Tuxtla in Veracruz, Mexico. *Wilson Bull.* 79: 163–187.

ANON. (1992a) Amazon 1992–final report: a Cambridge–RHBNC expedition to Colombia. Unpublished report.

ANON. (1992b) Timber news: Sri Lanka offers protection to forests. *TRAFFIC Bull.* 13(1): 32.

ANON. (1995) In Brief: the invisible rail. *World Birdw.* 17(3): 3.

ANON. (1996) 'Extinct' pheasant found in Vietnam. WWF Press release.

ANON. (1997a) In brief: Ke Go Nature Reserve in Vietnam. *World Birdw.* 19(1): 5.

ANON. (1997b) Exciting new find of Orange-necked Partridge. *World Birdw.* 19(2): 2.

ANTAS, P. T. Z. (1991) Status and conservation of seabirds breeding in Brazilian waters. Pp.141–158 in J. P. Croxall, ed. *Seabird status and conservation: a supplement.* Cambridge, UK: International Council for Bird Preservation (Techn. Publ. 11).

AOSNR (= Administrative Office of Shanxi Nature Reserves) (1990) [*Rare bird: Brown Eared-Pheasant.*] Taiyuan, China: Shanxi Popular Science Publishing House. (In Chinese.)

AOU (1995a) Forty-first supplement to the American Ornithologist' Union: check-list of North American birds. *Auk* 114: 542–552.

AOU (1995b) Fortieth supplement to the American Ornithologist' Union: check-list of North American birds. *Auk* 112: 819–830.

ARCHER, A. L. AND TURNER, D. A. (1993) Notes on the endemic species and some additional new birds occurring on Pemba Island, Tanzania. *Scopus* 16: 94–98.

ASH, J. S. (1979) A new species of serin from Ethiopia. *Ibis* 121: 1–7.

ASH, J. S. (1981) Field description of the Obbia Lark *Calandrella obbiensis*, its breeding and distribution. *Bull. Brit. Orn. Club* 101: 379–383.

ASH, J. S. (1987) Nigeria: surveys of selected bird conservation areas (wetlands and forests). Cambridge, UK: International Council for Bird Preservation.

ASH, J. S. (1990) Additions to the avifauna of Nigeria, with notes on distributional changes and breeding. *Malimbus* 11: 104–116.

ASH, J. (1991) The Grey-necked Picarthartes *Picathartes oreas* and Ibadan Malimbe *Malimbus ibadanensis* in Nigeria. *Bird Conserv. Internatn.* 1: 93–106.

ASH, J. S. AND GULLICK, T. M. (1990) *Serinus flavigula* rediscovered. *Bull. Brit. Orn. Club* 110: 81–83.

ASH, J. S. AND MISKELL, J. E. (1981) Present abundance of the Warsangli Linnet *Acanthis johannis. Bull. Brit. Orn. Club* 101: 396–398.

ASH, J. S. AND MISKELL, J. E. (1983) Birds of Somalia: their habitat, status and distribution. *Scopus* (Special Supplement) 1.

ASH, J. S. AND SHARLAND, R. E. (1986) *Nigeria: assessment of bird conservation priorities*. Cambridge, UK: International Council for Bird Preservation (Study Report 11).

ASH, J. S., DOWSETT, R. J. AND DOWSETT-LEMAIRE, F. (1989) New ornithological distribution records from eastern Nigeria. Pp.13–27 in R. J. Dowsett, ed. *A preliminary natural history survey of Mambilla Plateau and some lowland forests of eastern Nigeria*. Ely, UK: Tauraco Press (Tauraco Research Report 1).

ATKINS, J. D. (1992) A new location for the Ankober Serin *Serinus ankoberensis* near Debre Sina, Ethiopia. *Scopus* 16: 105–107.

ATKINS, J. D. AND HARVEY, W. G. (1994) Further sightings of an unnamed cliff swallow *Hirundo* sp. in Ethiopia. *Scopus* 18: 52–54.

ATKINSON, I. A. E. (1985) The spread of commensal species of *Rattus* to oceanic islands and their effects on island avifaunas. Pp.35–81 in P. J. Moors, ed. *Conservation of island birds*. Cambridge, UK: International Council for Bird Preservation (Techn. Publ. 3).

ATKINSON, I. A. E. AND BELL, B. D. (1973) Offshore and outlying islands. Pp.372–392 in G. R. Williams, ed. *The natural history of New Zealand*. Wellington: A. H. & A. W. Reed.

ATKINSON, P., PEET, N. AND ALEXANDER, J. (1991) The status and conservation of the endemic bird species of São Tomé and Príncipe, West Africa. *Bird Conserv. Internatn.* 1: 255–282.

ATKINSON, P. W., WHITTINGHAM, M. J., GÓMEZ DE SILVA GARZA, H., KENT, A. M. AND MAIER, R. T. (1993) Notes on the ecology, conservation and taxonomic status of *Hylorchilus* wrens. *Bird Conserv. Internatn.* 3: 75–85.

ATKINSON, P. W., DUTTON, J. S., PEET, N. B. AND SEQUEIRA, V. A. S., EDS. (1994a) *A study of the birds, small mammals, turtles and medicinal plants of São Tomé with notes on Príncipe*. Cambridge, UK: BirdLife International (Study Report 56).

ATKINSON, P. W., KOROMA, A. P., RANFT, R., ROWE, S. G. AND WILKINSON, R. (1994b) The status, identification and vocalisations of African fishing owls with particular reference to the Rufous Fishing Owl *Scotopelia ussheri*. *Bull. African Bird Club* 1: 67–72.

ATKINSON, P., ROBERTSON, P., DELLELEGN, Y., WONDAFRASH, M. AND ATKINS, J. (1996) The recent rediscovery of White-winged Flufftails in Ethiopia. *Bull. African Bird Club* 3: 34–36.

ATTIÉ, C. AND BRETAGNOLLE, V. (in prep.) A third record for the century of the Mascarene Petrel *Pseudobulweria aterrima* from Réunion Island, and comments on its current status.

BAHR, N. (1995) Additions to the list of new species of birds described from 1981–1990. *Bull. Brit. Orn. Club* 115: 114–116.

BAILLIE, J. AND GROOMBRIDGE, B., EDS. (1996) *1996 IUCN Red List of threatened animals*. Cambridge, UK: International Union for Conservation of Nature and Natural Resources.

BAKER, A. J., DAUGHERTY, C. H., COLBOURNE, R. AND McLENNAN, J. L. (1995) Flightless Brown Kiwis of New Zealand possess extremely subdivided population structure and cryptic species like small mammals. *Proc. Natn. Acad. Sci. USA* 92: 8254–8258.

BAKER, N. E. AND BAKER, E. M. (1990) A new species of

weaver from Tanzania. *Bull. Brit. Orn. Club* 110: 51–58.

VAN BALEN, S. AND GEPAK, V. H. (1994) The captive breeding and conservation programme of the Bali Starling (*Leucopsar rothschildi*). Pp.420–430 in P. J. S. Olney, G. M. Mace and A. T. C. Feistner, eds. *Creative conservation: interactive management of wild and captive animals*. London: Chapman and Hall.

VAN BALEN, S. AND HOLMES, D. A. (1993) Status and conservation of pheasants in the Greater and Lesser Sundas, Indonesia. Pp.40–49 in D. Jenkins, ed. *Pheasants in Asia 1992*. Reading, UK: World Pheasant Association.

BALMFORD, A. (1996) Extinction filters and current resilience: the significance of past selection pressures for conservation biology. *TREE* 11: 193–196.

BALMFORD, A. AND LONG, A. (1994) Avian endemism and forest loss. *Nature* 372: 623–624.

BALMFORD, A. AND LONG, A. (1995) Across-country analyses of biodiversity congruence and current conservation effort in the tropics. *Conserv. Biol.* 9: 1539–1547.

BANKS, P. F. (1976) Editorial: Chirinda Forest. *Rhodesia Sci. News* 10: 39.

BARBOSA, L. A. G. (1970) Carta fiteográfica de Angola. IICA: Luanda.

BARKER, J. R., HERLOCKER, D. J. AND YOUNG, S. A. (1989) Vegetal dynamics in response to sand dune encroachment within the coastal grasslands of central Somalia. *Afr. J. Ecol.* 27: 277–282.

BARKER, M. A. (1990) An investigation of avian endemism and protected areas in northern Central America. University of Stirling, Stirling (M.Sc. Thesis).

BARNES, K. (1996) Sites to save: Lake St Lucia. *World Birdw.* 18(2): 6–7.

BARNES, R., BUTCHART, S., CLAY, R., DAVIES, C. AND SEDDON, N. (1995) The conservation status of the Cordillera de Colán, northern Peru. *Cotinga* 3: 6–7.

BARRÉ, N. (1988) Une avifaune menacée: les oiseaux de la Réunion. Pp.167–196 in J.-C. Thibault and I. Guyot, eds. *Livre rouge des oiseaux menacés des régions françaises d'Outre-Mer*. Saint-Cloud: Conseil International pour la Protection des Oiseaux (Monogr. 5).

BEEHLER, B. (1985) Conservation of New Guinea rainforest birds. Pp.233–247 in A. W. Diamond and T. E. Lovejoy, eds. *Conservation of tropical forest birds*. Cambridge, UK: International Council for Bird Preservation (Techn. Publ. 4).

BEEHLER, B. M. (1993) Biodiversity and conservation of the warm-blooded vertebrates of Papua New Guinea. Pp.77–155 in B. M. Beehler, ed. *Papua New Guinea: conservation needs assessment*, 2. Boroko, Papua New Guinea: Department of Environment and Conservation, Government of Papua New Guinea.

BEEHLER, B. M., PRATT, T. K. AND ZIMMERMAN, D. A. (1986) *Birds of New Guinea*. Princeton: Princeton University Press.

BEENTJE, H. J. (1988) An ecological and floristic study of the forests of the Taita Hills, Kenya. *Utafiti* 1: 23–66.

BEGAZO, A. J. (1996) Ecology and conservation of the Yellow-faced Parrolet *Forpus xanthops*. *Cotinga* 6: 20–23.

BEICHLE, U. (1982) Untersuchungen zur Biologie und Systematik der Zahntaube *Didunculus strigirostris* (Jardine 1845). Kiel: Christian-Albrechts Universität (Doctoral dissertation).

BEICHLE, U. (1987) Lebensraum, Bestand und Nahrungs-aufnahme der Zahntaube, *Didunculus strigirostris. J. Orn.* 128: 75–89.

BEICHLE, U. AND MAELZER, M. (1985) A conservation programme for Western Samoa. Pp.297–299 in A. W. Diamond and T. E. Lovejoy, eds. *Conservation of tropical forest birds.* Cambridge, UK: International Council for Bird Preservation (Techn. Publ. 4).

BELL, B. D. (1991) Recent avifaunal changes and the history of ornithology in New Zealand. Pp.193–230 in B. N. Bell, R. O. Cossee, J. E. C. Flux, B. D. Heather, R. A. Hitchmough, C. J. R. Robertson and M. J. Williams, eds. *Acta XX Congressus Internationalis Ornithologici, Christchurch, New Zealand, 2–9 December 1990.* Wellington: New Zealand Ornithological Congress Trust Board.

BELL, B. D. AND ROBERTSON, C. J. R. (1994) Seabirds of the Chatham Islands. Pp.219–228 in D. N. Nettleship, J. Burger and M. Gochfeld, eds. *Seabirds on islands: threats, case studies, and action plans.* Cambridge, UK: BirdLife International (BirdLife Conservation Series no. 1).

BELL, H. L. (1970) Additions to the avifauna of Goodenough Island, Papua. *Emu* 70: 179–182.

BELLATRECHE, M. (1991) Deux nouvelles localisations de la Sitelle [sic] kabyle *Sitta ledanti* en Algérie. *Oiseau et R.F.O.* 61: 269–272.

BELLATRECHE, M. AND CHALABI, B. (1990) Données nouvelles sur l'aire de distribution de la Sittelle kabyle *Sitta ledanti. Alauda* 58: 95–97.

BELLINGHAM, M. AND DAVIS, A. (1988) Forest bird communities in Western Samoa. *Notornis* 35: 117–128.

BELTON, W. (1984–1985) Birds of Rio Grande Do Sul, Brazil. *Bull. Amer. Mus. Nat. Hist.* 178.

BENTON, T. G. AND SPENCER, T. (1995) The Pitcairn Islands: biogeography, ecology and prehistory. *Biol. J. Linn. Soc.* 56: 1–422.

BERGER, A. J. (1972) *Hawaiian birdlife.* Honolulu: University Press of Hawaii.

BERKMÜLLER, K., EVANS, T., TIMMINS, R. AND VONGPHET, V. (1995) Recent advances in nature conservation in the Lao PDR. *Oryx* 29: 253–260.

BEST, B. J. AND KESSLER, M. (1995) *Biodiversity and conservation in Tumbesian Ecuador and Peru.* Cambridge, UK: BirdLife International.

BHATTACHARJEE, P. C. (1995) Conservation of the birds of Assam plains. Pp.66–67 in L. Vijayan, ed. *Avian conservation in India.* Coimbatore, India: Salim Ali Centre for Ornithology and Natural History.

BHUSHAN, B. (1986a) Rediscovery of the Jerdon's or Double-banded Courser *Cursorius bitorquatus* (Blyth). *J. Bombay Nat. Hist. Soc.* 83: 1–14.

BHUSHAN, B. (1986b) Photographic record of the Jerdon's or Double-banded Courser *Cursorius bitorquatus. J. Bombay Nat. Hist. Soc.* 83 (Suppl.): 159–162.

BHUSHAN, B. (1992) Red Data Bird: Jerdon's Courser. *World Birdw.* 14(4): 12.

BIBBY, C. J. (1994) Recent past and future extinctions in birds. *Phil. Trans. Roy. Soc. Lond.* (B) 344: 35–40.

BIBBY, C. J. AND HILL, D. A. (1987) Status of the Fuerteventura Stonechat *Saxicola dacotiae. Ibis* 129: 491–498.

BIBBY, C. J. AND DEL NEVO, A. (1992) The first record of Fea's Petrel *Pterodroma feae* from the Azores. *Bull. Brit. Orn. Club* 111: 183–186.

BILIKI, M. (1993) Local conservation area ownership and management: Komarindi Catchment Conservation Area Project, Guadalcanal Province, Solomon Islands. Pp.108–113 in *Fifth South Pacific Conference on nature conservation and protected areas, 4–8 October 1993.* 2: *conference papers.* Apia, Western Samoa: South Pacific Regional Environment Programme.

BINFORD, L. C. (1989) *A distributional survey of the birds of the Mexican state of Oaxaca.* Washington, DC: American Ornithologists' Union (Orn. Monogr. 43).

BIRDSEY, R. A. AND WEAVER, P. L. (1982) *The forest resources of Puerto Rico.* New Orleans: So. For. Exp. Stn. USDA (For. Ser. Res. Bull SO-85).

BISHOP, K. D. (1982) Endemic birds of Biak Island. International Council for Bird Preservation survey. Unpublished report.

BISHOP, K. D. (1992) New and interesting records of birds in Wallacea. *Kukila* 6: 8–34.

BLACK, J. M., DUVALL, F., HOSHIDE, H., MEDEIROS, J., HODGES, C. N., SANTOS, N. AND TELFER, T. (1991) The current status of the Hawaiian Goose *Branta sandvicensis* and its recovery programme. *Wildfowl* 42: 149–154.

BLAKERS, M., DAVIES, S. J. J. F. AND REILLY, P. N. (1984) *The atlas of Australian birds.* Victoria: Royal Australasian Ornithologists' Union.

BLOM, A. (1990) List of the birds of the (future) Okapi Reserve and National Park. Unpublished (second) draft.

BLOT, J. (1985) Contribution a la connaissance de la biologie et de l'écologie de *Francolinus ochropectus* Dorst et Jouanin. *Alauda* 53: 244–256.

BOESMAN, P. AND CURSON, J. (1995) Grey-headed Warbler *Basileuterus griseiceps* in danger of extinction? *Cotinga* 3: 35–39.

BOND, R., CONVEY, P., SHARPE, C. AND VAREY, A. (1989) Cambridge Columbus zoological expedition to Venezuela 1988. Unpublished report.

BOONSONG, L. AND ROUND, P. (1991) *Birds of Thailand.* Bangkok: Saha Karn Bhaet.

BORCHSENIUS, F. (1997) Patterns of plant species endemism in Ecuador. *Biodiv. & Conserv.* 6: 379–399.

BORGHESIO, L. (in prep.) Observations on the ecology of *Tauraco ruspolii* and *T. leucotis* in south Ethiopia.

BORNSCHEIN, M. R., REINERT, B. L. AND TEIXEIRA, D. M. (1995) Um novo formicariidae do sul do Brasil (Aves, Passeriformes). Rio de Janeiro: Instituto Iguaçú de Pesquisa e Preservação Ambiental.

BOUCHET, P., JAFFRE, T. AND VEILLON, J.-M. (1995) Plant extinction in New Caledonia: protection of sclerophyll forests urgently needed. *Biodiv. & Conserv.* 4: 415–428.

BOURNE, W. R. P., BROOKE, M. DE L., CLARK, G. S. AND STONE, T. (1992) Wildlife conservation problems in the Juan Fernández Archipelago. *Oryx* 26: 43–51.

BOWDEN, C. G. R. AND ANDREWS, S. M. (1994) Mount Kupe and its birds. *Bull. African Bird Club* 1: 13–16.

BOWDEN, C. G. R. AND BOWDEN, E. M. (1993) The conservation of Mount Kupe, Cameroon. *Proc. 8th Pan-Afr. Orn. Congr. [Ann. Sci. Zool. Mus. Roy. Afrique Centr.]* 286: 231–235.

BOWEN, J. (1995) Protecting paradise. *World Birdw.* 17(4): 12–16.

BOWEN, J. (1996) Notes on the Vanuatu Megapode *Megapodius layardi* on Ambrym, Vanuatu. *Bird Conserv. Internatn.* 6: 401–408.

BOWEN, J. (1997) The status of the avifauna of Loru Protected Area, Santo, Vanuatu. *Bird Conserv. Internatn.* 7: 331–344.

BOWLER, J. AND TAYLOR, J. (1989) An annotated checklist of the birds of Manusela National Park, Seram (birds recorded on the Operation Raleigh Expedition). *Kukila* 4: 3–33.

BOWLER, J. AND TAYLOR, J. (1993) The avifauna of Seram. Pp.143–160 in I. D. Edwards, A. A. Macdonald and J. Proctor, eds. *Natural history of Seram.* Andover, UK: Intercept.

BRACE, R. C., HESSE, A. J. AND WHITE, A. G. (1995) The endemic macaws of Bolivia. *Cotinga* 3: 27–30.

BRADLEY, P. (1995) *Birds of the Cayman Islands.* Second edition. Unknown: Caerulea Press.

BRANDÃO, L. (1990) Avian endemism in Atlantic forests. Unpublished report.

BRASH, A. R. (1987) The history of avian extinction and forest conversion on Puerto Rico. *Biol. Conserv.* 39: 97–111.

BRATTSTROM, B. H. (1990) Biogeography of the Islas Revillagigedo. *J. Biogeogr.* 17: 177–183.

BRATTSTROM, B. H. AND HOWELL, T. R. (1956) The birds of the Revilla Gigedo Islands, Mexico. *Condor* 58: 107–120.

BRAZIL, M. A. (1991) *The birds of Japan.* London: Chistopher Helm.

BREEDLOVE, D. E., ED. (1981) *Introduction to the flora of Chiapas*, 1. First edition. San Francisco: California Academy of Sciences.

BREGULLA, H. L. (1992) *Birds of Vanuatu.* Oswestry, UK: Anthony Nelson.

BRETAGNOLLE, V. AND ATTIÉ, C. (1991) Status of Barau's Petrel (*Pterodroma baraui*): colony sites, breeding population and taxonomic affinities. *Col. Waterb.* 14: 25–33.

BRITTON, P. L., ED. (1980) *Birds of East Africa.* Nairobi: East Africa Natural History Society.

BROOKE, M. DE L. (1987) *The birds of the Juan Fernandez Islands, Chile.* Cambridge, UK: International Council for Bird Preservation (Study Rep. 16).

BROOKE, M. DE L. (1988) Distribution and numbers of the Masafuera Rayadito *Aphrastura masafuerae* on Isla Alejandro Selkirk, Juan Fernandez archipelago, Chile. *Bull. Brit. Orn. Club* 108: 4–9.

BROOKE, M. DE L. (1992) Sir Peter Scott Commemorative Expedition to the Pitcairn Islands 1991–1992. Expedition Report.

BROOKE, M. DE L. (1995a) The modern avifauna of the Pitcairn Islands. *Biol. J. Linn. Soc.* 56: 199–212.

BROOKE, M. DE L. (1995b) The breeding biology of the gadfly petrels *Pterodroma* spp. of the Pitcairn Islands: characteristics, population sizes and controls. *Biol. J. Linn. Soc.* 56: 213–231.

BROOKE, M. DE L. AND HARTLEY, I. R. (1995) Nesting Henderson Reed-warblers (*Acrocephalus vaughani taiti*) studied by DNA fingerprinting: unrelated coalitions in a stable habitat? *Auk* 112: 77–86.

BROOKE, M. DE L. AND JONES, P. J. (1995) The diet of the Henderson Fruit Dove *Ptilinopus insularis*. 1. Field observations of fruit choice. *Biol. J. Linn. Soc.* 56: 149–165.

BROOKE, M. DE L. AND ROWE, G. (1996) Behavioural and molecular evidence for specific status of light and dark morphs of the Herald Petrel *Pterodroma heraldica*. *Ibis* 138: 420–432.

BROOKS, T. AND BALMFORD, A. (1996) Atlantic forest extinctions. *Nature* 380: 115.

BROOKS, T. M., EVANS, T. D., DUTSON, G. C. L., ANDERSON, G. Q. A., ASANE, D. C., TIMMINS, R. J. AND TOLEDO, A. G. (1992) The conservation status of the birds of Negros, Philippines. *Bird Conserv. Internatn.* 2: 273–302.

BROOKS, T., DUTSON, G., GABUTERO, L. AND TIMMINS, R. (1995a) Siburan—key area for birds on Mindoro. *Oriental Bird Club Bull.* 21: 28–33.

BROOKS, T., MAGSALAY, P., DUTSON, G. AND ALLEN, R. (1995b) Forest loss, extinctions and last hope for birds on Cebu. *Oriental Bird Club Bull.* 21: 24–27.

BROOKS, T., DUTSON, G., KING, B. AND MAGSALAY, P. M. (1995c) An annotated check-list of the forest birds of Rajah Sikatuna National Park, Bohol, Philippines. *Forktail* 11: 121–134.

BROOKS, T. M., PIMM, S. L. AND COLLAR, N. J. (1997) Deforestation predicts the number of threatened birds in insular Southeast Asia. *Conserv. Biol.* 11: 382–394.

BROSSET, A. AND ERARD, C. (1986) *Les oiseaux des régions forestières du nord-est du Gabon*, 1. Paris: Société Nationale de Protection de la Nature.

BROUWER, J. AND GARNETT, S., EDS. (1990) *Threatened birds of Australia: an annotated list.* Moonee Ponds: Royal Australasian Ornithologists' Union (RAOU Report 68).

BROWN, K. S. JR AND BROWN, G. G. (1992) Habitat alteration and species loss in Brazilian forests. Pp.119–142 in T. C. Whitmore and J. A. Sayer, eds. *Tropical forest and extinction.* London: Chapman and Hall.

BRUDENELL-BRUCE, P. G. C. (1975) *The birds of New Providence and the Bahama Islands.* London: Collins.

BUCKINGHAM, D. L., DUTSON, G. C. L. AND NEWMAN, J. L. (1995) Birds of Manus, Kolombangara and Makira (San Cristobal) with notes on mammals and records from other Solomon Islands. Report of the Cambridge Solomons Rainforest Project 1990.

BUDEN, D. W. (1987) *The birds of the southern Bahamas: an annotated check-list.* London: British Ornithologists' Union (Check-list 8).

BULL, P. C., GAZE, P. D. AND ROBERTSON, C. J. R. (1985) *The atlas of bird distribution in New Zealand.* Wellington: Ornithological Society of New Zealand.

BURGESS, N. D. AND MLINGWA, C. O. F. (1993) Forest birds of coastal forests in East Africa. *Proc. 8th Pan-Afr. Orn. Congr. [Ann. Sci. Zool. Mus. Roy. Afrique Centr.]* 286: 295–301.

BURGESS, N. D., MWASUMBI, L. B., HAWTHORNE, W. J., DICKINSON, A. AND DOGGETT, R. A. (1992) Preliminary assessment of the distribution, status and biological importance of coastal forests in Tanzania. *Biol. Conserv.* 62: 205–218.

BURGESS, N., DE KLERK, H., FJELDSA, J. AND RAHBECK, C. (in press) A preliminary assessment of congruence between biodiversity patterns in Afrotropical forest birds and forest mammals. *Proc. 9th Pan-Afr. Orn. Congr.*

BURNEY, D. A. (1995) Theories and facts on Holocene environmental change before and after human colonisation. Pp.41–42 in B. D. Patterson, S. M. Goodman and J. L. Sedlock, eds. *Environmental change in Madagascar.* Chicago: Field Museum of Natural History.

BUTCHART, S. H. M., BROOKS, T. M., DAVIES, C. W. N., DHARMAPUTRA, G., DUTSON, G. C. L., LOWEN, J. C. AND

SAHU, A. (1996) The conservation status of forest birds on Flores and Sumbawa, Indonesia. *Bird Conserv. Internatn.* 6: 335–370.

BUTLER, D. AND MERTON, D. (1992) *The Black Robin: saving the world's most endangered bird.* Auckland: Oxford University Press.

BUTYNSKI, T. M. AND KALINA, J. (1993) Further additions to the known avifauna of the Impenetrable (Bwindi) Forest, southwestern Uganda (1989–1991). *Scopus* 17: 1–7.

BUTYNSKI, T. M., AGENONGA, U., NDERA, B. AND HART, J. F. (1997) Rediscovery of the Congo Bay (Itombwe) Owl *Phodilus prigoginei.* *Bull. African Bird Club* 4: 32–35.

BYERS, C., OLSSON, U. AND CURSON, J. (1995) *Buntings and sparrows: a guide to the buntings and North American sparrows.* Mountfield, UK: Pica Press.

CABANIUK, S., LEES, A. AND WRIGHT, S. (1995) *Integrating conservation and development: a future for the Sovi Basin, Waimaro.* Suva and Nelson: Native Lands Trust Board and Maruia Society.

CAHYADIN, Y. (1993) Tanimbar Corella on Yamdena. *Oriental Bird Club Bull.* 18: 55–56.

CAHYADIN, Y. AND ARIF, S. (1994) Status *Cacatua sulphurea abbotti* di Kepulauan Masalembu. Report to BirdLife Indonesia Programme.

CAHYADIN, Y., JEPSON, P. AND SYARIEF, M. (1994) *A rapid status assessment of Cacatua sulphurea sulphurea in South Sulawesi province, Indonesia.* Bogor: PHPA/ Birdlife International-Indonesia Programme (Laporan 3).

CAI GIKAN (1987) *Birds of Beijing.* Beijing: Beijing Press.

CAPPARELLA, A. P. (1986) Genetic variation in Neotropical birds: implications for the speciation process. Pp.1658 in H. Ouellet, ed. *Acta XIX Congressus Internationalis Ornithologici,* 2. Ottawa: National Museum of Natural Sciences/University of Ottawa Press.

CASTAÑEDA, P. G. (1993) Management planning for the Palawan Biosphere Reserve. *Nature & Res.* 29: 35–38.

CASTELLANOS, A. AND RODRÍGUEZ-ESTRELLA, R. (1993) Current status of the Socorro Mockingbird. *Wilson Bull.* 105: 167–171.

CEBALLOS, G. AND GARCÍA, A. (1995) Conserving Neotropical biodiversity: the role of dry forests in western Mexico. *Conserv. Biol.* 9: 1349–1356.

CHALABI, B. (1989) Du nouveau à propos de l'aire de distribution de la Sittelle kabyle (*Sitta ledanti*). *Aves* 26: 233–234.

CHAMPION, G. AND SETH, S. K. (1968) *A revised survey of the forest types of India.* Delhi: Manager of Publications.

CHAMPION, H. G. (1936) A preliminary survey of the forest types of India and Burma. *Indian Forest Recs.* 1: 1–286.

CHAPPUIS, C. AND ERARD, C. (1993) Species limits in the genus *Bleda* Bonaparte, 1857 (Aves, Pycnonotidae). *Z. Zool. Syst. Evolut.* 31: 280–299.

CHARDONNET, P. AND LARTIGES, A. (1992) *Gestion de la faune sauvage terrestre et vertébrée dans la Province sud de Nouvelle-Calédonie: avis et proposition.* Maison Alfort: IGF/ONC/CIRAD-EMUT.

CHEKE, A. S. (1987a) The ecology of the surviving native land-birds of Réunion. Pp.301–358 in A. W. Diamond, ed. *Studies in Mascarene island birds.* Cambridge, UK: Cambridge University Press.

CHEKE, A. S. (1987b) An ecological history of the Mascarene Islands, with particular reference to extinctions and introductions of land vertebrates. Pp.5–89 in A. W. Diamond, ed. *Studies of Mascarene Island birds.* Cambridge, UK: Cambridge University Press.

CHEKE, A. S. (1987c) The ecology of the smaller land-birds of Mauritius. Pp.151–207 in A. W. Diamond, ed. *Studies in Mascarene island birds.* Cambridge, UK: Cambridge University Press.

CHEKE, A. S. (1987d) Observations on the surviving endemic birds of Rodrigues. Pp.364–402 in A. W. Diamond, ed. *Studies in Mascarene island birds.* Cambridge, UK: Cambridge University Press.

CHENG TSO-HSIN (1987) *A synopsis of the avifauna of China.* Beijing: Science Press.

CHRISTIDIS, L. AND BOLES, W. E. (1994) *The taxonomy and species of birds of Australia and its territories.* Melbourne: Royal Australasian Ornithologists Union (RAOU Monogr. 2).

CHRISTY, P. (1996) Príncipe Thrush rediscovered after more than 50 years. *Gulf of Guinea Conserv. Newsl.* 4: 2–3.

CLANCEY, P. A. (1971) *A handlist of the birds of southern Mozambique.* Lourenço Marques: Instituto de Investigação Científica de Mocambique.

CLARK, M. R. AND DINGWALL, P. R. (1985) *Conservation of islands in the southern ocean: a review of the protected areas of Insulantarctica.* Gland, Switzerland and Cambridge, UK: International Union for the Conservation of Nature and Natural Resources.

CLARK, R. (1986) *Aves de Tierra del Fuego y Cabo de Hornos.* Buenos Aires: Literature of Latin America.

CLAY, J. (1994) Nakanai '93: an Oxford University Expedition to New Britain Island, Papua New Guinea. Unpublished report.

CLEMENTS, F. A. (1992) Recent bird records from Bhutan. *Forktail* 7: 57–74.

CLOSE, I. (1995) To protect a Pacific forest: conservation in Vanuatu. *Forest and Bird* 276: 36–41.

CLOUT, M. N. AND CRAIG, J. L. (1995) The conservation of critically endangered flightless birds in New Zealand. *Ibis* 137 (Suppl. 1): 181–190.

CLUNIE, F. (1984) *Birds of the Fiji bush.* Suva: Fiji Museum.

COATES, B. J. (1985) *The birds of Papua New Guinea,* 1: *non-passerines.* Alderley, Australia: Dove.

COATES, B. J. (1990) *The birds of Papua New Guinea,* 2: *passerines.* Alderley, Australia: Dove.

COATES, B. J. AND BISHOP, K. D. (1997) *A guide to the birds of Wallacea: Sulawesi, the Moluccas and Lesser Sunda Islands, Indonesia.* Alderley, Austrlaia: Dove.

COIMBRA-FILHO, A. F. (1970) Sobre *Mitu mitu* (Linnaeus, 1766) e a validez das suas duas raças geográficas (Cracidae, Aves). *Revta. Bras. Biol.* 30: 101–109.

COLLAR, N. J. (1982) *Extracts from the Red Data Book for the Birds of Africa and Associated Islands.* Cambridge, UK: International Council for Bird Preservation.

COLLAR, N. J. (1993) The conservation status in 1982 of the Aldabra White-throated Rail *Dryolimnas cuvieri aldabranus.* *Bird Conserv. Internatn.* 3: 299–305.

COLLAR, N. J. (1996) Species concepts and conservation: a response to Hazevoet. *Bird Conserv. Internatn.* 6: 197–200.

COLLAR, N. J. AND ANDREW, P. (1988) *Birds to watch: the ICBP world check-list of threatened birds.* Cambridge, UK: International Council for Bird Preservation (Techn. Publ. 8).

COLLAR, N. J. AND LONG, A. J. (1996) Taxonomy and names of *Carpococcyx* cuckoos from the Greater Sundas. *Forktail* 11: 135–150.

COLLAR, N. J. AND STUART, S. N. (1985) *Threatened birds of Africa and related islands: the ICBP/IUCN Red Data Book*. Cambridge, UK: International Council for Bird Preservation, and International Union for Conservation of Nature and Natural Resources.

COLLAR, N. J. AND STUART, S. N. (1988) *Key forests for threatened birds in Africa*. Cambridge, UK: International Council for Bird Preservation (Monogr. 3).

COLLAR, N. J. AND WEGE, D. C. (1995) The distribution and conservation status of the Bearded Tachuri *Polystictus pectoralis*. *Bird Conserv. Internatn.* 5: 367–390.

COLLAR, N. J., ROUND, P. D. AND WELLS, D. R. (1986) The past and future of Gurney's Pitta *Pitta gurneyi*. *Forktail* 1: 29–51.

COLLAR, N. J., DEE, T. J. AND GORIUP, P. D. (1987) La conservation de la nature à Madagascar: la perspective du CIPO. Pp.97–108 in *Priorités en matière de conservation des espèces à Madagascar*. Gland, Switzerland: International Union for Nature Conservation and Natural Resources (Occasional Papers of the IUCN SSC).

COLLAR, N. J., GONZAGA, L. P., KRABBE, N., MADROÑO NIETO, A., NARANJO, L. G., PARKER, T. A. AND WEGE, D. C. (1992) *Threatened birds of the Americas: the ICBP/IUCN Red Data Book*. Cambridge, UK: International Council for Bird Preservation.

COLLAR, N. J., CROSBY, M. J. AND STATTERSFIELD, A. J. (1994) *Birds to watch 2: the world list of threatened birds*. Cambridge, UK: BirdLife International (BirdLife Conservation Series no. 4).

COLLAR, N. J., WEGE, D. C. AND LONG, A. J. (1997) Patterns and causes of endangerment in the New World avifauna. Pp. in J. V. Remsem, ed. *Studies in Neotropical ornithology honoring Ted Parker* (Ornithol. Monogr. 48).

COLLAR, N. J., MALLARI, N. A. D., TABARANZA, B. R., VILLASPER, J. AND LOWEN, J. C. (in press.) *Threatened birds of the Philippines*. Manila: Bookmark.

COLLINS, N. M. AND MORRIS, M. G. (1985) *Threatened swallowtail butterflies of the world*. Gland, Switzerland and Cambridge, UK: International Union for Conservation of Nature and Natural Resources.

COLLINS, N. M., SAYER, J. A. AND WHITMORE, T. C., EDS. (1991) *The conservation atlas of tropical forests: Asia and the Pacific*. London: Macmillan.

CONRY, P. J. (1988) High nest predation by brown tree snakes on Guam. *Condor* 90: 478–482.

CONSERVATION INTERNATIONAL, FUNDAÇÃO BIODIVERSITAS AND SOCIEDADE NORDESTINA DE ECOLOGIA (1995) Prioridades para Conservação da Biodiversidade da Mata Atlantica. C.I. & F.B.: Belo Horizonte.

COOPER, J. AND RYAN, P. G. (1994) *Management plan for the Gough Island Wildlife Reserve*. Edinburgh, Tristan da Cunha: Government of Tristan da Cunha.

CORDEIRO, N. J. AND KIURE, J. (1995) An investigation of the forest avifauna in the North Pare mountains, Tanzania. *Scopus* 19: 9–26.

COWLES, G. S. (1987) The fossil record. Pp.90–100 in A. W. Diamond, ed. *Studies of Mascarene Island birds*. Cambridge, UK: Cambridge University Press.

CRACRAFT, J. A. (1983) Species concepts and speciation analysis. *Curr. Orn.* 1: 159–187.

CRACRAFT, J. (1985) Historical biogeography and patterns of differentiation within the South American avifauna: areas of endemism. Pp.49–84 in P. A. Buckley, M. S. Foster, E. S. Morton, R. S. Ridgely and F. G. Buckley, eds. *Neotropical ornithology*. Washington, DC: American Ornithologists' Union (Orn. Monogr. 36).

CRACRAFT, J. (1986) Origin and evolution of continental biotas: speciation and historical congruence within the Australian avifauna. *Evolution* 40: 977–996.

CRAIG, R. J. AND TAISACAN, E. (1994) Notes on the ecology and population decline of the Rota Bridled White-eye. *Wilson Bull.* 106: 165–168.

CRAMP, S. ET AL. (1977–1994) *The birds of the western Palearctic*, 2. Oxford: Oxford University Press.

CROME, F. H. J. (1993) Post world heritage bird conservation problems in north east Queensland. Pp.93–104 in C. P. Catterall, P. V. Driscoll, K. Hulsman, D. Muir and A. Taplin, eds. *Birds and their habitats: status and conservation in Queensland*. St Lucia, Queensland: Queensland Ornithological Society.

CROSBY, M. J. (1991) Little-known Oriental bird: Silver Oriole. *Oriental Bird Club Bull.* 14: 32–35.

CROSBY, M. J. (1994) Mapping the distributions of restricted-range bird species to identify global conservation priorities. Pp.145–154 in R. Miller, ed. *Mapping the diversity of nature*. London: Chapman and Hall.

CROSBY, M. J. (1995) From the field. *Oriental Bird Club Bull.* 21: 68–73.

CROSBY, M. J. (1996) Threatened birds in the eastern Himalayas. *OBC bulletin* 23: 21–23.

CROSBY, M. J. (in prep.) Emei Leaf Warbler *Phylloscopus emeiensis* at Fanjing Shan, eastern Guizhou province, China.

CROSBY, M. J., STATTERSFIELD, A. J., COLLAR, N. J. AND BIBBY, C. J. (1994) Predicting avian extinction rates. *Biodiv. Let.* 2: 182–185.

CROXALL, J. P. AND GALES, R. (in press) Assessment of the conservation status of albatrosses. Pp. 46–65 in G. Robertson and R. Gales *Albatross biology and conservation*. Chipping Norton, Australia: Surrey Beatty & Sons.

CROXALL, J. P., MCINNES, S. AND PRINCE, P. A. (1984) The status and conservation of seabirds at the Falkland Islands. Pp.271–292 in J. P. Croxall, P. G. H. Evans and R. W. Schreiber, eds. *Status and conservation of the world's seabirds*. Cambridge, UK: International Council for Bird Preservation (Techn. Publ. 2).

CRUSZ, H. (1984) Parasites of the endemic and relict vertebrates: a biogeographical review. Pp.321–352 in C. H. Fernando, ed. *Ecology and biogeography in Sri Lanka*. The Hague: W. Junk.

CURIO, E. (1994) Ornithological observations during a (preliminary) Philippines Conservation Expedition in 1993. *Ökol. Vögel* 16: 613–623.

CURIO, E., DIESMOS, A. C., MALLARI, N. A. D. AND ALTAMIRANO, R. A. N. (1996) The Mindoro Scarlet-collared Flowerpecker—an alleged single island endemic. *J. Orn.* 137: 361–365.

CURSON, J. (1989) South Andaman Island. *Oriental Bird Club Bull.* 10: 28–31.

CUTHBERT, R. J. AND DENNY, M. J. H. (1995) Population estimate of the Seychelles Brush Warbler *Acrocephalus seychellensis* on Aride Island, Seychelles, May 1995. Report to Aride Management Committee RSNC.

CYRUS, D. AND ROBSON, N. (1980) *Bird atlas of Natal.* Pietermaritzburg: University of Natal.

DAHL, A. L. (1980) *Regional ecosystems survey of the South Pacific area.* Noumea: South Pacific Commission (Technical Paper 179).

DAI BO (1996) A summary report on the survey of Sichuan Hill-partridge. Unpublished report.

DANIELSEN, F., POULSEN, M. K., JENSEN, A., HEEGAARD, M. AND JOKOBSEN, O. F. (1991) *Conservation of biological diversity in the Sierra Madre mountains of Isabela province, the Philippines.* Manila and Copenhagen: Department of Environment and Natural Resources, BirdLife International and Danish Ornithological Society.

DANIELSEN, F., JENSEN, A., MIRANDA, H. AND CALEDA, M. (1992) *A preliminary survey of the Philippine Eagle* Pithecophaga jefferyi *and the conservation of the northern Sierra Madre mountains in the Philippines.* Manila: Department of Environment and Natural Resources, and International Council for Bird Preservation.

DANIELSEN, F., BALETE, D. S., CHRISTENSEN, T. D., HEEGAARD, M., JAKOBSEN, O. F., JENSEN, A., LUND, T. AND POULSEN, M. K. (1994) *Conservation of biological diversity in the Sierra Madre Mountains of Isabela and southern Cagayan Province, the Philippines.* Manila and Copenhagen: Department of Environment and Natural Resources, BirdLife International and Danish Ornithological Society.

DANKS, A. AND CALVER, M. C. (1993) Diet of the Noisy Scrub-bird *Atrichornis clamosus* at Two Peoples Bay, south-western Western Australia. *Emu* 93: 203–205.

DATHE, H. AND NEUFELDT, I. A., EDS. (1978) *Atlas der verbreitung Palaearktischer vögel,* 7. Berlin: Akademie Verlag.

DATHE, H. AND NEUFELDT, I. A., EDS. (1980) *Atlas der verbreitung Palaearktischer vögel,* 8. Berlin: Akademie Verlag.

DATHE, H. AND NEUFELDT, I. A., EDS. (1982) *Atlas der verbreitung Palaearktischer vögel,* 10. Berlin: Akademie Verlag.

DAVIDSON, P., STONES, T. AND LUCKING, R. (1995) The conservation status of key bird species on Taliabu and the Sula Islands, Indonesia. *Bird Conserv. Internatn.* 5: 1–20.

DAVIES, A. G. AND PALMER, P. D. (1989) Conservation of forest resources in Sierra Leone. Unpublished report for the FAO Joint Inter-agencies Forestry Sector Review.

DAVIS, S. D., DROOP, S. J. M., GREGERSON, P., HENSON, L., LEON, C. J., VILLA-LOBOS, J. L., SYNGE, H. AND ZANTOVSKA, J. (1986) *Plants in danger: what do we know?* Gland, Switzerland: International Union for Conservation of Nature and Natural Resources.

DAVISON, G. W. H. (1992) *Birds of Mount Kinabalu, Borneo.* Sabah, Malaysia: Natural History Publications (Borneo) Sdn. Bhd. and Kohtas Sabah Berhad.

DEAN, W. R. J., HUNTLEY, M. A., HUNTLEY, B. J. AND VERNON, C. J. (1987) Notes on some birds of Angola. *Durban Mus. Novit.* 14: 43–92.

DEAN, W. R. J., MILTON, S. J., WATKEYS, M. K. AND HOCKEY, P. A. R. (1991) Distribution, habitat preference and conservation status of the Red Lark *Certhilauda burra* in Cape Province, South Africa. *Biol. Conserv.* 58: 257–274.

DEFENSE MAPPING AGENCY (1984–1988) Operational navigation charts. St Louis, Miss: Defense Mapping Agency Aerospace Center.

DEKKER, B. G. (1992) Secondary plant cover on upland slopes. Marquesas Islands, French Polynesia. *Atoll Res. Bull.* 363: 1–36.

DEKKER, R. AND ARGELOO, M. (1993) Bruijn's Brush-turkey *Aegopodius bruijnii* remains a mystery. *Megapode Newsl.* 7: 15–17.

DELACOUR, J. AND AMADON, D. (1973) *Curassows and related birds.* New York: American Museum of Natural History.

DELGADO (1985) A new subspecies of the Painted Parakeet (*Pyrrhura picta*) from Panama. Pp.17–20 in P. A. Buckley, M. S. Foster, E. S. Morton, R. S. Ridgely and F. G. Buckley, eds. *Neotropical ornithology.* Washington, DC: American Ornithologists' Union (Orn. Monogr. 36).

DEMENT'EV, G. P. AND GLADKOV, N. A., EDS. (1968) *Birds of the Soviet Union,* 6. Jerusalem: Israel Program for Scientific Translations.

DEMENT'EV, G. P. AND GLADKOV, N. A., EDS. (1970) *Birds of the Soviet Union,* 5. Jerusalem: Israel Program for Scientific Translations.

DEMEY, R. AND FISHPOOL, L. D. C. (1991) Additions and annotations to the avifauna of Côte d'Ivoire. *Malimbus* 12: 61–86.

DIAMOND, A. W. (1984) Biogeography of Seychelles land birds. Pp.487–504 in D. R. Stoddart, ed. *Biogeography and ecology of the Seychelles.* The Hague: W. Junk.

DIAMOND, A. W. AND KEITH, G. S. (1980) Avifaunas of Kenya forest islands. I–Mount Kulal. *Scopus* 4: 49–55.

DIAMOND, J. M. (1976) Recommendations for minimising enviromental costs of mining on Rennell. Unpublished report to the Central Planning Office, Government of the Solomon Islands.

DIAMOND, J. M. (1985) New distributional records and taxa from the outlying mountain ranges of New Guinea. *Emu* 85: 65–91.

DIAMOND, J. (1986) The design of a nature reserve system for Indonesian New Guinea. Pp.485–503 in M. E. Soulé, ed. *Conservation biology: the science of scarcity and diversity.* Sunderland, Mass.: Sinaeur.

DIAMOND, J. M. (1987) Extant unless proven extinct? Or, extinct unless proven extant? *Conserv. Biol.* 1: 77–79.

DIAMOND, J. (1991a) A new species of rail from the Solomon Islands and convergent evolution of insular flightlessness. *Auk* 108: 461–470.

DIAMOND, J. M. (1991b) The avifaunas of Rennell and Bellona islands. Pp.127–168 in T. Wolff, ed. *The natural history of Rennell Island, British Solomon Islands: Scientific results of the Noona Dan Expedition (Rennell Section, 1962) and the Danish Rennell Expedition, 1965,* 8 (*Zoology*). Copenhagen: University of Copenhagen.

DIAMOND, J. M. AND BISHOP, K. D. (1994) New records and observations from the Aru Islands, New Guinea region. *Emu* 94: 41–45.

DICKERMAN, R. W. (1965) The juvenile plumage and distribution of *Cassidix palustris* (Swainson). *Auk* 82: 268–270.

DICKINSON, E. C., KENNEDY, R. S. AND PARKES, K. C. (1991) *The birds of the Philippines: an annotated check-list.* Tring, UK: British Ornithologists' Union (Check-list 12).

DIESMOS, A. C. AND PEDREGOSA, M. D. G. (1995) The conservation status of threatened species of bleeding-hearts (Columbidae) and hornbills (Bucerotidae) in the Philippines. Unpublished.

DINERSTEIN, E., OLSON, D. M., GRAHAM, D. J., WEBSTER, A. L., PRIMM, S. A., BOOKBINDER, M. P. AND LEDEC, G. (1995) *A conservation assesssment of the terrestrial ecoregions of Latin America and the Caribbean*. Washington, DC: World Bank.

DINESEN, L., LEHMBERG, T., SVENDSEN, J. O. AND HANSEN, L. A. (1993) Range extensions and other notes on some restricted-range forest birds from West Kilombero in the Udzungwa Mountains, Tanzania. *Scopus* 17: 48–59.

DINESEN, L., LEHMBERG, T., SVENDSEN, J. O., HANSEN, L. A. AND FJELDSÅ, J. (1994) A new genus and species of perdicine bird (Phasianidae, Perdicini) from Tanzania: a relict form with Indo-Malayan affinities. *Ibis* 136: 3–11.

DING CHANG-QING AND ZHENG GUANG-MEI (1993) A radio-tracking study of habitat selection and movements by Cabot's Tragopan in the 1991 breeding season. Pp.76–79 in D. Jenkins, ed. *Pheasants in Asia 1992*. Reading, UK: World Pheasant Association.

DING PING AND ZHUGE YANG (1990) The ecology of Elliot's Pheasant in the wild. Pp.65–68 in D. A. Hill, P. J. Garson and D. Jenkins, eds. *Pheasants in Asia 1989*. Reading, UK: World Pheasant Association.

DIRZO, R. AND GARCÍA, M. C. (1992) Rates of deforestation in Los Tuxtlas, a Neotropical area in southeast Mexico. *Conserv. Biol.* 6: 84–90.

DISSING, H., JORGENSEN, M. F. AND JENSEN, S. (1990) Pakistan and Xinjiang. Unpublished report to DAFIF (Danish Ornithological Society).

DOBSON, A. P., RODRIGUEZ, J. P., ROBERTS, W. M. AND WILCOVE, D. S. (1997) Geographic distribution of endangered species in the United States. *Science* 275: 550–553.

DODMAN, T. (1995) A survey to investigate the status and distribution of the Black-cheeked Lovebird *Agapornis nigrigenis* in south-west Zambia. *Bull. African Bird Club* 2: 103–105.

DOUMENGE, C. AND RENARD, Y. (1989) *La conservation des ecosystemes forestiers de l'île de la Réunion*. Gland, Switzerland: International Union for the Conservation of Nature and Natural Resources.

DOUTHWAITE, R. J. (1987) Lowland forest resources and their conservation in southern Somalia. *Environ. Conserv.* 14: 29–35.

DOWELL, S. D. (1995) Current status and future prospects for the Sichuan Hill-partridge. *WPA News* 49: 6–13.

DOWSETT, R. J. (1985) The conservation of tropical forest birds in Central and Southern Africa. Pp.197–212 in A. W. Diamond and T. E. Lovejoy, eds. *Conservation of tropical forest birds*. Cambridge, UK: International Council for Bird Preservation (Techn. Publ. 4).

DOWSETT, R. J. AND DOWSETT-LEMAIRE, F., EDS. (1993) *A contribution to the distribution and taxonomy of Afrotropical and Malagasy birds*. Liege: Tauraco Press (Tauraco Research Report 5).

DOWSETT, R. J. AND FORBES-WATSON, A. D. (1993) *Checklist of birds of the Afrotropical and Malagasy regions*. Liège: Tauraco Press.

DOWSETT-LEMAIRE, F. (1989) Ecological and biogeographical aspects of forest bird communities in Malawi. *Scopus* 13: 1–80.

DOWSETT-LEMAIRE, F. (1990) Eco-ethology, distribution and status of Nyungwe Forest birds. Pp.31–85 in R. J. Dowsett, ed. *Enquête faunistique et floristique dans la Forêt de Nyungwe, Rwanda*. Ely, UK: Tauraco Press

(Tauraco Research Report 3).

DOWSETT-LEMAIRE, F. AND DOWSETT, R. J. (1990) Enquête faunistique et floristique dans la Forêt de Nyungwe au Rwanda: buts, statut de la forêt et recommandations. Pp.1–9 in R. J. Dowsett, ed. *Enquête faunistique et floristique dans la Forêt de Nyungwe, Rwanda*. Ely, UK: Tauraco Press (Tauraco Research Report 3).

DOWSETT-LEMAIRE, F., DOWSETT, R. J. AND BULENS, P. (1993) Additions and corrections to the avifauna of Congo. *Malimbus* 15: 68–80.

DROLLET, J. (1990) Bird conservation in Polynesia. Paper presented to the XX ICBP World Conference.

DUCKWORTH, J. W., EVANS, T. D. AND TIMMINS, R. J. (1993) *A wildlife and habitat survey of the Xe Piane National Biodiversity Conservation Area*. Vientiane, Laos: National Office for Nature Conservation and Watershed Management.

DUCKWORTH, J. W., TIMMINS, R. J. AND COZZA, K. (1993) A wildlife and habitat survey of Phou Xang He proposed protected area. Vientiane, Laos: National Office for Nature Conservation and Watershed Management (unpublished report).

DUKE, G. (1994) Mountains, forests and pheasants. *World Birdw.* 16(1): 10–13.

DUPON, J. F. (1986a) *The effects of mining on the environment of high islands: a case study of nickel mining in New Caledonia*. Noumea, New Caledonia: SPREP (Environmental case studies; South Pacific study 1).

DUPON, J. F. (1986b) *Wallis and Futuna: man against the forest*. Noumea, New Caledonia: SPREP (Environment case studies; South Pacific study 2).

DU PUY, D. J. AND MOAT, J. (1996) A refined classification of the primary vegetation of Madagascar based on the underlying geology: using GIS to map its distribution and to assess its conservation status. Pp.205–218 in W. R. Lourenco, ed. *Proceedings of the International Symposium on the biogeography of Madagascar*. Paris: ORSTOM.

DUTSON, G. (1993) A sighting of *Ficedula* (*crypta*) *disposita* in Luzon, Philippines. *Forktail* 8: 144–147.

DUTSON, G. C. L. (1995) The birds of Salayar and the Flores Sea Islands. *Kukila* 7: 129–141.

DUTSON, G. C. L. AND NEWMAN, J. L. (1991) Observations on the Superb Pitta *Pitta superba* and other Manus endemics. *Bird Conserv. Internatn.* 1: 215–222.

DUTSON, G. C. L., EVANS, T. D., BROOKS, T. M., ASANE, D. C., TIMMINS, R. J. AND TOLEDO, A. (1992) Conservation status of birds on Mindoro, Philippines. *Bird Conserv. Internatn.* 2: 303–325.

DUTSON, G. C. L., MAGSALAY, P. M. AND TIMMINS, R. J. (1993) The rediscovery of the Cebu Flowerpecker *Dicaeum quadricolor*, with notes on other forest birds on Cebu, Philippines. *Bird Conserv. Internatn.* 3: 235–243.

DUTTON, J. (1994) Introduced mammals in São Tomé and Príncipe: possible threats to biodiversity. *Biodiv. and Conserv.* 3: 927–938.

EAMES, J. C. (1995) Endemic birds and protected area development on the Da Lat Plateau, Vietnam. *Bird Conserv. Internatn.* 5: 491–523.

EAMES, J. C. AND NGUYEN CU (1994) *A management feasibility study of Thuong Da Nhim and Chu Yang Sin Nature Reserves on the Da Lat Plateau, Vietnam*. Hanoi: WWF Vietnam Programme.

EAMES, J. C., ROBSON, C. R., NGUYEN CU AND TRUONG VAN LA (1992) *Forest bird surveys in Vietnam 1991*. Cambridge, UK: International Council for Bird Preservation (Study Report 51).

EAMES, J. C., LAMBERT, F. R. AND NGUYEN CU (1994) A survey of the Annamese Lowlands, Vietnam, and its implications for the conservation of Vietnamese and Imperial Pheasants *Lophura hatinhensis* and *L. imperialis*. *Bird Conserv. Internatn.* 4: 343–382.

EAMES, J. C., LAMBERT, F. R. AND NGUYEN CU (1995a) Rediscovery of the Sooty Babbler *Stachyris herberti* in central Vietnam. *Bird Conserv. Internatn.* 5: 129–135.

EAMES, J. C., LE TRONG TRAI AND NGUYEN CU (1995b) Rediscovery of the Grey-crowned Crocias *Crocias langbianis*. *Bird Conserv. Internatn.* 5: 525–535.

EASTWOOD, C. (1996) Kavieng, Djaul and Mussau Island, New Ireland: a trip report. *Muruk* 8: 28–32.

EDWARDS, I. D. (1993b) Introduction. Pp.1–12 in I. D. Edwards, A. A. Macdonald and J. Proctor, eds. *Natural History of Seram, Maluku, Indonesia*. Andover, UK: Intercept Ltd.

EDWARDS, I. D., MACDONALD, A. A. AND PROCTOR, J., EDS. (1993) *Natural history of Seram, Maluku, Indonesia*. Andover, UK: Intercept.

EDWARDS, M. (1993a) Saving the bird—saving the forest. *People and the Planet* 2: 14–15.

ELGOOD, J. H. (1988) Rediscovery of *Malimbus ibadanensis* Elgood, 1958. *Bull. Brit. Orn. Club* 108: 184–185.

ELGOOD, J. H. (1992) The range of *Malimbus ibadanensis*. *Bull. Brit. Orn. Club* 112: 205–207.

ELLIOTT, G., WALKER, K. AND BUCKINGHAM, R. (1991) The Auckland Island Rail. *Notornis* 38: 199–209.

ELMQVIST, T., ED. (1993) *The rain forest and the flying foxes: an introduction to the rain forest perserves on Savai'i, Western Samoa*. Salelologa, Western Samoa: Fa'asao Savai'i Society.

ELMQVIST, T., RAINEY, W. E., PIERSON, E. D. AND COX, P. A. (1994) Effects of tropical cyclones Ofa and Val on the structure of a Samoan lowland rain forest. *Biotropica* 26: 384–391.

ENGBRING, J. (1988) *Field guide to the birds of Palau*. Koror, Palau: Conservation Office and Bureau of Education.

ENGBRING, J. (1992) *A 1991 survey of the forest birds of the Republic of Palau*. Honolulu: US Fish and Wildlife Service.

ENGBRING, J. AND RAMSEY, F. (1989) *A 1986 survey of the forest birds of American Samoa*. US Fish and Wildlife Service.

ENGBRING, J., RAMSEY, F. L. AND WILDMAN, V. J. (1990) *Micronesian forest bird surveys, the Federated States: Pohnpei, Kosrae, Chuuk, and Yap*. Honolulu: US Fish and Wildlife Service.

ENGLEMAN, D. (1994) The field editor's report. *Toucan* 20: 4–5.

ENKERLIN, E. C. (1995) Comparative ecology and reproductive biology of three species of Amazona parrots in northeastern Mexico. Texas A&M University (Ph.D. Dissertation).

ENTWISTLE, A. AND CORP, N. (1997) Status and distribution of the Pemba flying fox *Pteropus voeltzkowi*. *Oryx* 31: 135–142.

ERARD, C. (1975) Une nouvelle alouette du sud de l'Ethiopie. *Alauda* 43: 115–124.

ERARD, C. AND COLSTON, P. R. (1988) *Batis minima* (Verreaux) new for Cameroon. *Bull. Brit. Orn. Club* 108: 182–184.

ESCALANTE-PLIEGO, P. AND PETERSON, A. T. (1992) Geographic variation and species limits in middle American woodnymphs (*Thalurania*). *Wilson Bull.* 104: 205–219.

EVANS, M. I. (1993) Iraq marshes doomed. *Orn. Soc. Middle East Bull.* 31: 28–29.

EVANS, M. I. (1994) *Important Bird Areas in the Middle East*. Cambridge, UK: BirdLife International (BirdLife Conservation Series no. 2).

EVANS, M. I., DUCKWORTH, J. W., HAWKINS, A. F. A., SAFFORD, R. J., SHELDON, B. C. AND WILKINSON, R. J. (1992a) Key bird species of Marojejy Strict Nature Reserve, Madagascar. *Bird Conserv. Internatn.* 2: 201–222.

EVANS, S. M., FLETCHER, F. J. C., LOADER, P. J. AND ROOKSBY, F. G. (1992b) Habitat exploitation by landbirds in the changing Western Samoan environment. *Bird Conserv. Internatn.* 2: 123–129.

EVANS, T. D. AND ANDERSON, G. Q. A., EDS. (1992) *A wildlife survey of the East Usambara and Ukaguru mountains, Tanzania*. Cambridge, UK: International Council for Bird Preservation (Study Report 53).

EVANS, T. D. AND ANDERSON, G. Q. A. (1993) Results of an ornithological survey in the Ukaguru and East Usambara mountains, Tanzania. *Scopus* 17: 40–47.

EVANS, T. D., MAGSALAY, P., DUTSON, G. C. L. AND BROOKS, T. M. (1993) The conservation status of the forest birds of Siquijor, Philippines. *Forktail* 8: 89–96.

EVANS, T. D., WATSON, L. G., HIPKISS, A. J., KIURE, J., TIMMINS, R. J. AND PERKIN, A. W. (1994) New records of Sokoke Scops Owl *Otus ireneae*, Usambara Eagle Owl *Bubo vosseleri* and East Coast Akalat *Sheppardia gunningi* from Tanzania. *Scopus* 18: 40.

EWNHS (1996) The conservation of key biodiversity sites and the Important Bird Areas (IBAs) project in Ethiopia. Ethiopian Wildlife and Natural History Society.

EYRE, L. A. (1987) Jamaica: test case for tropical deforestation. *Ambio* 16: 6.

FAABORG, J., DUGGER, K. M., ARENDT, W. J., WOODWORTH, B. L. AND BALTZ, M. E. (1997) Population declines of the Puerto Rican Vireo in Guánica Forest. *Wilson Bull.* 109: 195–202.

FANSHAWE, J. (1991) Saving Sokoke. *World Birdw.* 13(3): 10–11.

FANSHAWE, J. (1993) Red Data Bird: Sokoke Scops Owl. *World Birdw.* 15(1): 18–19.

FAO (1982a) *National conservation plan for Indonesia. 3: Java and Bali*. Bogor: Food and Agriculture Organisation of the United Nations (Field Report 36).

FAO (1982b) *National conservation plan for Indonesia. 6: Sulawesi*. Bogor: Food and Agriculture Organisation of the United Nations (Field Report 35).

FAO (1982c) *National conservation plan for Indonesia. 4: Nusa Tenggara*. Bogor: Food and Agriculture Organization of the United Nations (Field Report 44).

FAO (1982d) *National conservation plan for Indonesia. 7: Maluku and Irian Jaya*. Bogor: Food and Agriculture Organisation of the United Nations (Field Report 18).

FARAMALALA, M. H. (1988) Etude de la végétation de Madagascar à l'aide des données spaciales. Univ. Paul Sabatier de Toulouse (Doctoral Thesis).

FARAMALALA, M. H. (1995) Formations végétales et domaine

forestier national de Madagascar. Conservation International.

FEARNSIDE, P. M. (1990) The rate and extent of deforestation in Brazilian Amazonia. *Environ. Conserv.* 17: 213–226.

FEARNSIDE, P. (1996) Brazil. Pp.229–248 in C. S. Harcourt and J. A. Sayer, eds. *The conservation atlas of tropical forests: the Americas,* 1. New York and London: Simon & Schuster.

FINCH, B. W. AND McKEAN, J. L. (1987) Some notes on the birds of the Bismarks [*sic*]. *Muruk* 2: 3–28.

FISHPOOL, L. D. C., DEMEY, R., ALLPORT, G. AND HAYMAN, P. V. (1994) Notes on the field identification of the bulbuls (Pycnonotidae) of Upper Guinea, 1: the genera *Criniger, Bleda* and *Andropadus. Bull. African Bird Club* 1: 32–38.

FITZPATRICK, J. W. AND O'NEILL, J. P. (1986) *Otus petersoni,* a new screech-owl from the eastern andes, with systematic notes on *O. colombianus* and *O. ingens. Wilson Bull.* 98: 1–14.

FITZPATRICK, J. W., TERBORGH, J. W. AND WILLARD, D. E. (1977) A new species of Wood-wren from Peru. *Auk* 94: 195–201.

FJELDSÅ, J. (1992) Biogeographic patterns and evolution of the avifauna of relict high altitude woodlands of the Andes. *Streenstrupia* 18: 9–62.

FJELDSÅ, J. AND KRABBE, N. (1990) *Birds of the high Andes.* Copenhagen: [Copenhagen and] Svendborg Zoological Museum, University of Copenhagen and Apollo Books.

FJELDSÅ, J. AND LOVETT, J. C. (1997) Biodiversity and environmental stability. *Biodiv. and Conserv.* 6: 315–323.

FJELDSÅ, J. AND MAYER, S. (1996) Recent ornithological surveys in the Valles region, southern Bolivia and the possible role of Valles for the evolution of the Andean avifauna. Centre for Research on the Cultural and Biological Diversity of Andean Rainforests: The Danish Environmental Research Programme.

FLINT, P. (1995) Separation of Cyprus Pied Wheatear from Pied Wheatear. *Brit. Birds* 88: 230–241.

FLINT, P. R. AND STEWART, P. F. (1983) *The birds of Cyprus.* London: British Ornithologists' Union (Check-list 6).

FORERO, E. (1989) Colombia. Pp.355–361 in D. G. Campbell and H. D. Hammond, eds. *Floristic inventory of tropical countries.* New York: New York Botanical Garden.

FORRESTER, B. C. (1993) *Birding Brazil: a check-list and site guide.* Privately published.

FORRESTER, B. C. (1995) Brazil's northern frontier sites: in search of two Rio Branco endemics. *Cotinga* 3: 51–54.

FORSHAW, J. M. (1989) *Parrots of the world.* Third (revised) edition. London: Blandford Press.

FORSHAW, J. M. AND COOPER, W. T. (1981) *Parrots of the world.* Second edition. Melbourne and London: Lansdowne Editions.

FOSTER, R. B., PARKER III, T. A., GENTRY, A. H., EMMONS, L. H., CHICCHÓN, A., SCHULENBERG, T., RODRÍGUEZ, L., LAMAS, G., ORTEGA, H., ICOCHEA, J., WUST, W., ROMO, M., CASTILLO, J. A., PHILLIPS, O., REYNEL, C., KRATTER, A., DONAHUE, P. K. AND BARKLEY, L. J. (1994) *The Tambopata–Candamo reserved zone of southeastern Perú: a biological assessment.* Washington, DC: Conservation International (RAP Working Papers 6).

FRANCIS, I. S., PENFORD, N., GARTSHORE, M. E. AND

JARAMILLO, A. (1992) The White-breasted Guineafowl *Agelastes meleagrides* in Taï National Park, Côte d'Ivoire. *Bird Conserv. Internatn.* 2: 25–60.

FRASER, B. J. AND HENSON, S. M. (1996) *Survey of endemic bird species on Gunung Lompobattang, South Sulawesi.* Bogor, Indonesia: PHPA/BirdLife International.

FRASER, M. W. AND BRIGGS, D. J. (1992) New information on the *Nesospiza* buntings at Inaccessible Island, Tristan da Cunha, and notes on their conservation. *Bull. Brit. Orn. Club* 112: 191–205.

FRASER, M. W., RYAN, P. G. AND WATKINS, B. P. (1988) The seabirds of Inaccessible Island, South Atlantic Ocean. *Cormorant* 16: 7–33.

FRASER, M. W., DEAN, W. R. J. AND BEST, I. C. (1992) Observations on the Inaccessible Island Rail *Atlantisia rogersi*: the world's smallest flightless bird. *Bull. Brit. Orn. Club* 112: 12–22.

FRASER, M. W., RYAN, P. G., DEAN, W. R. J., BRIGGS, D. J. AND MOLONEY, C. L. (1994) Biology of the Tristan Thrush *Nesocichla eremita. Ostrich* 65: 14–25.

FRIEDMANN, H. AND WILLIAMS, J. G. (1968) Notable records of rare or little-known birds from western Uganda. *Rev. Zool. Bot. Afr.* 77: 11–36.

FRITTS, T. H. (1988) *The brown tree snake,* Boiga irregularis, *a threat to Pacific islands.* Washington, DC: US Fish and Wildlife Service (Biol. Rep. 88/31).

FRY, C. H. AND SMITH, D. A. (1985) A new swallow from the Red Sea. *Ibis* 127: 1–6.

FRY, C. H., KEITH, S. AND URBAN, E. K. (1988) *The birds of Africa,* 3. London: Academic Press.

GAGNÉ, W. C. (1988) Conservation priorities in Hawaiian natural systems. *BioScience* 38: 264–271.

GAMAUF, A. AND TEBBICH, S. (1995) Re-discovery of the Isabela Oriole *Oriolus isabellae. Forktail* 11: 170–171.

GARDNER, A. S. AND FISHER, M. (1994) How the forest lost its trees: Just So storytelling about *Juniperus excelsa* in Arabia. *J. Arid Environments* 26: 299–301.

GARNETT, S., ED. (1993) *Threatened and extinct birds of Australia.* Second (corrected) edition. Moonee Ponds, Victoria: Royal Australasian Ornithologists Union (RAOU Report 82).

GARRIDO, O. (1992) Natural and man-induced evolutionary shifts in the birds of some Cuban cays. *Bird Conserv. Internatn.* 2: 1–6.

GARTSHORE, M. E., TAYLOR, P. D. AND FRANCIS, I. S. (1995) *Forest birds in Côte d'Ivoire.* Cambridge, UK: BirdLife International (Study Report 58).

GASTON, A. J. (1984) Is habitat destruction in India and Pakistan beginning to affect the status of endemic passerine birds? *J. Bombay Nat. Hist. Soc.* 81: 636–641.

GATTER, W. AND GARDNER, R. (1993) The biology of the Gola Malimbe *Malimbus ballmanni* Wolters 1974. *Bird Conserv. Internatn.* 3: 87–103.

GENTRY, A. (1989) North-west South America (Colombia, Ecuador and Peru). Pp.393–399 in D. G. Campbell and H. D. Hammond, eds. *Floristic inventory of tropical countries.* New York: New York Botanical Garden.

GENTRY, A. H. (1992) Tropical forest biodiversity: distributional patterns and their conservational significance. *Oikos* 63: 19–28.

GIBBS, D. (1994) Undescribed taxa and new records from the Fakfak Mountains, Irian Jaya. *Bull. Brit. Orn. Club* 114. 4–12.

GIBBS, D. (1996a) Mountain Eared Nightjar in Arfak Mountains, Irian Jaya: range extension and first description of nest and egg. *Dutch Birding* 18: 246–247.

GIBBS, D. (1996b) Notes on Solomon Island birds. *Bull. Brit. Orn. Club* 116: 18–25.

GIBSON, D. (1992) The Nyungwe Forest: saving its biodiversity. *Zoonooz* 65: 6–10.

GILLIARD, E. T. AND LECROY, M. (1967) Results of the 1958–1959 Gilliard New Britain Expedition. 4: annotated list of birds of the Whiteman Mountains, New Britain. *Bull. Amer. Mus. Nat. Hist.* 135: 173–216.

GILMAN, E. C. (1997) Community based and multiple purpose protected areas: a model to select and manage protected areas with lessons from the Pacific Islands. *Coastal Managem.* 25: 59–91.

GÓMEZ DE SILVA, H. AND AGUILAR RODRÍGUEZ, S. (1994) The Bearded Wood-Partridge in central Veracruz and suggestions for finding and conserving the species. *Euphonia* 3: 8–12.

GONZAGA, L. P. AND PACHECO, J. F. (1995) A new species of *Phylloscartes* (Tyrannidae) from the mountains of southern Bahia, Brazil. *Bull. Brit. Orn. Club* 115: 88–97.

GONZAGA, L. P., PACHECO, J. F., BAUER, C. AND CASTIGLIONI, G. D. A. (1995) An avifaunal survey of the vanishing montane Atlantic forest of southern Bahia, Brazil. *Bird Conserv. Internatn.* 5: 279–290.

GONZALES, P. C. AND KENNEDY, R. S. (1990) A new species of *Stachyris* babbler (Aves: Timaliidae) from the island of Panay, Philippines. *Wilson Bull.* 102: 367–379.

GONZALEZ, J. C. T. (1996) The status of the birds of Ursula Island, Palawan, Philippines. *Oriental Bird Club Bull.* 23: 38–41.

GOODMAN, S. M. (1993) A reconnaissance of Ile Sainte Marie, Madagascar: the status of the forest, avifauna, lemurs and fruit bats. *Biol. Conserv.* 65: 205–212.

GOODMAN, S. M. AND INGLE, N. R. (1993) Sibuyan Island in the Philippines—threatened and in need of conservation. *Oryx* 27: 174–180.

GOODMAN, S. M., WILLARD, D. E. AND GONZALES, P. C. (1995) The birds of Sibuyan Island, Romblon Province, Philippines, with particular reference to elevational distribution and biogeographic affinities. *Fieldiana Zool.* N.S, 82: 1–57.

GOODMAN, S. M., LANGRAND, O. AND WHITNEY, B. M. (1996) A new genus and species of passerine from the eastern rain forest of Madagascar. *Ibis* 138: 153–159.

GOODMAN, S. M., HAWKINS, A. F. A. AND DOMERGUE, C. (1997) A new species of vanga (Vangidae, *Calicalicus*) from southwestern Madagascar. *Bull. Brit. Orn. Club* 117: 5–10.

GORE, M. E. J. AND WON, PYONG-OH (1971) *The birds of Korea*. Seoul: Royal Asiatic Society.

GOSS, K. F. AND CHATFIELD, J. (1993) Landcare groups in Western Australia: the role of self help groups in restoring degraded farmland. Pp.281–293 in D. A. Saunders, R. J. Hobbs and P. R. Ehrlich, eds. *The reconstruction of fragmented ecosystems*. Chipping Norton, New South Wales: Surrey Beatty (Nature Conservation 3).

GRAVES, G. R. (1992) The endemic land birds of Henderson Island, southeastern Polynesia: notes on natural history and conservation. *Wilson Bull.* 104: 32–43.

GRAVES, G. R. (1993) Relic of a lost world: a new species of sunangel (Trochilidae: *Heliangelus*) from 'Bogotá'. *Auk* 110: 1–8.

GRAVES, G. R. AND OLSON, S. L. (1987) *Chlorostilbon bracei* Lawrence, an extinct species of hummingbird from New Providence Island, Bahamas. *Auk* 104: 296–302.

GRAVES, G. R., O'NEILL, J. P. AND PARKER, T. A. (1983) *Grallaricula ochraceifrons*, a new species of antpitta from northern Peru. *Wilson Bull.* 95: 1–6.

GREEN, A. J. (1993) *The status and conservation of the Marbled Teal* Marmaronetta angustirostris. Slimbridge, UK: International Waterfowl and Wetlands Research Bureau (IWRB Spec. Publ. 23).

GREEN, A. J. AND CROSBY, M. J. (1992) The historical range of the White-winged Wood Duck in Indonesia. *Kukila* 6: 1–7.

GREEN, M. J. B. AND GUNAWARDENA, E. R. N. (1993) *Conservation evaluation of some natural forests in Sri Lanka*. Colombo: Forest Department in association with UNDP/FAO/IUCN.

GREENWAY, J. C., JR. (1967) *Extinct and vanishing birds of the world*. Second (revised) edition. New York: Dover Publications.

GRETTON, A., KOHLER, M., LANSDOWN, R. V., PANKHURST, T. J., PARR, J. AND ROBSON, C. (1993) The status of Gurney's Pitta *Pitta gurneyi*, 1987–1989. *Bird Conserv. Internatn.* 3: 351–367.

GRIMMETT, R. (1991) Little known Oriental bird: Biddulph's Ground Jay. *Oriental Bird Club Bull.* 13: 26–29.

GRIMMETT, R. F. A. AND JONES, T. A. (1989) *Important Bird Areas in Europe*. Cambridge, UK: International Council for Bird Preservation (Techn. Publ. 9).

GRIMMETT, R. AND TAYLOR, H. (1992) Recent bird observations from Xinjiang Autonomous Region, China, 16 June to 5 July 1988. *Forktail* 7: 139–146.

GROOMBRIDGE, B., ED. (1992) *Global biodiversity: the status of the Earth's living resources*. London: Chapman & Hall.

GUYOT, I. AND THIBAULT, J.-C. (1988) La conservation de l'avifaune des iles Wallis et Futuna. Pp.125–142 in J.-C. Thibault and I. Guyot, eds. *Livre rouge des oiseaux menaces des regions françaises d'outre-mer*. Saint-Cloud, France: Conseil International pour la Protection des Oiseaux.

HADDEN, D. (1981) *Birds of the north Solomons*. Wau, Papua New Guinea: Wau Ecology Institute (Handbook 8).

HAFFER, J. (1967) Speciation in Colombian forest birds west of the Andes. *Amer. Mus. Novit.* 2294: 1–57.

HAFFER, J. (1975) *Avifauna of north-western Colombia, South America*. Bonn: Zoologisches Forschunginstitut und Museum Alexander Koenig (Bonner Zool. Monogr. 7).

HAFFER, J. (1992) The history of species concepts and species limits in ornithology. *Bull. Brit. Orn. Club* 112A (Centenary Suppl.): 107–158.

HAFFER, J. (1997) Essentialistisches und evolutionäres Denken in der systematischen Ornithologie des 19. und 20. Jahrhunderts. *J. Orn.* 138: 61.

HAHN, I. AND RÖMER, U. (1996) New observations of the Masafuera Rayadito *Aphratura masafuerae*. *Cotinga* 6: 17–19.

HAIG, S. M., BALLOU, J. D. AND DERRICKSON, S. R. (1993) Genetic considerations for the Guam Rail. *Re-introduc-*

tion News 7: 11–12.

VAN HALEWYN, R. AND NORTON, R. L. (1984) The status and conservation of seabirds in the Caribbean. Pp.169–222 in J. P. Croxall, P. G. H. Evans and R. W. Schreiber, eds. *Status and conservation of the world's seabirds.* Cambridge, UK: International Council for Bird Preservation (Techn. Publ. 2).

HALL, B. P. AND MOREAU, R. E. (1962) A study of the rare birds of Africa. *Bull. Brit. Mus. (Nat. Hist.) Zool.* 8: 313–378.

HALL, B. P. AND MOREAU, R. E. (1970) *An atlas of speciation in African passerine birds.* London: British Museum (Natural History).

HALLOY, S., GONZÁLEZ, J. A. AND GRAU, A. (1994) *Proyecto de creación del Parque Nacional Aconquija (Tucumán, Argentina): report no. 4.* Tucumán: Fundacíon Miguel Lillo (Nature Conservation Series 9).

HAMBLER, C., NEWING, J. AND HAMBLER, K. (1993) Population monitoring for the flightless rail *Dryolimnas cuvieri aldebranus. Bird Conserv. Internatn.* 3: 307–318.

HAMILTON, A. C. (1981) The Quaternary history of African forests: its relevance to conservation. *Afr. J. Ecol.* 19: 1–6.

HAMILTON, A. C. (1984) *Deforestation in Uganda.* Oxford: Oxford University Press/East Africa Wildlife Society.

HAMILTON, A. C. AND BENSTED-SMITH, R., EDS. (1989) *Forest conservation in the East Usambara Mountains Tanzania.* Gland, Switzerland and Cambridge, UK: International Union for Conservation of Nature and Natural Resources.

HANNECART, F. (1988) Les oiseaux menacés de la Nouvelle Calédonie et des îles proches. Pp.143–165 in J.-C. Thibault and I. Guyot, eds. *Livre rouge des oiseaux menacés des régions françaises d'outre-mer.* Saint-Cloud: Conseil International pour la Protection des Oiseaux (Monogr. 5).

HARCOURT, C. S. AND SAYER, J. A., EDS. (1996) *The conservation atlas of tropical forests: the Americas.* New York: Simon and Schuster.

HARDY, J. W. (1965) Evolutionary and ecological relationships between three species of blackbirds (Icteridae) in central Mexico. *Evolution* 21: 196–197.

HARDY, J. W. AND DICKERMAN, R. W. (1965) Relationships between two forms of the Red-winged Blackbird in Mexico. *Living Bird* 4: 107–129.

HARRAP, S. (1992) Little known West Palearctic birds: Algerian Nuthatch. *Birding World* 5: 154–156.

HARRAP, S. AND QUINN, D. (1996) *Tits, nuthatches and treecreepers.* London: A. & C. Black (Helm Identification Guides).

HARRIS, M. P. (1982) *A field guide to the birds of Galápagos.* Revised edition. London: Collins.

HARRISON, M. J. S. (1990a) A recent survey of the birds of Pagalu (Annobon). *Malimbus* 11: 135–143.

HARRISON, C. S. (1990b) *Seabirds of Hawaii: natural history and conservation.* Ithaca and London: Cornell University Press.

HARRISON, J. A., ALLAN, D. G., UNDERHILL, L. G., HERREMANS, M., TREE, A. J., PARKER, V. AND BROWN, C. J. (1997) *The atlas of southern African birds.* Johannesburg: BirdLife South Africa.

HART, J. K. (1991) Conservation of the Lear's Macaw: management of an endangered species. Pp.48–51 in J. Clinton-Eitniear, ed. *Proceedings of the First Meso-*

american Workshop on the Conservation and Management of Macaws. San Antonio, Texas: Center for the Study of Tropical Birds, Inc. (Misc. Publ. 1).

HASEGAWA, H. (1984) Status and conservation of seabirds in Japan, with special attention to the Short-tailed Albatross. Pp.487–500 in J. P. Croxall, P. G. H. Evans and R. W. Schreiber, eds. *Status and conservation of the world's seabirds.* Cambridge, UK: International Council for Bird Preservation (Techn. Publ. 2).

HASEGAWA, H. (1991) Red Data Bird: Short-tailed Albatross. *World Birdw.* 13(2): 10.

HAUGE, P., TERBORGH, J., WINTER, B. AND PARKINSON, J. (1986) Conservation priorities in the Philippine archipelago. *Forktail* 2: 83–91.

HAWKINS, A. F. A. (1994) Forest degradation and the Western Malagasy Forest bird community. University of London (Ph.D. Dissertation).

HAWKINS, F. (1993) An integrated biodiversity conservation project under development: the ICBP Angola Scarp Project. *Proc. 8th Pan-Afr. Orn. Congr. [Ann. Sci. Zool. Mus. Roy. Afrique Centr.]* 286: 279–284.

HAY, R. (1986) *Bird conservation in the Pacific Islands.* Cambridge, UK: International Council for Bird Preservation (Study Report 7).

HAYES, F. E. (1996) Project Sabrewing: status, ecology and behaviour of the White-tailed Sabrewing (*Campylopterus ensipennis*) on Tobago, West Indies. Unpublished report.

HAYNES, A. M., SUTTON, R. L. AND HARVEY, K. D. (1989) Conservation trends, and the threats to endemic birds in Jamaica. Pp.827–838 in C. A. Woods, ed. *Biogeography of the West Indies: past, present, and future.* Gainesville, Florida: Sandhill Crane Press.

HAZEVOET, C. J. (1992) A review of the Santiago Purple Heron *Ardea purpurea bournei,* with a report of a new colony. *Bird Conserv. Internatn.* 2: 15–23.

HAZEVOET, C. J. (1994) Status and conservation of seabirds in the Cape Verde Islands. Pp.279–293 in D. N. Nettleship, J. Burger and M. Gochfeld, eds. *Seabirds on islands: threats, case studies and action plans.* Cambridge, UK: BirdLife International (BirdLife Conservation Series no. 1).

HAZEVOET, C. J. (1995) *The birds of the Cape Verde Islands.* Tring, UK: British Ornithologists' Union (Checklist 13).

HAZEVOET, C. J. (1996) Conservation and species lists: taxonomic neglect promotes the extinction of endemic birds, as exemplified by taxa from eastern Atlantic islands. *Bird Conserv. Internatn.* 6: 181–196.

HEANEY, L. R., RICKART, E. A., TABARANZA, B., GONZALES, J. C., MALLARI, A. AND PETERSON, A. T. (1993) Survey of vertebrate diversity in Mt Katanglad Nature Park, Mindanao. Final report for 1992 and 1993. Unpublished.

HEATH, M. F. AND LONG, A. J. (1991) Habitat, distribution and status of the Azure-rumped Tanager *Tangara cabanisi* in Mexico. *Bird Conserv. Internatn.* 1: 223–254.

HEATH, M. F., PAYNE, A. J. AND EVANS, M. I. (in prep.) Important Bird Areas in Europe (fully revised).

HE FEN-QI (1992) News on the Sichuan Hill Partridge. *WPA News* 36: 33.

HE FEN-QI AND LU TAI-CHUN (1991) Changes in status and distribution of China's pheasants. *WPA News* 31: 19–24.

HEREDIA, B., ROSE, L. AND PAINTER, M., EDS. (1996) *Globally threatened birds in Europe: action plans.* Strasbourg,

France: Council of Europe and BirdLife International.

HERMES, N. (1985) *Birds of Norfolk Island*. Norfolk Island: Wonderland Publications.

HERNÁNDEZ CAMACHO, J. I., SÁNCHEZ, H., PARDO, J. L. AND CASTAÑO URIBE, C., EDS. (undated [c.1990]) *Guia del sistema de parques nacionales de Colombia*. Bogotá: INDERENA.

HERREMANS, M., LOUETTE, M. AND STEVENS, J. (1991) Conservation status and vocal and morphological description of the Grand Comoro Scops Owl *Otus pauliani* Benson 1960. *Bird Conserv. Internatn.* 1: 123–133.

HESSE, A. J. (1997) The Blue-throated Macaw in the wild: a cuase for concern. *AFA Watchbird* 24: 10–15.

HESSE, A. AND JAMMES, L. (1994) A preliminary assessment of the distribution of the Blue-throated Macaw *Ara glaucogularis*, Beni, Bolivia. Unpublished report.

HIGUCHI, H. AND KAWAJI, N. (1989) Ijima's Willow Warbler *Phylloscopus ijimae* of the Tokara Islands, a new breeding locality, in southwest Japan. *Bull. Biogeog. Soc. Japan* 44: 11–15.

HILL, M. O. (1979) *TWINSPAN: A FORTRAN program for arranging multivariate data in an ordered two-way table for classification of the individuals and attributes*. Ithica, New York: Cornell University.

HILTY, S. L. AND BROWN, W. L. (1986) *A guide to the birds of Colombia*. Princeton: Princeton University Press.

HIPKISS, A. J., WATSON, L. G. AND EVANS, T. D. (1994) The Cambridge–Tanzania Rainforest Project 1992: brief account of ornithological results and conservation proposals. *Ibis* 136: 107–108.

HOBDY, R. (1993) Lana'i—a case study: the loss of biodiversity on a small Hawaiian Island. *Pac. Sci.* 47: 201–210.

HOCKEY, P. A. R. (1987) The influence of coastal utilisation by man on the presumed extinction of the Canarian Black Oystercatcher *Haematopus meadewaldoi* Bannerman. *Biol. Conserv.* 39: 49–62.

HOCKEY, P. A. R., ALLAN, D. G., REBELO, A. G. AND DEAN, W. R. J. (1988) The distribution, habitat requirements and conservation status of Rudd's Lark *Heteromirafra ruddi* in South Africa. *Biol. Conserv.* 45: 255–266.

HOCKEY, P. A. R., UNDERHILL, L. G., NEATHERWAY, M. AND RYAN, P. G. (1989) *Atlas of the birds of the southwestern Cape*. Cape Town: Cape Bird Club.

HOLDAWAY, R. N. (1994) Chatham Islands ornithology: a tribute to Sir Charles A. Fleming K.B.E., D.Sc., F.R.S., F.R.S.N.Z. 1916–1987. *Notornis* 41 (Suppl. 1): 1–208.

HOLMES, D. A. (1996) Sumatra bird report. *Kukila* 8: 9–56.

HOLYOAK, D. T. AND THIBAULT, J.-C. (1984) Contribution à l'étude des oiseaux de Polynésie orientale. *Mem. Mus. Natn. Hist. Nat. Ser. A, Zool.* 127: 1–209.

HOLYOAK, D. T. AND THIBAULT, J.-C. (in prep.) *Checklist of the birds of the Pacific islands*. British Ornithologists' Union.

HOU, H. Y. (1979) The vegetation map of China. Beijing: map publisher of the People's Republic of China.

HOWARD, P. C. (1991) *Nature conservation in Uganda's tropical forest reserves*. Gland, Switzerland: International Union for the Conservation of Nature and Natural Resources.

HOWARD, R. AND MOORE, A. (1991) *A complete checklist of the birds of the world*. Second edition. London: Academic Press.

HOWELL, S. N. G. (1993) Taxonomy and distribution of the hummingbird genus *Chlorostilbon* in Mexico and northern Central America. *Euphonia* 2: 25–37.

HOWELL, S. N. G. AND ROBBINS, M. B. (1995) Species limits of the Least Pygmy-Owl complex. *Wilson Bull.* 107: 7–25.

HOWELL, S. N. G. AND WEBB, S. (1989) Notes on the Honduran Emerald. *Wilson Bull.* 101: 642–643.

HOWELL, S. N. G. AND WEBB, S. (1992a) Observations of birds from Isla Guadalupe, México. *Euphonia* 1: 1–6.

HOWELL, S. N. G. AND WEBB, S. (1992b) A little-known cloud forest in Hidalgo, México. *Euphonia* 1: 7–11.

HOWELL, S. N. G. AND WEBB, S. (1995a) *A guide to the birds of Mexico and northern Central America*. Oxford: Oxford University Press.

HOWELL, S. AND WEBB, S. (1995b) Species status of the Chestnut-throated Huet-Huet *Pteroptochos castaneus*. *Bull. Brit. Orn. Club* 115: 171–177.

HOWELL, T. R. AND CADE, T. J. (1953) The birds of Guadalupe Island in 1953. *Condor* 56: 283–294.

DEL HOYO, J., ELLIOT, A. AND SARGATAL, J., EDS. (1992) *Handbook of the birds of the world*. 1: *Ostrich to ducks*. Barcelona: Lynx Edicions.

DEL HOYO, J., ELLIOTT, A. AND SARGATAL, J., EDS. (1994) *Handbook of the birds of the world*. 2: *New World vultures to guineafowl*. Barcelona: Lynx Edicions.

HUBER, O. AND ALARCÓN, C. (1988) *Mapa de la vegetación de Venezuela*. Caracas: Ministério del Ambiente y de los Recursos Naturales Renovables (División de Vegetación) and the Nature Conservancy.

HUECK, K. (1978) *Los bosques de Sudamérica; ecología, composición e importancia económica*. Eschborn, Germany: Sociedad Alemania [*sic*] de Cooperacion [*sic*] Técnica.

HUGHES, R. H. AND HUGHES, J. S. (1992) *A directory of African wetlands*. Cambridge, UK: World Conservation Union, United Nations Environment Programme and World Conservation Monitoring Centre.

HULM, P. (1995) Robinson's Crusoe's Islands face an uncertain future. *Plant Talk* 2: 19–21.

HUMMELINCK, P., ED. (1957) *Studies on the fauna of Curaçao and other Caribbean islands*, 7. The Hague: Martinus Nijhoff.

HUNT, G. (1996a) Environmental variables associated with population patterns of the Kagu *Rhynochetos jubatus* of New Caledonia. *Ibis* 138: 778–785.

HUNT, G. R. (1996b) Manufacture and use of hook-tools by New Caledonian crows. *Nature* 379: 249–251.

HUNT, G. R., HAY, R. AND VELTMAN, C. J. (1996) Multiple Kagu *Rhynochetos jubatus* deaths caused by dog attacks at a high-altitude study site on Pic Ningua, New Caledonia. *Bird Conserv. Internatn.* 6: 295–306.

HUNTER, B., ED. (1994) *The statesman's year-book*. One hundred and thirty first edition. London: Macmillan.

HUNTER, N., CARTER, C. AND MLUNGU, E. (1996) Recent observations in the Udzungwa and Uluguru mountains, central Tanzania. *Bull. African Bird Club* 3: 96–98.

HUNTLEY, B. J. (1992) Biodiversity: Angolan environmental status quo assessment report. Prepared for the IUCN Regional Office for southern Africa, Harare, Zimbabwe.

ICBP (1992) *Putting biodiversity on the map: priority areas for global conservation*. Cambridge, UK: International Council for Bird Preservation.

ICHIDA, N. (in press) Sites to save: Yambaru, Japan. *World Birdwatch*.

INDRAWAN, M., FUJITA, M. S., MASALA, Y. AND PESIK, L. (1993) Status and conservation of Sula Scrubfowl *Megapodius bernsteinii* (Schlegel 1866) in Banggai Islands, Sulawesi. *Trop. Biodiv.* 1: 113–130.

INGRAM, G. B. (1992) Fragmentation: towards an expanded model on the vulnerability of forest habitats on islands. *Malayan Nat. J.* 45: 94–121.

INGRAM, G. B. (1994) Institutional obstacles to conservation: Fergusson Island, Papua New Guinea. *Pacific Affairs* 67: 26–45.

INSKIPP, C. (1989) *Nepal's forest birds: their status and conservation*. Cambridge, UK: International Council for Bird Preservation (Monogr. 4).

INSKIPP, C. AND INSKIPP, T. (1991) *Birds of Nepal*. Second edition. London: Christopher Helm.

INSKIPP, C. AND INSKIPP, T. P. (1993a) Birds recorded in a visit to Bhutan in autumn 1991. *Forktail* 8: 97–112.

INSKIPP, C. AND INSKIPP, T. P. (1993b) Birds recorded during a visit to Bhutan in spring 1993. *Forktail* 9: 121–142.

INSTITUTE OF GEOGRAPHY, CHINESE ACADEMY OF SCIENCES AND STATE PLANNING COMMITTEE, STATE ECONOMIC INFORMATION CENTRE, INSTITUTE OF STATISTICS AND STATE STATISTICAL BUREAU, EDS. (1994) *The national economic atlas of China*. Hong Kong: Oxford University Press.

IRWIN, M. P. S. (1979) The Zimbabwe Rhodesian and Moçambique highland avian endemics: their evolution and origins. *Honeyguide* 99: 5–11.

IRWIN, M. P. S. (1981) *The birds of Zimbabwe*. Salisbury: Quest Publishing.

ISLER, M. L. AND ISLER, P. R. (1987) *The tanagers: natural history, distribution, and identification*. Washington, DC: Smithsonian Institution Press.

IUCN (1990) *IUCN Directory of South Asian protected areas*. Gland, Switzerland: International Union for the Conservation of Nature and Natural Resources.

IUCN (1992a) *Protected areas of the world: a review of national systems. 4: Nearctic and Neotropical*. Gland, Switzerland and Cambridge, UK: International Union for Conservation of Nature and Natural Resources.

IUCN (1992b) *Protected areas of the world: a review of national systems. 3: Afrotropical*. Gland, Switzerland and Cambridge, UK: International Union for Conservation of Nature and Natural Resources.

IUCN (1992c) *Protected areas of the world: a review of national systems. 1: Indomalaya, Oceania, Australia and Antarctic*. Gland, Switzerland and Cambridge, UK: International Union for Conservation of Nature and Natural Resources.

IUCN (1992d) *Protected areas of the world: a review of national systems. 2: Palaearctic*. Gland, Switzerland and Cambridge, UK: International Union for the Conservation of Nature and National Resources.

IUCN (1993) *Nature reserves of the Himalaya and mountains of Central Asia*. Gland, Switzerland and Cambridge, UK: International Union for Conservation of Nature and Natural Resources.

IUCN (1995) *The Fly River Catchment, Papua New Guinea—a regional environmental assessment*. Boroko, Papua New Guinea and Gland, Switzerland: Department of Environment and Conservation, and International Union for Nature Conservation and Natural Resources.

IUCN/SSC (1994) *IUCN Red List Categories*. Gland, Switzerland: IUCN Species Survival Commission.

IUCN/UNEP (1986a) *Review of the protected areas system in the Afrotropical realm*. Gland, Switzerland: International Union for Conservation of Nature and Natural Resources.

IUCN/UNEP (1986b) *Review of the protected areas system in the Indo-Malayan realm*. Gland, Switzerland: International Union for Conservation of Nature and Natural Resources.

IUCN/UNEP (1986c) *Review of the protected areas system in Oceania*. Gland, Switzerland: International Union for Conservation of Nature and Natural Resources.

JACKSON, M. H. (1985) *Galapagos: a natural history guide*. Calgary, Canada: Calgary University Press.

JACOBI, J. D. AND ATKINSON, C. T. (1995) Hawaii's endemic birds. Pp.376–381 in E. T. LaRoe, ed. *Our living resources: a report to the nation on the distribution, abundance, and health of US plants, animals, and ecosystems*. Washington, DC: US Department of the Interior, National Biological Service.

JAFFE, M. (1994) *And no birds sing*. New York: Simon and Schuster.

JAFFRÉ, T. (1993) The relationship between ecological diversity and floristic diversity in New Caledonia. *Biodiv. Let.* 1: 82–87.

JAFFRÉ, T., MORAT, P. AND VEILLON, J.-M. (1994) La flore: caractéristiques et composition floristique des principales fromations végétales. *Bois et Forets Tropiques* 242: 7–30.

JEHL, J. R. (1972) On the cold trail of an extinct petrel. *Pacif. Disc.* 25: 24–29.

JEHL, J. R. AND EVERETT, W. T. (1985) History and status of the avifauna of Isla Guadalupe, Mexico. *Trans. San Diego Soc. Nat. Hist.* 20: 313–336.

JENKINS, M. D., ED. (1987) *Madagascar: an environmental profile*. Cambridge, UK: International Union for Conservation of Nature and Natural Resources.

JENNINGS, M. C. (1991) Arabian endemics for lumpers and splitters. *Phoenix* 8: 10–14.

JENNINGS, M. C., AL SALAMA, M. I. AND FELEMBAN, H. M. (1988) *Report on an ornithological survey of the Asir National Park, Saudi Arabia: 29 June to 18 July 1987*. Sandy, UK: Ornithological Society of the Middle East (Techn. Report 4).

JENSEN, F. P. (1983) A new species of sunbird from Tanzania. *Ibis* 125: 447–449.

JENSEN, F. P. AND BRØGGER-JENSEN, S. (1992) The forest avifauna of the Uzungwa Mountains, Tanzania. *Scopus* 15: 65–83.

JEPSON, P. (1993) Recent ornithological observations from Buru. *Kukila* 6: 85–109.

JEPSON, P. (1995) *Summary report of an evaluation of boundaries for a protected area in the Tanimbar Islands, South-east Maluku*. Bogor, Indonesia: PHPA/BirdLife International (Memorandum Teknis 1).

JEPSON, P. AND MONK, K. A. (1995) *A review of the protected areas system on Sumbawa Island, West Nusa Tenggara, in relation to biodiversity conservation*. Bogor, Indonesia: PHPA/BirdLife International (Laporan 4).

JEPSON, P., RAIS, S., ORA, A. B. AND RAHARJANINGTRAH, W. (1996) *Evaluation of protected area network for the* conservation of forest values on Sumba Island, East Nusa Tenggara. Bogor, Indonesia: PHPA/BirdLife International-Indonesia Programme (Laporan 5).

JOHNSON, A. W. (1967) The birds of Chile and adjacent regions of Argentina, Bolivia and Peru, 2. Buenos Aires: Platt Establicimientos Gráficos.

JOHNSON, N. (1995) Biodiversity in the balance: approaches to setting geographic conservation priorities. Washington, DC: Biodiversity Support Programme.

JOHNSON, T. H. AND STATTERSFIELD, A. J. (1990) A global review of island endemic birds. Ibis 132: 167–180.

JONES, C. G. (1987) The larger land-birds of Mauritius. Pp.208–300 in A. W. Diamond, ed. Studies of Mascarene Island birds. Cambridge, UK: Cambridge University Press.

JONES, C. (1994b) Birds survive Cyclone Hollanda. On the Edge 70: 6.

JONES, C. G. AND HARTLEY, J. (1995) A conservation project on Mauritius and Rodrigues: an overview and bibliography. Dodo (J. Jersey Wildl. Preserv. Trust) 31: 40–65.

JONES, M. J., LINSLEY, M. D. AND MARSDEN, S. J. (1995a) Population sizes, status and habitat associations of the restricted-range bird species of Sumba, Indonesia. Bird Conserv. Internatn. 5: 21–52.

JONES, D. N., DEKKER, R. W. R. J. AND ROSELAAR, C. S. (1995b) The megapodes. Oxford: Oxford University Press.

JONES, D., COCKLIN, C. AND CUTTING, M. (1995c) Institutional and landowner perspectives on wetland management in New Zealand. J. Environ. Mgmt 45: 143–161.

JONES, P. J. (1994a) Biodiversity in the Gulf of Guinea: an overview. Biodiv. and Conserv. 3: 772–784.

JONES, P. J. AND TYE, A. (1988) A survey of the avifauna of São Tomé and Príncipe. Cambridge, UK: International Council for Bird Preservation (Study Report 24).

JONES, P. J., BURLISON, J. P. AND TYE, A. (1991) Conservação dos ecossistemas florestais na República democrática de São Tomé e Príncipe. Gland, Switzerland and Cambridge, UK: International Union for Conservation of Nature and Natural Resources.

JONES, P., SCHUBEL, S., JOLLY, J., BROOKE, M. DE L. AND VICKERY, J. (1995d) Behaviour, natural history, and annual cycle of the Henderson Island Rail Porzana atra (Aves: Rallidae). Biol. J. Linn. Soc. 56: 167–183.

JOUVENTIN, P. AND MICOL, T. (1995) Conservation status of the French subantarctic islands. Pp.31–41 in P. R. Dingwall, ed. Progress in conservation of the subantarctic islands. Gland, Switzerland and Cambridge, UK: International Union for Conservation of Nature and Natural Resources.

JOUVENTIN, P., STAHL, J.-C., WEIMERSKIRCH, H. AND MOUGIN, J.-L. (1984) The seabirds of the French subantarctic islands and Adélie Land, their status and conservation. Pp.609–625 in J. P. Croxall, P. G. H. Evans and R. W. Schreiber, eds. Status and conservation of the world's seabirds. Cambridge, UK: International Council for Bird Preservation (Techn. Publ. 2).

JUNIPER, T. AND YAMASHITA, C. (1990) The conservation of Spix's Macaw. Oryx 24: 224–228.

JUVIK, J. O., JUVIK, S. P. AND HAMILTON, L. S. (1992) Altitudinal resource zonation versus vertical control: land use conflict on two Hawaiian mountains. Mtn Res. Develop. 12: 211–226.

KANYAMIBWA, S. (1995) Viewpoint: war and conservation. World Birdw. 17(2): 24.

KATTI, M., SINGH, P., MANJREKAR, D., SHARMA, D. AND MUKHERJEE, S. (1992) An ornithological survey of eastern Arunachal Pradesh, India. Forktail 7: 75–89.

KAWAJI, N., HIGUCHI, H. AND HORI, H. (1989) A new breeding record of the Izu Island Thrush Turdus celaenops from the Takara Islands, southwest Japan. Bull. Brit. Orn. Club 109: 93–95.

KEAST, A. (1961) Bird speciation on the Australian continent. Bull. Mus. Comp. Zool. 123: 307–495.

KEITH, S., URBAN, E. K. AND FRY, C. H. (1992) The birds of Africa, 4. London: Academic Press.

KENNEDY, R. S., GONZALES, P. C. AND MIRANDA, H. C. (1997) New Aethopyga sunbirds (Aves: Nectariniidae) from the island of Mindanao, Philippines. Auk 114: 1–10.

KIEW, B. H. (1994) The highland road: environmental risk and public concern. Malayan Naturalist 48: 23–25.

KING, B. (1987) Wild sighting of Brown Eared Pheasant. WPA News 15: 14.

KING, B. (1989a) Birds observed at Huang Nian Shan, Mabian County, southern Sichuan, China. Forktail 4: 63–68.

KING, B. (1989b) Birds observed at Dafengding Panda Reserve, Mabian County, southern Sichuan, China. Forktail 4: 69–76.

KING, B. (1994) A possible sighting of Diabolical Eared-nightjar Eurostopodus diabolicus in Sulawesi. Oriental Bird Club Bull. 19: 56–57.

KING, B. AND LIAO WEI-PING (1989) Hainan Island bird notes. Hong Kong Bird Rep. 1988: 88–101.

KING, B. F., DICKINSON, E. C. AND WOODCOCK, M. W. (1975) A field guide to the birds of south-east Asia. London: Collins.

KING, C. (1984) Immigrant killers: introduced predators and the conservation of birds in New Zealand. Auckland: Oxford University Press.

KING, C. E. AND NIJBOER, J. (1994) Conservation considerations for crowned pigeons, genus Goura. Oryx 28: 22–30.

KING, W. B. (1978–1979) Red Data Book, 2: Aves. Second edition. Morges, Switzerland: International Union for Conservation of Nature and Natural Resources.

KIRCH, P. V., FLENLEY, J. R., STEADMAN, D. W., LAMONT, F. AND DAWSON, S. (1992) Ancient environment degradation. Natn. Geogr. Res. 8: 166–179.

KNOX, A. G. (1990) Identification of crossbill and Scottish Crossbill. Brit. Birds 83: 89–94.

KOMDEUR, J. (1994) Conserving the Seychelles Warbler Acrocephalus sechellensis by translocation from Cousin Island to the islands of Aride and Cousine. Biol. Conserv. 67: 143–152.

KOMDEUR, J., BULLOCK, I. D. AND RANDS, M. R. W. (1991) Conserving the Seychelles Warbler Acrocephalus sechellensis by translocation: a transfer from Cousin Island to Aride Island. Bird Conserv. Internatn. 1: 177–185.

KONYUKHOV, N. B. AND MCCAFFERY, B. J. (1993) Second record of a Bristle-thighed Curlew from Asia and first record for the former Soviet Union. Wader Study Group Bull. 70: 22–23.

KOSTER, S. H. AND BUTYNSKI, T. M. (undated) Status of avifauna on Bioko Island (Fernando Poo), Equatorial Guinea. Unpublished.

KRABBE, N., DESMET, G., GREENFIELD, P., JÁCOME, M., MATHEUS, J. C. AND SORNOZA, M. F. (1994) Giant Antpitta *Grallaria gigantea*. *Cotinga* 2: 32–34.

KRATTER, A. W. (1995) Status, habitat and conservation of the Rufous-throated Antthrush *Formicarius rufifrons*. *Bird Conserv. Internatn.* 5: 391–404.

KROLL, J. C. (1980) Habitat requirements of the Golden-cheeked Warbler: management implications. *J. Range Management* 33: 60–65.

KUEHLER, C. (1992) Polynesian Ultramarine Lory translocation successful. *CBSG News* 3: 33.

KUEHLER, C., LIEBERMAN, A., VARNEY, A., UNITT, P., SULPICE, R. M., AZUA, J. AND TEHEVINI, B. (1997) Translocation of Ultramarine Lories *Vini ultramarina* in the Marquesas Islands: Ua Huka and Fatu Hiva. *Bird Conserv. Internatn.* 7: 69–80.

KULA, G. R., KINBAG, F. AND UNKAU, C. (undated) *Fauna survey report on west coast timber area, Manus Province*. Boroko, Papua New Guinea: Department of Environment and Conservation (Conserv. Study Rep. 2).

KUTAC, E. A. AND CARAN, S. C. (1994) *Birds and other wildlife of south central Texas*. Austin: University of Texas Press.

LACK, D. (1976) *Island biology illustrated by the land birds of Jamaica*. Oxford: Blackwell Scientific Publications.

LAMARCHE, B. (1980–1981) Liste commentée des oiseaux du Mali. [List of birds of Mali.] *Malimbus* 2: 121–158, 3: 73–102. (In French.)

LAMBERT, D. AND MORITZ, C., EDS. (1995) Biological conservation in New Zealand. *Pac. Conserv. Biol.* 2: 1–123.

LAMBERT, F. R. (1992) The status of the Philippine Cockatoo *Cactua haematuropygia* in Palawan and the Sulu Islands, Philippines. Unpublished report.

LAMBERT, F. R. (1993a) Some key sites and significant records of birds in the Philippines and Sabah. *Bird Conserv. Internatn.* 3: 281–297.

LAMBERT, F. R. (1993b) Trade, status and management of three parrots in the North Moluccas, Indonesia: White Cockatoo *Cacatua alba*, Chattering Lory *Lorius garrulus* and Violet-eared Lory *Eos squamata*. *Bird Conserv. Internatn.* 3: 145–168.

LAMBERT, F. AND WOODCOCK, M. (1996) *Pittas, broadbills and asities*. Mountfield, UK: Pica Press.

LAMBERT, F. R., EAMES, J. C. AND NGUYEN CU (1994) *Surveys for endemic pheasants in the Annamese lowlands of Vietnam, June-July, 1994: status of and conservation recommendations for Vietnamese Pheasant Lophura hatinhensis and Imperial Pheasant L. imperialis*. Gland, Switzerland and Cambridge, UK: International Union for Nature Conservation and Natural Resources.

LAMMERTINK, J. M. AND ROJAS TOMÉ, J. (1995) Preliminary report on the Sierra de Huicholes and northern Nayarit field work of the Mexican Mountain Forest–Imperial Woodpecker project. Unpublished report.

LAMMERTINK, J. M., ROJAS-TOMÉ, J. A., CASILLAS-ORONA, F. M. AND OTTO, R. L. (1996) *Status and conservation of old-growth forests and endemic birds in the pine-oak zone of the Sierra Madre Occidental, Mexico*. Amsterdam: Institute for Systematics and Population Biology.

LAMMERTINK, M. (1996) The lost empire of the Imperial Woodpecker. *World Birdw.* 18(2): 8–11.

LAMMERTINK, M. AND ESTRADA, A. R. (1995) Status of the Ivory-billed Woodpecker *Campephilus principalis* in Cuba: almost certainly extinct. *Bird Conserv. Internatn.* 5: 53–60.

LANGRAND, O. (1990) *Guide to the birds of Madagascar*. New Haven: Yale University Press.

LANGRAND, O. AND GOODMAN, S. M. (1995) Monitoring Madagascar's ecosystems: a look at the past, present, and future of its wetlands. Pp.204–214 in T. B. Herman, S. Bondrup-Nielsen, J. H. M. Willison and N. W. P. Munro, eds. *Ecosystem monitoring and protected areas*. Wolfville, Nova Scotia: Science and Management of Protected Areas Association.

LANGRAND, O. AND WILMÉ, L. (1993) Protection des zones humides et conservation des especes d'oiseaux endemiques de Madagascar. *Proc. 8th Pan-Afr. Orn. Congr.* [*Ann. Sci. Zool. Mus. Roy. Afrique Centr.*] 286: 201–209.

LANNING, D. V., MARSHALL, J. T. AND SHIFLETT, J. T. (1990) Range and habitat of the Colima Warbler. *Wilson Bull.* 102: 1–13.

LANYON, S. M., STOTZ, D. F. AND WILLARD, D. E. (1990) *Clytoctantes atrogularis*, a new species of antbird from western Brazil. *Wilson Bull.* 102: 571–580.

LAURANCE, W. F. (1993) Research challenges and opportunities in the Wet Tropics of Queensland World Heritage Area. *Pac. Conserv. Biol.* 1: 3–6.

LAWTON, J. H. (1996) Population abundances, geographic ranges and conservation: 1994 Witherby Lecture. *Bird Study* 43: 3–19.

LEARY, T. (1991) *Solomon Islands: state of the environment report*. [Honiara]: Environment and Conservation Division, Ministry of Natural Resources, Solomon Islands.

LECROY, M. AND DIAMOND, J. (1995) Plumage variation in the Broad-billed Fairy-wren *Malurus grayi*. *Emu* 95: 185–193.

LECROY, M., PECKOVER, W. S., KULUPI, A. AND MANSEIMA, J. (1984) *Bird observations on Normanby and Fergusson, D'Entrecasteaux Islands, Papua New Guinea*. Boroko, Papua New Guinea: Division of Wildlife (Wildlife in Papua New Guinea 83/1).

LEE, P. C., THORNBACK, J. AND BENNETT, E. L. (1988) *Threatened primates of Africa. The IUCN Red Data Book*. Gland, Switzerland and Cambridge, UK: International Union for Conservation of Nature and Natural Resources.

LEES, A. (1989) A representative national parks and reserves system for Fiji's tropical forests. Nelson: Mauria Society (Mauria Society Policy Reports Series no. 9). Draft version prepared for the approval of the Fiji Native Land Trust Board, Ministry of Tourism, and National Trust for Fiji.

LEES, A. (1991) *A protected forests system for the Solomon Islands*. Nelson, New Zealand: Maruia Society.

LEGGE, V. (1983) *A history of the birds of Ceylon*, 1. Second edition. Dehiwala: Tisara Prakasakayo.

LENCIONI-NETO, F. (1994) Une nouvelle espèce de *Chordeiles* (Aves, Caprimulgidae) de Bahia (Brésil). *Alauda* 62: 241–245.

LENS, L., DUCHATEAU, L. AND BENNUN, L. (1996) How grassland fragmentation and change in land-use affect Sharpe's Longclaw *Macronyx sharpei*, a Kenyan highland endemic. Pp.57 in *Ninth Pan-African Ornithological Congress: programme and book of abstracts*. [Accra]: Ghana Wildlife Society.

LEONARD, P. AND BEEL, C. (1996) Lake Lufira Weaver *Ploceus reichardi*—new to Zambia. *Zambia Orn. Soc. Newsl.* 26: 3–5.

LEPOFSKY, D. (1992) Arboriculture in the Mussau Islands, Bismarck Archipelago. *Econ. Bot.* 46: 192–211.

LÉTOCART, Y. (1992) Sauvegarde du cagou huppé (*Rhynochetos jubatus*) dans le Parc de la Rivière Bleue. Internal report for the Service de l'Environnement et de la Gestion des Parcs et Réserves de la Province Sud, Nouméa, New Caledonia.

LEWIS, A. (1993) Birding in Tanimbar and Kai. *Oriental Bird Club Bull.* 18: 52–54.

LEWIS, A. AND POMEROY, D. (1989) *A bird atlas of Kenya.* Rotterdam: A. A. Balkema.

LEWIS, R. E. (1988) Mt Apo and other national parks in the Philippines. *Oryx* 22: 100–109.

LEWTHWAITE, R. W. (1996) Forest birds of southeast China: observations during 1984–1996. *Hong Kong Bird Rep.* 1995: 150–203.

VAN DER LINDE, M. (1995) A further record of the Isabela Oriole *Oriolus isabellae* from Baggao, Cagayan Province, northern Philippines. *Forktail* 11: 171.

LIPPENS, L. AND WILLE, H. (1976) *Les oiseaux du Zaïre.* La Presidence de la Republique du Zaïre.

LIU HUAN-JIN AND LIU, B. S. (1991) *The Brown-eared Pheasant.* Beijing: China Forestry Publishing House.

LIU NAI-FA AND ZHANG BING-MEI (1989) Koslov's Accentor. *Chinese Wildl.* 48: 34.

LIU NAI-FA, CHEN XIAO-YUENG AND HE DE-KUI (1996) Habitat selection of Przewalski's Rock Partridge in Lanzhou. *Acta Zool. Sin.* 42 (Suppl.): 83–89.

LIVERSIDGE, R. (1996) A new species of pipit in southern Africa. *Bull. Brit. Orn. Club* 116: 211–215.

LI WENHUA AND ZHAO XIAN-JING (1989) *China's nature reserves.* Beijing: Foreign Languages Press.

LI XIANG-TAO (1993) Surveys of the Brown Eared-pheasant in Dongling Mountain, Beijing. Pp.139–140 in D. Jenkins, ed. *Pheasants in Asia 1992.* Reading, UK: World Pheasant Association.

LI XIANG-TAO (1995) Recent research on Brown Eared-pheasants at Dongling Mountain, Beijing. Pp.35–38 in D. Jenkins, ed. *Annual review of the World Pheasant Association 1993/94.* Reading, UK: World Pheasant Association.

LI XIAO-LIU, TAN HONG-ZHI, CHENG CAI-AN AND ZHANG ALI-LI (1990) Ecological studies on the White-browed Hill Partridge. Pp.84 in D. A. Hill, P. J. Garson and D. Jenkins, eds. *Pheasants in Asia 1989.* Reading, UK: World Pheasant Association.

LONEY, M. (1996) Normanby trees threatened. *The Eastern Star* 109, 1 April: 1.

LONG, A. J. (1994) The importance of tropical montane cloud forests for endemic and threatened birds. Pp.79–106 in L. S. Hamilton, J. O. Juvik and F. N. Scatena, eds. *Tropical montane cloud forests.* New York: Springer-Verlag (Ecology).

LONG, A. J. (1996) Establishing conservation priorities using endemic birds. Pp.35–46 in C. S. Harcourt and J. A. Sayer, eds. *The conservation atlas of tropical forests: the Americas.* New York and London: Simon & Schuster.

LONG, A. J., CROSBY, M. J., STATTERSFIELD, A. J. AND WEGE, D. C. (1996) Towards a global map of biodiversity: patterns in the distribution of restricted-range birds. *Glob. Ecol. Biogeog. Letters* 5: 281–304.

LONG, Y. C. AND KIRKPATRICK, R. C. (1991) A preliminary report on the Yunnan Snub-nosed Monkey (*Rhinopithecus bieti*). *Asian Primates* 1: 1–4.

LOOPE, L. L. AND MEDEIROS, A. C. (1995) Strategies for long-term protection of biological diversity in rainforests of Haleakala National Park and East Maui, Hawaii. *Endang. Spec. Update* 12: 1–5.

LORENCE, D. H. AND MENDOZA, A. G. (1989) Oaxaca, Mexico. Pp.253–269 in D. G. Campbell and H. D. Hammond, eds. *Floristic inventory of tropical countries.* New York: New York Botanical Garden.

LOUETTE, M. (1988a) Les oiseaux de Comores. *Ann. Mus. Afr. Centrale (Zool.)* (8) 255: 1–192.

LOUETTE, M. (1988b) La conservation des oiseaux de Mayotte (Maore). Pp.197–207 in J.-C. Thibault and I. Guyot, eds. *Livre rouge des oiseaux menacés des régions françaises d'Outre Mer.* Saint-Cloud: Conseil International pour la Protection des Oiseaux (Monogr. 5).

LOUETTE, M. (1990) A new species of nightjar from Zaïre. *Ibis* 132: 349–353.

LOUETTE, M. AND BENSON, C. W. (1982) Swamp-dwelling weavers of the *Ploceus velatus/vitellinus* complex, with the description of a new species. *Bull. Brit. Orn. Club* 102: 24–31.

LOUETTE, M. AND STEVENS, J. (1992) Conserving the endemic birds on the Comoro Islands. I: General considerations on survival prospects. *Bird Conserv. Internatn.* 2: 61–80.

LOUETTE, M., STEVENS, J., BIJNENS, L. AND JANSSENS, L. (1988) *Survey of the endemic avifauna of the Comoro Islands.* Cambridge, UK: International Council for Bird Preservation (Study Report 25).

LOUETTE, M., NERI, F. AND STEVENS, J. (1993) Distribution et abondance des oiseaux forestiers de Mayotte (Océan Indien). *Oiseau et R.F.O.* 63: 115–126.

LOVEGROVE, R., MANN, I., MORGAN, G. AND WILLIAMS, I. ([1989]) Tuamotu Islands expedition March–April 1989: report of an expedition to ascertain the status of Red Data Book species in the Tuamotu Archipelago (French Polynesia). Unpublished.

LOVEGROVE, T., BELL, B. AND HAY, R. (1992) *The indigenous wildlife of Western Samoa: impacts of Cyclone Val and a recovery management strategy.* Wellington: New Zealand Department of Conservation.

LOWEN, J. C., BARTRINA, L., CLAY, R. P. AND TOBIAS, J. A. (1996) *Biological surveys and conservation priorities in eastern Paraguay.* Cambridge, UK: CSB Conservation.

LUCKING, R. S. (1997) Hybridization between Madagascan Red Fody *Foudia madagascarensis* and Seychelles Fody *Foudia sechellarum* on Aride, Seychelles. *Bird Conserv. Internatn.* 7: 1–6.

LUDLOW, F. (1951) The birds of Kongbo and Pome, southeast Tibet. *Ibis* 93: 547–578.

LUDLOW, F. AND KINNEAR, N. B. (1933–1934) A contribution to the ornithology of Chinese Turkestan. *Ibis* 13: 240–259, 440–473, 658–694.

MACDONALD, A. A. (1995) Distribution of Blue Crowned Pigeon *Goura cristata* on north Seram. *Bull. Brit. Orn. Club* 115: 33–35.

MACGREGOR, J. (1887) Notes supplementary to Major Butler's catalogue of birds of the Deccan and south Mahratta country. *Stray Feathers* 10: 435–442.

MACKINNON, J., ED. (in press) *Protected areas system*

review of the Indo-Malayan Realm. Hong Kong and Canterbury, UK: Asian Bureau for Conservation.

MACKINNON, J. AND MACKINNON, K. (1986) Review of the protected areas system in the Indo-Malayan realm. Gland, Switzerland and Cambridge, UK: International Union for Conservation of Nature and Natural Resources.

MACKINNON, J. AND PHILLIPPS, K. (1993) A field guide to the birds of Borneo, Sumatra, Java and Bali. Oxford: Oxford University Press.

MACKINNON, J., BI FENG-ZHOU, QUI MING-JIANG, FAN CHUAN-DAO, WANG HAI-BIN, YUAN SHI-JUN, TIAN AN-SHUN AND LI JIANG-GUO (1989) National conservation management plan for the Giant Panda and its habitat. Beijing and Gland, Switzerland: Ministry of Forestry and World Wide Fund for Nature.

MACKINNON, J. L., FULLER, R., HARPER, M. E., HUGH-JONES, T., KNOWLES-LEAK, R., RAHMAN, D., ROBB, D. AND VERMEULEN, J. (1994) Halmahera '94: a University of Bristol expedition to Indonesia. Final Report.

MACLEAN, G. L. (1984) Roberts' birds of Southern Africa. Cape Town: John Voelcker Bird Book Fund.

MACLEOD, H. L. (1987) The conservation of Oku Mountain Forest, Cameroon. Cambridge, UK: International Council for Bird Preservation (Study Report 15).

MACLEOD, H. AND PARROTT, J. (1992) Conservation of the Kilum (Oku) mountain forests in the Bamenda Highlands of Cameroon. Proc. 7th Pan-Afr. Orn. Congr.: 447–451.

MADGE, S. AND BURN, H. (1988) Wildfowl. London: Christopher Helm.

MADGE, S. AND BURN, H. (1993) Crows and jays: a guide to the crows, jays and magpies of the world. Mountfield, UK: Helm Information.

MADGE, S. C. AND REDMAN, N. J. (1989) The existence of a form of cliff swallow Hirundo sp. in Ethiopia. Scopus 13: 126–129.

MAGNIN, G. AND YARAR, M. (1997) Important Bird Areas in Turkey. Istanbul: Dogal Hayati Koruma Dernegi.

MAGSALAY, P. M. (1993) Rediscovery of four Cebu endemic birds (Philippines). Asia Life Sci. 2: 141–148.

MAGSALAY, P., BROOKS, T., DUTSON, G. AND TIMMINS, R. (1995) Extinction and conservation on Cebu. Nature 373: 294.

MAGUIRE, B. (1970) On the flora of the Guayana Highland. Biotropica 2: 85–100.

MAJUMDAR, N. AND BRAHMACHARI, G. K. (1988) Major grassland types of India and their bird communities: a conservation perspective. Pp.205–214 in P. D. Goriup, ed. Ecology and conservation of grassland birds. Cambridge, UK: International Council for Bird Preservation (Techn. Publ. 7).

MALLARI, N. A. D. AND JENSEN, A. (1993) Biological diversity in northern Sierra Madre, Philippines: its implication for conservation and management. Asia Life Sci. 2: 101–112.

MALTBY, E., ED. (1994) An environmental and ecological study of the marshlands of Mesopotamia. Exeter, UK: AMAR Appeal Trust.

MANI, M. S., ED. (1974) Ecology and biogeography in India. The Hague: W. Junk.

MANN, C. F. (1987) A checklist of the birds of Brunei Darussalam. Brunei Mus. J. 6: 170–212.

MARANTZ, C. A. AND REMSEN, J. V. JR (1991) Seasonal distribution of the Slaty Elaenia, a little-known migrant of South America. J. Field Orn. 62: 162–172.

MARCHANT, S. AND HIGGINS, P. J., EDS. (1990) Handbook of Australian, New Zealand and Antarctic birds. 1: Ratites to ducks. Melbourne: Oxford University Press.

MARKS, J. S. AND REDMOND, R. L. (1994) Migration of Bristle-thighed Curlews on Laysan Island: timing, behavior and estimated flight range. Condor 96: 316–330.

VAN MARLE, J. G. AND VOOUS, K. H. (1988) The birds of Sumatra. London: British Ornithologists' Union (Checklist 10).

MARSHALL, A. G. (1973) A start to nature conservation in the New Hebrides. Biol. Conserv. 5: 67–69.

MARSHALL, A. P. (1992) Censusing Laysan Ducks Anas laysanensis: a lesson in the pitfalls of estimating threatened species populations. Bird Conserv. Internatn. 2: 239–251.

MARSHALL, A. P. AND BLACK, J. M. (1992) The effect of rearing experience on subsequent behavioural traits in Hawaiian Geese Branta sandvicensis: implications for the recovery programme. Bird Conserv. Internatn. 2: 131–147.

MARTENS, J. AND ECK, S. (1991) Pnoepyga immaculata n.sp., eine neue bodenbewohnende Timalie aus dem Nepal-Himalaya. J. Orn. 132: 179–198.

MARTENS, J. AND ECK, S. (1995) Towards an ornithology of the Himalayas: systematics, ecology and vocalizations of Nepal birds. Bonn: Zoologisches Forschungsinstitut, und Museum Alexander Koenig (Bonn. Zool. Monogr. 38).

MARTÍN, A., NOGALES, M., HERNÁNDEZ, M. A., LORENZO, J. A., MEDINA, F. M. AND RANDO, J. C. (1996) Status, conservation and habitat selection of the Houbara Bustard Chlamydotis undulata fuertaventurae on Lanzarote (Canary Islands). Bird Conserv. Internatn. 6: 229–239.

MARTÍNEZ-GÓMEZ, J. E. AND CURRY, R. L. (1996) The conservation of the Socorro Mockingbird Mimodes graysoni in 1993–1994. Bird Conserv. Internatn. 6: 271–283.

MARTÍNEZ-MORALES, M. A. (1996) The Cozumel Curassow: abundance, habitat preference and conservation. Cambridge University (M.Phil. Thesis).

MARTINS, R. P. (1996) Taxonomic treatment of endemic taxa in Socotra. Orn. Soc. Middle East Bull. 17: 81–82.

MA SHI-LAI, HAN LIAN-XIAN, LAN DAO-YING, JI WEI-ZHI AND HARRIS, R. B. (1995) Faunal resources of the Gaoligongshan region of Yunnan, China: diverse and threatened. Environ. Conserv. 22: 250–258.

MATURIN, S. (1994) Destination Vanuatu: protecting forests in the South Pacific. Forest and Bird 271: 38–43.

MAUERSBERGER, G., WAGNER, S., WALLSCHLAGER, D. AND WARTHOLD, R. (1982) Neue Daten zur Avifauna mongolica. Mitt. Zool. Mus. Berlin 58: 11–74.

MAY, R. M. (1990) Taxonomy as destiny. Nature 347: 129–130.

MAYR, E. (1945) Birds of the southwest Pacific: a field guide to the birds of the area between Samoa, New Caledonia and Micronesia. New York: Macmillan.

MAYR, E. AND PHELPS, W. H. (1967) The origin of the bird fauna of the southern Venezuelan highlands. Bull. Amer. Mus. Nat. Hist. 136: 269–328.

McCORMACK, G. AND KÜNZLE, J. (1990) Kakerori—Rarotonga's endangered flycatcher. Cook Islands Conservation Service.

References

MCCORMACK, G. AND KÜNZLE, J. (1993) The 'Ura or Rimatara Lorikeet (*Vini kuhlii*): its former range, its present status and conservation priorities. Paper presented at the Manu Conference, Tahiti, November 1993.

MCCORMACK, G. AND KÜNZLÉ, J. (1996) The 'Ura or Rimatara Lorikeet *Vini kuhlii*: its former range, present status, and conservation priorities. *Bird Conserv. Internatn.* 6: 325–334.

MCCULLOCH, N. (1996) The Seychelles Magpie Robin: first steps on the road to recovery. *Bull. African Bird Club* 3: 81–84.

MCGOWAN, P. J. K. AND GARSON, P. J. (1995) *Pheasants: status survey and conservation action plan 1995–1999.* Gland, Switzerland: International Union for Nature Conservation and Natural Resources and World Pheasant Association.

MCGOWAN, P. J. K., DOWELL, S. D., CARROLL, J. P. AND AEBISCHER, N. J. (1995) *Partridges, quails, francolins, snowcocks and guineafowl: status survey and conservation action plan 1995–1999.* Cambridge, UK: International Union for Nature Conservation and Natural Resources.

MCGUIGAN, C. (1987) Ornithology report. Pp.10–27 in S. L. Tetlow, ed. *Cambridge Conservation Study 1985: Taita Hills, Kenya.* Cambridge, UK: International Council for Bird Preservation (Study Report 19).

MEDEIROS, A. C., LOOPE, L. L. AND HOBDY, R. W. (1993) Conservation of cloud forests in Maui county (Maui, Molokai, and Lana'i), Hawaiian Islands. Pp.142–148 in L. S. Hamilton, J. O. Juvik and F. N. Scatena, eds. *Tropical montane cloud forests: proceedings of an international symposium.* Honolulu: East-West Center.

MEDWAY, LORD AND WELLS, D. R. (1976) *The birds of the Malay Peninsula,* 5. London: H. F. and G. Witherby.

MEES, G. F. (1995) On *Malacocincla vanderbilti* de Schauensee & Ripley, and *Malacocincla perspicillata* (Bonaparte) (Aves, Timaliidae). *Proc. Kon. Ned. Akad. v. Wetensch.* 98: 63–68.

MEES, G. F. (1997) On the identity of *Heterornis senex* Bonaparte. *Bull. Brit. Orn. Club* 117: 67–68.

MEYER, J.-Y. (1996) Status of *Miconia calvescens* (Melastomataceae), a dominant invasive tree in the Society Islands (French Polynesia). *Pac. Sci.* 50: 66–76.

MEYER DE SCHAUENSEE, R. (1970) *A guide to the birds of South America.* Wynnewood, Penn.: Livingston Publishing Company for the Academy of Natural Sciences of Philadelphia.

MEYER DE SCHAUENSEE, R. (1982) *A guide to the birds of South America.* Wynnewood, Penn.: Livingston Publishing Company for the Academy of Natural Sciences of Philadelphia (reprinted with addenda by ICBP Pan-American Section).

MEYER DE SCHAUENSEE, R. (1984) *The birds of China.* Oxford: Oxford University Press.

MEYER DE SCHAUENSEE, R. AND PHELPS, W. H. (1978) *A guide to the birds of Venezuela.* Princeton: Princeton University Press.

MEYERS, J. M., VILELLA, F. J. AND BARROW, W. C. (1993) Positive effects of Hurricane Hugo: record years for Puerto Rican Parrots nesting in the wild. *Endangered Species Techn. Bull.* 18: 1,10.

MEZA, J. (1989) Informe anual del proyecto 'conservación del Picaflor de Juan Fernández *Sephanoides fernandensis'*.

Invierno 1988–otoño 1989. [Santiago]: Corporación Nacional Forestal.

MILBERG, P. AND TYRBERG, T. (1993) Naive birds and noble savages—a review of man-caused prehistoric extinctions of island birds. *Ecography* 16: 229–250.

MIRSKY, E. N. (1976) Song divergence in hummingbird and junco populations on Guadalupe Island. *Condor* 78: 230–235.

MITCHELL, A. (1989) Nicobar Pigeon nesting colonies in Irian Jaya. *Kukila* 4: 51–52.

MITTERMEIER, R. A. (1988) Primate diversity and the tropical forest. Case studies from Brazil and Madagascar and the importance of the megadiversity countries. Pp.145–154 in E. O. Wilson, ed. *Biodiversity.* Washington, DC: National Academy Press.

MITTERMEIER, R. A., WERNER, T. B. AND LEES, A. (1996) New Caledonia—a conservation imperative for an ancient land. *Oryx* 30: 104–112.

MOELIKER, C. W. AND HEIJ, C. J. (1995) The rediscovery of *Monarcha boanensis* (Aves: Monarchidae) from Boano Island, Indonesia. *DEINSEA* 2: 123–143.

MOLLOY, J. AND DAVIS, A. (1992) *Setting priorities for the conservation of New Zealand's threatened plants and animals.* Wellington: New Zealand Department of Conservation.

MONNET, C., THIBAULT, J. AND VARNEY, A. (1993) Stability and changes during the twentieth century in the breeding landbirds of Tahiti (Polynesia). *Bird Conserv. Internatn.* 3: 261–280.

MONROE, B. L. (1968) *A distributional survey of the birds of Honduras.* Anchorage, Kentucky: American Ornithologists' Union (Orn. Monogr. 7).

MOORCROFT, D. (1996) Anjouan Expedition '95. University of Newcastle upon Tyne. Unpublished report.

MOORS, P. J., ATKINSON, I. A. E. AND SHERLEY, G. H. (1992) Reducing the rat threat to islands. *Bird Conserv. Internatn.* 2: 93–114.

MORAT, P., VEILLON, J.-M. AND MACKEE, H. S. (1984) Floristic relationships of New Caledonian rain forest phanerograms. Pp.71–128 in F. J. Radovsky, P. H. Raven and S. H. Sohmer, eds. *Biogeography of the tropical Pacific.* Kansas: ASC.

MOREAU, R. E. (1966) *The bird faunas of Africa and its islands.* London: Academic Press.

MOREL, G. J. AND CHAPPUIS, C. (1992) Past and future taxonomic research in West Africa. *Bull. Brit. Orn. Club (Centenary Suppl.)* 112A: 217–224.

MORIN, M. P. (1992) The breeding biology of an endangered Hawaiian honeycreeper, the Laysan Finch. *Condor* 94: 646–667.

MORIN, M. P. AND CONANT, S. (1994) Variables influencing population estimates of an endangered passerine. *Biol. Conserv.* 67: 73–84.

MORONY, J. J., BOCK, W. J. AND FARRAND, J. (1975) *Reference list of the birds of the world.* New York: Department of Ornithology, American Museum of Natural History.

MOSCHIONE, F. N. AND SAN CRISTÓBAL, J. (1993) Registro del Payador Negro *Diglossa carbonaria* para la Argentina. *Hornero* 13: 307.

MOURER-CHAUVIRÉ, C. AND MOUTOU, F. (1987) Découverte d'une forme récemment éteinte d'ibis endémique insulaire de l'île de la Réunion *Borbonibis latipes* n. gen. n. sp. *C. R. Acad. Sci. Paris* (II) 305: 419–423.

MOURER-CHAUVIRÉ, C., BOUR, R. AND RIBES, S. (1995) Was the Solitaire of Réunion an ibis? *Nature* 373: 568.

MOYER, D. (1995) *The status of Fischer's Lovebird Agapornis fischeri in the United Republic of Tanzania.* Cambridge, UK: International Union for Conservation of Nature and Natural Resources.

MOYER, J. T. (1993) [*Miyake-jima naturalist.*] Tokyo: Dobutsu-sha. (In Japanese.)

MULLER, T. AND TIMBERLAKE, J. (1992) Areas for plant conservation in Zimbabwe. *Zimbabwe Sci. News* 26(10/12): 88–95.

MUNN, C. A. (1995) Lears Macaw: a second population confirmed. *Psittascene* 7: 1–3.

MWAF (= Mauritian Wildlife Appeal Fund) (1992) Report 1990–1992. Unpublished.

MYERS, N. (1988a) Threatened biotas: 'hotspots' in tropical forests. *Environmentalist* 8: 1–20.

MYERS, N. (1988b) Environmental degradation and some economic consequences in the Philippines. *Environ. Conserv.* 15: 205–214.

MYERS, N. (1990) The biodiversity challenge: expanded hot-spots analysis. *Environmentalist* 10: 243–256.

NACINOVIC, J. B. AND TEIXEIRA, D. M. (1989) As aves de Fernando de Noronha: uma lista sistemática anotada. *Revta. Bras. Biol.* 49: 709–729.

NASH, S. V. (1993) Concern about trade in Red-and-blue Lories. *TRAFFIC Bull.* 13: 93–96.

NATIONAL RESEARCH COUNCIL (1992) *The scientific bases for the preservation of the Hawaiian Crow.* Washington, DC: National Academy Press.

DE NAUROIS, R. (1973) Lés Ibis des iles de S.Tomé et du Prine: leur place dans le groupe des *Bostrychia* (=*Lampribis*). *Arc. Mus. Boc.* 4: 157–173.

NAVARRO, A. G. (1992) Altitudinal distribution of birds in the Sierra Madre del Sur, Guerrero, Mexico. *Condor* 94: 29–39.

NAVARRO, A. G. AND ESCALANTE PLIEGO, P. (1993) Aves. Pp.443–501 in *Historia natural del Parque Ecologico Estatal Omiltemi, Chilpancingo, Guerrero, México.* México: CONABIO-UNAM.

NAVARRO, A. G., PETERSON, A. T., ESCALANTE, B. P. AND BENÍTEZ, H. (1992) *Cypseloides storeri*, a new species of swift from Mexico. *Wilson Bull.* 104: 55–64.

NECHAEV, V. A. (1989) The status of Normann's [*sic*] Greenshank *Tringa guttifer* in the USSR. *Asian Wetland News* 2: 11,14.

NEGRET, A. J. AND CAVALCANTI, R. (1985) Censo poblacional de duas aves da região de Brasília: *Scytalopus novacapitalis* e *Melanopareia torquata* (Rhinocryptidae). Pp.271 in A. C. Z. Amaral and E. H. M. do Amaral, eds. *Resumos, XII Congresso Brasileiro de Zoologia.* Campinas: Editora da UNICAMP.

NELSON, R. AND HORNING, N. (1993) AVHRR-LAC estimates of forest area in Madagascar, 1990. *Int. J. Remote Sensing* 14: 1463–1475.

NEWMARK, W. D. (1991) Tropical forest fragmentation and the local extinction of understorey birds in the East Usambara Mountains, Tanzania. *Conserv. Biol.* 5: 67–78.

NEWTON, S. F. AND NEWTON, A. V. (1996) Seasonal changes in the abundance and diversity of birds in threatened juniper forest in the southern Asir mountains, Saudi Arabia. *Bird Conserv. Internatn.* 6: 371–392.

NICOLL, M. E. AND LANGRAND, O. (1989) *Madagascar: revue de la conservation et des aires protegéés.* Gland, Switzerland: World Wide Fund for Nature.

NIX, H. A. AND SWITZER, M. A. (1991) *Rainforest animals: atlas of vertebrates endemic to Australia's wet tropics.* Canberra: Australian National Parks and Wildlife Service.

NJOROGE, P. AND BENNUN, L. (1996) Status and conservation of Hinde's Babbler *Turdoides hindei*, a threatened species in agricultural landscape. Pp.21 in *Ninth Pan-African Ornithological Congress: programme and book of abstracts.* [Accra]: Ghana Wildlife Society.

NORES, M. (1986) Nuevos registros para aves de Argentina. *Hornero* 12: 304–307.

NORES, M. (1995) Insular biogeography of birds on mountain-tops in north western Argentina. *J. Biogeogr.* 22: 61–70.

NORES, M. AND YZURIETA, D. (1983) Especiación en las Sierras Pampeanas de Córdoba y San Luis (Argentina), con descripción de siete nuevas subespecies de aves. *Hornero* Extr.: 88–102.

NORTON, W. J. E. (1975) Notes on the birds of the Sierra Nevada de Santa Marta, Colombia. *Bull. Brit. Orn. Club* 95: 109–115.

NOSKE, R. A. (1995) At the crossroads of two avifaunas—Timor. *Oriental Bird Club Bull.* 21: 34–38.

NOSKE, R. AND SALEH, N. (1993) Report to LIPI: the status of lowland forest birds in West Timor. Unpublished.

OATLEY, T. B. AND TINLEY, K. L. (1987) The forest avifauna of Gorongosa Mountain, Mozambique. *Ostrich* 14 (Suppl.): 57–61.

OGDEN, J. (1995) The long-term conservation of forest diversity in New Zealand. *Pac. Conserv. Biol.* 2: 77–90.

OLDFIELD, S. (1987) *Fragments of Paradise: a guide for conservation action in the UK dependent territories.* Oxford: Pisces.

OLIVER, W. L. R. AND SANTOS, I. B. (1991) *Threatened endemic mammals of the Atlantic Forest region of southeast Brazil.* Jersey, Channel Islands: Jersey Wildlife Preservation Trust (Spec. Sci. Report 4).

OLROG, C. C. (1979) *Nueva lista de la avifauna Argentina.* Tucumán: Ministerio de Cultura y Educación, Fundación Miguel Lillo (*Opera Lilloana* 27).

OLSEN, P. D. (1996) Re-establishment of an endangered subspecies: the Norfolk Island Boobook Owl *Ninox novaeseelandiae undulata. Bird Conserv. Internatn.* 6: 63–80.

OLSON, D. M. AND DINERSTEIN, E. (1997) *The global 200: conserving the world's distinctive ecoregions.* Washington, DC: World Wildlife Fund-US.

OLSON, S. L. (1981) Natural history of vertebrates on the Brazilian islands of the mid South Atlantic. *Nat. Geogr. Soc. Res. Rep.* 13: 481–492.

OLSON, S. L. (1986) An early account of some birds from Mauke, Cook Islands, and the origin of the 'Mysterious Starling' *Aplonis mavornata* Buller. *Notornis* 33: 197–208.

OLSON, S. L. (1992) Requiescat for *Tricholimnas conditicius*, a rail that never was. *Bull. Brit. Orn. Club* 112: 174–179.

OLSON, S. L. (1994) The endemic vireo of Fernando de Noronha (*Vireo gracilirostris*). *Wilson Bull.* 106: 1–17.

OLSON, S. L. AND JAMES, H. F. (1982) Fossil birds from the Hawaiian Islands: evidence for wholesale extinction by man before western contact. *Science* 217: 633–635.

OLSON, S. L. AND JAMES, H. F. (1994) A specimen of Nukupu'u (Aves: Drepanidini: *Hemignathus lucidus*) from the island of Hawai'i. *Pac. Sci.* 48: 331–338.

OLSON, S. L. AND JOUVENTIN, P. (1996) A new species of small flightless duck from Amsterdam Island, southern Indian Ocean (Anatidae: Aves). *Condor* 98: 1–9.

OLSSON, U. (1995) Little known Oriental bird: Koslov's Bunting *Emberiza koslowi*. *Oriental Bird Club Bull.* 21: 39–43.

OLSSON, U., ALSTRÖM, P. AND COLSTON, P. R. (1993) A new species of *Phylloscopus* warbler from Hainan Island, China. *Ibis* 135: 2–7.

ORNAT, A. L. AND LYNCH, J. F. (1990) Landbird communities of the coastal dune scrub in the Yucatán Peninsula: species composition, ecology, and zoogeographic affinities. *Vida Silvestre Neotropical* 2: 21–30.

ORNAT, A. L., LYNCH, J. F. AND MACKINNON DE MONTES, B. (1989) New and noteworthy records of birds from the eastern Yucatán Peninsula. *Wilson Bull.* 103: 390–409.

OSBORNE, P. E. AND TIGAR, B. J. (1992) Priorities for bird conservation in Lesotho, southern Africa. *Biol. Conserv.* 61: 159–169.

OSBORNE, P. L. (1995) Biological and cultural diversity in Papua New Guinea: conservation, conflicts, constraints and compromise. *Ambio* 24: 231–237.

OTANI, C. (1995) Tibetan Rosefinch *Kozlowia roborowskii* sightings on the Tibetan plateau. *Oriental Bird Club Bull.* 21: 46–47.

OTTENWALDER, J. A. (1992) Recovery plan for the conservation of the Hispaniolan Crossbill in southern Haiti. Prepared for the Macaya National Park Project/University of Florida, MacArthur Foundation and USAID/Haiti.

PACHECO, J. F. AND GONZAGA, L. P. (1995) A new species of *Synallaxis* of the *ruficapilla/infuscata* complex from eastern Brazil (Passeriformes: Furnariidae). *Ararajuba* 3: 3–11.

PACHECO, J. F., WHITNEY, B. M. AND GONZAGA, L. P. (1996) A new genus and species of furnariid (Aves: Furnariidae) from the cocoa-growing region of southeastern Bahia, Brazil. *Wilson Bull.* 108: 397–433.

PALLISER, T. (1992) An unknown rail sighted in West New Britain. *Muruk* 5: 62–63.

PALUDAN, K. (1959) On the birds of Afghanistan. *Vidensk. Medd. Dansk. Naturh. For.* 122: 1–332.

PANDE, P., KOTHARI, A. AND SINGH, S. (1991) *Directory of national parks and sanctuaries in Andaman and Nicobar Islands: management status and profiles.* New Delhi: Indian Institute of Public Administration.

PARK, G., HAY, R., WHISTLER, A. AND LOVEGROVE, T. (1992) *The conservation of biological diversity in the coastal lowlands of Western Samoa.* Wellington: New Zealand Department of Conservation.

PARKER, T. A. AND BAILEY, B. (1991) *A biological assessment of the Alto Madidi region and adjacent areas of northwest Bolivia, May 18—June 15, 1990.* Washington, DC: Conservation International.

PARKER, T. A. AND ROCHA, O. (1991) Notes on the status and behaviour of the Rusty-necked Piculet *Picumnus fuscus*. *Bull. Brit. Orn. Club* 111: 91–92.

PARKER, T. A., SCHULENBERG, T. S., KESSLER, M. AND WUST, W. H. (1995) Natural history and conservation of the endemic avifauna in north-west Peru. *Bird Conserv. Internatn.* 5: 201–231.

PARYSKI, P., WOODS, C. A. AND SERGILE, F. (1989) Conservation strategies and the preservation of biological diversity in Haiti. Pp.855–878 in C. A. Woods, ed. *Biogeography of the West Indies: past, present, and future.* Gainesville, Florida: Sandhill Crane Press.

PASCAL, J. P. (1988) *Wet evergreen forests of the Western Ghats of India. Ecology, structure, floristic composition and succession,* 20. India: Institut Francais de Pondicherry.

PATEL, A. D. AND LIN, Y. (1989) *History of wildlife conservation in Taiwan.* Taiwan: Council of Agriculture (COA Forestry Series 207).

PAULSON, D. D. (1994) Understanding tropical deforestation: the case of Western Samoa. *Environ. Conserv.* 21: 326–332.

PAYNE, R. B. (1997) The Mali Firefinch *Lagonosticta virata* in Senegal. *Malimbus* 19: 39–41.

PEARCE, F. (1993) Draining life from Iraq's marshes. *New Scientist* 138: 11–12.

PEARCE-HIGGINS, J. W. (1996) Seedeaters in the Noel Kempff Mercado National Park, Bolivia. *Cotinga* 5: 69–71.

PEARMAN, M. (1989) Observaciones de *Sicalis luteocephala*, una nueva especie para la Argentina. *Nuestras Aves* 20: 5.

PEARMAN, M. (1990) Behaviour and vocalizations of an undescribed canastero *Asthenes* sp. from Brazil. *Bull. Brit. Orn. Club* 110: 145–153.

PEARMAN, M. AND ABADIE, E. I. (in press) Mesopotamia grasslands and wetlands survey, 1991–1993: conservation of threatened birds and habitat in north-east Argentina.

PEET, N. B. AND ATKINSON, P. W. (1994) The biodiversity and conservation of the birds of São Tomé and Príncipe. *Biodiv. and Conserv.* 3: 851–867.

PENAFIEL, S. R. (1993) The biological and hydrological values of the mossy forests in the central cordillera mountains, Philippines. Pp.171–175 in L. S. Hamilton, J. O. Juvik and F. N. Scatena, eds. *Tropical montane cloud forests: proceedings of an international symposium.* Honolulu: East-West Center.

PENG YAN-ZHANG, WEI JIAN-HAO, YANG LAN, LIU GUANG-ZUO AND ZHENG BAO-LAI (1980) [*Report on studies of vertebrates in the Gaoligong mountain district. 2: birds.*] Beijing: Scientific Publishing House. (In Chinese.)

PERERA, A. AND ROSABAL, P. (1986) Las áreas protegidas en Cuba. *Silvestres* 2: 13–17.

PÉREZ DEL VAL, J., FA, J. E., CASTROVIEJO, J. AND PURROY, F. J. (1994) Species richness and endemism of birds in Bioko. *Biodiv. and Conserv.* 3: 868–892.

PETERS, D. S. (1996) *Hypositta perdita* n. sp., eine neue Vogelart aus Madagaskar (Aves: Passeriformes: Vangidae). *Senckenbergiana Biol.* 76: 7–14.

PETERS, J. L. (1934–1987) *Checklist of the birds of the world.* Cambridge, Mass.: Harvard University Press.

PETERSON, A. T. (1993) Species status of *Geotrygon carrikeri*. *Bull. Brit. Orn. Club* 113: 166–168.

PIDGEON, M. (1996) An ecological survey of Lake Alaotra and selected wetlands of central and eastern Madagascar in analysing the demise of Madagascar Pochard *Aythya innotata*. *Work. Grp Birds Madag. Reg.* 6: 17–19.

PINTO, O. M. DE O. (1952) Redescobrimento de *Mitu mitu* (Linné) no nordeste do Brasil (est. de Alagoas). Provada a independência de *Mitu tuberosus* (Spix) como espécie à parte. *Pap. Avuls. Dep. Zool. São Paulo* 10: 325–334.

POOLE, C. (1994) Around the Orient. *Oriental Bird Club Bull.* 20: 15–23.

PORTER, R. F. AND MARTINS, R. P. (1996) Southern Yemen and Socotra: the report of the OSME survey in spring 1993. *Sandgrouse* 17: 1–188.

PORTER, R. F. AND STONE, F. (1996) An introduction to Socotra and its birds. *Orn. Soc. Middle East Bull.* 17: 73–80.

POULSEN, M. K. (1995) The threatened and near-threatened birds of Luzon, Philippines, and the role of the Sierra Madre mountains in their conservation. *Bird Conserv. Internatn.* 5: 79–115.

POULSEN, M. K. (in press) *Conserving biodiversity on Buru: biodiversity conservation priorities on Buru with special reference to the proposed Kepalat Mada reserve.* Bogor: PHPA/BirdLife Indonesian Programme.

PRATT, H. D. (1980) Intra-island variation in the 'Elepaio on the island of Hawai'i. *Condor* 82: 449–458.

PRATT, H. D. (1993) *Enjoying birds in Hawaii: a birdfinding guide to the fiftieth state.* Honolulu: Mutual Publishing.

PRATT, H. D. (1994) Avifaunal change in the Hawaiian Islands, 1893–1993. *Stud. Avian Biol.* 15: 103–118.

PRATT, H. D., BRUNER, P. L. AND BERRETT, D. G. (1987) *A field guide to the birds of Hawaii and the tropical Pacific.* Princeton: Princeton University Press.

PRENDERGAST, J. R., QUINN, R. M., LAWTON, J. H., EVERSHAM, B. C. AND GIBBONS, D. W. (1993) Rare species, the coincidence of diversity hotspots and conservation strategies. *Nature* 365: 335–337.

PRICE, O., WOINARSKI, J. C. Z., LIDDLE, D. L. AND RUSSELL-SMITH, J. (1995) Patterns of species composition and reserve design for a fragmented estate: monsoon rainforests in the Northern Territory, Australia. *Biol. Conserv.* 74: 9–19.

PRIGOGINE, A. (1972) Description of a new green bulbul from the Republic of Zaire. *Bull. Brit. Orn. Club* 92: 138–141.

PRIGOGINE, A. (1985) Conservation of the avifauna of the forests of the Albertine Rift. Pp.277–295 in A. W. Diamond and T. E. Lovejoy, eds. *Conservation of tropical forest birds.* Cambridge, UK: International Council for Bird Preservation (Techn. Publ. 4).

PROCTER, J. (1984) Floristics of the granitic islands of the Seychelles. Pp.209–220 in D. R. Stoddart, ed. *Biogeography and ecology of the Seychelles Islands.* The Hague: W. Junk (Monogr. Biol. 55).

PRUM, R. O. (1994) Species status of the White-fronted Manakin, *Lepidothrix serena* (Pipridae), with comments on conservation biology. *Condor* 96: 692–702.

PRYS-JONES, R. P. AND DIAMOND, A. W. (1984) Ecology of the land birds of the granitic and coralline islands of the Seychelles, with particular reference to Cousin Island and Aldabra Atoll. Pp.529–558 in D. R. Stoddart, ed. *Biogeography and ecology of the Seychelles Islands.* The Hague: W. Junk (Monogr. Biol. 55).

QUINNELL, R. AND BALMFORD, A. (1988) A future for Palawan's forests? *Oryx* 22: 30–35.

RAHMANI, A. (1988) Grassland birds of the Indian Subcontinent: a review. Pp.187–204 in P. D. Goriup, ed. *Ecology and conservation of grassland birds.* Cambridge, UK: International Council for Bird Preservation (Techn. Publ. 7).

RAMANAMPAMONJY, J. R. (1995) Rencontre inattendue avec le Râle d'Olivier (*Amaurornis olivieri*) au Lac Bemamba. *Work. Grp. Birds Madag. Reg.* 5. 5–7.

RAMDAS, L. A. (1974) Weather and climatic patterns. Pp.99–134 in M. S. Mani, ed. *Ecology and biogeography in India.* The Hague: W. Junk.

RAND, A. L. AND GILLIARD, E. T. (1967) *Handbook of New Guinea birds.* London: Weidenfeld and Nicolson.

RANDS, M. R. W. (1989) The conservation of endemic and migratory birds in Arabia. Pp.263–270 in A. H. Abu-Zinada, P. D. Goriup and I. A. Nader, eds. *Wildlife conservation and development in Saudi Arabia: proceedings of the First Symposium, Riyadh, February, 1987.* Riyadh: National Commission for Wildlife Conservation and Development (Publication 3).

RANE, U. (1984) Occurrence of the Whitebreasted Laughing Thrushes (*Garrulax jecdoni* Blyth) in Goa. *J. Bombay Nat. Hist. Soc.* 81: 474–475.

RASMUSSEN, P. C. AND COLLAR, N. J. (in prep.-a) Systematics of the Forest Owlet *Heteroglaux* (*Athene*) *blewitti*.

RASMUSSEN, P. C. AND COLLAR, N. J. (in prep.-b) A major specimen fraud in the Forest Owlet *Heteroglaux* (*Athene*) *blewitti*, with clarification of the historical record.

RATNAPALA, R. (1984) Land snails: distribution and notes on ecology. Pp.391–412 in C. H. Fernando, ed. *Ecology and biogeography of Sri Lanka.* The Hague: W. Junk.

REBELO, A. G. (1994) Using the Proteaceae to design a nature reserve network and determine conservation priorities for the Cape Floristic Region. Pp.375–396 in P. L. Forey, C. J. Humphries and R. I. Vane-Wright, eds. *Systematics and conservation evaluation.* Oxford: Clarendon Press (Systematics Association Special Volume 50).

REICHEL, J. D. (1991) Status and conservation of seabirds in the Mariana Islands. Pp.249–262 in J. P. Croxall, ed. *Seabird status and conservation: a supplement.* Cambridge, UK: International Council for Bird Preservation (Techn. Publ. 11).

REMSEN, J. V. (1985) Community organization and ecology of birds of high elevation humid forest of the Bolivian Andes. Pp.733–756 in P. A. Buckley, M. S. Foster, E. S. Morton, R. S. Ridgely and F. G. Buckley, eds. *Neotropical Ornithology.* Washington, DC: American Ornithologists' Union (Orn. Monogr. 36).

REMSEN, J. V. AND PARKER, T. A. (1995) Bolivia has the opportunity to create the planet's richest park for terrestrial biota. *Bird Conserv. Internatn.* 5: 181–200.

RENMAN, E. (1995) A possible new species of Scops Owl *Otus* sp. on Réunion. *Bull. African Bird Club* 2: 54.

REPPPROT (1990) *National overview of the regional physical planning programme for transmigration.* Chatham, UK: Overseas Development Natural Resources Institute.

RESIDE, J. (1991) Mataweli is alive and well: the search for the Santo Mountain Starling. *Wingspan* 4: 10–11.

RESTALL, R. L. (1996) A proposed new species of munia, genus *Lonchura* (Estrildinae). *Bull. Brit. Orn. Club* 116: 137–142.

REVILLE, B. J. AND STOKES, T. (1994) Conservation of seabirds on Christmas Island, Indian Ocean. Pp.244–257 in D. N. Nettleship, J. Burger and M. Gochfeld, eds. *Seabirds on islands: threats, case studies and action plans.* Cambridge, UK: BirdLife International (BirdLife Conservation Series no. 1).

REYNARD, G. B., GARRIDO, O. H. AND SUTTON, R. L. (1993) Taxonomic revision of the Greater Antillean Pewee. *Wilson Bull.* 105. 217–387.

RICHARDSON, M. E. (1984) Aspects of the ornithology of the Tristan da Cunha group and Gough Island, 1972–74. *Cormorant* 12: 123–199.

RIDGELY, R. S. AND GWYNNE, J. A. (1989) *A guide to the birds of Panama with Costa Rica, Nicaragua, and Honduras*. Second edition. Princeton: Princeton University Press.

RIDGELY, R. AND TUDOR, G. (1989) *The birds of South America*, 1. Oxford: Oxford University Press.

RIDGELY, R. S. AND TUDOR, G. (1994) *The birds of South America*, 2. Austin, Texas: University of Texas Press.

RIDLEY, H. N. (1890) Notes on the zoology of Fernando Noronha. *J. Linn. Soc. Zool.* 20: 473–570.

RILEY, J. (1995) University of York Talaud and Sangihe Expedition 1995: an assessment of the threatened endemic avifauna of the Sangihe and Talaud islands, northeast Indonesia. Unpublished report.

RINKE, D. (1986a) The status of wildlife in Tonga. *Oryx* 20: 146–151.

RINKE, D. (1986b) Notes on the avifauna of Niuafo'ou Island, Kingdom of Tonga. *Emu* 86: 82–86.

RINKE, D. (1989) The relationships and taxonomy of the Fijian parrot genus *Prospeia*. *Bull. Brit. Orn. Club* 109: 185–195.

RINKE, D. R. (1991) Birds of 'Ata and Late, and additional notes on the avifauna of Niuafo'ou, Kingdom of Tonga. *Notornis* 38: 131–151.

RINKE, D. (1993) Safe islands for the Malau. *OSNZ News* 69: 1.

RIPLEY, S. D. (1976) Reconsideration of *Athene blewitti* (Hume). *J. Bombay Nat. Hist. Soc.* 73: 1–4.

RIPLEY, S. D. (1982) *A synopsis of the birds of India, Pakistan together with those of Nepal, Bhutan, Bangladesh and Sri Lanka*. Bombay: Bombay Natural History Society.

RIPLEY, S. D. AND BEEHLER, B. M. (1989) Ornithogeographic affinities of the Andaman and Nicobar Islands. *J. Biogeogr.* 16: 232–332.

RIPLEY, S. D., SAHA, S. S. AND BEEHLER, B. M. (1991) Notes on birds from the Upper Noa Dihang, Arunachal Pradesh, northeastern India. *Bull. Brit. Orn. Club* 111: 19–27.

RISING, J. D. (1996) *A guide to the identification and natural history of the sparrows of the United States and Canada*. London: Academic Press.

RIZZINI, T. C., ED. (1979) *Tratado de fitogeografica do Brasil: aspectors sociológicos e floristicos*, 2. São Paulo: Universidade de São Paulo.

ROBBINS, M. B. AND RIDGELY, R. S. (1992) Taxonomy and natural history of *Nyctiphrynus rosenbergi* (Caprimulgidae). *Condor* 94: 984–987.

ROBBINS, M. B., ROSENBERG, G. H. AND SORNOZA MOLINA, F. (1994) A new species of cotinga (Cotingidae: *Doliornis*) from the Ecuadorian Andes, with comments on plumage sequences in *Doliornis* and *Ampelion*. *Auk* 111: 1–7.

ROBERTS, P. (1987) Is the Aldabra brush warbler extinct? *Oryx* 21: 209–210.

ROBERTS, P. (1988) Introduced birds on Assumption Island—a threat to Aldabra. *Oryx* 22: 15–17.

ROBERTS, T. J. (1991) *The birds of Pakistan*, 1. Karachi: Oxford University Press.

ROBERTS, T. J. (1992) *The birds of Pakistan*, 2. Karachi: Oxford University Press.

ROBERTSON, C. J. R. AND NUNN, G. B. (in press) Towards a new taxonomy for albatrosses. Pp. in G. Robertson, ed. *Albatross biology and conservation*. Chipping Norton, Australia: Surrey Beatty.

ROBERTSON, H. (1995c) Kakerori comeback. *OSNZ News* 42: 2–3.

ROBERTSON, H. A., HAY, J. R., SAUL, E. K. AND McCORMACK, G. V. (1994) Recovery of the Kakerori: an endangered forest bird of the Cook Islands. *Conserv. Biol.* 8: 1078–1086.

ROBERTSON, I. S. (1995) First field observations on the Sidamo Lark *Heteromirafra sidamoensis*. *Bull. Brit. Orn. Club* 115: 241–243.

ROBERTSON, I. S. (1995a) Notes on birds in Ethiopia. *Scopus* 19: 61–62.

ROBERTSON, I. S. (1996b) Recent reports. *Bull. African Bird Club* 3: 60–63.

ROBERTSON, P. A., DELLELEGN, Y., DEJENE, S., SHIMELIS, A., MARIAM, T. W. AND ALEMAYEHU, M. (in prep.) Harwood's Francolin *Francolinus harwoodi*: recent observations on its status, distribution, habitat requirements, behavior and threats.

ROBINET, O. AND SALAS, M. (1996) Absence of ship rat *Rattus rattus*, and Norway rat *Rattus norvegicus*, on Ouvea (Loyalty Islands, New Caledonia): consequences for conservation. *Pac. Conserv. Biol.* 2: 390–397.

ROBINET, O., BEUGNET, F., DULIEU, D. AND CHARDONNET, PH (1995) The Ouvéa parakeet—state of knowledge and conservation status. *Oryx* 29: 143–150.

ROBINET, O., BARRE, N. AND SALAS, M. (1996) Population estimate for the Ouvea Parakeet *Eunymphicus cornutus uvaeensis*: its present range and implications for conservation. *Emu* 96: 151–157.

ROBINSON, D. AND TRAILL, B. J. (1996) *Conserving woodland birds in the wheat and sheep belts of southern Australia*. Melbourne: Royal Australasian Ornithologists' Union (RAOU Conservation Statement 10).

ROBSON, C. R. (1986) Recent observations of birds in Xizang and Qinghai provinces, China. *Forktail* 2: 67–82.

ROBSON, C. (1989) Birdwatching areas: Omei Shan, Sichuan, China. *Oriental Bird Club Bull.* 9: 16–21.

ROBSON, C. R. (1990) Recent reports. *Oriental Bird Club Bull.* 12: 40–44.

ROBSON, C. R. (1993a) From the field. *Oriental Bird Club Bull.* 17: 49–53.

ROBSON, C. R. (1993b) From the field. *Oriental Bird Club Bull.* 18: 67–70.

ROBSON, C. R. (1994) From the field. *Oriental Bird Club Bull.* 20: 55–61.

ROBSON, C. R. (1995) From the field. *Oriental Bird Club Bull.* 22: 57–62.

ROBSON, C. R. (1996) From the field. *Oriental Bird Club Bull.* 23: 49–54.

ROBSON, C. R. (1997) From the field. *Oriental Bird Club Bull.* 25: 61–69.

ROBSON, C. R., EAMES, J. C., WOLSTENCROFT, J. A., NGUYEN CU AND TRUONG VAN LA (1989) Recent records of birds from Viet Nam. *Forktail* 5: 71–98.

ROBSON, C. R., EAMES, J. C., NEWMAN, M., NGUYEN CU AND TRUONG VAN LA (1991) Forest bird surveys in Vietnam 1989/90: final report. Cambridge, UK: International Council for Bird Preservation.

ROBSON, C. R., EAMES, J. C., NGUYEN CU AND TRUONG VAN

LA (1993a) Further records of birds from Viet Nam. *Forktail* 8: 25–52.

ROBSON, C. R., EAMES, J. C., NGUYEN CU AND TRUONG VAN LA (1993b) Birds recorded during the third BirdLife/Forest Birds Working Group expedition in Viet Nam. *Forktail* 9: 89–120.

ROCA, R., ADKINS, L., WURSCHY, M. C. AND SKERL, K. L. (1996) *Wings from afar: an ecoregional approach to conservation of neotropical migratory birds in South America*. Arlington: The Nature Conservancy.

ROCAMORA, G., RÉMIE, S., AH-KAN, J., CONSTANCE, P. AND NIOLE, D. (1997) Census of number of territorial and breeding pairs of the Black Paradise Flycatcher *Tersiphone corvina* on la Digue. Report to BirdLife International and the E.U. Division of Environment (MFAPE), Seychelles.

ROCAMORA, G., CHANG-SENG, L., LABOUDALLEN, V., LUCKING, R. AND RÉMIE, S. (in press) Monitoring rare and threatened species of birds in the granitic Seychelles. *Proc. 9th Pan-Afr. Orn. Congr.*

RODEWALD, P. G., DEJAIFVE, P. A. AND GREEN, A. A. (1994) The birds of Korup National Park and Korup Project Area, Southwest Province, Cameroon. *Bird Conserv. Internatn.* 4: 1–68.

RODGERS, W. A. (1993) The conservation of the forest resources of eastern Africa: past influences, present practices and future needs. Pp.283–331 in J. C. Lovett and S. K. Wasser, eds. *Biogeography and ecology of the rain forests of eastern Africa*. Cambridge, UK: Cambridge University Press.

RODRÍGUEZ-ESTRELLA, R., MATA, E. AND RIVERA, L. (1992) Ecological notes on the Green Parakeet of Isla Socorro, Mexico. *Condor* 94: 523–525.

RODRÍGUEZ-ESTRELLA, R., LEON DE LA LUZ, J. L., BRECEDA, A., CASTELLANOS, A., CANCINO, J. AND LLINAS, J. (1996) Status, density and habitat relationships of the endemic terrestrial birds of Socorro Island, Revillagigedo Islands, Mexico. *Biol. Conserv.* 76: 195–202.

ROSELAAR, C. S. (1992) A new species of mountain finch *Leucosticte* from western Tibet. *Bull. Brit. Orn. Club* 112: 225–231.

ROSELAAR, C. S. (1994) Notes on Sillem's Mountain-finch, a recently described species from western Tibet. *Dutch Birding* 16: 20–26.

ROUND, P. D. (1988) *Resident forest birds in Thailand: their status and conservation*. Cambridge, UK: International Council for Bird Preservation (Monogr. 2).

ROUND, P. D. AND TREESUCON, U. (1986) The rediscovery of Gurney's Pitta *Pitta gurneyi*. *Forktail* 2: 53–66.

ROWE, S. AND EMPSON, R. (1996) Distribution and abundance of the Tanga'eo or Mangaia Kingfisher (*Halcyon tuta ruficollaris*). *Notornis* 43: 35–42.

ROYAL BOTANIC GARDENS KEW (1995) Pakistan expedition 1995. Expedition Report.

ROZENDAAL, F. G. (1987) Description of a new species of bush warbler of the genus *Cettia* Bonaparte, 1834 (Aves: Sylviidae) for Yamdena, Tanimbar Islands, Indonesia. *Zool. Meded.* 61: 177–202.

ROZENDAAL, F. AND LAMBERT, F. (in prep.) The identity of *Pinarolestes sanghirensis* Oustalet (1879).

RUMPFF, H. (1992) Distribution, population structure and ecological behaviour of the introduced south-east Asian wolf snake *Lycodon aulicus capucinus* on Christmas Island, Indian Ocean. Report to the Australian Nature Conservation Agency, Canberra.

RUSSELL-SMITH, J. AND BOWMAN, D. M. J. S. (1992) Conservation of monsoon rainforest isolates in the Northern Territory, Australia. *Biol. Conserv.* 59: 51–63.

RYAN, P. G., MOLONEY, C. L. AND HUDON, J. (1994) Color variation and hybridization among *Nesospiza* buntings on Inaccessible Island, Tristan da Cunha. *Auk* 111: 314–327.

RYAN, T. P., COLLINS, C. T. AND KELSEY, T. R. (1995) Status and distribution of the Pygmy Swift in Venezuela. Cincinnati, Ohio: American Ornithologists' Union (Abstracts of the 113th Stated Meeting).

RZEDOWSKI, J., ED. (1978) *Vegetación de México*. First edition. México: Limusa.

RZEDOWSKI, J. (1993) Diversity and origins of the phanerogamic flora of Mexico. Pp.129–146 in T. P. Ramamoorthy, R. Bye, A. Lot and J. Fa, eds. *Biological diversity of Mexico: origins and distributions*. New York: Oxford University Press.

RZEDOWSKI, J. AND CALDERÓN DE RZEDOWSKI, G. (1989) Transisthmic Mexico (Campeche, Chiapas, Quintana Roo, Tabasco and Yucatán). Pp.270–280 in D. G. Campbell and D. H. Hammond, eds. *Floristic inventories of tropical countries*. New York: New York Botanical Garden.

SAFFORD, R. J. (1991) Status and ecology of the Mauritius Fody *Foudia rubra* and Mauritius Olive White-eye *Zosterops chloronothos*: two Mauritian passerines in danger. *Dodo (J. Jersey Wildl. Preserv. Trust)* 27: 113–138.

SAFFORD, R. J. (1993a) The Madagascar Teal *Anas bernieri*: a preliminary survey from Antsalova to Morondava. *Dodo (J. Jersey Wildl. Preserv. Trust)* 29: 95–102.

SAFFORD, R. J. (1993b) Rediscovery, taxonomy and conservation of the Anjouan Scops Owl *Otus capnodes* (Gurney 1889). *Bird Conserv. Internatn.* 3: 57–74.

SAFFORD, R. J. (1997a) A survey fo the occurrence of native vegetation remnants on Mauritius in 1993. *Biol. Conserv.* 80: 181–188.

SAFFORD, R. J. (1997b) The destruction of source and sink habitats in the decline of the Mauritius Fody, *Foudia rubra*, an island-endemic bird. *Biodiv. and Conserv.* 6: 513–527.

SAFFORD, R. J. (1997c) Distribution studies on the forest-living native passerines of Mauritius. *Biol. Conserv.* 80: 189–198.

SAFFORD, R. J. AND BEAUMONT, J. (1996) Observations on the biology of the Mauritius Cuckoo-shrike *Coracina typica*. *Ostrich* 67: 15–22.

SAFFORD, R. J. AND JONES, C. G. (in press) Strategies for land-bird conservation on Mauritius. *Conserv. Biol.*

SAFFORD, R. J., ASH, J. S., DUCKWORTH, J. W. AND TELFER, M. G. (1995) A new species of nightjar from Ethiopia. *Ibis* 137: 301–307.

SALAMAN, P. G. W., ED. (1994) *Surveys and conservation of biodiversity in the Chocó, south-west Colombia*. Cambridge, UK: BirdLife International (Study Report 61).

SALAMAN, P. G. W. (1995) The rediscovery of Tumaco Seadeater *Sporophila insulata*. *Cotinga* 4: 33–35.

SALAMAN, P. G. W. AND STILES, F. G. (1996) A distinctive new species of vireo (Passeriformes: Vireonidae) from the Western Andes of Colombia. *Ibis* 138: 610–619.

SALAS, S. H., RAMÍREZ, G., SCHIBILI, I., DE AVILA, A. AND AGUILAR, R. (1994) Analysis of the vegetation and current land use in the state of Oaxaca. II: Valles Centrales, Sierra Norte and Papaloapan region. Sociedad para el estudio de los recursos bióticos de Oaxaca, Asociación Civil (SERBO, AC). Unpublished report.

SANKARAN, R. (1993a) A study of the ecology, status and conservation perspectives of certain rare endemic avifauna of the Andaman and Nicobar Islands. Salim Ali Centre for Ornithology and Natural History.

SANKARAN, R. (1993b) *The status and conservation of the Nicobar Scrubfowl Megapodius nicobariensis.* Coimbatore, India: Salim Ali Centre for Ornithology and Natural History.

SANKARAN, R. (1995) The distribution, status and conservation of the Nicobar Megapode *Megapodius nicobariensis. Biol. Conserv.* 72: 17–25.

SANKARAN, R. (1997) Developing a protected area network in the Nicobar islands: the perspective of endemic avifauna. *Biodiv. and Conserv.* 6: 797–815.

SANSON, L. V. AND DINGWALL, P. R. (1995) Conservation status of New Zealand's subantarctic islands. Pp.85–106 in P. R. Dingwall, ed. *Progress in conservation of the subantarctic islands: proceedings of the SCAR/IUCN workshop on protection, research and management of subantartic islands, Paimpont, France, 27–29 April 1992.* Gland, Switzerland and Cambridge, UK: International Union for Conservation of Nature and Natural Resources (Conservation of the Southern Polar Region 2).

SANTAELLA, L. AND SADA, A. M. (1991) The avifauna of the Revillagigedo Islands, Mexico: additional data and observations. *Wilson Bull.* 103: 668–675.

SANTANA, E. C. (1991) Nature conservation and sustainable development in Cuba. *Conserv. Biol.* 5: 13–16.

SAUNDERS, D. AND INGRAM, J. (1995) *Birds of southwestern Australia: an atlas of changes in distribution and abundance of the wheatbelt fauna.* Chipping Norton, Australia: Surrey Beatty.

SAVIDGE, J. A. (1987) Extinction of an island forest avifauna by an introduced snake. *Ecology* 68: 660–668.

SAYER, J. A., HARCOURT, C. S. AND COLLINS, N. M., EDS. (1992) *The conservation atlas of tropical forests: Africa.* London: Macmillan.

SCHMIDL, D. (1982) *The birds of the Serengeti National Park Tanzania.* London: British Ornithologists' Union (Check-list 5).

SCHODDE, R. (1990) The bird fauna of the mallee—its biogeography and future. Pp.61–70 in J. C. Noble, P. J. Joss and G. K. Jones, eds. *The mallee lands: a conservation perspective.* Melbourne: CSIRO.

SCHODDE, R. AND MASON, I. J. (1991) Subspeciation in the Western Whipbird *Psophodes nigrogularis* and its zoogeographical significance, with descriptions of two new subspecies. *Emu* 91: 133–144.

SCHODDE, R. AND WEATHERLY, R. G. (1983) Campbell's Fairy-wren *Malurus campbelli*, a new species from New Guinea. *Emu* 82: 308–309.

SCHODDE, R., FULLAGAR, P. AND HERMES, N. (1983) *A review of Norfolk Island birds: past and present.* Canberra: Australian National Parks and Wildlife Service (Spec. Publ. 8).

SCHUBERT, A. (1993) Conservation of biological diversity in the Dominican Republic. *Oryx* 27: 115–121.

SCHUCHMANN, K.-L. (1978) Allopatrische Artbildung bei der Kolibrigattung *Trochilus. Ardea* 66: 156–172.

SCHULENBERG, T. S. AND BINFORD, L. C. (1985) A new species of tanager (Emberizidae, Thraupinae, *Tangara*) from southern Peru. *Wilson Bull.* 97: 413–420.

SCHULENBERG, T. S., GOODMAN, S. M. AND RAZAFIMA-HAIMODISON, J.-C. (1993) Genetic variation in two subspecies of *Nesillas typica* (Sylviinae) in south-east Madagascar. *Proc. 8th Pan-Afr. Orn. Congr.* [*Ann. Sci. Zool. Mus. Roy. Afrique Centr.*]: 173–177.

SCOTT, D. A. (1989) *A directory of Asian wetlands.* Gland, Switzerland and Cambridge, UK: International Union for Conservation of Nature and Natural Resources.

SCOTT, D. A., ED. (1993) *A directory of wetlands in Oceania.* Slimbridge, UK and Kuala Lumpur, Malaysia: International Waterfowl and Wetlands Research Bureau and Asian Wetland Bureau.

SCOTT, D. A. AND CARBONELL, M. (1986) *A directory of Neotropical wetlands.* Cambridge and Slimbridge, UK: International Union for Conservation of Nature and Natural Resources and International Waterfowl Research Bureau.

SCOTT, J. M., MOUNTAINSPRING, S., RAMSEY, F. L. AND KEPLER, C. B. (1986) *Forest bird communities of the Hawaiian Islands: their dynamics, ecology, and conservation.* California: Cooper Ornithological Society (Studies in Avian Biology 9).

SCOTT, J. M., DAVIS, F., CSUTI, B., NOSS, R., BUTTERFIELD, B., GROVES, C., ANDERSON, H., CAICCO, S., D'ERCHIA, F., EDWARDS, T. C., JR., ULLIMAN, J. AND WRIGHT, R. G. (1993) Gap analysis: a geographic approach to the protection of biological diversity. *Wildlife Monogr.* 123: 1–41.

SEDDON, N., CAPPER, D. R., EKSTROM, J. M., ISHERWOOD, I. S., MUNA, R., POPLE, R. G., TARIMO, E. AND TIMOTHY, J. (1996) Project Mount Nilo '95: discoveries in the East Usambara and Nguu Mountains, northern Tanzania. *Bull. African Bird Club* 3: 90–95.

SEITRE, R. AND SEITRE, J. (1991) *Causes de disparition des oiseaux terrestres de Polynésie Française.* Nouméa: South Pacific Regional Environment Programme (Occas. Pap. Series 8).

SEITRE, R. AND SEITRE, J. (1992) Causes of land-bird extinctions in French Polynesia. *Oryx* 26: 215–222.

SERPELL, J., COLLAR, N., DAVIS, S. AND WELLS, S. (1983) Submission to the Foreign and Commonwealth Office on the future conservation of Henderson Island in the Pitcairn Group. Unpublished report.

SESEGA, S. AND PARK, G. (1993) The conservation of biological diversity in the coastal lowlands of Western Samoa. Pp.71–76 in *Fifth South Pacific Conference on nature conservation and protected areas, 4–8 October 1993, 2: conference papers.* Apia, Western Samoa: South Pacific Regional Environment Programme.

SEVERINGHAUS, L. L. (1989) The status and conservation of Lanyu Scops Owl *Otus elegans botelensis.* Pp.423–429 in B.-U. Meyburg and R. D. Chancellor, eds. *Raptors in the modern world.* Berlin, London and Paris: World Working Group on Birds of Prey and Owls.

SEXTON, C. (1992) The Golden-cheeked Warbler. *Birding* 24: 373–376.

SHEIL, D. (1992) Tanzanian coastal forests—unique, threatened and overlooked. *Oryx* 26: 107–114.

SHERRY, T. W. (1985) Adaptation to a novel environment: food, foraging, and morphology of the Cocos Island

Flycatcher. Pp.908–920 in P. A. Buckley, M. S. Foster, E. S. Morton, R. S. Ridgely and F. G. Buckley, eds. *Neotropical ornithology*. Washington, DC: American Ornithologists' Union (Orn. Monogr. 36).

SHORT, L. L. (1982) *Woodpeckers of the world*. Greenville, Delaware: Delaware Museum of Natural History (Monogr. Ser. 4).

SIBLEY, C. G. AND AHLQUIST, J. E. (1990) *Phylogeny and classification of birds: a study in moelecular evolution*. New Haven and London: Yale University Press.

SIBLEY, C. G. AND MONROE, B. L. (1990) *Distribution and taxonomy of birds of the world*. New Haven: Yale University Press.

SIBLEY, C. G. AND MONROE, B. L. (1993) *A supplement to distribution and taxonomy of birds of the world*. New Haven: Yale University Press.

SICK, H. (1972) A ameaça da avifauna brasileira. Pp.99–153 in *Espécies da fauna brasileira ameaçadas de extinção*. Rio de Janeiro: Academia Brasileira de Ciências.

DA SILVA, J. M. C. (1989) Análise biogeográfica da avifauna de florestas do interflúvio Araguaia-São Francisco. Brasília: Universidade de Brasília (M.Sc. dissertation).

DA SILVA, J. M. C. AND OREN, D. C. (1992) Notes on *Knipolegus franciscanus*, an endemism [*sic*] of cental Brazilian forests. *Goeld. Zool.* 16: 1–9.

SIMPSON, B. B. AND HAFFER, J. (1978) Speciation patterns in the Amazonian forest biota. *Ann. Rev. Ecol. Syst.* 9: 497–518.

SINGH, P. (1995) Recent bird records from Arunachal Pradesh. *Forktail* 10: 65–104.

SINHA, A. R. P. (1992) Impacts of growing population and tourism on the endemic flora of Andaman and Nicobar Islands. *Environ. Conserv.* 19: 173–4,182.

SKERRETT, A. (1995) Seychelles Fody rediscovered in Amirantes. *Bull. African Bird Club* 2: 75.

SLUD, P. (1967) The birds of Cocos Island. *Bull. Amer. Mus. Nat. Hist.* 134: 261–296.

SMIL, V. (1984) *The bad earth: environmental degradation in China*. London: Zed Press.

SMIL, V. (1993) *China's environmental crisis: an enquiry into the limits of national development*. New York: M. E. Sharp.

SMITH, A., MOORE, D. AND HORNING, N. (1991a) *Madagascar biodiversity planning service: pilot study*. Armidale, Australia: University of New England.

SMITH, E. F. G., ARCTANDER, P., FJELDSÅ, J. AND GEDOW AMIR, O. (1991b) A new species of shrike (Laniidae: *Laniarius*) from Somalia, verified by DNA sequence data from the only known individual. *Ibis* 133: 227–235.

SMITH, F. D. M., MAY, R. M., PELLEW, R., JOHNSON, T. J. AND WALTER, K. S. (1993) Estimating extinction rates. *Nature* 364: 494–496.

SMITH, J. N. M. AND SWEATMAN, H. P. A. (1976) Feeding habits and morphological variation in Cocos Finches. *Condor* 78: 244–248.

SMITH, P. W. AND SMITH, S. A. (1989) The Bahama Swallow *Tachycineta cyaneoviridis*; a summary. *Bull. Brit. Orn. Club* 109: 170–180.

SMITH, T. B. AND McNIVEN, D. (1993) Preliminary survey of the avifauna of Mt Tchabal Mbabo, west-central Cameroon. *Bird Conserv. Internatn.* 3: 13–19.

SMYTHIES, B. E. (1981) *The birds of Borneo*. Third edition. Kuala Lumpur: Sabah Society and Malayan Nature Society.

SMYTHIES, B. E. (1986) *The birds of Burma*. Liss, Hampshire and Pickering, Ontario: Nimrod Press and Silvio Mattacchione.

SNOW, D. W., ED. (1978) *An atlas of speciation in African non-passerine birds*. London: British Museum (Natural History).

SNOW, D. W. (1980) A new species of cotinga from southeastern Brazil. *Bull. Brit. Orn. Club* 100: 213–215.

SNYDER, N. AND ENKERLIN, E. (1996) New parrot reserve in Mexico. *Psittascene* 8: 8–9.

SØRENSEN, U. G., BECH, J., HALBERG, K. AND KRABBE, E. (1997) Notes on the possible breeding of Prince Ruspoli's Turaco *Tauraco ruspolii*. *Bull. African Bird Club* 4: 29–30.

SPREP (1993) *Western Samoa: National Environment and Development Management Strategies (NEMS)*. Apia, Western Samoa: South Pacific Regional Environment Programme.

SPRINGER, M. S., HIGUCHI, H., UEDA, K., MINTON, J. AND SIBLEY, C. G. (1995) Molecular evidence that the Bonin Islands 'Honeyeater' is a white-eye. *J. Yamashina Inst. Ornithol.* 27: 66–77.

STANDLEY, P. C. (1930) Flora of Yucatan. *Publ. Field Mus. Nat. Hist., Bot. Ser.* 3: 157–492.

STATTERSFIELD, A. J. (in press) Identifying threatened species in the 'south' using new criteria. *Pac. Conserv. Biol.*

STAUS, N. (1994) Observations on the West Indian Whistling-duck in the Bahamas. *IWRB Threatened Waterfowl Res. Group Newsl.* 5: 13–14.

STEADMAN, D. W. (1989) Extinctions of birds in Eastern Polynesia: a review of the records and comparisons with other Pacific Island Groups. *J. Archaeol. Sci.* 16: 177–205.

STEADMAN, D. W. (1991) Extinct and extirpated birds from Aitutaki and Atiu, southern Cook Islands. *Pac. Sci.* 45: 325–347.

STEADMAN, D. W. (1995) Prehistoric extinctions of Pacific Island birds: biodiversity meets zooarchaeology. *Science* 267: 1123–1131.

STEVENS, J., LOUETTE, M., BIJNENS, L. AND HERREMANS, M. (1995) Conserving the endemic birds on the Comoro Islands, III: bird diversity and habitat selection on Ngazidja. *Bird Conserv. Internatn.* 5: 463–480.

STEYERMARK, J. A. (1979) Flora of the Guayana Highland: endemicity of the generic flora of the summits of the Venezuelan Tepuis. *Taxon* 28: 45–54.

STILES, F. G. (1996) A new species of Emerald Hummingbird (Trochilidae, *Chlorostilbon*) from the Sierra de Chiribiquete, southeastern Colombia, with a review of the *C. mellisugus* complex. *Wilson Bull.* 108: 1–27.

STILES, F. G. AND SKUTCH, A. F. (1989) *A guide to the birds of Costa Rica*. London: Christopher Helm.

STINSON, D. W., RITTER, M. W. AND REICHEL, J. D. (1991) The Mariana Common Moorhen: decline of an island endemic. *Condor* 93: 38–43.

STOKES, T. (1988) *A review of the birds of Christmas Island, Indian Ocean*. Canberra: Australian National Parks and Wildlife Service (Occas. Pap. 16).

STONE, C. P. AND LOOPE, L. L. (1987) Reducing negative effects of introduced animals on native biotas in Hawaii: what is being done, what needs doing, and the role of national parks. *Environ. Conser.* 14: 245–258.

STONE, P. B., ED. (1992) *The state of the world's mountains*. London: Zed Books.

STOTZ, D. F., FITZPATRICK, J. W., PARKER, T. A. AND MOSKOVITS, D. K. (1996) *Neotropical birds: ecology and conservation*. Chicago: University of Chicago Press.

STRAHL, S., ELLIS, S., BYERS, O. AND PLASSE, C. (1994) *Conservation assessment and management plan for Neotropical Guans, Curassows, and Chachalacas*. Apple Valley, MN: International Union for Nature Conservation and Natural Resources.

STRANGE, I. J. (1996) *The Striated Caracara Phalcoboenus australis in the Falkland Islands*. Falkland Islands: I. J. Strange.

STRESEMANN, E. AMD PORTENKO, L. A. (1971) *Prunella koslowi*. In E. Stresemann, L. A. Portenko and C. Mauersberger, eds. *Atlas der Verbreitung Palaearktischer*, 3. Berlin: Akademie-Verlag.

STRONACH, N. (1990) New information on birds in Serengeti National Park, Tanzania. *Bull. Brit. Orn. Club* 110: 198–202.

STUART, S. N. (1985) Rare forest birds and their conservation in Eastern Africa. Pp.187–196 in A. W. Diamond and T. E. Lovejoy, eds. *Conservation of tropical forest birds*. Cambridge, UK: International Council for Bird Preservation (Techn. Publ. 4).

STUART, S. N., ED. (1986) *Conservation of Cameroon montane forests*. Cambridge, UK: International Council for Bird Preservation.

STUART, S. N. AND JENSEN, F. P. (1985) The avifauna of the Uluguru Mountains, Tanzania. *Gerfaut* 75: 155–197.

STUART, S. N., JENSEN, F. P., BRØGGER-JENSEN, S. AND MILLER, R. I. (1993) The zoogeography of the montane forest avifauna of eastern Tanzania. Pp.203–228 in J. C. Lovett and S. K. Wasser, eds. *Biogeography and ecology of the rain forests of East Africa*. Cambridge, UK: Cambridge University Press.

SUBRAMANYA, S., PRASAD, J. N. AND KARTHIKEYAN, S. (1993) Status and habitat requirements of Yellow-throated Bulbul. Pp.111 in A. Verghese, S. Sridhar and A. K. Chakravarthhy, eds. *Bird conservation strategies for the nineties and beyond*. Bangalore: Ornithological Society of India.

SUBRAMANYA, S., PRASAD, J. N. AND KARTHIKEYAN, S. (1995) In search of the Yellow-throated Bulbul. *Sanctuary* 15: 68–70.

SUGDEN, A. M. (1982) The vegetation of the Serranía de Macuira, Guajira, Colombia: a contrast of arid lowlands and an isolated cloud forest. *J. Arnold Arboretum* 63: 1–30.

SUHERDIE, I. H. E., BASUKI, I. M., CAHYADIN, Y. AND POULSEN, M. (1995) *Preliminary evaluation of boundaries for a protected area in Halmahera, North Maluku*. Bogor: PHPA/BirdLife International-Indonesia Programme (Memorandum Teknis 8).

SUJATNIKA AND JEPSON, P. (1995) *Priority proposed protected areas for conservation of global biodiversity in Indonesia*. Bogor, Indonesia: PHPA/BirdLife International.

SUJATNIKA, JEPSON, P., SOEHARTONO, T. R., CROSBY, M. J. AND MARDIASTUTI, A. (1995) *Conserving Indonesian biodiversity: the Endemic Bird Area approach*. Bogor: BirdLife International Indonesia Programme.

SYKES, B. R. (1996) The status and identification of *Gorsachius* herons in southern Taiwan. *Oriental Bird Club Bull.* 23: 57–58.

TACCONI, L. (1995) *Participatory conservation in Malekula Island, Vanuatu*. Canberra: School of Economics and Management, University of New South Wales (Vanuatu Forest Conservation Research Report 10).

TACCONI, L. AND BENNETT, J. (1994) *The socio-economic assessment of the Erromango Kauri Protected Area*. Canberra: School of Economics and Management, University of New South Wales (Vanuatu Forest Conservation Research Report 5).

TAKAGI, M. AND HIGUCHI, H. (1992) Habitat preference of the Izu Islands Thrush *Turdus celaenops* and the effect of weasel introduction on the population of the thrush on Miyake Island. *Strix* 11: 47–57. (In Japanese.)

TAKEISHI, M. (1987) The mass mortality of Japanese Murrelet *Synthliboramphus wumizume* on the Koyashima Islet in Fukuoka. *Bull. Kitakyushu Mus. Nat. Hist.* 7: 121–131. (In Japanese.)

TARBOTON, W. R., KEMP, M. I. AND KEMP, A. C. (1987) *Birds of the Transvaal*. Pretoria: Transvaal Museum.

TARBURTON, M. K. (1990) Breeding biology of the Atiu Swiftlet. *Emu* 90: 175–179.

TAULEALO, T. I. (1993) *Western Samoa: state of the environment report*. Apia, Western Samoa: South Pacific Regional Environment Programme.

TAW (1994) *The Times atlas of the World*. Ninth comprehensive edition. London: Times Books.

TEIXEIRA, D. M. (1986) The avifauna of the north-eastern Brazilian Atlantic forests: a case of mass extinction? *Ibis* 128: 167–168.

TEIXEIRA, D. M. (1987) Notas sobre o 'gravatazeiro', *Rhopornis ardesiaca* (Wied, 1831) (Aves, Formicariidae). *Revta. Bras. Biol.* 47: 409–414.

TEIXEIRA, D. M. AND GONZAGA, L. P. (1983) A new antwren from northeastern Brazil. *Bull. Brit. Orn. Club* 103: 133–135.

TÉLLEZ-VALDÉS, O., CABRERA-CANO, E. F., LINARES-MAZARI, E. AND BYE, R., EDS. (1989) *Las plantas de Cozumel*. México, D.F.: Instituto de Biología.

TERBORGH, J. AND WINTER, B. (1983) A method for siting parks and reserves with special reference to Colombia and Ecuador. *Biol. Conserv.* 27: 45–58.

THACKWAY, R. AND CRESSWELL, I. D., EDS. (1995) *An interim biogeographic regionalisation for Australia: a framework for setting priorities in the national reserves system cooperative program. Version 4.0*. Canberra: Australian Nature Conservation Agency.

THIBAULT, J.-C. (1988) Menaces et conservation des oiseaux de Polynésie Française. Pp.87–124 in J.-C. Thibault and I. Guyot, eds. *Livre rouge des oiseaux menacés des régions françaises d'outre-mer*. Saint-Cloud: Conseil International pour la Protection des Oiseaux (Monogr. 5).

THIBAULT, J.-C. (1989) L'avifaune des îles Eiao et Hatuta'a (Polynésie, Pacifique Sud): modifications intervenues au XXᵉ siècle. *Oiseau et R.F.O.* 59: 305.

THIBAULT, J.-C. AND GUYOT, I. (1987) Recent changes in the avifauna of Makatea Island (Tuamotus, Central Pacific). *Atoll Res. Bull.* 300: 1–13.

THIBAULT, J.-C. AND VARNEY, A. (1991) Numbers and habitat of the Rapa Fruit-dove *Ptilinopus huttoni*. *Bird Conserv. Internatn.* 1: 75–81.

THIOLLAY, J.-M. (1985) The West African forest avifauna: a review. Pp.171–186 in A. W. Diamond and T. E. Lovejoy, eds. *Conservation of tropical forest birds*. Cambridge, UK: International Council for Bird Preservation (Techn. Publ. 4).

THIRGOOD, S. J. AND HEATH, M. F. (1994) Global patterns of endemism and the conservation of biodiversity. Pp.207–227 in P. L. Forey, C. J. Humphries and R. I. Vane-Wright, eds. *Systematics and conservation evaluation.* Oxford: Clarendon Press.

THOMAS, D. W. (1986) Vegetation in the montane forests of Cameroon. Pp.20–27 in S. N. Stuart, ed. *Conservation of Cameroon montane forests.* Cambridge, UK: International Council for Bird Preservation.

THOMPSON, H. S. (1993) Status of white-necked picathartes– another reason for the conservation of the Peninsula Forest, Sierra Leone. *Oryx* 27: 155–158.

THOMPSON, P. M. AND EVANS, M. I. (1992) The threatened birds of Ambatovaky Special Reserve, Madagascar. *Bird Conserv. Internatn.* 2: 221–237.

THORPE, R. I. AND ALLEN, D. S. (1996) Little-known Oriental bird: Roborovski's Rosefinch *Kozlowia roborowskii.* *Oriental Bird Club Bull.* 23: 45–47.

THORSELL, J. W., ed. (1985) *Conserving Asia's natural heritage: planning and management of protected areas in the Indomalayan Realm.* Gland, Switzerland: International Union for Conservation of Nature and Natural Resources.

THORSTROM, R. AND WATSON, R. T. (1997) Avian inventory and key species of the Masoala Peninsula, Madagascar. *Bird Conserv. Internatn.* 7: 99–115.

TIMMINS, R. J., EVANS, T. D. AND DUCKWORTH, J. W. (1993) *A wildlife and habitat survey of Dong Hua Sao proposed protected area.* Vientiane, Laos: National Office for Nature Conservation and Watershed Management.

TISDALL, C. (1994) *Setting priorities for the conservation of New Zealand's threatened plants and animals.* Second edition. Wellington: New Zealand Department of Conservation.

TOBIAS, J. A., CATSIS, M. C. AND WILLIAMS, R. S. R. (1993) Notes on scarce birds observed in southern and eastern Brazil: 24 July—7 September 1993. Unpublished report.

TOMIYAMA, K. AND SUZUKI, J. (1996) Save Anjima, a tiny island in the Ogasawara Archipelago, Japan. *BES Bull.* 27: 34–35.

TOMKOVICH, P. S. (1991) Three-year study of breeding Spoon-billed Sandpiper. *Asian Wetland News* 4: 17.

TOONE, B., ELLIS JOSEPH, S., WIRTH, R. AND SEAL, U. S. (1993) Conservation assessment and management plan for pigeons and doves: report from a workshop help 10–13 March 1993, San Diego, CA. ICBP Pigeon and Dove Specialist Group and IUCN/SSC Captive Breeding Specialist Group. Participants first draft.

TRAIL, P. W., MORRELL, T. AND TUALAULELEI, A. (1992) *Declines in land bird populations on Tutuila, American Samoa, 1986–1992.* American Samoa Department of Marine and Wildlife Resources (American Samoa Department of Marine and Wildlife Resources Biological Report Series 32).

TREVELYAN, R. (1995) The feeding ecology of Stephen's Lory and nectar availability in its food plants. *Biol. J. Linn. Soc.* 56: 185–197.

TRIGGS, S. J. AND DAUGHERTY, C. H. (1996) Conservation and genetics of New Zealand parakeets. *Bird Conserv. Internatn.* 6: 89–101.

TUCKER, G. M. AND HEATH, M. F. (1994) *Birds in Europe:*

their conservation status. Cambridge, UK: BirdLife International (BirdLife Conservation Series no. 3).

TURBOTT, E. G. (1990) *Checklist of the birds of New Zealand.* Third edition. Wellington: Ornithological Society of New Zealand.

TYE, A. (1993) Forest and bird conservation in the East Usambara Mountains, north-east Tanzania. *Proc. 8th Pan-Afr. Orn. Congr.* [*Ann. Sci. Zool. Mus. Roy. Afrique Centr.*] (286): 287–292.

TYE, H. (1986) The climate of the highlands of western Cameroon. Pp.18–19 in S. N. Stuart, ed. *Conservation of Cameroon montane forests.* Cambridge, UK: International Council for Bird Preservation.

TYLER, S. J. AND TYLER, L. (1996) The Rufous-throated Dipper *Cinclus schulzi* on rivers in north-west Argentina and southern Bolivia. *Bird Conserv. Internatn.* 6: 103–116.

TYMSTRA, Y. R. (1993) Some bird observations from the lower Apsuwa River, east Nepal. *Forktail* 8: 53–64.

UNEP, ED. (1995) *Global biodiversity assessment.* Cambridge, UK: Cambridge University Press.

URBAN, E. K., FRY, C. H. AND KEITH, S. (1986) *The birds of Africa*, 2. London: Academic Press.

USFWS (1990) *Native forest birds of Guam and Rota of the Commonwealth of the Northern Mariana Islands: recovery plan.* Portland, Oregon: US Fish and Wildlife Service.

VALQUI, T. (1994) The extinction of the Junín Flightless Grebe? *Cotinga* 1: 42–44.

VANE-WRIGHT, R. I., HUMPHRIES, C. J. AND WILLIAMS, P. H. (1991) What to protect?—Systematics and the agony of choice. *Biol. Conserv.* 55: 235–254.

VARISCO, D. M., ROSS, J. P. AND MILROY, A. (1992) *Biological diversity assessment of the Republic of Yemen.* Cambridge, UK: International Council for Bird Preservation (Study Report 52).

VARTY, N. (1991) The status and conservation of Jamaica's threatened and endemic forest avifauna and their habitats following Hurricane Gilbert. *Bird Conserv. Internatn.* 1: 135–151.

VARTY, N. AND HILL, J. E. (1988) Notes on a collection of bats from the riverine forests of the Jubba valley, southern Somalia, including two species new to Somalia. *Mammalia* 52: 533–540.

VARTY, N., BENCKE, G. A., BERNARDINI, L. DE M., DA CUNHA, A. S., FONTANA, C. S., GUADAGNIN, D. L., KINDEL, A., KINDEL, E., RAYMUNDO, M. M., RICHTER, M., ROSA, O. A. AND TOSTES, C. S. (1994) *Um plano de ação preliminar para o papagaio charão Amazona pretrei no sul do Brasil.* Porto Alegre, Brazil: Museu de Ciências e Tecnologia (Spec. Publ.).

VAURIE, C. (1960) Systematic notes on Palearctic birds. No.39. Caprimulgidae: A new species of *Caprimulgus.* *Amer. Mus. Novit.* 1985.

VAURIE, C. (1972) *Tibet and its birds.* London: H. F. and G. Witherby.

VAURIE, C. (1980) Taxonomy and geographical distribution of the Furnariidae (Aves, Passeriformes). *Bull. Amer. Mus. Nat. Hist.* 166.

VEITCH, C. R. (1989) The eradication of cats and sheep from Socorro Island. *North. Reg. Tech. Rep. Ser.* 11.

VELASCO-MURGÍA, M. (1982) Colima y las islas de Revillagedo. Colima: Universidad de Colima.

VERHEUGT, W. J. M., SKOV, H. AND DANIELSEN, F. (1993)

Notes on the birds of the tidal lowlands and floodplains of South Sumatra province, Indonesia. *Kukila* 6: 53–84.

VERVOORST, F. (1979) La vegetación del noroeste argentino y su degradación. *Ser. Conserv. Naturaleza, Fundación Miguel Lillo* 1: 5–9.

VIDAL, R. M., MACÍAS-CABALLERO, C. AND DUNCAN, C. D. (1994) The occurrence and ecology of the Golden-cheeked Warbler in the highlands of Northern Chiapas, Mexico. *Condor* 96: 684–691.

VIELLIARD, J. (1990) Uma nova espécie de *Asthenes* da serra do Cipó, Minas Gerais, Brasil. *Ararajuba* 1: 121–122.

VO QUY (1983) [A catalogue of the birds of Vietnam.] Pp.12–43 in L. N. Medvedev, ed. [*Fauna and ecology of the animals of Vietnam.*] Moscow: Nauka. (In Russian.)

VUILLEUMIER, F. AND MAYR, E. (1987) New species of birds described from 1976 to 1980. *J. Orn.* 128: 137–150.

VUILLEUMIER, F., LeCROY, M. AND MAYR, E. (1992) New species of birds described from 1981 to 1990. *Bull. Brit. Orn. Club* 112A (Centenary Supplement): 267–310.

WACE, N. M. AND HOLDGATE, M. (1976) *Man and nature in the Tristan da Cunha Islands*. Morges, Switzerland: International Union for Conservation of Nature and Natural Resources.

WADSWORTH, F. H. (1950) The development of the forest land resources of the Luquillo Mountains. University of Michigan (Ph.D. Thesis).

WAIYAKI, E. AND BENNUN, L. (1996) The avifauna of coastal forests in southern Kenya: status and conservation. Pp.51 in *Ninth Pan-African Ornithological Congress: programme and book of abstracts*. [Accra]: Ghana Wildlife Society.

WALDREN, S., FLORENCE, J. AND CHEPSTOW-LUSTY, A. J. (1995) Rare and endemic vascular plants of the Pitcairn Islands, south-central Pacific Ocean: a conservation appraisal. *Biol. Conserv.* 74: 83–98.

WALLACE, G. E. (1995) Following migrant birds to Cuba. *World Birdw.* 17(2): 16–19.

WALLACE, G. E., GONZÁLES ALONSO, H., McNICHOLL, M. K., RODRÍGUEZ BATISTA, D., OVIEDO PRIETO, R., LLANES SOSA, A., SÁNCHEZ ORIA, B. AND WALLACE, E. A. H. (1996) Winter surveys of forest-dwelling Neotropical migrant and resident birds in three regions of Cuba. *Condor* 98: 745–768.

WALTERS, M. (1995) On the status of *Ara tricolor* Bechstein. *Bull. Brit. Orn. Club* 115: 168–170.

WANG, J., WU, C., HUANG, G., YANG, X., CAI, Z., CAI, M. AND XIAO, Q. (1991) [*Field guide: birds of Taiwan.*] Taipei: Yashe Books Limited. (In Chinese.)

WARDILL, J. C. (1995) The report of the ornithological expedition to the Rawa Aopa Watumohai National Park, south-east Sulawesi, Indonesia. Unpublished report.

WATKINS, B. P. AND FURNESS, R. W. (1986) Population status, breeding and conservation of the Gough Moorhen. *Ostrich* 57: 32–36.

WATLING, D. (1983) Ornithological notes from Sulawesi. *Emu* 83: 247–261.

WATLING, D. (1986) Rediscovery of a petrel and new faunal records on Gau Island. *Oryx* 20: 31–34.

WATLING, D. (1988a) Notes on the status and ecology of the Ogea Flycatcher *Mayrornis versicolor*. *Bull. Brit. Orn. Club* 108: 103–112.

WATLING, D. (1988b) The effects of logging on Fijian wildlife. Paper presented at the National Trust for Fiji's second conservation congress.

WATLING, D. (1995) Notes on the status of Kuhl's Lorikeet *Vini kuhlii* in the Northern Line Islands, Kiribati. *Bird Conserv. Internatn.* 5: 481–489.

WATLING, D. AND CHAPE, S., EDS. (1992) *Environment Fiji: the national state of the environment report*. Gland, Switzerland: International Union for Conservation of Nature and Natural Resources.

WATLING, D. AND GILLISON, A. N. (1993) Endangered species in low elevation cloud forest on Gau Island, Fiji. Pp.217–223 in L. S. Hamilton, J. O. Juvik and F. N. Scatena, eds. *Tropical montane cloud forests: proceedings of an international symposium at San Juan, Puerto Rico 31 May-5 June 1993*. Honolulu: East-West Center.

WATSON, J., WARMAN, C., TODD, D. AND LABOUDALLON, V. (1992) The Seychelles magpie robin *Copsychus sechellarum*: ecology and conservation of an endangered species. *Biol. Conserv.* 61: 93–106.

WATSON, L. AND PERKIN, A. (undated) Biological survey results and conservation proposals from the foothill forests, East Usambara Mountains, Tanzania. Unpublished report.

WATSON, R. T. AND RABARISOA, R. (in press) Sakalava fishermen and Madagascar Fish-eagles: enhancing traditional conservation rules to control resource abuse that threatens a key breeding area for an endangered eagle. *Proc. 9th Pan-African Orn. Congr.*

WATSON, R. T., BERKELMAN, J., LEWIS, R. AND RAZAFINDRAMANANA, S. (1993) Conservation studies on the Madagascar Fish Eagle *Haliaeetus vociferoides*. *Proc. 8th Pan-Afr. Orn. Congr.* [*Ann. Sci. Zool. Mus. Roy. Afrique Centr.*] 286: 192–196.

WEBB, R. (1994) Africa round-up. *Bull. African Bird Club* 1: 59–65.

WEBB, R. (1995) Africa round-up. *Bull. African Bird Club* 2: 5–11.

WEBB, R. (1996) Africa round-up. *Bull. African Bird Club* 3: 74–79.

WEBB, R. AND SMITH, S. (1996) Degodi Lark *Mirafra degodiensis*, one of Africa's most poorly-known species. *Bull. African Bird Club* 3: 85–86.

WEGE, D. C. (1989) Conserving biological diversity: identifying areas of avian endemism as a tool for conservation. A case study from the Tepuis region of southern Venezuela and contiguous countries. University College London (M.Sc. thesis).

WEGE, D. (1993) Red Data Bird: Bare-necked Umbrellabird. *World Birdw.* 15(2): 18–19.

WEGE, D. C. (1996) Threatened birds of the Darién Highland, Panama: a reassessment. *Bird Conserv. Internatn.* 6: 191–195.

WEGE, D. (1997) Ecuador's Endemic Bird Areas. Pp.43–50 in R. S. R. Williams, B. J. Best and T. A. Heijnen, eds. *A guide to bird-watching in Ecuador and the Galápagos Islands*. Otley, UK: Biosphere Publications.

WEGE, D. C. AND LONG, A. J. (1995) *Key Areas for threatened birds in the Neotropics*. Cambridge, UK: BirdLife International (BirdLife Conservation Series no. 5).

WELCH, G. AND WELCH, H. (1988) Habitats and birds in Djibouti. *Walia* 11: 11–18.

WELCH, G. R. AND WELCH, H. J. (1992) *Djibouti III: migrant raptor count*. Saxmundham, UK: G. R. and H. J. Welch.

WELLS, D. R. (1985) The forest avifauna of western Malesia and its conservation. Pp.213–232 in A. W. Diamond and T. E. Lovejoy, eds. *Conservation of tropical forest birds*. Cambridge, UK: International Council for Bird Preservation (Techn. Publ. 4).

WENDT, T. (1993) Composition, floristic affinities, and origins of the canopy tree flora of the Mexican Atlantic slope rain forests. Pp.595–680 in T. P. Ramamoorthy, R. Bye, A. Lot and J. Fa, eds. *Biological diversity of Mexico: origins and distribution*. New York: Oxford University Press.

WETMORE, A. (1950) Additional forms of birds from the republics of Panama and Colombia. *Proc. Biol. Soc. Washington* 63: 171–174.

WETMORE, A. (1963) Records of birds from Panama. *Smithsonian Misc. Coll.* 145: 3–5.

WETMORE, A. (1972) *The birds of the Republic of Panama. 3: Dendrocolaptidae to Oxyruncidae*. Washington, DC: Smithsonian Institute.

WHISTLER, W. A. (1992) Vegetation of Samoa and Tonga. *Pac. Sci.* 46: 159–178.

WHISTLER, W. A. (1993) The cloud forest of Samoa. Pp.231–236 in L. S. Hamilton, J. O. Juvik and F. N. Scatena, eds. *Tropical montane cloud forests: proceedings of an international symposium at San Juan, Puerto Rico, 31 May–5 June 1993*. Honolulu: East-West Center.

WHITAKER, R. (1985) Endangered Andamans: managing tropical forests, a case study of the Andamans. Environmental Services Group, World Wildlife Fund-India and MAB India Department of Environment.

WHITE, C. M. N. AND BRUCE, M. D. (1986) *The birds of Wallacea (Sulawesi, the Moluccas and Lesser Sunda Islands, Indonesia): an annotated check-list*. London: British Ornithologists' Union (Check-list 7).

WHITE, F. (1983) *The vegetation of Africa: a descriptive memoir to accompany the UNESCO/AERFAT/UNSO vegetation map of Africa*. Paris: United Nations Educational Scientific and Cultural Organisation.

WHITEHEAD, P. J., BOWMAN, D. M. J. S. AND TIDEMANN, S. C. (1992) Biogeographic pattern, environmental correlates and conservation of avifauna in the Northern Territory, Australia. *J. Biogeogr.* 19: 151–161.

WHITMORE, T. C. (1984) *Tropical rain forests of the Far East*. Second edition. Oxford: Clarendon Press.

WHITNEY, B. M. (1994) A new *Scytalopus* tapaculo (Rhinocryptidae) from Bolivia, with notes on other Bolivian members of the genus and the *magellanicus* complex. *Wilson Bull.* 106: 585–614.

WHITNEY, B. (1996) Sites to save: Boa Nova, Brazil. *World Birdw.* 18(3): 9–11.

WHITNEY, B. M. AND PACHECO, J. F. (1994) Behavior and vocalizations of *Gyalophylax* and *Megaxenops* (Furnariidae), two little-known genera endemic to northeastern Brazil. *Condor* 96: 559–565.

WHITNEY, B. M. AND ROSENBERG, G. H. (1993) Behavior, vocalizations and possible relationships of *Xenornis setifrons* (Formicariidae), a little-known Choco endemic. *Condor* 95: 227–231.

WHITNEY, B. M., PACHECO, J. F. AND PARRINI, R. (1995) Two species of *Neopelma* in southeastern Brazil and diversification within the Neopelma/Tyranneutes complex: implications of the subspecies concept for conservation (Passeriformes: Tyrannidae). *Ararajuba* 3: 43–53.

WHITTAKER, A., CARVALHAES, A. M. P. AND PACHECO, J. F. (1995) Rediscovery of the Chestnut-headed Nunlet *Nonnula amaurocephala* in Amazonian Brazil. *Cotinga* 3: 48–50.

WHITTEN, A. J., HAERUMAN, H., ALIKODRA, H. S., THOHARI, M. (1987a) *Transmigration and the environment in Indonesia: the past, present and future*. Cambridge, UK: International Union for the Conservation of Nature and Natural Resources.

WHITTEN, A. J., DAMANIK, S., ANWAR, J. AND HISYAM, N. (1987b) *The ecology of Sumatra*. Yogyakarta: Gadjah Mada University Press.

WHITTEN, A. J., MUSTAFA, M. AND HENDERSON, G. (1987c) *The ecology of Sulawesi*. Yogyakarta: Gadjah Mada University Press.

WHITTEN, A. J., BISHOP, K. D., NASH, S. V. AND CLAYTON, L. (1987d) One or more extinctions from Sulawesi, Indonesia? *Conserv. Biol.* 1: 42–48.

WHITTEN, T. AND WHITTEN, J. (1992) *Wild Indonesia: the wildlife and scenery of the Indonesian archipelago*. London: New Holland.

WHITTINGHAM, M. J. AND ATKINSON, P. W. (1996) A species split in Mexico: Sumichrast's and Nava's Wren *Hylorchilus sumichrasti* and *H. navai*. *Cotinga* 5: 20–22.

WILES, G. J. AND CONRY, P. J. (1990) Terrestrial vertebrates of the Ngerukewid Islands Wildlife Preserve, Palau Islands. *Micronesica* 23: 41–66.

WILES, G. J., AGUON, C. F. AND DAVIS, G. W. (1995) The status and distribution of endangered animals and plants in northern Guam. *Micronesica* 28: 31–49.

WILEY, J. W. (1985) Bird conservation in the United States Caribbean. *Bird Conserv.* 2: 107–159.

WILLIAMS, A. J. (1984) The status and conservation of seabirds on some islands in the African sector of the southern ocean. Pp.627–635 in J. P. Croxall, P. G. H. Evans and R. W. Schreiber, eds. *Status and conservation of the world's seabirds*. Cambridge, UK: International Council for Bird Preservation (Techn. Publ. 2).

WILLIAMS, R. S. R. (in prep.) The rediscovery and doubtful validity of the Blue-wattled Bulbul *Pycnonotus nieuwenhuisii*.

WILLIAMS, R. S. R., BEST, B. J. AND HEIJNEN, T. (1997) *A guide to birdwatching in Ecuador and the Galápagos Islands*. Leeds, UK: Biosphere Publications.

WILLIS, E. O. AND ONIKI, Y. (1981) Notes on the Slender Antbird. *Wilson Bull.* 93: 103–107.

WILLIS, E. O. AND ONIKI, Y. (1991) Avifaunal transects across the open zones of northern Minas Gerais, Brazil. *Ararajuba* 2: 41–58.

WILLIS, E. O. AND ONIKI, Y. (1992) A new *Phylloscartes* (Tyrannidae) from southeastern Brazil. *Bull. Brit. Orn. Club* 112: 158–165.

WILMÉ, L. (1994) Status, distribution and conservation of two Madagascar bird species endemic to Lake Alaotra: Delacour's grebe *Tachybaptus rufolavatus* and Madagascar Pochard *Aythya innotata*. *Biol. Conserv.* 69: 15–21.

WILSON, J. R. AND CATSIS, M. C. (1990) A preliminary survey of the forests of the 'Itombwe' mountains and the Kahuzi-Biega National Park extension, east Zaire, July-September 1989. [London]: World Wide Fund for Nature, Institut Zaïrois pour la Conservation de la Nature, and the Fauna and Flora Preservation Society. Unpublished.

WILSON, K.-J. (1993) Observations of the Kurämoó (*Vini peruviana*) on Aitutaki Island, Cook Islands. *Notornis* 40: 71–75.

WINKER, K., RAMOS, M. A., RAPPOLE, J. H. AND WARNER, D. W. (1992) A note on *Campylopterus excellens* in southern Veracruz with a guide to sexing captured individuals. *J. Field Orn.* 63: 339–343.

WITTEMAN, G. J., BECK, R. E., PIMM, S. L. AND DERRICKSON, S. R. (1990) The decline and restoration of the Guam Rail, *Rallus owstoni*. *Endang. Spec. Update* 8: 36–39.

WOINARSKI, J. C. Z. (1992) Biogeography and conservation of reptiles, mammals and birds across north-western Australia: an inventory and base for planning an ecological reserve system. *Wildl. Res.* 19: 665–705.

WOOD, P. (1993) The Gola Rain Forest Conservation Programme in Sierra Leone. *Proc. 8th Pan-Afr. Orn. Congr.* [*Ann. Sci. Zool. Mus. Roy. Afrique Centr.*] (286): 217–222.

WOODS, R. W. (1988) *Guide to birds of the Falkland Islands*. Oswestry, UK: Anthony Nelson.

WOODS, R. W. (1993) Cobb's Wren *Troglodytes* (*aedon*) *cobbi* of the Falkland Islands. *Bull. Brit. Orn. Club* 113: 195–207.

WUNDERLE, J. JR, LODGE, D. J. AND WAIDE, R. B. (1992) Short-term effects of Hurricane Gilbert on terrestrial bird populations on Jamaica. *Auk* 109: 148–166.

WU ZHIKANG, LI ZHUMEI, YU ZHIGANG AND JANG HONG (1994) Birdwatching areas: Tuoda (also Toada or Tuode) Forest Farm. *Oriental Bird Club Bull.* 19: 24–29.

WWF/IUCN (1994) *Centres of plant diversity: a guide and strategy for their conservation*, 1: *Europe, Africa, South West Asia and the Middle East*. Cambridge, UK: World Wide Fund for Nature and International Union for Conservation of Nature and Natural Resources.

WWF/IUCN (1994–1995) *Centres of plant diversity: a guide and strategy for their conservation*, 2: *Asia, Australasia and the Pacific*. Cambridge, UK: International Union for Conservation of Nature and Natural Resources.

WWF/IUCN (1997) *Centres of Plant Diversity: a guide and strategy for their conservation*, 3: *North America, Middle America, South America, Caribbean Islands*. Cambridge, UK: World Wide Fund for Nature and the International Union for the Conservation of Nature and Natural Resources.

WWFJ (1984) *Conservation of the Nansei Shoto: part 1*. Tokyo: World Wildlife Fund Japan.

WWFJ (1985) *Conservation of the Nansei Shoto: part 2*. Tokyo: World Wildlife Fund Japan.

XU LONG-HUI, LIU ZHEN-HE, LIAO WEIPING, LI XIAO-HUI, YU SI-MIAN, QIU JIN-CHANG, ZHOU YU-YUAN, DENG JU-XIE AND GUAN GUAN-XUN (1983) *The birds and mammals of Hainan island*. Canton Province: Animal Division, Entomological Institute.

YATIM, S. H. (1993) The status and distribution of pheasants in Peninsular Malaysia. Pp.28–39 in D. Jenkins, ed. *Pheasants in Asia 1992*. Reading, UK: World Pheasant Association.

YORKSTON, H. D. AND GREEN, P. T. (1997) The breeding distribution and status of Abbott's booby (Sulidae: *Papasula abbotti*) on Christmas Island, Indian Ocean. *Biol. Conserv.* 79: 293–302.

YOUNG, H. G., SAFFORD, R. J., GREEN, A., RAVONJIARISOA, P. AND RABARISOA, R. G. M. (1993) Survey and capture of the Madagascar Teal *Anas bernieri* at Lac Bemamba, Madagascar, July–August 1992, July 1993. *Dodo* (*J. Jersey Wildl. Preserv. Trust*) 29: 77–94.

YOUNG, L., ZHENG GUANG-MEI AND ZHANG ZHENG-WANG (1991) Winter movements and habitat use by Cabot's Tragopan *Tragopan caboti* in southeastern China. *Ibis* 133: 121–126.

ZAIMECHE, S. E. (1994) The consequences of rapid deforestation: a North African example. *Ambio* 23: 136–140.

ZHAO JI, ZHENG GUANG-MEI, WANG HUA-DONG AND XU JIA-LIN (1990) *The natural history of China*. London: Collins.

ZHENG GUANG-MEI AND ZHANG ZHENG-WANG (1993) The distribution and status of pheasants in China. Pp.15–19 in D. Jenkins, ed. *Pheasants in Asia 1992*. Reading, UK: World Pheasant Association.

ZHOU GUANG-YI (1995) Influences of tropical forest changes on environmental quality in Hainan province, P. R. of China. *Ecological Engineering* 4: 223–229.

ZIMMERMAN, D. A., TURNER, D. A. AND PEARSON, D. J. (1996) *Birds of Kenya and northern Tanzania*. London: Helm.

ZINK, R. M. AND MCKITRICK, M. C. (1995) The debate over species concepts and its implications for ornithology. *Auk* 112: 701–719.

ZINO, F. AND BISCOITO, M. (1994) Breeding seabirds in the Madeira archipelago. Pp.172–185 in D. N. Nettleship, J. Burger and M. Gochfeld, eds. *Seabirds on islands: threats, case studies, and action plans*. Cambridge, UK: BirdLife International (BirdLife Conservation Series no. 1).

INDEX OF RESTRICTED-RANGE SPECIES

Page numbers refer to the start of EBA or Secondary Area accounts in which the species occurs. Introductory chapters and appendices are not covered by this index. (For a taxonomic listing of restricted-range species, together with their EBAs or Secondary Areas, see Appendix 1, p. 679.)

G